The Royal Horticu

GARDENER'S
YEARBOOK
1997

The Royal Horticultural Society
GARDENER'S YEARBOOK
1 9 9 7

EDITORS
CHARLES QUEST-RITSON & CHRISTOPHER BLAIR

MACMILLAN

First published in 1994 by Pan Macmillan Limited
This Edition published in 1997 by Macmillan,
an imprint of Macmillan Publishers Ltd
25 Eccleston Place, London SW1W 9NF
and Basingstoke

Associated companies throughout the world

ISBN 0-333-672186

Note: Whilst every care has been taken to ensure that the information
contained in this directory is both accurate and up-to-date, neither the
editor nor the publisher accept any liability to any party for loss or
damage occurred by reliance placed on the information contained in this
book or through omissions or errors, howsoever caused.

A CIP catalogue record for this book is available from
the British Library.

The opinions expressed in this work are the opinions of the authors and
not of the publishers or the Royal Horticultural Society.

Data management and typesetting by
Hodgson Williams Associates, Tunbridge Wells and Cambridge
Printed and bound in Great Britain by
Mackays of Chatham Plc, Chatham, Kent

Contents

Introduction

Welcome to this fully updated edition of *The RHS Gardener's Yearbook*. As always we aim to include as much information as possible about every aspect of the British horticultural scene for the year. There are details of gardening events for the whole of 1997; concise and incisive descriptions of nurseries and gardens in the British Isles; lists of garden designers and specialist societies; reviews of books and shows; information on courses for both amateur and professional and much more besides. Recent legislation has made the riches of European nurseries easier to obtain than ever: we list some of the best and explain the rules on importing plants. This year cyber-gardening joins these pages also, with a collection of horticultural internet sites.

The contents page at the front will point you towards the broad subject categories we use, such as Professional services or Garden supplies. To find information about a specific company, organisation, or subject, turn to the index at the back: it should take you straight to the page you need. In the listings of gardens and of nurseries and garden centres, the entries appear by the county. This makes the book easy to use when you are travelling or planning a visit, but a little care is needed. We try to give the county where the garden or nursery is physically located rather than just the postal address. Last year saw the start of the creeping abolition of counties in England as the unit of local government; Scotland's regions and the counties in Wales have already gone. Few people are familiar with all these developments, so we have stuck to the 1974 counties of England and Wales and to the Scottish regional divisions with three exceptions. The counties of Avon, Cleveland and Humberside were deeply unpopular: we have redistributed their entries to Gloucestershire and Somerset, Co. Durham, North and East Yorkshire and Lincolnshire. This may not be ideal, but if you get into difficulty the index should put you straight.

A degree of selection has been necessary to keep the book within its bounds but we hope that there are few serious omissions. We rely to a great extent on information which has been submitted to us by third parties. Not everyone who was approached has replied — or replied in time — and this explains some gaps. Inclusion or exclusion should not be construed as a recommendation or condemnation.

A number of common abbreviations are used freely throughout the text, including AGS – the Alpine Garden Society; EU – the European Union; MAFF – Ministry of Agriculture, Fisheries and Food; NCCPG – National Council for the Conservation of Plants and Gardens; NGS – National Gardens Scheme; RHS – Royal Horticultural Society; RNRS – Royal National Rose Society; and SGS – Scotland's Garden Scheme.

The editors are very grateful to the many people who have helped in the compilation of this work. First and foremost we want to thank all the garden owners, nurseries, horticulturists, colleges, societies, products suppliers and everyone else who has responded to our requests for information. We are greatly indebted to them, and regret that it is not always possible to give each the personal attention which they are due. Particular thanks go the staff of the Alpine Garden Society; the Met Office at Bracknell; English Heritage; the National Trust; the NCCPG; the Northern Horticultural Society; Chris Philip and Tony Lord of the *RHS Plant Finder* and especially Ruth Anders, Eilidh Fursman, Rosie Harkness, Alan Leslie, Anne Louise Limm, Suzanne Mitchell, Karen Wilson and others at the Royal Horticultural Society.

We must also acknowledge the considerable input of others who have worked with us on this project: Julian Ashby; John Hodgson; Barbara Levy; and our editor at Macmillan, Dominic Taylor. Finally thanks are due for their patience and endeavours to Madeline Quest-Ritson and Camilla Blair; and above all to Brigid Quest-Ritson, whose labours are represented throughout these pages.

Join the RHS for a year of gardening
inspiration

Did you know that RHS membership offers the same excellent combination of information and inspiration as the RHS Gardener's Yearbook?

ADVICE AND IDEAS ON EVERY ASPECT OF GARDENING!

For just £25 (plus £7 one-off enrolment fee), *RHS* members receive a unique package of benefits that attracts keen gardeners and garden lovers alike. Key privileges include ☞ a **FREE** monthly copy of the gardening magazine *The Garden* (worth £33 alone) ☞ **FREE** exclusive access to *RHS* experts at Wisley for expert advice ☞ **FREE** entrance to 24 gardens throughout Britain, including Wisley ☞ privileged tickets to the world's best flower shows including Chelsea and Hampton Court Palace Flower Shows.

SAVINGS THAT HELP PROTECT BRITAIN'S GARDENING HERITAGE

As a member you will have saved £40 after just two visits to Wisley for you and a friend, two members' tickets to Chelsea and two copies of *The Garden*! And your subscription also enables us to continue our extensive programme of education, conservation and scientific work.

SPECIAL OFFER TO READERS OF THE *RHS Gardener's Yearbook*

Call us today on 0171 • 821 3000 for further details. If you quote code 897 when you join the *RHS*, we'll reduce your first year subscription by £5 to just £27!

Offer valid until 31 October 1997. Please quote CODE 897. ☞

Calendar

The calendar, with a week to a page, lists hundreds of gardening events up and down the country, and some international dates too. They include lectures and talks, shows, workshops and demonstrations, garden walks, and plant sales. In order to cram in as much as possible, the details are deliberately concise. Many entries give a contact number. For the rest, further information can frequently be found through entries in other sections of the book – say for a society or a garden. Turn to the index at the back first. A few abbreviations are used: these are identified in the Introduction. A number of organisations, including the Royal Horticultural Society, have such extensive pro-grammes that to save space, and avoid repetition, refer-ences to their events appear in shortened form. The titles of these organisations and some booking details are given below (RHS centres appear first).

Many events, especially those organised by societies or the National Trust must be booked: if in doubt, check. Although we take care to be as accurate as possible, our information has to be obtained well in advance. Arrange-ments can change at short notice, so do check with the organisers or in the press nearer the time, especially if you intend to travel any distance.

The attitude of societies towards admitting non-mem-bers to their lectures and events varies. More details appear in the Societies section. In general, though, clubs and societies exist for their members, so if you are interested in their events you should think about becoming a member. National societies who have local groups should be able to put you in touch with one near you. Most societies also hold open shows and plant sales (the AGS and NCCPG among them): the public is more than welcome at these events.

Royal Horticultural Society

A note on RHS events: members can bring a guest to most events, although guests pay a higher charge. When book-ing, it helps if you write the name of the event on the outside of the envelope. You will also need to enclose an SAE and quote your membership number and a daytime phone number with your payment. A list of courses, walks and demonstrations for each RHS centre can be obtained from RHS Courses and Events, PO Box 38, Ashford, Kent TN25 6PR. Enclose an SAE, and write the name of the RHS centre which you are interested in on your envelope. The RHS monthly journal, *The Garden*, publishes up to date information on events at all RHS gardens and several others to which members have access, including those at Harlow Carr, Ness and the Hillier Arboretum.

RHS Hyde Hall

The RHS Garden, Hyde Hall, Rettendon, Chelmsford, Essex CM3 8ET. A few walks and demonstrations are held at the garden (see also Gardens section, under Essex), but other events take place at nearby Writtle College, Writtle, Chelmsford. Apply in advance to the Administrator at the garden for tickets for both venues; for further information call 01245 400256.

RHS at Pershore

RHS Regional Centre at Pershore, Pershore College of Horticulture, Avonbank, Pershore, Hereford & Worces-ter WR10 3JP. Courses are also held at Kings Heath Park, Birmingham. Write to the Administrative Secretary in advance for tickets for the numerous events at both loca-tions: further details from 01386 554609.

RHS Lectures

For tickets to both the regional and London lectures, apply in writing to RHS Lectures, 80 Vincent Square, London SW1P 2PE. Tickets are normally free for RHS members.

RHS Rosemoor

The RHS Garden, Rosemoor, Great Torrington, Devon EX38 8PH. For tickets to the regular demonstrations and walks you should write to the Administrator. Some dem-onstrations are also staged at Cannington College, Bridg-water. The booking procedure is the same. (See also the Gardens section, under Devon). More details are available on 01805 624067.

RHS Wisley

The society's flagship garden (see also entry in Gardens section, under Surrey). Walks, demonstrations and other events are held throughout the year at the RHS Garden, Wisley, Woking, Surrey GU23 6QB. Events must be booked in advance. Write to the Director at Wisley. For more information ring 01483 224234.

RHS Flower Show, Westminster

The Westminster Flower Shows take place regularly throughout the year in the RHS Halls in London. The main venue is the New Hall in Greycoat Street, and larger shows also fill the Old Hall in nearby Vincent Square. The nearest underground stations are St James's Park and Victoria. Recorded information is available on 0171 828 1744. RHS members are admitted free.

Other Events Organisers

AGS

The Alpine Garden Society is based at Avon Bank, Pershore, Hereford & Worcester WR10 3JP. The society (see Societies section also) organises alpine shows nationwide, and has many active regional groups with their own events programmes (01386 554790).

Brogdale

Courses at the Brogdale Horticultural Trust's collection in Kent (see Gardens and Societies sections) should be booked in advance: Brogdale Road, Faversham, Kent ME13 8XZ (01795 535286). There is a substantial discount for Friends of Brogdale.

Harlow Carr

Harlow Carr Botanical Gardens, Crag Lane, Harrogate, North Yorkshire HG3 1QB. The home of the Northern Horticultural Society (see also entries in the Gardens and Societies sections). Walks and demonstrations in the garden are free, and there is no need to book. Contact the Education Officer for details of courses (01423 565418).

HDRA Ryton

Ryton on Dunsmore, Coventry, West Midlands CV8 3LG (01203 303517). Ryton Organic Gardens are the home of the Henry Doubleday Research Association (there's also a new garden in Yalding, Kent). Contact the Marketing Department for details of their distinctive courses.

Hillier Arboretum

Sir Harold Hillier Gardens and Arboretum, Jermyns Lane, Ampfield, Romsey, Hampshire SO51 0QA. The gardens and grounds (see Gardens section) are now managed by Hampshire County Council. Meet in the car park for walks: no need to book. You must book in advance for the workshops and some of the other events (01794 368787).

Ness

Ness Botanic Gardens, Ness, Neston, Cheshire L64 4AY (0151 353 0123). The gardens (see Gardens section also) belong to the University of Liverpool: card holders and card carrying members of the RHS, Northern Horticultural Society and Friends of RBG Kew are admitted free. No need to book for lectures, which are free although the normal garden admission charge applies. Most other events should be booked in advance.

NT: National Trust

Almost all events require prior booking: contact the property itself or the regional National Trust office which is listed in the local phone directory. The National Trust's head office is at 36 Queen Anne's Gate, London SW1H 9AS (0171 222 9251). Members are admitted free to the Trust's many gardens: enquiries about membership may be made on 0181 464 1111.

Primrose Fairs

Organisers of a series of Rare and Unusual Plant Fairs, held in the Midlands and East Anglia. All Fairs are open from 10 am – 4 pm, and entry is £2 (01636 830756).

Rare Plant Fairs

Attended by specialist nurseries, these Fairs in the south of England are organised by Derry Watkins of Special Plants (see Nurseries section also) and Maureen Willson (0117 9691570). Special Plants also runs courses at Cold Ashton (01225 891686).

NCCPG

The National Council for the Conservation of Plants and Gardens is based at The Pines, Wisley Garden, Woking, Surrey GU23 6QP (01483 211465). There is a strong network of county groups which organise a wide range of events including plant sales and lectures (see also Societies section).

Westonbirt

The Forestry Commission's Westonbirt Arboretum, Gloucestershire (see also in Gardens section) runs regular workshops and other events. Tickets can be booked by post or telephone from: Westonbirt Arboretum, Tetbury, Gloucestershire GL8 8QS (01666 880220).

EVENTS	DIARY	
		MON 30
		TUE 31
Walk; New Year's Day Tour, Hillier Arboretum: 11 am. • Walk; Felbrigg Hall, Norfolk (NT).	Henry Broughton, Lord Fairhaven, b. 1900; created garden at South Walsham Hall, Norfolk	WED 1
	Sir Harold Hillier, b. 1905; nurseryman and arboriculturist (Hillier Arboretum, Hampshire)	THU 2
		FRI 3
	Rev. Stephen Hales, d. 1761; (*Halesia*)	SAT 4
Open Day; Bawsinch Reserve, Trees in winter, Scottish Wildlife Trust.	Thomas Nuttall, b. 1786; botanist and rhododendron collector	SUN 5

DIARY		EVENTS
MON 6		Demonstration; Your garden in January, RHS Pershore at Kings Heath Park: 2 pm.
TUE 7		Demonstration: Your garden in January, RHS Pershore: 2 pm. • Lecture; Crystal Palace Park, Irene Seijo, London Historic Parks and Gardens Trust, Burlington House: 7 pm. • Classic FM Gardener's Forum recording, Birmingham Botanical Gardens & Glasshouses.
WED 8	Sir Herbert Maxwell, b. 1845; plantsman	Demonstration: Propagating glasshouse plants, RHS Wisley: 2 pm.
THU 9		Demonstration: Cloches in the garden, RHS Pershore: 2 pm.
FRI 10	Nicolas Culpeper, d. 1654; herbalist	Lecture; River conservation on the Upper Thames, Graham Scholey: BBONT, Hungerford (01488 668235). • Lecture; Flowers of Crete and the Eastern Mediterranean, Jack Smith, Cheshire Wildlife Trust: Wilmslow.
SAT 11	William Curtis, b. 1746; founder of *The Botanical Magazine*	Demonstration; Getting the best out of your greenhouse, RHS Pershore at Kings Heath Park: 2 pm. • Walk; Seeds in winter, Greenbank Garden, Strathclyde: 2.30 pm.
SUN 12	George Loudon, d. 1714; designer at Chatsworth and Castle Howard	Demonstration: Propagation of glasshouse plants, RHS Wisley: 10.30 am. • Walk; Winter colour, RHS Wisley: 10.30 am. • Lecture; Australian botanic gardens, Prof. Marrs, Ness: 2 pm. • Workshop; Conifer identification, Westonbirt Arboretum.

EVENTS

DIARY

	Hon. Vicary Gibbs, d. 1932; creator of garden at Aldenham	MON **13**

RHS Lecture; The development of a coastal garden, Simon Goodenough: Ayr. • Demonstration: Ornamental fruit garden design, RHS Pershore: 2 pm.

Walter Hood Fitch, d. 1892; illustrated Hooker's *Rhododendrons of Sikkim-Himalaya*

TUE **14**

Lecture; Silvers and greys, Jack Gingell, RHS Rosemoor: 11 am. • RHS Lecture; Herbaceous plants and borders, Bill Tait: Aberdeen. • Walk; Heaven Scent, Hillier Arboretum: 2 pm.

WED **15**

Demonstration: Interesting brickwork, RHS Hyde Hall at Writtle: 10 am. • Lecture; Plants for clay soils, Hilary Twigg, RHS Pershore: 2 pm. • Lecture; Scottish Ferns, Stuart Lindsay, Scottish Wildlife Trust. • Lecture; Spring in Patagonia, John Blanchard, AGS Exeter Group, St Thomas High School. • Winter Walk; Harlow Carr: 2 pm. • Lecture; The Perfumery Garden: Rediscovering English flower oils, Dr Peter Wilde, Chelsea Physic Garden.

Sir Jeremiah Colman, d. 1942; orchid breeder and mustard manufacturer

THU **16**

Wassailing the Quarry Orchard, Buckland Abbey, Devon (NT).

Rev. John Ray, d. 1705; early naturalist

FRI **17**

18 – 26 January; Orchids for all fortnight, RHS Wisley. • Demonstration: Introduction to propagation facilities, RHS Pershore: 10 am. • Lecture; Principles of planting, Anna Pavord, NCCPG Dorset: 2.30 pm. • Lecture; Exhibiting at Chelsea, David Hitchcock, Wilts. & Avon HPS. • Workshop; Grafting trees and shrubs, Westonbirt Arboretum.

Sir Andrew Balfour, b. 1630; co-founder of Edinburgh Botanic Garden

SAT **18**

Walk; Heaven Scent, Hillier Arboretum: 2 pm.

SUN **19**

DIARY	EVENTS
MON **20** Ferdinand Bauer, b. 1760; botanical artist	Demonstration; Winter pruning, RHS Pershore at Kings Heath Park: 2 pm.
TUE **21**	21 – 22 January; RHS Flower Show, Westminster: 11 am – 7 pm. Ornamental plant and botanical paintings competitions. • RHS Lecture; Cacti and their native habitats, Nigel Taylor, Westminster. • Lecture; Bagatelle and Giverny, Duncan Coombs, RHS Pershore: 2 pm. • Lecture; Glis Glis, Stephen Carter: BBONT, Great Missenden (01442 822669). • Workshop; Grafting trees and shrubs, Westonbirt Arboretum.
WED **22** George Bunyard, d. 1919; pomologist and rosarian	Demonstration: DIY garden machinery, RHS Hyde Hall at Writtle: 2 pm. • Workshop; Hands-on grafting, Hillier Arboretum: 10.30 am. • Walk; Heaven Scent, Hillier Arboretum: 2 pm. • Also: RHS Flower Show: 10 am – 5 pm.
THU **23**	Demonstration: Designing on a budget, RHS Pershore: 2 pm. • National Trust Lecture; Osterley House and Park: Reunification, the last five years, Anthea Palmer, 66 Portland Place: 6.30 pm. • Talk-in; National Pot Leek Society, Choppwell: 8 pm.
FRI **24** Henry Merryweather, b. 1839; nurseryman ('Bramley's Seedling')	
SAT **25** Lionel de Rothschild, b. 1882; creator of Exbury Gardens, Hampshire	Workshop; Painting with winter in mind using watercolours, RHS Pershore: 10 am – 4 pm. • Burns Night supper, Ness: 7.30 pm.
SUN **26** Hugh, 5th Earl Annesley, b. 1831; creator of garden at Castlewellan, Co. Down	Walk; Heaven Scent, Hillier Arboretum: 2 pm. • Walk; In search of the hawfinch, Fountains Abbey and Studland Royal (NT).

EVENTS	DIARY	
Demonstration; Planning the vegetable garden for home and show, RHS Pershore at Kings Heath Park: 2 pm.	Lord Grenfell, d. 1925; president of the RHS	MON 27
Lecture; 1997 varieties of vegetables, Dick Neath, RHS Pershore: 2 pm.	Mark Fenwick, d. 1945; creator of garden at Abbotswood, Gloucestershire	TUE 28
29 – 30 January; Garden, Leisure and Groundsmanship Exhibition, Dublin. Trade only (00 353 1 2694022). ● Course; Propagation of ornamentals and vegetables, RHS Rosemoor.	Lord Digby, d. 1964; creator of garden at Minterne, Dorset	WED 29
Lecture; The right tree for your garden, Peter Goodbury, RHS Pershore: 2 pm. ● Lecture; A gardener's palette, Andrew Lawson, University of Oxford Botanic Garden. ● Also: Garden, Leisure and Groundsmanship Exhibition.	George Ehret, b. 1708; botanical artist	THU 30
	Hugh Falconer, d. 1865; botanist in India (*Rhododendron falconeri*)	FRI 31
Workshop; Bench grafting of ornamentals, RHS Pershore: 10 am.		SAT 1
Walk; Changing face of Wisley, RHS Wisley: 10.30 am. ● Walk; Evergreen extravaganza, Hillier Arboretum: 2 pm. ● Open Day; Moseley Old Hall, Staffs (NT).	Aylmer Bourke Lambert, b. 1761; botanist	SUN 2

DIARY		EVENTS
MON 3	Col. Frederick Bailey, b. 1882; soldier and botanist (*Meconopsis baileyi* syn. *betonicifolia*)	3 – 8 February; Winter Artists' workshop week: Painting from nature, RHS Rosemoor. • Demonstration; Your garden in February, RHS Pershore at Kings Heath Park: 2 pm. • Lecture; Gardening for wildlife, Campbell Ferguson, Scottish Wildlife Trust: South Queensferry.
TUE 4	Jacob Bobart, d. 1680; first gardener at Oxford Botanic Garden	Demonstration; Your garden in February, RHS Pershore: 2 pm. • Lecture; Lead sculpture from Hyde Park Corner in the 18th century, John Davis, London Historic Parks and Gardens Trust, Burlington House: 7 pm.
WED 5	John Lindley, b. 1799; botanist and bibliophile	Demonstration: Growing plants under glass, RHS Wisley: 2 pm. • Walk; Changing face of Wisley, RHS Wisley: 10.30 am. • Lecture; Castle Hill, Hal Moggridge, Garden History Society, Piccadilly. • Workshop; Hands-on trees, Hillier Arboretum: 10.30 am.
THU 6	Sir Lancelot 'Capability' Brown, d. 1783; landscaper	6 – 9 February; Springfields Horticultural Exhibition, Spalding (01775 724843). • Lecture; Designing an organic garden, Maggi Brown, RHS Pershore: 2 pm. • Course; Hellebores, RBG Kew (0181 332 5623).
FRI 7	George Maw, d. 1912; (*Monograph of Genus Crocus*)	Springfields Horticultural Exhibition continues.
SAT 8	John Sipthorp, d. 1796; botanist	8 – 12 February; Camellia Festival, American Camellia Society, Georgia. • Lecture; Wild flowers of Western Australia, Franklyn Perring, NCCPG Cambs.: 2.30 pm. • Course; Winter: seasonal day course, University of Oxford Botanic Garden. • Walk; Winter in the potting shed, Greenbank Garden, Strathclyde: 2.30 pm. • Also: Springfields Horticultural Exhibition.
SUN 9	William Bartram, b. 1739; American botanist	Demonstration: Growing plants under glass, RHS Wisley: 10.30 am. • Lecture; 'In the footsteps of Forrest', Lady Skelmersdale, RHS Rosemoor: 2 pm. • Lecture; Arctic plants in the wild, Dr Jacqueline Potter, Ness: 2 pm. • Also: Springfields Horticultural Exhibition.

EVENTS

DIARY

Demonstration; Early spring bulbs, including Cyclamen, RHS Pershore at Kings Heath Park: 2 pm. • Lecture; Insight into seeds, Terry Underhill, South Devon AGS: Dartington Hall: 7.30 pm.	Rev. William Colenso, d. 1899; botanist in New Zealand — **MON 10**
RHS Lecture; London's Royal Parks, David Welch: Chelmsford. • Demonstration: Early vegetable crops, RHS Pershore: 2 pm. • Lecture; Rhododendrons, Dr George Hargreaves, Cornwall Garden Society; Liskeard: 7.30 pm. • Lecture; *Hemerocallis*, Diana Grenfell, Wilts. & Avon HPS.	Robert Gathorne-Hardy, d. 1973; garden writer — **TUE 11**
RHS Lecture; Water features for gardens large and small, Frank Hardy: Shrewsbury. • Flower Arranging Demonstration: The plant hunters, Pamela Howard-Spink, RHS Wisley: 10 am. • Lecture; Les Bois des Moutiers, Robert Mallet, Garden History Society, Piccadilly. • Demonstration; Art of the gardener: practical gardening techniques, Rowallane Garden, Co. Down (NT): 2.30 pm. • Lecture; Rhododendrons, Dr George Hargreaves, Cornwall Garden Society, Falmouth: 2.30 pm.	Charles Darwin, b. 1809; naturalist — **WED 12**
Demonstration: Growing on from plug plants, RHS Pershore: 2 pm. • Lecture; Deserts of Southwestern USA, Louise Bustard, Glasgow Botanic Garden.	Sir Joseph Banks, b. 1743; botanist (*Banksia*) — **THU 13**
14 – 17 February; Painting flowers in watercolour course, RBG Kew (0181 332 5623).	**FRI 14**
Rose pruning demonstration and talk, with RNRS, Hosford's Geranium & Garden Centre, Co. Cork: 3 pm.	E. H. Wilson, b. 1876; collector (*Magnolia wilsonii*) — **SAT 15**
Walk; Winter, Cliveden, Bucks. (NT): 11 am. • Lecture; Rambles in the Cascade Mountains, P. Cunnington, Ness: 2 pm. • Jam & Marmalade Stall, Friends of Ness: 12.45 pm.	**SUN 16**

DIARY   EVENTS

MON **17**	Reginald Farrer, b. 1880; plant collector	Demonstration; Repair and maintenance of hard landscape features, RHS Pershore at Kings Heath Park: 2 pm.
TUE **18**	Clarence Elliott, d. 1969; nurseryman and plantsman	18 – 19 February; RHS Flower Show, Westminster: 11 am – 7 pm. Ornamental plant and botanical paintings competitions. Includes British Iris Society competition (01728 832650). ● RHS AGM, Old Hall: 2 pm. ● Lecture; The early 18th century landscape garden, David Whitehead, RHS Pershore: 2 pm. ● Lecture; A naturalist in Iceland, Mike Phillips, Scottish Wildlife Trust: Kirkintilloch.
WED **19**	William Nesfield, b. 1793; garden designer at Arley Hall, Cheshire and RBG Kew	RHS Flower Arranging Demonstration: Westminster. ● Walk; Winter interest, RHS Hyde Hall at Writtle: 2 pm. ● Course: Barks and stems, RHS Rosemoor. ● Lecture; Fonthill, Dr Christopher Thacker, Garden History Society, Piccadilly. ● Lecture; Gardening: an unnatural virtue, Prof. David Rankin, NCCPG Ayr: 7.30 pm. ● Course; Introduction to permaculture, HDRA Ryton. ● Also: RHS Flower Show: 10 am – 5 pm.
THU **20**		Demonstration: Growing cherry tomatoes, RHS Pershore: 2 pm. ● Preserving Herbaria, Linnean Society: 4.30 pm. ● Lecture; Adventurous gardening, Stephen Lacey, University of Oxford Botanic Garden. ● Guided Walk; Harlow Carr: 2 pm. ● Lecture; The Perfumery Garden: Essential oils in aromatherapy, Julia Lawless, Chelsea Physic Garden.
FRI **21**	John Lewis, d. 1963; retailer and creator of Longstock Water Gardens, Hampshire	RHS Lecture; Plants with impact, Jim Gardiner: Isle of Wight. ● Lecture; The AGS China expedition, Peter Cunnington: AGS North Wales Group, Llanfairfechan: 7.30 pm. ● Gardeners' Question time, UEA, NCCPG Norfolk: 7.30 pm.
SAT **22**		RHS Lecture; Plants and gardens of Scotland, John Bassford: Bournemouth. ● Workshop; Fruit tree pruning, RHS Pershore: 10 am – 4 pm. ● AGM & Lecture; Sikkim in the monsoon, Peter Cunnington, NCCPG Hants: 2 pm. ● Snowdrop Study Day, East Lambrook Manor, Somerset.
SUN **23**	Sir William Chambers, b. 1723; architect at Kew	Lecture; Carnivorous plants in Western Australia, W. Bopp, Ness: 2 pm. ● Workshop; Evergreen trees and shrubs, Westonbirt Arboretum. ● Little things mean a lot, Birmingham Botanical Gardens & Glasshouses.

EVENTS

DIARY

Demonstration; Growing your own bedding plants, RHS Pershore at Kings Heath Park: 2 pm. • Lecture and bulb display, Victoria Hall, Dunblane, SRGC: 10 am (01786 824064).	Lord Mitford, b. 1837; bamboo expert **MON** **24**
Lecture; Unusual conifers, Frank Hardy, RHS Pershore: 2 pm.	George Don, d. 1856; plant collector **TUE** **25**
Demonstration: Practical gardening, RHS Wisley: 2 pm. • Course; Orchid festival: Flower arranging, RBG Kew (0181 332 5623). • Lecture; Butterstream, Jim Reynolds, Garden History Society, Piccadilly. • Lecture; South African plants in Lancashire, Dr Wofferden, NCCPG Cheshire: 7.30 pm.	 **WED** **26**
RHS Lecture; What makes a garden great, Allen Paterson: Bristol. • Demonstration: Germinating your RHS seeds, RHS Pershore: 2 pm. • National Trust Lecture; From private demesne to public place: accommodating visitors at Fountains Abbey and Studland Royal, Edward Cullinan, 66 Portland Place: 6.30 pm. • Lecture; Chrysanthemums, Andrew Pinkerton, Scottish National Chrysanthemum & Dahlia Society.	Mrs C. W. Earle, d. 1925; popular gardening writer **THU** **27**
	 FRI **28**
1 – 2 March; Siberian husky meet, Grimsthorpe Castle, Lincs. • 1 – 2 March; Spring pruning demonstrations, RNRS, St Albans. • Lecture; Alan Bloom, Bressingham Plant Centre, Norfolk (01379 687464): 11 am. • AGS Early Spring Show, Harlow: 12 pm (01245 473982). • Garden Open; Spring opening, Saltram, Devon (NT). • Course; Taxonomy day, University of Oxford Botanic Garden. • Daffodil displays, Holland Arms Garden Centre, Gwynedd. • Lecture; Flowers of the Alaska Wilderness, Alan Flack in aid of St Francis Hospital, Zambia, Kentisbeare Village Hall, nr Cullompton: 7.30 pm. • Demonstration; Rose pruning (in Dutch), Pépinières Louis Lens, Oudenburg, Belgium.	Lady Clara Vyvyan, d. 1976; Cornish gardener and writer **SAT** **1**
Demonstration: Practical gardening, RHS Wisley: 10.30 am. • AGM and Leek Sale; National Pot Leek Society, Pelaw and District Social Club, Heworth: 10 am. • Lecture; From Cairns to Hobart: four months in Australia, J. Irons, Ness: 2 pm. • AGM; British Orchid Council, Solihull. • Walk; Spring in your step, Hillier Arboretum: 2 pm. • Also: RNRS Rose pruning demonstrations.	Christopher Lloyd, b. 1921; garden writer **SUN** **2**

12 March

Diary

Events

Mon **3**	Batty Langley, d. 1751; landscaper	RHS Lecture; Structural plants: foliage and form in the garden, Christopher Bailes: Cambridge. • Demonstration; Your garden in March, RHS Pershore at Kings Heath Park: 2 pm.
Tue **4**		RHS Lecture; Bulbs for the smaller garden, Brian Mathew: Derby. • Demonstration: Your garden in March, RHS Pershore: 2 pm. • Lecture; From fields to gardens: the history of Lincoln's Inn Fields, Susan Palmer, London Historic Parks and Gardens Trust, Burlington House: 7 pm. • Course; Orchid Festival: Flower Arranging, RBG Kew (0181 332 5623). • Lecture; From Paxton, Scottish Borders to Patagonia, South America, Laurie Campbell, Scottish Wildlife Trust: Lothian group. • Lecture and Lunch; Nymans, West Sussex (NT).
Wed **5**		Demonstration: Rose pruning, RHS Wisley: 2 pm. • Demonstration: Seasonal shrub pruning, RHS Hyde Hall at Writtle: 7 pm. • Workshop; Camellias, Jennifer Trehane, RHS Rosemoor: 10.30 am. • RHS Lecture; Entente horticulturale: a view of gardening either side of the Channel, Gillian Mawrey: Fishguard. • AGM and lecture, Success with unusual plants, James Compton, RHS Pershore: 6.45 pm. • Lecture; Ninfa, Countess of Pietromarchi, Garden History Society, Piccadilly.
Thu **6**	General Sir Henry Collett, b. 1836; botanist and introducer of *Rosa gigantea*	6 – 9 March; Antiques Fair, Tatton Park, Cheshire (NT) (01277 365319). • Lecture; Secret gardens and plants of Worcestershire, Jane Carr and Terry Dagley, RHS Pershore: 2 pm. • Lecture; Lothian botany at the millennium, Dr Philip Smith, Scottish Wildlife Trust: Lothian group. • Course; Bulbs, RBG Kew (0181 332 5623).
Fri **7**		Lecture; Organic gardening, Michael Pollock, Cornwall Garden Society, Penzance: 7.30 pm. • Also: Antiques Fair, Tatton Park (NT).
Sat **8**	William Roscoe, b. 1753; (*Roscoea*)	8 – 9 March; London Orchid Show, RHS Old Hall, Westminster: 10 am – 5 pm. • 8 – 23 March; Garden crafts fortnight, RHS Wisley. • 8 – 9 March; Garden design weekend, RHS Pershore. • 8 – 16 March; New England Flower Show, Bayside Exposition Center, Boston MA (00 1 617 536 9280). • AGM; Royal National Rose Society, Piccadilly. • AGS Loughborough Show, Burleigh Community College: 12 pm (01509 261626). • Walk; Spring pruning, Greenbank Garden, Strathclyde: 2.30 pm. • Lecture; Liliums, Duncan Coombs, NCCPG E. Dorset: 2.30 pm. • Seed Study Day, Sparsholt College, Hardy Plant Society members only. • Lecture; Organic gardening, Michael Pollock, Cornwall Garden Society, Probus: 2.30 pm. • Lecture; Pulmonarias, Joe Sharman, NCCPG Cambs.: 2.30 pm. • Demonstration; Rose pruning (in French), Pépinières Louis Lens, Oudenburg, Belgium. • Also: Antiques Fair, Tatton Park (NT).
Sun **9**	John Fothergill, b. 1712; physician and gardener (*Fothergilla*)	Demonstration: Rose pruning, RHS Wisley: 10.30 am. • Graft while-u-wait, Brogdale. • Lecture; Chester Zoological Gardens, Dr G. McGregor Reid, Ness: 2 pm. • Also: London Orchid Show: 10 am – 4 pm; Antiques Fair, Tatton Park (NT); New England Flower Show.

EVENTS

Demonstration; Propagation of house plants, RHS Pershore at Kings Heath Park: 2 pm. • Lecture; Fritillaries, Kevin Pratt, NCCPG Staffs. • Lecture; In search of the dinosaur daisy, Graham Nicholls, South Devon AGS, Dartington Hall: 7.30 pm. • Also: New England Flower Show.

Lecture; New perennial garden at Cowley Manor, Noël Kingsbury. RHS Pershore: 2 pm. • Lecture and Lunch; Nymans, West Sussex (NT). • Demonstration: Growing plants from seed, Glasgow Botanic Garden: 2 pm. • Course; Orchids for beginners, RBG Kew (0181 332 5623). • Also: New England Flower Show.

Demonstration: Container gardening, RHS Wisley: 2 pm. • RHS Lecture; Better gardens by design, David Stevens: Ponteland. • Lecture; Great gardens and their makers: Belsay Hall, Stephen Anderton, Garden History Society, Piccadilly. • Lecture; Ninfa, Charles Quest-Ritson; British Italian Society at the Linnean Society, Piccadilly: 6.30 pm (0171 495 5536). • Gardeners' Question Time, lunch etc., Wilts. & Avon HPS. • Also: New England Flower Show.

13 – 14 March; Course: Knot gardens: design and maintenance, Anne Jennings, Museum of Garden History. • 13 – 15 March; National Show and Annual Convention, American Daffodil Society, Jackson, Mississippi. • RHS Lecture; The greatest show on earth, Nigel Colborn: Beverley. • Lecture; Introducing fritillaries, Michael Jefferson Brown, RHS Pershore: 2 pm. • Lecture; Return to Siberia, Graham Bell, Scottish Wildlife Trust: Galashiels. • Lecture; A gardener's perspective on the gardens of Ireland, John Anderson, University of Oxford Botanic Garden. • Lecture; The trees in our gardens, Hugh McAllister, Glasgow Botanic Garden, Hillhead Library: 7.30 pm. • Wine tasting, Ness: 7.30 pm. • Also: New England Flower Show.

14 – 24 March; SET 97 – Science, Engineering and Technology Week. • 14 – 16 March; Arley Antiques Fair, Arley Hall, Cheshire. • Also: New England Flower Show.

15 – 16 March; Ambleside Daffodil and Spring Flower Show (01539 432252). • 15 – 16 March; Rose pruning demonstrations, Henry Street Garden Centre, Berks. • Lecture; Gardens in and around Wiltshire, Christopher Thacker, Wiltshire Gardens Trust: 2.30 pm. • AGS/ SRGC Morecambe Show, Lancaster & Morecambe College of Further Education: 12 pm (01253 394993). • Walk; Healing herbs, RBG Edinburgh, Scottish Wildlife Trust: Lothian branch. • NCCPG Ayr, Microprogation study day at SAC Auchincruive. • National Auricula & Primula Society (Southern) Show, RHS Wisley.

Demonstration: Container gardening, RHS Wisley: 10.30 am. • SET 97 Lecture; Understanding growth in plants: principles of pruning, Dr H. McAllister, Ness: 2 pm. • AGM; The Daffodil Society. • Table top sale, Birmingham Botanical Gardens & Glasshouses. • Lecture and Annual Meeting, Claire Laberge, Canadian Rose Society, Civic Garden Centre, Toronto: 2 pm.

DIARY

Hugh Johnson, b. 1939; author and wine expert

MON

10

Frederick Balfour, b. 1873; creator of arboretum at Dawyck, Borders

TUE

11

John Aubrey, b. 1626; naturalist and antiquarian

WED

12

George Forrest, b. 1873; plant collector (*Rhododendron forrestii*)

THU

13

FRI

14

Rev. George Engleheart, d. 1936; daffodil breeder

SAT

15

SUN

16

DIARY		EVENTS
MON **17**	Ferdinand Bauer, d. 1826; botanical artist	Demonstration; Pruning of roses and shrubs, RHS Pershore at Kings Heath Park: 2 pm.
TUE **18**		18 – 19 March; RHS Flower Show, Westminster: 10.30 am – 7 pm. Includes Early Camellia, Rhododendron and Daffodil competitions, and ornamental plant competition. ● RHS Masters Memorial Lecture; The grim reaper in the garden: welcome friend and dreadful enemy, Prof. David Ingram, Westminster. ● Demonstration: Ornamental fruit garden preparation and planting, RHS Pershore: 2 pm. ● Lecture and Lunch; Nymans, West Sussex (NT). ● Lecture; RBG Kew (0181 332 5623).
WED **19**		Demonstration: Vegetables, RHS Wisley: 2 pm. ● Flower Arranging Demonstration: Nature the designer, Edna Johnson, RHS Wisley: 10 am. ● Demonstration: Knowing and growing hardy annuals, RHS Rosemoor at Cannington: 2 pm. ● Lecture and AGM; A seasonal look at Glasgow's parks, James McMahon, Scottish Wildlife Trust: Glasgow. ● Lecture; Ornamental medicinal plants in Bhutan, Chris Chadwell, NCCPG Ayr: 7.30 pm. ● Course; Growing from seed, HDRA Ryton.
THU **20**	Sir Isacc Newton, d. 1727; scientist and apple grower	Demonstration: Open-ground grafting of ornamentals and fruit, RHS Pershore: 2 pm. ● Lecture; Fritillaries in the open garden, Kevin Pratt, NCCPG Dorset: 7.30 pm. ● Spring Walk; Harlow Carr: 2 pm. ● Lecture; The glory of the Cape, Michael Upward, AGS Exeter Group, St Thomas High School. ● Course; Planting up containers, Special Plants (01225 891686). ● Lecture; The Perfumery Garden: Plants, perfume and people – possible panaceas or potential problems?, Anthony Dweck, Chelsea Physic Garden. ● Lecture; Wild orchids of the Appennines, Assocciazione per la Diffusione di Piante per Amatori.
FRI **21**	Wilfrid Fox, b. 1876; creator of Winkworth Arboretum, Surrey	Len Beer Lecture; The Shahjah Gardens: creating Eden in the desert, Philip Swindells: AGS North Wales, Bangor: 7.30 pm. ● AGM & Lecture; My world of plants, Terry Read, NCCPG Norfolk: 7.30 pm.
SAT **22**	Sir James Horlick, b. 1886; creator of Achamore Gardens, Strathclyde	22 – 23 March; Show, Lyon Saint Priest chateau, Rhone. ● Workshop; Plant portraits using coloured pencils, RHS Pershore: 10 am – 4 pm. ● Heather Society roadshow at Hillier Arboretum: 11 am. ● AGS Kent Show, Rainham: 12 pm (01474 703822). ● AGM & Lecture; Hybridisation: where do we go from here?, Raymond Evison, British Clematis Society, Writtle College. ● AGM; Hardy Plant Society, Ark Conference Centre, London. ● Edinburgh Show, Fairmilehead Parish Church Hall, SRGC: 11.30 am (0131 4475277). ● AGM; British & European Geranium Society, Peasley Cross, St Helens, Lancs.
SUN **23**	Augustine Henry, d. 1930; plant collector (*Lilium henryi*)	Walk; Early flowering trees and shrubs, RHS Wisley: 10.30 am. ● Demonstration: Vegetables, RHS Wisley: 10.30 am. ● SET 97 Lecture; Why some plants like acid soils, Prof. R. Marrs, Ness: 2 pm. ● Bonsai Sale, Birmingham Botanical Gardens & Glasshouses.

EVENTS	DIARY	
Walk; Early flowering trees and shrubs, RHS Wisley: 10.30 am. • Demonstration; Hardy annuals, RHS Pershore at Kings Heath Park: 2 pm.	Mark Catesby, b. 1682; botanist and artist	MON **24**
Demonstration: Planting and sowing vegetables, RHS Pershore: 2 pm. • RHS Lecture; Britain in Bloom, Ashley Stephenson, Southampton. • Lecture and Lunch; Nymans, West Sussex (NT).	John Standish, b. 1814; nurseryman	TUE **25**
Demonstration: Soils and mulches, RHS Rosemoor: 11 am. • RHS Lecture; Species and small-flowered Clematis, Raymond Evison: Kidderminster. • Lecture; Climbing wall plants, Denis Bradshaw, NCCPG Kent. • Workshop; Shrub pruning, Hillier Arboretum: 10.30 am.	Robert Bolton, d. 1949; sweet pea breeder	WED **26**
Lecture; Living willow in design, RHS Pershore: 2 pm. • Rare Plants Fair; Battersea Town Hall: 11 am – 4 pm (0117 9691570). • National Trust Lecture; Croome: a garden scene out of a morass, Jeffrey Haworth, 66 Portland Place: 6.30 pm. • Lecture; Dahlias, Ian Thorburn, Scottish National Chrysanthemum & Dahlia Society.	Charles Raffill, d. 1951; plantsman	THU **27**
28 – 31 March; Sale of fruit trees and bushes, Brogdale.		FRI **28**
29 – 31 March; Craft Fair, Arley Hall, Cheshire. • 29 – 31 March; Reigate and Redhill Garden & Flower Show (01202 870928). • 29 – 31 March; Easter Festival: National Festival Circus, Tatton Park, Cheshire (NT) (01565 750250). • 29 – 30 March; Show, Le Pradet, Toulon. • AGS Cleveland Show, Fairfield: 12.30 pm (01429 231791). • AGS South West Show, Exeter: 12 pm, St Thomas High School (01404 881213). • Primula Show, Oliver Bird Hall, Solihull, National Auricula & Primula Society (Mid and West). • Easter Egg Hunt; Dunster Castle, Somerset (NT). • Also: Plant Sale, Brogdale.	Sir Edwin Lutyens, b. 1869; architect	SAT **29**
Easter treasure hunt, Hillier Arboretum. • NGS Open Day; Pulmonarias, Glebe Cottage Plants, Devon: 2 – 5 pm. • Rare & Unusual Plant Fair; Fulbeck Hall, Lincs., Primrose Fairs: 10 am – 4 pm. • Workshop; Magnolias, Westonbirt Arboretum. • Also: Craft Fair, Arley Hall; Plant Sale, Brogdale; Reigate and Redhill Show; Easter Festival, Tatton Park.	Easter Sunday	SUN **30**

DIARY   EVENTS

MON   William Dallimore, b.   Daffodil day; Plants for sale. High Beeches, West Sussex: 1 – 5 pm. •
31   1871; supervised   Also: Craft Fair, Arley Hall; Reigate and Redhill Show; Easter Festival,
       Bedgebury National   Tatton Park.
       Pinetum, Kent

TUE   1 – 4 April; Children's activities, Glasgow Botanic Garden. • Walk; Ham
1   House, London (NT): 2 pm & 3 pm. • Course; The Georgian garden,
                                 Caroline Holmes, Museum of Garden History. • Walk; Winter into
                                 spring, Mottisfont Abbey, Hampshire (NT): 2 pm. • Easter Egg hunt,
                                 Westonbirt Arboretum.

WED   J. J. Dillenius, d. 1747;   2 – 4 April; Calling eager earthkeepers: environmental programme for 8 –
2   German botanist   11 year olds, Westonbirt Arboretum. • 2 – 20 April; Exhibition:
                                 Adventures in the ink garden, Philip Shaw, Museum of Garden History. •
                                 Lectures; Recognising and preventing pest damage, Andrew Halstead;
                                 Plant diseases and disorders, Chris Prior, RHS Wisley: 10.30 am and
                                 2 pm. • Workshop; Baskets from the hedgerow, Hillier Arboretum:
                                 9.30 am. • Lecture; St Kilda, Dr J. Morton Boyd, Scottish Wildlife Trust:
                                 Peebles group.

THU   3 – 6 April; Garden design course, Robin Williams, RHS Wisley. •
3   Lectures; Plant diseases and disorders, Chris Prior; Recognising and
                                 preventing pest damage, Andrew Halstead, RHS Wisley: 10.30 am and
                                 2 pm. • Lecture; Success with garden pinks, David Hitchcock, RHS
                                 Pershore: 2 pm. • Lecture; Garden artistry, Helen Dillon, University of
                                 Oxford Botanic Garden. • Lecture; Cottage gardening in England and
                                 America, Margaret Hensel, Museum of Garden History (0171 401 8865).

FRI   Ronald Gunn, b. 1808;   Local seed exchange, Threave, NCCPG Dumfries & Galloway. • Badger
4   collector (*Eucalyptus*   evening for children, Westonbirt Arboretum. • Tour of rose gardens,
       gunnii)   Heydon House & Heydon Chapel, Bermuda Rose Society.

SAT   5 – 6 April; Basketry Course, RBG Kew (0181 332 5623). • International
5   Symposium, International Violet Association, Dawlish, Devon: 10 am –
                                 5 pm. • AGS Nottingham Show, Mapperly: 11.30 am (01623 512672). •
                                 Stirling Show, with lecture, SRGC. • National Auricula & Primula
                                 Society (Southern) Show, Village Hall, Datchet, Berks. • Rare Plants Fair;
                                 The Pavilion, Bath: 11 am – 4 pm (0117 9691570). • Getting the garden
                                 ready, Speke Hall (NT) (0151 427 7231). • Walk; Claremont Gardens,
                                 Surrey (NT): 2 pm. • Lecture; Euphorbias and unusual perennials, Roger
                                 Turner, NCCPG E. Dorset: 2.30 pm. • Course; Georgian furniture,
                                 Altamont Garden, Co. Carlow. • Walk; Daffodils, Speke Hall (NT): 2 pm.

SUN   Henry Broughton, Lord   Walk; 'Bloomin' wonderful', Hillier Arboretum: 2 pm. • Workshop; Wild
6   Fairhaven, d. 1973; art   flowers of Westonbirt, Westonbirt Arboretum. • Concert; Brass Band,
       collector and garden maker Borde Hill Garden, W. Sussex: 2 – 4 pm.

EVENTS

DIARY

7 – 11 April; Children's activities, Glasgow Botanic Garden. ● RHS Lecture; Foliage in the garden, Michael Jefferson Brown: St Andrews. ● Demonstration; Your garden in April, RHS Pershore at Kings Heath Park: 2 pm. ● Lecture; In paradise with David Rose, South Devon AGS, Dartington Hall: 7.30 pm.		Mon 7
Demonstration: Your garden in April, RHS Pershore: 2 pm. ● Lecture; London's green underbelly, Todd Longstaffe-Gowan, London Historic Parks and Gardens Trust, Burlington House: 7 pm. ● Workshop; Propagating plants from cuttings, Glasgow Botanic Garden. ● Walk; Ham House, London (NT): 2 pm & 3 pm. ● Course; Decoupage trays, Belinda Ballantine, Englefield House Garden, Berks.	John Claudius Loudon, b. 1783; (*Encyclopedia of Gardening*)	Tue 8
Demonstration: Sinks and troughs, RHS Wisley: 2 pm. ● Walk; With David Masters, Nymans, West Sussex (NT): 2.30 pm. ● Children's Event: Photography day, Hillier Arboretum: 10.30 am – 3 pm. ● Special interest day, Waddesdon Manor, Bucks.	Francis Bacon, Viscount St Albans, d. 1626; Lord Chancellor and writer	Wed 9
RHS Lecture; Gardens of the National Trust, John Sales: Woodbridge: 2 pm. ● Demonstration: Easy rules for pruning, RHS Pershore. ● Taste of the Orient: Chinese meal and lecture on Chinese flora, Ness: 7 pm.	William Purdom, b. 1880; plant collector	Thu 10
11 – 13 April; 100th County Spring Flower Show, Heligan Gardens, Cornwall. ● 11 – 13 April; Spring Gardening & Country Show, Capel Manor, London. ● 11 – 13 April; AGM & Spring visit, The Hebe Society, Writtle College. ● RHS Lecture; Shrubaceous planting: mixing shrubs and herbaceous plants for effect, Dennis Woodland: Nottingham. ● Badger evening for children, Westonbirt Arboretum.	Benjamin Maund, d. 1864; publisher (*Botanic Garden*)	Fri 11
12 – 13 April; Alpine weekend, RHS Rosemoor. Lecture and official opening of Alpine Terrace. ● Lecture and walk; Flowering bulbs, RHS Hyde Hall at Writtle: 10 am. ● Lecture; Plant introductions in the last three years, Stepehn Page, RHS Pershore: 10 am. ● AGS/ SRGC Northumberland Show, Hexham: 12 pm (01661 871974). ● Walk; Propagating herbaceous plants, Greenbank Garden, Strathclyde: 2.30 pm. ● Rare Plants Fair; Court Gardens, Marlow: 11 am – 4 pm (0117 9691570). ● AGS Dublin Show, Cabinteely Community School: 1.30 pm (00 353 12862616). ● Exhibition; Sculpture by Philip Jackson, Pashley Manor, East Sussex. Continues until 11 July.	William Kent, d. 1748; landscaper	Sat 12
13 – 14 April; Show, Dinard, Ille et Villaine. ● Lecture; Sinks and troughs, RHS Wisley: 10.30 am. ● Alpine weekend: demonstrations and displays, RHS Rosemoor. ● Pulmonaria Study Day, Southern Counties Group, Hardy Plant Society members only. ● Rare & Unusual Plant Fair; Bressingham Plant Centre, Elton Hall, Cambs., Primrose Fairs: 10 am – 4 pm. ● Orchid Show, Birmingham Botanical Gardens & Glasshouses. ● Walk; Spring, Wallington Hall, Northumberland (NT): 2 pm. ● Also: County Spring Flower Show, Cornwall; Hebe Society, Spring visit; Spring Show, Capel Manor.	Robert Fortune, d. 1880; plant hunter	Sun 13

DIARY

EVENTS

MON **14**	Walter Bentley, d. 1953; creator of garden at Quarry Wood, Berkshire	14 – 25 April; Kew School of Botanical Illustration, RBG Kew (0181 332 5623). ● Walk; Rock garden, alpine meadow and alpine house, RHS Wisley: 10.30 am. ● Demonstration; Making an alpine trough, RHS Pershore at Kings Heath Park: 2 pm.
TUE **15**	Rev. Adam Buddle, d. 1715; (*Buddleja*)	15 – 16 April; RHS Flower Show, Westminster: 10.30 am – 7 pm. Includes Daffodil Show and AGS London Show, and Main Camellia and ornamental plant competitions. ● RHS Lecture; Development of the Jerusalem Botanic Garden, Dr Michael Avishai, Westminster. ● Flower Arranging Demonstration: Designing for spring, Craig Bullock, RHS Wisley: 10 am. ● Lecture; British poisonous plants, Michael Leech, RHS Pershore: 2 pm. ● AGM; National Viola & Pansy Society, Court Oak Methodist Church, Harborne: 7.45 pm. ● Course; Britain's vanishing vegetables, Alan Gear, Englefield House Garden, Berks.
WED **16**	Charles, 3rd Lord Aberconway, b. 1913; president of the RHS (1961 – 84)	16 – 20 April; European Orchid Congress, Geneva. ● Lecture; Garden styles of the 19th century, John Addison, RHS Rosemoor at Cannington: 2 pm. ● Lecture; The modern planstman's garden, Jim Reynolds, NCCPG Ayr: 7.30 pm. ● Walk; Meet the gardener, Hinton Ampner, Hampshire (NT): 2.15 pm. ● Walk; Claremont Gardens, Surrey (NT): 2.30 pm. ● Lecture & AGM; Perennials of the 90s, Graham Rice, Wiltshire Gardens Trust: Bradford on Avon. ● Also: RHS Flower Show: 10 am – 5 pm.
THU **17**	Col. Frederick Bailey, d. 1967; soldier and botanist	Lecture; Euphorbias – probably the best plant in the world, Tim Walker, RHS Pershore: 2 pm. ● Lecture; Flowers and gardens through embroidery, Thomasina Beck, Kingston Maurward, NCCPG Dorset: 7.30 pm. ● Guided Walk; Harlow Carr: 2 pm. ● Lecture; Plant hunting in Japan, Tel de Bordes, Glasgow Botanic Garden, Hillhead Library: 7.30 pm. ● Lecture; Plants from recent exhibitions, Jack Elliott, AGS Exeter Group.
FRI **18**	Erasmus Darwin, d. 1802; scientist and poet (*Botanic Garden*)	18 – 20 April; Gardening course, with visits, Altamont Garden, Co. Carlow. ● 18 – 20 April; La Landriana Show, Tuscany. ● Demonstration: Summer herbaceous borders, RHS Hyde Hall: 11 am. ● Plant Sale and Show; AGS North Wales Group, UNCW, Bangor: 7.30 pm.
SAT **19**	Adrian Haworth, b.1768; (*Haworthia*)	19 – 20 April; Grow '97: The Gardening Experience, Sandown Exhibition Centre, Surrey. ● 19 – 20 April; City of Belfast Spring Flower Show. Includes Northern Ireland Daffodil Group show. ● 19 – 20 April; Ragley Hall Spring Gardeners' Weekend (0121 7114728). ● 19 – 20 April; Solihull Horticultural Society Show, with Daffodil Society Show. ● 19 – 20 April; Garden Festival, Borde Hill Garden, W. Sussex. ● 19 – 20 April; Journeés des plantes, Arboretum de Balaine, Villeneuve sur Allier (00 33 470 43 36 91). ● AGS East Lancashire Show, Deane School: 11.30 am (0161 6825542). ● Rare Plants Fair; Pittville Pump Room, Cheltenham: 11 am – 4 pm (0117 9691570). ● West of England Primula & Auricula Show, Saltford, National Auricula & Primula Society. ● Perth Show, Rodney Pavilion, SRGC: 12 pm (01250 874715).
SUN **20**	Peter Barr, b. 1820; botanist and daffodil breeder	Pulmonaria Open Day, Stillingfleet Lodge Nurseries, N. Yorks: 1.30 – 5 pm. ● Plant Sale; Calke Abbey, Derbyshire (NT) (0115 983 0278): 11 am – 5 pm. ● Spring Plant Fair, Pashley Manor Gardens, East Sussex (01580 200692). NCCPG Plant sale, Capel Manor, London.

EVENTS

DIARY

Demonstration; Planting an alpine trough, RHS Pershore at Kings Heath Park: 2 pm.	**MON** **21**
Cincinnati Flower & Garden Show, USA. In association with the RHS. Gala Evening (001 513 5790259). • RHS Lecture; Herbaceous miscellany, Paul Ingwersen: Aberystwyth. • Lecture; Restoration of Croome Court, Simon Rose, RHS Pershore: 2 pm. • Workshop; Small plants for small gardens, Glasgow Botanic Garden.	James Anderson, d. 1842; botanist and plant collector (*Carex andersonii*) **TUE** **22**
23 – 27 April; Cincinnati Flower & Garden Show, USA. In association with the RHS (001 513 5790259). • 23 April – 11 May; Exhibition: Beth Chatto's garden through the eye of the painter, Jean Burns, Museum of Garden History. • Lecture; Biological pest control, Andrew Halstead, RHS Wisley: 2 pm. • Turf Day; Preparation, establishment and maintenance of fine turf, RHS Rosemoor. • RHS Lecture; Something nasty in the garden, Pippa Greenwood: Taunton.	Harold Comber, d. 1969; plant collector and lily breeder **WED** **23**
24 – 27 April; Harrogate Spring Flower Show, Great Yorkshire Showground (01423 561049). Includes AGS North of England Show (0114 2346720). • 24 – 27 April; Course: Introduction to botanical drawing and painting, Pauline Dean, RHS Wisley. • Demonstration: Unusual water features, RHS Hyde Hall at Writtle: 10 am. • RHS Lecture; Plants and sights of New Zealand, Jock Davidson: Redruth. • Lecture; Formal herb garden, Kim Hurst, RHS Pershore: 2 pm. • Plant Sale; Scottish National Chrysanthemum & Dahlia Society.	Sir Jeremiah Colman, b. 1859; mustard maker and orchid breeder **THU** **24**
25 – 27 April; National Bonsai Convention & Exhibition, Bournemouth. • 25 – 27 April; Show, St Jean de Beauregard, Essone. • Walk; *Malus* collection, RHS Hyde Hall: 11 am. • Walk; Tree gazing, Westonbirt Arboretum.	**FRI** **25**
26 – 27 April; Turf weekend, RHS Rosemoor. • 26 – 27 April; North of England Orchid Society, Centenary Show, Stockport. • Workshop; Propagation by division, RHS Pershore: 10 am. • National Auricula & Primula Society (Southern) Show, Village Hall, Datchet, Berks. • AGS Ulster Show, Greenmount College, Muckamore: 1 pm (012657 41288). • Demonstration; Art of the gardener: practical gardening techniques, Rowallane Garden, Co. Down (NT): 2.30 pm. • Plant Sale; Wilts. & Avon Group, Hardy Plant Society, St Margaret's Hall, Bradford on Avon: 9 am. • Early opening at Hillier Arboretum: 6.30 am. Breakfast available. • Ballymena Show, Broughshane (01266 861216). • Auricula Show, Arden School, Knowle, National Auricula & Primula Society (Mid and West). • NCCPG Plant Sale, Glasgow Botanic Garden: 10 am – 1 pm. • Rose Sale; Canadian Rose Society, Civic Garden Centre, Toronto.	Sam McGredy II, d. 1926; rose breeder **SAT** **26**
Turf Weekend; demonstrations and events, RHS Rosemoor. • Walk; Trees, shrubs and herbaceous perennials, RHS Wisley: 10.30 am. • Plant Sale and Garden Open, The Pines Garden, NCCPG Kent: 2 – 5 pm. • Plants and Gardens Spring Fair, Museum of Garden History: 10.30 am – 4 pm. • Walk; Woods in spring, Cliveden, Bucks. (NT): 11 am.	Lawrence Johnston, d. 1958; creator of Hidcote Manor, Gloucestershire **SUN** **27**

DIARY	EVENTS
MON **28** Charles Sturt, b. 1795; botanist of Australia	Walk; Trees, shrubs and herbaceous perennials, RHS Wisley: 10.30 am. ● Demonstration; Hanging baskets and containers, RHS Pershore at Kings Heath Park: 2 pm.
TUE **29** Rev. Samuel Goodenough, b. 1743; founder and first treasurer of the Linnean Society	29 – 30 April; RHS Flower Show, Westminster: 11 am – 7 pm. Includes Tulip, Main Rhododendron, Late Daffodil and ornamental plant competitions. With RNRS and Bonsai Kai competitions. ● RHS Lecture; The formal garden: principles and practicalities, Sir Roy Strong, Westminster: 2.15 pm. ● RHS/RNRS Courtney Page Memorial Lecture; Chinese puzzles: the search for the origins of the Chinese roses, Roger Phillips, Westminster: 6 pm. ● Lecture; Pulmonarias for flowers and foliage, Jennifer Hewitt, RHS Pershore: 2 pm. ● Walk; Spring, Mount Stewart, Co. Down (NT): 7.30 pm. ● Workshop; Choosing and growing houseplants, Glasgow Botanic Garden.
WED **30** Sir Gerald Loder, Lord Wakehurst; creator of Wakehurst Place, West Sussex	30 April – 1 May; Ayrshire Agricultural Show, Ayr Racecourse. ● Walk; Tough nuts for tight places, RHS Rosemoor: 11 am. ● Demonstration: Colourful containers, RHS Rosemoor: 2 pm. ● Walk; Gardens in spring, Cliveden, Bucks. (NT): 11 am. ● Also: RHS Flower Show: 10 am – 5 pm.
THU **1** Joseph Addison, b. 1672; writer and theorist	1 – 5 May; Tulip Festival, Pashley Manor Gardens, East Sussex. ● 1 – 4 May; European Bonsai Association Congress, Brugges, Belgium. ● Visit; To RHS Wisley, RHS Pershore. ● Walk; Meet the gardener, Emmetts Garden, Kent (NT): 7 pm. ● Course; Pruning and propagating, RBG Kew (0181 332 5623).
FRI **2** Alan Titchmarsh, b. 1949; broadcaster	2 – 5 May; Wimborne Minster Flower Festival. ● 2 – 4 May; Tre Giorni di Masino, near Turin (00 39 11 660 4339). ● Lecture & AGM; Bermuda Rose Society. ● Also: Tulips, Pashley Manor; Bonsai Congress.
SAT **3** George Sherriff, b. 1898; plant hunter	3 – 5 May; Hardy geranium weekend, Croftway Nursery, West Sussex. ● 3 – 5 May; Bath Spring Flower Show, Royal Victoria Park (01225 448433). ● 3 – 5 May; Spalding Flower Festival, Springfields (01775 724843). ● 3 – 5 May; Cactus and succulent show, Capel Manor, London. ● 3 – 5 May; Bonsai Weekend, Leonardslee Gardens, W. Sussex. ● 3 – 4 May; Show, La Roche Guyon, Val d'Oise. ● Workshop; Softwood cuttings, RHS Pershore: 10 am. ● AGS East Anglia Show, Sudbury: 12.30 pm (01787 247627). ● Walk; Claremont Gardens, Surrey (NT): 2 pm. ● AGS East Cheshire Show, Ryles Park County High School (01625 423894). ● Glasgow Show, Milngavie Town Hall, SRGC: 12 pm (0141 6377781). ● Walk; Dawn chorus, Westonbirt Arboretum: 4.30 am.
SUN **4**	4 – 5 May; Leicestershire County Show, Loughborough (01509 646786). ● 4 – 5 May; South of England Spring Show, Ardingly (01444 892700). ● International Dawn Chorus Day: nationwide events; Urban Wildlife Trust (0121 666 7474). ● Orchid Society of Great Britain Spring Show, Syon Park: 11 am – 4 pm. ● Spring Plant Fair, Newby Hall, N. Yorks. ● Walk; Winkworth Arboretum, Surrey (NT): 10.30 am. ● Walk; Spring tour, Hillier Arboretum: 2 pm. ● Open Day; Show auriculas, Lingen Nursery & Garden, Shropshire. ● Workshop; Cherries, Westonbirt Arboretum.

EVENTS

DIARY

Demonstration; Your garden in May, RHS Pershore at Kings Heath Park: 2 pm. • Bluebell day; Plants for sale. High Beeches, West Sussex: 1 – 5 pm. • NCCPG Plant Sale, Wimpole Hall, Cambs. (NT). • Flower Fair; Hergest Croft Gardens, H & W. • Open weekend; Rhododendrons at Hydon Nurseries, Surrey. • Spring Plant Sale, Friends of Ness Gardens: 10 am.	Hugh Dickson, d. 1904; rose breeder	**MON** **5**
Demonstration: Your garden in May, RHS Pershore: 2 pm. • Course; Flowers in watercolour, Jenny Jowett, Englefield House Garden, Berks. • Course; The Victorian garden, Caroline Holmes, Museum of Garden History. • Lecture; Tradescant and Sloane, Arthur MacGregor, Museum of Garden History. • Walk; Ham House, London (NT): 2 pm & 3 pm. • Also: Craft & Garden Show, Exbury Gardens.		**TUE** **6**
Demonstration: Summer hanging baskets, RHS Hyde Hall at Writtle: 7 pm. • Walk; Nymans, West Sussex (NT): 2.30 pm. • Lecture; Nigel Colborn, Bressingham Plant Centre, Dorney Court, Berks.: 7.30 pm. • Walk; Spring tour, Hillier Arboretum: 2 pm. • Lecture; Parterres, Caroline Holmes, Waddesdon Manor, Bucks. • Walk; Claremont Gardens, Surrey (NT): 2.30 pm. • Walk; Bluebells, Speke Hall (NT): 2 pm. • Also: Craft & Garden Show, Exbury Gardens.	E. A. Bowles, d. 1954; plantsman and writer	**WED** **7**
8 – 14 May; Well dressing, Tissington, Derbyshire. Tissington Nursery open throughout. • 8 – 12 May; Show, Société Bretonne du Rhododendron, Trevarez. • Guided Walk; Harlow Carr: 2 pm.	Thomas Baines, d. 1875; artist, explorer and botanist (*Aloe bainesii*)	**THU** **8**
9 – 11 May; Malvern Spring Gardening Show, TCAS Showground. Includes RHS show. See Shows section also: 9 am – 6 pm.	Charles Turner, d. 1885; nurseryman	**FRI** **9**
10 – 11 May; Blossom and flower festival, Brogdale. • 10 – 11 May; Herts. Garden Show, Knebworth (01795 474660). • 10 – 11 May; Varietas Florum, Cloître des Jacobins, Saint Sever, Landes. • Plant Sale; In aid of Motor Neurone Disease Association, Englefield House Garden, Berks.: 11 am – 4 pm. • Early opening at Hillier Arboretum: 6.30 am. Breakfast available. • Course; Paper making, RBG Kew (0181 332 5623). • Demonstrations: Hanging baskets, Holland Arms Garden Centre, Gwynedd. • Walk; Dawn chorus, Westonbirt Arboretum: 4.30 am. • Walk; Garden design, Greenbank Garden, Strathclyde: 2.30 pm. • Course; Spring: seasonal day course, University of Oxford Botanic Garden. • Also: Malvern Spring: 9 am – 6 pm.	Rev. H. H. d'Ombrain, b. 1818; rosarian	**SAT** **10**
Walk; Wisley's birds, RHS Wisley: 10.30 am. • Demonstration: Propagating hardy plants, RHS Wisley: 10.30 am. • Walk; Spring tour, Hillier Arboretum: 2 pm. • Rare & Unusual Plant Fair; Ryton Organic Gardens, Primrose Fairs: 10 am – 4 pm. • Walk; For NGS, Wallington Hall, Northumberland (NT): 2 pm. • Plantsman's Day, Plant Fair, Dunham Massey, Greater Manchester (NT): 11 am – 5 pm. • Workshop; Green woodworking, Westonbirt Arboretum. • Also: Malvern Spring: 9 am – 5 pm; Blossom festival, Brogdale; Herts. Garden Show.	Margaret, Duchess of Portland, b. 1715; botanist and patron (The Portland Rose)	**SUN** **11**

DIARY	EVENTS
MON **12** Reginald Cory, d. 1934; philanthropist and garden maker (Dyffryn Botanic Garden, South Glamorgan)	12 – 16 May; Plants in focus course, RBG Kew (0181 332 5623). • Demonstration; Using your greenhouse to full capacity, RHS Pershore at Kings Heath Park: 2 pm.
TUE **13**	Demonstration: Garden design: the hot border, RHS Pershore: 2 pm. • Outing; Cornwall Garden Society to Lancarffe. Members only. • Workshop; Flower photography, Glasgow Botanic Garden. • Course; Plants for people, Hew Prendergast, Englefield House Garden, Berks. • Walk; Ham House, London (NT): 2 pm & 3 pm.
WED **14** Mary Delany, b. 1700; paper flower artist	14 – 16 May; Royal Ulster Show, Balmoral (01232 665225). • Flower Arranging Day School; From both sides now, Vivienne O'Sullivan, RHS Wisley: 10 am. • Demonstration; Propagating hardy plants, RHS Wisley: 2 pm • Walk; Vegetable garden and potager, RHS Rosemoor. • Walk; Spring tour, Hillier Arboretum: 2 pm. • Lecture; Plants for problem places, Beth Chatto, Museum of Garden History. • Special interest day, Waddesdon Manor, Bucks. • Walk; Flowering shrubs, followed by wine, bread, cheese, Westonbirt Arboretum: 7 pm. • Walk; Claremont Gardens, Surrey (NT): 2.30 pm.
THU **15**	15 May – 30 June; Exhibition: The making of a museum, Museum of Garden History. • 15 – 17 May; Devon County Show, Exeter (01392 444777). • 15 – 18 May; International Clematis Society General Meeting, Sagamihara City, Japan. • Demonstration: Hanging baskets and containers, RHS Pershore: 2 pm. • Walk; Garden design, Greenbank Garden, Strathclyde: 7.30 pm. • Guided Walk; Harlow Carr: 2 pm.
FRI **16** Henry Elwes, b. 1846; dendrologist and collector (*Galanthus elwesii*)	16 – 17 May; Shropshire & West Mid Show, Showground, Shrewsbury (01743 362824). • 16 – 18 May; Journées des Plantes, Courson, near Paris (0033 164 58 90 12). See also Shows section. • 16 – 18 May; Rassemblement des Pepinieristes Collectionneurs, Gaujacq, Landes. • Walk; Summer evening, Waddesdon Manor, Bucks.
SAT **17** George Glenny, d. 1874; popular gardening writer	AGS Midland Show, Solihull: 11.30 am (0121 5202699). • Aberdeen Show, Ruthrieston West Church Hall, SRGC: 12 pm (01224 318617). • Lecture; Plants for scent and colour, Brenda Jones, Wilts. & Avon HPS. • Demonstrations: Hanging baskets, Holland Arms Garden Centre, Gwynedd. • Walk in the woods, Waddesdon Manor, Bucks.: 1.30 & 3.30 pm. • Morning bird watch, Ness: 9 am.
SUN **18**	Walk; May-time medley, RHS Wisley: 10.30 am. • National Trust Spring Plant Fairs at about 50 NT properties nationwide: see Shows section. • Plant Sale; Quenington Old Rectory, Gloucs.; Gloucestershire Gardens & Landscape Trust: 11 am – 4 pm. • Walk; Propagation, The Vyne, Hampshire (NT): 2.30 pm. • Greville Day; Edwardian celebrations, Polesden Lacey, Surrey (NT). • Workshop; Green woodworking, Westonbirt Arboretum. • Plant Market, Birmingham Botanical Gardens & Glasshouses. • Rare Plants Fair; Dyrham House, near Bath: 11 am – 4 pm (0117 9691570). • Walk; Late spring, Cragside, Northumberland (NT): 2 pm. • Plant Sale; For NCCPG, Lydney Park Gardens, Gloucs. • Walk; Spring tour, Hillier Arboretum: 2 pm.

EVENTS   DIARY

Walk; May-time medley, RHS Wisley: 10.30 am. • Demonstration; Late spring colour, RHS Pershore at Kings Heath Park: 2 pm. • Walk; Meet the gardener, Sheffield Park, East Sussex (NT): 2 pm.	**MON** **19**
20 – 23 May; Chelsea Flower Show, Royal Hospital Grounds: 8 am – 8 pm. Includes NAFAS flower arrangement marquee. See also Shows section. • Walk; Ham House, London (NT): 2 pm & 3 pm. • Walk; Meet the gardener, Hinton Ampner, Hampshire (NT): 2.15 pm.	Richard Cox, d. 1845; brewer ('Cox's Orange Pippin') **TUE** **20**
Demonstration: Watering techniques, RHS Hyde Hall at Writtle: 2 pm. • Walk; Spring tour, Hillier Arboretum: 2 pm. • Walk; Claremont Gardens, Surrey (NT): 2.30 pm. • Also: Chelsea Flower Show: 8 am – 8 pm.	Alexander Pope, b. 1688; poet and gardener **WED** **21**
National Trust Lecture; Lyme Park: a chameleon in disguise, James Rothwell, 66 Portland Place: 6.30 pm. • Walk; Meet the gardener, Emmetts Garden, Kent (NT): 7 pm. • Also: Chelsea Flower Show: 8 am – 8 pm.	Margaret Mee, b. 1909; botanical artist **THU** **22**
23 – 25 May; Hadlow '97 Convention; 75th anniversary conference, British Iris Society, Kent. • 23 – 25 May; Painting Course, Altamont House & Gardens, Co. Carlow. • Also: Chelsea Flower Show: 8 am – 5 pm.	**FRI** **23**
24 May – 1 June; Christie's Garden Festival week. Organised by the Historic Houses Association (South East): gardens include Pashley Manor Gardens in East Sussex and Boughton Monchelsea Place (01622 743120) and St Mary's House (01903 816205) in Kent. • 24 – 25 May; Herts. County Show, Redbourn (M1, J9) (01582 792626). • 24 – 26 May; Woburn Abbey Gardening Festival (0121 711 4728). • 24 – 25 May; Plant Fair, Killerton House, Devon (NT). • 24 May – 1 June; Open week and Fern exhibition, Glasgow Botanic Garden. • 24 – 26 May; Arts & Crafts Festival, Exbury Gardens, Hampshire. • 24 – 26 May; Mid Sussex Craft Show, Borde Hill Garden, W. Sussex. • Workshop; Planting hanging baskets and containers, RHS Pershore: 10 am. • AGS Southport Show, Lord Street South: 11.30 am (01204 61233). • Walk; Rhododendrons, Speke Hall (NT): 2 pm. • Also: British Iris Society convention.	**SAT** **24**
25 – 26 May; Country Show, Broadlands, Hants. • 25 – 26 May; Garden Fair for Christie's Garden Festival, Finchcocks, Goudhurst, Kent (01580 211702). • 25 – 27 May; Kent Garden Show, Detling (M2, J5) (01795 474660). • 25 May – 1 June; Gardens open for Christie's Festival, Chiddingstone Castle, Kent (01892 870347). • 25 – 26 May; Wine Festival with music and crafts for Christie's Garden Festival, Mount Ephraim Gardens, Kent. • Walk; Spring tour, Hillier Arboretum: 2 pm. • Rare Plants Fair; Tredegar House, Newport: 11 am – 5 pm (0117 9691570). • Let's face the music and dance with the WWF, Westonbirt Arboretum. • Garden Open; For Marie Curie Cancer Care, The Manor House, Birlingham: 2 – 5 pm.	John, 3rd Earl Bute, b. 1713; prime minister and botanist **SUN** **25**

DIARY

EVENTS

MON **26**	W. J. Bean, b. 1863; *Trees & Shrubs Hardy in the British Isles*	Surrey County Show, Stoke Park, Guildford (01483 414651). • Northumberland County Show, Corbridge (01434 344443). • Azalea day; Plants for sale. High Beeches, West Sussex: 1 – 5 pm. • Open weekend; Rhododendrons at Hydon Nurseries, Surrey. • AGM, International Dendrology Society, Piccadilly: 6 pm. • Walk; Tree gazing, Westonbirt Arboretum. • Also: Christie's Garden Festival; Country Show, Broadlands; Woburn Abbey Gardening Festival; Arts & Craft Festival, Exbury Gardens; Craft Fair, Borde Hill; Garden Fair, Finchcocks; Wine Festival, Mount Ephraim Gardens.
TUE **27**	Countess Amherst, d. 1863; plant collector and patron (*Amherstia*)	Walk; Meet the gardener, Scotney Castle Garden, Kent (NT): 2 pm. • Walk; Ham House, London (NT): 2 pm & 3 pm. • Walk; Spring into summer, Mottisfont Abbey, Hampshire (NT): 2 pm. • Concert; Telemann Ensemble, Glasgow Botanic Garden.
WED **28**		28 – 31 May; Royal Bath and West Show, Shepton Mallet (01749 822200). • 28 – 29 May; Staffordshire County Show, Stafford (01785 258060). • 28 – 29 May; Suffolk Show, Ipswich (01473 726847). • Workshop; Marie Curie Charity Study Day, RHS Rosemoor. • Walk; Spring tour, Hillier Arboretum: 2 pm. • Bat Walk; Dunster Castle, Somerset (NT). • Lecture; Ponds and bogs: the hard landscape, Hillier Arboretum: 7.30 pm. • Walk; Claremont Gardens, Surrey (NT): 2.30 pm. • Lecture & Walk; A garden in all seasons, Speke Hall (0151 427 7231). • Show; St Nicholas de la Grave, Tarn et Garonne.
THU **29**	Leopold de Rothschild, d. 1917; creator of Ascott, Buckinghamshire	Lecture; Salad days, using the unusual, RHS Pershore: 2 pm. • Workshop; Ponds and bogs: the soft landscape, Hillier Arboretum: 10.30 am. • Course; Queen's Garden, RBG Kew (0181 332 5623). • Children's Event; Riotous rainbows, Hillier Arboretum: 2 – 4 pm. • Walk; Wildlife of the night, The Vyne, Hampshire (NT): 8.30 pm. • Concert; Telemann Ensemble, Glasgow Botanic Garden.
FRI **30**	Alexander Pope, d. 1744; poet and gardener	30 May – 1 June; National Gardening Show, Strathclyde Country Park: 10 am – 6.30 pm. Includes RHS Show. See Shows section also. • 30 May – 1 June; Great Garden & Countryside Festival, Holker Hall, Cumbria (01539 558838). • Walk in the woods, Waddesdon Manor, Bucks.: 1.30 & 3.30 pm • Walk; Wildlife of the night, The Vyne, Hampshire (NT): 8.30 pm.
SAT **31**		31 May – 1 June; Iris picnic weekend, Croftway Nursery, West Sussex. • 31 May – 1 June; Southern Counties Game & Country Fair, Highclere Castle, Berks. • Lecture; Plants of South Africa, RHS Pershore: 10 am. • Demonstration; Art of the gardener: practical gardening techniques, Rowallane Garden, Co. Down (NT): 2.30 pm. • Walk; Early summer flowers, Bookham Commons, Surrey (NT): 2 pm.
SUN **1**	William Bull, d. 1902; orchid hybridiser	Walk; Champion trees at Hillier Arboretum: 2 pm. • Rare Plants Fair; Ashley Manor, Tetbury: 11 am – 5 pm (0117 9691570). • NGS Open Day; Geraniums, Glebe Cottage Plants, Devon: 2 – 5 pm. • Geranium Study Day, East Lambrook Manor, Somerset. • Walk; St Andrews Botanic Garden, Fife. • Pipes & Drums, Glasgow Botanic Garden. • Concert; Brass Band, Borde Hill Garden, W. Sussex: 2 – 4 pm.

EVENTS

DIARY

2 – 5 June; Tour of Belgian gardens, Wiltshire Gardens Trust. • Demonstration; Your garden in June, RHS Pershore at Kings Heath Park: 2 pm.

Vita Sackville West, d. 1962; creator of Sissinghurst Castle, Kent

MON

2

Demonstration: Propagating plants for glasshouse display, RHS Hyde Hall at Writtle: 7 pm. • Demonstration: Your garden in June, RHS Pershore: 2 pm. • Walk; Ham House, London (NT): 2 pm & 3 pm. • Course; The Edwardian garden, Caroline Holmes, Museum of Garden History.

Robert, 8th Baron Petre, b. 1713; introduced *Camellia japonica*

TUE

3

4 – 6 June; AGM & Conference, National Society of Allotment & Leisure Gardeners. • Walks; Eco-friendly garden; Don't be a slave to your garden, RHS Rosemoor: 11 am and 2 pm. • Walk; Flowering shrubs, followed by wine, bread, cheese, Westonbirt Arboretum: 7 pm. • Walk; Stream garden, Speke Hall (NT): 2 pm. • Walk; Claremont Gardens, Surrey (NT): 2.30 pm.

Nathaniel Ward, d. 1868; inventor of Wardian case

WED

4

5 – 8 June; Rose and summer flower festival, Pashley Manor Gardens, East Sussex. • 5 – 7 June; Royal Cornwall Show, Wadebridge (01208 812183). • 5 – 7 June; South of England Show, Ardingly (01444 892700). • 5 – 7 June; Guernsey Flower Show, Cambridge Park (01481 43667). • Lecture; Design: vertical gardening, Fiona Hope, RHS Pershore: 2 pm. • Also: National Society of Allotment & Leisure Gardeners Conference.

George Loddiges, d. 1846; nurseryman and artist (*Botanical Cabinet*)

THU

5

6 – 8 June; The Garden Show, Stansted Park, Hampshire: 10 am – 5 pm. Includes lectures, stands and exhibitions. • 6 – 8 June; NCCPG National AGM, hosted by Strathclyde group, Glasgow Caledonian University. Includes garden tours, lectures and plant sales. • 6 – 8 June; Gardening course with visits, Altamont Garden, Co. Carlow. • 6 – 8 June; Garden Festival, Ness. • Demonstrations: Planting containers, RHS Hyde Hall: 11 am, 2 pm. • Also: Rose festival, Pashley Manor; Royal Cornwall Show; South of England Show; National Society of Allotment & Leisure Gardeners Conference; Guernsey Flower Show.

Robert Brown, d. 1858; botanist and president of Linnean Society (*Rosa brunonii*)

FRI

6

7 – 15 June; Wildlife Week. Over 300 events organised by the Wildlife Trusts (01522 544400). • 7 – 15 June; National Herb Week. • 7 – 8 June; Orchid Fayre, Tatton Park, Cheshire. • 7 – 8 June; Bonsai Show, Capel Manor, London. • 7 – 8 June; Craft Fair, Castle Bromwich Hall, West Midlands. • 7 – 8 June; Gardeners' Fair, Burton Agnes Hall Gardens, Humberside. • Plant Sale; NCCPG E. Dorset: 10 am – 12 noon. • AGS Summer South Show, Merrist Wood College: 11.30 am (01932 346390). • Open Day; Pershore College of Horticulture. • Concert; Bishop Grosseteste College concert, Grimsthorpe Castle, Lincs. • Walk; Claremont Gardens, Surrey (NT): 2 pm.

SAT

7

Walk; Summer, RHS Wisley: 10.30 am. • NCCPG Plant Sale, Belsay Hall, Northumberland: 10 am – 4 pm. • World Environment Day celebration, Ness: 2 pm. • Walk; Early summer, Wallington Hall, Northumberland (NT): 2 pm. • Pansies & violas event, Dudmaston, Shropshire (NT): 2 – 5.30 pm. • Rare & Unusual Plant Fair; Dingle Plants & Gardens, Stamford, Primrose Fairs: 10 am – 4 pm.

Joseph Paxton, d. 1865; designer of Crystal Palace

SUN

8

DIARY		EVENTS
MON 9	E. F. Warburg, d. 1966; botanist (*Quercus warburgii*)	Demonstration; Softwood cuttings, RHS Pershore at Kings Heath Park: 2 pm.
TUE 10	Sir Cecil Hanbury MP, d. 1936; owner and improver of La Mortola gardens	10 – 12 June; Three Counties Agricultural Show, Malvern (01684 892751). • Lecture; Gardens from the far east, Andrew Boorman, RHS Hyde Hall: 7 pm. • Rose Clinic; Mottisfont Abbey, Hampshire (NT): 6.45 pm. • Course; Atmospheric watercolour, Wendy Jelbert, Englefield House Garden, Berks. • Walk; Ham House, London (NT): 2 pm & 3 pm.
WED 11		11 – 15 June; BBC Gardeners' World Live, NEC Birmingham: 9 am – 7pm. Includes RHS show. See also Shows section. • 11 – 12 June; Early Summer Flower Show, Howard Davis Park, Jersey (01534 37227). • 11 – 12 June; Twelfth Night, Theatre Set-Up, Dunster Castle, Somerset (NT). • Walk; Summer, RHS Wisley: 10.30 am. • Demonstration: Summer treatment of grapes, RHS Wisley: 10.30 am. • Workshop; Miniature kitchen gardens, Hillier Arboretum: 10.30 am. • Walk; Claremont Gardens, Surrey (NT): 2.30 pm. • Lecture; Parterres, Caroline Holmes, Waddesdon Manor, Bucks. • Walk; Tree gazing, Westonbirt Arboretum. • Also: Three Counties Show.
THU 12		Demonstration: Summer treatment of grapes, RHS Wisley: 10.30 am. • Walk; Rhododendrons, Cragside, Northumberland (NT): 7 pm. • Walk; Estate and woodland walk, Polesden Lacey, Surrey (NT): 6.30 pm. • Also: BBC Gardeners' World Live: 9 am – 7 pm; Three Counties Show; Twelfth Night, Dunster Castle; Early Summer Flower Show, Jersey.
FRI 13		13 – 15 June; Essex County Show, Chelmsford (01733 234451). • 13 – 17 June; Thomas Hardy's Wessex: Flower Festival, NAFAS display, Hillier Arboretum: 11 am – 5 pm. • 13 – 15 June; Summer Antiques Fair, Arley Hall, Cheshire. • Opera; Dyrham Park, Avon (NT). • Also: BBC Gardeners' World Live: 9 am – 7 pm.
SAT 14	Cecil Andrews, d. 1951; botanist	Plant Fair; Saltram House, Devon (NT). • Concert; Four Seasons by candlelight, Grimsthorpe Castle, Lincs. • Walk; Pests and diseases, Greenbank Garden, Strathclyde: 2.30 pm. • Lecture; Holland Arms Garden Centre, Gwynedd. • Course; Flower arranging, Altamont Garden, Co. Carlow. • Opera; Madame Butterfly, How Caple Court, H & W. • National Show, British & European Geranium Society, Oakwood School, Horley, Surrey (01293 516237): 2 – 5 pm. • Opera; Dyrham Park, Avon (NT). • Walk; Guided rose walk (in Dutch), Pépinières Louis Lens, Oudenburg, Belgium. • Also: BBC Gardeners' World Live: 9 am – 7 pm; Essex County Show; Flower Festival, Hillier Arboretum.
SUN 15		Demonstration: Management of protective crops, RHS Wisley: 10.30 am. • National Pelargonium Show, Capel Manor, London. • Midland Bonsai Society Annual Show, Birmingham Botanical Gardens. • Open Day; *Iris sibirica*, Lingen Nursery & Garden, Shropshire. Contribution to NCCPG. • Bonsai Show, Birmingham Botanical Gardens & Glasshouses. • Also: BBC Gardeners' World Live: 9 am – 6 pm; Essex County Show; Flower Festival, Hillier Arboretum.

EVENTS

DIARY

16 – 20 June; Aspects of gardening course, RBG Kew (0181 332 5623). • Demonstration; New plants for your garden, RHS Pershore at Kings Heath Park: 2 pm.

William Paul, b. 1822; rose nurseryman and breeder

MON 16

17 – 18 June; Cheshire County Show, Tabley (01829 760020). • Demonstration: Ornamental fruit garden: maintenance and training, RHS Pershore: 2 pm. • Walk; Plants from high places, University of Oxford Botanic Garden: 7 pm. • Rose Clinic; Mottisfont Abbey, Hampshire (NT): 6.45 pm. • Walk; Ham House, London (NT): 2 pm & 3 pm.

TUE 17

18 – 19 June; Lincolnshire Show, Grange de Lings (01522 522900). • Flower Arranging Demonstration; Here comes the bride, Molly Watson, RHS Wisley: 10 am. • Walk; Fragrant and aromatic plants, RHS Hyde Hall at Writtle: 2 pm. • Demonstration: Hardy and tender perennials, RHS Rosemoor at Cannington: 2 pm. • Walk; Summer, Cliveden, Bucks. (NT): 11 am. • Walk; Meet the gardener, Hinton Ampner, Hampshire (NT): 2.15 pm. • Walk; Claremont Gardens, Surrey (NT): 2.30 pm.

William Cobbett, d. 1835; journalist, writer and horticultural economist

WED 18

19 – 22 June; Course: Botanical drawing and painting, Pauline Dean, RHS Wisley. • 19 – 22 June; Royal Highland Show, Ingliston (0131 3332444). • Lecture and tour; Maintaining the Pershore tropical house, RHS Pershore: 2 pm. • Walk; Pests and diseases, Greenbank Garden, Strathclyde: 7.30 pm. • Guided Walk; Harlow Carr: 2 pm. • Lecture; The Colorado plateau, Chris Norton, AGS Exeter Group, St Thomas High School. • Walk; Azaleas, Dunham Massey, Cheshire (NT): 7 pm.

Sir Joseph Banks, d. 1820; botanist

THU 19

20 – 22 June; Garden of England Flower Show. • 20 – 21 June; Music and Fireworks, Borde Hill Garden, W. Sussex. (subject to confirmation)

C. Quest-Ritson. b. 1947; old rose expert

FRI 20

21 June – 6 July; Riot of roses fortnight, RHS Wisley. • 21 – 22 June; Festival of Gardening at Midsummer, Hatfield House, Herts. (01707 262823). • 21 – 22 June; Organic gardening weekend, HDRA Ryton. • 21 – 22 June; Enfield Rose & Horticultural Show, Capel Manor, London. • 21 – 22 June; Mid Sussex Country Show, Borde Hill Garden, W. Sussex. • Course; Plant and garden photography, RHS Hyde Hall at Writtle. • Lecture; Old-fashioned roses, Michael Marriott, RHS Pershore: 10 am. • AGS Summer North Show, Pudsey Civic Hall: 11.30 am (01246 415097). • Concert and Fireworks, Highclere Castle, Berks. • Phlomis Open Day; Just Phlomis, Gloucs.: 2 – 5 pm. • Walk; Guided rose walk (in French), Pépinières Louis Lens, Oudenburg, Belgium.

Sir Thomas Hanbury, b. 1832; creator of gardens at La Mortola and benefactor of Wisley to RHS

SAT 21

Workshop: Propagating Mediterranean plants, RHS Rosemoor: 11 am. • Walk; Mediterranean plants, RHS Rosemoor: 2 pm. • Open Day; Kittoch Mill Hosta Garden, Strathclyde: 2 – 5 pm. • Rare Plants Fair; The Old Rectory, Burghfield: 11 am – 5 pm (0117 9691570). • Rare & Unusual Plant Fair; Bressingham Plant Centre, Elton Hall, Cambs., Primrose Fairs: 10 am – 4 pm. • National Rose Show, Canadian Rose Society, Civic Garden Centre, Toronto.

SUN 22

DIARY		EVENTS
MON **23**	Eleanor Sinclair Rohde, d. 1950; writer	
TUE **24**		24 – 25 June; RHS Flower Show, Westminster: 11 am – 7 pm. Includes ornamental plant and British National Carnation Society competitions. ● RHS Lecture; Horticulture and nature conservation, Lord Selbourne, Westminster. ● Demonstration: Medicinal herbs and their uses, RHS Pershore: 2 pm. ● Workshop; Perennials 1, Glasgow Botanic Garden. ● Walk; Ham House, London (NT): 2 pm & 3 pm. ● Rose Clinic; Mottisfont Abbey, Hampshire (NT): 6.45 pm.
WED **25**	David Douglas, b. 1799; plant collector (Douglas Fir)	25 – 26 June; Royal Norfolk Show, New Costessey (01603 748931). ● Demonstration: Pruning shrubs, RHS Wisley: 2 pm. ● Lecture; Roses of China, Roger Phillips, Hinton St Mary Manor, NCCPG Dorset. ● Walk; Claremont Gardens, Surrey (NT): 2.30 pm. ● Also: RHS Flower Show: 10 am – 5 pm.
THU **26**	Rev. Gilbert White, d. 1793; naturalist	Walk; Roses, RHS Hyde Hall: 11 am. ● Demonstration: Design: the natural pool, RHS Pershore: 2 pm. ● National Trust Lecture; 20th century icons: from Willow Road to Forthlin Road and beyond, Kenneth Powell, 66 Portland Place: 6.30 pm. ● Also: Royal Norfolk Show.
FRI **27**	Allan Cunningham, d. 1839; botanist and collector	27 – 28 June; Royal Windsor Rose and Horticultural Society Summer Show, Home Park (01753 852352). Includes National Sweet Pea Society, Provincial Show. ● 27 – 29 June; Gardeners' Weekend, Hever Castle, Kent (01732 865224). ● 27 – 29 June; Anglian Flower & Garden Show, Wimpole Hall, Cambs. (NT). ● Walk; Roses, RHS Hyde Hall: 11 am.
SAT **28**	Robert Stephenson Clarke, b. 1862; creator of Borde Hill, Sussex	28 – 29 June; RNRS National Southern Show, Squires Garden Centre, Twickenham. ● 28 – 29 June; Middlesex Show, Uxbridge (0181 8661367). ● 28 – 29 June; Newbury Garden & Leisure Show, Chieveley (01635 247111). ● 28 – 29 June; The Garden Event at West Dean, West Sussex (01243 811205). ● 28 – 29 June; Ipswich Flower Show, Suffolk Showground (01473 401733). ● 28 – 29 June; Delphinium Society Show, RHS Wisley: 12 – 7 pm. ● 28 – 29 June; Southern Geranium & Pelargonium Society exhibition, Hillier Arboretum: 11 am – 5 pm. ● 28 – 29 June; Garden Festival, Barton under Neederwood, Staffs. Includes South Staffs. Bonsai Society Exhibition. ● 28 – 29 June; Garden Festival, Benington Lordship, Herts. ● Lecture; English roses, Holland Arms Garden Centre, Gwynedd. ● Demonstration; Art of the gardener: practical gardening techniques, Rowallane Garden, Co. Down (NT): 2.30 pm.
SUN **29**	Henry Doubleday, d. 1875; Quaker scientist	29 June – 4 July; International Heritage Rose Conference, Cambridge. ● Demonstration: Pruning shrubs, RHS Wisley: 10.30 am. ● Rare Plants Fair; The Manor House, Birlingham: 11 am – 5 pm (0117 9691570). ● Open Day; RNRS Rose 2000 Appeal, Elton Hall, Cambs.: 2 – 6 pm. ● Walk; Wild flowers and wild flower management, The Vyne, Hampshire (NT): 11 am.

EVENTS   DIARY

30 June – 6 July; NAFAS National Show, Telford Exhibition Centre. ● 30 June – 3 July; The Royal Show, Stoneleigh (01203 696969).	Sir Joseph Hooker, b. 1817; botanist **MON** **30**
Lecture; An evening with Hyde Hall's roses, RHS Hyde Hall: 7 pm. ● Demonstration: Your garden in July, RHS Pershore: 2 pm. ● Workshop; Perennials 2, Glasgow Botanic Garden. ● Walk; Ham House, London (NT): 2 pm & 3 pm. ● Rose Clinic; Mottisfont Abbey, Hampshire (NT): 6.45 pm. ● Also: NAFAS National Show; Royal Show.	Henry Doubleday, b. 1808; Quaker scientist **TUE** **1**
Demonstration: Budding fruit trees, RHS Wisley: 10.30 am. ● Lecture and walk; Plants for tropical butterflies, RHS Hyde Hall at Writtle: 2 pm. ● Walk; Summer evening, Waddesdon Manor, Bucks. ● Walk; Claremont Gardens, Surrey (NT): 2.30 pm. ● Opera; Magic Flute by Musical Theatre Kernow, Dunster Castle, Somerset (NT). ● Also: NAFAS National Show; Royal Show.	Augustine Henry, b. 1857; collector **WED** **2**
Lecture; Designing with tender perennials, RHS Pershore: 2 pm. ● Wildflower Walk; Harlow Carr: 2 pm. ● Course; Herb topiary, Anne Jennings, Museum of Garden History. ● Outing; Wiltshire Gardens Trust to Mapperton & Chettle. ● Musical gala evening, Capel Manor, London. ● Also: NAFAS National Show; Royal Show.	**THU** **3**
4 – 6 July; Southampton Balloon & Flower Festival (01703 832525). ● 4 – 6 July; Festival of food, drink and dance, Grimsthorpe Castle, Lincs. ● 4 – 10 July; Indoor Fuchsia Show, Deutsche Dahlien-, Fuchsien- und Gladiolen-Gesellschaft. ● Demonstration: Pruning shrubs, RHS Hyde Hall: 11 am. ● Concert; Jazz in the Park, Dyrham Park, Avon (NT). ● Also: NAFAS National Show.	Sir Thomas Raffles, d. 1826; (*Rafflesia*) **FRI** **4**
5 – 6 July; Rose weekend; Lectures, walks, demonstrations and advice, RHS Rosemoor. ● 5 – 6 July; Summer fruits family fun weekend, Brogdale. ● 5 – 6 July; Gardeners' Weekend at Shugborough Hall (0121 7114728). ● 5 – 6 July; Open weekend, Capel Manor, London. ● AGS Cheltenham Show, Pittville School: 12 pm (01242 510144). ● Walk; Claremont Gardens, Surrey (NT): 2 pm. ● Concert; Fireworks and orchestral concert, Arley Hall, Cheshire. ● Theatre, Highclere Castle, Berks. ● Concert; Music of the 60s & 70s, Dyrham Park, Avon (NT). ● Jazz Concert; Acker Bilk, Westonbirt Arboretum. ● Course; The potager, Altamont Garden, Co. Carlow.	Bishop Henry Compton, d. 1713; botanist and creator of Fulham Palace, London **SAT** **5**
Market Bosworth Show. Includes National Sweet Pea Society National Show. ● Open Day; Kittoch Mill Hosta Garden, Strathclyde: 2 – 5 pm. ● Walk; Midsummer, Wallington Hall, Northumberland (NT): 2 pm. ● Rose Fayre; Bressingham Plant Centre, Elton Hall, Cambridgeshire. ● Rare & Unusual Plant Fair; Fulbeck Hall, Lincs., Primrose Fairs: 10 am – 4 pm. ● Walk; Choosing perennials, Hillier Arboretum: 2 pm. ● Walk; St Andrews Botanic Garden, Fife. ● Workshop; Wild flowers of Westonbirt, Westonbirt Arboretum. ● Concert; Brass Band, Borde Hill Garden, W. Sussex: 2 – 4 pm. ● Concert; Afternoon music, Highclere Castle, Berks.	Sir Harry Veitch, d. 1924; nurseryman and orchidist **SUN** **6**

DIARY		EVENTS
MON 7	Henry Hoare, b. 1705; created Stourhead, Wiltshire	Demonstration; Your garden in July, RHS Pershore at Kings Heath Park: 2 pm. • Also: Dance festival, Grimsthorpe Castle.
TUE 8	Rev. James Backhouse, b. 1794; nurseryman and botanist	8 – 13 July; Hampton Court Palace Flower Show: 10 am – 5 pm. Preview Day. Includes NAFAS exhibit. See also Shows section. • 8 – 10 July; Great Yorkshire Show, Harrogate (01423 561536). • Lecture; Lilies for your garden, Duncan Coombs, RHS Pershore: 2 pm. • Walk; Plants for people, University of Oxford Botanic Garden: 7 pm. • Walk; Ham House, London (NT): 2 pm & 3 pm.
WED 9	Rev. Keble Martin, b. 1877; botanist in Britain	9 – 13 July; RNRS British Rose Festival at Hampton Court. • 9 – 13 July; Fête Champêtre, Claremont Gardens, Surrey (NT) (01372 459950). • Walk; Hylands Park. Contact RHS Hyde Hall. • Walk; Nymans, West Sussex (NT): 2.30 pm. • Also: Hampton Court: 10 am – 7.30 pm; Great Yorkshire Show.
THU 10	Sir F. Stern, d. 1967; creator of Highdown, West Sussex	10 – 12 July; Kent County Show, Detling (01622 630975). • 10 – 12 July; Theatre by Off the Ground Productions, Ness. • Lecture; Garden design, Susanna Brown, RHS Pershore: 2 pm. • Also: Hampton Court Palace Flower Show: 10 am – 7.30 pm; Great Yorkshire Show; Fête Champêtre, Claremont Garden.
FRI 11	E. C. Buxton, d. 1925; plantsman (Geranium 'Buxton's Blue')	11 – 13 July; Painting course, Altamont House & Gardens, Co. Carlow. • 11 – 12 July; 20s Summer follies, Packwood House, West Midlands (NT). • Opera; Gala evening, Opera Brava, Westonbirt Arboretum. • Also: Hampton Court Palace Flower Show: 10 am – 7.30 pm; Kent County Show; Theatre, Ness; Fête Champêtre, Claremont Garden.
SAT 12	David Douglas d. 1834; plant collector	12 – 19 July; Island of Jersey Floral Festival (0171 493 5278). • 12 – 13 July; Gardeners Weekend, Castle Bromwich Hall, West Midlands. • 12 – 13 July; Antiques festival, Grimsthorpe Castle, Lincs. • 12 – 13 July; Dagenham Town Show (0181 252 8137). • 12 – 13 July; South Staffs. Bonsai Society Exhibition, Shugborough Hall. • 12 – 13 June; Canadian miniature rose show, Sheridan Gardens Mall, Etobicoke, Ontario. • Walk; Summer foliage, Greenbank Garden, Strathclyde: 2.30 pm. • Walk; Herbaceous border and rose garden, Speke Hall (NT): 2 pm. • Course; Natural dyeing, RBG Kew (0181 332 5623). • Opera; Carmen, Opera Brava, Westonbirt Arboretum. • Also: Hampton Court Palace Flower Show (includes RNRS Great Summer Rose Show): 10 am – 7.30 pm; Kent County Show; Theatre, Ness; Fête Champêtre, Claremont Garden.
SUN 13	John Clare, b. 1793; nature poet	Plant Sale; Potticks House, Bradford on Avon, Wiltshire Gardens Trust: 2 pm. • Walk; Rivers and woodlands, Mottisfont Abbey, Hampshire (NT): 2 pm. • Garden Party, Borde Hill Garden, W. Sussex. • Also: Hampton Court Palace Flower Show (includes RNRS Great Summer Rose Show): 10 am – 5.30 pm; Gardeners Weekend, Castle Bromwich; Dagenham Town Show; South Staffs. Bonsai Exhibition; Jersey Floral Festival; Fête Champêtre, Claremont Garden; Canadian • Miniature Rose Show.

EVENTS   DIARY

14 – 18 July; Children's activities, Glasgow Botanic Garden. • Demonstration; The sweet pea year, RHS Pershore at Kings Heath Park: 2 pm. • Also: Jersey Floral Festival.	**MON** **14**
15 – 17 July; East of England Show, Peterborough (01733 234451). • Lecture; 1,000 years of gardens in 120 minutes, Andrew Boorman, RHS Hyde Hall: 7 pm. • Lecture; Update on Pershore's *Penstemon* collection, Bob Hares, RHS Pershore: 2 pm. • Walk; Meet the gardener, Chartwell, Kent (NT): 2 pm. • Walk; Ham House, London (NT): 2 pm & 3 pm. • Walk; Meet the gardener, Hinton Ampner, Hampshire (NT): 2.15 pm. • Also: Jersey Floral Festival.	William Robinson, b. 1838; writer (*The English Flower Garden*) **TUE** **15**
16 – 19 July; Theatre by Action Theatre Transport Productions, Ness. • Flower Arranging Demonstration: Gifts from the garden, Sheila Macqueen, RHS Wisley: 10 am. • Demonstration: Pruning fruit, RHS Wisley: 10.30 am. • Demonstration; Siting, designing and stocking the garden pond, RHS Rosemoor at Cannington: 2 pm. • Walk; Claremont Gardens, Surrey (NT): 2.30 pm. • Children's Day; Dunster Castle, Somerset (NT). • Also: East of England Show; Jersey Floral Festival.	**WED** **16**
17 – 20 July; Art in Action, Waterperry Gardens, Oxfordshire. • Demonstration: Summer colour in the rock garden, RHS Pershore: 2 pm. • Guided Walk; Harlow Carr: 2 pm. • Walk; Summer foliage, Greenbank Garden, Strathclyde: 7.30 pm. • Walk; Summer colour, Dunham Massey, Cheshire (NT): 7 pm. • Course; Introduction to woodland crafts, RBG Kew (0181 332 5623). • Also: East of England Show; Theatre, Ness; Jersey Floral Festival.	Rev A. T. Boscawen, d. 1939; creator of garden at Ludgvan, Cornwall **THU** **17**
18 – 20 July; Gardening course with visits, Altamont Garden, Co. Carlow. • Walk; Herbaceous perennials and half-hardy plants, RHS Hyde Hall: 11 am. • Also: Art in Action, Waterperry Gardens; Theatre, Ness; Jersey Floral Festival.	James Bateman, b. 1811; botanist and writer (*Orchidaceae of Mexico and Guatemala*) **FRI** **18**
19 – 20 July; RNRS National Northern Rose Show, Ormesby Hall, Middlesbrough. • 19 – 20 July; Dartford Festival, Central Park (01322 343056). • 19 – 20 July; Rose open weekend, Henry Street Garden Centre, Berks. • 19 – 20 July; Arley Flower Festival, Arley Hall, Cheshire. Includes Shakespeare play. • 19 – 20 July; Country Fair, Holkham Hall, Norfolk (01328 710227). • Outing; To Hodnant Hall, RHS Pershore. • Annual Show; National Viola & Pansy Society, St John's Church, Harborne. • Open Air Classical Extravaganza, with fireworks, Wilton House, Wilts. • Fordingbridge Show, Godshill (01425 652772).	Thomas Blaikie, d. 1838; landscaper and writer (*Diary of a Scotch Gardener at the French Court*) **SAT** **19**
Demonstration: Pruning fruit, RHS Wisley: 10.30 am. • Walk; Annuals and herbaceous plants, bedding, borders and trials, RHS Wisley: 10.30 am. • Campanula & Herbaceous Open Day, Lingen Nursery & Garden, Shropshire. • Walk; NGS Day tour, The Vyne, Hampshire (NT): 2.30 pm. • Plants and people: demonstrations and displays, Hillier Arboretum: 11 am – 5 pm. • NGS Open Day; Campanulas, Glebe Cottage Plants, Devon: 2 – 5 pm. • NGS Open Day; Hughenden Manor, Bucks (NT). • NGS Open Day and Walk; Cragside, Northumberland (NT).	**SUN** **20**

DIARY		EVENTS
MON **21**		21 – 24 July; Royal Welsh Show, Builth Wells (01982 553683). • Demonstration; Summer colour, RHS Pershore at Kings Heath Park: 2 pm. • Walk; Annuals and herbaceous plants, bedding, borders and trials, RHS Wisley: 10.30 am.
TUE **22**	Charles Babington, d. 1895; Cambridge botanist (*Allium babingtonii*)	22 – 23 July; RHS Flower Show, Westminster: 11 am – 7 pm. Includes Summer Fruit & Vegetable, ornamental plant and Delphinium Society competitions. • RHS Flower Arranging Demonstration: Westminster. • RHS Lecture; Lilies, Terry Wagg, Westminster. • Demonstration: Vegetables: crop care, RHS Pershore: 2 pm. • Walk; Ham House, London (NT): 2 pm & 3 pm. • Children's Event: Nests and homes, Hillier Arboretum: 2 – 4 pm. • Walk; Summer, Mount Stewart, Co. Down (NT): 7.30 pm. • Also: Royal Welsh Show.
WED **23**		Walk; Foliage, RHS Hyde Hall at Writtle: 2 pm. • Walk; Annuals and biennials, RHS Rosemoor: 11 am. • Walk; Meet the gardener, Packwood House, West Midlands (NT) 7 pm. • Workshop; A wild day, Hillier Arboretum: 10 am. • Course; Edible landscaping, HDRA Ryton. • Walk; Claremont Gardens, Surrey (NT): 2.30 pm. • Lecture & Walk; A garden for all seasons, Speke Hall (NT) (0151 427 7231). • Also: RHS Flower Show: 10 am – 5 pm; Royal Welsh Show.
THU **24**	Montagu Allwood, d. 1958; breeder of carnations and pinks	24 – 27 July; CLA Game Fair, Castle Ashby, Northants (01256 389434). • Demonstration: Ornamental fruit garden: summer pruning, RHS Pershore: 2 pm. • National Trust Lecture; Building in harmony: the relationship of modern architecture to traditional surroundings, George Perkin, 66 Portland Place: 6.30 pm.
FRI **25**	William Forsyth, d. 1804; co-founder of the RHS (*Forsythia*)	25 – 26 July; Border Union Show, Kelso (01573 224188). • 25 – 27 July; Royal Lancashire Show, Astley Park (01254 813769). • 25 – 27 July; St Helens Show, Sherdley Park (01744 456991). • Concert; Hatchlands Park, Surrey (NT) (01372 451596). • Also: CLA Game Fair.
SAT **26**	Joseph Arnold, d. 1818; botanist (*Rafflesia arnoldii*)	26 – 27 July; Fuchsia weekend, Bressingham Plant Centre, Norfolk. With Gouldings Fuchsias. • 26 – 27 July; Arley Garden Festival, Arley Hall, Cheshire: 10 am – 5 pm. • 26 – 27 July; Fuchsia Show, Capel Manor, London. • Malton Show. • Abergavenny & Border Counties Show, Llanwenarth. • Demonstration; Art of the gardener: practical gardening techniques, Rowallane Garden, Co. Down (NT): 2.30 pm. • Concert; An evening at the Proms, English National Orchestra, for the NT, Westonbirt Arboretum. • Concert; Hatchlands Park, Surrey (NT) (01372 451596). • Also: CLA Game Fair; Border Union Show; Royal Lancashire Show; St Helens Show.
SUN **27**		International Bog Day; events nationwide organised by the Wildlife Trusts (01522 544400). • Clematis Day; Roseland House Nursery, Cornwall: 2 – 5 pm. • Workshop; Ornamental grasses, Hillier Arboretum: 10.30 am. • NGS Open Day; Glebe Cottage Plants, Devon: 2 – 5 pm. • Concert; Hatchlands Park, Surrey (NT) (01372 451596). • Also: Arley Garden Festival: 10 am – 5 pm; Fuchsia weekend, Bressingham; CLA Game Fair; Border Union Show; Royal Lancashire Show; St Helens Show; Fuchsia Show, Capel Manor.

EVENTS

DIARY

28 July – 10 August; Children's fortnight, Marston Exotics. ● Demonstration; Cuttings from your garden, RHS Pershore at Kings Heath Park: 2 pm.	Abraham Cowley, d. 1667; botanist and poet **MON** **28**
29 – 31 July; New Forest & Hampshire County Show, Brockenhurst (01590 622400). ● Outing and lecture; To Ryton Organic Gardens, RHS Pershore. ● Walk; Plant hunters, University of Oxford Botanic Garden: 7 pm. ● Walk; Ham House, London (NT): 2 pm & 3 pm.	E. B. Anderson, d. 1971; plantsman and writer **TUE** **29**
Cardigan & District Agricultural Show, Briscwm Fields (01239 615438). ● Nantwich & South Cheshire Show, Dorfold Hall Park (01270 780306). ● Sandringham Flower Show (01485 540860). ● Walk; Claremont Gardens, Surrey (NT): 2.30 pm. ● Walk; Rose garden, Speke Hall (NT): 2 pm. ● Also: New Forest Show.	**WED** **30**
Demonstration: Summer pruning of shrubs, RHS Pershore: 2 pm ● Guided Walk; Harlow Carr: 2 pm. ● Also: New Forest Show.	Robert Gathorne-Hardy, b. 1902; writer **THU** **31**
1 – 31 August; Art exhibition by Sally Ann Nunn, Barry Peckham and Richard Tratt, Hillier Arboretum: 11 am – 5 pm. ● 1 – 3 August; Portsmouth & Southsea Show, Southsea Common (01705 834146). ● 1 – 3 August; South East Garden Festival, Historic Dockyard, Chatham (01795 844939). ● 1 – 3 August; Craft Show, Broadlands, Hants.	Lord Digby, b. 1894; creator of garden at Minterne, Dorset **FRI** **1**
2 – 17 August; Family fortnight, RHS Wisley. ● 2 – 3 August; Open Weekend, Thompson & Morgan, Poplar Lane, Ipswich. ● 2 – 3 August; Organic gardening weekend, HDRA Ryton. ● 2 – 5 August; International Society of Arboriculture Conference, Salt Lake City. ● Children's workshop, RHS Pershore: 10 am. ● Oswestry & District Show, Park Hall (01691 654875). ● Brecon County Show (01568 708760). ● Dumfries & Lockerbie Show, Park Farm (01461 203551). ● Course; Herbs: cultivation, cooking and cures, Altamont Garden, Co. Carlow. ● Walk; Claremont Gardens, Surrey (NT): 2 pm. ● Jazz Concert; Sudeley Castle & Gardens, Gloucs. ● Also: Craft Show, Broadlands; South East Garden Festival; Portsmouth & Southsea Show.	Joseph Thomson, d. 1895; botanist in Africa **SAT** **2**
Walk; Choosing shrubs, Hillier Arboretum: 2 pm. ● Bud while-u-wait, Brogdale. ● Walk; Late summer, Wallington Hall, Northumberland (NT): 2 pm. ● NGS Open Day; Glebe Cottage Plants, Devon: 2 – 5 pm. ● Open Day; For NGS & RNRS, Tissington Hall Gardens, Derbyshire. ● Concert; Brass Band, Borde Hill Garden, W. Sussex: 2 – 4 pm. ● Walk; St Andrews Botanic Garden, Fife. ● Concert; BBC Big Band, Grimsthorpe Castle, Lincs. ● Fuchsia Show, Borde Hill Garden, W. Sussex. ● Also: Open Weekend, Thompson & Morgan; Craft Show, Broadlands; South East Garden Festival; Portsmouth & Southsea Show.	Sir Joseph Paxton, b. 1801; garden designer **SUN** **3**

DIARY		EVENTS
MON 4	John Tradescant, Snr, b. 1608; royal gardener	4 – 29 August; Exhibition: The flowering of the letter, Museum of Garden History. • 4 – 5 August; Turriff Show, The Haughs (01888 563991). • Demonstration; Summer pruning of trees and shrubs, RHS Pershore at Kings Heath Park: 2 pm.
TUE 5	S. T. Edwards, b. 1768; botanical artist	Demonstration: Your garden in August, RHS Pershore: 2 pm. • Walk; Ham House, London (NT): 2 pm & 3 pm. • Also: Turriff Show.
WED 6	Thomas Laxton, d. 1893; nurseryman	6 – 7 August; Bakewell Show (01629 812736). • 6 – 7 August; Taunton Flower Show (01823 271597). • 6 – 7 August; Summer Flower Show, Howard Davis Park, Jersey (01534 37227). • Flower Arranging Demonstration: Spry summer, Fred Wilkinson, RHS Wisley: 10 am. • North Devon Agricultural Show, Barnstaple (01769 560205). • Walk; Claremont Gardens, Surrey (NT): 2.30 pm.
THU 7	Johann Graefer, d. 1802; botanist and garden designer	7 – 8 August; South Show, Samares Manor, Guernsey (01481 36673). • Outing; To Powis Castle, RHS Pershore. • Walk; University of Oxford Botanic Garden: 7 pm. • Children's Event: Dinosaurs and dragons, Hillier Arboretum: 2 – 4 pm. • Also: Taunton Flower Show; Bakewell Show; Jersey Summer Flower Show.
FRI 8	Lady Amelia Hume, d. 1809; gardener	8 – 17 August; Bonsai Summer School, Greenwood Gardens, Notts. • Concert and fireworks; Broadlands, Hampshire. • Opera; Dyrham Park, Avon (NT). • Theatre; The Tempest, Packwood House, West Midlands (NT). • Also: South Show, Guernsey.
SAT 9	Edward Kent Balls, b. 1892; collector	9 – 10 August; RNRS National Show for Miniature Roses, St Albans. • 9 – 10 August; Craft Fair, Grimsthorpe Castle, Lincs. • 9 – 10 August; Howden Agricultural & Horticultural Show (01430 431811). • Orkney Agricultural Show, Bignold Park (01856 771441). • Course; Summer: seasonal day course, University of Oxford Botanic Garden. • Flower Show, Broadlands, Hampshire. • Walk; Assessing the garden for change, Greenbank Garden, Strathclyde: 2.30 pm. • Opera; Dyrham Park, Avon (NT). • Theatre; The Tempest, Packwood House, West Midlands (NT).
SUN 10	Frank Ludlow, b. 1885; plant collector	10 – 11 August; Modern rose show, Norsk Roseforening, Freia Park, Oslo. • Walk; Heathers all year round, RHS Wisley: 10.30 am. • Borders Day with RHSE, RHS Rosemoor. • Annual Picnic; Sturford Mead, Corsley, Wiltshire Gardens Trust. • Concert and Teddy Bears Picnic, Highclere Castle, Berks. • Also: RNRS Miniature Rose Show; Craft Fair, Grimsthorpe Castle; Howden Show.

EVENTS

DIARY

Walk; Heathers all year round, RHS Wisley: 10.30 am.	James Pulham, d. 1898; ('Pulhamite stone') **MON 11**
12 – 13 August; Anglesey Show, Gwalchmai (01407 720072). • Demonstration: Permanent plants for pots and containers, RHS Pershore: 2 pm. • Walk; Hydrangeas, Dunham Massey, Cheshire (NT): 7 pm. • Walk; Ham House, London (NT): 2 pm & 3 pm. • Walk; Holiday Fun, Mottisfont Abbey, Hampshire (NT): 2 pm.	Rev. Samuel Goodenough, d. 1827; founder of Linnean Society **TUE 12**
13 – 14 August; West Show, L'Erée, Guernsey (01481 36673). • Demonstration: Propagation, The Mead Nursery, Wiltshire Gardens Trust. • Walk; Claremont Gardens, Surrey (NT): 2.30 pm. • Walk; Herbaceous border, Speke Hall (NT): 2 pm. • Also: Anglesey Show.	**WED 13**
14 – 15 August; Wisley Flower Show, RHS Wisley: 10 am – 6 pm. See Shows section also. • 14 – 15 August; United Counties Show, Camarthen (01267 232141). • Battle of the Flowers, St Helier, Jersey (01534 30178). • Guided Walk; Harlow Carr: 2 pm. • Walk; Formal garden in summer, Cragside, Northumberland (NT): 7 pm. • Walk; Estate and woodland walk, Polesden Lacey, Surrey (NT): 6.30 pm. • Walk; Evening tour, Lyme Park, Cheshire (NT). • Walk; Assessing the garden for change, Greenbank Garden, Strathclyde: 7.30 pm. • Children's Event: Ground under foot, Hillier Arboretum: 2 – 4 pm. • Also: West Show, Guernsey.	James Dickson, d. 1822; (*Dicksonia*) **THU 14**
15 – 16 August; Shrewsbury Flower Show, The Quarry (01743 364051). • 15 – 17 August; Ambleside Summer Flower Show, Borrans Road (01539 432252). • Also: Wisley Flower Show: 10 am – 5 pm; United Counties Show.	**FRI 15**
16 – 17 August; Bolton Show, Leverhulme Park (01204 522311 Ext. 4070). • 16 – 17 August; Hartlepool Show, Jesmond Road (01429 266522 Ext. 3403). • 16 – 17 August; As You Like It, Sudeley Castle & Gardens, Gloucs. • 16 – 17 August; Family Festival, Hillier Arboretum. • Skelton Agricultural & Horticultural Show, Hutton-in-the-Forest. • Family Barbecue, Ness: 2 pm. • Also: Shrewsbury Flower Show; Ambleside Flower Show.	**SAT 16**
Gentian day; Plants for sale. High Beeches, West Sussex: 1 – 5 pm. • Summer Plant Fair, Pashley Manor Gardens, East Sussex (01580 200692). • Open Day; For SGS, with plant sale, Glasgow Botanic Garden. • Also: Shakespeare, Sudeley Castle; Bolton Show; Hartlepool Show; Family Festival, Hillier Arboretum.	Lord Lambourne, b. 1847; RHS president (*Malus* 'Lord Lambourne') **SUN 17**

DIARY		EVENTS
MON 18		
TUE 19	Ellen Willmott, b. 1858; plantswoman and patron	19 – 20 August; RHS Flower Show, Westminster: 11 am – 7 pm. Includes Gladiolus, ornamental plant and Saintpaulia and Houseplant Society competitions and botanical photographs. • 19 – 21 August; Pembrokeshire Show, Withybush (01437 764331). • RHS Lecture, Westminster. • Walk; The gardener's palette, University of Oxford Botanic Garden: 7 pm. • Walk; Blackford Pond bat walk, Scottish Wildlife Trust: 8.30 pm. • Walk; Ham House, London (NT): 2 pm & 3 pm.
WED 20	Huttleston, Lord Fairhaven, d. 1966; creator of garden at Angelesey Abbey, Cambridgeshire	20 – 21 August; North Show and Battle of Flowers, Samarez Park, Guernsey (01481 36673). • Walk; Claremont Gardens, Surrey (NT): 2.30 pm. • Walk; Meet the gardener, Hinton Ampner, Hampshire (NT): 2.15 pm. • Course; Focus on fruit, HDRA Ryton. • Also: RHS Flower Show: 10 am – 5 pm; Pembrokeshire Show.
THU 21	James McBean, d. 1910; orchid nurseryman	21 – 23 August; Southport Flower Show (01704 547147). • 21 – 25 August; Chelmsford Spectacular (01245 490490 Ext. 2411) • Denbighshire & Flintshire Show, Denbigh (01352 712131). • Walk; University of Oxford Botanic Garden: 7 pm. • Children's Event: Fruit and nut cases, Hillier Arboretum: 2 – 4 pm. • Also: Pembrokeshire Show.
FRI 22		Lecture and Visit; Iford Manor, Wiltshire Gardens Trust. • Also: Southport Flower Show; Chelmsford Spectacular.
SAT 23	F. C. Puddle, d. 1952; creator of Bodnant Gardens, Clwyd	23 – 24 August; British Orchid Growers Association August Fayre, Elcot Park, Newbury. • 23 – 25 August; Festival of Gardening at Audley End, Essex (0121 711 4728). • 23 – 25 August; Craft Fair, Highclere Castle, Berks. • Poynton Show, Poynton Park (01625 872065). • Theatre; Twelfth Night, Dyrham Park, Avon (NT). • Also: Southport Flower Show; Chelmsford Spectacular.
SUN 24	A. W. Haworth, d. 1833; cactus botanist (*Haworthia*)	24 – 25 August; Havering Show, Hornchurch (A124). • 24 – 25 August; City of Swansea Summer Show (01792 635428). • 24 – 25 August; Canons Ashby Country Show, Northants. • NGS Open Day; Glebe Cottage Plants, Devon: 2 – 5 pm. • Also: Chelmsford Spectacular; Festival of Gardening, Audley End; BOGA Autumn Fayre; Craft Fair, Highclere Castle, Berks.

EVENTS   DIARY

Aylsham Show (01263 732432). • Fundraising day, Dunster Castle, Somerset (NT). • Madresfield Show (01684 576604). • Also: Chelmsford Spectacular; Swansea Summer Show; Havering Show; Canons Ashby Country Show; Craft Fair, Highclere Castle, Berks.	MON 25
26 August – 6 September; Floral safari, WAFA seminar, Durban SA. • Walk; Ham House, London (NT): 2 pm & 3 pm. • Walk; Moths, bats and owls, Glasgow Botanic Garden.	TUE 26
27 – 29 August; Bristol Flower Show (01980 611485). • Walk; Ferns, RHS Rosemoor: 11 am. • Walk; Claremont Gardens, Surrey (NT): 2.30 pm.	Lionel, 2nd Baron Rothschild, d. 1937; (*Gloriosa rothschildiana*) · WED 27
28 – 30 August; Ayr Flower Show (01292 282842). • Monmouthshire Show, Vauxhall Grounds, Monmouth (01291 691160). • Guided Walk; Harlow Carr: 2 pm. • Children's Event: Friend or foe: the world of fungi, Hillier Arboretum: 2 – 4 pm. • Also: Bristol Flower Show.	Neil McEacharn, b. 1885; creator of Villa Taranto · THU 28
29 – 31 August; Painting course, Altamont House & Garden, Co. Carlow. • Also: Bristol Flower Show; Ayr Flower Show.	FRI 29
Demonstration; Art of the gardener: practical gardening techniques, Rowallane Garden, Co. Down (NT): 2.30 pm. • Bulb festival starts, Holland Arms Garden Centre, Gwynedd. • Also: Ayr Flower Show.	Marianne North, d. 1890; botanical artist · SAT 30
Plant Sale; Calke Abbey, Derbyshire (NT) (0115 983 0278): 11 am – 5 pm. • Greville Day; Edwardian celebrations, Polesden Lacey, Surrey (NT).	Huttleston, Lord Fairhaven, b. 1896; creator of garden at Anglesey Abbey, Cambridgeshire · SUN 31

DIARY		EVENTS
MON 1		Demonstration; Your garden in September, RHS Pershore at Kings Heath Park: 2 pm.
TUE 2	Marion Cran, d. 1942; garden writer	Demonstration: Your garden in September, RHS Pershore: 2 pm. • Walk; Ham House, London (NT): 2 pm & 3 pm.
WED 3	Sir Frederick Moore, b. 1857; Irish botanist	3 – 28 September; Exhibition: Favourite flowers, Sue Clark, Museum of Garden History. • 3 – 4 September; Cheltenham Flower Show, Town Hall (01242 514867). • Workshop; What's up Doc?, Hillier Arboretum: 10.30 am. • Walk; Claremont Gardens, Surrey (NT): 2.30 pm.
THU 4		Lecture; Passion flowers, John Vanderplank, RHS Pershore: 2 pm. • Children's Event: Noise in the garden, Hillier Arboretum: 2 – 4 pm. • Also: Cheltenham Flower Show.
FRI 5		5 – 8 September; Heather Society Conference, Newton Rigg College (01449 711220). • 5 – 7 September; Dundee Flower Show (01382 434000).
SAT 6		Plant Sale; Auction, RHS Pershore: 10 am. • Dorchester Show (01305 264249). • Kingsbridge Show, East Allington. • Moreton-in-Marsh Show (01608 651908). • Walk; Claremont Gardens, Surrey (NT): 2 pm. • Course; Trees, Altamont Garden, Co. Carlow. • Also: Dundee Flower Show; Heather Society Conference.
SUN 7		Walk; Fruit, with tasting, RHS Wisley: 10.30 am. • National Dahlia Society Annual Show, RHS New Hall, Westminster (01628 473500). • Beningbrough Autumn Plant Fair, Beningbrough Hall, N. Yorks. (NT). • Seed collecting, Hall Farm Nursery, Lincs. • Walk; Fruitacopia, Hillier Arboretum: 2 pm. • Walk; September glory, Wallington Hall, Northumberland (NT): 2 pm. • Walk; St Andrews Botanic Garden, Fife. • Concert; Brass Band, Borde Hill Garden, W. Sussex: 2 – 4 pm. • Also: Dundee Flower Show: Heather Society Conference.

EVENTS

DIARY

8 – 21 September; September Festivities including art and flower arranging exhibitions, RHS Rosemoor. • 8 – 11 September; NAFAS National Assembly, Ormskirk. • Walk; Fruit, with tasting, RHS Wisley: 10.30 am. • Demonstration; Bulb planting, RHS Pershore at Kings Heath Park: 2 pm. • Also: Heather Society Conference.	**MON** **8**
Demonstration: Planning for late summer colour, RHS Pershore. • Walk; Ham House, London (NT): 2 pm & 3 pm. • Walk; Late summer, Mottisfont Abbey, Hampshire (NT): 2 pm. • Walk; Meet the gardener, Chartwell, Kent (NT): 2 pm. • Also: NAFAS National Assembly.	Captain William Bligh, b. 1754, introducer of bread fruits to the West Indies — **TUE** **9**
Turf Day; Demonstrations, RHS Rosemoor. • Walk; Writtle's horticultural facilities, RHS Hyde Hall at Writtle: 2 pm. • Course; Naturalistic flower painting, RBG Kew (0181 332 5623). • Walk; Claremont Gardens, Surrey (NT): 2.30 pm. • Special interest day, Waddesdon Manor, Bucks. • Course; Save your own seed, HDRA Ryton. • Also: NAFAS National Assembly.	George Bentham, d. 1884; taxonomist — **WED** **10**
11 – 14 September; Course: Botanical drawing and painting: a further step, Pauline Dean, RHS Wisley. • RHS Lecture; RBG Edinburgh and its satellites, John Main: Macclesfield. • Lecture; Touch of Tulipmania, Michael Jefferson Brown, RHS Pershore: 2 pm • Westmorland County Show, Kendal (01539 567804). • Also: NAFAS National Assembly.	Hon. Charles Hamilton, d. 1786; garden at Painshill, Surrey — **THU** **11**
12 – 14 September; Harrogate Autumn Flower Show, Hookstone Oval. Includes RNRS Great Autumn Rose Show, and National Dahlia Society Northern Show. See also Shows section. • 12 – 15 September; Dahlia Show, Deutsche Dahlien-, Fuchsien- und Gladiolen-Gesellschaft.	Gordon Rae, b. 1938; Director General of RHS — **FRI** **12**
13 – 14 September; Cider festival, Brogdale. • 13 – 14 September; Harvest Gardening Festival, Ragley Hall (0121 7114728). • Outing; To St Annes Vineyard, RHS Pershore. • Penistone Show (0114 2887816). • Bulb & Dried Flower Sale, Greenbank Garden, Strathclyde: 11 am – 5 pm. • Romsey Show, Broadlands, Hants. (01794 517521). • Open Day; Friends update, Glasgow Botanic Garden. • Also: Harrogate Autumn Flower Show.	Hon. Sir David Bowes-Lyon, d. 1964; president of the RHS — **SAT** **13**
Town & Country Show, New Costessey, Norfolk (01603 748931). • Rare Plants Fair; The Royal Free Hospital, Hampstead: 11 am – 5 pm (0117 9691570). • Heritage Open Day, with free garden entry, Hillier Arboretum. • Walk; September in the formal garden, Cragside, Northumberland (NT): 2 pm. • Bulb & Dried Flower Sale, Greenbank Garden, Strathclyde: 11 am – 5 pm. • National Heritage Day; Charity Fete, Creagh Gardens, Co. Cork. • Car boot sale, Friends of Ness Gardens. • Also: Harrogate Autumn Flower Show; Cider festival, Brogdale; Harvest Gardening Festival, Ragley Hall.	Alicia Amherst, d. 1941; garden historian — **SUN** **14**

DIARY	EVENTS
MON **15** André le Nôtre, d. 1700; Louis XIV's gardener	15 – 19 September; Botany for beginners course, RBG Kew (0181 332 5623). • RHS Lecture; Scent in the garden, Stephen Lacey: Middlesbrough. • Demonstration; Trees for small gardens, RHS Pershore at Kings Heath Park: 2 pm. • Rose Day; tours, talks and demonstrations in association with Stydd Nursery, at Dalemain, Cumbria.
TUE **16** Robert Fortune, b. 1812; collector; introduced tea to India from China	16 – 17 September; RHS Great Autumn Flower Show, Westminster: 10 am – 7 pm. • RHS Lecture; Organic gardening at Ryton, Bob Sherman, Westminster: 2.15 pm. • RHS/Gardeners Company Lecture; Where on earth did you get that?, Brian Hiley, Westminster: 6 pm. • RHS Lecture; Compatible companions for informal rose plantings, Hazel le Rougetel: Ross on Wye. • Demonstration: Mini vegetables for small households, RHS Pershore: 2 pm. • Walk; Ham House, London (NT): 2 pm & 3 pm. • Walk; Meet the gardener, Hinton Ampner, Hampshire (NT): 2.15 pm. • Course; Taking cuttings 1, Special Plants (01225 891686).
WED **17** Peter Barr, b. 1820; botanist and daffodil breeder	RHS Lecture; Hatton fruit gardens at East Malling, Brian Self, Westminster. • Flower Arranging Day School; Shades of autumn, Mary Gwyther, RHS Wisley: 10 am. • Members' Evening; Reception and open forum with Pippa Greenwood, RHS Rosemoor: 6.30 pm. • Demonstration: Introduction to viticulture, RHS Hyde Hall at Writtle: 6 pm. • Frome Cheese Show, Showfield (01373 463600). • Walk; Claremont Gardens, Surrey (NT): 2.30 pm. • Workshop; Winter hanging baskets, Hillier Arboretum: 2 pm. • National Trust properties, free admission day. • Also: RHS Great Autumn Flower Show: 10 am – 5 pm.
THU **18** George Paul, d. 1921; rose nurseryman	Lecture; Plants with personality, RHS Pershore: 2 pm. • Walk; Bulb care, Greenbank Garden, Strathclyde: 7.30 pm. • Walk; Estate and woodland, Polesden Lacey, Surrey (NT): 6.30 pm.
FRI **19** George Sherriff, d. 1962; plant hunter	19 – 21 September; Garden Craft Fair, RHS Rosemoor. • 19 – 21 September; Centenary Jubilee celebrations, Deutsche Dahlien-, Fuchsien- und Gladiolen-Gesellschaft, Mainau.
SAT **20** Percy Cane, b. 1881; writer and designer (Dartington Hall, Devon)	20 – 21 September; Newbury & Royal County of Berkshire Show, Chieveley (01635 247111). • 20 – 22 September; Flower arranging course, Altamont Garden, Co. Carlow. • 20 – 21 September; Dahlia Festival, Aylett Nurseries, Herts. • Workshop: Semi-ripe cuttings, RHS Pershore: 10 am. • AGS Wirral Show, West Cheshire Arts Centre: 12 pm (0151 6481072). • Annual Show; National Pot Leek Society. • Stokesley Show (01642 713209). • AGM and Symposium, Martineau Club, Birmingham, National Auricula and Primula Society (Mid and West). • Also: Garden Craft Fair, RHS Rosemoor; Jubilee celebrations, Mainau.
SUN **21**	Newbury & Royal County of Berkshire Show; Aylett's Dahlia Festival; Jubilee celebrations, Mainau; and Garden Craft Fair, RHS Rosemoor continue.

EVENTS	DIARY	
Demonstration; Autumn hanging baskets and containers, RHS Pershore at Kings Heath Park: 2 pm. • Nidderdale Show, Pateley Bridge (01423 770888).	John Bartram, d. 1777; botanist	MON 22
Demonstration: Sweet peas for early fragrance and flower, RHS Pershore: 2 pm. • Course; History of Gardens 1, Louise Bustard, Glasgow Botanic Garden. • Walk; Ham House, London (NT): 2 pm & 3 pm.		TUE 23
Demonstration: Lawn maintenance, RHS Wisley: 2 pm. • Demonstration: Patio garden: design, materials and plants, RHS Rosemoor at Cannington: 2 pm. • Course; Ornamental grasses, Special Plants (01225 891686). • Walk; Claremont Gardens, Surrey (NT): 2.30 pm. • Course; Compost making, HDRA Ryton.		WED 24
25 – 28 September; Course: Botanical drawing and painting, Pauline Dean, RHS Wisley. • Lecture; Carnivorous plants, Paul Gardner, RHS Pershore: 2 pm. • Course; Taking cuttings 1, Special Plants (01225 891686).		THU 25
Demonstration: Planting, RHS Hyde Hall: 11 am.		FRI 26
27 – 28 September; Malvern Autumn Show, TCAS Showground: 9 am – 6 pm. Includes RHS Show. See also Shows section. • 27 – 28 September; End of season plant sale, Pashley Manor Gardens, East Sussex. • 27 – 28 September; Dahlia Festival, Aylett Nurseries, Herts. • Lecture; Plant aberrations, Martin Cragg Barber, Wilts. & Avon HPS. • Demonstration; Art of the gardener: practical gardening techniques, Rowallane Garden, Co. Down (NT): 2.30 pm. • Variegated Plants Study Day, Berkshire Group, Hardy Plant Society members only.		SAT 27
Demonstration: Lawn maintenance, RHS Wisley: 10.30 am. • Walk; Autumn family walk, The Vyne, Hampshire (NT): 2 pm. • Also: Plant sale, Pashley Manor; Malvern Autumn Show: 9 am – 5 pm; Aylett's Dahlia Festival.	Sir Henry Wickham, d. 1928; plant collector	SUN 28

DIARY		EVENTS
MON **29**		Demonstration; Autumn colour, RHS Pershore at Kings Heath Park: 2 pm.
TUE **30**	James Aitchison, d. 1898; botanist in India (*Rosa ecae*)	Lecture; Garden design 1, Dennis Neate, RHS Hyde Hall at Writtle: 7 pm. • Lecture; Fresh herbs for the kitchen, Kim Hurst, RHS Pershore: 2 pm. • Course; History of gardens 2, Louise Bustard, Glasgow Botanic Garden. • Walk; Ham House, London (NT): 2 pm & 3 pm.
WED **1**		Demonstration: Glasshouse and conservatory management, RHS Wisley: 2 pm. • Walk; Autumn tour, Hillier Arboretum: 2 pm. • Workshop; Food for thought, Hillier Arboretum: 1 pm. • Course; Taking cuttings 1, Special Plants (01225 891686).
THU **2**		Workshop; Winter hanging baskets and containers, RHS Pershore: 2 pm.
FRI **3**		3 – 5 October; Canterbury Cathedral flower festival, NAFAS.
SAT **4**	Franz Bauer, b. 1758; botanical artist	4 – 5 October; Spring Show, Queensland Rose Society, Brisbane. • Course; Paper making, RBG Kew (0181 332 5623). • Demonstration: Flower arranging for beginners, Glasgow Botanic Garden. • Walk; Trees of Morden Hall Park, Surrey (NT): 2 pm. • Lecture; Putting your garden to bed, Duncan Travers, Wiltshire Gardens Trust. • Course; Irish silver, Altamont Garden, Co. Carlow. • Also: Flower festival, Canterbury.
SUN **5**	Sir Moritz Schomburgk, b. 1811; botanist	Demonstration: Glasshouse and conservatory management, RHS Wisley: 10.30 am. • Pumpkin day; Demonstrations, walk and lunch, and competitions, RHS Rosemoor. • RHS Lecture; Work of the world conifer conservation project, Martin Gardner: Ness. • Walk; Autumn tour, Hillier Arboretum: 2 pm. • South of England Autumn Show, Ardingly (01444 892700). • Walk; St Andrews Botanic Garden, Fife. • Also: Flower festival, Canterbury.

EVENTS   DIARY

6 – 17 October; Exhibition: Intimate places, Tom King, Museum of Garden History. • Demonstration; Your garden in October, RHS Pershore at Kings Heath Park: 2 pm.	**MON** **6**
7 – 8 October; RHS Flower Show, Westminster: 11 am – 7 pm. Includes Autumn Fruit & Vegetable, ornamental plant and British National Carnation Society competitions. • RHS VMH Centenary Lecture; Victorian gardening, Peter Thoday, Westminster. • Demonstration: Your garden in October, RHS Pershore: 2 pm. • Walk; Meet the gardener, Scotney Castle Garden, Kent (NT): 2 pm. • Walk; Ham House, London (NT): 2 pm & 3 pm. • Lecture; The hanging gardens of Babylon, Stephanie Dalley, Museum of Garden History. • Course; History of gardens 3, Louise Bustard, Glasgow Botanic Garden. • Course; Conservatory gardening, Special Plants (01225 891686).	**TUE** **7**
8 – 9 October; Autumn Fruit, Flower & Vegetable Show, Jersey (01534 37227). • Demonstration: Paths and patios, RHS Wisley: 10.30 am. • Lecture; Garden design 2, RHS Hyde Hall at Writtle: 7 pm. • Walk; Foliage garden, RHS Rosemoor: 11 am. • RHS Lecture; Around the world on a garden, Roy Lancaster: Dorchester. • Walk; Autumn tour, Hillier Arboretum: 2 pm. • Course; Planning with plants, HDRA Ryton. • Also: RHS Flower Show: 10 am – 5 pm.	George Hibbert, d. 1837; (*Hibbertia*) **WED** **8**
RHS Lecture; Container gardening: pots and plants for all situations, Ray Waite: Cheltenham. • Demonstration: Drying flowers from your garden, RHS Pershore: 2 pm. • Lecture; People, plants and places: Yunnan, China, John Main, Glasgow Botanic Garden: Hillhead Library: 7.30 pm. • Also: Autumn Show, Jersey.	William Aiton, d. 1849; superintendent of RBG, Kew **THU** **9**
10 – 12 October; Arley Antiques Fair, Arley Hall, Cheshire. • 10 – 12 October; American Rhododendron Society western Conference in San Jose, CA. • RHS Lecture; Making the right choices: selecting particular varieties for special situations, Tim Miles: Brecon.	Thomas Fairchild, d. 1729; raised first scientific hybrid (*Dianthus caryophyllus* × *barbatus*) **FRI** **10**
11 – 12 October; Garden design weekend, RHS Pershore. • 11 – 12 October; RNRS Autumn pruning demonstrations, Gardens of the Rose, St Albans. • 11 – 12 October; Les Journeés de l'Arbre, Arboretum National des Barres (00 33 238 97 62 21). • Walk; Care of wall plants, Greenbank Garden, Strathclyde: 2.30 pm. • Also: Arley Antiques Fair.	Alexander Dickson, d. 1890; founder of rose nursery **SAT** **11**
Walk; Autumn colour, RHS Wisley: 10.30 am. • Lecture; The Dorset heaths: their biology and conservation, Prof. Marrs, Ness: 2 pm. • Autumn splendour; Plants for sale. High Beeches, West Sussex: 1 – 5 pm. • Walk; Autumn tour, Hillier Arboretum: 2 pm. • Also: RNRS Autumn pruning demonstrations; Arley Antiques Fair; Journeés de l'Arbre, Barres.	Thomas Rochford, d. 1901; nursery founder **SUN** **12**

DIARY	EVENTS
MON **13** Mary Kingsley, b. 1862; botanist and traveller	Walk; Autumn colour, RHS Wisley: 10.30 am. • Demonstration; Semi-ripe cuttings, RHS Pershore at Kings Heath Park: 2 pm. • RHS Lecture; Role of botanical gardens in plant conservation, John Simmons: York.
TUE **14**	Demonstration: Paths and patios, RHS Wisley: 2 pm. • RHS Lecture; Mountain Plants of Tasmania, Brian Halliwell: Edinburgh. • Lecture; Pumpkins and squashes, RHS Pershore: 2 pm. • RHS/NCCPG Lecture; RHS Pershore: 7.30 pm. • Course; History of gardens 4, Louise Bustard, Glasgow Botanic Garden. • Walk; Ham House, London (NT): 2 pm & 3 pm. • Course; Fungus foray, RBG Kew (0181 332 5623).
WED **15** George Russell, d. 1951; lupin breeder	RHS Lecture; Plant hunting in Western China, Christopher Grey-Wilson: RHS Rosemoor: 2.30 pm. • Flower Arranging Demonstration: Memories of autumn, Pamela Howard-Spink, RHS Wisley: 10 am. • Walk; Autumn tour, Hillier Arboretum: 2 pm. • Lecture; Parterres, Caroline Holmes, Waddesdon Manor, Bucks.
THU **16** Stefan Buczacki, b. 1945; writer and broadcaster	RHS Lecture; Courageous gardening, Stephen Anderton: Melton Mowbray. • Lecture; Keeping the garden fit and healthy organically, RHS Pershore: 2 pm. • Walk; Meet the gardener, Emmetts Garden, Kent (NT): 2 pm. • Autumn Walk; Harlow Carr: 2 pm. • Lecture; 101 ways of growing alpines, Frank Tindall, AGS Exeter Group, St Thomas High School.
FRI **17** Thomas Rivers, d. 1877; fruit hybridiser	17 – 19 October; Journées des Plantes de Courson, near Paris (0033 164 58 90 12). See also Shows section.
SAT **18** Nicolas Culpeper, b. 1616; herbalist	18 October – 2 November; Autumn fruits fortnight, RHS Wisley. • 18 – 21 October; Apple Day celebrations, Brogdale. • 18 – 19 October; Apple Day celebrations at Highfield Garden Centre, Gloucs. Tasting, craft stalls. • 18 – 24 October; Annual Plant Sale, Killerton House, Devon (NT). • AGS Sussex Show, Horsham: 11.30 am (01323 843611). • AGM; Friends of Ness Gardens: 10 am. • Also: Courson.
SUN **19** Sir Thomas Browne, b. 1605, d. 1682; writer (*The Garden of Cyrus*)	Plant sale and autumn colour, Benington Lordship, Herts. • Walk; Autumn tour, Hillier Arboretum: 2 pm. • Walk; Woods in autumn, Cliveden, Bucks. (NT): 11 am. • Lecture; Is their too much yellow in our gardens? P. Cunnington, Ness: 2 pm. • Walk; Autumn, Wallington Hall, Northumberland (NT): 2 pm. • Walk; Seeds and things, The Vyne, Hampshire (NT): 2 pm. • Walk; Autumn leaves and fruit, Cragside, Northumberland (NT): 2 pm. • Apple day celebrations at: Highfield Garden Centre; Brogdale; Hughenden Manor, Bucks, HDRA Ryton. • Also: Courson.

EVENTS   DIARY

Demonstration; Collecting and preserving flowers, RHS Pershore at Kings Heath Park: 2 pm. • Walk; Meet the gardener, Sheffield Park, East Sussex (NT): 2 pm. • Also: Apple Day celebrations at Brogdale.	Friedrich Welwitsch, d. 1872; botanist **MON** **20**
RHS Lecture; Irish gardens and their plants, Charles Nelson: Durham. • Demonstration: Apple Day celebrations, RHS Pershore: 2 pm. • Walk; Autumn, Glasgow Botanic Garden: 2 pm. • Course; Basic Botany, RBG Kew (0181 332 5623). • Course; History of gardens 5, Louise Bustard, Glasgow Botanic Garden. • Walk; Ham House, London (NT): 2 pm & 3 pm. • Also: Apple Day celebrations at Brogdale.	**TUE** **21**
22 – 25 October; Exhibition of Elizabeth Dowle's fruit watercolours, with specimens from Brogdale, at Pashley Manor, East Sussex. • Lecture; Pressing Autumn leaves, RHS Hyde Hall at Writtle: 2 pm. • Lecture; Gardens of the 20th century, John Addison, RHS Rosemoor at Cannington: 2 pm. • RHS Lecture; Perennial pleasures: hardy plants for every garden, Trevor Bath: Mold. • Course; Basic Botany, Wakehurst Place (0181 332 5623). • Walk; Autumn tour, Hillier Arboretum: 2 pm. • Course; Focus on fruit, HDRA Ryton.	James Cocker, d. 1880; nurseryman **WED** **22**
23 – 26 October; Garden Design Course, Robin Williams, RHS Wisley. • 23 October – 16 November; Ceramics and pottery with a botanical theme, Claudia Clare, Museum of Garden History. • Demonstration: Pruning roses: ramblers, shrubs and climbers, RHS Hyde Hall: 11 am. • RHS Lecture; The gardens in the Great Park at Windsor, John Bond: Birmingham. • Outing; To Westonbirt, RHS Pershore. • Walk in the woods, Waddesdon Manor, Bucks.: 1.30 & 3.30 pm.	Rev. H. H. d'Ombrain, d. 1905; rosarian **THU** **23**
24 – 26 October; American Rhododendron Society northeast Conference, Allentown, Pennsylvania. • Demonstration: Pruning roses: ramblers, shrubs and climbers, RHS Hyde Hall: 11 am.	Marianne North, b. 1830; botanical artist **FRI** **24**
25 – 26 October; Craft Fair, Arley Hall, Cheshire. • 25 – 27 October; World Bonsai Friendship Federation, Seoul. • Workshop; Painting with Autumn in mind with watercolours, RHS Pershore: 10 am. • Ghosts, ghouls and witches activity day, Dunster Castle, Somerset (NT). • Plant Sale; Rowallane Garden, Co. Down (NT): 2.30 pm. • Walk; Autumn colours, Mount Stewart, Co. Down (NT): 2.30 pm.	James Sowerby, d. 1822; botanical artist **SAT** **25**
Plant Sale; Rowallane Garden, Co. Down (NT): 2.30 pm. • Family ghost tour, Dunster Castle, Somerset (NT). • Lecture; Seattle, Victoria and the Butchart Gardens, D. Wakeham, Ness: 2 pm. • Walk; Autumn tour, Hillier Arboretum: 2 pm. • Walk; Autumn tints, Hatchlands Park, Surrey (NT): 10 am. • Apple Day celebrations, Killerton House, Devon (NT). • Christmas Market, Birmingham Botanical Gardens & Glasshouses. • Also: Arley Craft Fair.	**SUN** **26**

DIARY		EVENTS
MON **27**	Rev. Clarence Bicknell, b. 1842; botanist on the Riviera	Demonstration; Bonsai for beginners, RHS Pershore at Kings Heath Park: 2 pm.
TUE **28**	Collingwood Ingram, b. 1880; *Prunus* expert	RHS Lecture; Beautiful plants and gardens, Archie Skinner, Oxford. • Lecture; Gardens of Roberto Burle-Marx, Noël Kingsbury, RHS Pershore: 2 pm. • Walk; Ham House, London (NT): 2 pm & 3 pm. • Walk; Autumn into winter, Mottisfont Abbey, Hampshire (NT): 2 pm.
WED **29**		Demonstration: Digging, composting and manuring, RHS Wisley: 2 pm. • Demonstration: Tree planting, RHS Rosemoor: 11. 30 am. • Walk; Trees, RHS Rosemoor: 2 pm. • RHS Lecture; Year-round bulb garden, Christine Skelmersdale: Sheffield. • Workshop; Practical composting, Hillier Arboretum: 10 am. • Workshop; The natural garden, Hillier Arboretum: 1.30 pm. • Walk; Autumn tour, Hillier Arboretum: 2 pm.
THU **30**	John Kennedy, b. 1759; nurseryman (*Kennedia*)	30 – 31 October; Ghost tours, Dunster Castle, Somerset (NT). • Lecture; *Streptocarpus* and other gesneriads, Rex Dibley, RHS Pershore: 2 pm. • Course; Growing plants for sale, Special Plants (01225 891686). • Children's Event: Winnie Witch gets ready for Halloween, Hillier Arboretum: 2 – 4 pm. • Halloween activities, Glasgow Botanic Garden.
FRI **31**	John Evelyn, b. 1620; naturalist and diarist	RHS Lecture; Hardy plants for autumn and winter interest, Ken Burras: Peterborough. • Halloween Evening: Ghost & Ghoul supper, Ness: 7.30pm. • Halloween activities, Glasgow Botanic Garden. • Also: Ghosts, Dunster Castle.
SAT **1**	Russell Page, b. 1906; writer and broadcaster	1 – 2 November; Christmas Fayre, Highclere Castle, Berks. • RHS Lecture; Creating a cottage garden, Sue Phillips: Windermere.
SUN **2**	John Waterer, d. 1868; nurseryman	Demonstration: Digging, composting and manuring, RHS Wisley: 10.30 am. • Lecture; Sefton Park Palm House, Dr J. Edmondson, Ness: 2 pm. • Walk; Firecrackers, Hillier Arboretum: 2 pm. • Also: Christmas Fayre, Highclere Castle, Berks.

EVENTS	DIARY	
Demonstration; Your garden in November, RHS Pershore at Kings Heath Park: 2 pm.	Robert Stephenson Clarke, d. 1948; creator of Borde Hill, West Sussex	MON 3
4 – 5 November; RHS Flower Show, Westminster: 11 am – 7 pm. Includes ornamental plant and botanical paintings competitions. • RHS Lecture; One hundred years of gardening at Hergest Croft, Elizabeth Banks, Westminster. • Demonstration: Your garden in November, RHS Pershore: 2 pm. • Workshop; Orchids for all, Glasgow Botanic Garden.	Alan Mitchell, b. 1922; dendrologist and tree measurer	TUE 4
Demonstration: Introduction to ornamental grasses, RHS Hyde Hall at Writtle: 2 pm. • Course; Organic gardening, City & Guilds, HDRA Ryton. • Also: RHS Flower Show: 10 am – 5 pm.	Richard Bradley, d. 1732; Cambridge botanist and writer	WED 5
RHS Lecture; Plant hunting for Kew, Tony Schilling: Bath. • Demonstration: Protecting tender plants over winter, RHS Pershore: 2 pm.	Frank Kingdon Ward, b. 1885; plant collector	THU 6
Charity fireworks display, Broadlands, Hampshire.	William Dallimore; d. 1959; dendrologist	FRI 7
8 – 9 November; National Chrysanthemum Society Show, RHS Westminster (01788 569039). • Walk; Soil management, Greenbank Garden, Strathclyde: 2.30 pm.		SAT 8
Lecture; Mr Bulley's garden 100 years on, J. Hulme, Ness: 2 pm. • Also: National Chrysanthemum Society Show.	Thomas Bridges, d. 1865; introducer of *Victoria amazonica*	SUN 9

DIARY		EVENTS
MON **10**	Robert Harkness, d. 1920; rose nurseryman	10 – 14 November; Schools week, HDRA Ryton. ● RHS Lecture; Unusual forms of climbing shrubs for walls, fences and pergolas, Roy Cheek: Preston. ● Demonstration; A futuristic approach to gardening, RHS Pershore at Kings Heath Park: 2 pm.
TUE **11**	E. J. Lowe, b. 1825; pteridologist	RHS Lecture; From the mountains to your garden: alpines for everyone, Michel Upward: Glasgow. ● Lecture; Capability Brown and his imitators, David Whitehead, RHS Pershore: 2 pm.
WED **12**		Demonstration: Pruning fruit trees and bushes, RHS Wisley: 10.30 am. ● Lecture; A tour of Irish gardens, John Chesters, RHS Rosemoor: 2 pm. ● Lecture; Approach to winter, Michael Leech, Museum of Garden History.
THU **13**		
FRI **14**	Rev. A. Foster-Melliar, d. 1904; rosarian	Demonstration: Pruning fruit trees and bushes, RHS Wisley: 10.30 am.
SAT **15**		15 – 16 November; Craft fair, RHS Rosemoor. ● 15 – 16 November; Craft show, Broadlands, Hants. ● 15 – 18 November; Management of small woodlands course, HDRA Ryton. ● Workshop; Hardwood cuttings, RHS Pershore: 10 am.
SUN **16**		Demonstration: Pruning fruit trees and bushes, RHS Wisley: 10.30 am. ● Lecture; Ness: the strategy for the next 100 years, Prof. R. Marrs, Ness: 2 pm. ● Also: Craft fair, RHS Rosemoor; Craft show, Broadlands.

EVENTS	DIARY	
Demonstration; Pests and diseases in your garden, RHS Pershore at Kings Heath Park: 2 pm.	Rev. William Colenso, b. 1841; botanist (*Myosotis colensoi*)	MON 17
RHS Lecture; Colour in the small garden, Tim Walker: Altrincham. ● Lecture; Introduction to fruit tree pruning, Tony Edgeley, RHS Pershore: 2 pm.		TUE 18
Demonstration: Winter treatment of grapes – indoor and out, RHS Wisley: 10.30 am. ● RHS Lecture; Flower shows at home and abroad, John Mattock: Norwich. ● Christmas Fayre course, Ness: 10 am. ● Lecture; People, plants and places, Paul Miles, Museum of Garden History (0171 401 8865).	Thomas Meehan, d. 1901; collector (*Meehania*)	WED 19
RHS Lecture; Gardens without borders, Alan Mason: Bath. ● Christmas sale of RHS goods, RHS Pershore: 2 pm. ● Lecture; The tuberous Corydalis, Brian Mathew, AGS Exeter Group, St Thomas High School.	Penelope Hobhouse, b. 1929; gardener and writer	THU 20
RHS Lecture; The potager: a decorative vegetable garden, Joy Larkcom: Belfast.		FRI 21
Demonstration: Planting fruit trees and bushes, RHS Hyde Hall at Writtle: 10 am. ● Workshop; Fruit tree pruning, RHS Pershore: 10 am.		SAT 22
Walk; Bamboos at Rosemoor, RHS Rosemoor: 10 am. ● Lecture; Every plant has a story: some horticultural reminiscences, Ness: 2 pm. ● Walk; Conifers, Cragside, Northumberland (NT): 2 pm.	Charles Babington, b. 1808; botanist (*Allium babingtonii*)	SUN 23

DIARY	EVENTS
MON **24**	Demonstration; Pot plants in winter, RHS Pershore at Kings Heath Park: 2 pm.
TUE **25** John Downie, d. 1892; nurseryman (*Malus* 'John Downie')	25 – 26 November; RHS Flower Show, Westminster: 11 am – 7 pm. Includes Late Apple & Pear, ornamental plant and botanical paintings competitions; and Orchid Society of Great Britain Autumn Show. • RHS Lecture; The Alpine Garden Society's expedition to China, Chris Brickell, Westminster. • Lecture; Great gardens of Cornwall, Duncan Coombs, RHS Pershore: 2 pm.
WED **26** Henry Elwes, d. 1922; dendrologist and collector	26 November – 7 December; National Tree Week (0171 828 9928). • RHS Lecture; Lessons from the Victorian walled garden, Peter Thoday: Consett. • Workshop; Traditional Christmas decorations in straw and rush, Hillier Arboretum: 9.30 am. • Course; Organic gardening: City & Guilds, HDRA Ryton. • Also: RHS Flower Show: 10 am – 5 pm.
THU **27** James Bateman, d. 1897; orchidist and writer	Demonstration; Making worms work for you, RHS Pershore: 2 pm. • Course; Taking cuttings 2, Special Plants (01225 891686). • Course; Focus on fruit, HDRA Ryton.
FRI **28**	
SAT **29** Gertrude Jekyll, b. 1843; garden designer and writer	
SUN **30** Sir Isaac Balfour, d. 1922; Edinburgh botanist	Lecture; Plant nutrition and growing systems: grow bags, rock wool etc., Dr K. Hardwick, Ness: 2 pm. • Friends' Craft Fair, Birmingham Botanical Gardens & Glasshouses.

EVENTS	DIARY	
Demonstration; Your garden in December, RHS Pershore at Kings Heath Park: 2 pm.	William Dykes, d. 1925; iris breeder	MON 1
Demonstration: Your garden in December, RHS Pershore: 2 pm.	Sir Alfred Parsons, b. 1847; botanical artist (*Genus Rosa*)	TUE 2
Flower Arranging Demonstrations; Christmas decorations, George Smith, RHS Wisley: 10 am and 2 pm. ● Demonstration: Pruning fruit trees and bushes, RHS Hyde Hall at Writtle: 2 pm. ● Course; Organic gardening: City & Guilds, HDRA Ryton.		WED 3
Demonstration: Garden design using computers, RHS Pershore: 2 pm.	Hugh Armytage-Moore, d. 1954; creator of Rowallane, Co. Down	THU 4
	Constance Spry, b. 1886; flower arranger and writer	FRI 5
6 – 7 December; Christmas Fayre, Brogdale. ● Christmas Evening, Arley Hall, Cheshire. ● 6 – 9 December; Management of small woodlands course, HDRA Ryton.		SAT 6
Lecture; Research on ivies in the wild and in cultivation, Dr H. McAllister, Ness: 2 pm. ● Walk; Advent walk, Hillier Arboretum: 2 pm. ● Christmas Day, Arley Hall, Cheshire. ● Advent event, with carols, Hillier Arboretum: 2 – 4 pm. ● Christmas Fayre, Brogdale. ● Christmas Bazaar, Borde Hill Garden, W. Sussex. (subject to confirmation)	Captain William Bligh, d. 1817; Master of *The Bounty* (*Blighia*, akee fruit)	SUN 7

DIARY		EVENTS
MON **8**	Gertrude Jekyll, d. 1932; garden designer and writer	Demonstration; Hardwood cuttings, RHS Pershore at Kings Heath Park: 2 pm.
TUE **9**	Lord Penzance, d. 1899; rose hybridiser (Rose 'Lord Penzance')	9 – 10 December; RHS Christmas Show, Westminster: 11 am – 7 pm. • RHS Flower Arranging Demonstration: Westminster. • Lecture; Winter fragrance for home and garden, Peter Goodburgh, RHS Pershore: 2 pm.
WED **10**	George Maw, b. 1832; collector and *Crocus* expert	Demonstration: Christmas crafts from the garden, RHS Rosemoor: 11 am. • Lecture; Annual Christmas lecture, Dunster Castle, Somerset (NT). • Workshop; Decorating with evergreens, Hillier Arboretum: 1 pm. • Course; Organic gardening: City & Guilds, HDRA Ryton. • Also: RHS Christmas Show: 10 am – 5 pm.
THU **11**	Franz Bauer, d. 1840; botanical artist	
FRI **12**	Erasmus Darwin, b. 1731; scientist and poet (*Botanic Garden*)	Workshop; Flowers at Christmas, Hillier Arboretum: 10.30 am. • Laudamus, Dunster Castle, Somerset (NT).
SAT **13**		Walk; Trees and shrubs, Greenbank Garden, Strathclyde: 2.30 pm. • Christmas Evening, Arley Hall, Cheshire. • Laudamus, Dunster Castle, Somerset (NT).
SUN **14**	John Loudon, d. 1843; writer and landscaper	Lecture; RHS Rosemoor. • Christmas Day, Arley Hall, Cheshire.

EVENTS

DIARY

15 - 19 December; Christmas week celebrations at Ness: special lunches and evening meals. • Demonstration; Winter colour in your garden, RHS Pershore at Kings Heath Park: 2 pm.

Hugh, 5th Earl Annesley, d. 1908; creator of Castlewellan, Co. Down

MON

15

16 - 19 December; Christmas at Packwood House, West Midlands (NT). • Workshop; Christmas flower arranging, RHS Pershore: 10 am.

TUE

16

Charles Hurst, d. 1947; Cambridge geneticist; hybridiser with roses and orchids

WED

17

Christmas Plant Sale, RHS Pershore: 2 pm.

Philip Miller, d. 1771; writer

THU

18

AGM and seed exchange; AGS Exeter Group, St Thomas High School.

FRI

19

Sir Reginald Blomfield, b. 1856; garden designer and writer

SAT

20

Charles Lawson, d. 1873; nurseryman (*Cupressus lawsonii*)

SUN

21

DIARY	EVENTS
MON **22**	
TUE **23** Sir Thomas Neame, b. 1885; founder of East Malling Research Station	
WED **24** Frances, Vicountess Wolseley, d. 1936; gardener	
THU **25** Christmas Day	
FRI **26** John Fothergill, d. 1780; amateur botanist	
SAT **27** Sir Thomas Gage, d. 1820; plant collector (*Gagea*)	
SUN **28** Joseph Arnold, b. 1782; botanist (*Rafflesia arnoldii*)	

EVENTS	DIARY	
	G. P. Baker, d. 1951; textile manufacturer and alpine botanist	MON 29
	Isabella Preston, d. 1965; Canadian hybridiser of *Syringa*	TUE 30
		WED 31
		THU 1
		FRI 2
		SAT 3
		SUN 4

Shows

NOTES FROM THE SHOWS IN 1996

Ups & Downs

The show scene is changing. Shows are becoming more commercial. Gone are those genteel days when nurserymen were content to consider their exhibits at horticultural shows as an advertisement for orders that would come to them later in the season. They want to come away knowing that they have reached their target, both for advance orders and for sales at the show itself. And the big sponsors, who use a show like Chelsea as an inexpensive means of obtaining major media exposure, are becoming more hard-nosed too. We noticed that one of the gardens which won a gold medal at Chelsea last year did not bear a fancy title like 'The Spirit of Gertrude Jekyll' but was crudely known from start to finish as 'The Preferred Direct Garden', after the insurance company which sponsored it. Getting the right designer so that you win the desired publicity is a serious business nowadays, particularly when Chelsea gets much better media coverage than Hampton Court. Christian Aid employs the shock-advertising techniques of Benetton to convey its message to visitors: land-mines in the earth may not be the sort of design which wins them a gold medal, but it certainly makes it clear why Christian Aid is calling for your support.

It follows that there is tremendous competition for a place at a great show in peak condition like Chelsea, but rather less for one that has not proved its value in the open market. Exhibitors and would-be exhibitors need to know which shows are doing well and which are not. We can tell them which shows are on the up. The Malvern Spring Gardening Show, for example, had over 130 applications from nurseries but space for only 90 stands in the Floral Halls. Attendance figures at BBC Gardener's World Live show at NEC Birmingham were up 11% at 124,000. It was a good show, too: the RHS awarded 26 gold medals to exhibitors, the highest number ever made at the event. BBC Gardener's World Live is the largest show after Chelsea and Hampton Court, and the RHS has run the floral marquee since the show began in 1993. It is, however, an open secret that the RHS was not entirely happy with the way that the show was run, so it came as no surprise to learn that, with effect from this year, the Society would take responsibility for the 'editorial content' of the show. It will also take control of the management, presentation and promotion of the event. Another show which saw an increase in attendance last year, up some 13% on 1995, was the Great Garden & Countryside Festival at Holker Hall early in June.

Scotland's National Gardening Show is the first completely new show that the RHS has launched since it first set up the Chelsea Flower show in the early years of this century. Modelled on the Hampton Court show, whose success has exceeded all expectations, Scotland's National Gardening Show will attract nurserymen and visitors from both sides of the border. It will include show gardens, floral marquees, exhibits by specialist societies and displays of garden equipment. This new event forms part of the Society's commitment to creating a real presence in every part of the United Kingdom: the Society's membership in the whole of Scotland amounts to less than one tenth of its membership in Surrey alone. It is an imbalance which the RHS feels that it must address if it can fairly claim to call itself a truly national institution.

Some of the lesser-known shows are also worth visiting. One of the most interesting last year was *Fungus 100*, the centenary exhibition of the British Mycological Society which took place in the Old Hall in September and brought together experts from all over the world for a three-day congress. Naturally, exhibits of fruiting fungi contributed much to its success. And the RHS Orchid Show in March showed renewed vigour again last year: we were particularly impressed by the quality of its exhibits and competitions. The Wisley Show, meanwhile, suffers from over-popularity. This creates pressure upon such facilities as the restaurant, car parks and loos. Last year it was held in conjunction with the annual show of the National Sweet Pea Society, and the marquee was deliciously sweet with their scent: this year the British Gladiolus Society will be the lucky society to share the Wisley show with the RHS, and the event will be scaled down to provide a more specialist focus.

It should also be said that some shows are on the down. The promoters killed off the new spring show at Southport, christened *Florilegia*, before it was even born. The idea of a three-day show over the May Bank Holiday was unpopular with nurserymen who thought they could do better by staying in their nurseries at what is one of their busiest weekends of the year. Some nurserymen were also disappointed by attendances at the Harrogate Spring show: it will be interesting to see whether it fares better this year when the show moves out of the middle of the town and up to the Great Yorkshire Showground. Running a successful show requires good organisers, good exhibitors and the right sort of visitors in just the right numbers. All the parties need each other. The organisers must promote the show, finance it and monitor its quality; the exhibitors must bring with them a good display and need to be convinced that their time and money are better spent at the show than they would be back home on the nursery; and the punters must come in a constant flow, and praise what they see in the best possible way by ordering lots of plants from the exhibitors. By and large, the RHS gets it right, but some visitors to the late November show at Westminster wondered whether even the Society was having a problem in filling its space. One journalist suggested that the Society would be prudent to consider whether some simplification of its Westminster programme might be appropriate. That said, the RHS has the happy knack in particular of attracting new exhibitors to all its shows: there can be no doubt, for example, that much interest was aroused by the first appearance at a Westminster show of Scotts Clematis Nursery and Wyevale Nurseries at the late Spring Show on 30 April & 1 May. It was also good to see Kelways of Langport back for the first time for quite a while: their tree paeonies made a great impression on visitors for the size and opulence of their flowers. Most were hybrids of *Paeonia suffruticosa*, old and new, Japanese and European, but a new American cultivar called 'High Noon' attracted much attention. It has good clear lemon-yellow flowers and, unusually for a tree paeony, a distinct scent.

Stalwart Institutions

The RHS is very well supported by scientific and research institutions. The Royal Botanic Gardens at Kew, for example, are regular exhibitors. Their presence at RHS shows serves to emphasise the close links which the Society enjoys with the world of botany and conservation and the importance which Kew attaches to good horticultural practice. At the show on 23 & 24 January Kew was awarded a Cultural Commendation for a large plant of *Helleborus vesicarius* in full bloom in a vast pot, some 30ins. deep. The flowers of this rare endemic of the Amanus Mountains near Antioch in Southern Turkey are small and green, with a striking purple rim to the segments, though it is the huge, inflated seed pods later in the year which are the most remarkable characteristic of this species. Difficult to grow in our climate, we were told that the secret of its successful cultivation is to ensure that *Helleborus vesicarius* has lots of water throughout its winter growing season: otherwise, it goes into premature aestivation. Likewise, the Royal Botanic Garden, Edinburgh, organised a most handsome exhibit at Chelsea last year. Working in association with the Alpine Garden Society, Kew, Ness, Wisley and such individuals as Elizabeth Strangman, they were able to exhibit a large number of plants which are seldom seen in the south of England. The huge flowers of *Meconopsis punicea*, and *M. grandis* attracted particular attention but close examination showed that their rock garden stand was planted with *Sorbus reducta* and dwarf rhododendrons near its summit, and endless smaller alpines in between: among them were *Nomocharis aperta*, anaphalis, drabas and saussureas, all growing under collectors' numbers. The Chelsea Physic Garden is another regular at RHS shows. At the Great Autumn Show it dedicated an exhibit to the plants which are used in pharmaceutical medicine: source plants were curiously juxtaposed with neat dispensary cartons of the drugs derived from them. It certainly made an impact.

The RHS Garden at Wisley can always be relied upon to send a substantial exhibit up to the New Hall, especially when there is less competition for stands from the trade. At the show on 23 & 24 July, which is not one of the more exciting ones, they showed 13 cultivars of radishes grown from seed at Wisley in a current RHS trial. At the show on 8 & 9 October they brought pumpkins and squashes from the demonstration plots in the model vegetable garden and trials fields. This was echoed by a glorious display of gourds by Caroline Boisset, an amateur member of the RHS from Leicestershire, at the next show early in November. Her pumpkins, cucumbers, marrows, squashes, gourds and courgettes (including nine *Cucumus* species, most of them tiny and covered in spines like a conker) came in every imaginable size and colour: striped and spotted, orange, yellow, green, white or grey. At the same show, Wisley displayed a magnificent exhibition of apples and pears, the largest seen at an RHS show for a long time. This was matched by a display of 100 varieties of top fruit exhibited by two RHS members, Douglas Bolingbroke from Cirencester and Gerald Edwards from Pinner. Unusual varieties included an early 19th-century pear called 'Seckle' and such seldom-seen apples as 'Austin Russet' and 'Wanstall Pippin'.

Stalwart Nurseries

The RHS is very well supported by a hard core of loyal nurserymen. It is hard to imagine a show without Burncoose Nurseries, Brian Hiley, P W Plants or the Botanic Nursery. But the outstanding exhibitor for us last year was Bluebell Nursery. Month after month they showed us new cultivars and species of small ornamental trees and gardenworthy shrubs. In February they exhibited the rare blackstemmed willow *Salix myrsinifolia* 'Nigricans', the big-leaved holly *Ilex perado* 'Platyphylla', and the form of *Acer × conspicuum* known as 'Phoenix' which has salmon-coloured stems in winter and is altogether more vigorous than the better-known *Acer pensylvanicum* 'Erythrocladum'. In March they brought us the compact form of the Chinese Judas tree *Cercis chinensis* 'Avondale' which is so good for small gardens and the seldomseen *Prinsepia chinensis* in flower. In April it was the privet-like lilac *Syringa pinnatifolia* and a purple-leaved form of the Turkish hazel *Corylus colurna* which caught our eye on Bluebell's stand At the late spring show on 30 April & 1 May they showed a new form of *Cercidiphyllum japonicum* called 'Rotfuchs', with new leaves which are very dark purple in colour. At Chelsea they brought us the fern-leaved form of *Rhamnus frangula* 'Aspleniifolia' whose leaves are so reduced that they appear linear, and *Quercus robur* 'Compacta', a dwarf and slow-growing form of our native English oak which is not yet available in commerce but should one day make an excellent small tree for small gardens. In July they exhibited the rare yellow-flowered shrub *Lonicera insularis*, so new to cultivation that it is not mentioned in *The New RHS Dictionary of Gardening*. In August their eye-catcher was *Maackia chinensis* in full flower, a striking sight with its erect white racemes and long, dark, pinnate leaves. And at the show on 8 & 9 October they brought up *Sambucus sieboldiana* var. *coreana* with leaflets so indented as to resemble a dissected form, as well as a graceful form of our native oak *Quercus robur* 'Pectinata' with highly dissected leaves and a dwarf-growing form *Quercus robur* 'Nana'. And one could tell the same story of other loyal nurserymen who bring up an endless series of perfect exhibits, beautifully mounted and full of interesting plants, to all the 'fortnightly' Westminster shows throughout the year.

Botanical exhibitions

No-one who has seen the expansion of entries in the Society's botanical art competitions can fail to be impressed by the high standard of the work which is now exhibited at the Westminster shows. The same is true of the originality of their subject matter and its treatment by artists. The outright winner of the competition at the show on 23 & 24 January was Jenny Jowett, who tutors the botanical illustration course which John Nash started at Flatford Mill in 1947. Her watercolours of *Galanthus* species and cultivars at that show were widely held to be the best that have ever been seen.

The exhibits which Dr Brent Elliott mounts from the Society's collections at the Lindley Library are invariably well chosen and accompanied by an interesting critique. At the Westminster show on 30 April & 1 May the theme was 'Women in Horticulture', and the display included books by Jane Loudon, Gertrude Jekyll and Alicia Amherst. At the Great Autumn Show on 17 & 18 September it relied on newspaper cartoons of RHS shows in the 1930s, gently satirising the horticultural aspirations of the visitors. At the show on 5 & 6 November the tables were turned. The exhibit was of photographs taken in the 1860s in a formal Victorian garden and recently acquired by the Lindley Library: members were asked to help to identify the garden.

Floral Committee B

Among the most valuable additions to the Westminster shows last year were the regular displays of species and cultivars of a given genus by members of the Floral B committee. This is the committee which assesses exhibits of trees and shrubs. Readers will remember that the exhibits began in 1995, when members of the committee showed a vast number of *Sorbus* species at one of the autumn shows. It followed up this initial venture by bringing two further collections of shrubs – *Sarcococca* and *Viburnum tinus* cultivars – to the show on 23 & 24 January last year. Visitors were able to compare some ten cultivars of this useful winter-flowering evergreen viburnum and a dozen different sarcococcas. The scent of the sarcococcas carried all over the upper part of the Hall, and species like *Sarcococca confusa* bore blue-black fruit as well as flowers. We noted at the time that this is exactly the sort of exhibit which only the RHS can muster and makes the Westminster shows so rewarding to plant-lovers. At the show on 20 & 21 August, members of Floral B committee mounted an exhibit of *Hypericum* from the Myriandera section of the genus. There were over 100 of them, many grown under collectors' numbers. At one extreme were the very large-flowered popular hybrids like 'Rowallane' and 'Hidcote': at the other were such comparatively small-flowered species as *H. kalmianum* and *H. buckleyi*. Then, at the show on 8 and 9 October, the committee assembled an even larger collection of *Cotoneaster* species. It was backed up by an exhibit from the National Collection owned by Romsey Gardens Nursery in Hampshire. For many visitors, the infinite variation between species was an eye-opener: many had never seen the huge purple fruits of *C. wilsonii*, the glossy black berries of *C. hummelii* or the large leaves of *C. affinis* which makes a small tree as much as 5m high. But the exhibit had something for experts and enthusiasts too: they could study the very different forms of *C. cavei* collected by Tony Schilling under SCHL 2147 and Maurice Foster under MF902. We hope that more species of cotoneaster will be grown in gardens as a result of this exhibit and that Floral B continues to amaze and educate us with the quality and variety of their exhibits.

Competitions

Sometimes it is in the competitions that visitors to RHS shows have an opportunity to see plants which are seldom offered commercially. *Mahonia siamensis* from Swansea Botanic Gardens stole the show on 12 & 13 March: its golden-yellow flowers have red backs to the petals, giving it a much richer appearance than most other species in cultivation. The spring show of the Alpine Garden Society can be relied upon to winkle out of enthusiasts' greenhouses a large number of good plants that are seldom seen in cultivation. At the Westminster show on 16 & 17 April, an Award of Merit was made to *Astragalus coccineus*, so rare that it is not yet available from any nursery in UK, with startling scarlet flowers and grey pinnate leaves, typical of the genus. The AGS actually has a competitive class for a plant 'new or rare in cultivation' and last year it was won by a pan of *Ranunculus* 'Essex', a natural hybrid with large white flowers between *R. amplexicaulis* and *R. parnassifolius*. It was originally found by C H Hammer and awarded a PC in 1957 but subsequently almost lost to cultivation. The entire stock now known descends from a single plant given to Capt. P J Erskine of Petersfield in 1986. The story underlines how precarious is the survival in cultivation of many alpine plants and what skillful propagators are the devoted alpinists.

At the late spring show there was an exceptionally large entry in the *Rhododendron* competitions but, because of the late season, many exhibits were of species and hybrids that might normally be seen at a March show in Westminster. There was much praise among the rhododendron fraternity for the forms and hybrids of *Rhododendron niveum* from Clyne Gardens in Swansea, none of which bore cultivar names. In the Saint-paulia & Houseplant Society's competition in August, the annual award for the best house-plant in the show was made to Mr C. Christotolou of Twickenham for a handsome two-foot plant of *Alocasia × amazonica*, beautifully grown and surrounded by leaves. This is a plant which carries the society's Award of Garden Merit and yet is listed by only one nurseryman in *The RHS Plant Finder*.

National Collections

Among the most rewarding exhibits for the regular visitor to the Westminster shows are the exhibits of a single genus which are sometimes mounted by a NCCPG National Collection holder. At the AGM show on 20 & 21 February, Rowden Gardens devoted their stand to cultivars of *Ranunculus ficaria*, of which they have a National Collection. It tied in with a fascinating article about the many variants of celandine which have been found in recent years in February's edition of *The Garden*, written by John Carter, one of the owners of Rowden Nursery. The variations are legion and, as with cyclamen, many of the best are in the leaves, which differ in shape, colouring, mottling and variegation. Some, including 'Holly', are indented; there were several purple-leaved forms; and most attractive among the many on Rowden Gardens' stand was a pale form with particularly regular segments called 'Limelight'. At the show on 12 & 13 March the most stunning exhibit was a selection of willows from the National Collection of *Salix* held by C M Newsholme of Devon. These included *S. subopposita*, a small spreading shrub from Japan; the trailing *S.* 'Nakamurana Yezoalpina', also from Japan; and *S. canariensis* from the Canary Islands and Madeira. One of the most unusual and eye-catching was *S.* 'Maerd Brno' which is a cross between *S. magnifica* and *S. × erdingeri* and has bright pinky-orange catkins on dark red stems. The National Collection comprises 245 species of *Salix* and 213 cultivars, ranging from large lowland willows to the smallest Arctic-alpine species. Another highly educational exhibit was the display at Hampton Court of oleanders from the French National Collection held by Pép. Filippi of Mèze, in the Hérault. We were told that some cultivars are hardy down to −15°C, and that others are suited to a temperate climate, so it is to be hoped that we shall begin to see these popular Mediterranean shrubs in English gardens. But perhaps the star turn in the NCCPG's tent at Hampton Court was John Vanderplank's exhibit of *Passiflora*: it included the newly-introduced *Passiflora quadrifaria* with bright orange flowers and the first plants ever to be seen at a show of *Passiflora lourdesae*, a species which John Vanderplank has helped to save from extinction.

Not all such exhibits come from National Collection holders. At the Malvern Autumn show, for example, one of the best stands was an exhibit of 235 potato cultivars which was mounted by Dave Chappell, an amateur from south Wales, with contributions from many fellow-members of the National Vegetable Society. A fascinating exhibit of *Pelargonium* species at the show on 16 & 17 April was put up by the Chelsea Physic Garden jointly with the Natural History Museum. Dominated by huge specimens of *P. cordifolium* and *P. papilionaceum* with striking flowers, the exhibit was manned by Dr Mary Gibbs, who works on the taxonomy of *Pelargonium* at the Natural History Museum, and was designed to show the diversity of the genus. This was exemplified by the two Madagascan species on show: the insignificant, weedy *P. madagascariense* and the lanky *P. caylae*. Stranger still were *P. lanceolatum*, whose long, glaucous leaves are as far removed from the typical 'geranium' as is possible to imagine, and a pot of *P. laevigatum* whose leaves are almost linear.

Plants

New plants are sometimes first shown at RHS shows some years before they will be introduced commercially. At the show on 23 & 24 January, the Bluebell Nursery exhibited a small plant – their only specimen – of a variegated form of *Drimys lanceolata*. They have named it 'Peter Clough' to commemorate the ex-head gardener at Inverewe who first discovered it as a sport. Robert Vernon, one of the proprietors of Bluebell Nursery, reckons that we will have to wait four or five years before he will have enough material to introduce this desirable novelty. Hopleys Plants used the show on 16 & 17 April to introduce their new yellow-leaved form of *Helleborus foetidus* called 'Chedglow' which was available immediately and featured on the front cover of their new catalogue. Glendedd Violets of Lincolnshire used the same occasion to exhibit 'Chantaspring', their first yellow-flowered hybrid *Saintpaulia*: it is perhaps rather more interesting than exciting, but none of the rather more substantial yellow hybrids which have been bred in the USA in recent years has yet been introduced commercially. The appearance of 'Chantaspring' at Westminster did not prevent the

Northern Horticultural Society from claiming that the new cultivar would make its public debut at the Harrogate Spring show ten days later. But, to be fair to the NHS, Chanctonbury Nursery did choose The Harrogate Spring show to introduce the first pure white alstroemeria. At the Westminster show on 30 April & 1 May Four Seasons Nursery showed new forms of *Pulsatilla vulgaris*, including the pearly-pink 'Barton's Pink', which they hope to introduce for sale shortly. Blackmore & Langdon introduced a new white Picotee begonia 'Coppelia' at BBC Gardener's World Live Show and Woodfields Bros. introduced their latest lupin hybrid 'Gay Search'. At the show on 5 & 6 November Coghurst Nurseries showed the new Australian Paradise strain of scented *Camellia sasanqua* hybrids, which will be extremely useful late-autumn-flowering shrubs if they prove suitable for the English climate. Coghurst lists about twenty cultivars and advises that they probably do best in a coolhouse or conservatory so that they are protected from rain.

Garden Exhibits

Last year, the RHS judges decided that the best garden at the Chelsea Flower Show was one which celebrated the influence of Vita Sackville-West on gardening. It had elements from Sissinghurst such as thick brick walls and a pastiche of the famous nut platt where full-sized coppice hazels were underplanted with woodland plants. It was a conventional choice, which did much to re-assure those designers who have in the past criticised the Society for giving its top prize to designs which they consider outlandish, wayward or unreal. But there is always someone who is not happy. Last year the Society came in for criticism from a different school of designers who complained that Julie Toll's woodland garden (another gold medallist) in a grove of birch, spruce, willow and rowan, did nothing to teach people how to improve their home environment. The RHS Council, always scrupulous to investigate complaints fairly, is reviewing their judging of such exhibits. The Tudor Rose award at Hampton Court went to Sainsbury's Homebase for the Good Ideas Garden designed by the father-and-son team of Robin Williams and Robin Templar Williams. Once again, the judges' choice was not universally popular, but this time it was the traditional nurseries and garden centres who eyed Sainsbury's Homebase with some misgivings. The manager on the stand retorted that 'the horticulture world has to start taking us a bit more seriously now'. For us, however, one of the most intriguing gardens at Hampton Court was the Four Seasons Garden supported by Marks & Spencers: smoke rose from a pile of leaves on the autumn section of their exhibit. We were told that the smoke was created by the unlikely process of blowing compressed air through vegetable oil.

Hampton Court is taking over from Chelsea as the launch pad for new roses. Last year, no fewer than 17 new varieties were launched. Among them were 'Road to Free-dom', 'Too Hot to Handle', 'Maureen Lipman' and 'Joanna Lumley': we have certainly seen a sea-change in the names given to roses in recent years. Naturally, the RHS now came in for criticism because of the way that television personalities are increasingly used to gain the attention of trigger-happy press photographers. But it seems to us that the promoters are just adapting to changes which have already happened in society as a whole: if comedy actresses sell a rose, then let us have them by the barrowload. We would have thought that a much more serious error of taste (over which the RHS has unfortunately no control) was the choice of an ignorant novice with a pretty face as the presenter of the BBC television programme on Chelsea instead of an experienced horticultural presenter like Alan Titchmarsh. Here again the RHS has no control: but someone is always quick to blame the Society.

The Chelsea Flower Show

But back to the glories of Chelsea. Inside the Great Marquee were some magnificent set pieces from local authorities which must have cost their sponsors a fortune. Birmingham City Council's exhibit (jointly mounted with Dunlop) celebrated 100 years of motoring: its vertical bedding and vast banks of African marigolds and poinsettias won a gold medal from the RHS. It is generally agreed that some of the local authority displays were more successful than others. The Gateshead NBC display, consisting of three large spheres, was perhaps too bold for Chelsea tastes. On the other hand, the Borough of Torbay had a wonderfully humorous montage of plants trained and tied into wire frames to celebrate the Lyceum. It included an entire orchestra, its audience, some strange figures on stage, and even a BBC cameraman.

The exhibit that we most enjoyed was Bridgemere Garden World's. It showed the different types of plant that have been popular over the last 100 years. They divided their stand into four segments. The first represented plants that were popular in gardens at the turn of the century, including Sinkins pinks and early rambling roses. Next came the arrangement of plants that were fashionable between the wars: hybrid strains of foxglove and colum-bines, *Dianthus* 'Doris' and herbaceous paeonies like *Paeonia* 'Mme Calot'. The period between the 1960s and the 1980s was stocked with *Paeonia* 'Bowl of Beauty', *Viburnum* × *carlcephalum* and *Rosa* 'Frensham': how

nice it is to be reminded of such plants. Finally Bridgemere predicted the plants we would all grow in our gardens in the future: *Viola pedata*, new hybrids of *Geranium*, lots of diascias and all those new clematis which are coming out of eastern Europe.

Trends

And what were the trends and fashions at last year's Chelsea that street-wise journalists are always so keen to spot? We thought that much more money was being spent on presentation. This is not confined to big-budget prestige projects like the more glamorous gardens. At its most simple, it means employing outside experts to make the most of your exhibit. Highfield Nurseries had their stand designed by Julian Dowle: he created a great sense of space on what was rather a small stand. Peter Beales placed his roses to grow up pergolas and trellises. Some of the pots were wired on halfway up, like an elaborate flower arrangement. When the flowers are tied into place, all you see is a mass of blossom which conceals the pots. It creates the bowery effect which was strongly in evidence at Chelsea last year. Pergolas and trellises are not the only props that have become more popular: temples and obelisks were widely used, as was quite a lot of tumble-down garden sheddery. If all these artifices suggest that gardening has become the pastime of control freaks, then it is worth noting that there was also more emphasis upon plants in their habitats. Natural gardening has brought in a desire for ferns and grasses which were much more widely used in displays than they were five years ago.

RHS Gold Medals at the Chelsea Flower Shows in 1996

Gardens. Best garden Award: Harpers & Queen, & Cartier (Views of an English Garden: The Spirit of Vita Sackville-West). Other Gold Medals: British Sky Broad-casting (New England Cottage Garden); Evening Standard ES Magazine (A London Roof Garden for the Nineties); Preferred Direct Insurance & Julian Dowle (The Preferred Direct Garden); Pro Carton (A Forest Garden); Roger Platts (Living Rooms); Van Hage Design Company (A Japanese Artist's Garden); Wyevale Garden Centres (A Touch of Paradise).

Nurseries: African Violet Centre (saintpaulias); The Alpine Garden Society & The Royal Botanic Garden Edinburgh (a Chinese landscape); Jacques Amand (bulbous plants); Ashwood Nurseries (national collection of lewisias); David Austin Roses (roses); Barbados Horticultural Society (flowers from Barbados); Peter Beales Roses (old-fashioned and climbing roses);

Birmingham City Council (ornamental & tender plants); Bloms Bulbs (tulips); Bressingham gardens (hardy plants); Cheshire Herbs (herbs); Craig House Cacti (California) (cacti, euphorbias & succulents); Dibleys (streptocarpus); Flowers & Gardens of Melbourne (indigenous plants of Australia); Fryer's Nurseries (roses); Fuchsiavale Nurseries (fuchsias); Glebe Cottage Plants (herbaceous plants); Glenedd (saintpaulias); Goldbrook Plants (hostas & associated plants); Greenacre Nursery (carnations & pinks); The Hardy Plant Society (hardy herbaceous perennials); Hardy's Cottage Garden Plants (herbaceous perennials and shrubs); Heron's Bonsai (bonsai); Hillier Nurseries (trees, shrubs, roses & ground-cover plants); The Hop Shop (dried flowers, herbs, grasses & hop bines); Ichiyo School of Ikebana (floral arrangements); Interflora (FTDA) British Unit (floral arrangements); Jekka's Herb Farm (medicinal, culinary & aromatic herbs); Kirstenbosch, South Africa (flowers from South Africa); Mallet Court Nursery (acers); Marston Exotics (carnivorous plants); McBean's Orchids (orchids); Ken Muir (strawberries); Oakleigh Nurseries (fuchsias & pelargoniums); The Orchid Society of Great Britain (orchids); P W Plants (foliage plants, perennials, grasses & Bamboos); Plant Lovers (cacti & succulents); Rickards Hardy Ferns (hardy & half-hardy ferns, including tree-ferns); Diane Sewell (sweet peas); Peter J Smith (alstroemerias); Toobees Exotics (succulent plants); Torbay Borough Council (carpet bedding: Apollo re-opens The Lyceum); Tropical Rain Forest (bromeliads); J Walkers Bulbs (daffodils); Webbs of Wychbold (Sun Flower Street: an Englishman's home is his castle); Medwyn Williams (vegetables); Woodfield Bros. (lupins); The Eric Young Orchid Foundation (orchids).

Horticultural Shows

Ayr Flower Show

South Ayrshire District Council, Burns House, Burns Statue Square, Ayr KA7 1UT
☎ 01292 612000
CONTACT   Mr P. M. Gibbs, Parks & Environment Dept
DATES   28 August to 30 August
LOCATION   Rozelle Park, Ayr
OPEN   28: 1 pm – 9 pm; 29: 9.30 am – 9 pm; 29: 9.30 am – 6 pm
PARKING AND TRAVEL   Parking on site

This continues to be a popular event in south-west Scotland, attracting many exhibitors from both sides of the border.

BBC Gardeners' World Live

Royal Horticultural Society, PO Box 313, 80 Vincent Square SW1P 2PE
☎ 0171 630 7422
DATES   11 June to 15 June
LOCATION   National Exhibition Centre, Birmingham
OPEN   11 – 14 June: 9 am – 7 pm; 15 June: 9 am – 6 pm

TICKETS   11 – 14 June: Members: £9 (£7.50 after 3 pm); Public: £11 (£7.50); 15 June: Members: £9 (£7.50 after 3 pm); Public: £11 (£7.50). Children £5. Ticket hotline: 0121 767 4505
GROUPS   £9.50
PARKING AND TRAVEL   Parking on site

Now run by the RHS, this showed has improved steadily with its mixture of displays and demonstrations. The NEC location, though slightly lacking atmosphere, has easy access and parking and there is a distinct buzz. Attractions include a large out-of-London RHS show in a big marquee and feature gardens. Members' and group rate tickets must be booked in advance.

Chelsea Flower Show

Shows Department, Royal Horticultural Society, 80 Vincent Square SW1P 2PE
☎ 0171 630 7422/ 649 1885
CONTACT   See the January edition of *The Garden*
DATES   20 May to 23 May
LOCATION   Royal Hospital, Chelsea, London
OPEN   20 – 22 May: 8 am to 8 pm; 23 May: 8 am to 5 pm
TICKETS   20, 21 May (members only): £17 (£10 from 3.30 pm; £6 from 5.30 pm); 22 May: Members £14; Public £24; 23 May: Members £12; Public £21
GROUPS   No discounts for groups
PARKING AND TRAVEL   Parking in Battersea Park, with free shuttle bus. Public transport recommended (Sloane Square underground or shuttle from Victoria station)

The world famous annual flower show remains the most prestigious event in the horticultural calendar. Nurseries, societies and charities create display stands and gardens in the huge marquee, and outside in the grounds of The Royal Hospital. An exceptional range of garden furniture, machinery and other products is displayed outside, and items can be bought or ordered. Press attention usually centres on the 24 display gardens: months of work goes into these beautifully staged displays which only last a week. There is a large flower arranging marquee and a pavilion devoted to garden designers. Numbers are restricted, and even so the show is often very crowded. RHS members have two days set aside exclusively for them, and can buy tickets at preferential rates: see the January copy of *The Garden*. Early morning and late evening are the best times to visit; on the first three days cheaper, timed tickets are available in the afternoon and evening. There is a new 24-hour hotline for members of the public to buy tickets: 0171 344 4343.

The Garden Show

Stansted Park, Rowlands Castle
☎ 01243 372325
CONTACT   Lizzie Dymock
DATES   6 to 8 June
LOCATION   Stansted Park, off the B2148
OPEN   10 am – 5 pm each day
TICKETS   From Trentham Cottage, Tower Street, Emsworth Hants PO10 7BH
PARKING AND TRAVEL   Parking available

In addition to stands by nurseries and product suppliers, the show has a strong line up of lectures from leading garden writers and designers. An art exhibition accompanies the show, which also supports the Prince's Youth Business Trust.

The Great Garden and Countryside Festival

Holker Hall, Cark in Cartmel, Grange over Sands LA11 7PL

☎ 01539 558838

CONTACT   Show director
DATES   30 May to 1 June
LOCATION   Holker Hall, Cumbria: west of Grange over Sands on B5277 and B5278
OPEN   10 am – 6 pm on 30 & 31 May; 10 am – 5.30 pm on 1 June
TICKETS   Adults £6.50, OAPs £5.50, Children (12 – 16) £3
GROUPS   £5 for groups of 20 or more
PARKING AND TRAVEL   Free parking on site
FACILITIES FOR THE DISABLED   Disabled car & loos

The show covers horticulture, the countryside and the environment. In addition to displays by specialist nurseries, there will be modern as well as traditional crafts, advice centres, floral art demonstrations and product displays.

Grow 97

Protech Promotions, Grenfell House, Grenfell Avenue, Hornchurch RM12 4DN

☎ 01708 455907

DATES   19 to 20 April
LOCATION   Sandown Exhibition Centre, Esher

A new show devoted mainly to products, aimed at the general gardening public. In addition there are to be displays by nurseries and seminars and demonstrations.

Hampton Court Palace Flower Show

Shows Department, Royal Horticultural Society, 80 Vincent Square SW1P 2PE

☎ 0171 630 7422/ 344 9966

CONTACT   Shows department
DATES   9 July to 13 July; Preview day, 8 July
LOCATION   Hampton Court Palace, East Molesey, Surrey
OPEN   8 July: 10 am – 5 pm; 9 – 12 July: 10 am – 7.30 pm; 13 July: 10 – 5.30 pm
TICKETS   8: £22 (members only); 9: Members £17 (after 3 pm £10); 10 – 12: Members £13 (after 3 pm £8), Public £17 (£8); 13: Members £13 (after 3 pm £8), Public £17 (£10)
GROUPS   Reduced rates for affiliated societies, senior citizens and groups
PARKING AND TRAVEL   Parking £8 all day; £5 after 3 pm
FACILITIES FOR THE DISABLED   One escort admitted free

This is now the biggest gardening show of its kind in the world. Unlike Chelsea the exhibitors can sell direct from their stands on all days. The show is also recommended for those who now find Chelsea too crowded. The Royal National Rose Society's British Rose Festival is held at the show. A Gala Evening will be held on Preview Day with music and fireworks (0171 630 5999).

Harrogate Great Autumn Flower Show

The North of England Horticultural Society, 4a South Park Road, Harrogate HG1 5QU

☎ 01423 561049

CONTACT   Show organiser
DATES   12 to 14 September
LOCATION   Great Yorkshire Showground, Hookstone Oval, Harrogate
OPEN   9.30 am – 6 pm, but 5.30 pm on final day
TICKETS   £6.50, but £6 on last day
GROUPS   Groups rates available for parties of 10 or more
PARKING AND TRAVEL   Free on-site parking

As well as displays from nurseries and other trade stands, this show is particularly recommended for the society competitions (including dahlias and chrysanthemums), and for the Onion Weigh-in which will probably take place at 12 noon on the first day. There is a flower arrangement section too.

Harrogate Spring Flower Show

North of England Horticultural Society, 4a South Park Road, Harrogate HG1 5QU

☎ 01423 561049

CONTACT   Show secretary
DATES   24 to 27 April
LOCATION   Great Yorkshire Showground, Harrogate
OPEN   24 – 26 April: 9.30 am to 6 pm; 27 April: 9.30 am – 4.30 pm
TICKETS   Day tickets: 24, £8.50; 25, £7; 26, £7.50; 27, £6. Reduced afternoon rates daily, except Saturday 26 April
GROUPS   Discounts for party bookings
PARKING AND TRAVEL   Free parking

Run by the North of England Horticultural Society, the Spring Show moves out to the Great Yorkshire Showground for the first time this year. As well as trade stands from nurseries, the show includes the Alpine Garden Society's North of England Show. A shuttle bus service runs from Harrogate to the Showground every twenty minutes.

Journées des Plantes de Courson

Domaine de Courson, 91680 Courson Monteloup

☎ 00 33 164 58 90 12

DATES   16 – 18 May; 17 – 19 October
LOCATION   20 miles south of Paris
PARKING AND TRAVEL   On site

Prestigious French show with a unique atmosphere, held twice yearly in a country house setting near Paris. The show has strong British connections, including a number of regular exhibitors.

Malvern Autumn Show

Three Counties Agricultural Society, The Showground, Malvern WR13 6NW

☎ 01684 892751

DATES   27 to 28 September
LOCATION   Three Counties Showground
OPEN   27 September: 9 am – 6 pm; 28 September: 9 am – 5 pm
TICKETS   Members: £5 (£4 in advance); Public: £6 (£5 in advance); Family ticket (2 + 3): £12 (£10 in advance)
GROUPS   £4 for groups of 10 or more
PARKING AND TRAVEL   Free parking

Charming newish horticultural show which we highly recommend. Nursery displays and an RHS show (last year more gold medals were awarded here than at any RHS show before). Includes identification clinics for fruit and fungi and rural crafts displays.

Malvern Spring Gardening Show

Three Counties Agricultural Society, The Showground, Malvern WR13 6NW

☎ 01684 892751

CONTACT   Show secretary
DATES   9 May to 11 May
LOCATION   Three Counties Showground, Malvern
OPEN   9 – 10 May: 9 am – 6 pm; 11 May: 9 am – 5 pm
TICKETS   £8 (£6 if booked in advance); £5 for RHS and Three Counties Agricultural Society members (in advance)
GROUPS   £5.50 Affiliated Society groups of 10 or more
PARKING AND TRAVEL   Free car parking

The Malvern Spring Gardening Show is organised by the Three Counties Agricultural Society and the Royal Horticultural Society together. The dramatic setting and rural location give this show its own unique character. The exhibitors include a wide range of nurseries, both national and local, and numerous products and sundries stands. The RHS advisory team is present. There is also a large floral art section.

Scotland's National Gardening Show

Royal Horticultural Society, PO Box 313, 80 Vincent Square SW1P 2PE

☎ 0171 630 7422

DATES   30 May to 1 June
LOCATION   Strathclyde Country Park
OPEN   30 – 31 May: 10 am – 6.30 pm; 1 June: 10 am – 5 pm
TICKETS   £9 (Members £7, Public £8 in advance: Phone: 01698 507000)
GROUPS   £7.50 for groups of 10 or more
PARKING AND TRAVEL   Free

A new show, to be staged by the RHS in Strathclyde Country Park. As well as displays from nurseries from all over Great Britain, the show will include practical demonstrations.

Shrewsbury Flower Show

Quarry Lodge, Shrewsbury SY1 1RN

☎ 01743 364051

CONTACT   Show secretary
DATES   15 – 16 August
LOCATION   The Quarry, Shrewsbury
OPEN   15 August: 10.30 am – 10 pm; 16th August: 10 am – 10 pm
TICKETS   Adults £7.50, OAPs £6.50, Children £4.20, if bought in advance. Otherwise £9, £8 & £5 respectively at the gate
GROUPS   Sale or return terms available
PARKING AND TRAVEL   On-site parking free
FACILITIES FOR THE DISABLED   Disabled loos. Disabled parking by prior arrangement

A large, traditional flower show. The show closes with a fireworks display on both nights.

Southport Flower Show

42 Hoghton Street, Southport PR9 0PQ

☎ 01704 547147

CONTACT   Show administrator
DATES   21 August to 24 August
LOCATION   Victoria Park, Southport
OPEN   21–22 August: 9 am – 7 pm; 23 August: 9 am – 10 pm; 24 August: 9 am – 5.30 pm
TICKETS   Adults £8, OAPs £7, Children (12 – 16) £3, if pre-booked. But £9, £8 & £3.50 respectively at the gate.
GROUPS   15% off for groups of 20 or more: pre-booking essential
PARKING AND TRAVEL   No parking on site

This prestigious annual flower show, which hopes to draw over 100,000 visitors, is running for a fourth day this year for the first time. Nice northern flavour with lots of local nurseries who do not attend the numerous southern shows and some southerners who come to be beside the sea.

Spring Plant Fair Day

The National Trust, Spring Plant Fairs, PO Box 39, Bromley BR1 3XL

☎ 0181 315 1111

DATES   18 May
LOCATION   At around fifty National Trust properties nationwide
OPEN   Contact individual properties for details

A new and intriguing initiative from the National Trust. Around fifty properties will be hosting fund-raising plant fairs on the same day. Most will include plants supplied by volunteer growers: to register and receive an information pack contact the address above. Specialist nurseries will also attend some of the fairs. Properties in need of volunteers include: Aberdulais Falls; Acorn Bank Garden; Arlington Court; Attingham Park; Basildon Park; Beningbrough Hall; Berrington Hall; Blickling Hall; Bodiam Castle; Canons Ashby House; Castle Drogo; Claremont Gardens; Colby Woodland Garden; Compton Castle; Dinefwr Park; Dunster Castle; East Riddlesden Hall; Erddig; Fell Foot Park; Gibside; Ham House; Hanbury Hall; Heywood House; Hinton Ampner; Hughenden Manor; Kingston Lacy; Knole; Llanerchaeron; Lydford Gorge; Marsden Moor Estate; Nunnington Hall; Ormesby Hall; Osterley Park; Overbecks; Packwood House; Petworth House; Plas Newydd; Sheffield Park Garden; Sizergh Castle; Souter Lighthouse; Sutton House; The Vyne; Tintinhull House Garden; Treasurers House; Wallington Hall. The following properties will feature only specialist nurseries and so do not require volunteer growers: Biddulph Grange Garden; Cliveden; Clumber Park; Cotehele; Dyrham Park; Hatchlands Park; Lanhydrock; Powis Castle; and Trerice. For more details, contact the individual properties.

Wisley Flower Show

RHS Garden, Wisley, Woking GU23 6QB

☎ 01483 224234

DATES   14 to 15 August
LOCATION   RHS Garden, Wisley

OPEN   14 August: 10 am – 6 pm; 15 August: 10 am – 5 pm
TICKETS   Normal garden admission rates (£5); RHS members free
GROUPS   £4 for advance bookings of 10 or more
PARKING AND TRAVEL   Free parking

The setting in the garden at Wisley is a major attraction of this smallish show. The nurseries attending will be selling plants. This year the Flower Show hosts the British Gladiolus Society's Show.

3

A Digest of 1996 Gardening News

Several horticulturists received recognition in the New Year's Honours list. Rosemary Verey received an OBE, as did John Turner, the vice-principal of Writtle College. MBEs were awarded to Oliver Menhinnick, the charismatic head of horticulture at Lackham College and principal of the Horticultural Correspondence College, and Jim Fisk, the founder of Fisk's Clematis Nursery.

At the beginning of February, the publishers Michael Joseph announced that they would be publishing later this year *Mr McGregor* the first novel by 'gardening pundit Alan Titchmarsh'. It tells the story of a young, bare-chested television gardener whose attractions are so amazing that the viewing figures go rocketing. Michael Joseph describe the novel as 'very sexy, very funny, Jilly Cooper-ish'.

In February, Johnsons Seeds announced that they would be making the grass seed used on the pitch at Wembley Stadium (known as the 'Hallowed Turf') available for sale to the public. Johnsons Seeds have been responsible for the grass at the stadium for several years and their Wembley mix is designed to be hard-wearing, slow-growing and disease-resistant. Soccer fans are expected to be among the most avid purchasers. No doubt we shall see copycat products for sale in years to come, with ryegrass from Ibrox Park competing with Celtic Park and fescues from The Oval on sale alongside seed from Lords.

Gardeners at the Royal Botanic Gardens Kew went on strike at the beginning of March. The strike was in protest against a pay rise offer of 0.9% and the introduction of performance pay. It was the first piece of industrial action at Kew since the gardens were established more than two centuries ago. The dispute was soon settled.

The BSE scare, which began to dominate the national headlines at the end of March, raised an unusual question in the minds of many garden-owners: how safe are such fertilisers as bone-meal and 'hoof and horn'? The RHS was not found wanting: it had already stated in its existing guideline on the use of fertilisers that 'the handling of organic fertilisers derived from dead animals may present some health hazard if human pathogens survive the processing'. But the advice from MAFF was that there was no evidence of infectivity by BSE of blood and bones of slaughtered cattle, nor of farmyard manure carrying the organism. The RHS also pointed out that the loss of bone meal as a fertiliser should present no hardship to gardeners. Its principal ingredient is phosphate, which can be provided by dressings of rock phosphate or superphosphate. On 18 April, MAFF banned bone meal from sale and use as a fertiliser on agricultural land. It explained that the aim was to prevent ruminants from ingesting it. There was no restriction on the use of bone meal in private gardens.

During the course of last spring, specimens of over 300 rhododendrons were flown back from the Royal Botanic Garden in Edinburgh to their native China as part of a new conservation initiative. RBG Edinburgh is the leading centre for rhododendron scholarship and has in its collection over 200 species collected in China during the last 100 years. These original collections by such plant hunters as Forrest, Wilson, Rock and Kingdon-Ward often represent species which are under threat from deforestation in the wild. It was from these important historical plants that the 300 young plants were raised and flown to two botanic gardens in China, at Hua Xi and Guiyang. By returning material to their country of origin, the Royal Botanic Garden in Edinburgh is making a measurable contribution to conservation and biodiversity.

In May, Flora and Fauna International celebrated the first year's crop of snowdrops and aconites grown under its 'Indigenous Propagation Project' in the Turkish village of Dumlugöze. This conservation scheme was set up to address the international trade in wild bulbs. Until about ten years ago some 70 million bulbs were being trafficked through Holland each year, often marked as 'grown in Holland'. The problem was that campaigning for an immediate end to the trade would have caused considerable financial hardship to many poor people in Turkey for whom the bulb trade had become an important part of their income. Flora and Fauna International therefore set up a bulb farm as part of a project to tackle the problem on all levels. Villagers were shown how to propagate bulbs, rather than collecting them from the wild, to ensure that they received a sustainable income. The Turkish government was lobbied, in the hope of persuading it to reduce its quota for the export of wild bulbs and to ratify CITES. Importers and exporters were urged to deal only in cultivated bulbs. Both have been asked to sign a pledge (with a split infinitive) 'to never knowingly sell wild-collected bulbs': so have the retailers. Consumers have been asked to buy only from retailers who have signed that pledge. Flora and Fauna International point out that villagers can now look forward to a safe and secure income from land that would otherwise not be used, the traders are now trading with 'green' credentials and the gardeners get better quality bulbs. However, the problem of unscrupulous wild collections continues in other parts of the world. In the tropics the trade in orchids, cacti, palms, succulents and cycads is still widespread and illegal and wild collection on a vast scale is commonplace. Last year in Georgia, for example, six million snowdrops were collected from their natural habitat.

In May it was announced the Blooms of Bressingham had been bought by a Channel Islands based company called Flying Flowers for £2.26 million. In June Alan Bloom was awarded an MBE in the Queen's Birthday Honours: on 19 November he celebrated his 90th birthday.

In June the RHS joined forces with the Water Services Association to encourage Britain's 23 million gardeners to look at ways of conserving water in the garden. A new practical gardening guide *The Water Friendly Garden* gives advice on selecting plants, improving the retention of moisture in the soil, and watering efficiently during dry weather.

The garden pesticide Roseclear was banned by the Ministry of Agriculture in June. A routine test by the Pesticide Safety Directorate found that Roseclear in its undiluted form, carried ' a remote hazard of accidental eye damage', which resulted in its upgrading from a mild to a severe irritant. The ban was considered somewhat controversial. Miracle Garden Care claimed that 40 million bottles of the pesticide had been sold since 1982 and there had been only four reported cases of temporary eye irritation. A representative of the British Rose Growers Association said 'Roseclear has been used by the public for many years without problems. The actions are unjustified.' The Secretary of the Royal National Rose Society Lt. Col. Ken Grapes described it as a case of 'a perfectly acceptable product being taken out of circulation in the interest of protecting the idiot few'.

At the end of July, a plant of *Amorphophallus titanum* at RBG Kew came into flower for the first time for many years. The flower is the largest inflorescence in the plant kingdom, some 3m (10ft) high. It is also noteworthy for its disgusting scent, a 'mixture of jam and rotting meat' according to one account. The flowering brought a large number of curious visitors to see the spectacle, which lasted for little more than a couple of days, but not everyone agreed about the odour. 'It really was awful' said a member of Kew's staff, but many visitors said that they could barely smell it.

Whitefly is a serious pest of glasshouse crops, and a spreader of diseases: some 63 different plant viruses are known to be carried by it. It is a particular problem for commercial growers who buy their stocks from continental producers. In fact, the UK was made a protected zone for poinsettia cuttings – which means that they cannot be imported without a phytosanitary certificate – specifically to protect us from infection by whitefly, or *Bemisia tabaci* as it is properly known. In September, however, it was announced that a biological solution to the problem may be close. Ongoing trials of whitefly predators and parasites, jointly run by Biological Crop Protection and Wye College, have shown that a small beetle called *Delphastus pusillus* can eat up to 160 whitefly eggs a day but will feed upon the whitefly at every stage of their existence. Trials with *Delphastus pusillus* have been running in Holland for a couple of years and it is possible that the predator will be available in the UK shortly. The first users are likely to be glasshouse owners, botanic gardens and butterfly houses, but no doubt it will find its way through to amateur gardeners in due course.

At the start of October, the winners of the annual Britain in Bloom competition were announced. The principal winners were: Westminster (large city trophy); Oxford (city trophy); Nottingham (inner city trophy); Christchurch (town trophy); Alcester (small town trophy); Moffat, Dumfries & Galloway (small country town trophy); Stanwell, Surrey (urban community trophy); Hillsborough, Northern Ireland (large village trophy); Beddgelert, Gwynedd (village trophy); Bridlington (Asmer trophy for the best display of bedding plants); Carlisle (Beautiful Britain award for new and extensive landscaping).

Yorkshire Water lifted its hosepipe ban at last on 1 November. The ban was imposed sixteen months previously after the low rainfall of early 1995 had left water supply stocks well below average. Nevertheless, at the time of going to press, water restrictions were still in force for gardeners in some part of the north-west and south of England.

Obituaries

Millar Gault died on 12 March aged 92. Millar Gault was largely responsible for the transformation of Regent's Park in London into one of the finest amenity gardens in the world. As Superintendent he established such high standards for the Park's maintenance that they have been followed to this day. His career as a professional gardener began with an apprenticeship at Crathes Castle in Aberdeenshire. Later he served as head gardener to Nancy Astor at Cliveden in Buckinghamshire. His tenure of responsibility at Regent's Park ran from 1955 to 1969. Although Queen Mary's Garden in the Inner Circle at Regent's Park had been in existence for some years previously, Gault expanded and improved the display: the Rose Garden now contains some 60,000 roses which makes it one of the largest in the country. His *Dictionary of Roses in Colour* of 1971, written in partnership with Patrick Synge, a former editor of the RHS Journal, and published in collaboration with the RHS and the RNRS, remained the standard reference work on roses for nearly 20 years.

Geoff Hamilton was born on 12 August 1936 and died on 4 August 1996. Familiar to television audiences from his long-running *Gardeners' World* series, Hamilton made his garden at Barnsdale among the

best-known in the country. He was born in London, and had trained at Writtle College. From horticulture he moved into horticultural journalism, first on *Garden News*, and then as editor of *Practical Gardening*. But it was as the presenter of *Gardeners' World* that he found fame and fortune. His hands-on, easy-going affability made the programme one of the most-watched on BBC2, and it had a strong following even among non-gardeners, happy to unwind on a Friday evening in Barnsdale. The programme attracted its critics, as it tried to cater for a wider range of interests; but Hamilton escaped censure, a discernibly genuine and unpretentious presence at the show's centre. Despite his place in the mainstream, he followed his own beliefs, advocating an organic and environmental approach which was at odds with some entrenched industry opinions. Books followed in the same competent and unfussy style that characterised his television appearances, but it is for the latter that he will be remembered by a whole generation of gardeners whose interest was fostered by his broadcasts. There was a display of his books to commemorate him at the RHS show on 20 & 21 August. They made one realise what a protean intellect he had: he tackled every subject.

Sir Geoffrey Jellicoe died on 17 July. He was one of the greatest landscape architects: among his best known works are the gardens at Sutton Place in Surrey, Shute House in Wiltshire and Sandringham House in Norfolk which he designed for King George V & King George VI. His most monumental work may however prove to have been his last and largest: the Moodey Historical Gardens at Galveston, Texas, conceived as a three-dimensional history of mankind starting with a Garden of Eden. Jellicoe trained to be an architect at the Architectural Association and it was during his student days that he first toured Italy to study the country's famous gardens. The result was Jellicoe's first book, *The Italian Gardens of the Renaissance,* published in 1925 and now in its fifth edition. Perhaps the most important of his books was *The Landscape of Man* co-authored with his late wife Susan in 1975. In 1929 he helped to found the Institute of Landscape Architects and during the 1930s he worked in partnership with the great designer and philosopher of gardens, Russell Page. Although a great admirer of the Italian Renaissance and of the Central European baroque gardens (he wrote a book about them at a time when they were not at all fashionable) Jellicoe was essentially a modernist, a man with a restless intellect and interest in new ideas. This was evident too in his personality, for his cheerfulness, enthusiasm and optimism lent particular charm to his many friendships.

4

Weather Records

Review of 1995/96

During December 1995, a series of high pressure zones established themselves over the northern part of the British Isles, drawing in cold north-easterly winds across the southern part of Britain. Frosts of −5°C were regularly experienced over Devon and Somerset. From time to time rain-bearing lows came up from the south and collided with the highs. The result was a series of snow storms, intense but short-lived, before the snow turned to rain.

A particularly cold spell over the Christmas period brought Arctic temperatures to the whole of Britain. The worst snowstorm since 1955 delivered 40cm (15ins.) of snow to the Shetlands and the Western Isles, but violent blizzards whipped it into drifts as deep as 10m. Temperatures in parts of Highland fell below −20°C: by 29 December, the afternoon maximum temperature at Braemar was −15.3°C and a night-time temperature of −27°C at Altnaharra in Highland was claimed as the lowest ever recorded in the British Isles. On Boxing Day night the temperature at Glasgow airport sank to −18°C, the lowest recorded since 1940: by 29 December it had reached −20°C, an all-time record low. Thick snow fell as far south as the Midlands. The towns of Scarborough and Whitby were cut off from the rest of Yorkshire. Even in the south of England, the temperatures remained below freezing for nearly a week.

December 1995 was therefore the coldest in much of the UK since 1981. Nevertheless, the twelve months to 31 December 1995 were the warmest since records began in 1659: the average temperature was 10.7°C, some 0.5°C above the previous high in 1949.

For much of January 1996, the weather depended on the interchange between two systems: a large, stationary, high pressure zone over Russia and a series of Atlantic lows which approached the United Kingdom from the south or west. During the first three weeks of January, the lows brought weather that was mild, even warm, but the Siberian system established control around 24 January to bring easterly gales and sub-zero temperatures to the whole of the country for several days. One surprising result was that for much of the country January was the dullest since meteorologists first recorded sunshine hours in 1909 — some 48% of the average. On the other hand, February was the sunniest in Northern Ireland since records began in 1880.

March was cold, with temperatures at least 1°C lower than average throughout the country. By the end of the month, the season was three weeks late. A cartoon in The Times showed a weatherman desperately urging 'Spring' to arrive. The quality and quantity of the camellias in the competition at the Early Spring Show on 12 and 13 March were noticeably poorer than usual. The equinox came and went without gales or any wind other than a persistent south-easterly from the still cold mainland of Europe. March was also a dry month, with barely more than half the expected rainfall in any part of Britain. In Manchester the twelve months to the end of March were the driest on record, which augured ill for the water companies.

Wholesale nurseries and garden centres were affected by the poor weather: cold temperatures and cloudy skies do not bring out the customers in March and April, on which both rely for a high proportion of their business. At the RHS Westminster show on 16 and 17 April the long slow spring brought out so many competitors in the Camellia Competition that there was not enough room for them all on the stand, but late-flowering cultivars were conspicuous by their absence.

May was unusually cold: dry in the first half and wet in the second half, but cold until the last few days. North-easterly winds brought cold, bright, dry weather to most of the country. One consequence of the cold weather was that it culled a large proportion of queen wasps, active at this season, so that in much of the country wasp nests were not such a problem in late summer as, for example, in 1995. Knightshayes in Devon had a ground frost every morning from 1 to 15 May. There was snow on the west country moors on 19 May. Many visitors said that the Chelsea Flower Show was the coldest they could remember: throughout the month, no place in the whole of Britain reached a temperature of 20°C until 29 May.

June was an anticyclonic month: very sunny and dry, with warm days and cool nights. On 7 June, the temperature reached 32.9°C at Gravesend in Kent and Wattisham in Suffolk. A series of anticyclones took up residence on the continent and fed mild south-westerly airflows over much of the country, though it was warmer in the south and cooler in Scotland and there were several short-lived interruptions to the settled weather. During one such interlude – a cool snap between 19 and 21 June – some 42.6mm of rain fell at Bournemouth on 20 June, while the maximum temperature reached no higher than 12°C. Despite the generally warm weather, however, the season remained late and difficult. Roses were about two weeks late in flowering, and unsettled weather returned at the end of the month. Water-shortages remained topical: drought-busting and water-saving were popular themes in the exhibits at BBC Gardener's World Live. This contrasted with a report in *Garden News* on 19 June that a freak hailstorm had devastated the National Collection of *Artemisia* species in Cambridgeshire.

July began with north-westerly winds and changeable weather: sunshine and showers, and nowhere very warm. But anticyclones and south-westerly winds brought warmer weather from 10 July onwards. Temperatures peaked at 33.2°C at Rickmansworth on 22 July and were followed by thunderstorms, locally very heavy. By the end of the month, mean temperatures were slightly above average in most of Britain. August had variable weather: showery days would be followed by spells of fine, warm weather. Bill Giles, one of the old-style BBC weathermen, said that global warming was such a fact of life that he was going to plant olive trees in his south Oxfordshire garden. Thundery storms became more common again: 115mm of rain fell at Folkestone on 12 August. The end of the month

was again unsettled, and the Bank Holiday characterised by cool winds and showers.

September was very dry, the driest since 1959 in much of eastern England and the Midlands. The first three weeks were dominated by high pressure zones: Glasgow had no significant rain between 2 and 22 September. Changeable, windy weather set in on 23 September, but the month as a whole was warmer than usual, particularly in the west, sheltered from the north-easterly winds which accompanied the anticyclones. In East Anglia, the mean daily maxima were 1.5°C cooler than normal. Southerly and westerly winds persisted in October, making for one of the mildest Octobers on record. A sequence of anticyclones passed gently over the country until ex-hurricane Lili brought severe gales during 28 and 29 October: gusts exceeding 70 knots were recorded in southern England. Autumn colour came little and late: the robinias in Hyde Park were fully leaved and green still in December. But it was a marvellous autumn for fruit. Heavy crops of apples, pears and plums were reported from all parts of Britain. The wild hawthorns and sloes were better than many could remember. Did it all betoken a fearsome winter? No, said the experts: it was all the result of the hot weather we had in 1995, which ripened the flower buds that brought us the bumper pickings.

Weather Records

We are publishing complete weather records for the twelve months September 1995 to August 1996. The data, supplied by the Met. Office, has been collected at the Meteorological Stations at five important gardens around the British Isles: the Royal Botanic Garden, Edinburgh; the Royal Horticultural Society's Gardens at Wisley, Surrey; the University of Liverpool's Ness Gardens, Cheshire; and the National Trust's gardens at Trelissick, Cornwall; and Rowallane in Northern Ireland.

The information is given on a day by day basis, without averaging, so that readers can see the fluctuations within any period of their choice. Close study reveals patterns that may help to explain plant growth and offer a general guide to seasonal variations.

Date	Max (°C)	Min (°C)	Rainfall (mm)	Sunshine (hrs)	Date	Max (°C)	Min (°C)	Rainfall (mm)	Sunshine (hrs)
Sept 1995 01	16.9	9.1	9.6	nil	Nov 01	12.1	9.2	trace	4.2
02	14.0	11.1	55.9	nil	02	11.8	2.0	trace	7.1
03	16.1	9.8	0.1	4.1	03	8.7	0.4	nil	5.3
04	17.3	8.6	17.9	4.8	04	9.8	-0.7	nil	6.7
05	13.0	10.3	3.3	nil	05	10.6	0.7	nil	0.1
06	15.7	10.8	1.1	0.3	06	12.1	6.1	0.9	2.0
07	15.0	12.0	13.4	nil	07	14.7	7.5	0.3	2.2
08	16.3	12.6	6.4	nil	08	13.1	11.4	trace	nil
09	15.4	12.3	3.5	nil	09	8.9	0.5	trace	2.8
10	19.7	9.7	15.2	11.2	10	9.9	1.2	4.4	0.9
11	15.7	12.2	0.1	0.1	11	11.3	3.9	4.9	nil
12	16.7	11.0	nil	5.9	12	11.2	8.8	0.2	nil
13	17.2	10.0	4.0	8.0	13	11.6	10.3	trace	nil
14	15.4	8.0	nil	7.0	14	11.4	7.4	13.7	1.9
15	16.8	9.6	nil	5.1	15	8.9	6.4	38.2	nil
16	18.0	6.8	0.8	7.3	16	5.8	3.8	0.1	4.7
17	15.7	11.9	trace	0.8	17	4.7	-0.3	trace	3.2
18	16.6	11.5	4.1	5.9	18	6.1	-0.1	trace	4.3
19	15.0	11.4	0.4	0.2	19	10.5	0.9	trace	3.2
20	18.2	7.0	nil	9.8	20	11.7	-0.7	1.5	0.1
21	17.4	10.9	nil	4.0	21	11.9	1.8	0.2	0.3
22	16.1	12.2	0.1	5.2	22	12.4	8.2	nil	2.8
23	16.8	9.9	5.2	3.9	23	14.3	7.7	1.0	3.1
24	14.0	10.0	0.7	6.5	24	14.1	11.2	0.4	4.5
25	17.1	6.0	trace	0.9	25	9.6	8.3	5.3	2.7
26	13.8	9.4	2.2	8.5	26	9.9	0.2	0.3	1.2
27	11.5	6.4	nil	9.4	27	9.0	1.7	0.6	0.8
28	12.8	1.6	nil	8.9	28	9.4	4.4	2.0	0.1
29	13.1	6.1	nil	7.5	29	10.3	5.7	0.1	0.1
30	14.4	5.6	3.5	2.1	30	8.5	7.0	trace	nil
Oct 01	15.6	9.5	2.2	5.9	Dec 01	8.1	6.0	1.2	0.1
02	17.6	9.7	5.8	8.1	02	11.2	4.9	trace	nil
03	17.3	10.3	3.5	3.9	03	12.6	6.5	1.6	1.1
04	17.2	11.3	0.6	5.2	04	8.2	6.6	trace	0.1
05	14.8	10.5	1.3	6.9	05	6.1	2.5	1.7	nil
06	19.1	10.2	1.4	3.9	06	5.2	0.5	3.2	0.5
07	17.3	10.5	0.8	5.7	07	3.6	1.0	trace	3.3
08	19.8	11.6	nil	6.9	08	0.5	-3.7	nil	4.8
09	19.6	15.4	trace	3.4	09	7.9	-4.0	0.9	nil
10	15.8	8.4	nil	8.4	10	8.3	-1.5	trace	1.9
11	16.7	5.3	0.8	2.0	11	5.8	5.2	trace	nil
12	15.3	12.8	20.6	1.5	12	6.0	2.5	nil	0.7
13	14.0	10.3	0.5	nil	13	6.3	2.2	1.4	nil
14	15.6	10.6	trace	7.4	14	6.7	4.5	0.8	0.3
15	17.1	9.5	nil	1.4	15	7.7	4.0	3.5	0.5
16	16.5	11.5	trace	0.4	16	6.9	4.8	trace	1.0
17	18.2	14.5	trace	5.0	17	6.7	4.1	2.6	nil
18	13.7	8.5	nil	2.4	18	5.4	4.3	0.7	nil
19	15.0	10.8	1.3	3.2	19	4.2	4.1	trace	nil
20	11.6	4.3	trace	9.0	20	0.3	-3.0	nil	5.6
21	14.0	0.0	2.0	0.4	21	3.8	-7.0	5.6	nil
22	15.5	2.0	19.0	0.1	22	4.0	-3.0	13.1	nil
23	15.8	10.1	trace	0.1	23	4.4	2.0	0.9	3.2
24	18.4	9.8	3.3	0.7	24	2.7	-1.9	nil	3.8
25	14.2	7.4	7.7	5.4	25	1.2	-0.5	nil	0.4
26	14.8	8.3	10.3	1.6	26	-0.5	-5.1	nil	5.6
27	10.0	6.0	0.3	7.1	27	-2.5	-9.5	nil	5.7
28	11.5	6.0	trace	5.2	28	-2.0	-10.4	nil	5.7
29	11.4	1.7	1.2	1.4	29	0.5	-11.5	nil	nil
30	14.1	4.5	4.3	0.5	30	3.6	-11.5	nil	nil
31	13.3	8.5	6.0	nil	31	3.9	0.0	3.4	nil

Date	Max (°C)	Min (°C)	Rainfall (mm)	Sunshine (hrs)	Date	Max (°C)	Min (°C)	Rainfall (mm)	Sunshine (hrs)
Jan 1996 01	4.5	3.0	3.2	nil	Mar 01	10.3	0.2	nil	5.4
02	5.5	3.0	0.3	nil	02	10.6	2.9	nil	4.8
03	5.8	1.3	0.6	0.4	03	11.9	5.3	nil	0.3
04	6.5	3.0	0.4	nil	04	9.3	0.5	trace	2.6
05	7.0	3.0	0.6	nil	05	8.9	−1.0	nil	6.5
06	5.8	5.5	1.5	nil	06	11.5	2.1	0.1	4.6
07	9.0	3.7	0.1	0.9	07	8.2	5.2	0.2	3.2
08	11.5	4.4	1.7	nil	08	5.1	2.5	0.1	0.3
09	10.9	6.4	0.2	0.9	09	9.5	2.8	nil	4.5
10	9.2	6.3	trace	3.9	10	10.4	−1.4	nil	2.5
11	8.5	0.8	0.9	nil	11	8.4	1.3	7.0	nil
12	9.7	5.5	3.9	nil	12	2.8	1.7	7.6	nil
13	10.8	5.9	trace	3.8	13	2.7	−1.3	0.2	2.4
14	10.7	8.0	trace	nil	14	4.3	0.2	trace	1.6
15	11.6	7.8	trace	1.3	15	3.7	0.7	nil	nil
16	8.4	6.3	0.2	nil	16	3.8	2.3	4.9	nil
17	10.2	5.8	trace	nil	17	3.5	0.7	trace	nil
18	9.1	8.0	trace	1.2	18	4.9	2.2	0.1	nil
19	7.5	4.8	nil	nil	19	4.8	2.3	trace	nil
20	6.1	5.4	trace	nil	20	4.8	1.9	0.1	0.7
21	4.0	2.2	0.2	nil	21	6.2	1.9	0.2	nil
22	4.8	2.1	trace	nil	22	4.0	2.5	0.5	nil
23	3.9	3.1	nil	nil	23	5.4	1.9	trace	nil
24	3.9	2.6	nil	nil	24	9.0	−2.0	nil	7.0
25	1.8	0.3	2.0	1.7	25	4.8	2.6	0.3	nil
26	2.6	−0.6	3.3	2.8	26	6.5	2.0	nil	1.0
27	2.9	−0.4	4.8	nil	27	6.2	−1.3	0.8	2.2
28	4.2	0.3	0.1	2.2	28	7.9	1.4	trace	1.7
29	3.5	1.3	nil	0.3	29	8.2	1.5	nil	5.3
30	3.9	1.7	nil	nil	30	5.9	−0.4	nil	nil
31	2.9	2.4	nil	nil	31	9.0	2.0	nil	7.1
Feb 01	3.5	−0.2	nil	nil	Apr 01	7.3	2.5	nil	1.7
02	5.4	1.7	nil	4.9	02	9.5	2.1	nil	1.5
03	4.5	−1.4	nil	nil	03	10.7	5.2	nil	0.4
04	5.9	−0.4	trace	5.0	04	12.5	0.7	nil	8.7
05	2.6	−0.7	1.3	nil	05	14.1	0.0	nil	11.6
06	0.5	−1.4	4.7	nil	06	8.0	−1.5	nil	8.9
07	2.4	−1.3	2.0	nil	07	8.4	3.8	nil	nil
08	4.3	−3.0	1.1	6.6	08	16.5	2.6	nil	5.3
09	5.4	−3.2	2.6	1.9	09	16.7	5.6	0.7	7.7
10	9.8	1.3	1.5	2.8	10	10.5	7.8	9.8	nil
11	8.2	4.9	2.8	0.5	11	8.0	6.0	trace	nil
12	6.4	3.9	1.5	nil	12	4.8	3.5	trace	nil
13	5.6	1.8	0.1	3.5	13	7.4	1.4	nil	nil
14	6.7	−3.0	nil	4.1	14	9.2	3.2	0.6	nil
15	10.3	−1.5	0.3	nil	15	14.8	4.3	0.1	0.6
16	7.9	6.5	0.6	4.0	16	13.7	8.7	0.5	nil
17	8.7	3.7	2.7	3.2	17	12.2	8.4	3.6	1.7
18	6.9	2.5	1.4	3.4	18	12.5	5.6	2.0	5.3
19	3.6	1.0	0.8	3.8	19	14.8	6.3	0.1	11.5
20	4.7	−0.6	0.1	4.2	20	12.4	6.8	6.1	nil
21	4.7	−3.9	3.0	nil	21	11.7	5.6	3.3	0.3
22	7.3	0.0	0.1	3.9	22	15.0	4.9	6.7	13.1
23	8.7	3.2	1.2	1.3	23	10.7	6.3	4.0	nil
24	7.4	2.9	2.4	nil	24	13.7	6.5	0.1	4.1
25	6.4	−0.1	trace	8.4	25	13.0	7.0	nil	3.5
26	6.6	−3.3	nil	8.4	26	15.4	9.7	3.1	1.0
27	9.0	−0.5	trace	7.5	27	14.2	7.2	nil	10.4
28	9.1	−1.3	nil	8.3	28	11.7	5.4	0.3	3.8
29	11.8	1.8	nil	7.7	29	13.0	4.8	1.0	4.0
					30	7.5	4.5	3.4	0.9

Date	Max (°C)	Min (°C)	Rainfall (mm)	Sunshine (hrs)	Date	Max (°C)	Min (°C)	Rainfall (mm)	Sunshine (hrs)
May 01	6.1	2.5	7.0	nil	July 01	16.9	9.7	1.2	5.0
02	8.5	2.8	nil	11.6	02	17.5	9.0	3.1	5.3
03	10.2	2.0	trace	7.1	03	18.8	11.2	5.2	4.1
04	11.4	-0.5	0.2	7.2	04	17.5	9.0	3.0	7.8
05	12.8	2.4	3.3	8.7	05	16.3	10.1	nil	5.2
06	11.9	4.1	trace	7.1	06	16.9	9.7	nil	5.4
07	11.3	2.5	0.4	5.0	07	18.8	9.8	nil	8.0
08	12.0	2.3	nil	5.1	08	19.2	7.3	0.2	7.9
09	9.8	3.2	nil	14.1	09	21.6	12.1	nil	5.0
10	9.5	4.1	5.8	2.8	10	19.5	11.8	trace	4.0
11	8.2	3.5	0.4	nil	11	20.3	14.0	nil	5.7
12	11.5	5.5	nil	nil	12	16.9	12.5	trace	4.3
13	16.8	4.7	nil	14.0	13	19.5	12.0	trace	6.2
14	18.0	5.5	nil	6.1	14	19.2	11.2	nil	15.4
15	11.3	6.9	nil	4.1	15	18.8	7.3	nil	10.8
16	11.2	3.4	nil	5.6	16	18.5	5.2	nil	13.9
17	10.6	-1.0	0.7	9.2	17	22.0	8.9	nil	14.3
18	9.1	1.3	4.0	3.7	18	16.9	11.8	nil	5.4
19	10.8	4.6	2.2	0.1	19	22.3	10.1	nil	3.3
20	13.1	6.0	2.6	7.5	20	25.5	9.5	nil	13.7
21	14.2	6.3	0.6	7.0	21	24.5	11.3	11.0	4.1
22	14.1	4.8	1.1	0.6	22	20.9	14.8	1.0	0.4
23	15.5	8.7	1.7	12.5	23	20.2	14.8	13.6	1.3
24	15.3	6.4	trace	10.4	24	18.9	11.5	nil	7.0
25	15.5	8.6	nil	10.9	25	20.7	8.5	1.4	4.0
26	13.9	6.6	2.9	5.0	26	19.2	13.4	nil	10.6
27	16.0	7.9	nil	9.7	27	17.5	11.5	nil	1.8
28	14.9	6.3	2.1	nil	28	18.0	11.9	4.9	2.2
29	17.5	9.8	0.5	7.8	29	18.3	12.2	trace	3.2
30	17.4	10.5	6.5	0.1	30	17.4	12.2	0.2	0.9
31	14.8	10.6	1.1	12.2	31	18.1	10.3	nil	6.7
June 01	14.8	7.5	1.0	8.0	Aug 01	18.7	10.5	0.2	9.6
02	15.5	6.3	nil	8.3	02	18.6	9.4	nil	8.5
03	14.6	6.5	0.9	4.4	03	19.9	11.9	nil	6.3
04	18.6	8.9	0.2	13.4	04	21.7	9.4	nil	11.5
05	18.7	10.9	trace	3.3	05	23.9	13.4	nil	3.9
06	19.6	11.8	nil	12.6	06	17.1	12.4	7.0	1.2
07	21.0	10.8	nil	6.5	07	20.6	12.8	0.7	2.5
08	18.8	10.8	nil	13.5	08	18.7	11.8	0.8	0.9
09	17.8	10.1	1.3	0.9	09	21.8	10.4	1.1	7.3
10	17.9	12.3	0.8	5.2	10	19.7	13.9	10.7	5.7
11	18.1	11.4	3.0	2.2	11	20.5	10.3	trace	4.9
12	16.6	8.7	nil	12.6	12	22.2	10.7	nil	14.0
13	17.8	7.6	nil	9.9	13	19.8	12.5	nil	6.9
14	21.0	8.0	nil	14.8	14	20.4	13.1	nil	7.3
15	17.7	10.5	nil	15.3	15	22.9	9.5	nil	9.2
16	23.8	10.3	nil	10.6	16	20.7	12.8	nil	1.6
17	19.2	11.8	nil	13.5	17	23.2	9.6	nil	7.3
18	16.8	10.4	nil	3.6	18	25.9	14.8	nil	12.2
19	16.8	9.8	nil	3.5	19	21.9	11.9	3.0	2.7
20	14.6	5.5	nil	3.9	20	20.2	15.5	14.3	0.9
21	16.2	6.5	nil	5.1	21	17.4	13.2	3.8	3.0
22	18.7	6.9	nil	7.5	22	19.7	13.1	0.6	3.9
23	20.5	6.0	nil	13.6	23	20.1	12.0	7.1	10.3
24	21.8	8.6	nil	14.8	24	17.5	12.2	7.7	2.7
25	23.6	10.0	0.4	5.0	25	17.7	11.2	nil	4.8
26	17.7	13.0	nil	7.3	26	17.6	8.5	nil	5.5
27	18.0	9.5	2.7	1.5	27	16.8	12.5	nil	1.4
28	18.9	12.2	0.3	2.6	28	17.7	12.7	nil	5.3
29	18.2	10.6	0.4	3.4	29	19.3	9.3	nil	6.6
30	17.1	10.0	2.0	6.9	30	18.8	9.4	nil	4.9
					31	17.2	8.2	nil	2.4

Date	Max (°C)	Min (°C)	Rainfall (mm)	Sunshine (hrs)	Date	Max (°C)	Min (°C)	Rainfall (mm)	Sunshine (hrs)
Sept 1995 01	19.0	14.7	trace	0.2	Nov 01	13.4	3.4	nil	0.4
02	19.5	14.8	1.6	3.4	02	11.4	1.9	nil	4.3
03	19.7	5.7	nil	8.6	03	10.2	2.4	nil	4.2
04	21.6	7.2	nil	7.9	04	11.3	-2.4	nil	7.0
05	20.4	9.0	0.7	5.8	05	9.7	-1.5	nil	8.4
06	20.2	11.6	5.5	3.5	06	11.6	-4.4	nil	6.6
07	18.7	14.1	7.4	1.0	07	10.4	-0.2	nil	0.1
08	19.6	14.9	trace	1.2	08	14.6	3.3	nil	0.8
09	20.1	11.8	trace	7.6	09	12.9	10.0	6.2	nil
10	16.5	10.3	9.0	0.5	10	12.9	9.0	0.9	nil
11	20.4	13.0	2.5	8.2	11	14.7	7.8	2.3	0.6
12	17.5	11.2	4.2	6.0	12	13.9	12.5	2.2	nil
13	18.2	9.3	nil	5.7	13	15.0	10.2	0.1	4.0
14	17.7	7.5	2.5	2.7	14	14.0	6.6	3.0	3.2
15	17.4	10.0	4.7	2.3	15	14.6	9.2	1.6	4.4
16	16.7	11.2	3.1	0.1	16	12.3	9.4	2.1	2.0
17	19.0	12.4	0.1	2.2	17	5.1	-0.8	trace	4.2
18	18.3	11.4	18.5	0.3	18	7.1	-3.2	nil	7.1
19	17.8	14.2	trace	nil	19	9.4	-0.5	nil	7.0
20	17.8	10.6	nil	5.3	20	11.0	-1.8	nil	3.4
21	19.1	4.8	trace	10.2	21	10.5	0.4	trace	0.1
22	19.0	8.2	trace	5.9	22	12.9	9.0	nil	1.4
23	18.0	9.8	4.3	7.7	23	11.9	4.6	nil	nil
24	16.2	10.5	4.0	3.4	24	12.2	9.0	1.3	0.1
25	16.4	3.3	0.1	6.0	25	12.5	10.3	5.2	nil
26	17.6	12.5	21.7	nil	26	11.1	8.5	8.8	1.0
27	15.2	10.9	0.1	8.1	27	11.6	7.2	2.0	2.1
28	14.4	5.0	2.6	5.5	28	11.2	5.7	3.6	1.1
29	17.0	3.2	trace	8.0	29	11.5	8.4	trace	1.1
30	17.5	3.0	0.8	2.1	30	8.4	4.2	nil	nil
Oct 01	19.1	11.1	nil	7.2	Dec 01	12.0	5.3	1.5	nil
02	17.3	9.0	nil	2.5	02	12.8	8.4	0.5	nil
03	17.5	10.8	5.6	1.9	03	12.4	9.5	11.3	nil
04	16.8	13.5	2.5	0.4	04	6.4	5.4	0.1	nil
05	17.2	8.6	0.1	9.3	05	3.2	2.4	2.3	1.6
06	17.1	10.8	4.5	0.2	06	0.1	-2.4	2.8	nil
07	18.6	14.3	nil	nil	07	2.6	-1.1	0.1	nil
08	23.4	12.7	nil	9.7	08	5.6	-0.8	nil	4.4
09	22.8	13.7	nil	9.2	09	4.4	-5.4	nil	3.3
10	20.3	11.8	nil	2.8	10	2.0	-5.0	0.5	nil
11	21.2	10.4	nil	4.2	11	6.0	-1.8	0.1	4.8
12	22.4	15.0	nil	3.2	12	6.7	1.0	0.4	nil
13	21.5	13.1	nil	5.7	13	7.6	4.6	0.1	nil
14	20.8	12.1	nil	2.2	14	5.3	3.7	trace	0.7
15	18.4	10.3	nil	2.1	15	4.8	2.2	0.6	nil
16	19.4	10.3	nil	3.3	16	5.8	1.5	trace	nil
17	17.5	13.3	trace	nil	17	5.0	4.1	2.6	nil
18	15.2	11.2	trace	1.6	18	4.9	3.6	trace	nil
19	16.7	6.4	nil	4.0	19	5.9	3.6	28.7	nil
20	15.7	8.7	0.9	2.2	20	4.5	1.6	3.4	0.9
21	15.9	2.9	nil	7.6	21	12.1	0.0	15.8	nil
22	15.6	5.5	nil	5.4	22	13.5	1.6	6.2	0.4
23	16.7	4.2	nil	0.8	23	6.5	6.2	6.4	nil
24	19.7	9.6	3.3	8.1	24	5.1	3.0	trace	0.3
25	16.2	10.1	0.1	7.4	25	3.7	-1.2	nil	1.3
26	17.6	11.9	0.7	nil	26	1.4	-4.3	trace	5.2
27	16.0	13.5	nil	3.9	27	1.3	-3.4	nil	0.8
28	14.0	0.5	nil	5.2	28	0.2	-4.4	nil	2.3
29	13.7	3.4	nil	2.4	29	4.4	-6.8	nil	6.8
30	15.5	3.1	nil	5.6	30	2.5	-5.2	12.3	nil
31	16.1	0.5	nil	6.8	31	5.0	-1.0	0.4	nil

Date	Max (°C)	Min (°C)	Rainfall (mm)	Sunshine (hrs)	Date	Max (°C)	Min (°C)	Rainfall (mm)	Sunshine (hrs)
Jan 1996 01	6.4	1.0	trace	nil	Mar 01	7.5	0.2	1.5	nil
02	5.8	2.6	nil	nil	02	7.0	3.5	0.9	nil
03	6.0	3.0	nil	nil	03	7.8	5.0	1.3	nil
04	7.5	3.5	3.4	1.1	04	7.2	2.6	0.2	nil
05	8.0	5.5	3.0	nil	05	6.8	5.2	0.2	nil
06	12.5	6.5	6.0	nil	06	9.1	3.5	nil	2.1
07	10.8	6.2	2.4	1.1	07	4.3	1.5	trace	nil
08	12.0	7.7	22.9	nil	08	8.3	1.9	9.7	2.6
09	11.1	8.1	trace	nil	09	6.6	−0.5	0.4	nil
10	11.6	6.7	trace	0.7	10	9.4	−2.0	trace	7.5
11	10.4	5.3	1.7	nil	11	7.4	−3.5	trace	2.2
12	11.1	7.6	1.9	0.4	12	3.0	−1.5	nil	nil
13	11.7	10.0	nil	1.2	13	4.3	−0.7	nil	3.8
14	12.8	7.8	nil	3.3	14	6.1	−2.0	nil	4.4
15	10.4	4.0	trace	0.7	15	13.4	−0.6	nil	3.2
16	7.4	4.2	trace	nil	16	7.1	2.5	0.1	nil
17	12.1	3.8	trace	4.0	17	11.5	−0.4	nil	4.6
18	7.8	3.5	0.2	nil	18	11.8	0.8	0.1	1.8
19	8.2	4.0	0.2	nil	19	9.6	0.7	nil	1.1
20	4.3	3.8	trace	nil	20	7.2	1.9	3.8	nil
21	4.0	1.9	trace	nil	21	8.8	2.6	1.9	nil
22	6.5	2.1	trace	nil	22	11.1	0.5	5.0	nil
23	4.2	3.6	8.1	nil	23	14.7	6.9	trace	1.1
24	4.7	2.3	0.2	nil	24	9.4	7.7	nil	nil
25	−0.1	−0.1	trace	nil	25	10.6	5.1	13.4	0.2
26	−1.2	−3.1	trace	1.1	26	5.9	4.3	trace	nil
27	1.9	−5.4	0.8	3.2	27	6.1	0.1	nil	6.8
28	1.7	−4.3	trace	nil	28	9.9	−2.1	0.2	5.2
29	1.9	0.2	nil	nil	29	9.7	0.1	nil	6.7
30	4.5	0.3	nil	0.9	30	9.9	−2.5	nil	5.7
31	5.6	1.3	trace	6.3	31	6.9	0.7	trace	nil
Feb 01	5.1	−5.8	trace	4.7	Apr 01	7.8	−2.7	nil	3.1
02	2.6	−3.5	nil	0.7	02	9.0	−4.6	nil	7.4
03	5.3	−2.0	nil	3.8	03	9.2	−1.8	nil	10.3
04	4.8	−1.9	nil	1.4	04	11.6	−4.2	nil	9.9
05	1.1	−3.0	0.9	nil	05	12.6	−0.3	nil	8.6
06	−0.3	−1.4	0.2	nil	06	10.6	2.9	nil	1.0
07	1.4	−3.4	0.2	nil	07	11.4	5.3	nil	nil
08	6.3	−3.1	3.5	6.8	08	15.4	3.0	nil	4.1
09	7.1	−2.8	12.5	0.3	09	15.5	9.1	trace	1.3
10	10.3	4.0	0.5	2.8	10	11.5	6.6	0.4	nil
11	9.0	5.1	9.7	1.0	11	15.7	6.5	trace	3.5
12	5.9	3.6	0.7	0.8	12	9.4	6.3	13.3	0.3
13	5.3	2.0	trace	0.9	13	11.0	6.4	trace	9.3
14	5.9	1.8	trace	2.5	14	12.5	1.5	trace	0.7
15	6.6	−2.8	nil	nil	15	16.4	4.3	nil	1.5
16	12.1	0.0	nil	4.9	16	17.1	9.1	trace	0.7
17	10.4	6.1	3.0	3.9	17	15.9	9.8	trace	4.7
18	8.5	5.8	0.8	5.1	18	13.3	6.9	0.5	0.2
19	4.7	0.5	1.1	3.9	19	16.4	9.4	nil	0.6
20	1.1	−2.0	nil	1.4	20	22.4	8.5	nil	6.6
21	3.4	−2.2	1.0	3.0	21	21.0	8.0	trace	10.6
22	5.1	−3.9	0.4	0.3	22	11.1	7.0	9.9	nil
23	5.6	0.3	2.4	3.0	23	12.9	8.8	1.2	0.5
24	8.7	3.5	14.3	nil	24	14.5	6.8	trace	6.8
25	7.3	4.6	2.2	1.1	25	16.4	4.9	nil	10.4
26	10.0	1.1	trace	6.8	26	20.0	6.3	nil	2.2
27	11.2	−2.8	trace	5.8	27	20.9	4.6	nil	13.2
28	9.6	−1.9	trace	6.8	28	15.6	8.1	nil	5.8
29	10.7	−2.4	trace	7.8	29	12.1	1.8	nil	1.1
					30	12.9	2.8	0.3	3.3

Date	Max (°C)	Min (°C)	Rainfall (mm)	Sunshine (hrs)	Date	Max (°C)	Min (°C)	Rainfall (mm)	Sunshine (hrs)
May 01	15.5	6.9	0.5	5.9	July 01	18.9	11.7	2.1	3.7
02	11.3	6.8	nil	nil	02	18.9	9.9	trace	2.2
03	12.4	4.6	nil	4.6	03	17.1	10.7	0.6	0.4
04	12.1	−1.4	nil	6.3	04	18.3	10.6	11.8	3.2
05	12.9	−2.2	nil	3.7	05	20.8	8.1	15.3	3.1
06	15.3	−0.4	nil	10.7	06	18.0	10.2	5.9	4.2
07	15.9	−0.7	nil	13.1	07	20.3	8.5	trace	7.9
08	14.0	2.3	nil	13.3	08	19.5	8.8	nil	6.7
09	13.1	2.6	nil	7.5	09	19.9	10.5	trace	0.2
10	11.5	3.2	0.5	3.3	10	25.3	10.6	nil	6.8
11	12.5	0.0	nil	1.7	11	23.9	13.5	nil	4.2
12	14.8	4.5	nil	6.0	12	23.5	13.5	0.2	2.1
13	18.0	1.8	nil	11.3	13	23.3	14.5	nil	9.5
14	15.1	0.7	nil	6.0	14	24.3	16.1	nil	1.4
15	16.8	−0.3	nil	7.1	15	25.1	10.8	nil	13.5
16	10.8	0.8	7.6	0.1	16	21.2	8.8	nil	8.3
17	8.5	3.2	1.7	nil	17	23.8	8.9	nil	11.9
18	10.0	4.5	3.8	nil	18	26.7	5.6	nil	13.6
19	12.6	5.5	1.1	3.4	19	26.2	9.1	nil	10.5
20	15.5	5.5	0.3	12.1	20	27.8	9.8	nil	13.0
21	16.3	7.1	0.1	6.3	21	29.6	8.0	nil	12.1
22	13.9	8.5	4.1	0.1	22	30.5	10.5	nil	13.5
23	15.9	9.6	1.6	2.0	23	28.3	16.2	0.1	4.0
24	13.5	11.1	8.4	0.1	24	21.8	14.0	nil	2.1
25	17.4	7.0	1.1	4.2	25	25.2	7.5	nil	13.2
26	15.5	6.6	2.2	nil	26	29.0	10.2	0.2	9.3
27	16.2	10.0	2.5	1.2	27	23.0	15.3	0.3	0.7
28	16.5	2.4	0.1	2.1	28	23.5	15.0	0.9	1.1
29	21.2	11.7	trace	1.2	29	23.5	15.7	0.6	5.5
30	24.4	11.5	nil	11.6	30	24.1	12.9	1.6	0.6
31	19.0	11.9	2.4	11.7	31	23.7	14.2	nil	6.0
June 01	16.5	8.6	0.9	7.9	Aug 01	22.5	10.8	trace	3.3
02	18.8	6.3	nil	6.3	02	20.6	9.2	nil	2.6
03	18.8	5.3	0.2	7.5	03	23.3	7.5	nil	10.6
04	21.7	11.4	nil	14.1	04	24.6	8.2	nil	13.0
05	26.0	8.2	nil	13.7	05	26.6	11.7	trace	10.9
06	29.1	9.9	nil	13.8	06	21.1	15.1	nil	6.3
07	30.4	15.3	1.3	13.6	07	22.2	13.3	nil	3.5
08	21.4	14.1	trace	2.1	08	22.1	9.8	0.3	6.3
09	21.5	9.6	nil	13.4	09	20.6	13.0	6.0	0.3
10	23.3	8.9	nil	5.3	10	21.8	15.2	5.1	8.0
11	22.4	11.9	nil	4.5	11	20.3	12.6	9.4	3.3
12	20.9	11.5	nil	13.1	12	21.4	13.0	1.7	2.4
13	22.3	4.7	nil	13.7	13	23.2	12.9	nil	7.0
14	21.9	5.2	nil	13.2	14	21.9	15.3	nil	1.5
15	22.9	4.5	nil	13.2	15	21.4	14.8	nil	4.6
16	26.1	4.5	nil	13.5	16	25.8	12.1	nil	7.7
17	27.5	7.4	nil	9.1	17	27.4	11.3	nil	9.8
18	23.1	10.6	nil	11.3	18	29.3	11.4	nil	11.7
19	21.4	7.9	0.8	9.8	19	31.1	12.2	nil	11.8
20	16.1	8.8	0.6	0.2	20	23.8	11.7	0.4	1.1
21	17.3	7.5	trace	4.9	21	24.5	11.3	nil	9.5
22	16.8	6.5	nil	4.5	22	21.7	9.8	14.5	8.0
23	21.5	4.4	nil	9.2	23	20.6	13.8	2.5	6.1
24	22.2	7.6	nil	6.8	24	20.8	15.0	4.8	5.3
25	25.7	7.1	nil	10.8	25	19.4	14.2	1.4	4.1
26	25.9	10.3	0.5	6.3	26	20.5	10.4	0.2	7.9
27	23.8	15.7	trace	1.6	27	20.1	9.1	nil	6.4
28	19.0	13.6	1.0	0.3	28	20.4	7.0	3.0	4.8
29	17.4	11.4	nil	1.4	29	16.9	10.4	nil	nil
30	21.3	11.0	nil	2.4	30	17.5	9.9	0.1	2.1
					31	19.2	6.0	nil	3.6

Date	Max (°C)	Min (°C)	Rainfall (mm)	Sunshine (hrs)	Date	Max (°C)	Min (°C)	Rainfall (mm)	Sunshine (hrs)
Sept 1995 01	19.6	11.2	11.2	4.5	Nov 01	17.2	9.8	nil	4.4
02	17.3	12.6	3.3	5.7	02	13.0	5.2	nil	6.6
03	16.8	10.9	3.9	0.4	03	12.0	7.3	nil	3.7
04	17.9	10.7	52.3	2.5	04	10.1	2.0	nil	6.4
05	13.2	10.6	23.6	nil	05	9.7	0.3	nil	6.1
06	16.9	10.9	3.4	1.2	06	9.8	−0.7	trace	3.8
07	21.3	12.8	2.1	3.5	07	14.4	−0.7	0.1	0.3
08	17.1	12.8	nil	1.7	08	14.2	9.1	1.2	0.2
09	18.5	10.7	nil	7.3	09	10.6	6.7	0.1	2.6
10	19.7	9.4	22.4	4.5	10	8.4	0.9	3.0	nil
11	16.7	11.3	2.4	6.7	11	12.9	3.0	11.5	nil
12	19.1	10.2	nil	6.0	12	13.5	7.8	0.5	nil
13	18.7	8.3	nil	5.6	13	14.0	9.7	0.2	1.0
14	17.6	9.3	0.7	0.5	14	12.8	8.1	2.2	3.1
15	16.9	10.8	0.1	4.4	15	11.9	7.7	5.1	0.4
16	18.4	10.1	nil	5.1	16	6.3	4.3	0.1	nil
17	18.6	10.0	0.5	1.8	17	5.6	−0.1	nil	4.9
18	20.4	10.8	trace	5.4	18	8.6	−0.7	1.8	5.1
19	17.3	9.9	nil	3.9	19	10.4	0.6	trace	3.3
20	17.3	8.6	nil	5.9	20	8.6	2.4	4.3	0.1
21	18.2	10.1	nil	4.2	21	10.0	2.6	2.7	0.4
22	18.3	12.8	trace	1.9	22	11.6	6.9	0.2	1.8
23	18.9	9.5	13.2	8.8	23	12.8	5.2	0.2	0.1
24	13.7	11.6	0.6	6.0	24	11.8	10.1	9.6	0.1
25	18.9	7.6	5.7	4.1	25	9.5	5.4	0.8	2.2
26	15.4	11.1	1.6	1.6	26	10.1	5.4	trace	4.0
27	12.9	8.2	5.5	6.4	27	9.6	5.5	0.5	0.9
28	13.6	6.9	1.1	6.1	28	9.5	4.9	0.8	0.3
29	14.9	7.4	0.1	6.6	29	10.1	6.8	0.1	nil
30	15.5	6.4	1.4	2.1	30	7.9	4.7	trace	nil
Oct 01	16.7	10.1	0.4	7.8	Dec 01	9.5	6.3	nil	nil
02	19.0	9.9	0.2	2.4	02	11.1	6.5	0.4	nil
03	17.3	12.1	3.1	0.4	03	11.9	9.2	2.2	nil
04	17.6	12.7	nil	6.8	04	7.6	7.1	0.2	nil
05	17.0	8.0	1.0	6.8	05	4.1	3.2	0.2	0.8
06	18.4	10.6	1.7	1.3	06	3.5	0.0	1.0	0.7
07	18.3	12.3	0.1	0.6	07	1.5	−1.1	0.3	nil
08	24.9	12.8	nil	8.3	08	4.5	−1.9	trace	0.3
09	20.8	13.6	nil	6.7	09	6.1	−0.1	trace	0.7
10	18.8	9.5	trace	8.1	10	5.7	−1.1	nil	2.5
11	17.4	7.9	0.3	3.0	11	7.3	−1.6	trace	3.8
12	19.7	10.1	0.4	1.8	12	7.0	−0.6	trace	nil
13	16.5	11.2	trace	0.2	13	6.6	0.9	0.1	0.2
14	17.0	10.7	nil	0.3	14	6.9	3.5	nil	1.1
15	18.1	11.7	nil	5.4	15	5.9	2.0	nil	3.5
16	16.2	10.3	nil	0.2	16	6.7	−0.8	nil	3.9
17	18.6	12.0	0.5	2.8	17	4.6	1.1	0.4	nil
18	13.8	8.9	nil	3.0	18	4.9	2.8	nil	nil
19	17.9	8.7	nil	3.4	19	4.7	3.3	10.8	nil
20	14.8	9.7	nil	4.5	20	4.0	0.6	0.7	3.8
21	13.7	4.4	nil	5.3	21	3.4	−2.3	14.2	nil
22	16.2	7.2	nil	3.6	22	11.6	0.4	11.2	0.3
23	16.1	9.3	nil	2.6	23	4.7	1.5	0.3	nil
24	18.1	10.1	7.9	1.9	24	5.2	−0.5	3.8	0.8
25	14.6	7.1	0.4	6.0	25	3.0	−0.7	nil	2.6
26	16.5	7.6	0.7	0.3	26	1.9	−2.2	nil	4.0
27	14.3	8.6	trace	7.3	27	−0.6	−6.4	trace	4.0
28	12.8	4.8	nil	4.9	28	−2.9	−8.4	nil	nil
29	11.3	2.8	0.4	3.8	29	−0.4	−7.5	trace	1.8
30	14.2	6.4	nil	1.2	30	0.9	−7.4	3.6	nil
31	17.2	6.8	trace	4.1	31	1.6	−1.4	1.1	nil

Date	Max (°C)	Min (°C)	Rainfall (mm)	Sunshine (hrs)	Date	Max (°C)	Min (°C)	Rainfall (mm)	Sunshine (hrs)
Jan 1996 01	3.2	0.7	nil	nil	Mar 01	8.4	3.8	nil	9.5
02	4.6	1.5	nil	0.2	02	7.7	4.4	0.2	0.4
03	6.9	2.1	nil	0.2	03	7.3	4.3	nil	nil
04	8.1	4.6	0.7	nil	04	7.9	5.0	nil	nil
05	8.1	4.8	3.0	nil	05	7.4	4.5	nil	nil
06	8.8	5.0	8.0	nil	06	9.4	4.1	0.3	5.7
07	10.0	5.0	0.4	nil	07	10.1	4.2	nil	8.3
08	10.0	4.7	1.8	nil	08	7.8	2.5	4.0	1.5
09	11.4	6.1	0.5	1.1	09	8.0	2.1	trace	3.7
10	10.5	5.3	0.5	1.9	10	10.1	0.2	nil	3.8
11	9.3	5.1	1.3	nil	11	5.5	2.1	16.9	nil
12	11.2	6.6	2.3	0.2	12	0.4	−0.3	0.6	nil
13	10.4	8.5	nil	1.3	13	1.5	−1.4	nil	nil
14	10.1	8.5	nil	nil	14	4.7	−1.8	trace	0.2
15	9.1	7.0	trace	0.4	15	4.8	0.0	1.3	nil
16	7.1	1.5	trace	nil	16	4.9	1.2	trace	nil
17	8.5	1.8	trace	nil	17	9.1	1.7	nil	4.1
18	7.1	5.7	trace	nil	18	8.2	1.9	nil	0.7
19	7.2	5.6	trace	nil	19	7.9	3.1	nil	0.5
20	6.0	5.8	0.5	nil	20	7.0	2.9	6.0	0.1
21	2.7	0.7	0.2	nil	21	7.7	2.2	0.5	0.1
22	3.5	0.3	nil	nil	22	7.3	4.1	2.2	nil
23	2.8	0.2	1.1	nil	23	10.1	4.9	3.7	nil
24	2.2	0.8	nil	nil	24	9.0	6.2	1.2	nil
25	1.9	−0.8	trace	4.1	25	8.6	3.3	1.0	0.3
26	1.5	−2.0	0.5	3.2	26	6.4	3.4	0.9	nil
27	1.4	−2.7	0.3	nil	27	6.9	1.1	trace	10.2
28	2.3	−6.8	nil	0.9	28	9.0	−0.1	nil	6.1
29	1.9	−2.6	0.1	nil	29	9.1	3.1	nil	7.2
30	1.7	−0.2	nil	nil	30	7.3	−1.4	nil	6.9
31	0.9	−0.5	nil	nil	31	7.3	0.9	nil	nil
Feb 01	1.9	−4.5	nil	4.0	Apr 01	8.4	−1.8	0.7	7.3
02	2.5	−3.5	nil	nil	02	9.4	1.1	nil	6.4
03	4.9	−0.9	nil	2.9	03	11.3	4.3	nil	6.0
04	2.7	−2.0	nil	0.1	04	10.7	0.5	trace	10.2
05	1.6	−2.9	10.2	nil	05	13.2	−1.4	nil	10.3
06	−0.2	−2.0	3.7	nil	06	11.1	−0.3	nil	4.2
07	1.4	−6.1	0.3	nil	07	10.8	4.0	nil	3.2
08	5.6	−4.2	1.6	6.8	08	13.4	3.0	nil	0.9
09	7.1	−2.1	2.0	3.4	09	16.7	6.5	1.2	4.5
10	8.9	3.1	1.0	1.5	10	12.0	8.4	0.6	1.2
11	8.6	5.4	13.4	1.5	11	14.3	2.6	3.4	3.7
12	6.0	0.1	3.3	nil	12	6.3	5.4	10.3	nil
13	4.7	0.3	nil	0.2	13	7.1	0.3	0.2	nil
14	6.1	−1.4	nil	4.9	14	10.0	2.9	3.8	nil
15	9.5	−0.7	0.4	nil	15	14.6	3.9	0.5	0.5
16	9.2	3.4	0.1	5.7	16	13.1	9.8	3.6	nil
17	9.8	5.8	5.2	1.0	17	13.5	8.6	0.1	5.2
18	6.3	4.5	3.7	3.0	18	12.6	6.7	0.9	0.6
19	4.3	0.7	1.1	5.3	19	14.8	6.9	1.0	1.4
20	3.5	−2.1	trace	6.9	20	17.7	7.8	0.5	2.8
21	4.6	−1.6	2.2	2.6	21	19.4	7.4	3.1	2.1
22	5.4	−0.6	trace	1.2	22	15.2	6.6	18.2	4.6
23	7.9	0.8	2.1	0.2	23	13.7	6.6	1.0	4.3
24	8.5	3.1	0.3	1.2	24	13.4	7.4	trace	4.9
25	5.4	0.2	nil	0.5	25	14.1	6.2	nil	3.5
26	7.6	−0.9	nil	6.3	26	17.1	8.6	nil	9.5
27	9.6	−1.5	nil	8.8	27	12.7	8.0	trace	4.9
28	10.1	−1.6	nil	8.2	28	11.6	5.6	trace	5.6
29	8.6	0.3	nil	3.8	29	10.7	4.5	1.8	1.7
					30	10.8	5.8	8.6	0.2

Date	Max (°C)	Min (°C)	Rainfall (mm)	Sunshine (hrs)	Date	Max (°C)	Min (°C)	Rainfall (mm)	Sunshine (hrs)
May 01	12.2	4.4	0.9	0.7	July 01	15.9	10.6	2.1	3.8
02	8.6	6.3	trace	0.2	02	16.3	10.6	2.0	5.1
03	9.8	0.7	trace	7.0	03	17.0	10.7	1.9	4.4
04	10.4	1.2	nil	11.1	04	17.6	11.4	0.4	3.4
05	11.8	1.8	nil	11.6	05	15.4	11.6	trace	10.2
06	12.8	4.2	nil	6.5	06	15.5	10.0	trace	12.5
07	13.9	3.9	trace	8.2	07	14.9	7.1	0.1	2.0
08	12.5	1.7	trace	6.7	08	16.2	10.0	1.2	3.6
09	11.9	1.8	trace	7.7	09	15.3	12.2	0.5	0.5
10	12.6	1.4	0.6	5.8	10	20.3	12.8	nil	3.6
11	10.9	2.9	0.3	1.6	11	21.1	13.9	0.6	3.0
12	13.6	5.5	trace	4.7	12	19.7	15.1	nil	5.4
13	14.3	3.1	nil	11.9	13	23.2	11.6	nil	6.4
14	15.3	5.3	nil	9.7	14	17.5	14.7	nil	3.3
15	11.3	6.9	nil	1.1	15	18.0	10.7	nil	11.6
16	10.7	2.7	trace	3.1	16	20.3	7.9	nil	12.6
17	10.7	1.6	0.3	3.4	17	23.6	8.9	nil	12.9
18	10.1	1.5	8.4	3.7	18	25.9	10.4	nil	11.5
19	10.5	5.0	1.4	0.3	19	26.8	12.7	nil	12.1
20	15.0	5.3	nil	10.4	20	27.0	14.1	nil	13.0
21	15.2	5.2	1.1	11.5	21	26.9	13.5	nil	9.5
22	15.5	6.9	trace	1.4	22	26.9	13.4	nil	9.4
23	15.0	7.4	10.5	4.7	23	20.2	14.2	trace	7.2
24	14.8	9.7	trace	11.1	24	18.1	14.0	nil	4.7
25	12.8	6.8	1.0	3.4	25	21.6	10.3	nil	10.9
26	15.0	9.8	4.5	0.2	26	22.2	14.9	nil	2.5
27	15.2	9.8	0.1	3.1	27	19.4	11.2	1.0	7.0
28	17.6	5.9	1.2	0.6	28	19.6	11.3	7.6	0.9
29	16.3	11.1	2.7	2.1	29	21.7	13.8	0.1	5.7
30	22.9	11.8	trace	5.1	30	18.7	13.1	0.8	0.7
31	15.6	10.7	trace	11.6	31	19.2	13.1	nil	5.5
June 01	16.4	7.8	0.5	9.8	Aug 01	18.6	13.1	1.3	4.9
02	14.1	9.0	nil	2.5	02	18.1	13.0	trace	8.0
03	16.0	5.7	3.6	4.1	03	19.9	12.8	nil	5.3
04	20.4	10.3	nil	13.6	04	24.3	11.1	nil	11.9
05	20.1	9.6	nil	0.4	05	26.3	12.2	nil	4.8
06	21.8	12.5	0.2	8.2	06	17.4	15.4	12.5	nil
07	19.6	10.8	2.8	2.7	07	19.0	11.9	trace	6.2
08	16.7	9.6	trace	13.7	08	19.8	11.3	1.0	2.1
09	17.6	6.6	nil	3.1	09	21.7	11.3	1.6	6.3
10	19.8	13.5	0.4	4.9	10	20.8	13.6	1.5	6.5
11	19.0	12.7	4.1	3.2	11	19.1	11.2	6.7	3.6
12	16.0	8.9	trace	13.3	12	19.6	11.6	trace	9.9
13	17.4	7.3	nil	12.4	13	17.4	12.6	nil	10.9
14	19.7	7.1	nil	12.9	14	21.1	12.1	nil	11.2
15	23.6	9.0	nil	13.4	15	23.9	11.5	trace	7.7
16	24.9	10.9	nil	13.8	16	23.8	13.6	nil	4.6
17	22.9	11.7	nil	10.9	17	24.2	14.2	nil	3.7
18	16.1	10.5	nil	9.5	18	29.4	15.5	nil	11.5
19	21.3	8.3	nil	8.4	19	26.8	16.1	1.8	3.5
20	17.2	9.6	nil	9.1	20	19.1	16.0	2.0	nil
21	15.0	7.5	nil	11.9	21	21.0	14.8	trace	7.2
22	15.0	8.6	nil	8.5	22	20.3	12.7	1.8	3.5
23	15.9	9.5	nil	11.5	23	20.0	11.8	3.9	6.9
24	16.1	9.4	nil	9.9	24	18.3	12.5	15.9	1.5
25	22.1	8.2	2.9	7.6	25	18.2	12.6	5.3	4.8
26	16.4	11.8	trace	5.2	26	17.1	11.7	25.5	6.7
27	19.5	8.0	8.3	8.0	27	16.9	11.5	1.1	1.5
28	19.3	11.6	2.6	nil	28	17.9	10.4	2.2	3.4
29	15.1	11.3	0.6	3.1	29	16.4	11.4	0.3	6.0
30	17.2	11.0	0.7	nil	30	17.2	12.6	trace	5.3
					31	16.7	12.2	nil	6.3

Date	Max (°C)	Min (°C)	Rainfall (mm)	Date	Max (°C)	Min (°C)	Rainfall (mm)
Sept 1995 01	21.8	11.4	0.9	Nov 01	14.8	4.1	trace
02	19.3	14.7	1.6	02	13.5	6.2	trace
03	18.0	9.4	3.5	03	14.4	1.1	nil
04	17.1	12.7	1.3	04	13.0	4.0	nil
05	19.2	10.0	0.1	05	10.2	8.7	nil
06	16.8	6.5	31.9	06	12.0	6.0	nil
07	18.6	14.8	8.8	07	14.3	2.9	0.2
08	18.8	14.3	trace	08	14.3	7.3	0.1
09	19.5	11.7	10.2	09	12.9	8.2	1.3
10	19.6	13.2	9.7	10	13.4	5.8	10.7
11	19.6	12.2	2.4	11	13.7	6.7	7.7
12	17.3	6.9	0.2	12	14.8	6.7	0.2
13	20.0	8.0	5.5	13	16.5	10.3	trace
14	18.8	12.7	1.8	14	13.8	3.6	9.4
15	18.2	10.7	0.1	15	14.6	10.6	0.6
16	19.6	9.7	nil	16	14.5	8.6	2.5
17	19.3	11.3	1.6	17	8.3	1.7	0.5
18	20.3	10.7	0.2	18	8.0	−1.8	nil
19	17.8	14.3	nil	19	9.9	−4.5	trace
20	19.2	8.1	nil	20	12.4	−3.2	14.2
21	18.8	8.5	nil	21	15.4	6.8	1.5
22	19.2	7.0	0.4	22	13.2	7.2	0.1
23	18.3	9.3	8.3	23	12.9	6.4	5.2
24	15.7	11.8	trace	24	12.7	11.3	6.1
25	17.4	6.3	nil	25	11.0	6.6	2.0
26	17.3	13.9	12.9	26	10.4	3.4	11.6
27	15.9	13.1	0.1	27	11.9	6.4	4.1
28	15.6	6.3	2.3	28	12.3	6.0	16.9
29	14.8	4.8	7.2	29	13.0	8.4	1.4
30	18.3	10.8	1.0	30	11.6	9.8	10.5
Oct 01	17.6	13.7	0.3	Dec 01	12.7	9.0	6.2
02	19.1	8.7	trace	02	14.4	9.8	1.0
03	16.4	14.0	3.7	03	13.5	11.9	0.1
04	17.3	12.8	3.8	04	10.7	8.2	nil
05	17.1	9.7	11.5	05	4.9	2.7	nil
06	16.6	13.4	29.6	06	2.4	−2.9	trace
07	17.0	14.5	5.2	07	8.2	−3.3	1.3
08	19.5	13.7	nil	08	8.9	−1.5	trace
09	19.3	14.3	nil	09	8.2	−0.7	trace
10	19.1	9.5	nil	10	9.4	0.9	trace
11	14.7	8.7	nil	11	9.0	7.0	nil
12	15.3	13.5	nil	12	7.9	2.7	nil
13	15.1	13.7	nil	13	9.3	2.9	0.3
14	16.1	12.8	nil	14	6.8	2.5	nil
15	18.5	13.1	nil	15	4.4	2.4	0.4
16	16.7	13.5	2.5	16	9.3	1.9	10.5
17	18.8	14.4	0.1	17	8.6	4.3	0.6
18	14.4	11.3	nil	18	11.1	6.4	26.4
19	16.8	8.4	0.1	19	12.5	7.2	4.7
20	16.8	9.7	13.2	20	11.7	10.0	15.8
21	15.8	9.6	0.1	21	12.9	5.0	15.4
22	16.7	10.4	trace	22	12.5	10.0	7.3
23	16.5	12.4	0.4	23	11.6	9.5	2.0
24	16.5	12.9	14.9	24	7.7	1.5	0.6
25	16.0	8.2	0.1	25	7.1	−0.5	trace
26	15.5	12.9	11.7	26	5.7	−4.3	1.3
27	15.9	11.1	0.1	27	5.1	−4.2	0.2
28	13.5	4.1	1.5	28	5.3	−1.7	trace
29	14.9	9.1	trace	29	7.9	3.2	15.0
30	15.4	12.6	trace	30	8.5	4.0	18.8
31	15.7	12.5	trace	31	11.4	3.0	2.0

Date	Max (°C)	Min (°C)	Rainfall (mm)	Date	Max (°C)	Min (°C)	Rainfall (mm)
Jan 1996 01	11.2	3.8	0.7	Mar 01	8.2	−0.8	nil
02	12.1	7.0	trace	02	11.8	0.2	nil
03	11.0	7.5	16.7	03	11.5	3.4	nil
04	11.9	8.4	15.7	04	11.5	6.5	trace
05	9.5	8.3	3.8	05	9.3	4.9	nil
06	12.3	4.8	11.5	06	6.4	5.3	nil
07	12.7	8.5	16.3	07	10.3	0.2	0.1
08	12.8	5.4	9.8	08	5.3	−0.2	2.1
09	11.2	9.8	12.9	09	10.6	−0.4	trace
10	11.5	4.2	18.7	10	12.5	4.8	nil
11	12.3	4.3	16.5	11	9.8	3.6	trace
12	12.1	8.9	4.8	12	8.2	6.6	trace
13	10.9	7.0	18.3	13	6.0	4.3	nil
14	10.7	9.2	4.7	14	6.3	3.8	0.8
15	12.2	8.2	0.2	15	10.6	−1.2	1.7
16	10.4	8.6	trace	16	10.9	3.5	4.1
17	10.8	9.2	0.1	17	9.5	4.3	10.1
18	11.1	9.1	0.2	18	12.2	4.2	0.1
19	11.3	8.2	27.6	19	10.1	1.4	0.8
20	9.6	6.9	7.7	20	9.2	5.5	19.0
21	8.3	7.9	0.1	21	8.1	5.4	3.8
22	9.3	3.3	4.6	22	12.1	3.4	6.5
23	6.3	5.2	8.2	23	13.2	7.6	trace
24	8.2	0.4	9.2	24	12.5	9.0	4.0
25	3.5	0.4	0.1	25	9.1	7.4	5.7
26	−0.1	−2.0	trace	26	8.1	7.4	6.4
27	5.6	−5.4	trace	27	5.4	1.9	0.1
28	5.8	−3.1	nil	28	7.4	−2.7	trace
29	5.8	1.5	nil	29	11.0	1.0	trace
30	4.9	0.4	0.1	30	8.6	−0.2	trace
31	4.8	2.5	trace	31	9.3	1.1	trace
Feb 01	7.4	−2.8	trace	Apr 01	8.8	2.2	nil
02	7.4	0.8	nil	02	10.8	−3.3	nil
03	4.4	−0.4	nil	03	10.6	−0.3	nil
04	5.9	−4.1	0.9	04	8.8	4.3	nil
05	7.4	−2.8	31.5	05	9.7	4.2	nil
06	7.7	3.9	19.8	06	11.1	0.7	nil
07	5.7	0.9	5.6	07	12.0	6.8	nil
08	9.3	1.4	13.8	08	12.3	6.2	nil
09	11.2	4.2	6.8	09	11.6	9.7	5.0
10	10.1	5.8	2.4	10	13.6	9.9	trace
11	10.8	6.2	10.6	11	11.7	2.3	10.7
12	9.4	6.1	1.2	12	11.7	8.2	8.9
13	9.7	2.2	trace	13	9.6	6.0	0.2
14	9.7	−1.1	nil	14	11.6	5.2	2.7
15	9.2	−4.0	nil	15	12.2	8.7	0.6
16	11.7	−1.3	trace	16	11.7	9.8	16.1
17	10.4	7.5	1.6	17	14.4	8.5	0.2
18	9.5	7.0	3.7	18	13.1	9.3	4.8
19	6.7	1.8	nil	19	11.1	5.2	2.1
20	3.3	−0.3	trace	20	14.2	6.2	3.5
21	8.6	−3.2	4.1	21	13.0	9.1	2.6
22	9.4	1.6	0.1	22	14.2	7.9	5.0
23	10.9	2.2	8.1	23	12.7	7.1	0.8
24	10.1	6.7	7.5	24	13.4	5.0	0.2
25	9.0	3.7	0.5	25	15.7	4.6	trace
26	9.1	−1.2	trace	26	14.6	5.2	nil
27	10.0	−2.5	trace	27	16.7	4.8	nil
28	10.0	2.9	nil	28	14.4	4.2	nil
29	11.3	−2.6	nil	29	12.1	3.1	0.1
				30	11.7	5.6	2.1

Date	Max (°C)	Min (°C)	Rainfall (mm)	Date	Max (°C)	Min (°C)	Rainfall (mm)
May 01	11.9	3.5	7.9	July 01	17.4	11.8	0.5
02	12.6	8.5	0.8	02	17.8	12.4	1.5
03	12.0	5.2	trace	03	17.5	13.2	0.8
04	11.1	0.8	nil	04	18.0	10.9	6.9
05	12.0	0.4	nil	05	18.0	11.2	3.7
06	12.6	2.4	nil	06	17.2	8.2	3.0
07	15.2	2.5	nil	07	17.4	5.5	trace
08	15.0	1.6	nil	08	17.7	11.0	0.1
09	11.9	3.9	nil	09	19.5	12.2	trace
10	12.5	0.4	nil	10	21.7	12.3	trace
11	11.7	0.9	nil	11	19.0	14.1	2.2
12	13.0	0.5	nil	12	18.1	14.4	3.6
13	14.7	−0.3	nil	13	20.8	15.4	0.3
14	15.2	1.8	nil	14	22.6	15.3	nil
15	15.4	6.0	nil	15	22.6	11.2	nil
16	11.4	6.3	trace	16	17.2	11.4	nil
17	8.7	4.7	1.9	17	18.8	12.2	nil
18	11.3	5.8	26.9	18	20.8	9.3	nil
19	12.9	4.7	1.6	19	19.4	10.7	nil
20	14.0	4.7	2.7	20	21.4	8.3	nil
21	14.5	4.2	12.9	21	21.1	10.9	nil
22	14.9	9.7	3.1	22	24.1	11.7	nil
23	13.1	10.3	14.2	23	20.6	13.4	nil
24	14.1	11.4	0.2	24	20.0	14.6	nil
25	15.3	6.5	2.4	25	22.4	8.8	nil
26	15.7	7.2	0.9	26	24.9	10.3	0.1
27	15.3	11.5	trace	27	21.1	16.6	0.1
28	14.4	6.4	trace	28	21.2	15.1	2.9
29	17.3	11.4	trace	29	22.4	14.1	trace
30	14.9	10.7	trace	30	20.6	14.3	0.2
31	15.8	10.4	1.3	31	20.2	15.0	trace
June 01	15.5	7.6	0.1	Aug 01	21.0	13.4	nil
02	15.8	7.1	trace	02	19.7	9.8	nil
03	13.5	3.9	2.2	03	21.3	8.3	nil
04	17.0	8.6	trace	04	20.2	7.7	nil
05	20.2	10.7	nil	05	20.2	14.7	5.1
06	22.8	9.2	3.8	06	17.5	12.4	0.4
07	17.4	9.8	trace	07	20.5	10.2	trace
08	17.4	10.2	nil	08	18.4	10.3	6.5
09	15.7	8.1	2.5	09	19.3	13.6	1.7
10	18.4	12.9	0.8	10	18.8	12.2	13.8
11	16.5	13.3	0.3	11	19.2	12.4	0.1
12	16.8	9.0	trace	12	20.2	11.6	nil
13	17.5	5.4	nil	13	21.9	11.6	nil
14	18.6	6.6	nil	14	21.5	8.8	nil
15	18.1	10.5	nil	15	20.7	10.1	nil
16	20.1	12.6	nil	16	20.8	14.6	nil
17	22.9	10.5	nil	17	19.8	9.6	nil
18	23.3	9.8	nil	18	21.4	15.0	0.4
19	20.7	10.5	0.6	19	19.0	14.8	6.9
20	18.7	13.9	0.2	20	20.8	14.0	0.1
21	16.8	10.7	nil	21	19.1	10.3	nil
22	16.8	5.9	nil	22	19.0	10.7	10.7
23	19.0	5.9	nil	23	18.1	9.8	6.2
24	19.4	7.7	nil	24	18.7	11.5	1.9
25	16.5	7.2	trace	25	18.6	12.8	0.2
26	20.7	13.6	trace	26	18.8	9.1	1.6
27	19.6	7.9	nil	27	18.3	9.6	0.7
28	19.4	11.7	0.1	28	17.8	10.8	trace
29	17.0	12.7	0.6	29	17.4	12.1	trace
30	17.5	12.8	0.6	30	19.0	9.9	nil
				31	18.5	10.7	nil

Date	Max (°C)	Min (°C)	Rainfall (mm)	Date	Max (°C)	Min (°C)	Rainfall (mm)
Sept 1995 01	21.2	9.0	15.2	Nov 01	12.1	9.0	nil
02	17.5	9.6	5.1	02	11.5	6.0	nil
03	17.4	9.7	13.0	03	10.7	4.4	nil
04	16.6	11.8	3.0	04	11.3	5.2	nil
05	12.2	9.8	8.0	05	12.1	7.5	trace
06	15.7	10.3	0.1	06	12.2	2.4	trace
07	16.3	8.6	trace	07	14.3	7.8	nil
08	18.5	10.1	nil	08	12.9	8.9	1.0
09	18.0	8.7	trace	09	8.9	1.6	0.5
10	16.7	9.0	0.1	10	9.0	1.3	7.6
11	18.8	7.2	6.2	11	12.5	4.5	23.6
12	18.3	8.5	0.6	12	12.0	4.5	10.7
13	18.6	10.0	0.1	13	13.8	10.8	0.4
14	17.6	8.3	nil	14	10.6	3.2	18.2
15	17.5	7.8	trace	15	10.1	4.9	19.6
16	16.8	8.1	nil	16	5.7	4.2	0.2
17	18.2	5.1	nil	17	5.5	−2.4	nil
18	18.2	8.9	nil	18	5.7	−2.9	nil
19	18.0	8.1	nil	19	8.6	0.4	0.3
20	17.8	8.0	nil	20	12.0	0.0	6.7
21	17.5	7.2	0.6	21	13.3	7.3	0.2
22	16.6	11.9	0.5	22	11.4	6.3	trace
23	17.1	8.0	8.3	23	13.1	6.2	2.4
24	13.8	8.3	0.2	24	11.5	8.5	11.4
25	18.3	6.1	2.4	25	7.0	3.3	5.1
26	14.3	8.8	1.1	26	8.7	−1.3	2.2
27	11.0	5.9	5.0	27	8.6	2.7	17.5
28	13.3	8.1	0.1	28	9.7	1.7	0.5
29	14.5	2.6	0.2	29	11.1	8.3	1.2
30	14.1	4.0	8.1	30	9.6	7.6	4.3
Oct 01	15.0	8.9	0.1	Dec 01	11.6	7.6	4.5
02	16.6	9.1	3.8	02	12.4	8.0	4.0
03	15.5	7.6	17.5	03	10.7	10.5	0.1
04	14.8	10.3	0.1	04	8.2	2.9	3.0
05	15.0	6.9	17.4	05	5.3	2.2	10.2
06	17.0	9.6	0.1	06	4.1	0.0	2.2
07	16.2	6.1	1.8	07	2.9	1.1	5.3
08	19.3	12.0	0.3	08	6.4	−1.8	0.1
09	17.3	13.0	trace	09	8.5	−0.5	trace
10	15.8	7.3	nil	10	7.1	1.0	nil
11	15.0	5.2	1.5	11	6.1	0.3	nil
12	14.3	10.0	15.7	12	8.2	0.1	nil
13	17.0	10.1	0.2	13	6.6	0.9	nil
14	17.5	13.0	1.0	14	6.6	1.5	nil
15	17.8	13.3	0.1	15	6.0	2.5	trace
16	15.4	10.2	3.0	16	7.0	3.5	nil
17	16.7	12.3	nil	17	6.4	4.8	nil
18	13.6	4.0	0.1	18	5.8	2.6	1.5
19	15.3	8.9	nil	19	4.7	3.1	5.9
20	12.0	5.5	trace	20	3.6	−3.0	4.2
21	12.8	3.9	1.9	21	9.1	−5.2	21.0
22	14.4	7.5	5.6	22	5.4	3.2	5.8
23	14.8	12.1	4.6	23	3.7	2.5	5.3
24	14.6	11.9	14.7	24	1.7	−0.6	0.5
25	14.2	3.7	3.4	25	2.8	−2.5	0.7
26	13.8	7.5	6.3	26	−0.9	−4.7	nil
27	10.5	4.9	0.5	27	−1.5	−9.0	nil
28	10.0	1.1	trace	28	−0.4	−8.1	nil
29	14.4	1.5	6.9	29	2.0	−5.8	nil
30	15.7	5.0	nil	30	3.0	−0.6	3.8
31	15.8	7.8	0.1	31	6.2	0.1	12.8

Date	Max (°C)	Min (°C)	Rainfall (mm)	Date	Max (°C)	Min (°C)	Rainfall (mm)
Jan 1996 01	7.9	2.0	18.3	Mar 01	9.4	3.2	nil
02	9.3	5.6	0.7	02	7.3	3.4	nil
03	9.3	5.4	33.8	03	11.5	2.1	nil
04	9.1	6.9	20.3	04	7.6	2.8	nil
05	8.9	5.6	11.0	05	7.1	4.4	0.3
06	9.0	4.8	7.1	06	10.8	1.5	nil
07	9.3	5.5	0.6	07	9.7	0.0	trace
08	10.6	4.2	12.3	08	5.7	1.4	5.4
09	9.7	7.3	1.9	09	6.5	1.0	7.3
10	6.7	0.4	1.4	10	8.3	1.5	0.4
11	8.9	-0.1	15.7	11	8.6	4.8	9.1
12	9.1	5.6	17.1	12	6.9	6.1	24.3
13	9.8	6.5	17.8	13	1.3	-0.6	0.1
14	11.6	6.2	13.4	14	3.8	-0.4	4.6
15	10.3	7.7	0.1	15	4.3	0.3	0.2
16	8.7	3.9	nil	16	5.2	1.6	0.1
17	9.3	6.1	0.5	17	7.6	0.3	8.3
18	9.1	8.0	5.2	18	5.6	3.3	1.6
19	8.8	6.9	21.7	19	6.7	3.3	0.6
20	7.0	6.6	0.8	20	6.9	2.6	1.2
21	3.9	3.0	0.3	21	5.4	2.0	4.2
22	5.2	1.7	trace	22	5.6	2.3	0.2
23	4.2	2.2	nil	23	8.8	3.3	0.8
24	4.2	1.6	nil	24	6.3	4.4	2.2
25	2.7	0.6	trace	25	7.3	3.6	trace
26	1.6	-0.7	0.7	26	7.8	3.0	trace
27	3.4	-1.5	2.6	27	7.2	-3.2	trace
28	3.3	-1.6	trace	28	9.8	0.7	trace
29	3.1	-3.3	0.1	29	9.4	-1.5	nil
30	3.7	0.0	0.1	30	7.8	-2.2	nil
31	4.1	2.1	nil	31	7.6	0.0	nil
Feb 01	4.9	-4.1	nil	Apr 01	9.8	-2.6	nil
02	2.8	-4.7	nil	02	9.9	-1.7	trace
03	4.9	-4.0	1.4	03	11.5	-1.1	nil
04	5.4	-3.2	7.2	04	8.4	-0.1	nil
05	5.0	0.6	14.8	05	10.9	-1.7	nil
06	5.6	-0.6	0.1	06	10.4	-1.5	nil
07	3.1	-4.0	0.1	07	13.5	-0.9	nil
08	6.6	-0.6	25.8	08	16.9	4.2	nil
09	8.5	-1.2	3.5	09	10.6	4.7	5.0
10	8.1	5.3	3.8	10	14.9	7.1	0.1
11	7.7	5.0	12.2	11	11.3	0.3	9.1
12	8.1	0.6	0.2	12	6.0	5.3	12.8
13	6.6	0.2	nil	13	6.9	2.4	8.5
14	5.6	-3.6	nil	14	9.0	3.6	1.4
15	10.4	-1.5	0.4	15	11.6	5.7	7.3
16	9.0	4.5	0.7	16	13.0	7.7	17.2
17	9.5	4.6	12.6	17	13.1	4.0	5.8
18	7.1	2.5	4.0	18	15.3	5.0	2.3
19	5.5	-1.3	0.3	19	14.0	3.9	0.2
20	4.6	0.7	1.7	20	14.0	7.0	2.8
21	4.9	-3.0	1.8	21	13.9	7.6	7.3
22	7.3	-0.9	0.9	22	13.8	7.5	0.2
23	8.6	2.4	0.1	23	13.6	4.2	1.1
24	6.6	2.9	2.4	24	12.1	5.1	2.9
25	5.5	-2.0	trace	25	16.4	4.3	0.3
26	5.1	-3.8	trace	26	16.0	8.3	1.5
27	9.7	-3.5	trace	27	12.9	5.4	nil
28	9.9	-2.4	trace	28	10.8	3.3	trace
29	8.6	-1.6	nil	29	11.8	4.3	1.1
				30	11.8	0.0	14.8

Date	Max (°C)	Min (°C)	Rainfall (mm)	Date	Max (°C)	Min (°C)	Rainfall (mm)
May 01	9.3	0.0	6.1	July 01	16.0	9.3	1.6
02	9.3	2.9	trace	02	16.1	7.1	6.9
03	9.6	-2.0	nil	03	17.3	11.1	3.7
04	9.9	-1.0	0.3	04	17.0	8.5	0.7
05	11.0	-0.5	3.1	05	16.1	9.3	0.3
06	12.8	3.2	trace	06	15.8	5.7	nil
07	12.9	0.3	nil	07	15.6	7.3	nil
08	14.2	1.6	nil	08	17.9	8.3	0.1
09	11.6	2.2	nil	09	17.6	12.4	nil
10	11.0	-0.3	0.8	10	23.2	13.0	nil
11	10.2	2.1	nil	11	18.2	13.6	4.9
12	12.6	4.3	trace	12	17.9	10.9	nil
13	14.8	4.7	nil	13	20.9	10.6	nil
14	17.2	4.1	nil	14	17.7	12.0	nil
15	13.3	8.2	nil	15	17.3	9.0	nil
16	10.6	3.1	1.5	16	17.6	6.4	nil
17	11.2	0.6	nil	17	22.0	6.7	nil
18	11.9	0.4	1.0	18	23.5	5.5	nil
19	9.2	3.9	10.0	19	24.6	11.5	trace
20	14.3	4.6	4.9	20	24.6	9.1	trace
21	13.7	3.9	8.2	21	19.8	11.5	4.4
22	14.2	6.5	10.4	22	17.0	14.6	16.0
23	15.2	4.6	7.4	23	18.7	13.2	0.1
24	15.8	3.0	1.5	24	18.3	11.7	nil
25	14.9	6.4	0.8	25	22.6	8.5	3.2
26	14.6	5.4	12.4	26	18.9	13.4	0.2
27	16.1	8.1	6.0	27	17.6	9.5	4.7
28	16.6	6.8	2.6	28	14.0	11.0	1.4
29	17.3	9.7	8.3	29	19.2	12.5	0.2
30	12.1	8.0	2.0	30	19.0	10.9	0.8
31	14.7	8.4	0.8	31	18.6	10.9	0.1
June 01	15.6	5.9	3.3	Aug 01	16.6	10.5	6.0
02	15.3	3.0	7.8	02	18.5	10.8	nil
03	16.9	5.6	0.3	03	20.0	11.4	nil
04	18.2	7.6	2.5	04	20.0	9.8	1.3
05	17.8	8.8	1.0	05	15.2	13.5	13.1
06	17.8	6.9	trace	06	14.2	12.5	1.8
07	18.6	6.3	0.6	07	17.8	7.9	0.4
08	18.9	6.7	nil	08	16.0	11.9	4.6
09	13.0	9.1	4.6	09	17.5	10.4	10.1
10	18.9	10.6	3.4	10	19.7	10.1	0.1
11	17.5	10.4	6.0	11	21.1	9.5	0.1
12	16.4	7.3	0.1	12	20.0	9.9	nil
13	17.4	4.2	nil	13	19.2	11.6	nil
14	18.0	5.3	nil	14	20.3	8.6	nil
15	21.5	6.7	nil	15	21.4	8.5	nil
16	23.0	8.1	nil	16	20.2	12.0	nil
17	18.1	10.4	nil	17	20.4	13.4	nil
18	17.6	8.7	nil	18	21.7	13.7	nil
19	17.2	5.6	nil	19	18.2	14.0	0.3
20	17.4	5.9	nil	20	16.4	14.5	18.4
21	13.8	5.6	nil	21	19.1	12.7	4.3
22	15.6	4.0	nil	22	15.2	8.8	6.4
23	15.9	9.8	nil	23	19.0	7.4	0.2
24	16.9	10.5	nil	24	16.4	9.0	3.4
25	19.0	10.1	3.0	25	15.4	10.0	6.8
26	18.2	10.4	nil	26	15.9	11.1	3.2
27	18.5	8.0	2.9	27	19.0	10.2	0.2
28	18.3	12.5	0.5	28	18.0	8.2	4.9
29	16.5	10.4	1.3	29	16.3	6.5	0.1
30	16.0	11.0	4.0	30	15.6	10.4	trace
				31	17.9	6.6	nil

UK Societies

Specialist Societies

Alpine Garden Society

AGS Centre, Avon Bank, Pershore, Hereford & Worcester WR10 3JP

☎ 01386 554790   FAX 01386 554801

CONTACT   Bill Simpson (Secretary)
AIMS   To encourage interest in all aspects of alpine and rock garden plants
MEMBERSHIP   13,500
SUBSCRIPTIONS   £15 single; £18 joint
SERVICES   Lectures; associated gardens; seed scheme; library; publications; advice; awards; shows; journal; special interest and regional groups; outings; new rock garden at Pershore

Founded in 1929. The AGS caters for anyone interested in rock gardening or alpine plants. You join the national organisation which entitles you to numerous benefits including free entry to the twenty or so shows, the bulletin, the seed exchange scheme, and the advisory service. If you wish you can also join one of the 60 local groups: there is a small additional subscription which varies from group to group. You have to be a member of the national AGS in order to join. Local groups organise their own busy programmes of events, including lectures, shows and visits. The *Quarterly Bulletin of the Alpine Garden Society* is an authoritative illustrated magazine which covers alpines in cultivation and in the wild. The AGS organises guided expeditions to many countries for its members, and these are both popular and respected. They also publish monographs and alpine titles (including the mammoth new alpine encyclopedia), and members can use the slide and postal book libraries. At local level, AGS groups are an excellent and informal way to learn and develop an interest in alpines. Some groups are more active than others: it depends on local demand. Many of the lecturers are acknowledged experts, as will be some of the group members. The dates for the national shows, and a number of group events, appear in our calendar. Most local groups allow members to bring guests and will usually admit visitors for a small charge, though if you expect to attend regularly then you should really sign up properly. AGS headquarters can put you in touch with your nearest group. Active groups include the following: Bedfordshire, Berkshire, Birmingham, Bristol, East Cheshire, Cleveland, Cotswold and Malvern, North Cumbria, Derby, East Dorset, North East England, Exeter, Epping Forest, Hertfordshire, South Humberside, Ipswich, East Kent, Kent Medway,

East Lancashire, North Lancashire, Leicester, North London, Nottingham, Oxford, East Surrey, North Staffordshire, Southport, West Sussex, Ulster, North Wales, South Wales, Woking, East Yorkshire, West Yorkshire. The Society's newly-made rock garden at the AGS Centre, Pershore, is well worth a visit.

Australasian Plant Society

74 Brimstage Road, Heswall, Merseyside L60 1XQ
☎ 0151 342 1703

CONTACT   Jeff Irons
AIMS   To encourage the cultivation of Australian & New Zealand plants
MEMBERSHIP   100
SUBSCRIPTIONS   £6
SERVICES   Journal; outings

Members receive the twice-yearly newsletter and take part in an annual weekend visit. The society's excellent seedlist has many species which are not listed elsewhere.

Bonsai Kai

c/o 39 West Square, London SE11 4SP
☎ 0171 735 8476   FAX 0171 820 0941

CONTACT   Colin Ellis (Chairman)
MEMBERSHIP   150
SUBSCRIPTIONS   £12
SERVICES   Lectures; library; awards; shows; journal

Founded in 1961 as a group of The Japan Society and still affiliated to it. Bonsai Kai exhibits at two Westminster shows (March & October) to encourage interest in the art of bonsai: members have free admittance to those shows, for which Bonsai Kai also supplies judges to the RHS. Meetings take place at the RHS's Halls at 7 pm on the Tuesdays of RHS shows.

Botanical Society of the British Isles

c/o Dept of Botany, The Natural History Museum, Cromwell Road, London SW7 5BD

CONTACT   Hon. General Secretary
AIMS   The study of British and Irish flowering plants and ferns
MEMBERSHIP   2,000
SUBSCRIPTIONS   £18; reduced rate for junior members
SERVICES   Lectures; publications; advice; journal; outings; exhibition meetings

This association of amateur and professional botanists traces its history back to 1836. Three regular publications (*Watsonia*,

BSBI Abstracts and *BSBI News*) cover the society's activities, articles on the taxonomy and distribution of plants in the British Isles, and an annual bibliography. The society also arranges conferences, exhibitions and study trips, and undertakes research projects and surveys. Members have access to a panel of experts on the British flora and can buy works on British botany at reduced prices.

British & European Geranium Society
4 Higher Meadow, Clayton-le-Woods, Chorley, Lancashire PR5 2RS
☎ 01772 453383

CONTACT   Mrs Joan Hinchcliffe (Hon. Membership Secretary)
AIMS   To promote the Geranium (*Pelargonium*)
MEMBERSHIP   1,050
SUBSCRIPTIONS   £5 single; £7 double
SERVICES   Lectures; associated gardens; library; publications; advice; awards; shows; journal; special interest and regional groups; outings; plant finder

The British & European Geranium Society is dedicated to growing, hybridising and exhibiting pelargoniums. The society is divided into regional groups which organise programmes of events including lectures and shows. There is an annual national show; every other year a conference is also staged. Members receive three *Gazettes* and a *Year Book*. The society has other publications too. A new service is a computerised plant finder which has details of sources for any pelargonium which is available in Europe.

British Cactus & Succulent Society
1 Springwoods, Courtmoor, Fleet, Hampshire GU13 9SU
☎ 01252 622065

CONTACT   The Secretary
MEMBERSHIP   3,800
SUBSCRIPTIONS   £12 UK & EU; £13 other countries
SERVICES   Lectures; seed scheme; library; advice; shows; journal; outings

Founded in 1983 by the amalgamation of two earlier cactus and succulent societies, the BCSS is the premier national society with associated branches in more than 100 towns throughout the British Isles. Members receive the quarterly *Journal*, a quality magazine with a wide range of good articles. The yearbook *Bradleya* is available for an extra payment. There is a good choice of activities to cater for all interests.

British Clematis Society
The Tropical Bird Gardens, Rode, Bath, Somerset BA3 6QW
☎ 01373 830326   📠 01373 831288

CONTACT   Membership Secretary
AIMS   To encourage and extend clematis cultivation, and to share knowledge with fellow members
MEMBERSHIP   700
SUBSCRIPTIONS   £11 single; £16.50 joint; £12 Europe; £15 overseas; £17 overseas joint
SERVICES   Lectures; seed scheme; advice; shows; journal; outings; plant sales; demonstrations

A fast-growing society which organises meetings throughout the country and publishes a substantial illustrated journal, *The Clematis*, each year as well as supplements and newsletters. The society organises visits to gardens and nurseries. Members can obtain advice on clematis cultivation and join in the seed exchange programme. The society also produces a list of good clematis gardens and a list of clematis nurseries.

British Fuchsia Society
15 Summerfield Lane, Summerfield, Kidderminster, Hereford & Worcester DY11 7SA
☎ 01562 66688

CONTACT   Hon. Secretary
AIMS   To further interest in the cultivation of fuchsias
MEMBERSHIP   5,500
SUBSCRIPTIONS   £6 individual; £9 joint; £10 affiliated societies
SERVICES   Advice; shows; journal; special interest and regional groups; rooted cuttings

The British Fuchsia Society organises nine regional shows and a London show. Members receive the *Fuchsia Annual* and a twice-yearly bulletin, as well as three free rooted cuttings. They can also obtain advice from the society's experts either by post or telephone. Special interest groups are devoted to old cultivars and hybridising. Some three hundred societies are affiliated to the national society, many of which organise programmes of events and festivals.

British Gladiolus Society
24 The Terrace, Mayfield, Ashbourne, Derbyshire DE6 2JL
☎ 01335 345443

CONTACT   Hon. Secretary
AIMS   To stimulate interest in and improve gladiolus growing
MEMBERSHIP   400
SUBSCRIPTIONS   £10 single; £11 family
SERVICES   Lectures; seed scheme; library; publications; advice; awards; shows; journal; special interest and regional groups

Founded in 1926 the British Gladiolus Society stages three major shows each year: the National (at Wisley on 14 & 15 August this year), Southern and Northern. There are regional groups in Sussex and Buckinghamshire. Members keep in touch with society news through three bulletins and the yearbook, *The Gladiolus Annual*, which is published each spring. The society runs trials at three sites, and also has a book, slide and video library available for members and affiliated societies. Council members can advise on gladiolus cultivation, and the society raises money by distributing cormlets. A small range of booklets on showing and growing gladiolus is also available.

British Hosta & Hemerocallis Society
c/o Cleave House, Sticklepath, Okehampton, Devon EX20 2NN
☎ 01837 840481   📠 01837 840482

CONTACT   Hon. Secretary
AIMS   To foster interest in the cultivation of *Hosta* and *Hemerocallis*
MEMBERSHIP   240
SUBSCRIPTIONS   £8 single; £10 joint; £12 overseas

SERVICES   Lectures; library; advice; awards; journal; outings; annual plant auction

Founded in 1981, the British Hosta & Hemerocallis Society has members spread throughout the world. It publishes an annual bulletin, and regular newsletters to keep members informed of news and events. Garden visits and lectures are arranged, and members can borrow by post from the society's specialist and comprehensive library. An annual award is presented to a hosta and a hemerocallis. Expert advice is provided via the secretary. There are eight relevant NCCPG national collections.

The British Iris Society
The Old Mill House, Shurton, Stogursey, Somerset TA5 1QG

CONTACT   Hon. Secretary
AIMS   To encourage and improve the cultivation of irises
MEMBERSHIP   800
SUBSCRIPTIONS   £9 single
SERVICES   Lectures; seed scheme; library; publications; advice; awards; shows; journal; special interest and regional groups; plant sales scheme; lectures for clubs and societies

The British Iris Society was founded in 1922 and caters for all levels of interest in this varied genus. The illustrated and authoritative *Iris Year Book* is supplemented by three newsletters. The society's programme includes three annual shows and occasional lectures. There are regional groups in Mercia and Kent, and special interest groups for species, Japanese, Siberian and Pacific Coast irises. Members can borrow from the reference library, and the slide collection runs to some 5,000 items. As well as a plant sales scheme there is also a seed distribution scheme, and expert advice is available on request. New hybrids are trialled at Wisley, and the Dykes Medal is awarded to the best British bred hybrid in the trial. The society will celebrate its 75th anniversary this year with a four-day convention at Hadlow College, starting on 23 May.

British Ivy Society
14 Holly Grove, Huyton, Merseyside L36 4JA
☎ 0151 489 1083

CONTACT   Hon. Secretary
MEMBERSHIP   120
SUBSCRIPTIONS   £7.50
SERVICES   Advice; journal; outings

Members receive a newsletter and the informative and readable journal *Ivy* each year. They can obtain advice on *Hedera* cultivation.

The British National Carnation Society
3 Canberra Close, Hornchurch, Essex RM12 5TR
☎ 01708 441786

CONTACT   The Secretary
AIMS   To improve the cultivation of the *Dianthus* family
MEMBERSHIP   450
SUBSCRIPTIONS   £9 single; £10 joint
SERVICES   Lectures; publications; advice; shows; journal; discount coupon scheme

The British National Carnation Society organises several shows annually. Members receive the illustrated *Carnation Year Book* each year as well as two newsletters. New members can also choose one of the society's cultural booklets when they join. Medals and show cards are available for affiliated societies, and together the society and its affiliates hold area shows throughout the country. A coupon in the autumn newsletter gives a discount on plants from selected nurseries. A panel of experts can be called on to answer questions. Other societies can hire lectures: a fee is charged to non-affiliated societies.

British Orchid Council
P O Box 1072, Frome, Somerset BA11 5NY
☎ 01373 465746

CONTACT   Peter Hunt (Secretary)
MEMBERSHIP   5,000
SERVICES   Judges training scheme; panel of speakers

The BOC is a co-ordinating forum for amateur and professional orchid growers. Its members include over 50 local and regional societies, the British Orchid Growers' Association, the RHS, RBG Kew and other botanical institutions. The Society publishes a useful *Grower's & Buyer's Guide to Orchids* which lists all its members and what they offer.

The British Pelargonium & Geranium Society
75 Pelham Road, Bexleyheath, Kent DA7 4LY
☎ 01322 525947

CONTACT   Les Hodgkiss (Secretary)
AIMS   To promote interest in *Pelargonium*, *Geranium* and other Geraniaceae
MEMBERSHIP   1,200
SUBSCRIPTIONS   £6.50 single & affiliated societies
SERVICES   Seed scheme; advice; shows; journal; biennial conference; books on pelargoniums available by post

The British Pelargonium & Geranium Society was founded in 1951. It publishes a Year Book and three issues of *Pelargonium News* annually. The society's annual show, held in June, moves around the country, and includes classes for beginners and flower arrangers. Every other year a conference is held. Members can take advantage of a postal advisory service, and free seeds. They stage publicity and information stands at Chelsea, Malvern and the RHS Westminster shows, and encourage other societies to join as affiliated members.

British Pteridological Society
16 Kirby Corner Road, Canley, Coventry, West Midlands CV4 8GD
☎ 01203 715690

CONTACT   Hon. General Secretary
AIMS   To promote the study and cultivation of ferns and fern allies
MEMBERSHIP   800
SUBSCRIPTIONS   £15 single; £12 optional; £9 student; £25 subscriber
SERVICES   Lectures; seed scheme; publications; advice; journal; special interest and regional groups; outings; book sales service; plant exchange scheme

Now over 100 years old, this international society includes amateur and professional members. An annual *Bulletin* contains society news, whilst the *Pteridologist* prints articles and book reviews for the amateur enthusiast. The twice-yearly *Fern Gazette* includes more scientific papers: members who do not wish to receive this journal pay the lower optional subscription rate. According to the season activities include indoor meetings and field trips and garden visits. A spore exchange distributes fern spores from all over the world, whilst a postal plant exchange scheme helps members obtain rarely available or surplus plants. There are regional groups in Cumbria, South-East England, the Midlands, Wessex and North-East England. The society takes a stand at the Malvern Spring Show and the Southport Show. Members can obtain advice on fern cultivation through the Hon. General Secretary.

Carnivorous Plant Society
1 Orchard Close, Ringwood, Hampshire BH24 1LP

CONTACT   Steve Cottell
AIMS   To bring together all those interested in carnivorous plants
MEMBERSHIP   650
SUBSCRIPTIONS   £9 single; £10 Europe; £13 world
SERVICES   Seed scheme; advice; shows; journal; outings; plant search service

The Carnivorous Plant Society publishes an annual colour journal and four newsletters. They organise a number of events including visits to nurseries, field trips and open days. A plant search scheme is run, and members have free access to the seed bank. The information officer can provide advice on all topics.

The Cottage Garden Society
5 Nixon Close, Thornhill, Dewsbury, West Yorkshire WF12 0JA

CONTACT   Membership Secretary
AIMS   To promote and conserve cottage garden plants and to encourage cottage-style gardens
MEMBERSHIP   5,000
SUBSCRIPTIONS   £5 individual; £8 joint; £6 overseas; $20 USA
SERVICES   Lectures; seed scheme; publications; shows; journal; special interest and regional groups; list of members' gardens which can be visited

The Cottage Garden Society promotes and conserves worthwhile old-fashioned garden plants, and encourages owners of small gardens to garden in the cottage style. Members receive a quarterly bulletin and can take part in the annual seed distribution. The society has a growing number of regional and county groups: each organises lectures, meetings, visits and other events. The society hires out slides to members.

The Cyclamen Society
Tile Barn House, Standen Street, Iden Green, Benenden, Kent TN17 4LB

CONTACT   Peter Moore
AIMS   To further interest in and scientific knowledge of cyclamen
MEMBERSHIP   1,400
SUBSCRIPTIONS   £5 individual; £6 family; £7 overseas

SERVICES   Lectures; associated gardens; seed scheme; library; advice; awards; shows; journal; annual weekend conference

The Cyclamen Society has an international membership but is based in Britain. Its work includes research and conservation, whilst members benefit from the twice-yearly journal, a seed distribution scheme and access to expert advice through the society's advisory panel. It exhibits and stages shows, organises meetings and lectures, and maintains a specialist library of literature and slides on cyclamen.

Daffodil Society
The Meadows, Puxton, Weston-super-Mare BS24 6TF
☎ 01934 833641

CONTACT   Jackie Petherbridge (Secretary)
MEMBERSHIP   720
SUBSCRIPTIONS   £5 individual; £7.50 family
SERVICES   Seed scheme; publications; advice; shows; journal; special interest and regional groups

Established in 1898, the Society caters for breeders, exhibitors and lovers of daffodils. It also has over 200 affiliated societies as members. It is closely involved in the competitions at RHS Westminster shows and the Harrogate Spring show as well as running its own show at Solihull. Members receive the annual *Journal* in February and the *Newsletter* in July. In addition to the Seed Scheme, there are good opportunities to acquire new cultivars in the annual Bulb Lottery.

The Delphinium Society
Takakkaw, Ice House Wood, Oxted, Surrey RH8 9DW

CONTACT   Membership Secretary
AIMS   To encourage and extend the culture of delphiniums
MEMBERSHIP   1,400
SUBSCRIPTIONS   £5 single & joint; £6 overseas
SERVICES   Seed scheme; publications: *Simply Delphiniums*, £2.50; advice; awards; shows; journal

The Delphinium Society dates back to 1928. New members receive a mixed packet of seed when they join, and all members can buy the society's hand-pollinated seeds of garden hybrids and species. The illustrated *Year Book* is a unique source of information about the genus. Two shows, at which cups are awarded, are held each year: in June at Westminster, and in July at Wisley. Members gain free entry to the shows, and can also take advantage of advice on cultivation and a number of social events.

Epiphytic Plant Study Group
1 Belvidere Park, Great Crosby, Lancashire L23 0SP
☎ 0151 928 2770

CONTACT   Chris Dawson (Subscription Secretary)
MEMBERSHIP   175
SUBSCRIPTIONS   £7.25 UK; £8.50 overseas
SERVICES   Advice; journal

Originally an offshoot of the British Cactus & Succulent Society, the Study Group still has a particular interest in epiphyllums and similar plants. The principal benefit to members is the quarterly journal. Overseas subscribers in USA, Australia and New Zealand may pay to local representatives: details from Chris Dawson.

Federation of British Bonsai Societies

The Woodlands, New Hall Drive, Walmley, Sutton
Coldfield, West Midlands B76 1QX
☎ 0121 378 4837   📠 0121 311 1912
CONTACT   Administrative Officer
AIMS   To promote the art of Bonsai in the UK
MEMBERSHIP   77 clubs
SUBSCRIPTIONS   £40 society; £10 single; £20 commercial
SERVICES   Library; publications; advice; awards; shows;
journal; special interest and regional groups; outings; list of
lecturers

The Federation of British Bonsai Societies is the national
bonsai organisation, and is a member of the European Bonsai
Association. Most of its members are local societies and
nurseries. The Federation publishes a newsletter six times a
year giving members information on national and worldwide
bonsai events. Two national exhibitions are held each year,
and every other year up to 400 delegates attend a major bonsai
convention. This year the International convention will be in
October in Seoul, South Korea. FOBBS keeps a library of
slides, films and videos and can provide expert advice through
the secretary and chairman. The National Bonsai Collection is
held at Birmingham Botanic Gardens and Glasshouses; the
Scottish National Collection is at Malleny House in Lothian.

Fruit Group of the Royal Horticultural Society

80 Vincent Square, London SW1P 2PE
☎ 0171 630 7422   📠 0171 233 9525
CONTACT   Mavis Sweetingham
AIMS   To promote interest in the cultivation of fruit
MEMBERSHIP   400
SUBSCRIPTIONS   £3
SERVICES   Associated gardens; publications; shows; outings

Membership of the Fruit Group is open to all members of the
RHS. The Group exhibits at the Chelsea Flower Show, the
RHS Great Autumn Show, the Harrogate Autumn Show and
the Malvern Autumn Show. Members have the opportunity
to exhibit at RHS shows and join Group outings, but perhaps
the best meetings are those at Wisley, where they can study
the RHS's fruit collection at close quarters, in the company of
knowledgeable members of staff and other experts. These
meetings often have a practical aspect: the periodic organised
'gooseberry tastings' are not to be missed. The Group balances
its activities between top fruit and soft fruit, so that all
members' interests are accommodated within the annual programme. It has also set up sub-groups in the West Midlands
(based at Pershore) and the south west (run from Rosemoor):
more groups will follow shortly.

The Garden History Society

77 Cowcross Street, London EC1M 6BP
☎ 0171 608 2409
CONTACT   Linda Wigley
AIMS   To study garden history and preserve parks and
gardens
MEMBERSHIP   2,000
SUBSCRIPTIONS   £20

SERVICES   Lectures; journal; special interest and regional
groups; outings

Founded in 1965. Learned society which is concerned with
the study of garden and landscape history. It is also actively
involved in conservation and regularly advises local authorities on such issues. The twice-yearly journal Garden History
publishes new research, whilst regular newsletters carry details of conservation matters and society events. These events
include lectures and garden visits, at home and abroad. There
is a regional group in Scotland. Events are limited to society
members only but the public are admitted to the excellent
winter lectures in London.

The Hardy Plant Society

Little Orchard, Great Comberton, Pershore, Hereford &
Worcester WR10 3DP
☎ 01386 710317
CONTACT   Mrs Pam Adams (Adminstrator)
AIMS   To stimulate interest in growing hardy herbaceous
plants
MEMBERSHIP   11,000
SUBSCRIPTIONS   £10 single; £12 joint
SERVICES   Lectures; associated gardens; seed scheme; publi-
cations; advice; shows; journal; special interest and regional
groups; outings; slide library

The Hardy Plant Society has its own garden at the Pershore
College of Horticulture. Members join the national society and
can then choose to join one of the 33 regional groups. In
addition there six special interest groups (Grasses; Hardy
Geraniums; Half-hardy plants; Pulmonarias; Paeonies; and
Variegated plants) and a Correspondents Group for those who
cannot come to meetings. Two journals are sent to members
each year, along with regular newsletters. The national society
attends Chelsea and the RHS Westminster shows, whilst area
groups patronise local shows and arrange their own programmes of events. An annual seed distribution list is circulated to all members. Members benefit from a horticultural
advisory panel headed by the society's vice-president, and a
slide library from which they can borrow. The society is also
involved in conserving old cultivars and introducing new ones,
and has produced a number of useful publications. It has grown
fast in recent years, but managed the expansion well. The local
groups organise their own busy programmes of meetings, trips
and garden visits: the additional cost of joining such a group is
usually very small. Full details of the local and specialist groups
are available from the national society: only HPS members can
join a local or specialist group. Because all HPS events are for
HPS members only they are not included in our calendar.
Regional groups exist for the following areas: Berkshire; Buckinghamshire, Oxfordshire and Northamptonshire; Cambridgeshire and Bedfordshire; Cheshire; Cornwall; Cumbria; Devon;
Essex; Hampshire; Hereford & mid Wales; Hertfordshire;
Kent; Lincolnshire; Norfolk and Suffolk; North-East Eng-
land; North London; North-West England; North Yorkshire;
Nottinghamshire; Rutland; Shropshire; Somerset; Southern
Counties; South Pennines; South Wales; Sussex; Western
Counties; West Midlands; West Yorkshire; Wiltshire and

Avon; Worcestershire; Scotland & Northern Borders; Cork. There are also plans to start a group in Staffordshire.

The Heather Society
Denbeigh, All Saints Road, Creeting St Mary, Ipswich, Suffolk IP6 8PJ
☎ & [FAX] 01449 711220

CONTACT Administrator
AIMS To promote interest in heathers and provide a friendly meeting place for enthusiasts
MEMBERSHIP 850
SUBSCRIPTIONS £10 single; £12 joint
SERVICES Publications; advice; shows; journal; special interest and regional groups; slide library

The Heather Society was founded in 1963. Members receive the society's authoritative *Year Book*, which is edited by Dr Charles Nelson, and a twice-yearly bulletin of news and events. Competitions are held through the RHS at Westminster. A slide library is maintained, and expert advice on cultivation and other technical queries is available. Regional groups arrange a series of local events, and an annual weekend conference, linked to the AGM, is held at a different location each year. The national reference collections are at Wisley, Surrey and Cherrybank, Perth.

The Hebe Society
Rosemergy, Hain Walk, St Ives, Cornwall TR26 2AF
☎ 01736 795225

CONTACT Hon. Secretary
AIMS To encourage, conserve and extend the cultivation of hebe, parahebe and all New Zealand native plants
MEMBERSHIP 300
SUBSCRIPTIONS £6 single; £8 joint; £12 professional
SERVICES Publications; advice; shows; journal; special interest and regional groups

An international society, based in Britain. It was established in 1985, and has since expanded its brief to include other New Zealand plants. The society is affiliated to the New Zealand Alpine Garden Society. Quarterly issues of *Hebe News* keep members in touch with activities, and include botanical and horticultural articles. Local groups exist or are being formed in the north-west of England, Cornwall and the Cotswolds. The society maintains a slide library, operates a cutting exchange service and produces booklets about hebes and parahebes. Society members can also obtain written advice on request. Five National Collections are held by members.

Henry Doubleday Research Association (HDRA)
Ryton Organic Gardens, Ryton on Dunsmore, Coventry, West Midlands CV8 3LG
☎ 01203 303517   [FAX] 01203 639229

CONTACT Jackie Gear
AIMS To promote and advise on organic gardening, growing and food
MEMBERSHIP 21,000
SUBSCRIPTIONS £17 single; £20 joint

SERVICES Associated gardens; seed scheme; library; publications; advice; journal; special interest and regional groups; trials; product discounts

Europe's largest organic organisation. At the Ryton headquarters there is a ten-acre garden, and a reference library which members can use. Members are kept up to date with HDRA events through a quarterly magazine. In addition there are over fifty local groups around the country. The society provides free advice on organic gardening to its members, and they receive discounts on HDRA products and books. They can also join the Heritage Seed programme for £8 (£16 for non-members): this scheme propagates and preserves vegetable varieties which have been squeezed out of commerce by current legislation. Since they are not allowed to be sold, the HDRA gives them away to subscribers. Hand in hand with this project is *The Vegetable Finder*. The HDRA also carries out scientific research, consultancy work for industry and public bodies, and worldwide research and agricultural aid projects. Members are entitled to free entry to Brogdale, Harlow Carr, West Dean in West Sussex, the RHS gardens at Wisley, Hyde Hall & Rosemoor, and the Centre Terre Vivante near Grenoble.

The Herb Society
134 Buckingham Palace Road, London SW1W 9SA
☎ 0171 823 5583

CONTACT Nicola Hartopp
AIMS To bring together all who have an interest in herbs
MEMBERSHIP 2,400
SUBSCRIPTIONS £16 single; £14 senior citizens and under-18s
SERVICES Lectures; associated gardens; journal

Founded in 1927 as the Society of Herbalists, the Society is celebrating its 70th anniversary this year. It aims to bring together all with an interest in herbs. Members receive three copies of the Society's magazine *Herbs*, and four copies of the newsletter *Herbarium* each year. Seminars and workshops are arranged nationwide in appropriate settings. Information on suppliers, literature and all aspects of growing herbs is available to members. The Society's garden is part of the Henry Doubleday Research Association's new garden at Yalding in Kent.

Ichiyo School of Ikebana
4 Providence Way, Waterbeach, Cambridge, Cambridgeshire CB5 9QJ
CONTACT Mrs Eileen Gibson (President)
AIMS To introduce the art of Ikebana
MEMBERSHIP 60
SUBSCRIPTIONS £15
SERVICES Lectures; shows; journal

The School holds courses, workshops and demonstrations in Ikebana, and exhibits at major shows, including Chelsea and the RHS Westminster shows.

International Asclepiad Society
2 Keymer Court, Burgess Hill, West Sussex RH15 0AA
CONTACT L B Delderfield (Secretary)
AIMS To grow and study the Asclepiadaceae
SUBSCRIPTIONS £10

92   Specialist Societies

SERVICES   Lectures; seed scheme; library; publications; advice; journal; special interest and regional groups; outings; slide library

This society is British-based, but international: its members come from over 20 different countries. They tend to have a particular interest in succulents, though other members of the family are not neglected. The thrice-yearly journal Asklepios is a quality publication. So far as permitted by international regulations, the society organises a plant bank, a seed bank and a plant exchange scheme.

Japanese Garden Society
Groves Mill, Shakers Lane, Long Itchington, Warwickshire CV23 8QB
☎ 01926 632746

CONTACT   Mrs Kira Dalton
AIMS   To record, conserve and encourage Japanese-style gardens
MEMBERSHIP   450
SUBSCRIPTIONS   £20 single; £30 couple
SERVICES   Lectures; library; shows; journal; special interest and regional groups; outings

A new society which is devoted to gardens influenced by the Japanese tradition of design. It aims to compile a register of Japanese gardens in the UK, and to work for the conservation of existing gardens and the creation of new ones. Last year the Society organised a cherry blossom tour to Japan. It has six regional groups: members receive the quarterly journal Shakkei.

Lily Group of the Royal Horticultural Society
c/o Rosemary Cottage, Lowbands, Redmarley, Gloucester, Gloucestershire GL19 3NG
☎ 01452 840661

CONTACT   Dr A F Hayward (Membership Secretary)
AIMS   To encourage the cultivation of Lilium and related genera
MEMBERSHIP   530
SUBSCRIPTIONS   £5
SERVICES   Lectures; seed scheme; publications; awards; shows; journal; outings; bulb auction

Membership of the Lily Group is open to all members of the RHS. It is the largest lily society in Europe and the only one in Britain. Members receive three newsletters a year. Lectures are associated with RHS shows at Westminster (at least two a year), and the Group also exhibits at Hampton Court. There is an annual bulb auction at the late-autumn show and the Group issues its Seed List early in the year: it offers a remarkable choice of lily and Liliaceae seed sent by donors at home and abroad. Advice on all aspects of growing these plants is available from the General Secretary, via the RHS.

The Mammillaria Society
26 Glenfield Road, Banstead, Surrey SM7 2DG
☎ 01737 354036

CONTACT   Hon. Chairman
AIMS   To promote interest in the genus Mammillaria

MEMBERSHIP   450
SUBSCRIPTIONS   £6.50 UK; £7.50 Europe; £8.50 outside Europe
SERVICES   Seed scheme; publications; advice; journal

Founded in 1960. Its interests extend to Coryphantha and allied genera as well as Mammillaria. Members receive a quarterly illustrated Journal, and have access to specialised publications. There is an annual seed scheme, and advice is available to any member. Lecturers can be provided for other societies.

The Maple Society
4 Black Barn, High Street, Seal, Sevenoaks, Kent TN15 0AL
CONTACT   Alan Ball (Membership Secretary)
AIMS   To foster interest in the genus Acer
MEMBERSHIP   200
SUBSCRIPTIONS   £9 single; £13 family
SERVICES   Lectures; seed scheme; advice; journal; outings

The society aims to encourage the cultivation of maples and enable members to learn from each other. It promotes the study of the origins, botany, uses and cultural requirements of all maples. Roy Lancaster is its President and the society's activities last year included a four-day tour of Boskoop and Dutch botanic gardens. The newspaper is published quarterly and contains articles of high quality and interest.

Mesemb Study Group
Brenfield, Bolney Road, Ansty, West Sussex RH17 5AW
☎ 01444 441193   FAX 01444 454061

CONTACT   Suzanne Mace
AIMS   To further the study and knowledge of Mesembryanthemum and related genera
MEMBERSHIP   500
SUBSCRIPTIONS   £6 single; £9 overseas, airmail
SERVICES   Lectures; seed scheme; journal; research

Successor to the Mesembryanthemum Society, the Mesemb Study Group celebrated its 10th birthday last year. Members, about a third of whom live overseas, receive a quarterly bulletin and can take part in the annual seed list. Meetings are arranged irregularly, and announced in the quarterly bulletin. A larger event, often including a show, takes place every two or three years. Financial assistance is also available for some research projects.

The National Association of Flower Arrangement Societies
21 Denbigh Street, London SW1V 2HF
☎ 0171 828 5145   FAX 0171 821 0587

CONTACT   The Secretary
AIMS   To encourage of the love of flowers and demonstrate their decorative value
MEMBERSHIP   75,000
SUBSCRIPTIONS   Payable to local clubs
SERVICES   Lectures; library; publications; awards; shows; journal; special interest and regional groups; outings; book service

Founded in 1959. NAFAS is the umbrella organisation for nearly 1500 flower-arrangement clubs. The Association is very active in training and teaching arrangers of all skill levels. Local clubs organise demonstrations and competitions, and area groups stage exhibits at NAFAS and local shows. Regular flower festivals are organised to raise money for charitable causes, and arrangements in hospitals are another important part of the NAFAS activity. They also co-ordinate the flowers at Westminster Abbey, and do the arrangements for major occasions including royal weddings. *The Flower Arranger* is circulated quarterly; members can use the book service, and there is a book and slide library at the London headquarters. Prospective members should write to headquarters in the first instance: they will put you in touch with a local club. Subscriptions to these clubs vary and are usually modest. All clubs are represented at area level: the twenty-one areas are as follows: East of England; South-West, Scotland; North-East; Three Counties and South Wales; London and Overseas; Surrey; Wessex and Jersey; Home Counties; Berks, Bucks and Oxon; Mercia and North Wales; North West; Kent; Sussex; North Midlands; South Midlands; Devon and Cornwall; Northumberland and Durham; Dorset and Guernsey; Cheshire; Northern Ireland.

National Auricula and Primula Society (Midland & West Section)

6 Lawson Close, Saltford, Somerset BS18 3LB

☎ 01225 872893

CONTACT   Peter Ward (Hon. Sec.)

AIMS   To improve and encourage the cultivation of florists' auriculas

MEMBERSHIP   420

SUBSCRIPTIONS   £5 home; £6 abroad

SERVICES   Lectures; publications; advice; awards; shows; journal

Founded in 1900. Members receive the year book *Argus* and two newsletters every year. The society also publishes information sheets on cultivation, guides to varieties and a history of auriculas. Three shows are held a year, one at Saltford in Avon and two in the Midlands, at Solihull and Knowle. Plant sales are held at the society's shows: some varieties are not available commercially.

National Auricula and Primula Society (Southern Section)

67 Warnham Court Road, Carshalton Beeches, Surrey SM5 3ND

CONTACT   Hon. Secretary

AIMS   To improve and encourage the cultivation of auriculas and hardy primroses

MEMBERSHIP   400

SUBSCRIPTIONS   £7 home; £8 overseas

SERVICES   Lectures; publications; advice; awards; shows; journal; special interest and regional groups

Founded in 1876. Members receive a year book and an annual newsletter. Two shows are held: both usually in April. This year the Primula show is on 5 April and the Auricula show on 26 April, both at Datchett Village Hall. Plants are for sale at the shows. Members can seek advice on all aspects of primula cultivation and exhibition. The society has a third section

serving the North (146 Queens Road, Cheadle Hulme, Cheshire SK8 5HY).

National Begonia Society

33 Findern Lane, Willington, Derbyshire DE65 6DW

☎ 01283 702681

CONTACT   Hon. Secretary

AIMS   To promote and encourage the cultivation of all begonias

MEMBERSHIP   800

SUBSCRIPTIONS   £5 single; £6 joint; additional enrolment fee £1

SERVICES   Lectures; publications; advice; awards; shows; journal; special interest and regional groups

Established in 1948. The society encourages the cultivation of all types of begonia. New members receive a cultural handbook, and the journal appears three times a year. Meetings are arranged through the regional groups, five of which also organise an annual area show. In addition there is a national show with 26 classes. New cultivars can be submitted for awards to the floral committee. An advisory service is available through the secretary. The Society is producing a register of all known cultivars in cultivation.

National Chrysanthemum Society

George Gray House, 8 Amber Business Village, Amber Close, Tamworth, Staffordshire B77 4RD

☎ & [FAX] 01827 310331

CONTACT   Mrs Y Honnor

AIMS   To promote the chrysanthemum and offer advice

MEMBERSHIP   4,500

SUBSCRIPTIONS   £10 fellow; £9 senior fellow; £14 family; £5 junior

SERVICES   Publications; advice; awards; shows; journal; special interest and regional groups

The National Chrysanthemum Society holds two national shows each year: in Bingley Hall, Stafford (September) and the RHS Halls, Westminster (November). The advisory bureau helps with queries about chrysanthemums and handles membership enquiries.

National Council for the Conservation of Plants and Gardens

The Pines, Wisley Garden, Woking, Surrey GU23 6QB

☎ 01483 211465   [FAX] 01483 211750

CONTACT   Graham Pattison

AIMS   To encourage the conservation of plants and gardens

MEMBERSHIP   6,000

SUBSCRIPTIONS   Apply to local group for details

SERVICES   Lectures; publications; shows; journal; special interest and regional groups; outings

Founded in 1978. The NCCPG is divided into about 40 local and county groups who organise their own programmes of events. The national body works to preserve individual plants and endangered gardens. The society's most successful innovation has been the establishment of National Collections of genera (and part genera). These gather together as many representatives of the genus as possible and form a unique resource. Many can be visited: full details appear in the *1997 National Plant Collections Directory*, which is available from the NCCPG. As well as helping to establish organisations for the conservation of garden plants in Australia, France and the USA, the NCCPG has close relations with similar movements in Sweden (c/o Kenneth Lorentzon, Swedish University for Agricultural Science, Nursery Stock Research Faculty, Box 55, S-23053 Alnarp) and in Poland (c/o T J Nowak, Ogrod Botaniczny Uniwersytetu, ul. Sienkiewicza 22, 50-335 Wroclaw).

National Dahlia Society

19 Sunnybank, Marlow, Buckinghamshire SL7 3BL
☎ 01628 473500
CONTACT   General Secretary
AIMS   To promote the cultivation of dahlias
MEMBERSHIP   3,000
SUBSCRIPTIONS   £10.50 single; £8.50 OAPs; £11 affiliated society
SERVICES   Lectures; library; publications; advice; awards; shows; journal; special interest and regional groups; judging examinations; classification of new varieties

The National Dahlia Society holds two main shows: in London at the RHS and at Harrogate during the Autumn Show. It runs trials at Bradford and Wisley, and gives an annual award for the best new British and new overseas seedlings. Members receive the society journal twice a year, and can take part in its annual conference and lecture programme. There are about 900 affiliated societies: they can use the society's medals and certificates for their own shows. A range of books and pamphlets is available for members at reduced prices.

National Pot Leek Society

147 Sea Road, Fulwell, Sunderland SR6 9EB
☎ 0191 549 4274
CONTACT   Hon. Secretary
AIMS   To improve and encourage leek growing
MEMBERSHIP   2,000
SUBSCRIPTIONS   £5
SERVICES   Lectures; publications; advice; awards; shows; journal; items for sale

The society produces a yearbook and two newsletters for its members. Advice can be provided by letter or phone, and the society produces a growing guide *Sound All Round*, and a video *Growing Leeks with the Experts*. Among the items on sale are measuring equipment and charts. Most of the members live in the north-east of England.

National Society of Allotment and Leisure Gardeners

O'Dell House, Hunters Road, Corby, Northamptonshire NN17 1JE
☎ 01536 266576
CONTACT   Geoff Stokes
AIMS   To help all enjoy the recreation of gardening
MEMBERSHIP   104,000
SUBSCRIPTIONS   £6.45 single; £67 life membership; £1 per member for societies

SERVICES   Seed scheme; commercial seeds available at reduced prices; publications; advice; journal; special interest and regional groups; insurance

This national society was founded in 1930 for allotment holders and other gardeners. Members can join individually or as part of a gardening association: some 1,700 societies belong and 100+ local authorities. In return they receive the journal and are able to take advantage of NSALG's many services. These include substantial discounts on seeds ordered through the society, and special insurance for allotment property. The society provides free advice on horticultural subjects, and in particular on the legal aspects of allotment gardening, including threatened loss of land and other disputes. It can also advise on suitable forms for leases, rents and agreements. A range of leaflets and fact sheets is available, along with show stationery and awards.

The National Sweet Pea Society

3 Chalk Farm Road, Stokenchurch, High Wycombe, Buckinghamshire HP14 3TB
☎ 01494 482153
CONTACT   Hon. Secretary
AIMS   To encourage the cultivation and improvement of the sweet pea
MEMBERSHIP   1,400
SUBSCRIPTIONS   £12 single; £10 affiliated society; £15 overseas
SERVICES   Lectures; advice; awards; shows; journal; special interest and regional groups; joint RHS/ NSPS trials

The National Sweet Pea Society was founded in 1900. The society's *Annual* appears every June, and further Bulletins in February and September. The *Annual* is a substantial publication. Its two major shows are held in July this year: the National at Market Bosworth on 6 July and the Provincial in the grounds of Windsor Castle on 27 & 28 June: there may be a second Provincial Show. Each county has an area representative who arranges programmes for local members. The society actively promotes new varieties, and members can send their own seedlings to the trials at Wisley each year.

National Vegetable Society

56 Waun-y-Groes Avenue, Rhiwbini, Cardiff, South Glamorgan CF4 4SZ
☎ 01222 627994
CONTACT   I Garland (Hon. Sec.)
MEMBERSHIP   3,500
SUBSCRIPTIONS   £8 single; £9.50 joint; £11 & £14 societies
SERVICES   Library; publications; advice; awards; shows; journal; special interest and regional groups

The National Vegetable Society was founded in 1960 and caters for individual members and societies. The latter can use the NVS medals and award cards. Membership spans the expert and the novice vegetable grower. The new quarterly National Bulletin and the regional Bulletins that members receive contain advice on all aspects of growing and showing vegetables. A National Newsletter gives details of all Society activities. The National Vegetable Championships are held at a different location each year and major awards are presented at it. There are regional branches (Midland, Northern, Scottish, Southern, Welsh).

National Viola and Pansy Society

Cleeway, Eardington, Bridgnorth, Shropshire WV16 5JT
☎ 01746 766909

CONTACT John Snocken
AIMS To encourage the cultivation, exhibition and improvement of violas and pansies
MEMBERSHIP 120
SUBSCRIPTIONS £3
SERVICES Library; advice; shows; journal

Founded in 1911. The Midlands-based society encourages and popularises the growing of exhibition varieties, and helps its members with advice on propagation and cultivation. A newsletter is circulated irregularly, and there is an annual show at St John's Church, Harborne, (19 July this year). Surplus cuttings and plants form the basis for occasional exchanges.

Ohara School of Ikebana

Forresters, Sway Road, Lymington, Hampshire SO4 8LR
☎ 01590 672418

CONTACT Mrs A Sawano
AIMS To teach and promote the art of Ikebana
SUBSCRIPTIONS £12
SERVICES Lectures; shows; journal

Teaches the Ohara style of Ikebana, the Japanese art of flower-arranging. Three to four newsletters are produced each year, and members exhibit at flower, garden and Ikebana shows. Teachers are available throughout the UK and around the world.

Orchid Society of Great Britain

Athelney, 145 Binscombe Village, Godalming, Surrey GU7 3QL
☎ 01483 421423

CONTACT Hon. Secretary
AIMS To encourage amateur growers of orchids
MEMBERSHIP 1,200
SUBSCRIPTIONS £10 single; £12 double; £5 joining fee
SERVICES Lectures; library; publications; advice; awards; shows; journal; special interest and regional groups; outings; plant exchanges and sales

The nationwide orchid society. It produces an informative journal four times a year and stages two major shows annually. In addition there is a monthly meeting in the Napier Hall, London which may include a lecture and a show. The library lends books and slides, and members can obtain cultural advice in person or in writing from the Cultural Adviser. There is a plant exchange forum, and a sales table at most meetings. The society publishes a small booklet on orchid cultivation which is a useful introduction to the subject (£2.50).

Rhododendron, Camellia & Magnolia Group of the RHS

Netherton, Buckland Monachorum, Yelverton, Devon PL20 7NL
☎ & [FAX] 01822 854022

CONTACT Josephine Warren (Hon. Sec.)

AIMS To bring together all who share an interest in rhododendrons, camellias and magnolias
MEMBERSHIP 700
SUBSCRIPTIONS £15 Europe; £17.50 outside Europe (airmail)
SERVICES Lectures; associated gardens; publications; advice; awards; shows; journal; special interest and regional groups; outings

Membership is open to all members of the RHS. New members are assigned to the nearest regional branch and advised of the garden visits and lectures programme. The Group organises a Spring Tour and an Autumn Weekend, and mounts a display at the main Rhododendron Show at Vincent Square (29 & 30 April in 1997). The *Bulletin* is published three times a year. The *Yearbook* is issued in December for the following year.

The Royal Horticultural Society

P O Box 313, 80 Vincent Square, London SW1P 2PE
☎ 0171 834 4333

CONTACT Membership Department
AIMS The encouragement and improvement of the science, art and practice of horticulture in all its branches
SUBSCRIPTIONS £25 single; £12 student; £16 associate; £7 enrolment fee
SERVICES Lectures; associated gardens; seed scheme; library; publications; advice; awards; shows; journal; special interest and regional groups; outings

The premier horticultural society in the country and probably the world. Membership has grown steadily in recent years and the society's activities have expanded correspondingly. As well as the extensive gardens at Wisley in Surrey, there are now also regional gardens at Rosemoor, Devon and Hyde Hall, Essex and a regional centre at Pershore in the West Midlands. Reciprocal arrangements also give full and student members admission to Ness Gardens, Cheshire; the Sir Harold Hillier Gardens and Arboretum, Hampshire; Brogdale and Yalding in Kent; Trebah and Trewithen in Cornwall; The Garden House in Devon; Forde Abbey in Dorset; Ryton Organic Garden in Warwickshire; the Harlow Carr Botanical Gardens, North Yorkshire; and the Kalmthout Arboretum in Belgium; as well as the National Trust's gardens at Hidcote Manor, Gloucestershire; Bodnant, Clwyd; Sheffield Park, East Sussex; and Nymans, West Sussex. From 22 March 1997 a further seven gardens will be open free to members: Audley End, Essex; Belsay Hall, Northumberland; Brodsworth Hall, South Yorkshire; Osborne House, Isle of Wight; Walmer Castle, Kent; Westonbirt Arboretum, Gloucestershire. There is a full range of courses, lectures and demonstrations at the RHS gardens and Pershore, and a wide variety of regional and London lectures each year. Members are admitted to these events at concessionary rates, and free of charge to most lectures: you should apply for tickets in writing. The show programme is formed around the so-called fortnightly shows in the RHS Halls in Westminster (see our calendar for dates). The halls are less full on Tuesday evenings and on Wednesdays. The RHS and specialist societies hold plant competitions at these shows, and members can bring along plants for exhibition or cultural awards. Schedules are available from the RHS. Members no longer receive free entrance to Chelsea, but they can buy tickets at reduced prices and the Tuesday and Wednesday of Chelsea week are reserved for members. Members are entitled to reduced price admission to the increasing number of shows which the RHS now runs, among them the Hampton Court Palace Flower Show, BBC Gardener's World Live, Scotland's National Gardening Show and the established shows at Malvern. The illustrated RHS journal *The Garden* is sent free to members every month. Long a journal of record, the magazine is now back on form with a mixture of society news, horticultural and botanical articles. Its sister title is *The New Plantsman*: aimed at the specialist, there is a separate subscription. A number of other publications are produced, and the society promotes a collection of gardening titles in association with commercial publishers. RHS members are entitled to technical advice from the society's experts: this service is accessible by post, at the society's own shows and a number of other major events which it attends, and in person at Wisley. Members may use and borrow from the Lindley Library in Vincent Square: its holdings are of world standing. A distribution of seed from the Wisley garden is made each year for a nominal charge. The new class of associate member coincides with changes which have been made to the membership privileges. Membership cards are no longer transferable, and the benefits now apply to the named holder only. Members can enrol up to three people who live at their address as associate members: they are entitled to all the normal benefits except free entry to those gardens which are not owned by the RHS; only one copy of the journal is sent to each address. There are some specialist sections (an additional subscription is payable) for Fruit, Lilies, and Rhododendrons and Camellias. Behind the scenes the RHS is involved in scientific and technical horticulture, including its regular trial programme. The trials can be viewed at Wisley (Portsmouth field). The society liaises with national and trade organisations in the interests of horticulture, and is increasingly active in the international arena too. Our calendar lists many events that are organised by the RHS. Up to date information along with precise details of how to book, is published monthly in *The Garden* (which non-members can buy from newsagents). A recorded information line (0171 649 1885) gives details of forthcoming flower shows for members and non-members. A new direct line has been established for membership and subscription enquiries: 0171 821 3000.

The Royal National Rose Society

The Gardens of the Rose, Chiswell Green, St Albans, Hertfordshire AL2 3NR

☎ 01727 850461   🖷 01727 850360

CONTACT   Reception
AIMS   To promote the love of roses
MEMBERSHIP   15,000
SUBSCRIPTIONS   £15 single; £20 joint; £7 student; £5 extra for Historic Roses Group
SERVICES   Lectures; associated gardens; library; publications; advice; awards; shows; journal; special interest and regional groups; outings

Founded in 1876. The society has its headquarters near St Albans: the Gardens of the Rose display over 1,700 different roses. Members enter free. The society also maintains 12 regional rose gardens. An illustrated quarterly journal *The Rose* gives news of the society and the rose world, and there are regular shows including the British Rose Festival at the Hampton Court Palace Flower Show. The society always has hundreds of new roses on trial for awards at St Albans: the trial fields can be visited. There is a full advisory service for members and regular pruning demonstrations which anyone can attend (1 & 2 March 1997). There are regional groups in Yorkshire and the North West, and special interest sections for exhibitors and rose breeders (The Amateur Rose Breeders Association). For an additional £5 RNRS members can join the Historic Roses Group, which organises its own programme of events and visits. The RNRS Rose 2000 Development will enormously expand the activities of the Society and its garden.

The Saintpaulia & Houseplant Society

33 Church Road, Newbury Park, Ilford, Essex IG2 7ET
☎ 0181 590 3710

CONTACT   Hon. Secretary
AIMS   To grow better and more beautiful houseplants, and to help the public to do the same
MEMBERSHIP   920
SUBSCRIPTIONS   £4 single; £5 joint (£1.50 extra for overseas)
SERVICES   Lectures; library; publications; advice; shows; journal; special interest and regional groups; outings; *Saintpaulia* leaf distribution

The society is affiliated to the Royal Horticultural Society, and holds regular Tuesday evening meetings at the RHS, usually to coincide with the Westminster shows. There are competitions at the meetings, and an annual show in the New Hall at the August show. Members receive the bulletin four times a year. The society arranges visits and also has three local groups with their own programmes. Members can borrow from the society's specialist library, and take part in the annual leaf distribution. The society has expanded quickly in recent years.

Sedum Society

173 Colchester Road, West Bergholt, Colchester, Essex CO6 3JY

CONTACT   Ron Mills
AIMS   To preserve the species and hybrids of *Sedum*
MEMBERSHIP   140
SUBSCRIPTIONS   £7.50 UK; £12.50 Europe; US$22 USA/ Canada; £15 other
SERVICES   Seed scheme; advice; journal; slide library

The Sedum Society aims to be an international vehicle for promoting the genus. Central to achieving its purpose are the cuttings exchange scheme and seed distribution scheme. Members receive a quarterly newsletter with articles on nomenclature, taxonomy, cytology, cultivation and the history of sedums, including such related genera as *Rhodiola*, *Rosularia* and *Sinocrassula*.

The Sempervivum Society

11 Wingle Tye Road, Burgess Hill, West Sussex RH15 9HR
☎ 01444 236848

CONTACT   Peter Mitchell

AIMS   The promotion and cultivation of sempervivums and allied plants
MEMBERSHIP   225
SUBSCRIPTIONS   £5 for three newsletters
SERVICES   Library; publications; advice; journal

The Sempervivum Society was founded by Peter Mitchell more than 25 years ago, and he is still the guiding spirit. The main benefit which members receive is the newsletters, which come out irregularly. The society also aims to put members, half of whom are overseas, in touch with each other.

The Tomato Growers Club
27 Meadowbrook, Old Oxted, Surrey RH8 9LT
☎ 01883 715242

CONTACT   Colin Simpson
AIMS   To collect and maintain a seed library of open pollinated tomatoes
MEMBERSHIP   1,000
SUBSCRIPTIONS   Nil, a minimum purchase of £10 seed or plants in first year only
SERVICES   Seed scheme; journal

The club exists to preserve worthwhile strains of tomato varieties which are available to members for trialling, currently about 500 are on offer. There is an annual newsletter and seed catalogue in December. Members can get help with disease problems.

Wild Flower Society
Woodpeckers, Hoe Lane, Abinger Hammer, Dorking, Surrey
CONTACT   Mrs Pat Verrall (Hon. Gen. Sec.)
MEMBERSHIP   800
SUBSCRIPTIONS   £8 single; £12 family
SERVICES   Lectures; publications; special interest and regional groups

The society aims to promote a greater knowledge of field botany, especially among the young. Members receive three copies of *The Wild Flower* magazine and a copy of *The Wild Flower Diary*. This is a printed list of some 1,000 species which members are encouraged to use to record the plants they find each year.

Regional Societies (UK)

Avon Gardens Trust
30 Hurle Crescent, Abbots Leigh, Bristol BS8 2SZ
☎ 0117 974 1033

CONTACT   Malcolm Douglas
MEMBERSHIP   150
SUBSCRIPTIONS   £7.50 single; £10 family
SERVICES   Lectures; publications; journal; outings

The trust works to conserve the county's gardens through monitoring planning applications and advising owners on surveys and restoration plans. The twice-yearly *Newsletter* is readable and informative. Garden visits and other events are staged for members throughout the year. Last year they published *Thomas Goldney's Garden* by P K Stembridge which is available from the Trust (£3.50 incl. p & p).

BBONT
3 Church Cowley Road, Rose Hill, Oxford OX4 3JR
☎ 01865 775476   [FAX] 01865 711301
CONTACT   Lou Burns
MEMBERSHIP   12,000
SUBSCRIPTIONS   £16 single; £24 joint
SERVICES   Lectures; publications; advice; journal; special interest and regional groups; outings

Berkshire, Buckinghamshire and Oxfordshire Naturalists Trust has over ninety reserves across the three counties, including Bowdown Woods, Little Linford Wood and the Warburg Reserve.

Bedfordshire & Cambridgeshire, Northamptonshire & Peterborough Wildlife Trust
Enterprise House, Maris Lane, Trumpington, Cambridge CB2 2LE
☎ 01223 846363   [FAX] 01223 846085
CONTACT   Sue Magee (Membership Secretary)
MEMBERSHIP   12,000
SUBSCRIPTIONS   £16 single; £20 family
SERVICES   Lectures; publications; advice; journal; special interest and regional groups; outings

Formed by an amalgamation of the Northamptonshire Wildlife Trust with the Wildlife Trust for Bedfordshire & Cambridgeshire. The trust has a large number of reserves under management, including Totternhoe Knolls, High Wood and Hayley Wood.

Botanical Society of Scotland
c/o Royal Botanic Garden, Edinburgh, Lothian EH3 5LR
☎ 0131 459 0446
CONTACT   Hon. Secretary
AIMS   To promote the study of plants and exchange botanical information
MEMBERSHIP   450
SUBSCRIPTIONS   £12 basic; £25 including scientific publications
SERVICES   Lectures; publications; journal; special interest and regional groups; outings

Founded in 1836: formerly the Botanical Society of Edinburgh. Based in Edinburgh, with regional branches in Scotland, the society includes amateur and professional botanists. It holds regular lectures, conferences and field meetings. Its publications include a newsletter and a scientific journal.

Brecknock Wildlife Trust
1st Floor Office, 2 The Struet, Brecon, Powys LD3 7LH
☎ 01874 625708
MEMBERSHIP   1100
SUBSCRIPTIONS   Adults £12.50; Family £17
SERVICES   Lectures; publications; advice; journal; special interest and regional groups; outings

The trust looks after some 20 nature reserves in central Wales. The Autumn 1996 edition of the Trust's journal *Breconshire Wildlife & Naturalist* carried a major feature on wildlife gardening.

Cheshire Wildlife Trust
Grebe House, Reaseheath, Nantwich, Cheshire CW5 6DA
☎ 01270 610180   [FAX] 01270 610430
CONTACT Colin Storey
SUBSCRIPTIONS £16 single; £18 joint
SERVICES Lectures; publications; advice; journal; special
interest and regional groups; outings; ecological consultancy

Formerly the Cheshire Conservation Trust, the trust manages
over 40 reserves including Red Rocks Marsh and Swettenham
Meadows.

Cleveland Wildlife Trust
Bellamy House, Kirkleatham Old Hall, Kirkleatham, Redcar,
North Yorkshire TS10 5NW
☎ 01642 480033   [FAX] 01642 480401
CONTACT Director
MEMBERSHIP 2,500
SUBSCRIPTIONS £14 single; £18 joint
SERVICES Lectures; publications; advice; journal; outings

Formed in 1979 to protect wildlife in the county. They have
13 reserves in hand, including the deciduous woodland of
Saltburn Gill.

Cornwall Gardens Society
Top Meadow, St Germans Road, Callington, Cornwall
PL17 7EN
CONTACT Hon. General Secretary
AIMS To foster a love and knowledge of plants and
gardening
MEMBERSHIP 1,400
SUBSCRIPTIONS £10 single
SERVICES Lectures; publications; advice; shows; journal;
outings; garden openings

A scaled-down model of the RHS, with an excellent magazine,
good bulletins and a famous show at the end of March. They
also organise a garden opening scheme.

Cornwall Gardens Trust
Tredarvah Vean, Penzance, Cornwall TR18 4SU
☎ 01736 63473
CONTACT Membership Secretary
AIMS To preserve, enhance and recreate the gardens of
Cornwall
MEMBERSHIP 220
SUBSCRIPTIONS £10 single; £12.50 family
SERVICES Lectures; associated gardens; publications; advice;
awards; journal; outings

Formed in 1988, the Trust carries out conservation and preservation work, and organises special events and garden visits
for its members. It is putting much of its efforts at the moment
into assembling an archive of Cornwall garden records. The
annual *Journal* is a quality publication. A joint conference
with the Devon Gardens Trust is planned for later this year.

Cornwall Wildlife Trust
Five Acres, Allet, Truro, Cornwall TR4 9DJ
☎ 01872 273939   [FAX] 01872 225476
CONTACT Trevor Edwards

MEMBERSHIP 6,000
SUBSCRIPTIONS £15 single; £1 each for additional family
members
SERVICES Lectures; publications; advice; journal; outings

The trust has over 40 nature reserves covering 3000 acres.
Good sites for botanists include Peters Wood and
Ventongimps Moor.

Cumbria Wildlife Trust
Brockhole, Windermere, Cumbria LA23 1LJ
☎ 015394 48280   [FAX] 015394 48281
CONTACT The Secretary
MEMBERSHIP 3,500
SUBSCRIPTIONS Adults £15; Family £20
SERVICES Lectures; publications; journal; special interest
and regional groups; outings

Cumbria is the second largest county in England and has more
sites of national and international importance than any other.
The Trust looks after about 30 nature reserves and has a small
wildlife garden at Brockhole.

Derbyshire Wildlife Trust
Elvaston Castle, Derby DE72 3EP
☎ 01332 756610
CONTACT The Development Officer
MEMBERSHIP 4,000
SUBSCRIPTIONS £15 single; £20 family
SERVICES Lectures; publications; advice; journal; outings

The trust administers 49 reserves, including Cromford Canal
and Spring Wood. Volunteers collect seeds of wild trees and
shrubs. The trust has a series of open gardens in the summer.
It also publishes an excellent small book on *Wildlife Gardening* (£5.60 incl. p & p) which covers all aspects of the
subject, including how to design habitat gardens, make ponds,
and choose suitable plants for wildlife.

Devon Gardens Trust
Lucombe House, Devon County Council, County Hall,
Exeter, Devon EX2 4QW
☎ 01392 382252
CONTACT The Secretary
AIMS To preserve the gardens of Devon
MEMBERSHIP 400
SUBSCRIPTIONS £8 single; £12 joint (1996)
SERVICES Lectures; advice; journal; outings

A successful gardens trust, which surveys Devon gardens, and
works to protect their future. Members benefit from lectures,
special garden visits and seminars, and are kept informed of the
trust's research and conservation work.

Devon Wildlife Trust
Shirehampton House, 35-37 St David's Hill, Exeter, Devon
EX4 4DA
☎ 01392 79244   [FAX] 01392 433221
CONTACT Emma Davis
MEMBERSHIP 5,000
SUBSCRIPTIONS £15 Adults; £28 Family
SERVICES Lectures; publications; advice; journal; special
interest and regional groups; outings

The trust looks after more than 30 nature reserves covering over 2,500 acres.

Dorset Perennial Group

Ivy Cottage, Aller Lane, Ansty, Dorchester, Dorset DT2 7PX

☎ 01258 880053

CONTACT Hon. Secretary
MEMBERSHIP 390
SUBSCRIPTIONS £1
SERVICES Lectures; seed scheme; library; journal; outings

Dorset-based society which used to be the local Hardy Plant Society group: they are no longer connected with the HPS. The programme includes garden visits and talks.

Dorset Wildlife Trust

Brooklands Farm, Forston, Dorchester, Dorset DT2 7AA
☎ 01305 264620   [FAX] 01305 251120
CONTACT Conservation Officer
MEMBERSHIP 6,300
SUBSCRIPTIONS £12.50 single; £6 each additional person
SERVICES Lectures; publications; advice; journal; special interest and regional groups; outings

The trust looks after nearly 30 nature reserves including Fontmell Down and Kingcombe Meadows. A Wildlife Garden is being established at Preston near Weymouth.

Durham Wildlife Trust

Low Barns, Witton-le-Wear, Bishop Auckland, Co Durham DL14 0AG
☎ 01388 488728   [FAX] 01388 488529
MEMBERSHIP 3,500
SUBSCRIPTIONS Adults £15; Family £18
SERVICES Lectures; publications; advice; journal; special interest and regional groups; outings

The Trust manages some 27 nature reserves throughout the county and publishes its *Guide to Reserves*. There are eight local groups.

Dyfed Wildlife Trust

7 Market Street, Haverfordwest, Dyfed SA61 1NF
☎ 01437 765462   [FAX] 01437 767163
CONTACT Margaret Brooks
MEMBERSHIP 3,600
SUBSCRIPTIONS £15 single; £20 family
SERVICES Lectures; publications; advice; journal; outings

The trust, the second oldest in the country, manages 67 reserves including the acid heath of Dowrog Common. The Welsh Wildlife Centre is in Dyfed, at Cilgerran near Cardigan. The 200-acre reserve includes meadows, a reedbed, woodland and fresh and salt-water marsh.

Essex Wildlife Trust

Fingringhoe Wick Nature Reserve, South Green Road, Fingringhoe, Colchester, Essex CO5 7DN
☎ & [FAX] 01206 729678
CONTACT Gene Clifton
MEMBERSHIP 13,000
SUBSCRIPTIONS £17 single; £21 joint

SERVICES Lectures; associated gardens; publications; advice; journal; special interest and regional groups; outings

The trust manages over 80 reserves and has five conservation centres. Its reserves include the Danbury complex and Fingringhoe Wick. The trust also sells organic compost and wood chips and gives wildlife gardening advice.

Federation of Edinburgh & District Allotments & Gardens

2 South House Avenue, Edinburgh EH17 8EA
☎ 0131 664 1601

CONTACT The Secretary
AIMS To promote the interests of allotment and garden associations in Edinburgh
MEMBERSHIP 25 sites
SUBSCRIPTIONS £20 per site
SERVICES Seed scheme; advice; shows; journal; discounts on garden supplies

The Federation of Edinburgh & District Allotments and Gardens Associations represents about 1,300 individuals on 25 sites. Its main efforts recently have been directed at improving the management and facilities on council-run sites, and at making allotments part of the city's leisure provisions. A newsletter is circulated about three times a year and members can obtain seed through the federation. The annual flower and vegetable show is held on the last Saturday in August. Informal advice is available through other members, and they are planning to extend the range of membership services offered.

Friends of Brogdale

The Brogdale Horticultural Trust, Brogdale Farm, Faversham, Kent ME13 8XZ
☎ 01795 535286   [FAX] 01795 531710
AIMS Fruit research and conservation
MEMBERSHIP 1,500
SUBSCRIPTIONS £15 ordinary; £25 joint
SERVICES Lectures; advice; journal; grafting service

The Brogdale Experimental Horticultural Station was bought from the government by the Brogdale Trust in 1991 to safeguard its work. It carries out commercial research and trialling, and maintains exceptional reference collections of fruit varieties, including over 2,300 different apples. Friends receive free entry to the site, priority booking for events, and access to a Friday afternoon information line. There is also a quarterly newsletter.

Friends of the Royal Botanic Garden Edinburgh

The Royal Botanic Garden, Inverleith Row, Edinburgh EH3 5LR
CONTACT The Secretary
AIMS To support the garden and raise funds for its activities
SUBSCRIPTIONS £15 single; £20 family
SERVICES Lectures; associated gardens; journal

The Friends raise funds for and promote the work of the Royal Botanic Garden Edinburgh. There is no admission charge to this great garden, but friends have free entry to the three regional gardens (Logan, Dawyck and Younger). There is a regular newsletter, and a series of lectures and other social events.

Friends of the Royal Botanic Gardens Kew

Cambridge Cottage, Kew Green, Kew, Richmond, Surrey TW9 3AB
☎ 0181 332 5922   FAX 0181 332 5901
CONTACT   Dianne Owens
AIMS   Fund raising for Royal Botanic Gardens, Kew
MEMBERSHIP   17,000
SUBSCRIPTIONS   £30 single; £40 family; concessions for OAPs & students
SERVICES   Lectures; associated gardens; shows; journal; discounts in Kew and Wakehurst Place shops; guest passes

The Friends of the Royal Botanic Gardens, Kew is a relatively new organisation: its aim is to raise funds for Kew's work, hence the highish subscription. That said, free entry to Kew and Wakehurst Place is a valuable benefit for regular visitors, and many will enjoy helping the scientific and conservation work which is carried out from Kew. The Friends' journal *Kew*, published three times a year, is colourful and outstandingly good. Lectures are given monthly throughout the year, and there is an annual plant auction in the autumn. Friends receive discounts on shop purchases, and six complimentary day passes to the gardens for their guests.

Glamorgan Wildlife Trust

Fountain Road, Tondu, Bridgend, Mid Glamorgan CF32 0EH
☎ 01656 724100
MEMBERSHIP   1,000
SUBSCRIPTIONS   £15 joint
SERVICES   Lectures; publications; advice; journal; special interest and regional groups; outings

The Glamorgan Wildlife Trust administers 47 reserves from woodland to coastal sites, including reserves on the Gower peninsula and Melincourt Falls.

Gloucestershire Gardens & Landscape Trust

Room 3, The Annexe, The Old Memorial Hospital, Sheep Street, Cirencester, Gloucestershire GL7 1QW
☎ 01285 643066
CONTACT   Elisabeth Ridler (Chief Executive)
AIMS   To conserve gardens and landscape
MEMBERSHIP   170
SUBSCRIPTIONS   £12 single; £20 joint
SERVICES   Lectures; advice; journal; outings

The trust exists to protect valuable gardens and landscapes. As well as conservation work it has a programme of lectures, garden visits and other events for members. One of the most dynamic of the county garden trusts.

Gwent Wildlife Trust

16 White Swan Court, Monmouth, Gwent NP5 3NY
☎ 01600 715501   FAX 01600 715832
CONTACT   John Harper
MEMBERSHIP   1,500

SUBSCRIPTIONS   £15 single; £18 joint
SERVICES   Lectures; publications; advice; journal; outings

The trust was started in 1963 and now has over thirty reserves including Magor Marsh, its first purchase, and Cleddon Shoots. Local groups offer a comprehensive programme of members' events. Members receive the quarterly magazine *Wild about Gwent.*

Hampshire Gardens Trust

Jermyns House, Jermyns Lane, Ampfield, Romsey, Hampshire SO51 0QA
☎ 01794 367752 (mornings)   FAX 01794 368520
CONTACT   The Secretary
AIMS   To care for Hampshire's gardens and parks
MEMBERSHIP   450
SUBSCRIPTIONS   £10 single; £15 joint
SERVICES   Lectures; library; advice; journal; outings; research into Hampshire's historic gardens and landscapes

The first of the county gardens trusts, formed with help from Hampshire County Council in 1984, and in every way the model still for all other such trusts. The trust is active in conservation and education work, and has an excellent programme of events for members.

Herefordshire Nature Trust

25 Castle Street, Hereford HR1 2NW
☎ 01432 356872
MEMBERSHIP   1,400
SUBSCRIPTIONS   £12 single; £15 joint
SERVICES   Publications; advice; journal; special interest and regional groups; outings

The trust manages over 40 reserves in the county, including those at Great Doward and the woods at Lea and Pagets.

Herts & Middlesex Wildlife Trust

Grebe House, St Michael's Street, St Albans, Hertfordshire AL3 4SN
☎ 01727 858901   FAX 01727 854542
MEMBERSHIP   7,000
SUBSCRIPTIONS   £15 single; £20 joint
SERVICES   Lectures; publications; advice; journal; outings

The trust looks after some 44 reserves including Old Park Wood and the old chalk downland of Therfield Heath. It has an active programme of events for members in both counties.

Isle of Wight Gardens Trust

Cassies, Billingham, Newport, Isle of Wight PO30 3HD
CONTACT   Membership Secretary
SUBSCRIPTIONS   £5 individual; £7.50 joint
SERVICES   Lectures; journal; outings

The trust helps to record the island's parks and gardens and to assist in their conservation. Talks and garden visits are staged for members, and they can also get involved in conservation work.

Kent Trust for Nature Conservation

Tyland Barn, Sandling, Maidstone, Kent ME14 3BD
☎ 01622 662012   FAX 01622 671390
CONTACT   Public Relations Officer

MEMBERSHIP 10,000
SUBSCRIPTIONS £19.50 single; £24.50 family
SERVICES Lectures; publications; advice; journal; special interest and regional groups; outings

The Kent Trust looks after 45 reserves which cover some 5,000 acres, including Yockletts Bank, Sladden Wood, Park Gate Down and Hothfield Common.

Lancashire Wildlife Trust

Cuerdon Park Wildlife Centre, Shady Lane, Bamber Bridge, Preston, Lancashire PR5 6AU
☎ 01772 324129   📠 01772 628849
MEMBERSHIP 3,500
SUBSCRIPTIONS £15 Adults; £20 Family
SERVICES Lectures; advice; journal; special interest and regional groups; outings

The Trust manages some 33 nature reserves containing over 2,000 acres of wildlife habitat. It has been particularly active in the campaign to protect limestone pavement.

Leicestershire and Rutland Trust for Nature Conservation

1 West Street, Leicester LE1 6UU
☎ 0116 2553904
CONTACT John Coleman
SUBSCRIPTIONS £15 single; £5 each additional person
SERVICES Lectures; publications; advice; journal; special interest and regional groups; outings

The trust manages 37 reserves including Cribb's Meadow and the woodland at Prior's Coppice.

The Lincolnshire Trust for Nature Conservation

Banovallum House, Manor House Street, Horncastle, Lincolnshire LN9 5HF
☎ 01507 526667   📠 01507 525732
CONTACT Mary Edwards (Promotions Officer)
MEMBERSHIP 9,700
SUBSCRIPTIONS £17 single; £23 joint
SERVICES Lectures; publications; advice; journal; special interest and regional groups; outings

The trust (one of the RSNC wildlife trusts) was founded in 1948 and manages over 100 sites including Little Scrubbs Meadow in the Wolds and the dunes at Saltfleetby-Thed-dlethorpe. Send a stamped addressed envelope for details of events for 1997: several wildlife gardens are opening for the trust this year.

London Historic Parks & Gardens Trust

Duck Island Cottage, St James's Park, London SW1
☎ 0171 839 3969
CONTACT Diana Eyre (Secretary)
MEMBERSHIP 300
SUBSCRIPTIONS £12 adults; £6 concessions
SERVICES Lectures; publications; advice; journal; outings

Founded in 1994, to encourage greater protection for the capital's parks and gardens, the society has already completed a survey of 1200 sites throughout Greater London and embarked upon an educational programme. Members receive a quarterly newsletter. The upmarket journal *The London Gardener* follows an 18th-century format: its articles are scholarly and enjoyable. A series of excellent winter lectures at the Linnean Society seems set to become a regular feature.

Marcher Apple Network

Orchard Barn, Ocle Pychard, Hereford, Hereford & Worcester HR1 3RB
☎ 01432 820304
CONTACT John Aldridge
AIMS To rescue and preserve old cultivars of apples
SUBSCRIPTIONS Adults £2; Children 50p
SERVICES Lectures; associated gardens; advice; journal; outings

This society was formed by a group of people living in the Welsh Marches with the aim of rescuing old apple cultivars from extinction. They identify old trees, propagate them and establish new orchards to preserve them. They also organise events to celebrate and encourage the revival of interest in traditional fruit varieties.

Montgomeryshire Wildlife Trust

Collot House, 20 Severn Street, Welshpool, Powys SY21 7AD
☎ 01938 555654   📠 01938 556161
CONTACT Susan Roach (Membership Secretary)
MEMBERSHIP 1,000
SUBSCRIPTIONS £15 single; £18 joint
SERVICES Lectures; publications; advice; journal; special interest and regional groups; outings

The trust has 12 reserves under management including Llyn Mawr, Roundton Hill and Dyfnant Meadows.

National Bonsai Society

30 Dunbar Road, Southport PR8 4RD
☎ 01704 564271
CONTACT Tom Ball
AIMS To promote, educate and further interest in bonsai throughout the UK
MEMBERSHIP 300
SUBSCRIPTIONS £8.50 single; £12 joint
SERVICES Lectures; library; publications; advice; awards; shows; journal

Despite its grand title, which dates from the time when it was almost the only bonsai society in the country, the National Bonsai Society operates to all purposes as a local club. It meets on the third Tuesday of every month (except in December) at 7.45 pm in the Harry Livingstone Hall, Princes Street, Southport. Visitors are welcome at these meetings and pots and containers may be bought at a discount.

Norfolk Wildlife Trust

72 Cathedral Close, Norwich NR1 4DF
☎ 01603 625540   📠 01603 650593
MEMBERSHIP 15,000
SUBSCRIPTIONS £18 individual; £24 joint

SERVICES   Lectures; publications; advice; journal; special interest and regional groups; outings

Founded in 1927, this is the oldest county nature trust. It maintains 38 reserves across the county including East Wretham Heath in the Breckland and the pingos (glacial craters) of Thompsons Heath. The latest acquisition, the Ebb-Flow Marshes near Horning, is a site for the rare crested buckler fern.

North of England Horticultural Society
4A South Park Road, Harrogate, North Yorkshire
HG1 5QU
☎ & ＦＡＸ 01423 561049

CONTACT   A Ravenscroft (Show Director)
MEMBERSHIP   65
SUBSCRIPTIONS   £18

This is the company which organises the Harrogate shows in spring and autumn. Members are entitled to entry to both shows.

The North of England Rose, Carnation and Sweet Pea Society
94 Hedgehope Road, Westerhope, Newcastle upon Tyne
NE5 4LA
☎ 0191 271 0971

CONTACT   General Secretary
AIMS   To further interest in the three named flowers, and gardening in general
MEMBERSHIP   300
SUBSCRIPTIONS   £2.50
SERVICES   Lectures; library; publications; advice; awards; shows; journal; special interest and regional groups; outings

The society – Rosecarpe, for short – was founded in 1938. Its interests extend beyond its three main flowers. Members can attend the regular meetings, usually on the first Monday of most months in the Civic Centre, Gateshead, for lectures or demonstrations. The four shows play an important part in the society's life, notably the Gateshead Spring and Summer Flower Shows organised in association with the Metropolitan Borough Council, and two Rosecarpe Flower Shows. Trophies are presented at all shows. An annual yearbook is produced, and members can also borrow the society's books and videos, and draw on the advice of the society's experts. Rosecarpe attends other shows and horticultural college events, and is affiliated to the national Rose, Carnation, Sweet Pea and Daffodil societies.

North Wales Wildlife Trust
376 High Street, Bangor, Gwynedd LL57 1YE
☎ 01248 351541

CONTACT   Morgan Parry
SUBSCRIPTIONS   £15 single; £20 joint
SERVICES   Lectures; publications; advice; journal; outings

The trust has 34 reserves in North Wales including mixed woodland at Ddol Uchaf and the dunes of Morfa Bychan.

Northern Horticultural Society
Harlow Carr Botanical Gardens, Crag Lane, Harrogate, North Yorkshire HG3 1QB
☎ 01423 565418   ＦＡＸ 01423 530663

CONTACT   Barry Nuttall
AIMS   To promote the science and practice of horticulture
MEMBERSHIP   11,000
SUBSCRIPTIONS   £20
SERVICES   Lectures; associated gardens; seed scheme; library; publications; advice; awards; journal; special interest and regional groups

Founded in 1947, the Northern Horticultural Society is a focus for gardeners in the north of England. Members receive free entrance to the Harlow Carr Botanical Gardens which are the society's headquarters. The annual programme includes a series of day and longer courses throughout the year at the garden. The garden also trials vegetable and flower varieties specifically for their suitability to northerly climates, and visitors can assess the new and unreleased varieties which are undergoing trial. An illustrated journal, *The Northern Gardener*, appears four times a year. Members can also take advantage of the seed scheme, the reference and lending library, and an advisory service (in writing only). There are special interest sections for alpines, bonsai, bulbs, delphiniums, ferns, rhododendrons and roses. A reciprocal arrangement with the Royal Horticultural Society allows free access to some of the RHS gardens. Some of the society's events are listed in our calendar.

Northern Ireland Daffodil Group
77 Ballygowan Road, Hillsborough, Co Down, Northern Ireland BT26 6EQ

CONTACT   Richard McCaw (Secretary)
MEMBERSHIP   100
SUBSCRIPTIONS   £7.50 for 1 year; £18 for 3 years
SERVICES   Lectures; shows; journal; annual bulb auction

Daffodils are a major interest in Northern Ireland. The NIDG has many affiliated societies, who exhibit at the City of Belfast Spring Show (19 & 20 April this year). It also issues two newsletters a year to all members.

Northumberland Wildlife Trust
The Garden House, St Nicholas Park, Jubilee Road, Newcastle upon Tyne
☎ 0191 284 6884   ＦＡＸ 0191 284 6794

CONTACT   Sallyanne Flemons
MEMBERSHIP   5,000
SUBSCRIPTIONS   Adults £15; Family £22
SERVICES   Lectures; publications; advice; journal; special interest and regional groups; outings

The Trust looks after a number of nature reserves in the county and is building a wildlife garden at St Nicholas Park in Newcastle.

Nottinghamshire Historic Gardens Trust
1 Sandfield Road, Toton, Nottingham NG9 6LT
☎ 0115 981 9911 Ext 350

CONTACT   James Beard (Secretary)
SUBSCRIPTIONS   £10 single; £18 family
SERVICES   Lectures; advice; journal; outings

Launched in 1994 to care for parks and garden landscapes in the county of Nottingham. The trust keeps a register of gardens and assists in their surveying and recording. Members enjoy a programme of lectures, garden visits and other events.

Nottinghamshire Wildlife Trust
310 Sneinton Dale, Nottingham NG3 7DN
☎ 0115 958 8242   📠 0115 924 3175
CONTACT   John Ellis
MEMBERSHIP   2,500
SUBSCRIPTIONS   £15 single; £20 joint
SERVICES   Lectures; publications; advice; journal; special interest and regional groups; outings

Formed in 1963. The trust looks after 50 reserves including Tresswell Wood and Eakring Meadows.

Radnorshire Wildlife Trust
Warwick House, High Street, Llandrindod Wells, Powys LD1 6AG
☎ & 📠 01597 823298
CONTACT   Alison Davies
MEMBERSHIP   800
SUBSCRIPTIONS   £12 single; £15 Joint; £8 unwaged
SERVICES   Lectures; publications; advice; journal; special interest and regional groups; outings

In this sparsely populated county the trust manages reserves which include Bailey Einon and the newly acquired Pentrosfa Mire. There is an Information Centre and shop in Llandrindod Wells.

The Rose Society of Northern Ireland
10 Eastleigh Drive, Belfast, Northern Ireland BT4 3DX
CONTACT   R Brooks (Secretary)
SUBSCRIPTIONS   £5
SERVICES   Lectures; advice; shows; journal; outings

The Royal Caledonian Horticultural Society
28 Silverknowes Southway, Edinburgh EH4 5PX
☎ 0131 336 5488   📠 0131 336 1847
CONTACT   Hon. Secretary
AIMS   The improvement of horticulture in all its branches
MEMBERSHIP   700
SUBSCRIPTIONS   £10 single; £12.50 family
SERVICES   Lectures; library; publications; advice; awards; shows; journal; special interest and regional groups; outings

The Royal Caledonian Horticultural Society was founded in 1809. It publishes an annual *Journal*, and a newsletter *Preview* three times a year. There is a regular lecture programme, fortnightly from October to April, whilst in the summer months a series of garden visits takes place. The society's president is the custodian of their library. There is an annual spring show and an AGM, at which the society presents three prestigious awards: the Queen Elizabeth the Queen Mother Medal, the biennial Neill Prize to a botanist, and the Scottish Horticultural Medal, the number of whose recipients is limited to 50.

The Scottish Allotments and Gardens Society
14/1 Hoseasons Gardens, Edinburgh, Lothian EH4 7HQ
CONTACT   The Secretary
AIMS   To promote the interests of allotment holders
MEMBERSHIP   780
SUBSCRIPTIONS   £1 individuals; sites £1 per plot
SERVICES   Seed scheme; advice; awards; journal; grants for gardeners

Long-established organisation which promotes the interests of allotment holders and societies. You can either join as an individual or as an entire site, in which case your subscription depends on the number of plots. There is a bi-monthly newsletter, and a discount seed scheme. SAGS also receives funds to assist needy gardeners with the upkeep of their plots.

Scottish National Chrysanthemum & Dahlia Society
41 Mosspark Road, Coatbridge, Strathclyde ML5 2HG
☎ 01236 434042
CONTACT   Joe Gartshore (Secretary)
MEMBERSHIP   240
SUBSCRIPTIONS   £5 individual; £3 over-65s
SERVICES   Lectures; advice; awards; shows; journal

The annual show is held in Stirling early in September each year. Members may also attend the monthly meetings held in Glasgow on the last Thursday in every month from October to April (except December). The Society's annual is called *Impact* and contains articles on every aspect of growing, breeding and exhibiting. Some 40 local societies are affiliated to the Society: they are entitled to receive lists of approved judges and to award the SNC&DS Silver Medal and Certificate of Merit at their shows.

Scottish National Sweet Pea, Rose & Carnation Society
72 West George Street, Coatbridge, Lanarkshire ML5 2DD
☎ 01236 42916
CONTACT   The Secretary
AIMS   To encourage the growing and showing of the named flowers in Scotland
MEMBERSHIP   100
SUBSCRIPTIONS   £3
SERVICES   Associated gardens; advice; awards; shows; journal

The Scottish National Sweet Pea, Rose & Carnation Society produces an annual Year Book in November, and holds a show in August. Some 28 trophies are awarded annually. Sweet Peas and roses are trialled in Glasgow, at Bellahouston Park and Tollcross Park respectively. There is an informal advisory service.

Scottish Orchid Society
164 Eskhill, Penicuik, Lothian EH26 8DQ
☎ 01968 677075
CONTACT   Alan Benson (Secretary)
MEMBERSHIP   200
SUBSCRIPTIONS   £10 single; £15 joint

SERVICES   Advice; shows; journal; special interest and regional groups

Founded in 1958, the society helped to host the World Orchid Conference in 1993: the Royal Mail issued a set of stamps to commemorate the occasion. The society's own activities take place through its regional groups in Aberdeen, Tayside, Edinburgh, Glasgow and Perth. Growing and showing are important to members.

Scottish Rhododendron Society

Stron Ailne, Colintraive, Argyll, Strathclyde PA22 3AS
☎ 01700 841285

CONTACT   Hon. Secretary
AIMS   To encourage the cultivation of Rhododendrons
MEMBERSHIP   265
SUBSCRIPTIONS   £19.50
SERVICES   Lectures; associated gardens; seed scheme; publications; advice; awards; shows; journal; special interest and regional groups; outings; automatic membership of the American Rhododendron Society

The Scottish Rhododendron Society was founded just over ten years ago to provide a forum at which Scottish growers could meet and exhibit. Many of the best Scottish rhododendron gardens belong, but about a third of the members live outside Scotland. A newsletter is produced three times a year, and there are at least two meetings annually. Their national show, at a different venue each year, is probably the top show in Britain for rhododendrons. Members can purchase a range of books at reduced prices, seek specialist advice through the secretary, and gain free admission to Arduaine Gardens in Strathclyde. The society is also a chapter of the excellent American Rhododendron Society, and members automatically belong directly to the American society too. This gives them the scholarly quarterly journal, access to all the other ARS chapters (from Denmark and Holland to India), and the opportunity to raise seeds from the ARS seed bank. Last year the Society hosted the ARS Annual Convention at Oban with great aplomb.

Scottish Rock Garden Club

P O Box 14063, Edinburgh, Lothian EH10 4YE

CONTACT   Sandy Leven (Publicity Manager)
AIMS   To promote the cultivation of alpine and peat garden plants
MEMBERSHIP   4,500
SUBSCRIPTIONS   £10 single; £12 family; £13 overseas
SERVICES   Lectures; seed scheme; library; publications; advice; awards; shows: organised by ten of the local groups; journal: twice yearly; special interest and regional groups; slide library; annual conference

Founded in 1933 this is now the largest horticultural society in Scotland, with overseas members in thirty-eight countries. There are regional groups in Aberdeen, Ayr, Belford, Dundee, Edinburgh, Glasgow, Inverness, Kircudbright, Moray, Newcastle, Oban, Penrith, Perth, Renfrew, Stirling, St Andrews and Thurso. Each local group is responsible for organising a programme of events including lectures, and some members also open their gardens. The society journal, The Rock Garden, appears twice a year: it is a well-produced and authoritative magazine which covers rock garden plants both in cultivation and in the wild. The seed exchange scheme is among the best of its kind.

Scottish Wildlife Trust

Cramond House, Cramond Glebe Road, Edinburgh EH4 6NS
☎ 0131 312 7765   📠 0131 312 8705

CONTACT   Development Officer
MEMBERSHIP   15,000
SUBSCRIPTIONS   £15 single; £25 family
SERVICES   Lectures; publications; advice; journal; special interest and regional groups; outings

Formed in 1964, the national wildlife conservation body in Scotland is growing steadily. They have over 100 reserves under management including Red Moss of Balerno, Rahoy Hills and Seaton Cliffs. The junior wing, Scottish Wildlife Watch, is particularly active.

Shropshire Wildlife Trust

167 Frankwell, Shrewsbury, Shropshire SY3 8LG
☎ 01743 241691   📠 01743 366671
MEMBERSHIP   2,000
SUBSCRIPTIONS   Adults £16; Family £20
SERVICES   Lectures; publications; advice; journal; special interest and regional groups; outings

The Trust manages a number of nature reserves: the latest, at Melverley Farm, was opened last year.

Somerset Gardens Trust

St Peter's Vicarage, 62 Eastwick Road, Taunton, Somerset TA2 7HD

CONTACT   Membership Secretary
SUBSCRIPTIONS   £10 single; £15 joint
SERVICES   Lectures; journal; outings

Works to conserve and protect Somerset's parks and gardens. As well as conservation and education work, talks and garden visits are arranged.

Somerset Wildlife Trust

Fyne Court, Broomfield, Bridgwater, Somerset TA5 2EQ
☎ 01823 451587   📠 01823 451671

CONTACT   Stephanie Leland
MEMBERSHIP   10,000
SUBSCRIPTIONS   £12 single; £2 for additional members
SERVICES   Lectures; associated gardens; library; publications; advice; shows; journal; special interest and regional groups; outings; wildflower gardening group

The trust now has more than 60 reserves under management, including Greater Westhay in the Somerset Levels. There is a wildflower gardening group.

Staffordshire Gardens & Parks Trust

c/o Planning Department, South Staffordshire District Council, Wolverhampton Road, Codsall, Wolverhampton WV8 1PX

CONTACT   The Secretary

AIMS   To record and encourage the conservation of parks and gardens
MEMBERSHIP 100
SUBSCRIPTIONS £7.50 single; £10 joint
SERVICES Lectures; advice; journal; outings; training; exhibitions

The trust aims to record the county's most valuable gardens and work for their conservation. Members can assist in this task, and take part in study visits. Meetings and lectures are held in Stafford.

Suffolk Wildlife Trust
Brooke House, The Green, Ashbocking, Ipswich, Suffolk IP6 9JY
☎ 01473 890089   FAX 01473 890165
CONTACT Antonia Coppen
MEMBERSHIP 12,000+
SUBSCRIPTIONS £16 single; £17 joint
SERVICES Publications; advice; journal; outings; education

One of the largest of the county wildlife trusts, with some 75 reserves. A current concern is the effect of ground water levels on many of these reserves.

Surrey Gardens Trust
c/o Planning Department, Surrey County Council, County Hall, Kingston on Thames, Surrey KT1 2DT
☎ 0181 541 9419
CONTACT The Secretary
MEMBERSHIP 220
SUBSCRIPTIONS £10 single; £15 joint
SERVICES Lectures; advice; journal; outings; research; restoration work

Members receive a twice-yearly newsletter, and there is a programme of lectures and garden visits. Those wanting more active involvement may train as recorders, carry out archive research and assist on garden improvement projects. The trust is making a study of Jekyll gardens in the county.

Surrey Wildlife Trust
School Lane, Pirbright, Woking, Surrey GU24 0JN
☎ 01483 488055   FAX 01483 486505
CONTACT Martin Newman (Director)
MEMBERSHIP 5,000
SUBSCRIPTIONS £18 single; £24 household
SERVICES Lectures; publications; advice; journal; special interest and regional groups; outings

The Surrey Wildlife Trust looks after 24 nature reserves including Nower Wood and the Graeme Hendrey Wood.

Sussex Wildlife Trust
Woods Mill, Henfield, West Sussex BN5 9SD
☎ 01273 492630   FAX 01273 494500
CONTACT The Secretary
MEMBERSHIP 9,000
SUBSCRIPTIONS £16 single; £20 joint
SERVICES Lectures; publications; advice; journal; special interest and regional groups; outings

Formed in 1961, the trust now looks after about 40 separate nature reserves including The Mens, over 7,000 acres in total. Among the attractions at the Woods Mill headquarters is managed hazel coppice. There is an active junior section called 'Watch in Sussex'.

Ulster Wildlife Trust
Ulster Wildlife Centre, 3 New Line, Crosgar, Co. Down BT30 9EP
☎ 01396 830282   FAX 01396 830888
CONTACT Paul Watterson
MEMBERSHIP 2,500
SUBSCRIPTIONS Adults £15; Family £20
SERVICES Lectures; publications; advice; journal; special interest and regional groups; outings

Founded in 1977, the Trust manages some 20 major nature reserves in Northern Ireland. It is particularly active in educational efforts to improve children's awareness of the importance of nature conservation. There is a visitor centre at Crossgar.

Urban Wildlife Trust, The West Midlands Wildlife Campaign
Unit 310 Jubilee Trades Centre, 130 Pershore Street, Birmingham B5 6ND
☎ 0121 666 7474   FAX 0121 622 6443
CONTACT Wendy Burnett
MEMBERSHIP 900
SUBSCRIPTIONS £15 household; £8 concessions
SERVICES Publications; advice; journal; wildflower nursery

Urban group which encourages and advises on the formation of wildlife areas. They have an environmental centre at Winson Green, and a wildflower nursery.

Wakefield & North of England Tulip Society
70 Wrenthorpe Lane, Wrenthorpe, Wakefield, West Yorkshire WF2 0PT
CONTACT Hon. Secretary
AIMS   The growing, breeding and showing of English florists' tulips
MEMBERSHIP 300
SUBSCRIPTIONS £4; £5 family
SERVICES Seed scheme; publications; awards; shows; journal; outings

This long-established society, devoted to florists' tulips, publishes an annual journal and holds two shows each year. Other events include formal and informal meetings and garden visits. Surplus bulbs are distributed in October. *The English Tulip and its History* is available from the society, as are slide lectures.

Warwickshire Wildlife Trust
Brandon Marsh Nature Centre, Brandon Lane, Coventry CV3 3GW
☎ 01203 302912   FAX 01203 639556
CONTACT Andy Tasker
MEMBERSHIP 4,500

SUBSCRIPTIONS £16 single; £20 family

SERVICES Lectures; publications; advice; journal; special interest and regional groups; outings; environmental consultancy

Formerly the Warwickshire Nature Conservation Trust. They manage over 50 reserves including Ryton Woods and Ufton Fields.

Welsh Historic Gardens Trust

Coed-y-Ffynnon, Lampeter Valley, Narberth SA67 8UJ

☎ & 🆗 01834 833196

CONTACT Trust Secretary

AIMS To assist in and initiate conservation of gardens and designed landscapes in Wales

MEMBERSHIP 550

SUBSCRIPTIONS £10 single; £15 family

SERVICES Lectures; advice; journal; special interest and regional groups; outings

Through the trust office and local branches this organisation assists and initiates the conservation of important gardens, parks and landscapes. Members can become involved in research, surveying and other conservation work which is carried out at branch level. The Newsletter is informed and informing, while the Trust is also planning a Conference this year on the restoration and conservation of historic gardens which will be aimed at Conservation Officers in the new local authorities.

Wildlife Trust for Bristol, Bath and Avon

Bristol Wildlife Centre, Jacob Wells Road, Bristol BS8 1DR

☎ 0117 926 5490   🆗 0117 929 7273

MEMBERSHIP 3,500

SUBSCRIPTIONS £15 single; £5 for every extra member

SERVICES Lectures; publications; advice; journal; outings

Formed in 1980, this is the new name for the Avon Wildlife Trust. It manages some 30 nature reserves including Brown's Folly above Bathford.

Wiltshire Gardens Trust

Treglisson, Crowe Lane, Freshford, Bath, Somerset BA3 6EB

CONTACT Hon. Secretary

MEMBERSHIP 540

SUBSCRIPTIONS £10 single; £15 joint

SERVICES Lectures; seed scheme; library; publications; journal; special interest and regional groups; outings

This group doubles as the county garden trust and (for an additional subscription) as the Wiltshire branch of the NCCPG. Their excellent programme of events includes lectures and garden visits. A four-day visit to nurseries and gardens in Belgium is planned this year.

Wiltshire Wildlife Trust

18–19 High Street, Devizes, Wiltshire SN10 1AT

☎ 01380 725670   🆗 01380 729017

CONTACT Marketing Officer

MEMBERSHIP 6,500

SUBSCRIPTIONS £16 single; £20 joint

SERVICES Lectures; publications; advice; journal; outings

Formerly the Wiltshire Trust for Nature Conservation. They look after nearly 40 reserves including a fritillary meadow at Upper Waterhay (late April).

Yorkshire Wildlife Trust

10 Toft Green, York, North Yorkshire YO1 1JT

☎ 01904 659570   🆗 01904 613467

MEMBERSHIP 8,000

SUBSCRIPTIONS £17 single; £25 joint (1996)

SERVICES Lectures; publications; advice; journal; special interest and regional groups; outings

Founded in 1946, and now managing over 80 nature reserves covering 6,000 acres in Yorkshire and North Humberside. Sites of interest to botanists include Grass Wood and Spurn Head.

6

International & Overseas Societies

AAT Garten- und Teichfreunde Luxemburgs

44 rue de Bois, L-4421 Soleuvre, Luxemburg
CONTACT Henri Regenwetter (President)
SUBSCRIPTIONS Lfr 400
SERVICES Lectures; seed scheme; publications; advice; shows; journal; special interest and regional groups; outings

The Luxemburg horticultural society: British expats working for the EU will find themselves at home here.

African Violet Society of America Inc

P O Box 3609, Beaumont, TX 77704, U.S.A.
☎ 00 1 409 839 4725
CONTACT Cindy Chatelain
MEMBERSHIP 11,000
SUBSCRIPTIONS US$18 US; US$20.50 abroad
SERVICES Lectures; library; publications; advice; shows; journal; special interest and regional groups; plant sales

This thriving society, which celebrated its 50th anniversary last year, opens the world of African Violets to all home-owners and gardeners. It also acts as the International Registration Authority for *Saintpaulia* and publishes the *Master Variety List of African Violets* (available on paper or on disk) which lists all registered cultivars since 1949 – tens of thousands of them! Members receive the bi-monthly magazine *African Violet*: several of the advertisers offer more than 600 varieties for sale.

American Bamboo Society

750 Krumkill Road, Albany, NY 12203, U.S.A.
☎ 00 1 518 458 7618   FAX 00 1 518 458 7625
CONTACT Michael Bartholomew (Newsletter Editor)
MEMBERSHIP 1,050
SUBSCRIPTIONS US$30
SERVICES Publications; advice; journal; special interest and regional groups; outings; rare plant auction

The American Bamboo Society is for everyone who is interested in the cultivation, appreciation and use of 'woody grasses' – amateurs, aesthetes, horticulturists, botanists, conservationists and craftsmen. Members receive a bi-monthly newsletter and a scientific annual. There are seven chapters, all in the US.

American Begonia Society

157 Monument Road, Rio Dell, CA 95562-1617, U.S.A.
CONTACT John Ingles Jr (Membership Secretary)
SUBSCRIPTIONS US$17 US; US$27 overseas surface; US$37 air mail
SERVICES Seed scheme; library; advice; shows; journal; special interest and regional groups

The ABS has 52 chapters in the US and good working relations with other national *Begonia* societies. The society's bi-monthly publication *The Begonian* has articles on cultivation, taxonomy, latest scientific research and propagation. The seed bank offers seed of species and cultivars by mail.

American Bonsai Society

P O Box 1136, Puyallup, WA 98371-1136, U.S.A.
☎ 00 1 206 841 8992
CONTACT Patricia De Groot
MEMBERSHIP 1,425
SUBSCRIPTIONS US$24 single; US$35 airmail
SERVICES Library; shows; journal; special interest and regional groups; big annual convention

A co-ordinating body for bonsai enthusiasts all through the USA. Members receive the quarterly *Bonsai* journal: the society also publishes a directory of North American bonsai societies.

American Camellia Society

One Massee Lane, Fort Valley, GA 31030, U.S.A.
☎ 00 1 912 967 2358   FAX 00 1 912 967 2083
CONTACT Helen Bryan

MEMBERSHIP 3,800
SUBSCRIPTIONS US$25 single; US$27.50 joint. Abroad: US$28 single; $31 joint
SERVICES Lectures; associated gardens; library; publications; advice; awards; shows; journal; special interest and regional groups

The American Camellia Society is based in Massee Lane Gardens. Members have free admission to the gardens and greenhouses. They run workshops and courses. There is an extensive library, gift shop and gallery. The Society celebrated its 50th anniversary last year. This year's annual Convention will be at Atlanta, Georgia, from 19 to 22 February.

American Conifer Society

827 Brooks Street, Ann Arbor, MI 48103-3161, U.S.A.

CONTACT Charlene & Wade Harris
AIMS To encourage the development, conservation and propagation of dwarf and unusual conifers
MEMBERSHIP 1,200
SUBSCRIPTIONS US$25 single/joint; US$32 overseas
SERVICES Lectures; seed scheme; advice; shows; journal; special interest and regional groups; outings; plant sales

A thriving international society – the best in its field – with an excellent Bulletin and a long calendar of events and tours. Members may attend regional meetings throughout the USA and Canada. The emphasis is upon conifers that are dwarf or unusual.

American Daffodil Society Inc

1686 Grey Fox Trails, Milford, Ohio 45150, U.S.A.
☎ 00 1 513 248 9137   [FAX] 00 1 513 248 0898

CONTACT Mary Lou Gripshover (Executive Director)
MEMBERSHIP 1,400
SUBSCRIPTIONS US$20
SERVICES Publications; awards; shows; journal

The society runs about 40 shows throughout the USA. Membership includes a subscription to the quarterly The Daffodil Journal, a substantial publication with good articles. The National Show & Annual Convention will be at Jackson, Mississippi, on 13 – 15 March 1997.

American Dianthus Society

P O Box 22232, Santa Fe, NM 87502-2232, U.S.A.
☎ 00 1 505 438 7038

CONTACT Rand Lee
MEMBERSHIP 250
SUBSCRIPTIONS US$15 US; US$18 Canada/Mexico; US$20 overseas
SERVICES Seed scheme; journal; slide library

The society aims to encourage Americans to grow more pinks and to preserve heirloom varieties. The society's quarterly magazine The Gilliflower Times claims to be the only publication in the world devoted to Dianthus. Rand Lee is the author of The Dianthus Encyclopedia.

American Fuchsia Society

County Fair Building, 9th Avenue & Lincoln Way, San Francisco, CA 94122, U.S.A.

CONTACT Philip Scherer (Corresponding Secretary)

MEMBERSHIP 1,100
SUBSCRIPTIONS US$17; US$30 airmail
SERVICES Lectures; library; publications; journal; special interest and regional groups; outings

This West Coast society has 24 branches in California and Oregon. The bi-monthly Bulletin offers a range of articles on cultivation, new varieties and local shows. Members may also take part in a cuttings exchange.

American Gloxinia & Gesneriad Society

c/o Horticulture Society of New York, 128 W. 58th Street, New York, NY 10019, U.S.A.

CONTACT Membership Secretary
SUBSCRIPTIONS US$20 US; US$25 abroad

American Hemerocallis Society

1454 Rebel Drive, Jackson, Miss. 39211, U.S.A.

CONTACT Executive Secretary
MEMBERSHIP 9,600
SUBSCRIPTIONS US$18 US; US$25 Canada & overseas
SERVICES Associated gardens; seed scheme; publications; awards; shows; journal; special interest and regional groups

The Society's quarterly publication The Daylily Journal is both colourful and informative: it has articles on cultivation, hybridisation, new cultivars and forthcoming events. There are dozens of advertisements by nurseries in the States, where Hemerocallis are a major horticultural interest.

American Hepatica Society

195 North Avenue, Westport, CT 06880, USA

CONTACT Paul Held
MEMBERSHIP 50
SERVICES Seed scheme; advice; journal

A new society for Hepatica enthusiasts around the world.

American Hibiscus Society

P O Box 321540, Cocoa Beach, FL 32932-1540, U.S.A.
☎ 00 1 407 783 2576   [FAX] 00 1 407 783 2576

CONTACT Executive Secretary
MEMBERSHIP 2,000
SERVICES Lectures; seed scheme; publications; advice; awards; shows; journal

The society was founded in 1950 and its members come from 49 countries. It now has 20 chapters, almost all in Texas, Florida and the Virgin Islands. Hybridisation and the raising of new varieties are an important part of the society's activities: members have access to the society's seed bank and the quarterly magazine is called The Seed Pod. The annual convention will take place 19 – 22 June 1997 at Fort Lauderdale in Florida.

American Hosta Society

7802 NE 63rd Street, Vancouver, WA 98662, U.S.A.

CONTACT Robyn Duback
MEMBERSHIP 2,700
SUBSCRIPTIONS US$19 single; US$25 Canada; US$35 overseas

SERVICES Lectures; associated gardens; publications; advice; shows; journal; special interest and regional groups; outings; registration of new cultivars; sales

The society brings together the activities of *Hosta* enthusiasts throughout North America. Nearly 50 local and state *Hosta* societies are amalgamated into six US regions, with a seventh for Canada. The *Hosta Yearbook* has details of all the societies' activities and a complete membership list. The quarterly *Hosta Journal* carries good articles on botany, classification, cultivation and new varieties from correspondents in the US and abroad. The society also publishes a source list of some 30 US nurseries offering quality *Hosta* plants and acts as the international registrar for new varieties: some 62 in 1994 alone.

American Iris Society
8426 Vinevalley Drive, Sun Valley, CA 91352, U.S.A.

CONTACT Jeanne Clay Plank (Secretary)
MEMBERSHIP 7,000
SERVICES Lectures; associated gardens; seed scheme; library; publications; advice; awards; shows; journal; special interest and regional groups

American Orchid Society
6000 South Olive Avenue, West Palm Beach, FL 33405-4199, U.S.A.
☎ 00 1 561 585 8666   [FAX] 00 1 561 585 0654

CONTACT Lee Coke (Executive Director)
MEMBERSHIP 30,000+
SUBSCRIPTIONS US$36 US; US$42 abroad
SERVICES Lectures; library; publications; advice; awards; shows; journal; special interest and regional groups

A large (and growing) society with members all over the world and more than 500 affiliated societies, the AOS celebrated its 75th birthday in 1996. Members receive the monthly *AOS Bulletin*, a substantial publication with over 100 pages, many in full colour: the advertisements alone are an education. The *Awards Quarterly* and the society's scientific review *Lindleyana* are published separately.

American Penstemon Society
1569 South Holland Court, Lakewood, CO 80232, U.S.A.

CONTACT Ann Bartlett (Membership Secretary)
MEMBERSHIP 450
SUBSCRIPTIONS US$15
SERVICES Seed scheme; library; journal

Members have access to the Seed Exchange (15 free packets a year) as well as receiving the quarterly *Bulletin of the American Penstemon Society* which has articles on collecting, cultivation and hybridisation.

American Peony Society
250 Interlachen Road, Hopkins, Minn. 55343, U.S.A.

SUBSCRIPTIONS US$7.50
SERVICES Publications; journal

The Canadian Peony Society is a subsection of the APS.

American Primrose, Primula & Auricula Society
41801 S.W. Burgasky Rd., Gaston, OR 97119, U.S.A.

CONTACT Addaline Robinson (Treasurer)
MEMBERSHIP 750
SUBSCRIPTIONS US$21
SERVICES Seed scheme; library; shows; journal; special interest and regional groups

The society brings together everyone in North America who is interested in the genus *Primula*, and gives equal attention to auriculas, candelabras, alpine species and garden varieties. The society has eight local chapters, including British Columbia and Alaska, but the greatest concentration of members is in Washington state. Members receive the society's quarterly *The Primrose*. The national show will be on 5 & 6 April this year.

American Rhododendron Society
P O Box 1380, Gloucester, VA 23061, U.S.A.
☎ 00 1 804 693 4433
CONTACT Executive Director
MEMBERSHIP 6,000

Represented in UK by the Scottish Rhododendron Society.

North American Rock Garden Society
P O Box 67, Millwood, NY 10546, U.S.A.
☎ 00 1 914 762 2948

CONTACT Executive secretary
MEMBERSHIP 4,500
SUBSCRIPTIONS US$25 or £17
SERVICES Lectures; associated gardens; seed scheme; library; publications; awards; journal; special interest and regional groups

The society offers an excellent quarterly journal and a long seed list: as a result, it has many members in the UK.

American Rose Society
P O Box 30,000, 8877 Jefferson Paige Road, Shreveport, LA 71130-0030, U.S.A.
☎ 00 1 318 938 5402   [FAX] 00 1 318 938 5405

CONTACT Membership Secretary
MEMBERSHIP 24,000
SUBSCRIPTIONS US$32 US; US$40 foreign
SERVICES Lectures; associated gardens; library; publications; advice; awards; shows; journal; special interest and regional groups; outings

The world's largest rose society, founded in 1892 and based in the 118-acre Gardens of the American Rose Center. It has nearly 400 affiliated societies and a steady membership. Traditionally concerned with modern roses, it has recently made a bid to lead the heritage rose movement. The monthly *American Rose Magazine* and the yearly *American Rose Annual* are quality publications.

Amici della Passiflora
Via Roma 11/B, I-26010 Ripalta Cremasca (CR), Italy
☎ & [FAX] 00 39 373 68441

CONTACT Dr Maurizio Vecchia

AIMS   To exchange Passion Flower seeds and plants

A small association for amateur botanists and owner-gardeners who are interested in the genus, which flourishes particularly well in a Mediterranean climate.

Arbeitskreis für Mammillarienfreunde

Schusterfeld 12c, D-32139 Spenge, Germany

SUBSCRIPTIONS   DM 70, plus DM 20 joining fee

SERVICES   Seed scheme; shows; journal; special interest and regional groups; plant exchange

The German society for the study of mammillarias has a quarterly newsletter.

Arche Noah

Margarethenstraße, A-3500 Krems, Austria

The Austrian society for the conservation of old fruit and vegetable cultivars.

ARIDES

24, rue des Saulzaies, F-44800 St Herblain, France

CONTACT   Joël Lodé

SUBSCRIPTIONS   FF 150

SERVICES   Seed scheme; publications; shows; journal; special interest and regional groups

ARIDES is an acronym for one of those long names so beloved of French societies: it stands for *Association des recherches et d'informations sur les déserts et les succulents*. The main benefits to foreign members are the excellent seed scheme (some 1,500 items) and its publications, including the quarterly *Cactus Aventures* and the *Encyclopédie des cactées et succulents*.

Asociación Española de la Rosa

Rosaleda Ramon Ortiz, Parque del Oeste, E-28008 Madrid, Spain

☎ 00 34 91 542 0430

SUBSCRIPTIONS   Ptas 4,000

SERVICES   Lectures; shows; journal

Asociatiei Amicii Rozelor din România

RO-3400 Cluj 1, C.P. 86, Romania

☎ 00 40 95 14 71 38

CONTACT   Dr Stefan Wagner (President)

MEMBERSHIP   1,000

SUBSCRIPTIONS   US$8

SERVICES   Lectures; shows; journal; outings; pruning days

The Romanian rose society is based in Cluj and has grown fast in recent years. Members receive the bulletin *Rosarium* twice a year and have access to the society's library. The society is an active member of the World Federation of Rose Societies.

Association Française Culture et Protection des Orchidées

23 rue d'Alsace, F-92300 Levallois Perret, France

CONTACT   Mme N Rigal (Secretary)

MEMBERSHIP   160

SERVICES   Publications; journal

A small society for amateur enthusiasts. The Society's journal *Orchidées: Culture et Protection* is quarterly and has

excellent articles, well illustrated with line drawings and colour photographs.

Association Française pour la Conservation des Espèces Végétales

Mairie de Mulhouse, 2, rue Pierre Curie, F-68200 Mulhouse, France

☎ 00 33 3 89 32 59 67   [FAX] 00 33 3 89 32 59 09

CONTACT   Gabriel Alziar (Secretary)

AIMS   Plant Conservation in France

SUBSCRIPTIONS   FF 150 single; FF 300 associations

SERVICES   Lectures; publications; journal; conferences

The AFCEV is an umbrella organisation for all conservation groups in France: the closest UK parallel is BGCI. It has over 100 institutional members, with about 20 individual members as associates. Scientific stations, botanic gardens, nature conservation groups, regional trusts and specialist plant societies are among its members. The magazine *Floraison* has articles on a wide variety of botanical and horticultural conservation activities. Its *Guide des Jardins Botaniques de France* is one of the best guides to French gardens. The AFCEV also publishes the proceedings of its annual conferences: last year's, at Nice in October, concentrated on the problem of invasive exotic introductions.

Association Française des Amateurs de Bégonias

11, rue Myrha, F-75018 Paris, France

☎ 00 33 1 42 62 84 89

MEMBERSHIP   170

SUBSCRIPTIONS   FF 150

SERVICES   Lectures; advice; shows; journal; outings

Founded in 1988 as a forum for both amateurs and professionals and much concerned with the vast number of *Begonia* species grown in collections throughout France. There is a quarterly newsletter and members participate in lectures and shows in every region.

Association of Australian Begonia Societies

79 Chuter Street, Stafford, Queensland 4053, Australia

CONTACT   Peter Henderson (Chairman)

An umbrella organisation for: The Begonia Society of Western Australia Inc, 34 Waterton Way, Cooloongup WA 6168; The New South Wales Begonia Society Inc, 2/283 Jersey Road, Woollabra 2025, NSW; The Queensland Begonia Society, 24 Lexham Street, Bald Hills, Queensland 4036; The South Australian Begonia Society, P O Box 116, Stirling 5152 South Australia; The Victorian Begonia Society Inc, 74 Railway Place, Macedon 3440 Victoria. UK begoniaphiles generally rate this and the American Begonia Society as the two foreign societies they enjoy belonging to most.

The Association of Societies for Growing Australian Plants

P O Box 38, Woodford, NSW 2778, Australia

☎ & [FAX] 00 61 47 58 66 37

CONTACT   Membership Officer

AIMS To promote the establishment and breeding of Australian native plants

MEMBERSHIP 10,000

SUBSCRIPTIONS A$26 ordinary; A$20 concessional; A$44 overseas

SERVICES Lectures; associated gardens; seed scheme; publications; advice; shows; journal; special interest and regional groups; outings

This is the address of the NSW branch: there are branches in Canberra (41 Jamieson Crescent, Kambah, ACT 2902), Queensland (PO Box 586, Fortitude Valley, Qld 4006), South Australia (5 Marram Terrace, Largs North, SA 5016), Tasmania (GPO Box 1353P, Hobart, Tasmania 7001), Victoria (17 Craig Court, Heathmont, Vic. 3135), and Western Australia (PO Box 64, Nedlands, WA 6009). Each is supported in turn by a network of district groups. All members of the Association receive the highly illustrated quarterly journal *Australian Plants* and each society publishes a periodic newsletter or bulletin of state news and events. The major benefit for overseas members is the opportunity to acquire seeds of wild plants from all over Australia.

Association pour la Sauvegarde du Patrimoine Fruitier

4, avenue de la Résistance, F-30270 Saint Jean-du-Gard, France

☎ 00 33 4 66 85 33 37   FAX 00 33 4 66 86 19 66

AIMS Preserving the heritage fruit of France

MEMBERSHIP 570

SUBSCRIPTIONS FF 150

SERVICES Lectures; publications; advice; shows; journal; outings

A conservation group devoted to fruit – everything from apples and pears to olives and figs. The quarterly bulletin *Fruits Oubliés* is subtitled *Revue de Pomologie Vivante* and *Sauve qui Pomme*. English-speakers may address enquiries directly to: Brian Wills, 345 Chemin de Tavion, 30140 Anduze (Tel: 00 33 4 66 61 73 08; Fax: 00 33 4 66 61 72 63).

Associazione Italiana Amatori Piante Succulente

Viale Piave 68, I-20060 Pessano (MI), Italy

☎ 00 39 2 9504404

CONTACT Mariangela Costanzo

MEMBERSHIP 2,350

SUBSCRIPTIONS Lit. 40,000

SERVICES Publications; shows; journal; special interest and regional groups

Founded in 1979, the society has branches in every province of Italy. Its quarterly review *Piante Riviste* has many articles or abstracts in English, and also publishes a yearly *Annuario*.

Associazione Italiana della Fuchsia

Piazza Cavour, 15, I-27025 Gambolò (PV), Italy

☎ 00 39 381 938763

CONTACT Agnese Mandrino (Secretary)

MEMBERSHIP 250

SUBSCRIPTIONS Lit. 25,000

SERVICES Lectures; advice; shows; journal

Founded in 1992 to increase appreciation of fuchsias in Italy. Members receive a quarterly bulletin and can attend talks and shows, which are mostly in the north of Italy. They also run a cuttings exchange. The society will take part in the *Tre giorni per il giardino* at Masino in May.

Associazione Italiana della Rosa

Roseto Niso Fumagalli, Villa Reale, I-20052 Monza (MI), Italy

☎ 00 39 39 320994   FAX 00 39 39 2086237

CONTACT Sgra Luciana Lupi Timini

SUBSCRIPTIONS Lit. 50,000

SERVICES Lectures; associated gardens; publications; advice; journal; outings

The Italian rose society runs a trials ground at Monza, in the gardens of the old Sforza castle. Last year it hosted the European Regional Conference of the World Federation of Rose Societies.

Associazione Italiana di Orchidologia

c/o Dipartimento di Biologia Vegetale, Università degli Studi 'La Sapienza', Piazzale A Moro, 5 – 00185 Roma, Italy

☎ 00 39 6 49912818

CONTACT Dr Sabine Riess (President)

MEMBERSHIP 250

SUBSCRIPTIONS Lit. 50,000

SERVICES Lectures; seed scheme; publications; shows; journal; special interest and regional groups

The Italian orchid society publishes two editions a year of its review: it is written in both English and Italian. There are many local lectures, shows and other events, but the national conference will be at Viterbo 3 – 5 October.

Associazione Italiana Rose Antiche e Storiche

Via Trancia, 4, I-00100 Roma, Italy

The Italian heritage rose society.

Associazione per la Diffusione di Piante per Amatori

c/o Orto Botanico del Comune di Lucca, Via del Giardino Botanico, 14, I-55100 Lucca, Italy

☎ & FAX 00 39 583 442160

CONTACT The Secretary

MEMBERSHIP 600

SUBSCRIPTIONS Lit. 30,000

SERVICES Lectures; associated gardens; seed scheme; advice; journal; outings

A society for amateur plantsmen, based at the botanic garden in Lucca, where there are fortnightly lectures throughout the winter months. Members receive two copies of the Newsletter a year: the spring edition is a substantial list of seed donated by botanic gardens and other donors; the autumn edition comprises articles, advice, book reviews, plant wants etc. There is an active programme of visits and excursions.

Auckland Lily Society
34 Maungakiekie Avenue, Greenlane, Auckland 1005, New Zealand
☎ 00 64 9 520 2826

CONTACT   Betty Gross (Secretary)
MEMBERSHIP   175
SERVICES   Lectures; seed scheme; library; shows; journal

An active lily society, whose members are involved in showing and breeding as well as running a good programme of events.

Australian Garden History Society
c/o Royal Botanic Gardens, Birdwood Avenue, South Yarra, Victoria 3141, Australia
☎ 00 61 39 650 5043

CONTACT   Jackie Courmadias (Executive Officer)
MEMBERSHIP   1,300
SUBSCRIPTIONS   A$38
SERVICES   Lectures; library; publications; journal; special interest and regional groups; outings

This vigorous society has one or two branches in each of the states, each of which has a programme of events for its members. Its primary aim is to promote interest in garden history: much of its work is concentrated upon the 19th and early 20th century. The Society's journal *Australian Garden History* is an impressive work which combines scholarship with readability. It encompasses horticulture, landscape design, architecture and botanical history. There are six issues a year.

Australian Lilium Society
P O Box 208, Monbulk, Victoria 3793, Australia
☎ 00 61 3 9763 6832   FAX 00 61 3 9753 1999

CONTACT   Robyn Miller (Hon. Sec.)
MEMBERSHIP   600
SUBSCRIPTIONS   A$16 single; A$24 double; A$28 overseas
SERVICES   Lectures; seed scheme; library; shows; journal; outings; bulb sales

An active society, based in Melbourne, with separate shows in January for trumpet varieties and oriental lilies as well as a general show. There are monthly lectures and general meetings throughout the year and the International Lily Conference will be held in Tasmania this year. The seed lists (two every year) contain some interesting Australian-raised hybrids.

Azalea Society of America
P O Box 34536, West Bethesda, MD 20827-0536, U.S.A.

CONTACT   Membership Chairman
AIMS   Promote knowledge of and interest in Azaleas
MEMBERSHIP   900
SUBSCRIPTIONS   US$25
SERVICES   Advice; journal; special interest and regional groups

Established in 1977, the Society is spread over nine chapters, mainly in the old Confederate states where azaleas are such a feature of gardens. The Society is concerned with conservation and actively seeks out old azalea cultivars for propagation and research.

Begonia Werkgroep Nederland
9 Gaelstraat, NL-2291 SG Wagengingen, The Netherlands
CONTACT   Beatrice Van der Laan (President)

Belgische Orchideënvereniging
O L Vrouwestraat 8, B-2070 Ekeren/Antwerp, Belgium
The Belgian orchid society.

Bermuda Rose Society
P O Box PG 162, Paget PG BX, Bermuda
☎ 00 1 809 296 0416

CONTACT   Jennie Watlington (President)
MEMBERSHIP   100
SUBSCRIPTIONS   US$15
SERVICES   Associated gardens; shows; journal

Members are involved in the identification and conservation of old roses, particularly the old tea roses that grow well in Bermuda's climate. Members are expected to attend meetings or resign from the society, so no foreign members are permitted.

Blue Mountain Rhododendron Society of New South Wales
15 Warrigal Street, Blackheath 2785, NSW, Australia
CONTACT   Norman Campbell (Supervisor)
SUBSCRIPTIONS   A$5 single; A$10 family
SERVICES   Lectures; associated gardens; journal

Bonsai Clubs International
7026 North Lake Drive, Fox Point, WI 53217-3636, U.S.A.
AIMS   To foster an appreciation and knowledge of Bonsai
MEMBERSHIP   20,000
SUBSCRIPTIONS   US$32
SERVICES   Lectures; library; shows; journal; special interest and regional groups

Bonsai Klubas Vilnius
Tilto 19-21, 2001 Vilnius, Lithuania
CONTACT   Darius Armonas (President)
AIMS   To promote the art of Bonsai in Lithuania
MEMBERSHIP   50
SUBSCRIPTIONS   10 litas annual fee; 15 litas joining fee
SERVICES   Lectures; exhibitions

The club was founded in 1994: the Bonsai tradition is new in Lithuania but has taken root quickly. Meetings are held every second Wednesday and there are two annual shows in Vilnius. No newsletter yet, but the Club gets good publicity in the national and gardening press and would appreciate closer contacts with bonsai societies and experts in western Europe.

Botanical Society of South Africa
Kirstenbosch, Claremont, Cape Town 7735, South Africa
☎ 00 27 797 2090   FAX 00 27 797 2376

CONTACT   Diana Peters
AIMS   Conservation, cultivation, study and use of native southern African plants
MEMBERSHIP   23,000
SUBSCRIPTIONS   R53 single; R72 family (both overseas rates)

SERVICES Lectures; associated gardens; seed scheme; publications; outings

Based at Kirstenbosch in Cape Province, the society has for many years been very successful in spreading information about the rich native flora of South Africa. Members have free entry to all the many regional gardens which it runs throughout the republic, as well as Kirstenbosch itself. The chief benefit to overseas members is the generous annual allocation of seed of native Cape species. The Society's exhibits at Chelsea and Hampton Court have for many years been one of the sensa-tions of the Chelsea Flower Show and, latterly, of the Hamp-ton Court Flower Show too.

Cactus & Succulent Society of America
P O Box 3010, Santa Barbara, CA 93130, U.S.A.

CONTACT Louise Lippold
MEMBERSHIP 3,700
SUBSCRIPTIONS US$30 US; US$35 overseas
SERVICES Lectures; seed scheme; library; advice; shows; journal; special interest and regional groups; outings

The leading society in its field, with a good number of members from Europe and many affiliated societies all over North America. All members receive the impressive bi-monthly *Cactus and Succulent Journal*. The society also publishes a scientific journal *Haseltonia*.

Canadian Begonia Society
70 Enfield Avenue, Toronto, Ontario M8W 1T9, Canada

CONTACT Miree Lex (President)

Canadian Chrysanthemum & Dahlia Society
140 Centennial Road, Scarborough, Ontario M1C 1Z5, Canada

CONTACT Roy Fox (Secretary)
MEMBERSHIP 100
SUBSCRIPTIONS C$12 home members; C$15 USA & overseas
SERVICES Lectures; shows; journal

This Toronto-based society was founded in 1959 and has grown steadily since then. Monthly meetings throughout the year alternate between dahlias and dendranthemas and culmi-nate in four shows in September/October.

Canadian Gladiolus Society
189 Trudeau Drive, Bowmanville, Ontario L1C 1B9, Canada
☎ 00 1 905 697 2284

CONTACT Heidi Haines (Secretary)

Canadian Rose Society
c/o 10 Fairfax Crescent, Scarborough, Ontario M1L 1Z8, Canada
☎ 00 1 416 757 8809   FAX 00 1 416 757 4796

CONTACT Paul & Anne Graber
AIMS Enjoyment of the rose, the 'Queen of Flowers'
MEMBERSHIP 900
SUBSCRIPTIONS C$21 single; C$23 family; C$30 overseas
SERVICES Lectures; associated gardens; library; advice; shows; journal

One of the world's oldest rose societies, founded in 1913, and particularly active in Ontario and Quebec. Members have free access to the Canadian National Rose Show and the demonstration gardens. *The Canadian Rose Annual* is an authoritative publication which regularly carries detailed assessments by the society's members of the newer roses and their performance in Canadian growing conditions.

Colorado Water Garden Society
528 S. Alcott, Denver, CO 80219, U.S.A.
☎ 00 1 303 922 9559

CONTACT Mary Mirgon
AIMS To encourage greater use of water in the landscape
MEMBERSHIP 150
SUBSCRIPTIONS US$10 single; US$15 family
SERVICES Lectures; journal; outings; plant sales

Water gardens and water plants are the driving forces behind this small state-based society.

Conservatoire National des Plantes Médicinales, Aromatiques et Industrielles
route de Nemours, F-91490 Milly-la-Forêt, France

CONTACT Claude Genevelle
SUBSCRIPTIONS FF 125
SERVICES Seed scheme; shows; journal

Les Croqueurs de Pommes
Maison des Associations, B P 702 – Belfort Cedex, France

CONTACT The Secretary
AIMS Conservation of old fruit varieties
MEMBERSHIP 2,800
SUBSCRIPTIONS FF 110 home members; FF 130 abroad
SERVICES Lectures; shows; journal; tastings

The 'Apple Munchers' society is subtitled 'Association Na-tionale des Amateurs Bénévoles pour la Sauvegarde des Variétés Fruitières en Voie de Disparition.' It aims to protect regional and local fruit varieties and prevent their disappear-ance and in this, and in raising public awareness, it has been very successful since its foundation in 1978. It teaches mem-bers how to graft and take cuttings. Publicity, education, shows, publications, research, advice and relations with similar organisations abroad are all part of its remit. In addition to its 2,800 members, it has 25 affiliated regional groups throughout France. There are over 4,000 varieties of apple alone in France.

Cryptanthus Society
3508 Seltzer, Plano, TX 75023, U.S.A
☎ 00 1 214 596 7074

CONTACT Carole Richtmyer
MEMBERSHIP 350
SUBSCRIPTIONS US$10 US; US$15 elsewhere
SERVICES Shows; journal

Cryptanthus are a genus of bromeliads from eastern Brazil. There are hundreds of cultivars with beautiful leaf markings. The society has a biennial plant show and sale. The slim quarterly *Journal* has news from members and mouth-watering illustrations.

Cucurbit Network
P O Box 560483, Miami, FL 33256, U.S.A.
MEMBERSHIP   250
SUBSCRIPTIONS   US$10 single
SERVICES   Seed scheme; publications

Dedicated to the conservation and cultivation of Cucurbitaceae throughout the world, the Network publishes a twice-yearly newsletter and mans a web site:
http://probe.nalusda.gov:00/otherdocs/cgc/tcn.

Cymbidium Club of Australia Inc
1 Cliff Avenue, Peakhurst, NSW 2210, Australia
☎ 00 61 2 5335148
CONTACT   Helen Schultz (Secretary)

An umbrella organisation for the state-based Cymbidium Clubs in Australia. These include The Cymbidium Club of South Australia Inc, The Cymbidium Club of Western Australia and The Cymbidium Orchid Society of Victoria Inc.

Cymbidium Society of America Inc
P O Box 2244, Orange, CA 92669, U.S.A.
CONTACT   Membership Secretary
MEMBERSHIP   1,300
SERVICES   Awards; journal; special interest and regional groups

Czech Rosa Club
Livornská 440, 109 00 Praha 10, Czech Republic
☎ 00 42 2 2417 2736   📠 00 42 2 2417 2024
CONTACT   Dr Josef Thomas
MEMBERSHIP   800
SERVICES   Lectures; journal; special interest and regional groups

Dahlia Society of India
4, Thakur Ramkrishna Park Row, Calcutta 700025, India
CONTACT   K Samadder (Hon. Sec.)
MEMBERSHIP   270
SUBSCRIPTIONS   Rs.10 or US$15
SERVICES   Lectures; publications; advice; shows; journal

The Society holds monthly discussion classes in Calcutta: its shows are mainly in January and February. The Society encourages the raising of new varieties and, jointly with the Indian National Horticultural Board, has published a useful handbook *Dahlia Breeding.*

Dansk Bonsai Selskab
Hvidkildev'nget 7, DK-5230 Odense M., Denmark
CONTACT   Aase Wilberg
MEMBERSHIP   600
SUBSCRIPTIONS   Dkr 75
SERVICES   Shows; journal; special interest and regional groups

The Danish bonsai society has a bi-monthly magazine.

Dansk Fuchsia Klub
Solbakken 17, DK-4400 Kalundborg, Denmark
CONTACT   Bendte Hartwig
MEMBERSHIP   1,300

SUBSCRIPTIONS   Dkr 135
SERVICES   Library; shows; journal; special interest and regional groups

The Danish fuchsia club publishes five editions a year of its magazine *Fuchsia.*

Dansk Iris- og Liljeklub
Klovermaksvej 9, Hylke, DK-8660 Skanderborg, Denmark
☎ 00 45 86 53 84 48
CONTACT   Lars Pedersen (Secretary)
AIMS   Promoting the cultivation of irises and lilies in Denmark
MEMBERSHIP   300
SUBSCRIPTIONS   Dkr 90 annual fee; Dkr 100 entry fee
SERVICES   Lectures; seed scheme; library; advice; shows; journal; outings; bulb sales

Dedicated principally to irises and lilies, but extending to some other Iridaceae and Liliaceae, this is a thriving small society. Members enjoy a quarterly bulletin, several garden visits in summer months, and an annual show at Kolding in July. All members receive a list of bulbs for sale in September and a seed list in December.

Dansk Orchide Klub
Edisonvej 1 B, DK-1856 Frederiksberg C., Denmark
CONTACT   Inger Lomborg
MEMBERSHIP   450
SUBSCRIPTIONS   Dkr 230
SERVICES   Lectures; publications; shows; journal; special interest and regional groups

As well as publishing ten editions of the magazine *Orchideer* (in Danish, Norwegian and Swedish), the Danish orchid society runs about ten shows a year.

Det Danske Rosenselskab
Kirkedalsvej 63, Rårup, DK-7130 Juelsminde, Denmark
☎ 00 45 7568 5232   📠 00 45 7568 5746
CONTACT   Peter Jordt
MEMBERSHIP   830
SUBSCRIPTIONS   Dkr 110
SERVICES   Publications; advice; shows; journal; special interest and regional groups; outings

The Danish rose society publishes a quarterly journal *Rosen-Nyt.*

Deutsche Bromelien-Gesellschaft
Steiler Weg 15, D-57076 Siegen, Germany
CONTACT   Ursula Börner
SUBSCRIPTIONS   DM 55
SERVICES   Seed scheme; shows; journal; plant sales

Deutsche Dahlien- Fuchsien- und Gladiolen-Gesellschaft e V
Drachenfelsstraße 9a, D-53177 Bonn, Germany
☎ 00 49 228 35 58 35   📠 00 49 228 35 58 37
CONTACT   Elisabeth Göring
MEMBERSHIP   650
SUBSCRIPTIONS   DM 60
SERVICES   Lectures; journal

Founded in 1897, the society is celebrating its centenary this year. There will be a conference for European fuchsia societies (16 societies from 12 countries) in Berlin 6 – 8 July and a big celebration at Insel Mainau on Lake Constance 19 – 21 September. Members receive three issues of the magazine *Rundbriefe* a year and the annual *Jahrbuch* which is a substantial publication (170 pages) with useful reports and articles. There is a panel of experts to advise on problems of cultivation.

Deutsche Dendrologische Gesellschaft

Hawstraße 28, D-54290 Trier, Germany

CONTACT Wolfgang Schönherr
SUBSCRIPTIONS DM 40
SERVICES Advice; journal; special interest and regional groups; outings

The German dendrological society is very active, and strong in all its branches throughout the country. The annual *Mitteilungen der DDG* is an authoritative publication.

Deutsche Kakteen-Gesellschaft e V

Volksdorfer Weg 231, D-22393 Hamburg, Germany
☎ & FAX 00 49 40 6004356

CONTACT Renate Siebke (Hon. Sec.)
MEMBERSHIP 6,500
SUBSCRIPTIONS DM 60 in Germany; DM 65 abroad
SERVICES Lectures; seed scheme; library; publications; advice; awards; shows; journal; special interest and regional groups; outings; plant sales

Founded in 1892, and one of the most distinguished horticultural associations in Europe. The Society has about 130 affiliated local groups, and specialist working groups for *Astrophytum, Echinopsis, Gymnocalycium, Rebutia* and *Tephrocactus*. There is a large lending library of specialist books for members' use. The society also publishes a list of about 40 specialist cactus nurseries in Germany. The illustrated monthly journal *Kakteen und andere Sukkulenten* is of high quality, with informative articles of botanical and horticultural interest.

Deutsche Kameliengesellschaft

Stahlbühlring 96, D-68526 Ladenburg, Germany

CONTACT Gerhard Kasimir
SUBSCRIPTIONS DM 50
SERVICES Lectures; publications; shows; journal; special interest and regional groups; outings

A branch of the International Camellia Society.

Deutsche Rhododendron Gesellschaft

Botanischer Garten u. Rhododendron-Park, Marcusallee 60, D-28359 Bremen, Germany
☎ 00 49 421 361 3025 FAX 00 49 421 361 3610

CONTACT Julia Westhoff
AIMS To promote rhododendrons and other evergreen shrubs
MEMBERSHIP 1,100
SUBSCRIPTIONS DM 40 single; DM 50 double

SERVICES Lectures; associated gardens; publications; awards; shows; journal; special interest and regional groups; outings

This Bremen-based society is a fair match for the RHS Rhododendron Group. Its publications illustrate its botanical and horticultural qualities: the *Jahrbuch* is an authoritative scientific publication while the handsomely illustrated quarterly magazine *Immergrüner Blätte* is of more horticultural interest but of equally high standard. In addition to the seed exchange, members are entitled to take a number of cuttings and pollen from the Rhododendronpark in Bremen: the Rhododendronpark is Germany's answer to the Savill Gardens and Valley Gardens in Windsor Great Park. The society gives awards to new *Rhododendron* cultivars and mounts a big exhibition every four years (the next will be in 1998). Its annual study tours are a feature of its events programme: last year the group visited Irish gardens, and this year they are going to Potsdam and Berlin.

Dionée

41 rue Henri II Plantagenêt, F-76100 Rouen, France

CONTACT Pierre Sibille
SUBSCRIPTIONS FF 100
SERVICES Seed scheme; shows; journal; special interest and regional groups; outings

Subtitled *Association pour les amateurs de plantes carnivores*, this is the French carnivorous plant society. The main benefit for overseas members is the tri-annual magazine *Dionée*.

Dunedin Rhododendron Group

222 Balmacewen Road, Dunedin, New Zealand
☎ 00 64 466 7567

CONTACT David Temple (Treasurer)
MEMBERSHIP 600
SUBSCRIPTIONS NZ$19 single; NZ$21 family
SERVICES Lectures; library; shows; journal; outings; annual plant distribution

The group holds about 15 meetings a year. Its *Bulletin* is a substantial publication, with articles on botany, hybridisation, cultivation, plant hunting, gardens and nurseries.

Europäische Bambusgesellschaft

John-Wesley-Str. 4, D-63584 Gründau/Rothenbergen, Germany
☎ 00 49 6051 17451

CONTACT Frau Edeltraud Weber
MEMBERSHIP 700
SUBSCRIPTIONS DM 50
SERVICES Lectures; seed scheme; journal; outings; slide library

This vigorous German bamboo society has members all over Europe. The quarterly *Bambusbrief* has good articles on every aspect of bamboo botany, cultivation and use. Last year the society visited China to see bamboos growing in the wild.

Europäische Liliengesellschaft e V
Rabenweg 4, D-89250 Senden, Germany
☎ 00 49 7309 5487

CONTACT Wolfgang Salzborn
MEMBERSHIP 150
SUBSCRIPTIONS DM 40
SERVICES Seed scheme; shows; journal

A young, but growing, German-based lily society, with a seed list and annual bulb sale.

The Federation of Rose Societies of South Africa
Box 95738, Waterkloof 0145, South Africa
☎ 00 27 12 5451244

CONTACT G W Dams (Hon. Sec.)
MEMBERSHIP 4000
SERVICES Shows; journal

This is an umbrella organisation for some sixteen local rose societies within the republic. The Federation publishes an annual and organises the national convention in October. Each member society has its own programme of events.

Fous de Palmiers
BP 600, F-83403 Hyères-les-Palmiers Cedex, France
☎ 00 33 4 94 65 85 08

AIMS To encourage the planting and cultivation of palm-trees
MEMBERSHIP 450
SUBSCRIPTIONS FF 200 single; FF 250 double
SERVICES Lectures; seed scheme; journal; outings

The *Association des Amateurs de Palmiers* was founded in 1989 as a chapter of the International Palm Society. Its members are 'crazy' about palm-trees and seek to encourage the cultivation of as many varieties as possible. They have a very active programme of events, including foreign tours, and the six-monthly journal *Le Palmier* is a high quality publication. *Les Fous de Palmiers* will be of particular interest to UK members as the most active group of palm-lovers in Europe.

Freie Vereinigung der Eibenfreunde
Dachauerstr. 52, D-82256 Fürstenfeldbruck, Germany
CONTACT Thomas Scheeder
SUBSCRIPTIONS DM 15
SERVICES Lectures; journal; outings

The only society we know of that is devoted to the cultivation and promotion of yews.

Fructus
Waisenhausstrasse 4, CH-8820 Wadenswil, Switzerland

Gesellschaft der Heidefreunde
Lütjenmoor 66, D-22850 Norderstedt, Germany
☎ 00 49 40 5256259   FAX 00 49 40 5217267

CONTACT Jürgen Schröder
MEMBERSHIP 280
SUBSCRIPTIONS DM 45 single; DM 55 joint
SERVICES Lectures; advice; shows; journal; outings

The German Heather society is very active, especially in the north-west of the country. In September they are running a two-week trip to South Africa.

Gesellschaft der Staudenfreunde
Meisenweg 1, D-65975 Hattersheim, Germany
☎ & FAX 00 49 6190 3642

CONTACT Geschäftsführer (Secretary)
MEMBERSHIP 4,000
SUBSCRIPTIONS DM 50 single; DM 75 double
SERVICES Lectures; seed scheme; journal; special interest and regional groups

The German Perennial Society developed from the Iris and Lily Society but now encompasses all kinds of hardy perennials. There are over 30 regional and five special interest groups (alpines, *Hemerocallis*, lilies, paeonies and wildflowers) which all organise their own lectures and outings. Members receive the excellent quarterly journal *Der Staudengarten*, which is comparable to *The Hardy Plant*. The society's seed scheme centres on an annual list, not confined to perennials, which offers about 4,000 items. We strongly recommend all Hardy Planters to consider membership.

Gesellschaft für Fleischfressende Pflanzen im deutschsprachigen Raum
Dreherstr. 115, D-40625 Düsseldorf, Germany
CONTACT Klaus-Peter Dickscheidt
SUBSCRIPTIONS DM 45
SERVICES Seed scheme; journal

The German carnivorous plant society has a bi-annual newsletter called *Das Taublatt* and an exchange of plants as well as seeds.

Gesellschaft Schweizer Staudenfreunde
Wettsteinstr. 6, CH-8332 Russikon, Switzerland
CONTACT Walter Good
SUBSCRIPTIONS SFr 45, but SFr 55 abroad
SERVICES Lectures; seed scheme; library; journal; special interest and regional groups; outings

The Swiss hardy plant society publishes *Schweizer Staudengärten* twice a year and runs a scheme whereby its members club together to buy new plants from abroad, mainly from the USA.

Gesellschaft Schweizerischer Rosenfreunde
Bahnhofstr. 11, CH-8640 Rapperswil, Switzerland
☎ 00 41 55 272409

CONTACT Dr Theodor Zwygart (President)
MEMBERSHIP 3,500
SUBSCRIPTIONS SFr 40
SERVICES Lectures; library; advice; awards; shows; journal; special interest and regional groups; outings

The Swiss rose society: *Rosa Helvetica* is its annual. Most articles are in German, but some are in French or Italian. Members also receive a monthly newsletter *Das Kleine Rosenblatt* which is more concerned with practical problems of cultivation. As well as cultivated varieties, the Society is interested in wild roses and the taxonomy of the many species native to Switzerland. The Society carries out trials at an alpine test garden: hardiness is of paramount importance.

Hardy Plant Society Mid-Atlantic Group

49 Green Valley Road, Wallingford, PA 19086, U.S.A.

CONTACT   Jean Schumacher
MEMBERSHIP   850
SUBSCRIPTIONS   US$15 single; US$18 double
SERVICES   Seed scheme; journal; special interest and regional groups; outings; plant sales (two each year)

Members receive the quarterly *Newsletter*. There are special interest groups for geraniums, hellebores, native plants, salvias, variegated plants and shade-loving plants, any of which may be joined by paying a US$3 supplement.

Heliconia Society International

Fairchild Tropical Gardens, 10901 Old Cuttler Road, Miami, FL 33156, U.S.A.

MEMBERSHIP   550
SUBSCRIPTIONS   US$35 single; US$40 family
SERVICES   Lectures; publications; journal; outings

The society is concerned not only with Heliconias but also with such related plants as bananas, cannas, gingers and strelitzias. It is US-based, but truly international: for example, the August 1995 edition of its *Bulletin* contained articles from members in Germany, Australia, Hawaii and the Netherlands, as well as mainland USA. The next biennial conference will be in Singapore.

Hemerocallis Europa

Homburg 14, D-79761 Waldshut-Tiengen, Germany
☎ & 🖷 00 49 7741 63068

CONTACT   Matthias Thomsen-Stork
MEMBERSHIP   50
SUBSCRIPTIONS   DM 50
SERVICES   Lectures; seed scheme; shows; journal; trial gardens

Germany-based but bilingual (German & English) society that seeks to study, evaluate and popularise the best daylilies for Europe. It has members in eight European countries. The society encourages the breeding of new varieties, and runs trials for their garden-worthiness in Germany and at Ventnor Botanic Gardens in the Isle of Wight. Members receive three newsletters and a substantial Yearbook.

Heritage Rose Foundation

1512 Gorman Street, Raleigh, NC 27606-2919, U.S.A.
☎ & 🖷 00 1 919 834 2591

CONTACT   Charles Walker (President)
MEMBERSHIP   600
SUBSCRIPTIONS   US$10 US; US$12 Bermuda, Canada & Mexico; US$15 elsewhere
SERVICES   Lectures; associated gardens; library; journal; outings

The Foundation is concerned to conserve old roses, especially those which are no longer available commercially. It has just

decided to establish its own garden where rare and unnamed old varieties may be preserved, studied and propagated.

Holly Society of America Inc

11318 West Murdock, Wichita, KS 67212-6609, U.S.A.
☎ 00 1 316 721 5668

CONTACT   Hon. Secretary
MEMBERSHIP   550
SUBSCRIPTIONS   US$25
SERVICES   Lectures; seed scheme; publications; shows; journal; special interest and regional groups

The society was founded in 1947 and has six chapters in the US and one in Korea. The main benefit for non-US members is the quarterly *Holly Society Journal* with a mixture of scientific, horticultural and social reports. There is an exchange of cuttings and seeds at the annual meeting as well as a show with ten competitive classes. The society is the International Registration Authority for *Ilex* cultivars.

Hydroponic Society of America

P O Box 3075, Suite 218, San Ramon, CA 94583, U.S.A.
☎ 00 1 510 743 9605   🖷 00 1 510 743 9302

MEMBERSHIP   900
SUBSCRIPTIONS   US$30 North America; US$40 overseas
SERVICES   Lectures; advice; journal; outings; books for sale

The Society is the leading international society in its field: its mission is to disseminate information about every aspect of hydroponics and soilless growing. It does this mainly through its excellent newsletter *The Soilless Grower* whose articles by professionals and amateurs give details of commercial developments, R&D reports, new products, educational facilities and other news. Founded in 1980, the society is currently growing very fast and has members in 23 countries.

Indian Rose Federation

852 Napier Town, Jabalpur 482 001 (MP), India
☎ 00 91 761 315744   🖷 00 91 761 392042

International Aroid Society

P O Box 43-1853, Miami, FL 33143, U.S.A.
☎ 001 305 271 3767

CONTACT   Amy Donovan
MEMBERSHIP   500
SUBSCRIPTIONS $30
SERVICES   Lectures; publications; advice; awards; shows; journal; special interest and regional groups; plant exchange scheme

The Society is truly international, with members in most parts of the tropical world. It contributes to the Aroid Discussion group on the Internet called AROID-L. Bi-monthly meetings take place at the Fairchild Tropical Garden and the Annual Show and Plant Sale will be held there on 27 & 28 September. The Newsletter carries reports of aroid hunting expeditions and the activities of members worldwide while its flagship annual *Aroideana* has more in the way of scientific articles.

International Camellia Society

41 Galveston Road, East Putney, London SW15 2RZ

☎ 0181 870 6884   📠 0181 874 4633

CONTACT UK Membership Representative

AIMS To foster the love of camellias and maintain and increase their popularity throughout the world

MEMBERSHIP 1,700

SUBSCRIPTIONS £8.50 single; £11 joint

SERVICES Associated gardens; advice; shows; journal; special interest and regional groups; outings;

Founded in 1962. There are now members in 25 countries, including 360 in the UK. The society has several trial grounds around the country; the national collection is at Mount Edgcumbe, Cornwall. Members receive the *International Camellia Journal* annually, and a UK newsletter twice a year. The society takes a stand at the main spring shows, and holds weekend meetings in spring and autumn. Informal advice on camellias is available to members, as is a worldwide network of fellow enthusiasts.

The International Carnivorous Plant Society

c/o Fullerton Arboretum, California State University Fullerton, Fullerton, CA 92634, U.S.A.

MEMBERSHIP 828

SUBSCRIPTIONS US$15 US; US$20 elsewhere

SERVICES Seed scheme; publications; journal; special interest and regional groups

The society is dedicated to understanding, preserving, growing, selecting, propagating, studying and appreciating the natural flora of the earth, with special interest in carnivorous plants. There is an active internet group: new subscribers should send an e-mail to LISTPROC@OPUS.HPL.HP.COM.

International Clematis Society

115 Belmont Road, Harrow HA3 7PL

☎ 0181 427 5340

CONTACT Fiona Woolfenden

MEMBERSHIP 160

SUBSCRIPTIONS £16.50 UK

SERVICES Seed scheme; shows; journal; outings

The society is international in its membership and aspirations: it aims to provide a channel of communication for clematis growers across the world. Its main event is the annual tour, attended by international members, during which there are shows and meetings. This year's tour will be to Japan in May. Members receive an annual *Journal*. The excellent seed list contains up to 100 items.

International Dendrology Society

School House, Stannington, Morpeth, Northumberland NE61 6HF

☎ 01670 789621   📠 01670 789235

CONTACT The Secretary

AIMS To promote the study and conservation of trees, woody plants and shrubs

MEMBERSHIP 1,500

SUBSCRIPTIONS £25 single; £250 life

SERVICES Lectures; seed scheme; publications; journal; special interest and regional groups; outings; conservation and research; annual bursary

This prestigious international society has a worldwide membership. It encourages and helps fund conservation and research projects by registered charities, and has established a bursary to allow a dendrological student from Eastern Europe to study in the UK for a few months each year. The IDS holds a dendrological symposium every two years: last year's study of *Magnolia* at Windsor in April attracted considerable attention. Members also receive the *Year Book* and newsletters, and can take part in the seed exchange scheme and the excellent botanical tours. Membership is restricted, is at the invitation of existing members only, and is subject to the approval of the council.

International Geranium Society

P O Box 9274, Pasadena, CA 91109-2734, U.S.A.

CONTACT The Membership Secretary

SUBSCRIPTIONS US$12.50

A new society for geraniums and pelargoniums.

International Lilac Society

c/o The Holden Arboretum, 9500 Sperry Road, Kirtland, OH 44094-5172, U.S.A.

☎ 00 1 216 256 1110   📠 00 1 216 256 1655

CONTACT Dave Gressley

MEMBERSHIP 400

SUBSCRIPTIONS £10 single; £100 life membership

SERVICES Lectures; library; publications; advice; journal

In addition to receiving the informative *Quarterly Journal of the International Lilac Society*, members can purchase rare *Syringa* taxa and take part in the annual convention – this year in June on Mackinac Island, Michigan.

International Oak Society

P O Box 310, Pen Argyl, PA 18072-0310, U.S.A.

☎ 00 1 610 588 1037   📠 00 1 610 252 7064

AIMS To encourage the study and cultivation of the genus *Quercus*

MEMBERSHIP 380

SUBSCRIPTIONS US$15

SERVICES Seed scheme; publications; journal; triennial conferences (next one this year)

The society gives members all over the world an opportunity to acquire acorns of rare species. The annual conference will be 21 – 23 October at Huntington Gardens, California.

International Oleander Society Inc

P O Box 3431, Galveston, TX 77552-0431, U.S.A.

☎ 00 1 409 762 9334

CONTACT Elizabeth Head (Secretary)

MEMBERSHIP 200

SERVICES Lectures; associated gardens; seed scheme; publications; journal; cuttings scheme

Galveston is the Oleander City and the society has its reference collection of varieties at the Moody gardens there. The main publication is the quarterly *Nerium News*, but the society has also issued two videos on oleanders and their cultivation.

International Palm Society
P O Box 368, Lawrence, KS 66044, U.S.A.
CONTACT   Mrs Lynn McKamey

International Violet Association
Devon Violet Nursery, Rattery, South Brent, Devon TQ10 LG
☎ 01364 643033

CONTACT   Membership Secretary
AIMS   To bring together all those interested in the violet and its near relations
MEMBERSHIP   300
SUBSCRIPTIONS   £10 or $15
SERVICES   Lectures; advice; journal

A new and growing international society which originated in the USA, though the president is British. Its International Symposium this year will be held at The Manor House, Dawlish, on 5 April. Its aims include bringing the violet back into gardens, assisting in the preservation of its natural habitats, and recording and introducing new cultivars. Membership is not limited to growers and collectors. A newsletter is produced four times a year, and the president offers an advisory service to European members.

International Water Lily Society
92 London Road, Stapeley, Nantwich, Cheshire CW5 7LH
☎ 01270 628628   📠 01270 624188
CONTACT   The Treasurer (IWLS Europe)
AIMS   To further interest in all aspects of water gardening
MEMBERSHIP   2,000
SUBSCRIPTIONS   £15 single; £17.50 family
SERVICES   Lectures; library; awards; journal; special interest and regional groups; outings

The International Water Lily Society is based in the USA but has members in 23 countries of the world. The membership spans amateurs and professionals, and the society carries out a range of research and educational work, including hybrid registration. Members receive the quarterly journal. There are lectures at the British branch AGM in October.

Iris Society of Australia (NSW Region)
P O Box 11, Gordon, NSW 2072, Australia
CONTACT   Mrs Heather Pryor (Hon. Sec.)
MEMBERSHIP   120
SUBSCRIPTIONS   A$12 single; A$14 double
SERVICES   Lectures; library; advice; shows; journal

The NSW regional society has three branches in Sydney, Canberra and the Central West sub-region. The newsletter carries articles on local cultivation and hybridisation.

Iris Society of South Africa
P O Box 2924, Edenvale 1610, South Africa
CONTACT   Matilda Anderson (Secretary)
SUBSCRIPTIONS   £5 for UK Members
SERVICES   Advice; shows; journal; special interest and regional groups

Established in 1953, the society has about 100 members, plus some 21 affiliated societies. There is a National All Iris Show, usually early in October and members receive a twice-yearly Bulletin.

Irish Garden Plant Society
c/o National Botanic Gardens, Glasnevin, Dublin 9, Eire
MEMBERSHIP   600
SUBSCRIPTIONS   I£15 single; I£22 family
SERVICES   Lectures; seed scheme; publications; special interest and regional groups; outings; plant sales

Formed in 1981 as the Irish equivalent to the NCCPG, the Society has a particular mission to locate and propagate plants raised in Ireland, whether by amateurs or nurserymen. The Society exhibits at Chelsea and is the only group within Ireland that is registered with the NCCPG. There are branches in Munster and Northern Ireland, each with their own programme. Members receive a a quarterly newsletter as well as the society's journal *Moorea*, which has articles of a historical nature about Irish plants, gardens and gardeners.

Japan Begonia Society
2-1-11 Yakumo 2-Chome, Maguro-Ku, Tokyo 152, Japan
CONTACT   Tatsuo Suzuki (President)

Japan Rose Society
3-9-5 Oyamadai, Setagaya-ku, Tokyo 158, Japan
☎ & 📠 00 81 3 3702 9413
CONTACT   Takeo Nagata (Acting Chief Executive)
MEMBERSHIP   1,500
SUBSCRIPTIONS   ¥7,000; US$70 overseas
SERVICES   Lectures; associated gardens; library; advice; awards; shows; journal; special interest and regional groups; outings

The Japan Rose Society is concerned to spread a love of roses among the Japanese people. It has seven regional groups and runs the Tokyo International Trial Grounds for new rose varieties. Members receive free stocks of new varieties as one of their benefits, as well as a monthly Newsletter and an annual Bulletin. There are about ten lectures in the Tokyo area every year, exhibitions in spring and autumn, and study tours. The spring exhibition receives a visit from the Imperial royal family.

The Magnolia Society Inc
6616 81st Street, Cabin John, MD 20818, U.S.A.
☎ & 📠 00 1 301 320 4296
CONTACT   Hon. Secretary
MEMBERSHIP   600
SUBSCRIPTIONS   US$20 US; US$25 Canada & overseas
SERVICES   Lectures; associated gardens; seed scheme; library; publications; advice; awards; journal; outings

Founded in 1963 to promote the exchange of knowledge about magnolias, the Society is the major association devoted to this genus. Members receive the twice-yearly journal *Magnolia* as well as a newsletter. The journal has articles on cultivation, propagation, breeding and gardens. The society offers a seed exchange, library and registration service for new cultivars. This year's AGM will be held in Korea on 19 April; last year's was in England.

National Chrysanthemum Society Inc

10107 Homar Pond Drive, Fairfax Station, VA 22039-1650, U.S.A.

☎ 00 1 703 978 7981

CONTACT   Galen L Goss (Secretary)
MEMBERSHIP   1,500
SUBSCRIPTIONS   US$12.50
SERVICES   Lectures; publications; shows; journal; special interest and regional groups

Founded in 1944, primarily for amateur gardeners, the society now has specialist, expert and institutional members in the US and overseas. There are chapters throughout the US, each with its own programme of events and shows. The society's Annual Meeting and Show are hosted by a different chapter each year. Members receive the quarterly journal The Chrysanthe-mum devoted to articles on cultivation and showing. The society also publishes its own handbooks.

National Daffodil Society Inc

277 Fencourt Road, Fencourt R.D.1, Cambridge 2351, New Zealand

CONTACT   W T Hall

National Fuchsia Society (US)

11507 E. 187th Street, Artesia, CA 90701, U.S.A.

☎ 00 1 310 865 1806

CONTACT   Agnes Rietkerk
MEMBERSHIP   200
SUBSCRIPTIONS   US$15 single; US$30 overseas
SERVICES   Lectures; shows; journal; special interest and regional groups; plant sales

The society is based in California, and has four branches there. It aims to stimulate interest in the culture of fuchsias and promote social relationships. The main publication is a slim journal called The Fuchsia Fan.

National Rose Society of Australia

271b Balmore Road, North Balwyn, Victoria 3104, Australia

CONTACT   James Priestly
MEMBERSHIP   3,400

An umbrella organisation for the six state rose societies, the NRSA publishes The Australian Rose Annual.

National Rose Society of New Zealand

P O Box 66, Bunnythorpe, New Zealand

☎ 00 64 6 329 2700

CONTACT   Mrs Heather MacDonell (Secretary)
AIMS   To plant roses in the hearts and gardens of the people
MEMBERSHIP   8,600
SUBSCRIPTIONS   NZ$23 single
SERVICES   Lectures; library; publications; advice; shows; journal; special interest and regional groups; trials

New Zealand has the highest per capita membership of all national rose societies. It is divided between 44 regions, each with its own programme of events. The NRSNZ successfully hosted the World Rose Convention in Christchurch in 1994. Its trials test about 100 new varieties every year, but they

include fewer French and German roses than the RNRS trials. The New Zealand Rose Annual has high quality articles and illustrations: social inconsequences are kept to a minimum. It is supplemented by N.Z. Rosarian, a chatty, thrice-yearly bulletin.

Nationale Boomgaarden Stichting

Postbus 49, B-3500 Hasselt 1, Belgium

☎ & [FAX] 00 32 12 237001

CONTACT   Ludo Royen
MEMBERSHIP   2,000
SUBSCRIPTIONS   BFr 600
SERVICES   Lectures; publications; shows; journal; special interest and regional groups; outings; scion exchange

An active and enthusiastic Flemish society, dedicated to the conservation of fruit trees. It sustains the Belgian national collections of apples, pears, plums, cherries, quinces and med-lars. The quarterly journal Pomologia is an authoritative publication. The society will be much involved with organising the International Fruit Show Europom in Limburg in 1999.

Nederlands Belgische Vereniging van Liefhebbers van Cactussen

Prins Willem Alexanderlaan 104, NL-6721 AE Bennekom, The Netherlands

CONTACT   J M Smit-Reesink (Secretary)
MEMBERSHIP   2,500
SUBSCRIPTIONS   HFl 50
SERVICES   Seed scheme; library; publications; shows; journal; special interest and regional groups; outings

The Benelux Succulent society has many attractions, including a seed list of rare species and the attractive bi-monthly Suc-culenta. The 33 regional societies have their own programmes of events and shows.

Nederlandse Dahlia Vereniging

Postbus 50, NL-2180 AB Hillegom, The Netherlands

☎ 00 31 1719 15567

CONTACT   J P Lindhout (Secretary)
AIMS   To promote dahlia growing
MEMBERSHIP   225
SUBSCRIPTIONS   HFl 35 single
SERVICES   Lectures; shows; journal; special interest and regional groups

The Dutch Dahlia Society is well supported by professionals and amateurs alike: it has 100 nurseries among its members and 30 local Dahlia clubs. In addition to the society's annual, members receive the bulletin Dahlia Varia. The society runs trials for new seedlings at Hillegom and publishes the results.

Nederlandse Heidervereniging 'Ericultura'

Esdoornstraat 54, NL-6681 ZM Bemmel, The Netherlands

CONTACT   J Dahm

Dutch Heather society.

Nederlandse Kring van Fuchsiavrienden

Gratamastraat 28, NL-3067 SE Rotterdam, The Netherlands

☎ 00 31 20 4202514

CONTACT The Secretary
MEMBERSHIP 6,000
SUBSCRIPTIONS HFl 50 single, plus one-off joining fee of HFl 7.50
SERVICES Lectures; publications; advice; journal; special interest and regional groups; outings

Founded in 1965, the Dutch Fuchsia Society is a large and popular national institution. There are about 30 regional groups with their own programmes of events. The excellent Magazine *Fuchsiana* is sent to members every two months.

Nederlandse Lathyrus Vereniging

Kenyadreef 9, NL-3564 CM Utrecht, The Netherlands

☎ 00 31 30 261 1117

CONTACT J A M Halkes (Secretary)
MEMBERSHIP 190
SUBSCRIPTIONS HFl 18 single
SERVICES Seed scheme; shows

Founded in 1927. There is no formal application for membership, nor does the society issue a newsletter. However, it does organise shows for members only and run a seed bank.

Nederlandse Pelargonium en Geranium Vereniging

Zwaluwplein 11a, NL-1742 GD Schagen, The Netherlands

☎ 00 31 2240 15862

CONTACT Cees Piet
MEMBERSHIP 425
SUBSCRIPTIONS HFl 35
SERVICES Library; publications; shows; journal

Members may use the library, attend local events and receive the quarterly bulletin *Pelargonium & Geranium Nieuws*. NPGV offers six regional groups, a *Geranium* work group, a *Pelargonium* miniatures group and a *Pelargonium* species group.

Nederlandse Rozenvereniging

Cromhoutstraat 36, NL-6971 AV Brummen, The Netherlands

☎ 00 31 36 5324363

MEMBERSHIP 2,000
SUBSCRIPTIONS HFl 35 home; HFl 45 abroad
SERVICES Lectures; advice; shows; journal; outings

The Dutch rose society: members receive the quarterly *Rozenbulletin*. The society conducts international rose trials in the Westbroekpark in the Hague and is co-hosting the World Federation of Rose Societies meeting in June.

New Zealand Alpine Gardening Society

P O Box 2984, Christchurch, New Zealand

☎ 00 64 3 303 6119

CONTACT Joan Whillans
MEMBERSHIP 900

SUBSCRIPTIONS NZ$20 New Zealand members; NZ$25 overseas
SERVICES Lectures; seed scheme; library; shows; journal

The society aims to encourage and foster the study and cultivation of alpine and rock garden plants. Local members attend monthly meetings in Canterbury. There are two main benefits for overseas members: the high quality twice yearly *Bulletin* and the annual seed list with over 3,000 items.

New Zealand Fuchsia Society Inc

P O Box 11-082, Ellerslie, Auckland, New Zealand

CONTACT Miss Joan Byres

New Zealand Gladiolus Council

13 Ramanui Avenue, Hawera, Taranaka, New Zealand

New Zealand Lily Society Inc

P O Box 1394, Christchurch, New Zealand

CONTACT The Secretary
SUBSCRIPTIONS NZ$15 single; NZ$18 double; NZ$22 overseas
SERVICES Lectures; seed scheme; library; shows; journal

Ten meetings are held every year at Christchurch and a two-day show at the beginning of January. Members receive three bulletins a year: they contain articles on growing and showing lilies and information about the society's activities. The seed list contains some interesting tender species and hybrids.

Noordelijke Pomologische Vereniging

Sluisstraat 165, NL-9406 AX Assen, The Netherlands

Nordisk Kaktus Selskab

Tokkerupvej 1, DK-4640 Fakse, Denmark

CONTACT Hugo Jensen
MEMBERSHIP 600
SUBSCRIPTIONS Dkr 175
SERVICES Shows; journal; special interest and regional groups

This is the Danish cactus club, but many of its members are also Norwegian or Swedish. It runs some 10 meetings a year and publishes a quarterly bulletin *Kaktus*.

Norsk Roseforening

Smiuvegen 8, N-0892 Oslo, Norway

☎ & FAX 00 47 22 10 84 17

CONTACT Laila Finholth (Secretary)
AIMS Promoting the Rose in Norway, Scandanavia and abroad
MEMBERSHIP 1,300
SUBSCRIPTIONS NoKr 125 (Scandanavia only)
SERVICES Lectures; associated gardens; publications; advice; shows; journal; special interest and regional groups; outings

The Norwegian Rose Society is based in Oslo and has ten regional groups throughout the country. The main competition takes place on 5 July at the Tomb rose garden, south of Oslo, where the society also has a demonstration and trials garden. The society enjoys close relations with rose societies in other Nordic countries. The quarterly magazine *Rosebladet* has articles on choosing varieties, cultivation, events, and historical and scientific matters.

North American Gladiolus Council

Box 70, Belgrade, ME 04917, U.S.A.

☎ 00 1 207 495 2244

CONTACT Robert Martin (Membership Secretary)
MEMBERSHIP 750
SUBSCRIPTIONS US$10 US; US$12.50 overseas
SERVICES Lectures; shows; journal; outings; bulb auctions; speakers' list

NAGC has about 45 affiliated societies throughout North America. It also trains judges, awards medals, and trials new hybrids. The quarterly *Bulletin* is a substantial publication. The marigold is described by the society as 'the international friendship flower'.

North American Heather Society

P O Box 101, Highland View, Alstead, NH 03602, U.S.A.

CONTACT Hon. Secretary

North American Lily Society Inc

P O Box 272, Owatonna, MN 55060, U.S.A.

☎ 00 1 507 451 2170

CONTACT Hon. Secretary
MEMBERSHIP 1,500
SUBSCRIPTIONS US$12.50
SERVICES Seed scheme; library; publications; advice; awards; shows; journal; special interest and regional groups

Founded in 1946, the society publishes an excellent *Quarterly Bulletin* and a *Yearbook*. The seed exchange is a valuable asset for non-US members.

North American Plant Collections Consortium

c/o A.A.B.G.A., 786 Church Road, Wayne, PA 19087, U.S.A.

One of two organisations in the USA which are equivalent to our NCCPG. This one is led by botanists.

North American Plant Preservation Council

c/o Sunshine Nursery, Renick, West Virginia 24966, U.S.A.

CONTACT B Glick

One of two organisations in the USA which are equivalent to our NCCPG. This one is led by a nurseryman.

Northeast Heather Society

P O Box 101 – Highland View, Alstead, NH 03602-0101, U.S.A.

☎ 00 1 603 835 6165

CONTACT Walter Wornick (Sec./Treas.)
MEMBERSHIP 400
SUBSCRIPTIONS US$5 for USA, US$7.50 overseas
SERVICES Lectures; journal; outings; plant sales; cuttings exchange; slide library

Members receive the quarterly newsletter *Heather Notes*. There are about 25 UK members.

Northwest Fuchsia Society

P O Box 33071, Seattle, WA 98133-0071, U.S.A.

CONTACT The Secretary
MEMBERSHIP 750
SUBSCRIPTIONS US$10 US; US$12 Canada or international
SERVICES Library; shows; journal; spring plant sale

An umbrella society with eleven member societies, two affiliates and two active special interest groups. The society publishes a monthly newsletter *The Fuchsia Flash* and has an extensive lending library.

Österreichische Gartenbau-Gesellschaft

Parkring 12, A-1010 Wien, Austria

☎ 00 43 512 84 16   FAX 00 43 512 84 17

MEMBERSHIP 4,500
SUBSCRIPTIONS ÖS 370 Austria; ÖS 470 abroad
SERVICES Lectures; library; shows; journal; special interest and regional groups; outings; educational courses

The Austrian horticultural society is the focus for all gardening interests in the country. The Austrian rose society *Österreichische Rosenfreunde* and fuchsia society *Fuchsienfreunde* operate within the main society and there are special interest groups for alpine plants, bromeliads, house plants, Ikebana and floral art. The monthly magazine *Garten* has a broad-based editorial policy: it is particularly useful for discovering what can be grown in a cold climate.

Österreichische Orchideengesellschaft

Postfach 300, A-1222 Wien, Austria

CONTACT Ing. Kurt Reif
SUBSCRIPTIONS ÖS 250
SERVICES Lectures; publications; shows; journal; special interest and regional groups

The parent organisation for orchid societies in Austria. It publishes a quarterly magazine *Orchideenkurier*.

Orchid Council of New Zealand

P O Box 181, Palmerston North, New Zealand

SERVICES Publications; advice; journal; special interest and regional groups; outings

Orchid Society of New South Wales Ltd

P O Box 333, Beverley Hills, NSW 2209, Australia

☎ 00 61 2 759 5948

CONTACT Joan Gleeson (Secretary)
MEMBERSHIP 420
SUBSCRIPTIONS A$16 single; A$20 double
SERVICES Lectures; shows; journal; special interest and regional groups

This Sydney-based society is the premier orchid society in Australia. Members receive *The Orchid Review*, a substantial quarterly with fully integrated colour and articles on every aspect of orchid growing, breeding and showing.

The Organisation of Plant Collections in Australia
c/o RBG Melbourne, Birdwood Avenue, South Yarra, Victoria 3141, Australia
This is the Australian equivalent of the NCCPG.

Pomologen-Verein e V
Meierkamp 1, D-49406 Eydelstadt-Gothel, Germany

Pomona
Via Bramante, 29, I-20154 Milano, Italy
☎ 00 39 2 3494775   [FAX] 00 39 2 33105281
CONTACT Dr Paolo Belloni
SERVICES Lectures; associated gardens; advice; special interest and regional groups; outings
An extremely active Italian society dedicated to the conservation of old fruit varieties, particularly of tree fruits. They have been very successful in raising public consciousness of the importance of protecting traditional cultivars of apples, pears, plums and peaches.

Queensland Orchid Society Inc
G.P.O. Box 2002, Brisbane, Queensland 4001, Australia
☎ 00 61 7 266 7125
CONTACT Maree Illingworth
MEMBERSHIP 400
SUBSCRIPTIONS A$18 single; A$20 family
SERVICES Lectures; shows; journal; special interest and regional groups
Founded in 1934, the society has about 70 affiliated societies: most have monthly meetings and one or two shows each year. Native Australian orchids are catered for as well as exotics.

Queensland Rose Society Inc
Box 1866, G.P.O. Brisbane, Queensland 4001, Australia
☎ 00 61 7 814 4714
CONTACT Fraser Harris (Hon. Sec.)
MEMBERSHIP 360
SUBSCRIPTIONS A$20
SERVICES Lectures; library; publications; advice; shows; journal; special interest and regional groups; outings
As well as The Australian Rose Annual members receive the quarterly The Queensland Rose and can attend the monthly meetings in Paddington. The Spring Show will be on 4 & 5 October at the Brisbane Botanic Gardens.

Rhododendronforeningen
Mariehoj 1, DK-2990 Nivå, Denmark
CONTACT Ida Tonnesen
MEMBERSHIP 600
SUBSCRIPTIONS Dkr 140
SERVICES Shows; journal; outings
The Danish rhododendron society is a chapter of the American Rhododendron Society. It publishes a quarterly magazine Rhodo-Nyt.

The Rock Garden Club Prague
Pod Zvonarkou 10, 120 00 Praha 2, Czech Republic
CONTACT Vojtech Holubec

MEMBERSHIP 1,200
SUBSCRIPTIONS US$20, plus US$5 for seed exchange
SERVICES Lectures; seed scheme; library; shows; journal
The Czechs have a long history of excellence with alpine plants. The Club's quarterly bulletin Skalnicky is published with English abstracts: more than 10% of its members live abroad. The annual seed list has about 2,500 items, many of them collected in central or eastern Europe.

Rose Hybridizers Association
21 South Wheaton Road, Horseheads, NY 14845, U.S.A.
☎ 00 1 607 562 8592
CONTACT Larry Peterson
MEMBERSHIP 450
SUBSCRIPTIONS US$8; US$10 abroad
SERVICES Associated gardens; library; publications; advice; awards; journal
All members are amateurs, and interested in breeding new roses. There is a quarterly newsletter and the Association meets twice a year during the American Rose Society National Conventions. Members use round robins to keep in touch.

Rose Society of New South Wales
Lot 9 Curramore Road, Jamberoo, NSW 2533, Australia
CONTACT Mrs S Kingsford (Hon. Sec.)

Rose Society of South Australia
29 Columbia Crescent, Modbury North, South Australia 5092, Australia
CONTACT Malcolm Watson

Rose Society of Tasmania
RSD 146, Cradoc Hill Road, Cradoc, Tasmania 7109, Australia
CONTACT J Cane

Rose Society of Victoria Inc
40 Williams Road, Blackburn, Victoria 3130, Australia
CONTACT Mrs D M Aitken (Hon. Sec.)

Rose Society of Western Australia
33 Lord Street, Bentley, WA 6102, Australia
☎ 00 61 9 458 6452
CONTACT Mrs B Gunther (Hon. Sec.)

Royal Horticultural Society of Ireland
Swanbrook House, Bloomfield Avenue, Morehampton Road, Dublin 4
☎ 00 353 1 668 4358
CONTACT Mrs Monica Nolan (Secretary)
AIMS To encourage a greater awareness of gardening and plants
MEMBERSHIP 1,200
SUBSCRIPTIONS I£15 single; I£21 joint
SERVICES Lectures; library; awards; shows; journal; outings
Founded in 1830, the society encourages people to make gardens and grow a wide variety of plants. Lectures, demonstrations, courses, garden visits and plant sales are held throughout the year. The newsletter (three a year) keeps members up to date with activities.

Sino-Himalayan Plant Association

81 Parlaunt Road, Slough, Berkshire SL3 8BE
☎ 01753 542823

CONTACT   Chris Chadwell (Secretary)
AIMS   To bring together and spread information on Sino-Himalayan flora
MEMBERSHIP   150
SUBSCRIPTIONS   £8 UK; £10 overseas
SERVICES   Lectures; associated gardens; seed scheme; library; journal; outings

Formed in 1990, this is an informal Association. Members receive a twice-yearly newsletter and meetings take place in varying venues around the country. There is a small display garden and a seed exchange.

Società Italiana del Bambù

Via Romana, 17, I-18012 Bordighera, Italy
☎ 00 39 184 264270   FAX 00 39 184 263527

CONTACT   Tito Schiva
AIMS   To promote the knowledge and cultivation of bamboos
MEMBERSHIP   70
SUBSCRIPTIONS   Lit. 40,000
SERVICES   Publications; journal; outings

The Italian bamboo society is based on the Riviera and has close relations with the French society nearby. The quarterly newsletter is one of the main benefits and promotes scientific research and economic uses for all bamboos.

Société Belge du Bégonia

Chemin de Lancre,4, B-4970 Coo, Belgium

CONTACT   Piron Gilles (Président)

Société Bretonne du Rhododendron

Kernéostic, Ménez-Rohou, F-29170 Fouesnant, France
☎ 00 33 2 98 56 27 23   FAX 00 33 2 98 56 23 25

CONTACT   Marc Colombel (Président)
MEMBERSHIP   80
SUBSCRIPTIONS   FF 170 single; FF 180 double
SERVICES   Lectures; seed scheme; publications; journal; outings; pollen bank

A newish society, in the part of France where rhododendrons are a major feature of gardens. Members receive four copies of the *Bulletin* a year, supplemented by circulars. The *Bulletin* contains articles on cultivation, species, hybrids, pests and diseases. There is an interesting programme of visits and lectures and the society will be holding its first show at Trevarez in Brittany from 8 to 12 May 1997.

Société des Amateurs de Jardins Alpins

43, rue Buffon, F-75005 Paris, France

MEMBERSHIP   600

The French alpine society is a regular exhibitor at French flower shows.

Société Française d'Orchidophilie

84, rue de Grenelle, F-75007 Paris, France
☎ 00 33 1 45 69 50 50

AIMS   Study, cultivation and conservation of orchids
MEMBERSHIP   1,500
SUBSCRIPTIONS   FF 250 France; FF 290 abroad
SERVICES   Lectures; library; publications; advice; shows; journal; outings; plant exchanges; pollen bank

The SFO is the most established orchid society in France. It is concerned as much with studying and conserving native orchids as with the cultivation and hybridisation of exotics. Its review *L'Orchidophile* has five issues a year and carries articles of high quality. The programme of events includes activities in every part of France, as well as trips abroad.

Société Française des Chrysanthémistes

53 rue Francis de Pressensé, F-69100 Villeurbane, France
☎ 00 33 4 78 93 48 33   FAX 00 33 4 78 23 65 07

CONTACT   Claude Chanteur (Sec. Gén.)
MEMBERSHIP   600
SUBSCRIPTIONS   FF 120, plus FF 10 joining fee
SERVICES   Shows; journal

Founded in 1896, the society celebrated its centenary last November with a Conference and Show at Bourges. Members receive the quarterly bulletin *Le Chrysanthème* and enjoy free entry to the society's shows.

Société Française des Iris et Plantes Bulbeuses

19, rue du Docteur Kurzenne, F-78350 Jouy en Josas, France
☎ 00 33 2 39 56 12 24

CONTACT   Mme Anne-Marie Chesnais
MEMBERSHIP   400
SUBSCRIPTIONS   FF 180 France; FF 210 abroad
SERVICES   Lectures; seed scheme; advice; outings; registration of new hybrids

Irises are very popular in France, where many more varieties are grown than in UK. Members of the French society receive the quarterly bulletin *Iris et Bulbeuses*, which has a mixture of articles about varieties, botany, breeding, new introductions and reports of events. The society is recovering well from a period of poor financial administration.

Société Française des Roses 'Les Amis des Roses'

Roseraie du Parc de la Tête d'Or, F-69006 Lyon, France
☎ 00 33 16 78 94 31 07

Société National d'Horticulture de France

84, rue de Grenelle, Paris F-75007, France
☎ 00 33 1 45 48 81 00

Société Nationale Belge 'Les amis de la Rose'

Korte Aststraat 12, B-9750 Huise-Zingem, Belgium
☎ & FAX 00 32 9 3848339

MEMBERSHIP   800

SUBSCRIPTIONS BFr 500 Belgium; BFr 600 abroad

SERVICES Publications; advice; shows; journal; outings

Members receive three newsletters a year, the annual *Rosa Belgica* and free entry to the society's shows. The society was founded in 1926 and is currently much involved in organising the Benelux Rose Convention in 1997.

The Society for Japanese Irises

9823 E. Michigan Avenue, Galesburg, MI 49053, U.S.A.

☎ 00 1 616 665 7500

CONTACT Robert A. Bauer (Membership Secretary)

AIMS The culture, appreciation & breeding of Japanese irises

MEMBERSHIP 620

SUBSCRIPTIONS US$3.50 single; US$4 double

SERVICES Lectures; library; publications; advice; journal; special interest and regional groups; outings; slide library

A section of the American Iris Society, with some outstanding professionals and experts among its members, but run primarily for amateurs. The Society holds its own trials, and encourages members to be involved in breeding improved varieties. The main publication is a twice-yearly *Review* with articles about activities, gardens, breeding and new varieties.

Society for Louisiana Irises

P O Box 40175, Lafayette, LA 70504, U.S.A.

AIMS To promote the five native species of *Iris* in Louisiana

MEMBERSHIP 460

SUBSCRIPTIONS US$7.50 single; US$9 family. Overseas US$10 & US$12

SERVICES Lectures; shows; journal; outings

An independent organisation, founded in 1941, and closely connected to the American Iris Society. The Society has international representatives in Australia, New Zealand and South Africa but not yet in the UK. The quarterly Newsletter has articles on hybridising and cultivation, reports of shows and meetings, and news of developments in the Iris world. Its book on *The Louisiana Iris* by Marie Caillet & Joseph K. Mertzweiller, published in 1988, is the standard work on the subject. The highlight of the society's year is the annual convention in April at Lafayette, in association with a flower show which is open to the public on the second and third day.

Society for Pacific Coast Native Iris

4333 Oak Hill Road, Oakland, CA 94605, U.S.A.

CONTACT Adele Lawyer

MEMBERSHIP 450

SUBSCRIPTIONS US$4 single; US$5 family

SERVICES Seed scheme; publications; journal

Members receive the SPCNI *Almanac* which is published twice yearly and contains articles on cultivation and where to find PCI species growing in the wild. The seed scheme gives access to wild-collected species and garden hybrids. The society will be running a field trip this year on 10 & 11 May to study species in the wild, based at Roseberg in Oregon.

Southern California Camellia Society

7475 Brydon Road, La Verne, CA 91750, U.S.A.

☎ 00 1 909 593 4894

CONTACT Bobbie Belcher (Secretary-Treasurer)

SUBSCRIPTIONS US$20 single

SERVICES Lectures; seed scheme; publications; shows; journal; outings

One of 13 regional Camellia societies throughout California with a good number of members in New Zealand and Australia where the climatic conditions are similar. Members receive *The Camellia Review* quarterly. The society's major publication is *Camellia Nomenclature*, issued every three years. Monthly meetings are held at Los Angeles County Arboretum and the society organises about 10 shows between December and March.

Succulent Society of South Africa

Private Bag X10, Brooklyn, 0011 Pretoria, South Africa

[FAX] 00 27 12 991 2988

SUBSCRIPTIONS £19 surface mail; £29.50 airmail

SERVICES Seed scheme; journal

The society's quarterly journal *Aloe* concentrates upon the rich succulent flora of southern Africa.

Svenska Rosensällskapet

Spireavägen 14, S-70375 Örebro, Sweden

☎ & [FAX] 00 46 19 314566

CONTACT Denise Andersson

MEMBERSHIP 1,400

SUBSCRIPTIONS SKr 130

SERVICES Lectures; publications; advice; shows; journal; special interest and regional groups; outings

Founded in 1987, the Swedish rose society has a flourishing membership and an active programme of events. There are ten regional branches throughout Sweden, each with their own programme of events throughout the year. The society enjoys close relations with the Norwegian, Danish and Finnish rose societies and together they mount an annual Nordic Rose weekend. The quarterly newsletter *Rosenbladet* is stylishly edited and has articles on cultivation, new varieties, hardiness and rose gardens to visit: it has a particularly good international perspective.

Szo. Czs. Martagon (Czech Lily Society)

Mochovská 33, 190 00 Praha 9, Czech Republic

CONTACT Dr Karel Veres (President)

MEMBERSHIP 250

SUBSCRIPTIONS CzK. 80

SERVICES Lectures; seed scheme; shows; journal; outings; bulb exchange

The Czech lily society has been operating at a high level for many years. Its quarterly Bulletin (in Czech) runs regular reports on Czech-raised hybrids: the autumn 1995 edition carried an interesting article on whether a number of cultivars that could loosely be ascribed to *Lilium martagon* var. *album* and var. *albiflorum* should in fact be regarded as hybrids of *Lilium martagon*.

Tasmanian Daffodil Council
103 Carella Street, Howrah 7018, Tasmania, Australia
☎ 00 61 02 478226

CONTACT   Mrs Mary Crow (Secretary)
MEMBERSHIP   110
SUBSCRIPTIONS   A$12 single; A$15 double; A$16 overseas
SERVICES   Advice; journal

By far the largest daffodil body in Australia, and growing steadily.

Unione Bonsaisti Italiani
Via G Brodolini, 14, I-63020 Montappone (AP), Italy
☎ & [FAX] 00 39 734 761022

CONTACT   The Secretary
SERVICES   Shows; journal

The parent organisation for bonsai clubs in Italy, where the art of bonsai thrives, particularly in the north of the country. The magazine *Notiziario* is a quality publication.

Verein Deutscher Rosenfreunde
Waldseestrasse 14, D-76530 Baden-Baden, Germany
☎ 00 49 7221 31302   [FAX] 00 49 7221 38337

CONTACT   Frau H Bartetzko
MEMBERSHIP   8,500
SUBSCRIPTIONS   DM 42 single; DM 50 double
SERVICES   Lectures; associated gardens; library; publications; advice; awards; shows; journal; special interest and regional groups; outings

Lieben Sie Rosen? Dann sollten Sie VDR Mitglied werden. The German rose society is the best-run rose society in Europe and offers good value to members abroad through its informative quarterly *Rosenbogen* and its quality *Jahrbuch.* The great rose gardens at Westfalen Park in Dortmund managed by the VDR are a model that every rose society could to advantage copy.

Vereinigung Deutscher Orchideenfreunde
Herderstr. 12a, D-85055 Ingolstadt, Germany
CONTACT   Mathilde Heiligtag
SERVICES   Lectures; publications; advice; shows; journal; special interest and regional groups

The parent organisation for orchid fans and local orchid clubs in Germany.

Victorian Orchid Club
P O Box 68, Officer, Victoria 3809, Australia
☎ 00 61 59 41 3917

CONTACT   Ms Judith Clark

Vlaamse Bonsai Vereniging
Klerkenstraat 27, B-8310 Brugge, Belgium
The Flemish bonsai society.

Vlaamse Irisvereniging
Hogeweg 111, B-2940 Stabroek, Belgium
CONTACT   Gilbert Versijwer
SUBSCRIPTIONS   BFr 600
SERVICES   Lectures; seed scheme; advice; shows; journal; special interest and regional groups

The Flemish *Iris* society runs plant exchanges which are not limited to irises but extend to other herbaceous plants, and publishes a quarterly magazine *Iris.*

Western Horticultural Society
P O Box 60507, Palo Alto, CA 94306, U.S.A.
CONTACT   Robert Young

World Pumpkin Confederation
Gowanda State Road, Collins, NY 14034, U.S.A.
☎ 00 1 716 532 5995   [FAX] 00 1 716 532 5690

CONTACT   Ray Waterman (President)
AIMS   Growing and studying pumpkins, melons & squashes
MEMBERSHIP   2,000
SUBSCRIPTIONS   US$15 US; US$20 Canada; US$25 other countries
SERVICES   Shows; journal; competitions

Largely devoted to competitions for the heaviest pumpkins, squashes and watermelons, the confederation has members, competitions and correspondents in 30 countries, including the UK. A prize of $50,000 is available to the first person to raise a 1,000 lb. pumpkin, which seemed a far cry when it was first offered in 1986 and the world record stood at 671 lb. But the current world record is 836 lb. so it is only a matter of time before someone claims the big one.

7

New Plants

Awards to New Plants from Trials, Shows & Exhibits

Introducing a new plant

New varieties and cultivars of plants don't just arrive in seed catalogues and nurseries. The Horticultural Research Institute called a full press conference last year to show off two of their new strawberries: one fruits non-stop from July to October, while the other has strawberries which are three inches in diameter and three ounces in weight. Some advances are the result of years of top secret work while others just turn up in someone's back garden. Either way, a keen eye and a good deal of patience are at least as important as scientific and horticultural knowledge in the business of breeding new varieties and cultivars of garden plants. Genetic engineering may change the picture one day, but raising new plants is as yet an area where in theory the amateur can compete with the professionals.

Plant breeding may be defined as the fixation of a desirable combination of genes in a cultivar. There are broadly two types of cultivar. First, there are clonal cultivars, propagated vegetatively, where a good genetic combination is maintained by avoiding the genetic mixing associated with sexual reproduction – the new roses like 'Molineux' that won prizes in the trials listed below are clonal cultivars. Second, there are seed-propagated cultivars, where genetic recombination is used to produce the desired genetic mix – the *Fleuroselect* winners listed below are an example. Both types are of great importance in horticultural crops.

For the amateur, there are two stages of development. First you have to breed or select a new cultivar which is genetically stable and good enough to be introduced. Then you have the problems of propagating it in sufficient quantities and marketing and selling your new variety or cultivar. Trial and error may be enough for the first stage, but you can turn to the specialist societies for advice also. Most will have knowledgeable members who can point you in the right direction and warn you against such

problems as genetic incompatibility between certain species or sections within a genus. Some societies are more active still and make breeding material available to their members. The Hardy Plant Society has published a useful booklet, *Raising New Plants*, which contains general information about the mechanics of plant breeding and details of how the society can help you take your hobby a stage further. The classic guide is W J C Lawrence's *Practical Plant Breeding*. Many books which are devoted to a particular genus include useful material on genetics and the techniques of plant breeding which are applicable to other genera.

Propagating and marketing a new plant are probably best left to the professionals, unless the plant is only likely to appeal to a small group of enthusiasts. You can test the water by sending your plant for trial at the RHS, the Royal National Rose Society, or one of the other societies which organises trials for specific genera. RHS members can also enter a plant for an award by taking it to one of the society's shows. The experts on the judging committees will assess its potential and may recommend the plant for an award or advise further trials.

A more high profile approach is to make a commercial nursery do the work for you. Keep an eye out for the nurseries which regularly bring novelties into commerce, and contact one which handles plants of the right type. The major seed companies for example are always looking out for new strains which they can promote in their annual catalogues. Some have formal schemes to encourage amateur hybridisers. Thompson & Morgan produces an easy to understand leaflet which explains its procedures and gives tips on how to get started, including some plants which are suitable for the beginner to experiment with.

Blooms of Bressingham is among the nurseries which are always interested in potential new additions to their list. We give the way they deal with new plants here as an illustration: expect a similar *régime* at other nurseries, though precise details may differ. In the first instance Blooms require a photograph and a letter which describes in what way the plant is different from existing varieties.

Their experienced staff will quickly recognise an improvement on the type. Do not send any plant material until they ask for it. If they think the plant may be of commercial quality, they will propagate and evaluate it for up to two years. They may also send it to their agents abroad or to National Collection holders for an opinion on its merits and for confirmation that it is sufficiently distinct to be introduced. During this period Blooms keep meticulous records of its growth and performance, and also inform you of its progress; they are always careful to acknowledge the original raiser. If it still looks good after trialling, they may consider taking out Plant Breeder's Rights for the plant, after discussing this with you. A financial settlement will need to be negotiated, and they will consider either buying your interest in the plant outright, or offering you a percentage on sales. A major new introduction would be marketed in Europe and the USA through their agents: the rights apply overseas too.

Self-satisfaction and local glory aside, there is a chance of making money from your intervention in nature's handiwork. Yet on your own the expense of registering your interest in the plant may prove prohibitive. You may seek the advice of a marketing consultant who specialises in horticultural novelties and can guide you through the legal maze of Plant Breeders' Rights: Genesis (9 Portland Street, King's Lynn, Norfolk PE30 1PB) have many new plants on their books, including the white-flowered *Aubrieta* 'Purity' and a dwarf-growing *Weigela*. The legislation in the *Plant Varieties and Seeds Act 1964* and the *Plant Breeders Rights (Fees) Regulations 1990* lays down stringent procedures including trials and evaluations. At every stage of the process a hefty fee is payable. The result has been that PBR is usually only resorted to – even by the trade – for plants that have the chance of outstanding commercial success and which are expensive to develop. The main categories are roses, chrysanthemums and pelargoniums. Look in *The RHS Plant Finder*, where such plants are marked.

From *The RHS Plant Finder* you will see that in some genera varieties proliferate for no good reason. Gardeners and nurseryman all suffer from indiscriminate introductions, which detract from the better plants and confuse the public. The following points, which echo the stages of the PBR system, offer some ground rules for hybridisers:

Make sure that a 'new' plant really is new. It could be growing somewhere else under a different name. In the past it was common for the same plant to circulate under several different names at once, and the confusion has not yet been eradicated. Don't add to this problem. Check against specimens in botanic gardens or the NCCPG National Collections: a trained eye may be needed.

Confirm that the plant is distinct in its ornamental features (as opposed to botanical characteristics). Find a variety that is closest to yours and note every way in which the two plants differ. If there is nothing else like it, you may be onto a winner.

Increase your stocks. This is not just a preliminary to distributing it. The form may not be stable or may be difficult to replicate. Bulk up the plants and grow them on to see how they behave. The recent introduction *Lavatera* 'Barnsley' seemed to have no drawbacks until it showed a tendency to revert back to the ordinary form of *Lavatera thuringiaca*.

If the plant is raised from seed, then you must make sure that it will come true from seed. You will require several generations of further crosses to develop a pure seed strain. That said, there is no need to be put off. Hybridising is fun and frequently addictive. All your attempts, even the disastrous ones, will produce unique results. Even if you never seem to be getting anywhere there is nothing to stop you from trying again. And again.

Finally, readers who are interested in new plants – who has got what, and why it is an improvement on existing cultivars – should subscribe to the new quarterly journal *Plants*. It is subtitled 'New, Rare & Elusive Plants: A Journal for New Plant Hunters' and costs £14 a year from Aquilegia Publishing, 2 Grange Close, Hartlepool, Cleveland TS26 0DU. The editor Dick van der Werff scours seed lists and nursery catalogues for their novelties and reports on them with wisdom and enthusiasm. It brings the excitement of plant-hunting to your armchair.

Trials

Many horticultural institutes, private and public, carry out tests and assessments on new and established varieties of plant. These include Fleuroselect, which is mainly concerned with annuals grown from seed for summer bedding; the Royal Horticultural Society, which runs both temporary and permanent trials of a very wide selection of annuals, perennials, shrubs, bulbs, fruit and vegetables; the Northern Horticultural Society, which tests the same range as the RHS, but limits its assessments to fewer varieties; and the Royal National Rose Society, which conducts three-year tests on over 200 new rose varieties every year. We report from all these institutions below. *Gardening from Which?* also undertakes useful trials of many types of plant, from annuals to trees, and publishes the results month-by-month in *Gardening from Which?* There is an emphasis upon established varieties, rather than novelties. The results of all these trials is a good test of what is on the market and what may be expected when the introducers have been able to bulk up their stocks to a commercial volume.

The Royal Horticultural Society

Some years ago, the RHS introduced a 'kite-mark' for good garden plants which receive the Award of Garden Merit. The symbol has the shape of a trophy and is now widely adopted by gardening publications and on plant tags at nurseries and garden centres. The trophy symbol simplifies the decision-making process for gardeners who want a plant which offers the best all-round garden value.

In order to qualify as an AGM plant, it should: be of outstanding excellence for garden decoration or use; be available in the trade; be of good constitution; and require neither highly specialist growing conditions or care. AGMs are only awarded after a period of assessment by the relevant committee of the RHS. That assessment may take the form of: a trial at one of the RHS gardens or similar venue; visits to specialist collections; round table discussions which draw on the expertise and experience of committee members.

Permanent trials are conducted at Wisley with border carnations, early-flowering chrysanthemums, daffodils, dahlias, day-lilies, delphiniums, garden pinks, irises and sweet peas. Permanent trials of camellias are situated on nearby Battleston Hill. These trials continue from year to year with periodic replanting, at which time additions and removals are made. Results of trials are published in the horticultural press and in publications of the RHS available to members on request from the trials office at Wisley.

There follows a selection of the AGM awards made at the Wisley Trials during 1996:

Bean, French Dwarf (green types in unheated tunnels): 'Aramis', 'Artigo', 'Ferrari', 'Forum', 'Irago', 'The Prince' (Suttons).

Cabbage (early red, non-storing types): 'Bavero', 'Red Flare', 'Reddy', 'Rodeo', 'Rondy', 'Rookie'.

Camellia: williamsii 'Saint Michael', williamsii 'Jenefer Carlyon', williamsii 'Tiptoe', 'Freedom Bell'.

Carnations, Border (RHS and British National Carnation Society): 'Claire Tautz', 'Natalie Saunders', 'Nichola Ann', 'Spinfield Lane'.

Carnations, Perpetual flowering: 'Ann Unitt', 'Dark Pierrot', 'Malaga', 'Pierrot' (syn. Kobusa).

Dahlia: 'Alan Melville', 'Allan Sparkes', 'Andrew Magson', 'Bridge View Aloha', 'Dark Stranger', 'Elmdon Hank', 'Freya's Thalia', 'Freya's Sweetheart', 'Hamari

Rosé', 'Harvest Inflammation', 'Harvest Samantha', 'Kenora Valentine', 'Little Dorrit', 'Omo', 'Peachette'.

Delphinium (RHS and Delphinium Society): 'Cassius', 'Our Deb', 'Thamesmead', 'Walton Gemstone'.

Endive: 'Atria', 'Elysée', 'Golda', 'Jeti', 'Pancalieri', 'Sally'.

Fennel: 'Atos', 'Carmo', 'Dover', 'Heracles', 'Zefa Fino'.

Fritillaria: *F. persica* 'Adiyaman'.

Gazania (from seed): 'Daybreak Bright Orange', 'Daybreak Garden Sun'.

Gazania (from plants): 'Dorothy', 'Michael', 'Northbourne', *G. rigens* var. *uniflora*.

Iris, Pacific Coast: 'Goring Ace'.

Iris spuria: 'Lydia Jane'.

Iris, Tall Bearded: 'Breakers', 'Cardew', 'Meg's Mantle', 'Morwenna', 'Phil Keen', 'Princess Sabra', 'Precious Heather', 'Severn Side', 'Cream Soda', 'Sherwood Pink', Sherwood Primrose', 'Apricorange', 'Nicola Jane'.

Lavatera (Annual, from seed): 'Beauty Formula Mixture', 'Pink Beauty', 'Salmon Beauty', 'Silver Cup (Tezier)', 'White Beauty', 'White Cherub'.

Narcissus, Miniature: 'April Tears', 'Chit Chat', 'Hawera', 'Pixie's Sister', 'Segovia', 'Sun Disc'.

Onion, Salad types (spring sown): 'Asian Queen', 'Beltsville Bunching', 'Emerald Isle', 'Feast Ishiko', 'Ishikura', 'Laser', 'Ramrod', 'Savel', 'White Spear'.

Pelargonium, Scented leaved: 'Candy Dancer', 'Charity', 'Citriodorum', 'Gemstone', 'Grace Thomas', 'Lara Starshine', 'Nervous Mabel', 'Orsett', 'Peter's Luck', 'Princeanum', 'Radula', 'Royal Oak', 'Sweet Mimosa'. Uniques: 'Bolero', 'Mystery', 'Roller's Satinique', 'Voodoo'.

Phygelius: *rectus* 'African Queen', *aequalis* 'Yellow Trumpet'.

Pieris: 'Sarabande', 'Prelude'.

Pinks, Garden (RHS and British National Carnation Society, cultivars for open border): 'Devon Carla', 'Devon General', 'Devon Pride', 'Diane', 'Oakwood Gillian Garforth', 'Oakwood Romance', 'Trisha's Choice', 'White Joy', 'Zoe's Choice'.

Radish (Round and French breakfast types): 'Cherry Bell (King)', 'Cyros', 'Flamboyant Sabina', 'French Breakfast', 'French Breakfast 3', 'Marabelle', 'Scarlet Globe', 'Sparkler', 'Summer Crunch', 'Tinto'.

Schizanthus (Glasshouse cultivation): 'Dwarf Bouquet Mixed', 'Sweet Lips'.

Spinach (Spring sown): 'Atlanta', 'Long Standing', 'Mazurka', 'Monnopa', 'San Felix', 'San Severo', 'Space', 'Spokane'.

Sweet Corn (super sweet, yellow types): 'Dickson', 'Dynasty', 'Fiesta', 'Golden Sweet', 'Gourmet', 'Northern Extra Sweet', 'Ovation', 'Punchline', 'Start Up'.

Harlow Carr (trials)

The Northern Horticultural Society carries out trials of flowers and vegetables at Harlow Carr near Harrogate, but these are less ambitious and rather more informal than the trials run by the Royal Horticultural Society at Wisley. Their main trial in 1996 was of gazanias grown from seed, which was particularly interesting for two reasons: first, because gazanias need high levels of sunlight, which Har-low Carr is seldom able to offer, and second, because they agreed to compare their results with the RHS's trials of gazanias from seed. Seed of seventeen different cultivars was sown in mid-March, grown on under glass and planted out at the beginning of June. The best performers were 'Dynastar Mixed', 'Splendens Mixed', 'Sunshine Creamy White' and 'Mini-Star Yellow', all of which began to flower by the end of June, reached a peak in mid-August and continued flowering until the first frosts. A second independent panel of judges concluded that 'Mini-Star Yellow' was the best of all. However, there is one impor-tant proviso: the RHS AGM-winner 'Daybreak Bright Orange' was not included in the Harlow Carr trials. It was however grown in the NHS's Fleuroselect trials, where it greatly impressed the judges. In fact, the British Bedding & Pot Plant Association was so impressed by 'Daybreak Bright Orange' that they have named it their 'plant of the year' for 1997.

The Fleuroselect Awards

Fleuroselect is an international marketing and sales organ-isation, based in the Netherlands, whose principal aim is to stimulate the breeding of new and better seed varieties. These are trialled anonymously for germination, growth, performance and flowering period at 25 trial grounds from Scandinavia to Southern Italy. Those which receive the most points are awarded the Fleuroselect Gold Medal: others receive the Fleuroselect Medal or Quality Mark. This year we are publishing all the new seed strains which have won a Fleuroselect Gold Medal since trials began in 1973. Please note that the botanical nomenclature which Fleuroselect uses is sometimes open to question and often just plain wrong: for instance, Dahlia variabilis is cor-rectly known as Dahlia hortensis. However, we have given Fleuroselect's chosen namings on this occasion to

help readers to identify them in seed catalogues. The list that follows amounts to an honours board of all the most distinguished seed strains which we have seen introduced over the last twenty years and more. It is by any reckoning an impressive achievement.

1973
Dianthus chinensis 'Snowflake' Goldsmith
Lavatera trimestris 'Tanagra' Vilmorin
Pelargonium zonale 'Sprinter' S&G Seeds

1974
Antirrhinum majus 'Orange Pixie' Goldsmith
Tagetes patula 'Showboat Yellow' Ferry Morse

1975
Callistephus chinensis 'Pinocchio' Royal Sluis
Dahlia variabilis 'Redskin' Waller
Dianthus chinensis 'Crimson Charm' Goldsmith
Dianthus chinensis 'Scarlet Charm' Goldsmith
Nicotiana affinis 'Crimson Rock' Clause
Tagetes patula 'Honeycomb' Panam

1976
Impatiens walleriana 'Miss Swiss' Mauser
Zinnia elegans 'Pink Ruffles' Bodger

1977
Calendula officinalis 'Fiesta Gitana' Royal Sluis
Helichrysum bracteatum 'Hot Bikini' Benary

1978
Lobularia maritima 'Wonderland' Booker
Salvia farinacea 'Victoria' Clause
Zinnia elegans 'Cherry Ruffles' Bodger
Zinnia elegans 'Yellow Ruffles' Bodger

1979
Dianthus caryophyllus 'Crimson Knight' Goldsmith
Lavatera trimestris 'Mont Blanc' Clause
Lavatera trimestris 'Silver Cup' S&G Seeds
Pelargonium zonale 'Red Express' Panam
Tagetes patula 'Orange Boy' Panam

1980
Coreopsis grandiflora 'Sunray' Tezier
Tagetes patula 'Queen Bee' Panam

1981
Verbena hybrida 'Tropic' Clause
Zinnia elegans 'Pacific Yellow' Bodger

1982
Dianthus caryophyllus 'Scarlet Luminette' Sakata

Dianthus chinensis 'Telstar Mixed' Takii
Gazania splendens 'Mini Star Yellow' Benary
Pelargonium zonale 'Red Elite' Goldsmith
Tagetes hybrida 'Florence' Royal Sluis
Tagetes patula 'Silvia' Daehnfeldt
Tagetes patula 'Yellow Jacket' Panam
Zinnia elegans 'Dasher Scarlet' Bodger

1983
Petunia grandiflora 'Red Picotee' Sakata

1984
Pelargonium zonale 'Cherry Diamond' Walz
Pelargonium zonale 'Scarlet Diamond' Walz

1985
Gazania splendens 'Mini Star Tangerine' Benary
Rudbeckia hirta 'Goldilocks' Booker

1986
Pelargonium peltatum 'Summer Showers' Panam

1987
Impatiens walleriana 'Starbright' Goldsmith

1988
Alyssum maritimum 'Snow Crystals' Royal Sluis
Dahlia variabilis 'Sunny Yellow' Takii
Verbena hybrida 'Sandy Scarlet' Clause
Verbena hybrida 'Showtime Belle' Panam

1989
Coreopsis grandiflora 'Early Sunrise' Panam
Dianthus hybrida 'Telstar Crimson' Takii
Lobelia speciosa 'Compliment Scarlet' Benary
Tagetes patula 'Disco Golden Yellow' Bodger
Tagetes patula 'Disco Orange' Bodger
Tagetes patula 'España Mix' Panam
Tagetes patula 'Orange Jacket' Panam

1990
Gazania splendens 'Garden Sun' Panam
Viola wittrockiana 'Jolly Joker' Benary

1991
Begonia tuberhybrida 'Pin Up' Benary
Cosmos bipinnatus 'Sonata' Royal Sluis
Dianthus hybrida 'Color Magician' Takii
Dianthus chinensis 'Raspberry Parfait' Goldsmith
Dianthus chinensis 'Strawberry Parfait' Goldsmith
Eschscholtzia californica 'Dalli' Sperling
Pelargonium hortorum 'Orange Appeal' Goldsmith
Viola wittrockiana 'Imperial Gold Princess' Takii
Viola wittrockiana 'Padparadja' Benary

1992
Callistephus chinensis 'Starlight Rose' Dittmar
Impatiens walleriana 'Mega Orange Star' Goldsmith
Salvia coccinea 'Lady-in-Red' Sahin
Tagetes patula 'Safari Tangerine' Bodger
Verbena hybrida 'Peaches & Cream' Sahin

1993
Limonium sinuatum 'Forever Gold' Sahin
Nierembergia hippomanica 'Mont Blanc' Takii
Verbena speciosa 'Imagination' Benary
Viola tricolor 'Imperial Frosty Rose' Takii

1994
Bellis perennis 'Robella' Röggli
Centaurea cyanus 'Florence Pink' Royal Sluis
Centaurea cyanus 'Florence White' Royal Sluis
Viola 'Velour Blue' Clause

1995
Fuchsia hybrida 'Florabelle' Panam
Lobelia speciosa 'Fan Scarlet' Benary
Nicotiana 'Havana Appleblossom' Daehnfeldt
Papaver orientale 'Pizzicato' Tezier

1996
Ammobium alatum 'Bikini' Benary
Petunia hybrida 'Lavender Storm' Goldsmith
Salvia farinacea 'Strata' Clause

1997
Gazania splendens 'Daybreak Orange' Panam
Delphinium 'Centurion Sky Blue' Röggli
Myosotis sylvatica 'Rosylva' Clause

International Rose Trials 1996: List of Awards made by the Trials Committee of the Royal National Rose Society

The list of roses receiving awards from the Royal National Rose Society is very much less interesting than it used to be when the varieties were released into commerce with proper names before being sent to trial. We are therefore fortunate that, once again, last year's winner of the President's International Trophy is already in commerce under the memorable Midlands name of 'Molineux'. It was an exceptional winner, by a very large margin, and is the first rose of David Austin's to win the RNRS's top prize. There are, however, three interesting points to emerge from the list that follows. First, there continues to be a strong move away from traditional hybrid teas and floribundas (now known to the RNRS, but to no-one else, as large-flowered roses and clustered-flowered roses respectively) towards ground cover, miniature and shrub roses of one sort or another. Second, despite the regrettable move away from disclosing the parentage of new roses, it is clear that certain lines are emerging which will have a significant influence on the future – in particular, the polyantha types like 'Eye Opener'. Third, the parents of the new roses, where they are actually disclosed, indicate a strong resurgence of interest in breeding from the early hybrids of *Rosa multiflora*: indeed, the 'ground-cover shrub rose' which received an award after only two years of trialling (and which rejoices in the name of R9) is by parentage a pure polyantha.

Please note that, in the list of winners which now follows, cultivars which have been given a popular name are shown in inverted commas e.g. 'MOLINEUX'. Names without inverted commas, e.g. HORCOEXIST, are provisional code-names or names used for registration.

The President's International Trophy for the best new seedling rose of the year, a Gold Medal and The Henry Edland Memorial Medal for the best scented rose:

'MOLINEUX' (AUSMOL). Shrub; yellow; bears clusters of very many double blooms; bushy growth, 2–4ft. Very good scent. Bred from 'Graham Thomas' × 'Golden Showers'. *David Austin, 1995.*

A Gold Medal and The Torridge Award for best amateur-raised award-winner:

HORCOEXIST. Shrub; gold, with red edges; bears clusters of very many single blooms; growth spreading and dense, 2–4ft; foliage neat and small. Little scent. [('Little Darling' × 'Anna Ford') × 'Sea Foam'] ×['Little Darling' × ('Hamburger Phönix' × 'Prelude')]. *Colin Horner, England.*

A Gold Medal was awarded to:

'TOP OF THE BILL' (Gensur). Ground cover shrub; bright mid-pink; bears clusters of very many semi-double blooms; growth bushy and spreading, 2–4ft. Good scent. 'Surrey' × unnamed seedling. *Genesis, England.*

Certificates of Merit were awarded to:

WAX 93. Shrub; pink with yellow eye; bears clusters of many single blooms; growth bushy, 4–6ft; foliage light green. Light scent. 'Anna Ford' seedling. *T L Watson, England.*

DICWORKER. Ground-cover shrub; red; bears clusters of very many single red blooms; growth bushy and spread-

ing, 2-4ft. Little scent. ('Snow Carpet' × unnamed seedling) × ('Little Prince' × 'Eye Opener'). *Dickson, Northern Ireland.*

DICKWHISTLE. Ground-cover shrub; pink; bears clusters of very many double blooms; growth spreading, 2–4ft. Light scent. Unnamed seedling × 'The Fairy'. *Dickson, Northern Ireland.*

SHERILOWSTRI. Dwarf Floribunda; salmon-orange with creamy stripe; bears clusters of several semi-double blooms; growth bushy, 1–2ft. Moderate scent. 'Summer Tan' × unnamed striped seedling. *Sheridan, England.*

791x90. Ground-cover shrub; pink with white eye; bears clusters of very many single blooms; growth dense and bushy; 2–4ft. Light scent. 'Flower Carpet' × unnamed seedling. *Noack, Germany.*

KORHASSI. Shrub; red; bears clusters of several double blooms; growth upright and bushy; 2–4ft; foliage has good autumn tints. Moderate scent. Kordes, Germany.

MACREDPARAP. Ground-cover shrub; red; bears clusters of blooms; growth bushy, spreading and dense, 2–4ft. Little scent. 'Sexy Rexy' × 'Eye Opener'. *McGredy, New Zealand.*

Trial Ground Certificates were awarded to:

DICWHYNOT. Ground-cover shrub; blush; bears clusters of many semi-double blooms; growth bushy and spreading, up to 2ft. Little scent. Unnamed seedling × 'The Fairy'. *Dickson, Northern Ireland.*

B826-88. Ground-cover shrub; salmon-orange with yellow eye; bears clusters of many double blooms; growth bushy and spreading, 2–4ft; foliage dark green and glossy. Moderate scent. *Interplant, Holland.*

DRISCOBERT. Dwarf Floribunda; red with yellow eye, cream reverse; bears clusters of very many semi-double blooms; growth bushy and spreading, 1–2ft. Little scent. *Driscoll, England.*

JON 8919. Dwarf Floribunda; red and silver blends; bears clusters of many semi-double blooms; growth spreading, 1–2ft. Light scent. C & K Jones, England.

'SORBET FRAMBOISE' (Delsorb). Floribunda; pink and white stripes; bears clusters of very many semi-double blooms; growth upright, 2–4ft. Moderate scent. 'International Herald Tribune' × unnamed seedling. *Delbard, France.*

KORVERPEA. Hybrid Tea; veined dusky red with gold reverse; bears many double blooms; growth upright, 2–4ft. Good scent. *Kordes, Germany.*

MEHNINA. Climbing miniature; dark red; bears clusters of several double blooms; climbs to 10ft. Little scent. ('Iceberg' × 'Anytime') × 'Eye Opener'. *Eurosa, England.*

KORVERLANDUS. Ground-cover shrub; bright cerise pink; bears clusters of very many double blooms; growth spreading, up to 2ft. Light scent. *Kordes, Germany.*

521-90. Shrub; pink; bears clusters of several single blooms; growth bushy, 2–4ft. Good scent. 'Flower Carpet' × unnamed seedling. *Noack, Germany.*

HARBOUNTY. Shrub; bright red; bears clusters of very many double blooms; growth bushy, 2–4ft; nice dark glossy foliage. Moderate scent. 'Sweet Magic' × unnamed seedling. *Harkness, England.*

'PRINCE REGENT' (Genpen). Shrub; dark wine-red; bears clusters of very many semi-double blooms; growth spreading, 2–4ft. Little scent. 'Marjorie Fair' × unnamed seedling. *Genesis, England.*

GENSEN. Shrub; glossy dark red with white fleck; bears clusters of very many semi-double blooms; growth spreading and arching, 4–6ft. Light scent. *Genesis, England.*

ARB 396. Shrub; red; bears clusters of several single blooms; growth spreading, 2–4ft; many lovely bright red hips. Good scent. *Meilland, France.*

PEAYANKEE. Hybrid Tea; peach pink; bears many double blooms; growth upright, over 4ft. Very good scent. 'Memory Lane' × 'Sweetheart'. *Limes New Roses, England.*

ALMAL. Dwarf Floribunda; apricot yellow; bears clusters of very many double blooms; upright growth, 1–2ft. Moderate scent. Sport of 'Sweet Dream'. *Hockenhull Roses, England.*

1581x90. Shrub; dusky pink; bears clusters of several semi-double blooms; growth bushy, 2–4ft. Moderate scent. Unnamed seedling × 'Gruß an Aachen'. *Noack, Germany.*

RUM.1.COOKSEN. Climber; pink; bears clusters of many semi-double blooms; climbs to 10ft. Light scent. *Rumwood Nurseries, England.*

HARBABBLE. Hybrid Tea; glossy salmon-pink; bears many double blooms; growth upright, 2–4ft. Good scent. Rose of the Year, 1997. 'Harold Macmillan' × 'Fellowship'. *Harkness, England.*

Awards made after the second year of trial:

R9. Ground-cover shrub; white; bears clusters of very many semi-double blooms; growth spreading, 2ft. Light scent. 'Sanders White' × 'Yesterday'. *M J Law, England.*

JP 90-3559-2. Floribunda; magenta with silver eye and reverse; bears clusters of very many semi-double blooms; growth upright, 2–4ft. Light scent. *Bear Creek Nurseries, USA.*

POL 89 8254-8. Dwarf Floribunda; light pink; bears clusters of many double blooms; growth spreading. 1–2ft. Moderate scent. *Poulsen, Denmark.*

Readers might like to be reminded of the other important trials which the RNRS has carried out at The Gardens of the Rose in recent years. They began in 1990 with the widely reported pruning trials, done in conjunction with *Gardening Which?* which found that the rough pruning of bushes to the same height with a hedgetrimmer (or secateurs) every spring is not only quicker and simpler than traditional techniques but also produces better results. Seven years on, the RNRS is certain that rough pruning not only does no harm to the roses but actually produces better flowering and leads to stronger growth. Once these results began to appear, year after year, the RNRS had to ask the question – why does rough pruning produce more and better flowers? It seems that the reason is that it leaves more little twiggy stems on the bushes and thus more foliage to manufacture the food that will produce the flowers. The RNRS is now extending the trial to evaluate the practice of deadheading in summer as well as carrying out trials on such topics as disease control, mulching and specific replant disease.

8

Nurseries & Garden Centres

We have chosen a range of nurseries from the smallest and most specialised to the largest of the garden centres. Between these two poles, there should be several to suit everyone's needs.

There are three ways of finding nurseries in this book. In this section they are listed by county. We have used the 1974 county names in England and Wales (as amended – which means omitting Avon, Cleveland and Humberside) and have adopted the old regional divisions of Scotland. The English counties are followed by Wales, Scotland, Northern Ireland, the Channel Islands, the Isle of Man, and Eire. To help plan a visit, nurseries have been ordered wherever possible into their geographical counties rather than by their postal address. Strict alphabetical order has been followed here so that, for example, the rose breeders R. Harkness & Co. are listed under 'R' and not 'H'. In addition, all nurseries and garden centres appear alphabetically in the index at the end of the book where initials and prefixes are disregarded (so 'Harkness & Co. R.'). Finally the next section, Nursery Specialities, lists many of the nurseries by specialisation. The county name appears there to help to locate the entry in the main listing. We have restricted this list to true specialists: those with an excellent general range are not included. These specialisations also appear in the main entry for each nursery or garden centre, where appropriate. Please note that the order in which the various specialisations are given is not necessarily a guide to their predominance at the nursery – that information is given in the main body of each entry.

Mail order is an issue which splits the trade. Most garden centres do not offer this service, nor will some traditional or smaller nurseries. We have indicated those who do. Buying by post obviously means that you cannot inspect the plants first. You still have a right to expect healthy specimens nonetheless. Remember that posted plants are likely to be smaller than normal, to save on space

and postage costs. They will also probably be sent in the dormant season when the plant will be better able to cope with the journey through the postal system, and when the nurseryman is less busy. Trees are usually sent by road carrier; roses travel cheaply in paper sacks. Other plants need careful and time-consuming packing for which you will have to pay.

Some nurseries have demonstration and display gardens: these are mentioned. On occasions we have had to consider whether to treat a site as a garden or a nursery. There is a trend for nurseries to sport a garden where the plants they grow can be seen in mature growth and for garden owners to offer plants in a nursery which in no time brings in more income than the garden openings themselves. See also the publications of the National Gardens Scheme and Scotland's Garden Scheme: a number of nurseries open regularly for these charities. Where nurseries have indicated that they hold a National Collection, we have included this information: it is probably best to ask the nursery directly about opening times, or consult *The National Plant Collections Directory 1997*. Other useful publications are a good road atlas for tracking down the nursery site, and a current copy of *The RHS Plant Finder*. Do buy the 1997/98 edition, and throw away earlier ones: some nurseries have become so exasperated by people telephoning to ask about plants which they have not stocked for some years, that they have asked to be taken out of *The RHS Plant Finder* altogether. This is most regrettable, and could easily be avoided if people made sure that they always use the current edition.

Garden centres usually observe fixed opening times. Traditional nurseries tend to open early and close at dusk. Opening hours at smaller nurseries may depend on shows and other commitments. Of course, some nurseries only operate by mail order: they do not open at all. If in doubt, phone first. Sunday trading laws have had a disastrous effect on large nurseries and garden centres in England and Wales: they are now open only for six hours on Sundays. It is high time that this ludicrous anomaly was corrected. Fortunately, smaller nurseries face no such restrictions.

ENGLAND

BEDFORDSHIRE

Bickerdike's Garden Centre
London Road, Sandy SG19 1DW
☎ 01767 680559   [FAX] 01767 680356
LOCATION   On A1
OPEN   9 am – 5.30 pm, Monday – Saturday, 10.30 am – 4.30 pm, Sundays
SHOP   Garden products
GARDEN   Display gardens

Garden centre under the same ownership as Brampton Garden Centre.

Bloms Bulbs Ltd
Primrose Nurseries, Melchbourne MK44 1ZZ
☎ 01234 782424/709099   [FAX] 01234 782495/709799
CONTACT   Sales Office
OPEN   9 am – 5 pm, Monday – Friday. Also 9 am – 12 noon, Saturdays, September only
SPECIALITIES   Bulbs
CATALOGUE   On request
MAIL ORDER   Yes
GARDEN   Display at Chenies Manor, Buckinghamshire, and Pashley Manor, East Sussex: see Gardens section
SHOWS   Malvern (Spring); Chelsea

Major bulb growers: their range covers hyacinth, daffodil, and tulip cultivars; they also have species and a wide selection of smaller bulbs.

Wyevale Garden Centre
Dunstable Road, Caddington, Luton LU1 4AN
☎ 01582 457313   [FAX] 01582 480716
REFRESHMENTS   Restaurant

BERKSHIRE

Bressingham Plant Centre
Dorney Court, Dorney, Windsor SL4 6QP
☎ 01628 669999   [FAX] 01628 669693
CONTACT   Peter Freeman (Manager)
LOCATION   On B3026, signed off A4
OPEN   9 am – 5.30 pm, daily except Christmas and Boxing Day
SPECIALITIES   Alpines; conifers; herbaceous perennials; shrubs
MAIL ORDER   See Bressingham Mail Order
REFRESHMENTS   Tea room
DESIGN SERVICE   Border Planning Service

SHOWS   Chelsea; BBC GW Live; Hampton Court

Blooms' first plant centre to be opened away from Norfolk: Alan Bloom inaugurated it in March 1993. They carry the huge range of perennials and conifers for which the company is renowned. The quality is also outstanding. Talks are held at the plant centre. Nigel Colborn will lecture on 7 May. Mail order is available directly from Norfolk: see Bressingham Mail Order.

Chris Chadwell – Freelance Botanist
81 Parlaunt Road, Slough SL3 8BE
☎ 01753 542823
CONTACT   Chris Chadwell
LOCATION   5 minutes from M4, Jct 5
OPEN   By appointment, May – July only
SPECIALITIES   Seeds; Himalayan plants
CATALOGUE   3 second-class stamps
MAIL ORDER   Yes, seeds
REFRESHMENTS   Garden visitors only
GARDEN   Kohli Memorial Garden, open by appointment, £2.00 donation suggested, which includes refreshments
SHOWS   RHS Westminster

Seeds from the Himalaya. You either subscribe for a share in a collecting expedition, or you can buy from his stocks. Other areas are also available. Many Himalayan species can be seen in the P. N. Kohli Memorial Botanic Garden: not large, but full of unusual species. Mr Chadwell is also secretary of the Sino-Himalayan Plant Association. There is now a small retail nursery for rarities.

Country Gardens
4A Bath Road, Hungerford RG17 0HE
☎ 01488 682916   [FAX] 01488 681718
CONTACT   Ray Cordrey (Manager)
OPEN   9 am – 6 pm, Monday – Saturday; 10.30 am – 4.30 pm, Sundays
SHOP   Patio and ponds
REFRESHMENTS   Coffee shop

Country Gardens
Garden Centre Roundabout, Bath Road, Thatcham RG18 3AN
☎ 01635 871760   [FAX] 01635 872124
CONTACT   Simon Baker (Manager)
LOCATION   30 sites in the south-east and south Midlands

The head office of a chain of 30 garden centres in southern England.

Country Gardens
Dedworth Road, Windsor SL4 4LH
☎ 01753 841791   [FAX] 01753 841754
CONTACT   Brendon Brady (Manager)
OPEN   9 am – 6 pm, Monday – Saturday; 10.30 am – 4.30 pm, Sundays
SHOP   Mowers
REFRESHMENTS   Coffee shop

Foxgrove Plants
Foxgrove, Enborne, Newbury RG14 6RE
☎ 01635 40554

CONTACT   Louise Vockins
LOCATION   West of Newbury
OPEN   10 am – 5 pm, Wednesday – Sunday, and Bank Holidays. Closed in August
SPECIALITIES   Alpines; snowdrops
CATALOGUE   £1 cheque or postal order
MAIL ORDER   Snowdrops only, January to April
SHOWS   RHS Westminster; Malvern (Spring); Malvern (Autumn); Harrogate (Spring); Chelsea; BBC GW Live; Hampton Court

This small nursery carries a pleasing range of hardy and cottage garden type plants, including several new *Saxifraga* cultivars from the Czech Republic. Their speciality is snowdrops: they have a number of species, forms and hybrids. A separate list is published early in the New Year (£1). The nursery will be at some AGS shows. Plantings can be undertaken, and terracotta pans are available to order. Except for snowdrops, the nursery no longer does mail order, but, given notice, plants can be collected from shows.

Henry Street Garden Centre
Swallowfield Road Nursery, Arborfield, Reading RG2 9JY
☎ 0118 9761223   FAX 0118 9761417

CONTACT   M. C. Goold
LOCATION   Off A327 in Arborfield
OPEN   9 am – 5.30 pm, Monday – Saturday; 10 am – 4 pm, Sundays
SPECIALITIES   Bedding plants; roses
CATALOGUE   On request
MAIL ORDER   Yes, bare root only
REFRESHMENTS   The Street Café
GARDEN   Rose fields open

Rose growers whose range covers all types, in mainly modern varieties. They also sell bedding plants, and carry a general stock at the garden centre. There will be pruning demonstrations on 15 – 16 March at the nursery, and a rose Open Weekend with guided tours 19 – 20 July.

Hillier Garden Centre
Priors Court Road, Hermitage, Newbury RG16 9TG
☎ 01635 200442   FAX 01635 200737

CONTACT   John Martin (Manager)
OPEN   9 am – 5.30 pm, Monday – Saturday; 10.30 am – 4.30 pm, Sundays

Hollington Nurseries
Woolton Hill, Newbury RG20 9XT
☎ 01635 253908   FAX 01635 254990

CONTACT   Judith or Simon Hopkinson
LOCATION   4 miles south of Newbury, off A343
OPEN   10 am – 5.30 pm, Monday – Saturday; 11 am – 5 pm, Sundays and Bank Holidays, March to September. Please telephone October to February
SPECIALITIES   Climbers; herbs
CATALOGUE   SAE plus 50p
MAIL ORDER   No
SHOP   Herb products
REFRESHMENTS   Tea room (summer only)
GARDEN   Display gardens in walled garden. Admission £1. Close ½ hour before nursery
DESIGN SERVICE   Hollington Nurseries

A large range of herbs and scented plants in containers, as well as roses to plant with them. Herb and wild flower seeds too. They run courses, and have a garden planning service. A series of informal lecture days is organised in June on using herbs in cookery, details available from March.

Kennedys Garden Centre
Cedar Cottage, Crown Lane, Farnham Royal, Slough SL2 3SG
☎ 01753 645627   FAX 01753 647392

CONTACT   Gillian Bristow (Manager)
OPEN   9 am – 6 pm, Monday – Saturday, April to September, close 5.30 pm, October to March; 10.30 am – 4.30 pm, Sundays
REFRESHMENTS   Café

Kennedys Garden Centre
Floral Mile, Hare Hatch, Twyford, Reading RG10 9SW
☎ 01734 403933   FAX 01734 403705

CONTACT   Ian Simpson (Manager)
OPEN   9 am – 6 pm, Monday – Saturday, April to September, close 5.30 pm, October to March; 10.30 am – 4.30 pm, Sundays

Kennedys Garden Centres Ltd (Head Office)
Kennedy House, 11 Crown Row, Bracknell RG12 3TH
☎ 01344 860022   FAX 01344 860175

Head office and administration only of this garden centre chain. The group's eleven garden centres, in the south and east, are listed separately. The sites are Church Lawford, Claygate, Croydon, Farnham Royal, Folkestone, Hailsham, Hare Hatch, Oxford, Stroud, Swindon and Wellingborough.

Wyevale Garden Centre
Forest Road, Binfield, Bracknell RG12 4HA
☎ 01344 869456   FAX 01344 869541
REFRESHMENTS   Restaurant

Wyevale Garden Centre
Heathlands Road, Wokingham RG11 3BG
☎ 01734 773055   FAX 01734 772949

BUCKINGHAMSHIRE

A J Palmer & Son
Denham Court Nursery, Denham Court Drive, Denham, Uxbridge UB9 5PG
☎ 01895 832035

CONTACT   Sheila or John Palmer
LOCATION   Middle of New Buckinghamshire golf course, near Denham country park
OPEN   Spring: 9 am – 5 pm, Monday – Saturday, 10 am – 1 pm, Sundays. Summer: 9 am – dusk, daily. Autumn: 9 am – 5 pm, Monday – Saturday, 10 am – 1 pm, Sundays. Closed January
SPECIALITIES   Roses

NEW FOR 1997   Rose 'Sunset Boulevard'
CATALOGUE   On request
MAIL ORDER   Yes, collection only for standards
GARDEN   Rose fields

Specialist rose growers with a range of mainly modern varieties. Opening times vary with the seasons and availability. Containerised plants are available in spring, from about mid February to June. From July to October the show field is open for viewing (near the Denham roundabout off the A40). Most of the stock is sold bare-rooted in November.

Buckingham Nurseries and Garden Centre

10 Tingewick Road, Buckingham MK18 4AE
☎ 01280 813556   FAX 01280 815491

CONTACT   P. L. Brown
LOCATION   1½ miles west of Buckingham, on A421
OPEN   Summer: 8.30 am – 6 pm, Monday – Friday, 9.30 am – 6 pm, Sundays; winter: 8.30 am – 5.30 pm, Monday – Friday, 9.30 am – 5.30 pm, Sundays
SPECIALITIES   Hedging; herbaceous perennials; trees
CATALOGUE   On request (September)
MAIL ORDER   Yes
SHOP   Retail garden shop
SHOWS   BBC GW Live

The nursery produces bare-root hedging and tree plants for ornamental and forestry use. There are some interesting varieties of trees and shrubs, with a growing list of herbaceous plants. A selection of container plants, including ones not listed in the catalogue, is sold from the garden centre.

Butterfields Nursery

Harvest Hill, Bourne End SL8 5JJ
☎ 01628 525455
LOCATION   Off B476
OPEN   9 am – 5 pm, usually
SPECIALITIES   Dahlias; pleiones
CATALOGUE   SAE
MAIL ORDER   Yes, pleiones only
GARDEN   Dahlia display during season
SHOWS   RHS Westminster; Malvern (Spring); Chelsea
NCCPG NATIONAL COLLECTIONS Pleione

Butterfields has two main but very different specialities: pleiones and dahlias. The Pleione species are backed up by an impressive list of hybrids. The dahlia range consists of named varieties for showing, flower arranging and garden use. You are advised to phone before visiting, in case they are at a show.

The Conifer Garden

Hare Lane Nursery, Little Kingshill, Great Missenden HP16 0EF
☎ 01494 890624   FAX 01494 862086
CONTACT   Mr or Mrs M. P. S. Powell
LOCATION   Directions in plant list
OPEN   11 am – 4.30 pm, Tuesday – Saturday
SPECIALITIES   Conifers
CATALOGUE   2 first-class stamps for plant list
MAIL ORDER   By arrangement
SHOWS   Harrogate (Spring)

Specialists in conifers of all sizes. The stock is container-grown, and the choice is extensive (over 500). Talks for garden clubs can be arranged.

Country Gardens

London Road, Beaconsfield HP9 1SH
☎ 01494 672522   FAX 01494 670379
CONTACT   Colin Rushby (Manager)
OPEN   9 am – 6 pm, Monday – Saturday; 10.30 am – 4.30 pm, Sundays

Great Gardens of England Ltd

Marlow Garden & Leisure Centre, Pump Lane South, Little Marlow SL7 3RB
☎ 01628 482716
CONTACT   Steve Walker
LOCATION   Off A404, between M4 and M40
OPEN   9 am – 5.30 pm, Monday – Saturday; 10.30 am – 4.30 pm, Sundays
REFRESHMENTS   Restaurant

This large garden centre has a wide range of plants and sundries of general interest.

Jardinerie Ltd

Studley Green, Stokenchurch, High Wycombe HP14 3UX
☎ 01494 483761   FAX 01494 482675
CONTACT   Paul Colson (Manager)
LOCATION   On A40 west of Studley Green
OPEN   9 am – 6 pm (5 pm in January & February); Monday – Saturday; 10.30 am – 4.30 pm, Sundays
SHOP   Gifts, floristry, conservatories, garden buildings, swimming pool centre
REFRESHMENTS   Café

Lower Icknield Farm Nurseries

Lower Icknield Way, Great Kimble, Aylesbury OX44 9PY
☎ 01844 343436   FAX 01865 343267
CONTACT   Mrs Baldwin
LOCATION   On B4009 between Longwick & Great Kimble
OPEN   9 am – 5.30 pm; daily; all year except Christmas – New Year
SPECIALITIES   Chrysanthemums; conservatory plants
CATALOGUE   SAE
MAIL ORDER   No
GARDEN   Two-acre display garden

Chrysanthemums, basket plants, patio plants, tender perennials and some hardy herbaceous plants are this nursery's specialities. All may be seen in their garden, where a backbone of permanent plantings is clothed with bedding plants. Very much a proper nursery: no sundries.

Morehavens Camomile Nurseries

28 Denham Lane, Gerrards Cross SL9 0EX
☎ 01494 871563
CONTACT   Ann Farmer
LOCATION   Telephone for directions
OPEN   Collection by arrangement
SPECIALITIES   Camomile for lawns
CATALOGUE   SAE

MAIL ORDER Yes, p & p included
GARDEN Gardens
Camomile lawns by first-class post.

Tamarisk Nurseries
Wing Road, Stewkley, Leighton Buzzard LU7 0JB
☎ & FAX 01525 240747

CONTACT Alan Cupit
LOCATION North Buckinghamshire, between Wing and Stewkley
OPEN 10 am – 5 pm, Saturday – Sunday, and Bank Holidays. Also some weekdays: phone first
SPECIALITIES Air plants; cacti and succulents; carnivorous plants; conservatory plants; orchids
CATALOGUE Yes
MAIL ORDER Yes

The range here includes cacti and airplants, as well as orchids, carnivorous plants, nerines, alpines and perennials. You are advised to phone first during the show season: they visit Capel Manor, Hatfield House, Suffolk Agricultural and the early and late Newbury shows among others.

Waddesdon Plant Centre & Nursery
Queen Street, Waddesdon, Aylesbury HP18 0JW
☎ 01296 658586   FAX 01296 658852

CONTACT P. Wilson or L. Bellis
LOCATION Between Aylesbury and Bicester on A41
OPEN 10 am – 5 pm, daily
REFRESHMENTS Ice cream
DESIGN SERVICE Waddesdon Plant Centre & Nursery

Bedding plants, herbs and herbaceous perennials. No longer connected with the nearby gardens.

Woodstock Orchids and Automations
Woodstock House, 50 Pound Hill, Great Brickhill, Milton Keynes MK17 9AS
☎ 01525 261352   FAX 01525 261724

CONTACT Bill Gaskell
OPEN By appointment only
SPECIALITIES Orchids
CATALOGUE SAE or 50p in stamps
MAIL ORDER Yes
SHOWS RHS Westminster; Malvern (Spring); Harrogate (Spring); Harrogate (Autumn); Southport; Chelsea; Hampton Court

Orchid specialist, wholesale and retail, with a very interesting list. They advise and instruct would-be growers.

Wyevale Garden Centre
Junction Avebury Boulevard/ Secklow Gate, Milton Keynes MK9 3BY
☎ 01908 604011   FAX 01908 664678

Wyevale Garden Centre
Newport Road, Woburn Sands, Milton Keynes MK17 8UF
☎ 01908 281161   FAX 01908 281142
REFRESHMENTS Restaurant

Wyevale Garden Centre
Aylesbury Road, Wendover, Aylesbury HP22 6BD
☎ 01296 623116   FAX 01296 625986
REFRESHMENTS Restaurant

CAMBRIDGESHIRE

Brampton Garden Centre
Buckden Road, Brampton, Huntingdon PE18 8NF
☎ 01480 453048   FAX 01480 414994

CONTACT Peter Bates
LOCATION Opposite RAF Brampton
OPEN 9 am – 5.30 pm, Monday – Saturday; 10.30 am – 4.30 pm, Sundays; 10 am – 5.30 pm, Bank Holidays
SHOP Garden sundries, garden furniture
REFRESHMENTS Coffee shop
GARDEN Display gardens

Full range of garden products, indoor and outdoor plants, garden buildings and garden furniture. Local delivery.

Bressingham Plant Centre
Elton Hall, Elton, Peterborough PE8 6SH
☎ 01832 280058   FAX 01832 280081

CONTACT Tom Green (Manager)
LOCATION On A605 8 miles west of Peterborough
OPEN 9 am – 5.30 pm, daily
SPECIALITIES Alpines; conifers; herbaceous perennials
CATALOGUE £2.50
MAIL ORDER See Bressingham Mail Order
REFRESHMENTS Hot drinks
GARDEN Elton Hall, Cambridgeshire, see Gardens section
DESIGN SERVICE Border Planning Service
SHOWS Chelsea; BBC GW Live; Hampton Court

This is Bressingham's newest venture, in the old walled kitchen garden at Elton Hall, with their classic specialities of well-grown alpines, herbaceous perennials and conifers, as well as a good range of climbers, herbs and shrubs. There will be a Rose Fair at the centre on 6 July.

Cambridge Bulbs
40 Whittlesford Road, Newton, Cambridge CB2 5PH
☎ 01223 871760

CONTACT Norman Stevens
SPECIALITIES Bulbs
NEW FOR 1997 Arum apulum, Crocus speciosus spp. ilgazensis, Fritillaria epirotica & many more
CATALOGUE SAE
MAIL ORDER Yes
SHOWS RHS Westminster

This newish company has made quite an impact on the special-ist bulb market. They say that their specialities are arums, corydalis, crocuses, fritillarias and irises, but the catalogue is also particularly strong on Calochortus, Arisaema, gageas and roscoeas and many other good things. Recommended.

Dingle Plants & Gardens

Stamford Road, Pilsgate, Stamford PE9 3HW
☎ 01780 740775   [FAX] 01780 740838

CONTACT   Margaret Handley
LOCATION   Less than 1 mile from Burghley House, on B1443
OPEN   10 am – 5 pm, 1 March to 14 November; and by appointment. Closed Sunday mornings
SPECIALITIES   Foliage plants; herbaceous perennials
CATALOGUE   3 first-class stamps
MAIL ORDER   Yes, minimum order £10
REFRESHMENTS   Picnics welcomed
GARDEN   Gardens

The range includes hardy shrubs, perennials, alpines, grasses and conifers. Most are chosen for their coloured or variegated foliage. Group and evening visits are welcome by prior arrangement. The nursery is just inside the Cambridgeshire boundary.

Elsworth Herbs

Avenue Farm Cottage, 31 Smith Street, Elsworth,
Cambridge CB3 8HY
☎ & [FAX] 01954 267414

CONTACT   Dr J. Twibell
OPEN   By appointment
SPECIALITIES   Herbs; Artemisia; Nerium oleander
CATALOGUE   For artemisias only: 2 first-class stamps
MAIL ORDER   Yes, minimum order £10
GARDEN   Garden
NCCPG NATIONAL COLLECTIONS Artemisia;   Nerium oleander

Insectivorous plants, herbs and cottage garden plants are available, but artemisias are the main attraction. The nursery holds the national collection of artemisias, and of Nerium oleander too.

Growing Carpets

Christmas Tree House, High Street, Guilden Morden,
Royston SG8 0JP
☎ 01763 852705

CONTACT   Eileen Moore
LOCATION   Off A505, follow signs for Guilden Morden
OPEN   11 am – 5 pm, Monday – Saturday, 17 March to 31 October. By appointment only from 1 November to 16 March
SPECIALITIES   Ground cover plants
NEW FOR 1997   Leptinella albida
CATALOGUE   £1
MAIL ORDER   Yes
GARDEN   Garden, including the whole nursery range

This ground-cover nursery offers container-grown plants, and especially spreading perennials and prostrate shrubs. They are happy to give advice. The nursery is signed from the road. The nursery will be at the Capel Manor NCCPG and Knebworth House Plant Sales.

Honeysome Aquatic Nursery

The Row, Sutton, Ely CB6 2PF
☎ 01353 778889

CONTACT   D. Littlefield

LOCATION   6 miles due west of Ely
OPEN   By appointment
SPECIALITIES   Aquatic plants; bog plants
CATALOGUE   2 first-class stamps
MAIL ORDER   Yes

Ornamental aquatics and oxygenators as well as bog and marginal plants. Their pool collections are useful for starting a new pond.

Meadowcroft Fuchsias

Church St Nurseries, Woodhurst, Huntingdon PE17 3BN
☎ 01487 823333

CONTACT   D. N. Pickard or R. C. Polhill
LOCATION   East of Huntingdon, off A141
OPEN   9 am – 6 pm, weekends and Bank Holidays
SPECIALITIES   Fuchsias; pelargoniums
CATALOGUE   3 second-class stamps
MAIL ORDER   Yes
DESIGN SERVICE   Meadowcroft Fuchsias
SHOWS   RHS Westminster; Chelsea; BBC GW Live; Hampton Court

Wholesale and retail fuchsia specialists, with thirty years' experience. Their range includes regal, zonal and ivy leaf pelargoniums.

Monksilver Nursery

Oakington Road, Cottenham CB4 4TW
☎ 01954 251555   [FAX] 01954 202666

CONTACT   Joe Sharman
LOCATION   North of Cambridge: between Oakington and Cottenham
OPEN   10 am – 4 pm, Friday – Saturday, March to June and October
SPECIALITIES   Herbaceous perennials; shrubs
NEW FOR 1997   Pulmonaria 'Blauhügel', Sedum 'Indian Chief'
CATALOGUE   6 first-class stamps
MAIL ORDER   Yes
GARDEN   Display gardens
NCCPG NATIONAL COLLECTIONS Galeobdolon; Lamium, Lathyrus; part Vinca

This remarkable nursery is deservedly fashionable. Monksilver specialises in finding and rescuing some really rare plants. Much of the stock is herbaceous, though there are also some desirable shrubs. A fifth of the catalogue changes each year. Three National Collections, and a part-collection, are held by the nursery.

Notcutts Garden Centre

Oundle Road, Orton Waterville, Peterborough PE2 5UU
☎ 01733 234600   [FAX] 01733 370592

CONTACT   Carl Miles (Manager)
LOCATION   Opposite Nene Park
OPEN   8.30 am – 5.30 pm, Monday – Saturday; 11 am – 5 pm, Sundays. Closes at 5 pm in winter
SHOP   Garden sundries, furniture, buildings, conservatories
REFRESHMENTS   Restaurant
DESIGN SERVICE   Notcutts Landscapes

Padlock Croft
19 Padlock Road, West Wratting CB1 5LS
☎ 01223 290383

CONTACT Susan or Peter Lewis
OPEN 10 am – 6 pm, Wednesday – Saturday, April to 15 October. Also open Bank Holiday Mondays and by appointment at other times
SPECIALITIES Campanulaceae
NEW FOR 1997 Selection of Lobelia
CATALOGUE 4 second-class stamps
MAIL ORDER No
GARDEN Padlock Croft, Cambridgeshire, see Gardens section
NCCPG NATIONAL COLLECTIONS Adenophera; Campanula; Platycodon; Symphyandra

This small nursery holds the National Collection of Campanula: a long list of species and cultivars forms the centre of the range. Other plants on offer include different members of the Campanulaceae. Recommended to enthusiasts.

Scotsdale Nursery & Garden Centre
120 Cambridge Road, Great Shelford, Cambridge CB2 5JT
☎ 01223 842777   FAX 01223 844340

CONTACT Caroline Owen
LOCATION 4 miles south of Cambridge, on A1301
OPEN 9 am – 5.30 pm (8 pm on Thursdays), daily; 10.30 am – 4.30 pm, Sundays
SHOP Garden sundries, furniture, fencing, gifts
REFRESHMENTS Tea room
DESIGN SERVICE Scotsdale Nursery & Garden Centre

Large garden centre with plants and associated products. Garden design and delivery service.

Simply Plants
17 Duloe Brook, Eaton Socon PE19 3DW
☎ 01480 475312

CONTACT Christine Dakin
LOCATION Near A1
OPEN By appointment and on open days
SPECIALITIES Bamboos; grasses
CATALOGUE 2 first-class stamps
MAIL ORDER Yes

The nursery specialises in grasses and bamboos, but has an increasing number of perennials and some shrubs. Wholesale and retail.

Thyme House Nursery
High Street, Manea, March PE15 0JA
☎ 01354 680412

CONTACT Mary Larham
LOCATION Behind post office
OPEN 8 am – 8 pm (or dusk, if sooner); daily; all year
SPECIALITIES Herbaceous perennials; roses; trees
NEW FOR 1997 New diascias, penstemons, fuchsias and geraniums
CATALOGUE 50p
MAIL ORDER No

An excellent all-purpose nursery with a wide range of plants of every kind. Roses and trees (both native & ornamental) are among their specialities, but they also have a good list of phormiums, penstemons and mints.

CHESHIRE

Arley Hall Nursery
Arley, Northwich CW9 6NB
☎ 01565 777479

CONTACT Jane Foster
LOCATION 5 miles west of Knutsford, signed from M6 and M56
OPEN 12 noon – 5.30 pm, Tuesday – Sunday and Bank Holidays, 5 April to 29 September
SPECIALITIES Herbaceous perennials
CATALOGUE 70p
MAIL ORDER No
REFRESHMENTS Restaurant adjoining gardens
GARDEN Arley Hall, Cheshire, see Gardens section

Arley Hall is famed for its herbaceous borders: the nursery concentrates on plants which can be seen growing there. There will be another Garden Festival on 26 – 27 July and study days during the summer.

Bellhouse Nursery
Bellhouse Lane, Moore, Warrington WA4 6TR
☎ 01925 740307   FAX 01925 740672

CONTACT Doreen Scott or Elaine Soens
LOCATION 2 miles off M56, Jct 11 towards Warrington
OPEN 10 am – 5 pm (4 pm in February), Wednesday – Monday, February to October
SPECIALITIES Herbaceous perennials; shrubs
NEW FOR 1997 Several sarcococcas
CATALOGUE £1
MAIL ORDER By arrangement
GARDEN Garden open

A young nursery which is building up a large and useful range of less common shrubs and perennials.

Bents Garden Centre and Nurseries
Warrington Road, Glazebury, Leigh WA3 5NT
☎ 01942 262066   FAX 01942 261960

CONTACT Ron Bent
LOCATION Near Leigh, just off A580 towards Warrington
OPEN 9 am – 8 pm, Monday – Friday; 9.30 am – 5 pm, Saturdays; 10.30 am – 4.30 pm Sundays
SPECIALITIES Herbaceous perennials; roses; shrubs
NEW FOR 1997 Special occasion roses
SHOP Garden sundries, gifts and aquatics
REFRESHMENTS Café
GARDEN Demonstration gardens

Garden centre with the usual range of ancillary products. The focus, however, is the 60-acre nursery which supplies hardy nursery stock. A wide range is sold within the garden centre.

Bridgemere Garden World

Bridgemere, Nantwich CW5 7QB

☎ 01270 521100 📠 01270 520215

LOCATION West of M6, Jct 15 and Jct 16
OPEN 9 am – 8 pm, daily, summer; 9 am – 5 pm, daily, winter
MAIL ORDER No
SHOP Garden sundries, gifts, foods
REFRESHMENTS Coffee shop & restaurant
GARDEN Bridgemere Garden World, Cheshire
SHOWS Chelsea; BBC GW Live

Astonishing 25-acre nursery-cum-garden theme park: the largest range of plants in the country including a 'Connoisseur's Corner'. The choice of houseplants is especially notable. Other attractions include five acres of gardens (£1.50 admission), and flower shows in summer.

C & K Jones

Goldenfields Nursery, Barrow Lane, Tarvin CH3 8JF

☎ 01829 740663 📠 01829 741877

CONTACT Christine Slatcher
LOCATION Chester
OPEN 8.30 am – 5 pm, daily
SPECIALITIES Roses
NEW FOR 1997 Rose 'Kathryn McGredy'
CATALOGUE £1
MAIL ORDER Yes
GARDEN Rose fields open June to September
SHOWS RHS Westminster; Harrogate (Autumn); Southport; BBC GW Live; Hampton Court; Ayr

Specialist rose growers: the rose fields are at Halghton, Clwyd. Their range includes all types, but they are especially good for newer varieties and introductions.

C M Dickinson

Nanney's Bridge Nursery, Church Minshull, Nantwich CW5 6DY

☎ 01270 522239 📠 01270 522523

CONTACT C. M. Dickinson
SPECIALITIES Grasses; herbaceous perennials
CATALOGUE SAE
MAIL ORDER No

Wholesale nursery providing a useful source of herbaceous perennials and grasses for landscapers and the trade, including *Erysimum* and *Penstemon* cultivars.

Caddick's Clematis Nursery

Lymm Road, Thelwall, Warrington WA13 0UF

☎ 01925 757196

CONTACT Mrs Caddick
LOCATION Near M6, Jct 20 (M56, Jct 9), by Thelwall viaduct
OPEN 10 am – 5 pm, Tuesday – Sunday, & Bank Holidays, February to October; 10 am – 4 pm, Tuesday – Saturday, November
SPECIALITIES Clematis
CATALOGUE £1
MAIL ORDER Yes
GARDEN Display gardens

Clematis specialists and enthusiasts. Their range of species and cultivars is probably the largest in the country. It's worth asking for ones that are not shown in the list.

Cheshire Herbs

Fourfields, Forest Road, Little Budworth, Tarporley CW6 9ES

☎ 01829 760578 📠 01829 760354

CONTACT Libby Riddell
LOCATION On A49, just north of A54 intersection
OPEN 10 am – 5 pm. Closed from Christmas to New Year
SPECIALITIES Herbs; seeds
CATALOGUE On request
MAIL ORDER Seeds only
SHOP Herb products
GARDEN Herb garden
SHOWS Southport; Chelsea; BBC GW Live; Hampton Court

An extensive range of pot-grown herbs are on sale, retail and wholesale. The small shop sells associated products, and seeds are available mail order. The nursery holds talks and courses.

Collinwood Nurseries

Mottram St Andrew, Macclesfield SK10 4QR

☎ 01625 582272

CONTACT Anthony Wright
LOCATION In the middle of the village, 2 miles east of Alderley Edge
OPEN 8.30 am – 5.30 pm, Monday – Saturday; 1 pm – 5.30 pm, Sundays. Closed Sundays January to March, July and August
SPECIALITIES Chrysanthemums
CATALOGUE On request; chrysanthemums only
MAIL ORDER Yes, no minimum order

In season general garden plants, bedding and cut flowers are available. The main focus, though, is chrysanthemums (*Dendranthema*): the comprehensive catalogue lists more than 200 – Koreans, rubellums, greenhouse and garden varieties.

F Morrey & Son

Forest Nursery, Kelsall, Tarporley CW6 0SW

☎ 01829 751342 📠 01829 752449

LOCATION 8 miles east of Chester on A54
OPEN 9 am – 5 pm, Monday – Saturday
SPECIALITIES Rhododendrons; roses; shrubs; trees
CATALOGUE 1 second-class stamp
MAIL ORDER No

A long-established family nursery. Their range includes trees and shrubs of all kinds, as well as conifers, heathers and roses. Notably good for rhododendrons and azaleas.

The Firs Nursery

Chelford Road, Henbury, Macclesfield SK10 3LH

☎ 01625 426422

CONTACT Fay Bowling
LOCATION 2 miles west of Macclesfield on A537, next to Cock Inn
OPEN 9.30 am – 5 pm, March to September. Closed Wednesdays and Sundays
SPECIALITIES Alpines; herbaceous perennials

NEW FOR 1997   *Cerinthe major* 'Purpurascens'
CATALOGUE   2 first-class stamps
MAIL ORDER   No
GARDEN   Gardens open with nursery

An interesting herbaceous list with some exciting novelties to reward the discriminating visitor. We noticed *Dierama co-operi* last year.

Fryer's Roses Ltd
Manchester Road, Knutsford WA16 0SX
☎ 01565 755455   📠 01565 653755

CONTACT   G. R. Fryer
LOCATION   On A50 north of Knutsford
OPEN   9 am – 5.30 pm, Monday – Saturday, 10.30 am – 4.30 pm, Sundays
SPECIALITIES   Roses
NEW FOR 1997   Rose 'Cheshire Regiment'
CATALOGUE   On request
MAIL ORDER   Yes
SHOP   Garden sundries, pots, dried flowers
GARDEN   July to October
SHOWS   Harrogate (Autumn); Southport; Chelsea; Hampton Court

Rose growers of largely modern roses. They have a garden centre carrying a full general range with a special rose centre. The rose fields can be visited in summer. They will be at the Great Yorkshire and Shrewsbury shows this year.

Goldenfields Nursery
Barrow Lane, Tarvin CH3 8JF
☎ 01829 740663   📠 01829 741877

CONTACT   Rachel Gilham
LOCATION   Chester
OPEN   9.30 am – 5 pm, daily
SPECIALITIES   Herbaceous perennials
CATALOGUE   £1
MAIL ORDER   Yes
DESIGN SERVICE   Yes
SHOWS   Malvern (Spring); Malvern (Autumn); Harrogate (Autumn); Southport; BBC GW Live; Hampton Court; Ayr

Cottage garden perennials by mail order and from the nursery, where a greater range is available. They attend lots of shows. The nursery operates from the same site as C & K Jones, and shares a catalogue.

Gordale Nursery & Garden Centre
Chester High Road, Burton, South Wirral L64 8TF
☎ 0151 336 2116   📠 0151 336 8152

CONTACT   Jill Nicholson
LOCATION   8 miles west of Chester, on A540
OPEN   9 am – 5 pm, winter; 9 am – 6 pm, summer. Open until 8 pm Thursdays
SHOP   Sundries, gifts, garden furniture
REFRESHMENTS   Coffee shop with home made cakes
GARDEN   Landscaped gardens

Garden centre with a general range of plants and garden products. Delivery service.

Grosvenor Garden Centre
Wrexham Road, Belgrave, Chester CH4 9EB
☎ 01244 682856   📠 01244 679036

CONTACT   Wendy Kettlewell
LOCATION   South of Chester, on B5445
OPEN   9 am – 6 pm (5 pm in winter), Monday – Saturday. 11 am – 5 pm, Sundays.
SHOP   Garden sundries, machinery, gifts
REFRESHMENTS   Orangery café
GARDEN   Sensory garden
DESIGN SERVICE   Druid Designs

Large garden centre with a full range of plants and products. Monthly lectures, and a design service through Kate Roscoe of Druid Designs.

Harold Walker
Oakfield Nurseries, Huntington, Chester CH3 6EA
☎ 01244 320731   📠 01244 342372

CONTACT   Barry Walker
LOCATION   Map in catalogue
OPEN   9 am – 5 pm daily, February to June
SPECIALITIES   Bedding plants; chrysanthemums
CATALOGUE   1 first-class stamp
MAIL ORDER   Yes
SHOWS   Malvern (Spring); Malvern (Autumn); Harrogate (Autumn); Southport

Chrysanthemum specialist, also selling fuchsias, bedding and basket and patio plants too. The range of mums includes exhibition, garden, cut flower and greenhouse varieties.

Lodge Lane Nursery
Bluebell Cottage, Lodge Lane, Dutton, Warrington WA4 4HP
☎ 01928 713718

CONTACT   Rod or Diane Casey
LOCATION   Lodge Lane is on A533 half-way between Runcorn & Northwich
OPEN   10 am – 5 pm, Wednesday – Sunday; 1 pm – 5 pm Tuesdays; mid March to early October
SPECIALITIES   Camellias; herbaceous perennials
NEW FOR 1997   150 new additions
CATALOGUE   2 first-class stamps
REFRESHMENTS   By arrangement
GARDEN   Bluebell Cottage

This is a garden-nursery, where many of the perennial plants growing in the 1½-acre garden may be bought at the nursery. It offers a large choice of diascias, penstemons, salvias, artemisias and asters as well as a good number of unusual plants. Advice on design and landscaping is also available. Recommended.

Okell's Nurseries
Duddon Heath, Tarporley CW6 0EP
☎ 01829 741512   📠 01829 741587

CONTACT   Gary Okell
LOCATION   On A51 between Nantwich and Chester
OPEN   9 am – 5 pm, daily. Closes at 7 pm, Saturday – Sunday, May and June

SPECIALITIES Heathers
NEW FOR 1997 *Calluna vulgaris* 'Dark Star' and *C. v.* 'Dark Beauty'
CATALOGUE On request
MAIL ORDER No
SHOP Garden sundries

This wholesale nursery produces heathers in variety (150) and quantity (2.6 million). They also have a retail garden centre which stocks heathers and a general range of plants and sundries.

One House Nursery

Buxton New Road, Rainow, Macclesfield SK11 0AD
☎ 01625 427087

CONTACT Louise Bayliss
LOCATION 2 miles from Macclesfield on A537 to Buxton
OPEN 10 am – 5 pm; daily
SPECIALITIES Alpines; herbaceous perennials; primulas; sempervivums
CATALOGUE 3 first-class stamps
MAIL ORDER Yes, for sempervivums
SHOWS Harrogate (Spring); Harrogate (Autumn)

This excellent north-country nursery has a good line in alpine and small herbaceous plants, as well as some dwarf conifers. They list only a fraction of the 600 sempervivums they grow, but offsets are often available from most of them. They also sell some 20 different cultivars of double primrose.

Phedar Nursery

Bunkers Hill, Romiley, Stockport SK6 3DS
☎ & FAX 0161 430 3772

CONTACT Will McLewin
LOCATION 3 miles east of Stockport
OPEN By appointment only
SPECIALITIES Paeonies; seeds; shrubs; hellebores
NEW FOR 1997 Chinese tree peony cultivars
CATALOGUE Large SAE plus 1 first-class stamp
MAIL ORDER Yes

A highly specialised source of authentic *Helleborus* and *Paeonia* species, which are only grown from collected material. They also offer fresh seed in August. Other plants from this research nursery include *Erythronium* and *Dodecatheon*. They pride themselves on accurate naming.

Pilkington Garden Centre

Bold Heath, Widnes WA8 3UU
☎ 0151 424 6264 FAX 0151 420 2110

CONTACT Philip Pilkington
LOCATION 2 miles east of M62, Jct 7 on A57
OPEN 9 am – 6 pm, daily, closes at 5 pm in winter
SHOP Garden sundries, floristry, aquatics, gifts
REFRESHMENTS Café

General garden centre with a full range of plants and products. Demonstrations held throughout the year.

Stapeley Water Gardens Ltd

London Road, Stapeley, Nantwich CW5 7LH
☎ 01270 623868 FAX 01270 624919

CONTACT Reception desk

LOCATION Signed from M6, Jct 16; 1 mile south of Nantwich
OPEN Daily, except Christmas Day. Opening times vary, phone to check
SPECIALITIES Aquatic plants; bog plants
CATALOGUE £1 cheque or postal order
MAIL ORDER Yes
SHOP Garden sundries, water equipment, furniture, gifts, books
REFRESHMENTS Restaurant, café, snack bar, coffee shop
GARDEN Stapeley Water Gardens Ltd, Cheshire, see Gardens section
SHOWS Chelsea; Hampton Court; Courson
NCCPG NATIONAL COLLECTIONS *Nymphaea*

A large water-gardening centre, with aquatic plants, marginals and poolside varieties as well as all the necessary equipment for ponds and pools. They hold the national water lily collection, here and at Burnby Hall, Humberside. Their French subsidiary (Etablissement Botanique Latour-Marliac) exhibits at Courson.

Ward Fuchsias

5 Pollen Close, Sale M33 3LS
☎ 0161 282 7434

CONTACT M. Ward
LOCATION Map in catalogue
OPEN 9.30 am – 5 pm, Tuesday – Sunday, February to June. Closed on Mondays
SPECIALITIES Fuchsias
NEW FOR 1997 *Fuchsia* 'Rachel Craig'
CATALOGUE On request
MAIL ORDER Yes, fuchsia cuttings only

Specialist fuchsia grower: cuttings by post, plants and hanging baskets at the nursery. Hostas, too.

Weaver Vale Garden Centre

Winnington Avenue, Winnington, Northwich CW8 4EE
☎ 01606 79965 FAX 01606 784480

CONTACT Neil Phelps (Manager)
LOCATION 2 miles north-west of Northwich on A533
OPEN 9 am – 6 pm, Monday – Saturday; 10.30 am – 4.30 pm, Sundays. Closes at 5 pm in winter
SHOP Garden sundries, machinery, conservatories, aquatics
REFRESHMENTS Coffee shop
GARDEN Demonstration gardens
DESIGN SERVICE Weaver Vale Garden Centre

Garden centre with indoor and outdoor plants and associated products. Landscaping and garden design service.

Wilmslow Garden Centre

Manchester Road, Wilmslow SK9 2JN
☎ 01625 525700 FAX 01625 539800

CONTACT Mrs S. Kaye
LOCATION Main road between Handforth and Wilmslow
OPEN 9 am – 6 pm, summer; 9 am – 5 pm, winter; 10 am – 5 pm, Sundays (all year). Also 8 pm closing, summer Thursdays
SHOP Garden sundries, furniture, machinery, pets
REFRESHMENTS Restaurant & coffee shop
DESIGN SERVICE Wilmslow Garden Centre
SHOWS Southport

Garden centre selling plants and products. They have a design and landscape capability, and a delivery service.

Wyevale Garden Centre
Green Lane, Timperley, Altrincham WA15 8QP
☎ 0161 980 6036   📠 0161 903 9321
OPEN   9 am – 6 pm, Monday – Saturday; 11 am – 5 pm, Sundays
REFRESHMENTS   Restaurant

Wyevale Garden Centre
Otterspool, Dooley Lane, Marple, Stockport SK6 7HE
☎ 0161 427 7211   📠 0161 449 7636
REFRESHMENTS   Restaurant

Wyevale Garden Centre
Forest Road, Tarporley CW6 9EE
☎ 01829 760433   📠 01829 760485
REFRESHMENTS   Restaurant

Wyevale Garden Centre
Wood Lane, Timperley, Altrincham WA15 7PJ
☎ 0161 904 0474   📠 0161 903 9376

CORNWALL

Bosvigo Plants
Bosvigo House, Bosvigo Lane, Truro TR1 3NH
☎ & 📠 01872 275774

CONTACT   Wendy Perry
LOCATION   ¼ of a mile from Truro centre. Leave A390 at Highertown (near Sainsburys): 500m down Dobbs Lane
OPEN   11 am – 6 pm, Wednesday – Saturday, March to September. Closed Sundays, Mondays and Tuesdays
SPECIALITIES   Herbaceous perennials
CATALOGUE   4 second-class stamps
MAIL ORDER   No
GARDEN   Bosvigo House, Cornwall, see Gardens section

An excellent list of mainly herbaceous perennials, with a discriminating eye for the best forms and an impressive number of new introductions, including a gold-leaved form of *Dahlia merckii* which occurred there as a seedling. The nursery will be open 10 am – 4 pm, Fridays and Saturdays in February for the sale of hellebores only. These are their selection of *Helleborus orientalis* hybrids sold in flower.

Boyton Nursery
Bragg's Hill, Boyton, Launceston PL15 9LP
☎ 01566 776474   📠 01566 777779
CONTACT   Susan Bean
OPEN   8.30 am – 5 pm, summer; 9 am – 4 pm, winter
SPECIALITIES   Herbaceous perennials; roses
CATALOGUE   2 first-class stamps
MAIL ORDER   No
REFRESHMENTS   Yes
GARDEN   Garden being made

Modern and old-fashioned roses, cottage garden perennials and fuchsias from this nursery. A Victorian garden is being made.

Bregover Plants
Middlewood, Launceston PL15 7NN
☎ 01566 782661
CONTACT   Jennifer Bousfield
LOCATION   Between Launceston and Liskeard on B3254
OPEN   11 am – 5 pm, Wednesday – Friday, mid-March to mid-October. Weekends and winter months by appointment
SPECIALITIES   Herbaceous perennials
NEW FOR 1997   *Viola odorata* 'Tanith', *Viola canina alba*
CATALOGUE   2 first-class stamps
MAIL ORDER   Yes, £2.50 minimum charge
GARDEN   Cottage garden and stock beds open by appointment

Mainly cottage garden, wild and woodland plants, including old varieties. The garden will be open as part of the Berriowbridge and Middlewood village opening for the NGS.

Brockings Exotics
Brockings Nursery, North Petherwin, Launceston PL15 8LW
☎ 01566 785533
CONTACT   Ian Cooke
LOCATION   Take signs to Otter Park, then continue into village centre
OPEN   By appointment only
SPECIALITIES   Conservatory plants; topiary; cannas; half-hardy plants
CATALOGUE   3 first-class stamps
MAIL ORDER   Yes, £15 minimum order
GARDEN   Display garden
DESIGN SERVICE   Brockings Exotics
NCCPG NATIONAL COLLECTIONS   *Canna; Solenostemon*

Brockings Exotics sell an outstanding collection of half-hardy perennials. Some are new, many are revived. Strengths include cannas, coleus, now *Solenostemon* (old, named varieties), and argyranthemums (20). The business is now almost entirely mail order.

Burncoose Nurseries
Gwennap, Redruth TR16 6BJ
☎ 01209 861112   📠 01209 860011
CONTACT   C. H. Williams
LOCATION   Between Redruth and Falmouth, on A393
OPEN   8.30 am – 5 pm, Monday – Saturday; 11 am – 5 pm, Sundays
SPECIALITIES   Camellias; conservatory plants; rhododendrons; magnolias
CATALOGUE   £1
MAIL ORDER   Yes
REFRESHMENTS   Tea room
GARDEN   Burncoose Gardens, Cornwall, beside the nursery
DESIGN SERVICE   Burncoose & South Down Nurseries
SHOWS   RHS Westminster; Malvern (Spring); Malvern (Autumn); Harrogate (Spring); Harrogate (Autumn); Southport; Chelsea; BBC GW Live; Hampton Court; Strathclyde

One of the great plantsman's nurseries, with a very large general range and a high proportion of unusual plants. Burncoose is particularly strong on flowering shrubs and trees, including magnolias, and good for tender and conservatory plants too. Look out for their masterly displays at horticultural shows: Burncoose is the most consistent winner of gold medals at Westminster. They go to shows abroad as well and will be at La Landriana Garden Fair, south of Rome, in April.

Carnon Downs Garden Centre

Quenchwell Road, Carnon Downs, Truro TR3 4LN
☎ 01872 863058   ▣ 01872 862162
LOCATION   On A39 between Truro and Falmouth at Carnon Downs
OPEN   9 am – 5 pm, Monday – Saturday; 10.30 am – 4.30 pm, Sundays; extended opening in spring
SHOP   Garden sundries, furniture and buildings; pets
REFRESHMENTS   Licensed restaurant

Garden centre with a large range of ancillary products including garden machinery. The plant centre includes a selection of plants suited to coastal conditions. They can deliver; on site there is also a working pottery and an adventure playground. Large Christmas section, from October.

Duchy of Cornwall Nursery

Cott Road, Lostwithiel PL22 0BW
☎ 01208 872668   ▣ 01208 872835
CONTACT   Andrew Carthew (Manager)
LOCATION   Lostwithiel, 1½ miles off A390
OPEN   9 am – 5 pm, Monday – Saturday; 10 am – 5 pm, Sundays. Closed Bank Holidays
SPECIALITIES   Conifers; herbaceous perennials; shrubs; trees, half-hardy plants
NEW FOR 1997   Berberis hypokerina, Deutzia corymbosa KR3820, Magnolia × loebneri 'Ballerina'
CATALOGUE   £2 appreciated
MAIL ORDER   No
SHOP   Garden sundries
REFRESHMENTS   Light refreshments available all day
GARDEN   Woodland walk

The nursery stocks an extensive general range of all types of plants as well as garden sundries. Varieties range from reliable old favourites to rare species and recent cultivars. They are especially good on tender perennials. Set in woods, there is a woodland walk centred on the nursery. They will be at the Royal Cornwall and Devon County Shows this year.

Elizabeth Smith

Downside, Bowling Green, Constantine, Falmouth TR11 5AP
☎ 01326 340787
CONTACT   Elizabeth Smith
OPEN   Mail order only
SPECIALITIES   Violets
NEW FOR 1997   Viola 'California', 'Donau'
CATALOGUE   SAE; January
MAIL ORDER   Yes

Mail-order nursery devoted exclusively to scented violets: single, double and Parma.

Hardy Exotics Nursery

Gilly Lane, Whitecross, Penzance TR20 8BZ
☎ 01736 740660   ▣ 01736 741101
CONTACT   Clive Shilton or Julie Smith or Ian Lowe
LOCATION   Off A30 east of Penzance
OPEN   Phone first – opening hours on answerphone
SPECIALITIES   Conservatory plants; hardy and half-hardy exotics
CATALOGUE   4 first-class stamps
MAIL ORDER   Yes
GARDEN   Demonstration garden
DESIGN SERVICE   Hardy Exotics

Eye-catching plants. Striking foliage and flowers, to enliven your garden, patio or conservatory. Design Service as well.

Lanhydrock Gardens

The National Trust, Lanhydrock Gardens, Bodmin PL30 5AD
☎ 01208 72220/ 73320 ▣ 01208 72220/ 74084
CONTACT   Mr Teagle
LOCATION   2 miles south east of Bodmin
OPEN   11 am – 4.30 pm, March to October
SPECIALITIES   Rhododendrons; shrubs
CATALOGUE   On request
MAIL ORDER   No
REFRESHMENTS   11 am – 5 pm, April to October
GARDEN   Lanhydrock, Cornwall, see Gardens section
NCCPG NATIONAL COLLECTIONS   Crocosmia

There are some herbaceous plants here, but the best of the list is shrubs. You would expect rhododendrons and azaleas, but there are also attractive Ceanothus and Deutzia cultivars.

Little Treasures Nursery

Wheal Treasure, Horsedowns TR14 0NL
☎ 01209 831978
CONTACT   B. Jackson
OPEN   10 am – 5 pm, Wednesday – Saturday, mid-March to September
SPECIALITIES   Herbaceous perennials; shrubs
CATALOGUE   4 first-class stamps
MAIL ORDER   Yes

Perennials, shrubs, climbers and herbs, both hardy and tender. Their eclectic selection concentrates on older and scented varieties. Mail order all year except August and December. Orders can be collected by arrangement. Visitors to the nursery should bring wellingtons if wet.

The Old Mill Herbary

Helland Bridge, Bodmin PL30 4QR
☎ & ▣ 01208 841206
CONTACT   Mr or Mrs R. D. Whurr
LOCATION   Helland Bridge: Map ref. 065717
OPEN   10 am – 5 pm, April to October; closed Wednesdays and 19 October
SPECIALITIES   Herbs
NEW FOR 1997   More medicinal herbs
CATALOGUE   6 first-class stamps
MAIL ORDER   No

GARDEN   Terraced and water garden, arboretum: admission £2.50

The nursery sells a range of culinary and medicinal herbs as well as some climbers, shrubs and trees. The garden, which includes herbs, bog plants, aquatics and a young arboretum, is open at the same times, but ring first.

Parkinson Herbs

Barras Moor Farm, Perran Ar Worthal, Truro TR3 7PE
☎ & 📠 01872 864380
CONTACT   Elizabeth Parkinson
LOCATION   On A39 between Truro and Falmouth
OPEN   9 am – 5 pm, daily
SPECIALITIES   Herbs
CATALOGUE   On request
MAIL ORDER   Yes, minimum order £5

The nursery sells herbs and aromatic plants. Lectures and demonstrations can be arranged, but only in Cornwall.

Porthpean House Gardens

Porthpean, St Austell PL26 6AX
☎ 01726 72888   📠 01726 70548
CONTACT   Mrs Petherick
LOCATION   1½ miles south-east of St Austell
OPEN   9 am – 5 pm, Monday – Friday
SPECIALITIES   Camellias
CATALOGUE   On request
MAIL ORDER   No
SHOWS   RHS Westminster

Camellia specialists, and regular award-winning camellia exhibitors at RHS Westminster.

R A Scamp

14 Roscarrack Close, Falmouth TR11 4PJ
☎ 01326 317959
CONTACT   Ron Scamp
OPEN   Mail order only
SPECIALITIES   Daffodils
CATALOGUE   2 first-class stamps
MAIL ORDER   Yes

One of the leading daffodil growers. The handsome catalogue lists a very wide range of all types of daffodil including miniatures, species and an increasing number of their own breeding. Strongly recommended.

Roseland House Nursery

Roseland House Chacewater, Truro TR4 8QB
☎ 01872 560451
CONTACT   C. Pridham
LOCATION   West of Truro, OS map reference 752444
OPEN   12 noon – 4 pm, Tuesdays, March to July
SPECIALITIES   Climbers; herbaceous perennials
CATALOGUE   2 first-class stamps
MAIL ORDER   Yes
REFRESHMENTS   Teas available
GARDEN   Garden opens for NGS

Climbers, including some clematis and a good choice of hardy and half-hardy (outside Cornwall) perennials. They will be at the Cornwall Garden Society Spring Show and the Royal Cornwall Show. There will be a clematis day on Sunday, 27 July, 2 – 5 pm.

Trebah Nursery

Trebah, Mawnan Smith, Falmouth TR11 5JZ
☎ 01326 250448   📠 01326 250781
CONTACT   Anne Black
LOCATION   6 miles south-west of Falmouth, signed from Mawnan Smith
OPEN   10.30 am – 5 pm, daily
SPECIALITIES   Conservatory plants; palms; pelargoniums; succulents, tree ferns
NEW FOR 1997   Lobelia excelsa, L. bridgesii
MAIL ORDER   No
REFRESHMENTS   In Garden Coffee Shop
GARDEN   Trebah Garden, Cornwall, see Gardens section

The plant centre draws on the collections at Trebah to offer plants suitable for the south west. Good Agave, Yucca and Lampranthus.

Trewithen Nurseries

Grampound Road, Truro TR2 4DD
☎ 01726 882764   📠 01726 882301
CONTACT   Glenys Cates
LOCATION   Trewithen
OPEN   Garden and nursery: 10 am – 5 pm, Monday – Saturday, March to September. Also, Sundays in April and May only; Nursery only: 8 am – 4.30 pm, Monday – Friday, October to February
SPECIALITIES   Camellias; climbers; rhododendrons
CATALOGUE   £1.20 & postage
MAIL ORDER   No
REFRESHMENTS   March to September, when gardens open
GARDEN   Trewithen, Cornwall

An interesting nursery, particularly for ornamental shrubs and climbers for acid soils and sheltered spots. A good choice of rhododendrons, camellias and magnolias.

Wall Cottage Nursery

Lockengate, Bugle, St Austell PL26 8RU
☎ 01208 831259
CONTACT   J. R. Clark
LOCATION   On A391, ¾ mile from A30 Bodmin bypass
OPEN   8.30 am – 5 pm, Monday – Saturday. Closed Sundays
SPECIALITIES   Rhododendrons
CATALOGUE   60p
MAIL ORDER   Yes, minimum order £15

Rhododendron and azalea specialist, with an extensive choice of species and hybrids. Visitors welcome, but they would prefer it if you can make an appointment.

Wyevale Garden Centre

Nut Lane, Hayle TR27 6LG
☎ & 📠 01736 753731
REFRESHMENTS   Restaurant

CUMBRIA

Beechcroft Nurseries

Bongate, Appleby CA16 6UE
☎ 017683 51201   📠 017683 52546

CONTACT Roger Brown
LOCATION Ask in Appleby
OPEN 8 am – 6 pm, Monday – Saturday; 11 am – 6 pm,
Sundays. Closed 14 December – 2 January
SPECIALITIES Shrubs; trees
CATALOGUE £2.50; SAE only for list of field-grown trees
MAIL ORDER Field-grown trees, November to April
DESIGN SERVICE Beechcroft Nurseries

A small nursery which specialises in hardy trees and shrubs:
both container and field-grown. The rest of the selection is
splendidly mixed, running from conifers to vegetables. Gardens designed and planted too.

Beetham Nurseries

Pool Darkin Lane, Beetham, Milnthorpe LA7 7QR
☎ 015395 63630   📠 015395 67784

CONTACT Michèle Briers
LOCATION Off A6 south of Milnthorpe
OPEN 9 am – 5.30 pm, daily, all year
SPECIALITIES Shrubs; trees
MAIL ORDER No

Nursery with an interesting range of trees, shrubs and perennials.

Boonwood Garden Centre

Gosforth, Seascale CA20 1BP
☎ 01946 725330

CONTACT Stanley Mossop
LOCATION Off A595
OPEN 9 am – 5 pm, daily
SPECIALITIES House plants; Achimenes
NEW FOR 1997 Smithiantha 'Temple Bells', Achimenes
'Strawberry Fields' and several new yellow cultivars
CATALOGUE Free
MAIL ORDER Yes
GARDEN Two display houses to visit in season
DESIGN SERVICE Boonwood Garden Centre

The leading specialists in Gesneriaceae, both nationally and
internationally. Their long list includes many distinguished old
names, while their hybridisation of Achimenes ensures a
constant stream of new cultivars. Their work with intergeneric
× Achimenantha hybrids is breaking new ground. Strongly
recommended.

Brownthwaite Hardy Plants

Fell Yeat, Casterton, Kirkby Lonsdale LA6 2JW
☎ 015242 71340

CONTACT Chris Benson
LOCATION Bull Pot Road in Casterton
OPEN 10 am – 5 pm, Tuesday – Sunday, April to October
SPECIALITIES Alpines; herbaceous perennials
CATALOGUE 3 first-class stamps
MAIL ORDER Yes

GARDEN Garden opens for NGS
DESIGN SERVICE Yes

This Pennine nursery grows and stocks a range of hardy
perennials and grasses. The plants can be seen in a garden
setting.

Halecat Garden Nurseries

Witherslack, Grange over Sands LA11 6RU
☎ 015395 52229

CONTACT M. Stanley or Y. Langhorn
LOCATION Signed off A590 between Grange and Levens
OPEN 9 am – 4.30 pm, Monday – Friday, all year
SPECIALITIES Herbaceous perennials; hydrangeas
CATALOGUE 45p
MAIL ORDER No
GARDEN Display garden

They specialise in species and cultivars of Hydrangea, and
also stock an attractive range of perennials for herbaceous and
mixed borders. The garden of the house is open at the same time.

Hartside Nursery Garden

Alston CA9 3BL
☎ & 📠 01434 381372

CONTACT N. Huntley
LOCATION 1¼ miles south-west of Alston on A686 Alston
to Penrith road
OPEN 9 am – 5 pm, Monday – Friday; 12.30 pm – 4 pm,
Saturdays, Sundays; March to October. Other months by
appointment
SPECIALITIES Alpines; ferns; primulas
CATALOGUE £1 each; 3 annually
MAIL ORDER Yes
GARDEN 12 acre wooded valley
SHOWS Malvern (Autumn); Harrogate (Spring); Harrogate
(Autumn); BBC GW Live; Hampton Court; Strathclyde; Ayr

The nursery specialises in alpines, particularly Primula, dwarf
shrubs and conifers, and hardy ferns: all grown in the North
Pennines at altitude. The substantial gardens are also open, and
there is a self-catering cottage available.

Hayes Gardenworld Ltd

Lake District Nurseries, Ambleside LA22 0DW
☎ 015394 33434   📠 015394 34153

LOCATION South of Ambleside on A591
OPEN 9 am – 6 pm, Monday – Saturday; 10.30 am – 4.30 pm,
Sundays
SHOP Garden sundries, greenhouses, conservatories, aquarium
REFRESHMENTS Coffee lounge
GARDEN Gardens open, as above
DESIGN SERVICE Hayes Garden World

Established over 200 years ago, and now a major tourist
attraction. The garden centre offers a full range of garden
products, plus a landscaping and construction service, and
assorted leisure activities.

Lingholm Gardens

Lingholm, Keswick CA12 5UA
☎ 017687 72003   📠 017687 75213

CONTACT Ian Stephenson

LOCATION 2 miles west of Keswick, signed from A66

OPEN 10 am – 5 pm, daily, 28 March to 31 October

SPECIALITIES Primulas; rhododendrons

MAIL ORDER No

REFRESHMENTS Tea room

GARDEN Lingholm, Cumbria, see Gardens section

The plant centre attached to these Lakeland gardens specialises in acid-loving plants, including *Meconopsis* and *Rhododendron*.

Muncaster Plants

Muncaster Castle, Ravenglass CA18 1RJ

☎ 01229 717357 [FAX] 01229 7171010

CONTACT A. J. or S. F. Clark

LOCATION Off A595 1 mile east of Ravenglass

OPEN 10 am – 4 pm, daily, April to September. By appointment October to March

SPECIALITIES Rhododendrons

CATALOGUE 3 first-class stamps

MAIL ORDER Yes

GARDEN Muncaster Castle, Cumbria, see Gardens section

The nursery at this famous garden has an exceptional collection of azaleas and rhododendrons. It includes rare species, many under famous collectors' numbers, older and newer hybrids.

T H Barker & Son

Baines Paddock Nursery, Haverthwaite, Ulverston LA12 8PF

☎ 015395 58236

CONTACT W. E. Thornley

LOCATION On B5278, 2 miles north of Holker Hall

OPEN 9.30 am – 5.30 pm, daily. Closed Tuesday mornings, Christmas Day and Boxing Day

SPECIALITIES Clematis

CATALOGUE £1

MAIL ORDER Yes

Lake District nursery specialising in clematis, both large flowered, small flowered and species. There is a growing range of cottage garden plants for collection. The nursery is hidden from the road: watch out for the green and gold signs.

Weasdale Nurseries

Newbiggin on Lune, Kirkby Stephen CA17 4LX

☎ 015396 23246 [FAX] 015396 23277

CONTACT Andrew Forsyth

LOCATION 7 miles from M6, Jct 38, off A685

OPEN 9 am – 5 pm. Plant collection by prior arrangement only

SPECIALITIES Hedging; shrubs; trees

CATALOGUE £2.50 cheque

MAIL ORDER Yes

Trees and shrubs by mail order, including ornamental, hedging and woodland species. Forty-five year's mail order experience, from a substantial list. The high situation on the Fells promises hardiness too.

Webbs Garden Centre

Burneside Road, Kendal LA9 4RT

☎ 01539 720068 [FAX] 01539 727328

LOCATION From M6, Jct 36 take A591 Kendal North road. Turn right downhill at roundabout, then left into Burneside Road

OPEN 9 am – 6 pm, Monday – Saturday; 10.30 am – 4.30 pm, Sundays

CATALOGUE General list

SHOP Garden sundries, floristry

REFRESHMENTS Restaurant

GARDEN Yes

Garden centre with plants and garden products – the home of the 'Webbs Wonderful' lettuce. Special events, competitions and demonstrations are held throughout the year.

DERBYSHIRE

Abbey Brook Cactus Nursery

Bakewell Road, Matlock DE4 2QJ

☎ 01629 580306 [FAX] 01629 55852

CONTACT Brian Fearn

LOCATION On A6 2 miles north of Matlock

OPEN 1 – 5 pm, daily. Opens 12.15 pm, Sundays. Closed Christmas Day, Boxing Day and New Year's Day

SPECIALITIES Cacti and succulents; heathers

CATALOGUE £1

MAIL ORDER Yes

SHOP Yes

REFRESHMENTS Yes

GARDEN 4 large glasshouses: ⅓ of an acre under glass

DESIGN SERVICE Yes

NCCPG NATIONAL COLLECTIONS *Conophytum*; *Haworthia*; *Lithops*

The leading UK cactus nursery, now mainly wholesale (1,000,000 plants in stock) but their retail catalogue lists 2,000 species and the nursery is worth a visit at any time of the year.

Birchwood Farm Nursery

Portway, Coxbench DE21 5BE

☎ 01332 880685

CONTACT Mr or Mrs H. S. Crooks

LOCATION Off A38 north of Little Eaton

OPEN 9 am – 5.30 pm, Monday – Tuesday, Thursday – Saturday. Closed Wednesdays and Sundays

SPECIALITIES Herbaceous perennials

REFRESHMENTS When garden open for NGS

GARDEN Garden opens for NGS and by appointment

Herbaceous perennials and shrubs, composts and fertilisers too.

Bluebell Nursery

Annwell Lane, Smisby, Ashby-de-la-Zouch LE65 2TA

☎ 01530 413700/01283 222091 [FAX] 01283 218282

CONTACT Robert or Suzette Vernon

LOCATION Off A50, by Mother Hubbard Inn, 1 mile north-west of Ashby-de-la-Zouch

OPEN   9 am – 5 pm, daily. Closed from Christmas Eve to 2 January
SPECIALITIES   Shrubs; trees
CATALOGUE   £1 plus 2 first-class stamps
MAIL ORDER   Yes
GARDEN   New 4-acre woodland garden open twice a month in summer for NGS
SHOWS   RHS Westminster; Malvern (Autumn); Chelsea; BBC GW Live

Dynamic and adventurous tree and shrub nursery with steady stream of new introductions. They are regular exhibitors at RHS Westminster shows.

Burrows Roses
Meadowcroft, Spondon Road, Dale Abbey, Derby DE7 4PQ
☎ 01332 668289

CONTACT   Diane Burrows
OPEN   Mail order only
SPECIALITIES   Roses
CATALOGUE   2 first-class stamps
MAIL ORDER   Yes
SHOWS   RHS Westminster; Malvern (Spring); Chelsea; Hampton Court

Specialist mail-order rose growers. The range is mostly of the modern types, especially hybrid teas of which they have a large number, including classic older varieties. They are careful to select roses with notably good scents.

Chatsworth Garden Centre
Calton Lees, Beeley, Matlock DE4 2NX
☎ 01629 734004   [FAX] 01629 735005

CONTACT   John Tarbatt
LOCATION   1 mile from Chatsworth House
OPEN   9 am – 5 pm, October – February; 9 am – 5.30 pm, March to September; 10.30 am – 4.30 pm, Sundays. Closed between Christmas and New Year
SHOP   Garden sundries, gifts
REFRESHMENTS   Coffee shop/restaurant

Garden centre with a range of indoor and outdoor plants, set in a former walled garden of the Chatsworth estate. Delivery service within 20-mile radius.

DHE Plants
Rose Lea, Darley House Estate, Darley Dale, Matlock DE4 2QH
☎ 01629 732512

CONTACT   Peter M. Smith
LOCATION   At Robert Young Garden Centre on A6 1½ miles north of Matlock
OPEN   10 am – 5 pm, Tuesday to Saturday; 10.30 am – 4.30 pm Sundays. Please phone first
SPECIALITIES   Alpines
CATALOGUE   2 first-class stamps
MAIL ORDER   Yes, no minimum order; October to April
REFRESHMENTS   Coffee shop
SHOWS   Harrogate (Autumn)

An alpine nursery whose stock includes particularly good choices of helianthemums (50), saxifrages (150) and sisyrinchi-ums (20). A regular attender at AGS and county shows. Retail stocks are now at Robert Young Garden Centre just north of Matlock.

Greenleaves Garden Centre Ltd
Birkin Lane, Wingerworth, Chesterfield S42 6RD
☎ 01246 204214   [FAX] 01629 580503

CONTACT   John Tarbatt
LOCATION   1 mile west of A61 Tupton roundabout
OPEN   9 am – 5 pm, October to February, 9 am – 5.30 pm, March to September, Monday – Saturday; 10.30 am – 4.30 pm, Sundays. Closed between Christmas and New Year
SHOP   Landscaping supplies

Garden centre, with local delivery service. They stock landscaping materials as well as plants, and have an advisory service.

The Herb Garden
Chesterfield Road, Hardstoft, Pilsley, Chesterfield S45 8AH
☎ 01246 854268

CONTACT   Lynne or Steve Raynor
LOCATION   Signed off A6175 and B6014
OPEN   10 am – 6 pm, daily, 15 March to 15 September
SPECIALITIES   Herbs
CATALOGUE   On request
MAIL ORDER   No
SHOP   Herb products
REFRESHMENTS   Tea room
GARDEN   Display gardens – donation of £1 per adult requested

There are four themed display gardens here, with around 300 culinary, medicinal and aromatic herbs for sale. Lots of different lavender.

Highgates Nursery
166a Crich Lane, Belper DE56 1EP
☎ 01773 822153

CONTACT   Mr or Mrs Straughan
LOCATION   Along unclassified road, signed to Ambergate and Ridgeway
OPEN   10 am – 4.30 pm, Monday – Saturday, early March to mid-October
SPECIALITIES   Alpines; rhododendrons
CATALOGUE   2 first-class stamps
MAIL ORDER   No
GARDEN   Display gardens

There are alpines in abundance at this specialist nursery, as well as a selection of dwarf rhododendrons.

Lea Gardens
Lea, Matlock DE4 5GH
☎ 01629 534380   [FAX] 01629 534260

CONTACT   Jon or Peter Tye
OPEN   10 am – 7 pm, 20 March to 16 July. Also by appointment for the rest of the year
SPECIALITIES   Rhododendrons
CATALOGUE   SAE plus 30p
MAIL ORDER   Yes, minimum order £15
REFRESHMENTS   Yes
GARDEN   Lea Gardens, Derbyshire, see Gardens section

The plants on sale reflect those which grow in the garden, notably *Rhododendron*, azaleas and *Kalmia*, with the tendency towards dwarf or low-growing varieties.

Matlock Garden Centre Ltd
Nottingham Road, Tansley, Matlock DE4 5FR
☎ 01629 580500   [FAX] 01629 580503

CONTACT   John Tarbatt
LOCATION   7 miles from M1, Jct 28
OPEN   9 am – 5 pm, October to February; 9 am – 5.30 pm, March to September. 10.30 am – 4.30 pm, Sundays. Closed between Christmas and New Year
SHOP   Aquatics
REFRESHMENTS   Restaurant

Garden centre with a hardy plant range and aquatics centre. Delivery within 20-mile radius.

Tissington Nurseries
Tissington, Ashbourne DE6 1RH
☎ 01335 390650   [FAX] 01773 853045

CONTACT   Derek or Sue Watkins
LOCATION   ¼ mile east of A515, in village centre. Tissington is 4 miles north of Ashbourne
OPEN   10 am – 6 pm, Wednesday – Sunday, Bank Holiday Mondays and Tuesdays, March to October
SPECIALITIES   Herbaceous perennials; shrubs
CATALOGUE   2 first-class stamps
MAIL ORDER   No
SHOWS   BBC GW Live

Peak District nursery with a conventional selection – best on herbaceous and alpine plants where the range, though not extensive, does concentrate upon the best available forms. *Veronica gentianoides* 'Tissington White' originated in the village. The nursery is open throughout Well Dressing week, 8 – 14 May this year. The gardens of Tissington Hall are open for the Royal National Rose Society on 2 August (2 pm – 5 pm).

Wyevale Garden Centre
Burton Road, Findern, Derby DE6 6BE
☎ 01332 514268   [FAX] 01332 513128
REFRESHMENTS   Restaurant

DEVON

Altoona Nurseries
The Windmill, Tigley, Dartington, Totnes TQ9 6DW
☎ 01803 868147

CONTACT   Paul Harber
LOCATION   1½ miles west of Totnes
OPEN   By appointment, any time
SPECIALITIES   Acers
CATALOGUE   SAE
MAIL ORDER   No

Specialists in Japanese acers, *Hamamelis* (witch hazels) and *Daphne*.

Ann & Roger Bowden
Hostas, Sticklepath, Okehampton EX20 2NN
☎ 01837 840481   [FAX] 01837 840482

CONTACT   Ann or Roger Bowden
LOCATION   20 miles west of Exeter, in centre of village
OPEN   By appointment only
SPECIALITIES   Hostas
CATALOGUE   3 first-class stamps
MAIL ORDER   Yes, no minimum order, low packing charges
GARDEN   National Collection of hybrid hostas
SHOWS   RHS Westminster; Malvern (Spring); Chelsea; BBC GW Live; Hampton Court
NCCPG NATIONAL COLLECTIONS   Hybrid *Hosta*

Hostas only, from a handsome catalogue with excellent photographs. Prices are fair and range from £2 for basic species to £15 for the latest imported hybrids. But the choice is magnificent: last year's catalogue offered 184 different hostas, of which 48 were new or re-introduced.

Ashford Garden Centre
Ashford, Barnstaple EX31 4BW
☎ 01271 42880   [FAX] 01271 23972

CONTACT   Miss J. Dellow
LOCATION   Between Barnstaple and Braunton on A361
OPEN   9 am – 5 pm, Monday – Saturday; 10.30 am – 4.30 pm, Sundays
SPECIALITIES   Herbaceous perennials
SHOP   Garden sundries, conservatories, mowers, pools
REFRESHMENTS   Tea room
GARDEN   2-acre show garden, with lake
DESIGN SERVICE   North Devon Garden Centre

General garden centre including all associated products. They have a landscaping department, and during the season a tropical butterfly house. The site is very attractive: it overlooks the Taw estuary.

Burnham Nurseries
Forches Cross, Newton Abbot TQ12 6PZ
☎ 01626 52233   [FAX] 01626 62167

CONTACT   Brian or Ann Rittershausen
LOCATION   Forches Cross: signed from A382
OPEN   10 am – 4 pm, daily
SPECIALITIES   Orchids
CATALOGUE   On request
MAIL ORDER   Yes
SHOP   Sundries
REFRESHMENTS   Light snacks
GARDEN   Visitor centre and display house
SHOWS   RHS Westminster; Chelsea; Hampton Court

A very extensive range of orchid species and hybrids. Plants can be seen growing in the display house: current admission is £1.50 for adults.

Churchills Garden Nursery
Exeter Road, Chudleigh TQ13 0DD
☎ & [FAX] 01626 852585

CONTACT   M. J. S. Henry
LOCATION   Off A38 at Chudleigh

OPEN 2 pm – 5 pm, Monday – Friday, 10 am – 5 pm, Saturdays, Sundays and Bank Holidays, mid-March to mid-October, and by appointment
SPECIALITIES Climbers; herbaceous perennials; shrubs; trees
NEW FOR 1997 About 100 new items every year
CATALOGUE 3 second-class stamps; published each March
MAIL ORDER No
GARDEN Four-acre private garden attached to the nursery

This is an excellent garden nursery. Everything is tried in the garden before finding its way into the nursery. The range of plants is exceptional: it is particularly strong on trees, shrubs and climbers. The list contains several rarities not available from other nurseries.

Decorative Foliage
Higher Badworthy, South Brent TQ10 9EG
☎ 01364 72768

CONTACT Amanda Hansford
LOCATION 1½ miles from South Brent
OPEN Phone first
SPECIALITIES Foliage plants
CATALOGUE 2 first-class stamps
MAIL ORDER Yes, no minimum order
GARDEN Garden

A small nursery with a good list of perennials and shrubs that have fine foliage and are useful for flower arranging.

Dulford Nurseries
Dulford, Cullompton EX15 2DG
☎ 01884 266361   [FAX] 01884 266663

CONTACT David or Jean Brent
LOCATION Off A373 by Keeper's Cottage Pub
OPEN 7.30 am – 4.30 pm; Monday – Friday; all year
SPECIALITIES Trees
CATALOGUE On request
MAIL ORDER Yes, road carrier

This nursery specialises in trees and shrubs. Its list has a wide selection across every genus of ornamental importance. They also sell bare-root hedging and forestry trees. Prices vary between the moderately expensive and the very reasonable. Worth investigating.

Elm Tree Nursery
Elm Tree Cottage, Cadbury, Exeter EX5 5LA
☎ & [FAX] 01392 861330

CONTACT Mike Saunders
OPEN Mail order only
SPECIALITIES Cyclamen
CATALOGUE 1 first-class stamp

A leading producer of hardy cyclamen: all their stock is grown from seed. Seed itself is available in late summer.

Endsleigh Garden Centre
Ivybridge PL21 9JL
☎ 01752 898989   [FAX] 01752 898990

CONTACT R. Taylor
LOCATION On A38, Plymouth side of Ivybridge
OPEN 9 am – 5 pm (6 pm during BST), daily
SHOP Garden machinery, buildings, pools, pets

REFRESHMENTS Tea room
GARDEN Demonstration gardens
DESIGN SERVICE Endsleigh Garden Centre

Garden centre with separate departments for associated products. They also run courses, workshops and exhibitions. Garden design and a delivery service are also offered.

Feebers Hardy Plants
1 Feebers Cottage, Westwood, Broadclyst EX5 3DQ
☎ 01404 822118

CONTACT Edna Squires
LOCATION 3 miles from Broadclyst, directions in catalogue
OPEN 10 am – 5 pm, Thursdays; 2 pm – 6 pm, Saturdays; March to July, September and October; or by appointment
SPECIALITIES South American plants
NEW FOR 1997 *Elegia capensis*, *Nerium oleander* 'Luteum Plenum'
CATALOGUE Large SAE with 38p stamp
MAIL ORDER Limited
GARDEN ¾-acre modern cottage garden

The heavy clay nursery soil influences the choice of hardy perennials. New plants from Chilean and Mexican seed are tested for hardiness during the winter. Advice is given for clay soil planting.

Glebe Cottage Plants
Pixie Lane, Warkleigh, Umberleigh EX37 9DH
CONTACT Carol Klein
LOCATION 4 miles south-west of South Molton
OPEN 10 am – 1 pm & 2 pm – 5 pm, Tuesday – Friday
SPECIALITIES Herbaceous perennials
CATALOGUE £1.50 & SAE
MAIL ORDER Yes
GARDEN Garden open, admission £1
SHOWS RHS Westminster; Malvern (Spring); Malvern (Autumn); Harrogate (Spring); Southport; Chelsea; Hampton Court; Courson

An exceptional list of perennials, with newly discovered species and promising cultivars. Carol Klein has a sharp eye for worthwhile new introductions, yet does not forget the reliable old classics, a talent recognised by five Gold Medals at Chelsea 1992-96. Her own garden is open during nursery hours (£1.50).

Greenway Gardens
Churston Ferrers, Brixham TQ5 0ES
☎ 01803 842382

CONTACT Roger Clark
LOCATION South-west of Galmpton, towards Greenway ferry
OPEN 2 pm – 5 pm, Monday – Friday, but 4.30 pm from November to March; 10 am – 12 noon, Saturdays. Closed Bank Holidays
SPECIALITIES Southern hemisphere trees and shrubs
CATALOGUE 3 first-class stamps
MAIL ORDER Yes, carrier at cost
GARDEN 2 walled nursery gardens open as above

An interesting list of mainly trees and shrubs. Specialities include southern hemisphere species, and plants grown from wild collected seed. Price varies with size so sounds like a place to visit if you are in the area.

H & S Wills
2 St Brannocks Park Road, Ilfracombe EX34 8HU
☎ 01271 863949

CONTACT   H. Wills
OPEN   Mail order only
SPECIALITIES   Sempervivums
CATALOGUE   SAE for list
MAIL ORDER   Yes, minimum order £3

Small mail-order-only nursery with a large choice of house-leeks: *Sempervivum*, *Jovibarba* and *Rosularia*, both species and cultivars.

The High Garden
Newton Ferrers PL8 1BW
☎ 01752 872528

CONTACT   F. Bennett
OPEN   By appointment
SPECIALITIES   Rhododendrons; *Pieris*
CATALOGUE   60p
MAIL ORDER   Yes

Young plants of *Rhododendron* species and hybrids, Japanese azaleas and *Pieris* are sold from a detailed list. Some *Skimmia* and *Camellia* also available.

Jack's Patch
Newton Road, Bishopsteignton, Teignmouth TQ14 9PN
☎ 01626 776996
LOCATION   Between Teignmouth and Newton Abbot on A381
OPEN   9 am – 5.30 pm, Monday – Saturday; 10 am – 5.30 pm, Bank Holidays; 10.30 am – 4.30 pm, Sundays
SHOP   Gifts
REFRESHMENTS   Jack's Kitchen
DESIGN SERVICE   Jack's Patch

Garden centre providing bedding plants and plants for small gardens among a general range. Most of the stock is grown at their own nurseries.

Kenwith Nursery
Blinsham, Beaford, Torrington, Winkleigh EX19 8NT
☎ 01805 603274   FAX 01805 603663
CONTACT   Gordon C. Haddow
LOCATION   1½ miles from RHS Garden Rosemoor on B3220 to Beaford
OPEN   10 am – 12 noon, 2 pm – 5 pm, Wednesday – Saturday. Other times by appointment
SPECIALITIES   Conifers
NEW FOR 1997   *Abies alba* 'Schwarzwald', *Cedrus deodara* 'Mountain Beauty', *Picea omorika* 'Karel', and several more dwarf conifers
CATALOGUE   3 first-class stamps
MAIL ORDER   Yes
GARDEN   Gardens contains over 2,000 dwarf conifers, many not grown elsewhere in the country

Just conifers: a very interesting and extensive collection of dwarf and slow-growing species and cultivars. They specialise in grafting. The nursery has moved and is now very convenient for RHS Rosemoor. Recommended for enthusiasts, who might also be interested in the comprehensive *World Checklist of Conifers* (from Landsman's Bookshop), which Mr Haddow co-wrote with Humphrey Welch.

Knightshayes Garden Trust
The Garden Office, Knightshayes, Tiverton EX16 7RG
☎ & FAX 01884 253264

CONTACT   01884 259010 (during opening hours)
LOCATION   Off A396 between Tiverton and Bampton
OPEN   10.30 am – 5.30 pm, daily, April to October
SPECIALITIES   Bulbs; herbaceous perennials; shrubs; trees
NEW FOR 1997   Collection of penstemon varieties, grass species and cultivars
MAIL ORDER   No
SHOP   National Trust shop
REFRESHMENTS   Restaurant
GARDEN   Knightshayes Gardens, Devon, see Gardens section

The nursery sells plants which look good in this National Trust garden, including bulbs and shrubs, with some new plants each year.

Marwood Hill Gardens
Barnstaple EX31 4EB
☎ 01271 42528

CONTACT   Dr J. A. Smart
LOCATION   Signed from A361
OPEN   11 am – 5 pm, daily
SPECIALITIES   Australian plants; bog plants; camellias; herbaceous perennials; New Zealand plants; trees
CATALOGUE   70p
MAIL ORDER   No
REFRESHMENTS   Sundays, Bank Holidays (April to October)
GARDEN   Marwood Hill Gardens, Devon, see Gardens section
NCCPG NATIONAL COLLECTIONS   *Astilbe; Iris ensata; Tolbaghia*

A charmingly varied and changing assortment of interesting trees, shrubs and perennials propagated from the well-known garden.

Nicky's Rock Garden Nursery
Hillcrest, Broadhayes, Stockland, Honiton EX14 9EH
☎ 01404 881213
CONTACT   Bob or Di Dark
LOCATION   6 miles east of Honiton, off midpoint of north/south road between A30 and A35. Map ref. ST 236027
OPEN   9 am – dusk, daily. Phone first
SPECIALITIES   Alpines
CATALOGUE   3 first-class stamps
MAIL ORDER   No
GARDEN   Display gardens

This nursery has a wide and changing selection of alpines and dwarf plants for rock gardens: bulbs, conifers and shrubs. Visitors are asked to phone for directions in advance.

Otter Nurseries Ltd

Gosford Road, Ottery St Mary EX11 1LZ

☎ 01404 815815　　🖷 01404 815816

CONTACT　Mrs P. Poole
LOCATION　1 mile from A30 (towards Ottery St Mary): turn at Brick Monument between Fenny Bridges and Fairmile
OPEN　9 am – 5.30 pm, Monday – Saturday; 10.30 am – 4.30 pm, Sundays. Closed Christmas and Boxing Day
SPECIALITIES　Herbaceous perennials
CATALOGUE　On request
MAIL ORDER　No
SHOP　Garden sundries, conservatories, greenhouses, machinery
REFRESHMENTS　Restaurant
DESIGN SERVICE　Otter Nurseries Ltd

Large garden centre with an excellent general range of plants – better than many specialist nurseries – especially conifers, perennials, shrubs and trees. They also have a nursery, so 80% of the plants are home-produced and there are stocks in excess of two million plants.

Perrie Hale Forest Nursery

Northcote Hill, Honiton EX14 8TH

☎ 01404 43344　　🖷 01404 47163

CONTACT　Judith Davey
LOCATION　1 mile north-east of Honiton
OPEN　Mid-November to early April for collection
SPECIALITIES　Hedging; trees
CATALOGUE　SAE
MAIL ORDER　Carriage can be arranged

Forest trees and hedging plants. This wholesale nursery is happy to deal with the public by appointment. They prefer you to collect, but small orders (under 200 plants) can be sent by carrier. They will be at the Devon County Show.

Peveril Clematis Nursery

Christow, Exeter EX6 7NG

☎ 01626 252937

CONTACT　Barry Fretwell
OPEN　10 am – 1 pm, 2 pm – 5.30 pm, Monday – Saturday; 10 am – 1 pm, Sundays. Closed Thursdays and Sunday afternoons
SPECIALITIES　Clematis
CATALOGUE　2 first-class stamps
MAIL ORDER　No
GARDEN　Clematis gardens

Barry Fretwell is a Clematis grower and hybridiser, author of 'Clematis as Companion Plants' (Cassell, 1994). The nursery offers an host of interesting species and large and small-flowered varieties.

Plant World Botanic Gardens

St Marychurch Road, Newton Abbot TQ12 4SE

☎ & 🖷 01803 872939

CONTACT　Ray Brown
OPEN　9.30 am – 5 pm, Thursday – Tuesday. Closed Wednesdays. Closed November – February
SPECIALITIES　Seeds

CATALOGUE　3 second-class stamps
MAIL ORDER　Seeds only
REFRESHMENTS　Award-winning farm-fresh ice-cream
GARDEN　Gardens divided into world habitat zones
NCCPG NATIONAL COLLECTIONS　Primula (captitatae); Primula (cortusoides); Primula (farinosae)

The nursery sells a selection of alpines, perennials and shrubs. There is an illustrated seed list with fresh material from the gardens and some interesting collected species. The gardens are planted out as special habitat zones.

The Plantsman Nursery

North Wonston Farm, Throwleigh, Okehampton EX20 2JA

☎ & 🖷 01647 231618

CONTACT　Guy & Emma Sisson
LOCATION　Directions in catalogue
OPEN　By appointment
SPECIALITIES　Climbers; conservatory plants
NEW FOR 1997　Schizophragma integrifolium, Clematis rehderiana
CATALOGUE　SAE
MAIL ORDER　Yes, minimum order £15
SHOWS　RHS Westminster

This young and expanding nursery has an interesting list of tender plants – the sort one sees in Mediterranean gardens. Many are climbers – asarinas, thunbergias and passion flowers, for instance – but there is also a good selection of such shrubs as daturas, Iochroma and Cestrum. Worth investigating.

Pleasant View Nursery & Garden

Two Mile Oak, Denbury, Newton Abbot TQ12 6DG

☎ 01803 813388

CONTACT　Christine Yeo
LOCATION　Take A381 from Newton Abbot: right at Two Mile Oak pub. Nursery is ³⁄₄ mile on the left
OPEN　10 am – 5 pm, Wednesday – Saturday, mid-March to October
SPECIALITIES　Shrubs; salvias
CATALOGUE　5 second-class stamps
MAIL ORDER　Yes, minimum order £20
GARDEN　Garden open Wednesday and Friday afternoons, May to September
NCCPG NATIONAL COLLECTIONS　Abelia; Salvia

The nursery carries a selection of rare shrubs for gardens and conservatories, and also a number of Salvia from the National Collection. They also hold the Abelia collection. The garden opens twice a week in season, and for the National Gardens Scheme on certain weekends. Groups and lectures by arrangement. Mrs. Yeo published a small book on Salvia last year.

Pounsley Plants

Pounsley Coombe, Spriddlestone, Brixton, Plymouth PL9 0DW

☎ & 🖷 01752 402873

CONTACT　Jane Hollow
LOCATION　Telephone or write for directions
OPEN　10 am – 5 pm most days, but check first
SPECIALITIES　Clematis; herbaceous perennials

NEW FOR 1997 *Adenophora coelestis* ACE 2455, *Clematis ranunculoides* ACE 2457
CATALOGUE SAE plus 2 first-class stamps
MAIL ORDER Yes, October to February only
GARDEN Garden open
DESIGN SERVICE Yes

A small nursery with perennials for cottage garden plantings, and some clematis and old roses too. Talks can be arranged and there is an advice centre, 'Plants for Places'. The nursery will be at local NCCPG plant sales.

R D Plants

Homelea Farm, Tytherleigh, Axminster EX13 7BG
☎ 01460 220206

CONTACT Lynda Windsor
LOCATION On A358, just inside the county boundary
OPEN 9 am – 1 pm, 2 pm – 5.30 pm, March to September. Phone first (between 8.30 and 9.30 am only)
SPECIALITIES Herbaceous perennials, woodland plants
NEW FOR 1997 *Anemone hupehensis* 'Crispa', *Anemone sylvestris* 'Elise Fellmann'
CATALOGUE 4 loose second-class stamps
MAIL ORDER Yes, mainland UK
GARDEN Small display area

Mainly herbaceous plants and alpines. Good for *Anemone, Epimedium, Ranunculus* and *Tropaeolum*. They will be at local NCCPG plant sales in spring and early summer.

RHS Enterprises Ltd

RHS Garden, Rosemoor, Great Torrington EX38 8PH
☎ 01805 624067   [FAX] 01805 622422
CONTACT J. Gingell
OPEN 10 am – 6 pm, April – September; 10 am – 5 pm, October – March
CATALOGUE No
MAIL ORDER No
SHOP Books, gifts
REFRESHMENTS Restaurant (garden)
GARDEN RHS Garden, Rosemoor, Devon, see Gardens section

There is an interesting selection of plants from the garden for sale here, as well as the new visitors centre. Numerous walks and demonstrations are held here (and at Cannington College, Bridgwater) throughout the year. Both are also open to non-RHS members.

Rowden Gardens

Brentor, Tavistock PL19 0NG
☎ 01822 810275

CONTACT J. R. L. Carter
LOCATION Phone for details
OPEN 10 am – 5 pm, Saturday – Sunday, and Bank Holiday Mondays. Other times by appointment
SPECIALITIES Aquatic plants; bog plants; herbaceous perennials; irises
CATALOGUE £1.50
MAIL ORDER Yes
REFRESHMENTS Available locally
GARDEN Garden

DESIGN SERVICE Rowden Gardens
NCCPG NATIONAL COLLECTIONS *Fallopia*; *Persicaria*; *Ranunculus ficaria*

Mostly aquatic and moisture-loving plants here. The choice of *Iris*, including *I. ensata* cultivars, is especially good. The nursery draws on the 3000 varieties in the garden. Groups welcome by arrangement: lectures available. They have a new National Collection, *Ranunculus ficaria*, the lesser celandine. They no longer attend shows, but will continue to introduce new plants.

Sampford Shrubs

Sampford Peverell, Tiverton EX16 7EW
☎ 01884 821164

CONTACT Martin Hughes-Jones or Sue Proud
LOCATION 1 mile from M5, Jct 27 and Tiverton Parkway station
OPEN 9 am – 5 pm (dusk if earlier), Thursday – Saturday; 10 am – 4 pm, Sundays. Closed over Christmas and January
SPECIALITIES Herbaceous perennials; rhododendrons; shrubs
NEW FOR 1997 *Arbutus xalapensis, Telekia speciosa, Dendranthema* 'Vagabond Prince'
CATALOGUE A5 SAE
MAIL ORDER Yes, winter only. £15 minimum order

A first-rate nursery that gets better and better every year. They offer a mixed collection of herbaceous plants and trees and shrubs, with a good selection of fruit. Their list is crammed with reliable varieties to grow. Plants are grown mainly in composted organic waste. They attend most of the NCCPG's Devon plant sales. This season they are again offering a small bonus for customers using public transport to visit the nursery.

Scotts Clematis

Lee, Ilfracombe EX34 8LW
☎ 01271 863366   [FAX] 01271 863003
CONTACT John and Marianne McLellan-Scott
LOCATION 3 miles west of Ilfracombe, towards Woolacombe
OPEN 10 am – 5 pm, March to October. Closed Mondays
SPECIALITIES Clematis
NEW FOR 1997 *Clematis integrifolia* 'Mariana', *Clematis pitcheri*
CATALOGUE A5 SAE
MAIL ORDER Yes, minimum order 4 plants
SHOWS RHS Westminster; Malvern (Spring); Malvern (Autumn); BBC GW Live; Hampton Court; Ayr; Courson

Clematis specialists, now producing in excess of 250 varieties at the nursery. In addition to attending shows in this country, they will be at shows in Belgium, France, Holland and Italy.

Silver Dale Nurseries

Shute Lane, Combe Martin EX34 0HT
☎ 01271 882539

CONTACT Roger Gilbert
LOCATION Knap Down, above Combe Martin
OPEN 10 am – 6 pm, daily
SPECIALITIES Fuchsias
NEW FOR 1997 *Fuchsia* 'Operetta' & F. 'Loxhore Posthorn'
CATALOGUE 3 first-class stamps

MAIL ORDER Yes, all year. No minimum order

Important fuchsia specialists, with a large catalogue listing about 700 cultivars. This includes over 200 hardy fuchsias, most of which may be seen in their show garden.

Southcombe Gardens
2 Willens Cottages, Mamhead, Kenton EX6 8HQ
☎ 01626 888947

CONTACT Mr or Mrs Wood
LOCATION Ask for map
OPEN By appointment
SPECIALITIES Alpines; grasses; herbaceous perennials
CATALOGUE £1
SHOWS RHS Westminster; Malvern (Spring); Malvern (Autumn); Harrogate (Spring); Harrogate (Autumn); Hampton Court; Courson

This youngish nursery is beginning to make an impact at shows. It specialises in plants for small gardens, especially rock-garden plants and small shrubs.

Stone Lane Gardens
Stone Farm, Chagford TQ13 8JU
☎ & FAX 01647 231311

CONTACT Kenneth Ashburner
LOCATION Between Whiddon Down and Drewsteignton
OPEN By appointment only
SPECIALITIES Alnus; Betula
NEW FOR 1997 Alnus fauriei, Alnus pendula, Alnus nitida, Betula chichibuensis, Betula delavayi
CATALOGUE £2
MAIL ORDER Yes
GARDEN Arboretum and water garden
NCCPG NATIONAL COLLECTIONS Alnus; Betula

Many rare species of Alnus and Betula, often of wild origin. Selected clones are also available as grafted plants. A sculpture exhibition is held in part of the arboretum from May to September.

Thornhayes Nursery
Dulford, Cullompton EX15 2DF
☎ 01884 266746   FAX 01884 266739

CONTACT Kevin Croucher
LOCATION 10 minutes from M5, Jct 28
OPEN By appointment only
SPECIALITIES Fruit; trees
CATALOGUE 4 first-class stamps
MAIL ORDER Yes

A retail and wholesale nursery. The stock is both open-ground and container-grown, and covers a broad spectrum of interesting ornamental and fruit trees, including some hard-to-get West Country apples (for cider, cooking and eating). The Sorbus, Pyrus and Crataegus are also good: dendrophiles should take a closer look.

Veryans Plants
Glebe, Coryton, Okehampton EX20 4PB
☎ 01822 860302 (day)

CONTACT Rebecca Miller
LOCATION 3 miles from A30

OPEN By appointment only
SPECIALITIES Herbaceous perennials
CATALOGUE 3 first-class stamps
MAIL ORDER Yes
SHOWS RHS Westminster; Malvern (Spring); Hampton Court

Young nursery with a plantsman's selection of cottage garden plants, especially alpines, woodlanders, groundcovers and low-growing herbaceous plants. The evening telephone number is 01566 783433.

The Water Garden Nursery
Wembworthy, Chulmleigh EX18 7SG
☎ 01837 83566

CONTACT John M. Smith
LOCATION Map in list
OPEN 9.30 am – 12.30 pm, 1.30 pm – 5 pm, Wednesday – Sunday
SPECIALITIES Aquatic plants; bog plants
CATALOGUE 3 first-class stamps
MAIL ORDER Yes
GARDEN Yes
DESIGN SERVICE Yes

Water lilies, bog plants and perennials for wet and dry margins.

Westfield Cacti
Kennford, Exeter EX6 7XD
☎ 01392 832921

CONTACT Ralph or Marina Northcott
LOCATION Kennford – at the end of the M5
OPEN 10 am – 5 pm, Wednesday – Sunday
SPECIALITIES Cacti and succulents; seeds
CATALOGUE 4 first-class stamps
MAIL ORDER Yes
REFRESHMENTS For groups only
GARDEN Show house open
SHOWS RHS Westminster; Malvern (Spring); Malvern (Autumn); Chelsea; BBC GW Live; Hampton Court

There is a huge choice of cacti and succulents at this retail and wholesale nursery. The stocks are also impressively large. Seeds and some books are also sold.

Whitehouse Ivies
Eggesford Gardens, Chulmleigh EX18 7QU
☎ 01769 580250   FAX 01769 581041

CONTACT Any staff member
LOCATION Off A377
OPEN 9 am – 6 pm, daily
SPECIALITIES Ivies
CATALOGUE £1
MAIL ORDER Yes
REFRESHMENTS Restaurant
GARDEN Yes
DESIGN SERVICE Design, construction and maintenance

The nursery has moved to Devon and is now part of??? The largest retail range of Hedera species and cultivars. Over 300 are now available, for climbing, trailing, topiary, ground cover and container use. Most of the business is mail order: the catalogue is fully illustrated. The nursery moves this year: write or telephone for details.

Withleigh Nurseries
Withleigh, Tiverton EX16 8JG
☎ 01884 253351
CONTACT   C. S. Britton
LOCATION   3 miles west of Tiverton on B3137
OPEN   9 am – 5.30 pm, Tuesday – Saturday. Also open Mondays, March to June
SPECIALITIES   Herbaceous perennials; shrubs
MAIL ORDER   No
GARDEN   Garden opens under NGS

A retail nursery with a range of bedding, herbaceous perennials and shrubs. Visitors are usually allowed in the garden too, which also opens under the NGS.

DORSET

Abbey Plants
Chaffeymoor, Bourton, Gillingham SP8 5BY
☎ 01747 840841
CONTACT   K. R. Potts
LOCATION   3 miles east of Wincanton, off A303
OPEN   10 am – 1 pm, 2 pm – 5 pm, Tuesday – Saturday, March to November. By appointment only December to February
SPECIALITIES   Roses; shrubs
MAIL ORDER   No
GARDEN   Chiffchaffs, Dorset, see Gardens section

The nursery sells a good range of flowering shrubs including roses, some grown on their own roots, with herbaceous and alpine plants.

Abbotsbury Gardens
Abbotsbury, Weymouth DT3 4LA
☎ 01305 871344/871412
CONTACT   D. Sutton
LOCATION   9 miles west of Weymouth, on the Dorset coast
OPEN   10 am – 5 pm, daily, March to October, 10 am – 3 pm, daily, November to March
SPECIALITIES   Half-hardy plants; sub-tropical plants
NEW FOR 1997   Several new palms
CATALOGUE   £2 plus large SAE (43p)
MAIL ORDER   Yes, minimum order £10
SHOP   Garden shop and plant centre
REFRESHMENTS   Yes
GARDEN   Abbotsbury Sub-Tropical Gardens, Dorset, see Gardens section

Attached to these famous gardens, the plant centre naturally specialises in tender and sub-tropical plants, including penstemons and salvias, and in species which give a tropical effect. Their handsome catalogue lists many rare species and cultivars.

Archangel Plants
186 Ringwood Road, Longham, Ferndown BH22 9AP
☎ 01202 872414
CONTACT   Carol Strafford or John Worrall

LOCATION   On A348, next to Angel Inn
OPEN   9 am – 5 pm, Monday – Thursday; 10 am – 4 pm Saturdays; 31 March to 30 September
SPECIALITIES   Herbaceous perennials
NEW FOR 1997   Achillea 'Terracotta', Euphorbia 'Golden Foam', Veronica montana 'Corinne Tremaine'
CATALOGUE   4 first-class stamps
MAIL ORDER   Yes, £10 minimum order

A small specialist nursery with a good list of perennials – often the larger sort that are the backbone of a border. Grasses, phlox, nepetas, kniphofias and sedums are well represented. They are hoping to move sites this year, so ring before visiting them to avoid disappointment.

Barthelémy & Co Nurseries
262 Wimborne Road West, Stapehill, Wimborne BH21 2DZ
☎ 01202 874283   FAX 01202 897482
CONTACT   John Skinner
LOCATION   On old A31 between Wimborne and Ferndown
OPEN   9 am – 5 pm, Monday – Saturday, 1 April to 19 December. Closed 1 pm – 2 pm
SPECIALITIES   Acers
CATALOGUE   SAE
MAIL ORDER   Yes

Specialist growers of acers. They have a large number of grafted A. palmatum varieties besides bare-root and pot-grown species seedlings.

Beacon Fuchsias
11 Tuckers Lane, Poole BH15 4BT
☎ & FAX 01202 685053
CONTACT   Alan or Nancy Franklin
LOCATION   1 mile north of Poole Bridge
OPEN   1 pm – 6 pm daily, February to June
SPECIALITIES   Fuchsias
NEW FOR 1997   5 exclusive new varieties from USA
CATALOGUE   2 first-class stamps
MAIL ORDER   Yes

There are over 400 fuchsias, varieties and species available in spring and summer. Bedding and patio plants, with a selection of pelargoniums, can be bought as well.

Bennetts Water Lily Farm
Water Gardens, Putton Lane, Chickerell, Weymouth DT3 4AF
☎ 01305 785150   FAX 01305 781619
CONTACT   J. Bennett
LOCATION   2 miles west of Weymouth, signed off B3157 Bridport road
OPEN   10 am – 5 pm, Tuesday – Sunday, April to August; 10 am – 5 pm, Tuesday – Saturday, September, Tuesday – Friday, October. Open on Bank Holidays
SPECIALITIES   Aquatic plants; bog plants; sempervivums; water lilies
CATALOGUE   3 first-class stamps
MAIL ORDER   Yes
SHOP   Gifts, pond supplies
REFRESHMENTS   Tea room, cream teas

GARDEN 6-acre site, with 100 varieties of water lilies

Water lilies, pond plants and marginals in abundance, as well as extensive display ponds. The flowering season is from to June to late September. They also have tropical varieties to tempt conservatory owners.

Birchdale Plants

9 Cowper Road, Moordown, Bournemouth BH9 2UJ
☎ 01202 521024

CONTACT Terry Bishop
OPEN By appointment only: phone first
SPECIALITIES Grasses
CATALOGUE 75p in stamps
MAIL ORDER Yes, £15 minimum order
SHOWS RHS Westminster; Malvern (Spring); Malvern (Autumn); Chelsea; BBC GW Live; Hampton Court

This nursery specialises in grasses and sedges, and has been one of the brightest stars at RHS shows in recent years. The catalogue is informative, and plants are reasonably priced.

C W Groves & Son

Nursery & Garden Centre, West Bay Road, Bridport DT6 4BA
☎ 01308 422654   FAX 01308 420888

CONTACT Clive or Diana Groves
LOCATION On A35 Bridport bypass, opposite Crown roundabout
OPEN 8.30 am – 5 pm, Monday – Saturday; 10.30 am – 4.30 pm, Sundays
SPECIALITIES Violas
CATALOGUE SAE
MAIL ORDER Yes
REFRESHMENTS Café
GARDEN Summer months: rose beds, asparagus beds, and demonstration vineyard

A traditional and family-run nursery-cum-garden centre, with a good general range. The firm was founded by the present owner's great-great-grandfather in 1866. Appropriately enough they also specialise in Victorian violets. These named violet cultivars are only sold by mail order, though. There are events during the season.

Cherry Tree Nursery (SWOP)

Off New Road Roundabout, Northbourne, Bournemouth BH10 7DA
☎ 01202 593537   FAX 01202 590626

CONTACT Jessica Davies
LOCATION Off A347 north of Bournemouth
OPEN 8.30 am – 3.30 pm, Monday – Friday; 9 am – 12 pm, Saturdays (most)
SPECIALITIES Climbers; conifers; shrubs
CATALOGUE Large SAE
MAIL ORDER No

Wholesale and retail nursery with an expanding range of shrubs, climbers and conifers. It is run by a charity which provides sheltered work opportunities for adults with mental health problems.

Cranborne Manor Garden Centre

Cranborne, Wimborne BH21 5PP
☎ 01725 517248   FAX 01725 517862

CONTACT Sandra Hewitt
LOCATION 10 miles north of Wimborne on B3078
OPEN 9 am – 5 pm, Monday – Saturday; 10 am – 5 pm, Sundays and Bank Holidays; March – December. 10 am – 4 pm, daily, January – February
SPECIALITIES Roses
CATALOGUE £1
MAIL ORDER Roses only; November to February
SHOP Pots and ornaments
REFRESHMENTS Wednesdays, weekends and Bank Holidays, April to September
GARDEN Cranborne Manor, Dorset. 9 am – 5 pm, Wednesdays only, March to September. See Gardens section

Among the general stock there is a good choice of herbaceous plants. The specialities, though, are old-fashioned roses and topiary specimens. If you go on a Wednesday (April to September) the garden is also open.

Global Orange Groves UK

P O Box 644, Poole BH17 9YB
☎ 01202 691699

CONTACT Mrs Oliver
LOCATION Horton Heath, near Wimborne
OPEN Weekends, when not exhibiting
SPECIALITIES Citrus
NEW FOR 1997 *Citrus bergamia*
CATALOGUE SAE
MAIL ORDER Yes
SHOWS Malvern (Spring); Hampton Court

Fruiting citrus trees in containers: they have 32 varieties, including lemons, mandarins and kumquats. Groups are offered a free talk and tour of the nursery. Their special summer and winter fertilisers are recommended for anyone with bedraggled and non-fruiting citrus.

Hardy Orchids Ltd

New Gate Farm, Scotchey Lane, Stour Provost, Gillingham SP8 5LT
☎ 01747 838368   FAX 01747 838308

CONTACT N. J. Heywood
LOCATION Stour Row turning off A30, 3½ miles west of Shaftesbury
OPEN Between 9 am – 5 pm, by appointment
SPECIALITIES Orchids (hardy)
CATALOGUE SAE
MAIL ORDER Yes
SHOP Orchid books and sundries

The business is devoted to hardy orchids, old and new books about them, and the materials needed to grow them. There will be open weekends on 31 May – 1 June and 14 – 15 June. The nursery will be at Newbury Show.

Holme Nurseries
West Holme Farm, West Holme, Wareham BH20 6AG
☎ 01929 554716   📠 01929 551616

CONTACT   Simon Goldsack
LOCATION   On B3070 between Wareham and Lulworth
OPEN   10 am – 5 pm, daily, 1 March to 31 October. Closed on Sundays from August onwards
CATALOGUE   £1
MAIL ORDER   No

General range, including herbaceous plants, shrubs, climbers and roses. Design and Landscape Construction is available and a free consultancy service.

Humphries Garden Centre
Littlemoor Road, Preston, Weymouth DT3 6AD
☎ 01305 834766   📠 01305 832708

CONTACT   Simon Lee or Rebecca Murphy
OPEN   9 am – 5.30 pm, Monday – Saturday; 10.30 am – 4.30 pm, Sunday
CATALOGUE   No
MAIL ORDER   No
SHOP   Garden sundries, pets, pond and pool equipment
REFRESHMENTS   Café
GARDEN   Wildlife garden

Macpennys Nurseries
154 Burley Road, Bransgore, Christchurch BH23 8DB
☎ 01425 672348

CONTACT   T. M. Lowndes
LOCATION   Between Christchurch and Burley
OPEN   9 am – 5 pm, Monday – Saturday; 2 pm – 5 pm, Sundays. Closed at Christmas and New Year
SPECIALITIES   Shrubs; trees
CATALOGUE   A4 SAE plus 50p
MAIL ORDER   Yes
GARDEN   4-acre woodland garden
DESIGN SERVICE   Yes

Long-established nursery with a reliable general range across the plant spectrum. The garden is open for the National Gardens Scheme at the same times. Talks and special openings can be arranged for groups.

Milton Garden Plants
Milton on Stour, Gillingham SP8 5PX
☎ & 📠 01747 822484

CONTACT   Sue Hardy
LOCATION   3 miles south of A303 at Mere
OPEN   8.30 am – 5 pm, Tuesday – Saturday and Bank Holidays; 10 am – 4.30 pm, Sundays. Closed Mondays
SPECIALITIES   Herbaceous perennials
CATALOGUE   £1.50 in stamps; perennials only
MAIL ORDER   No
GARDEN   Display gardens
DESIGN SERVICE   Milton Garden Plants

Family-run plant centre, with a good general range, notably of hardy perennials.

Naked Cross Nurseries
Waterloo Road, Corfe Mullen, Wimborne BH21 3SP
☎ 01202 693256

CONTACT   Peter French or Janet Paddon
LOCATION   Southern end of village
OPEN   9 am – 5.30 pm; Monday to Saturday; daily. 9.30 am – 5 pm Sundays
SPECIALITIES   Heathers
CATALOGUE   2 first-class stamps
MAIL ORDER   Yes

Family-run nursery with an excellent and long list of heathers: recommended.

Stewarts Country Garden Centre
God's Blessing Lane, Broomhill, Holt, Wimborne BH21 7DF
☎ 01202 882462   📠 01202 842127

CONTACT   Vincent Blood
OPEN   9 am – 5.30 pm, Monday – Friday, all year. 10 am – 4 pm, Sundays
SHOP   Sundries
REFRESHMENTS   Coffee shop

A good all-purpose garden centre whose origins date back to 1742. It offers gardening talks every Tuesday at 10.30 am and a series of events throughout the year.

Three Counties Nurseries
Marshwood, Bridport DT6 5QJ
☎ & 📠 01297 678257

CONTACT   Mr or Mrs D. C. Hitchcock
OPEN   Mail order only
SPECIALITIES   *Dianthus*
CATALOGUE   2 second-class stamps
MAIL ORDER   Yes
SHOWS   RHS Westminster; Malvern (Spring); Malvern (Autumn); Harrogate (Spring); Harrogate (Autumn); BBC GW Live; Hampton Court; Strathclyde

Dianthus specialists, with a wide choice of garden pinks, including laced, old-fashioned and modern hybrids. They also have alpine Dianthus and a new selection of named *D. barbatus* (Sweet Williams). Lectures by arrangement.

Trehane Camellia Nursery
Stapehill Road, Hampreston, Wimborne BH21 7NE
☎ & 📠 01202 873490

CONTACT   Lorraine Keets
LOCATION   Between Ferndown and Wimborne, off A31
OPEN   9 am – 4 pm, Monday – Friday, all year; 10 am – 4.30 pm, Saturday – Sunday, late February to end May and end September to end October or by appointment
SPECIALITIES   Camellias; blueberry plants
NEW FOR 1997   Range of *Kalmia*
CATALOGUE   £1.50 handbook
MAIL ORDER   Yes
GARDEN   Display house
SHOWS   RHS Westminster; Harrogate (Spring)

Wholesale and retail camellia growers. They have a wide choice of *Camellia* hybrids, and *Kalmia, Magnolia, Pieris* and azaleas. They also grow and sell blueberries and cranberries.

White Veil Fuchsias
Verwood Road, Three Legged Cross, Wimborne BH21 6RP
☎ 01202 813998
CONTACT   Robin Case
OPEN   9 am – 1 pm, 2 pm – 5 pm daily. Closed for lunch
SPECIALITIES   Fuchsias
NEW FOR 1997   Six new cultivars
CATALOGUE   2 first-class stamps
MAIL ORDER   Yes
SHOWS   RHS Westminster; Malvern (Spring); Chelsea; BBC GW Live; Hampton Court

Fuchsia specialists with a very comprehensive list of cultivars, old and new; they attend the major shows.

Wyevale Garden Centre
24 Wareham Road, Owermoigne, Dorchester DT2 8BY
☎ 01305 852324   📠 01305 854027
REFRESHMENTS   Restaurant

Wyevale Garden Centre
Van Dukes Garden Centre, 229–247 Wimborne Road West, Stapehill, Wimborne BH21 2DN
☎ 01202 874208   📠 01202 895335
REFRESHMENTS   Restaurant

CO. DURHAM

Beamish Clematis Nursery
Burntwood Cottage, Stoney Lane, Beamish DH9 0SJ
☎ & 📠 0191 370 0202
CONTACT   C. Brown or Jan Wilson
LOCATION   A693 from A1M to Beamish Village
OPEN   9 am – 5 pm, daily, February to November
SPECIALITIES   Clematis; climbers
MAIL ORDER   No

This retail nursery's main strength is clematis (over 300 varieties). Other ranges include *Lonicera* and *Hedera*, with ornamental trees and shrubs. Evening visits, with cutting demonstrations can be arranged for societies.

Eggleston Hall Gardens
The Cottage, Eggleston Hall, Eggleston, Barnard Castle DL12 0AG
☎ 01833 650403   📠 01833 650378
CONTACT   R. H. Gray or Gordon Long
LOCATION   Off the B6278: follow local signs
OPEN   10 am – 5 pm, daily
SPECIALITIES   Foliage plants
CATALOGUE   £1.50
MAIL ORDER   No
REFRESHMENTS   Drinks and ices
GARDEN   Garden open: 50p entrance charge (or £1 season ticket) covers nursery and garden

The gardens grow a varied selection of plants, with the emphasis on providing year-round material for flower arranging. The wide choice in the plant centre, with new plants added each year, reflects this balance.

Elly Hill Herbs
Elly Hill House, Barmpton, Darlington DL1 3JF
☎ 01325 464682
CONTACT   Nina Pagan
LOCATION   2 miles north-east of Darlington, map in catalogue
OPEN   9.30 am – 12.30 pm, 4 pm – 5.30 pm, daily, March to October. Phone first
SPECIALITIES   Herbs
CATALOGUE   Large SAE
MAIL ORDER   Herb book only (£4.75, inc. p & p)
REFRESHMENTS   By arrangement, for herb parties
GARDEN   Herb garden

A herb nursery selling herb plants and products. They organise herb parties and give conducted tours to groups. Their book, *Herbs and so on*, is available by post.

Elmridge Gardens Ltd
Coniscliffe Road, Darlington DL3 8DJ
☎ 01325 462710   📠 01325 363550
CONTACT   J. Blake
OPEN   8.30 am – 5.30 pm, daily (6.30 pm April to July)
SPECIALITIES   Bedding plants
CATALOGUE   On request
MAIL ORDER   No

Bedding, pot plants and shrubs.

Equatorial Plant Co
7 Gray Lane, Barnard Castle DL12 8PD
☎ & 📠 01833 690519
CONTACT   Dr R. Warren
LOCATION   South Durham
OPEN   By appointment only
SPECIALITIES   Orchids
CATALOGUE   SAE
MAIL ORDER   Yes
SHOWS   RHS Westminster

They specialise in laboratory-raised tropical orchids, which are sold at the right size for transplanting. They are active in conservation, including Brazil's coastal rain forest, where introductory orchid tours can be arranged. *Rhododendron vireya* are new this year. The nursery will be at Newbury Show on 29 – 30 June.

Klondyke Garden Centre (Chester-le-Street)
Lambton Park, Chester-le-Street DH3 4PZ
☎ 0191 385 5154   📠 0191 385 8481
CONTACT   David Welch (Manager)

Peter Barratt's Garden Centres (Stockton)
Yarm Road, Stockton on Tees TS18 3SQ
☎ 01642 613433   📠 01642 618185
CONTACT   Keith Crackett

OPEN 9 am – 5.30 pm
SPECIALITIES Shrubs; South American plants
SHOP Garden sundries, aquatics
REFRESHMENTS Yes
GARDEN Demonstration gardens
DESIGN SERVICE Peter Barratt's Garden Centres

General garden centre with garden and leisure products. Delivery and design service.

Robert W & R Bewley

Queens Road Nursery, 66 Queens Road, Blackhill, Consett DH8 0BW
☎ 01207 503263
OPEN Mail order only
SPECIALITIES Alpines
CATALOGUE 50p plus postage
MAIL ORDER Yes
SHOWS Harrogate (Spring); Harrogate (Autumn); Southport; BBC GW Live; Strathclyde; Ayr

Specialist nursery for alpine and rock-garden plants. Mail order only, but they attend many of the Northern shows, including the Royal, Holker Hall, the Royal Highland and will bring orders with them.

Rookhope Nurseries

Rookhope, Upper Weardale DL13 2DD
☎ 01388 517272

CONTACT Karen or Alan Blackburn
LOCATION 5 miles west of Stanhope, signed off A689
OPEN 9 am – 5 pm, daily, 15 March to 30 September
SPECIALITIES Alpines; herbaceous perennials
CATALOGUE 3 first-class stamps
MAIL ORDER Limited mail order
REFRESHMENTS Drinks and sweets
GARDEN Display gardens

Hardy garden plants, alpines, perennials and shrubs: all in wide variety. The nursery is high up in the Pennines so the plants are selected for the northern climate.

Strikes Garden Centre

299 Woodlands Road, Cockerton, Darlington DL3 9AA
☎ 01325 468474   [FAX] 01325 381970

CONTACT Caroline Burton (Manager)
LOCATION Near Cockerton Green
OPEN 9 am – 6 pm, Monday – Saturday; 10.30 am – 4.30 pm, Sundays
SHOP Gifts

Strikes Garden Centre

Urlay Nook Road, Eaglescliffe TS16 0PE
☎ 01642 780481   [FAX] 01647 788237

CONTACT Barrie Donaldson (Assistant Manager)
LOCATION Near Yarm
OPEN 9 am – 6 pm, Monday – Saturday; 10.30 am – 4.30 pm, Sundays
SHOP Gifts

Garden centre, with production nursery on the same site.

Town Farm Nursery

Whitton, Stockton on Tees TS21 1LQ
☎ 01740 631079

CONTACT David Baker
OPEN 10 am – 6 pm, Friday – Monday. Closed in winter
SPECIALITIES Alpines; herbaceous perennials; shrubs
CATALOGUE SAE
MAIL ORDER Yes
GARDEN 1-acre display garden

This nursery is a Mecca for keen gardeners in the north-east. David Baker lists an excellent selection of hardy alpines and perennials, both rare and classic. The magnificent display gardens are open for nursery visitors.

Westwinds Perennial Plants

Filpoke Lane, High Hesleden, Hartlepool TS27 4BT
☎ 0191 518 0225

CONTACT Harry Blackwood
LOCATION Off A1086 north of Hartlepool
OPEN 8 am – 8 pm, Saturday – Monday
SPECIALITIES Herbaceous perennials
NEW FOR 1997 Many new American hostas
CATALOGUE SAE
MAIL ORDER No
GARDEN Garden open

Herbaceous plant specialist (hostas, penstemons, hemerocallis, diascias, heucheras etc.), with an expanding range of climbers and shrubs too. Mailing-list customers get a brightly written newsletter.

ESSEX

Ausfern Nurseries UK Ltd

Tytherleigh House, Hubert Road, Brentwood CM14 4RF
☎ 01277 277606   [FAX] 01277 233585

CONTACT Neil Pike or Ed Pearman
LOCATION At Reeds Farm, Cow Watering Lane: back glasshouse entrance, Writtle
OPEN By appointment only: 9 am – 5 pm, daily
SPECIALITIES Australian plants; ferns; New Zealand plants; palms
NEW FOR 1997 New Xanthorrhoea cultivars
CATALOGUE From office address, £1
MAIL ORDER Yes
SHOWS Malvern (Spring); Malvern (Autumn); Harrogate (Spring); Harrogate (Autumn); Southport; Chelsea; BBC GW Live; Hampton Court; Ayr

Pommie outlet for Australian growers who conserve and propagate an intriguing range of tree and ground ferns and palms. Cash & carry only, with minimum £100 order.

B & H M Baker

Bourne Brook Nurseries, Greenstead Green, Halstead CO9 1RJ
☎ 01787 476367

CONTACT B. or H. M. Baker
LOCATION Halstead, Essex

OPEN   9 am – 4.30 pm, Monday – Friday; 9 am – 12 noon,
2 – 4.30 pm, Saturday – Sunday
SPECIALITIES   Fuchsias; house plants
CATALOGUE   20p plus first-class stamp
MAIL ORDER   No
GARDEN   Fuchsia stock plants on display late July to
September

This fuchsia specialist has a magnificent list of about 700
cultivars, and species and is particularly strong on old and
historic hybrids. A range of house plants is also available.

The Beth Chatto Gardens Ltd
Elmstead Market, Colchester CO7 7DB
☎ 01206 822007   ✆ 01206 825933
LOCATION   7 miles east of Colchester on A133
OPEN   9 am – 5 pm, Monday – Saturday, March to October;
9 am – 4 pm, Monday – Friday, November to February. Closed
Bank Holidays
SPECIALITIES   Herbaceous perennials
CATALOGUE   £2.50
MAIL ORDER   Yes, £20 minimum order
GARDEN   Beth Chatto Gardens, Essex, see Gardens section

The nursery is a prime source for out-of-the-ordinary plants.
The selection bears the stamp of a plantswoman with a discerning eye for effective plant combinations.

Bypass Nurseries
72 Ipswich Road, Colchester CO1 2YF
☎ 01206 865500   ✆ 01206 865810
CONTACT   Gina Zimmerman
OPEN   9 am – 5.30 pm, March to October; 9 am – 5 pm,
winter. 10.30 am – 4.30 pm, Sundays, all year
SHOP   Conservatories, greenhouses and flowers

A traditional garden centre supplying plants, and a range of
garden products through franchises. They also have a wholesale side as breeders and raisers of greenhouse cyclamen and
primroses. Delivery services available locally.

Cants of Colchester
Nayland Road, Mile End, Colchester CO4 5EB
☎ 01206 844008   ✆ 01206 855371
CONTACT   Angela Pawsey
LOCATION   North of Colchester, on A134
OPEN   Times vary: phone first
SPECIALITIES   Roses
NEW FOR 1997   Several new roses due this summer
CATALOGUE   On request
MAIL ORDER   Yes, fixed p & p rates
GARDEN   Rose fields are open from the end of June to late
September. Free entry, and no need to phone
SHOWS   Chelsea; Hampton Court

Cants is the oldest established UK rose nursery, best known
for 'Just Joey', one of the most popular roses of this century.
The range is mostly of modern varieties. Callers can obtain
containerised plants between April and August, and bare root
from November to March: they stress the need to phone
before visiting.

Copford Bulbs
Dorsetts, Birch Road, Copford, Colchester CO6 1DR
☎ 01206 330008
CONTACT   D. J. Pearce
LOCATION   South-west of Colchester, 2 miles off A12
OPEN   By appointment
SPECIALITIES   Cyclamen (hardy)
CATALOGUE   SAE
MAIL ORDER   Yes
GARDEN   By appointment

This small nursery now specialises in hardy cyclamen, but
daffodil enthusiasts may still persuade them to part with a few
of their exhibition bulbs.

The Cottage Garden
Langham Road, Boxted, Colchester CO4 5HU
☎ 01206 272269
CONTACT   Alison Smith
LOCATION   4 miles north of Colchester
OPEN   8 am (9.30 am on Sundays) – 5.30 pm; daily; spring &
summer. 8.30 am (9.30 am on Sundays) – 5.30 pm; Thursday
– Monday; autumn & winter
SPECIALITIES   Herbaceous perennials
MAIL ORDER   No
SHOP   Garden antiques, garden sundries
GARDEN   Display garden

The nursery sells home grown plants in variety, including
perennials and bulbs. Prices are modest. Also on sale are
garden sundries and garden antiques.

Country Gardens (Ongar)
Langford Bridge, Ongar Road CN15 0LB
☎ 01277 365485   ✆ 01277 365515
CONTACT   Pat Murray (Manager)
OPEN   9 am – 6 pm, Monday – Saturday; 10.30 am – 4.30 pm,
Sundays

County Park Nursery
384 Wingletye Lane, Hornchurch RM11 3BU
☎ 01708 445205
CONTACT   Graham Hutchins
LOCATION   2½ miles from M25, Jct 29. Off Wingletye Lane,
in Essex Gardens, Hornchurch
OPEN   9 am – 6 pm, Monday – Saturday; 10 am – 5 pm,
Sundays; from March to October. Closed Wednesdays. Open
in winter by appointment only
SPECIALITIES   Australian plants; New Zealand plants, hebe
NEW FOR 1997   Podocarpus 'County Park Fire',
Brachyglottis 'Silver Waves'
CATALOGUE   3 first-class stamps
MAIL ORDER   No
NCCPG NATIONAL COLLECTIONS   Coprosma; Parahebe

This small nursery specialises in Antipodean plants, many of
them grown from native seed. There are lots of hebes and
Parahebe, as well as clematis, Coprosma and other genera.
The main address is for postal enquiries only. The nursery
includes many specimen and stock plants.

Crowther Nurseries and Landscapes

Ongar Road, Abridge RM4 1AA
☎ 01708 688581   [FAX] 01708 688677

CONTACT   Ken Crowther
LOCATION   On A113 between Chigwell and Ongar, beside Stapleford Airdrome
OPEN   9 am – 5.30 pm, daily; closed over Christmas
MAIL ORDER   No
SHOP   Flower shop
REFRESHMENTS   Tea shop 10 am – 5 pm, with cream teas and home made cakes
GARDEN   BBC Essex display garden open daily, admission free
DESIGN SERVICE   Crowther Nurseries and Landscapes

Nursery and garden centre with a general range and a garden design and construction service. There are regular talks by Ken Crowther, who broadcasts for BBC Essex.

Flora Exotica

Pasadena, South Green, Fingringhoe, Colchester CO5 7DR
☎ 01206 729414

CONTACT   J. Beddoes
OPEN   Mail order only
SPECIALITIES   Carnivorous plants; lilies; New Zealand plants
CATALOGUE   £1.50
MAIL ORDER   Yes

Insectivorous plants by mail order: *Pinguicula*, *Utricularia* and *Nepenthe*, as well as a good choice of *Lilium* bulbs (eighty varieties) and orchids of every kind.

Frances Mount Perennial Plants

1 Steps Farm, Polstead, Colchester CO6 5AE
☎ 01206 262811

CONTACT   Frances Mount
LOCATION   8 miles from Colchester and Sudbury
OPEN   10 am – 5 pm, Tuesday, Wednesday, Saturday; 2 pm – 6 pm, Fridays
SPECIALITIES   Herbaceous perennials
CATALOGUE   3 first-class stamps
MAIL ORDER   Yes, minimum order £6
REFRESHMENTS   Only for groups booked in advance
GARDEN   Display garden

A small nursery whose stock includes hardy herbaceous perennials and, notably, over 65 varieties of hardy geraniums.

Glen Chantry

Ishams Chase, Wickham Bishops CM8 3LG
☎ 01621 891342

CONTACT   Sue Staines
LOCATION   Map in catalogue
OPEN   10 am – 4 pm, Fridays and Saturdays, 4 April to 18 October; on garden open days
SPECIALITIES   Alpines; herbaceous perennials
CATALOGUE   4 first-class stamps
MAIL ORDER   No
GARDEN   Garden opens for NGS (£1.50)

Small nursery with a developing collection of perennials and alpines, dwarf rhododendrons and conifers. Particular interests are *Iris*, *Monarda* and *Euphorbia*, and plants for white gardens.

Hull Farm Conifer Centre

John Fryer & Sons, Spring Valley Lane, Ardleigh, Colchester CO7 7SA
☎ 01206 230045   [FAX] 01206 230820

CONTACT   J Fryer & Sons
OPEN   10 am – 4 pm, daily
SPECIALITIES   Conifers
MAIL ORDER   No

Over 400 varieties of conifer, in a choice of sizes, but also rhododendrons, camellias and fruit trees. Open ground conifers available from November to April.

Ken Muir Nurseries

Honeypot Farm, Weeley Heath, Clacton on Sea CO16 9BJ
☎ 01255 830181   [FAX] 01255 831534

CONTACT   Ken Muir
LOCATION   Between Colchester and Clacton, off B1033
OPEN   10 am – 4 pm, daily. Closed Christmas and Boxing Day
SPECIALITIES   Fruit
CATALOGUE   3 first-class stamps
MAIL ORDER   Yes
SHOWS   RHS Westminster; Chelsea; BBC GW Live; Hampton Court

Fruit specialist with a substantial mail order business. If the lure of Honeypot Farm isn't enough in itself, then consider the wide range of strawberries, raspberries, other soft fruit and fruit trees. Some of the well known varieties are grown as slender columns, suitable for smaller gardens and tubs. Asparagus and Yoder chrysanthemums have been added to their range.

Langthorns Plantery

Little Canfield, Dunmow CM6 1TD
☎ & [FAX] 01371 872611

CONTACT   D. N. Cannon
LOCATION   Between Takeley and Great Dunmow, signed off A120
OPEN   10 am – 5 pm, daily. Closed Christmas to New Year
SPECIALITIES   Herbaceous perennials; shrubs
NEW FOR 1997   *Tricyrtis hirta* 'Nana'
CATALOGUE   £1
MAIL ORDER   No
REFRESHMENTS   Cold drinks only
GARDEN   Gardens open last week of month, March to October

Hardy plants of all kinds in a very varied and interesting range. The herbaceous section is especially good, and there are interesting alpines, shrubs and trees here too. Langthorns Garden is open the last week of each month.

Mill Race Nursery

New Road, Aldham, Colchester CO6 3QT
☎ 01206 242324   📠 01206 241616
CONTACT   Bill Mathews or Philip Bell
LOCATION   Ford Street, Aldham, off A604
OPEN   9 am – 5.30 pm, daily
SPECIALITIES   Herbaceous perennials; trees
CATALOGUE   SAE (A4) and 2 first class stamps
MAIL ORDER   No
SHOP   Garden sundries
REFRESHMENTS   Restaurant, picnic garden
GARDEN   Demonstration gardens
DESIGN SERVICE   Mill Race Landscapes Ltd
SHOWS   BBC GW Live; Hampton Court

A large nursery with a wide range of container grown stock, sold both wholesale and retail. Plant types include conifers, climbers, trees, shrubs, perennials and fruit trees and bushes. There is a picnic garden and boating on the River Colne.

Notcutts Garden Centre

Station Road, Ardleigh CO2 7RT
☎ 01206 230271   📠 01206 231205
CONTACT   Douglas Birt (Manager)
OPEN   8.30 am – 5.30 pm, Monday – Saturday; 11 am – 5 pm, Sundays. Closes 5 pm in winter
SHOP   Garden sundries, furniture, machinery
DESIGN SERVICE   Notcutts Landscapes
SHOWS   Chelsea; BBC GW Live; Hampton Court

Notcutts Garden Centre

Station Road, Ardleigh, Colchester CO7 7RT
☎ 01206 230271
LOCATION   On B1029
OPEN   8.30 am – 5.30 pm, Monday – Saturday; 11 am – 5 pm, Sundays. Closes at 5 pm in winter
SHOP   Garden sundries, furniture
GARDEN   Landscaped gardens
DESIGN SERVICE   Notcutts Landscapes

Plantworld

Burnam Road, South Woodham Ferrers, Chelmsford CM3 5QP
☎ & 📠 01245 320482
CONTACT   F. Waterworth
OPEN   By appointment
SPECIALITIES   *Tropaeolum speciosum*
CATALOGUE   £2
MAIL ORDER   Yes

A range of hardy perennials, with a speciality in *Tropaeolum speciosum*.

Rhodes & Rockliffe

2 Nursery Road, Nazeing EN9 2JE
☎ 01992 463693   📠 01992 440673
CONTACT   David Rhodes
LOCATION   Phone for directions
OPEN   By appointment only
SPECIALITIES   Begonias
NEW FOR 1997   More species and hybrids

CATALOGUE   2 first-class stamps
MAIL ORDER   Yes, minimum order £2.50
GARDEN   Open by appointment
SHOWS   RHS Westminster; Chelsea

Begonia specialists, with some out of the way species and hybrids.

Sheila Chapman Clematis

8 Dene Court, Chignall Road, Chelmsford CM1 2JQ
☎ 01245 422245   📠 01245 422293
CONTACT   Sheila Chapman
LOCATION   At Hanging Gardens Nurseries, Oxney Green on A414 Writtle by-pass
OPEN   9 am – 6 pm, daily, summer; 9 am – 5 pm, daily, winter
SPECIALITIES   Clematis
NEW FOR 1997   46 more *Clematis* varieties
CATALOGUE   4 first-class stamps

Specialist clematis nursery. The large selection encompasses species, newer hybrids and popular cultivars, over 400 in all. Pruning demonstrations are held each February: phone for details. There is a general plant range at the parent company, Hanging Gardens Nurseries, where the nursery is. The address above is for correspondence.

Three Suns Nursery

Spital Road, Maldon CM9 6SH
☎ 01621 853872
CONTACT   A. Thorogood
LOCATION   On A414 south of Maldon
OPEN   9 am – 5 pm, but phone first in season
SPECIALITIES   Pelargoniums
CATALOGUE   31p
MAIL ORDER   Yes
SHOWS   RHS Westminster; BBC GW Live; Hampton Court

Regal pelargonium specialist. There is a good collection of standards and a small general plant range.

Thurrock Garden Centre Ltd

South Road, South Ockendon RM15 6DU
☎ 01708 851991   📠 01708 859138
CONTACT   Graham or Emma Pinkerton or May Brisbane
LOCATION   Near Lakeside Shopping Centre, on B186
OPEN   9 am – 6 pm, Monday – Saturday; 10 am – 5 pm, Sundays. Close at 5.30 pm in winter
SHOP   Garden sundries, gifts, pets
REFRESHMENTS   Coffee shop

Garden centre with garden products. They have a good record in the Chelsea hanging basket competition: demonstrations and other events at the centre.

Trevor Scott Ornamental Grasses

Thorpe Park Cottage, Thorpe le Soken CO16 0HN
☎ & 📠 01255 861308
CONTACT   Trevor Scott
LOCATION   Thorpe le Soken, near Colchester; phone for directions
OPEN   By appointment only
SPECIALITIES   Grasses

CATALOGUE 5 first-class stamps
GARDEN Garden

A very wide range of grasses for all purposes and situations: there are some other interesting perennials too. No mail order now, but plants can be reserved for later collection. Visitors by appointment to the nursery and garden.

Wyevale Garden Centre
Cressing Road, Braintree CM7 8DL
☎ 01376 553043   📠 01376 553004
REFRESHMENTS Restaurant

Wyevale Garden Centre
Homelands Retail Park, Cuton Hall Lane, Springfield, Chelmsford CM2 5PX
☎ 01245 466466   📠 01245 451263
REFRESHMENTS Restaurant

Wyevale Garden Centre
Eastwood Road, Rayleigh SS6 7QA
☎ 01702 527331   📠 01702 421203

Wyevale Garden Centre
Nags Head Lane, Upminster Common RM14 1TS
☎ 01708 342469   📠 01708 376231
REFRESHMENTS Restaurant

GLOUCESTERSHIRE

Alan Phipps Cacti
62 Samuel White Road, Hanham, Bristol BS15 3LX
☎ 0117 960 7591
CONTACT Alan Phipps
LOCATION In centre of village: ask for directions
OPEN Phone first
SPECIALITIES Cacti and succulents
CATALOGUE SAE or two IRCs
MAIL ORDER Yes, smallish plants only
REFRESHMENTS Tea & biscuits

Cacti and succulent specialist with both a general and a collectors range of species. Telephone first before visiting to make sure someone is in. They also sell seed-grown cacti and succulents to retail and wholesale outlets. The mail order list is issued in April.

C S Lockyer
70 Henfield Road, Coalpit Heath, Bristol BS17 2UZ
☎ 01454 772219
CONTACT C. S. Lockyer
LOCATION Near M4, Jct 18 & Jct 19: map in catalogue
OPEN Most days; phone first
SPECIALITIES Fuchsias
CATALOGUE 4 first-class stamps
MAIL ORDER Yes
GARDEN Demonstration gardens
SHOWS RHS Westminster; Malvern (Spring); Chelsea; BBC GW Live; Hampton Court

A specialist fuchsia grower, with young plants of both tender and hardy varieties. They run a members club and hold regular talks and demonstrations at the nursery to pass on the experi-

ence of over 35 years in the business. There is a video 'Fuchsias: The Easy Way' available from the nursery. Look out for them at shows in the south and west.

Chris Pattison (Nurseryman)
Brookend, Pendock GL19 3PL
☎ & 📠 01531 650480
CONTACT Chris Pattison
LOCATION Gloucestershire, Worcestershire border, near M50, Jct 2
OPEN 9 am – 5 pm, Monday – Friday
SPECIALITIES Alpines; shrubs
CATALOGUE 3 first-class stamps
MAIL ORDER No
SHOWS Malvern (Spring); Malvern (Autumn)

Small retail and wholesale nursery offering alpines and shrubs, including dwarf *Daphne* cultivars and Japanese *Acer*, all container-grown at the nursery. They visit some specialist plant sales.

Four Counties Nursery
Todenham, Moreton in Marsh GL56 9PN
☎ 01608 650522   📠 01608 650591
CONTACT Sandra Taylor
LOCATION Cotswolds
OPEN 9 am – 6 pm, Monday – Saturday, 25 March to 21 October; 9 am – 5 pm, Monday – Saturday, 22 October to 24 March. Also 11 am – 5 pm, Sundays, all year
SPECIALITIES Conservatory plants; trees; citrus
CATALOGUE £1 plus SAE
MAIL ORDER No
REFRESHMENTS Café
GARDEN Italian demonstration gardens

Four Counties have an extensive range of trees and specimen shrubs, most of it propagated on-site, as well as herbaceous and alpine plants. In addition, they also specialise in conservatory plants, including citrus trees.

Highfield Garden Centre
Bristol Road, Whitminster, Gloucester GL2 7PB
☎ 01452 741444   📠 01452 740750
CONTACT Mr T. R. Greenway
LOCATION On A38 ½ mile from M5, Jct 13
OPEN 9 am – 6 pm, Monday – Saturday; 10.30 am – 4.30 pm, Sundays
NEW FOR 1997 Medlars, Mulberries
CATALOGUE On request
MAIL ORDER Yes
SHOP Sundries, tools
REFRESHMENTS Coffee shop
GARDEN Yes
DESIGN SERVICE Yes
SHOWS RHS Westminster; Malvern (Spring); Malvern (Autumn); Chelsea; BBC GW Live; Hampton Court

Highfield Nurseries' garden centre. Apple Day celebrations will be held on 18 – 19 October with around 70 varieties on display and to taste.

Highfield Nurseries

School Lane, Whitminster, Gloucester GL2 7PL
☎ 01452 740266   📠 01452 740750

CONTACT   Mr T. R. Wellington
LOCATION   Off A38, ½ mile from M5, Jct 13
OPEN   9 am – 4 pm, Monday – Friday. Closed Saturdays and Sundays
SPECIALITIES   Fruit
NEW FOR 1997   Unusual fruit trees
CATALOGUE   On request
MAIL ORDER   Yes
REFRESHMENTS   At garden centre
SHOWS   RHS Westminster; Malvern (Spring); Malvern (Autumn); Chelsea; BBC GW Live; Hampton Court

Large nurseries with an extensive all round range – good choice of fruit trees and bushes. They have a garden centre nearby.

Hoo House Nursery

Hoo House, Gloucester Road, Tewkesbury GL20 7DA
☎ 01684 293389

CONTACT   Julie Ritchie
LOCATION   2 miles south of Tewkesbury on A38
OPEN   2 pm – 5 pm, Monday – Saturday
SPECIALITIES   Alpines; herbaceous perennials
CATALOGUE   3 first-class stamps; specify retail or mail order
MAIL ORDER   Yes, October to March only
NCCPG NATIONAL COLLECTIONS   Platycodon; Gentiana asclepiadea

A mixed range of alpines and herbaceous plants, The nursery also holds two NCCPG National Collections.

Hunts Court Garden & Nursery

Hunts Court, North Nibley, Dursley GL11 6DZ
☎ 01453 547440

CONTACT   T. K. Marshall
LOCATION   B4060 from Wootton-under-Edge to North Nibley, turn right at cross roads, then keep left
OPEN   9 am – 5 pm, Tuesday – Saturday, Bank Holiday Mondays in spring; NGS Sundays. Closed August
SPECIALITIES   Roses; shrubs
CATALOGUE   3 second-class stamps
MAIL ORDER   No
REFRESHMENTS   NGS Sundays only
GARDEN   Hunts Court Garden, Gloucestershire, see Gardens section
DESIGN SERVICE   Yes

The nursery has a large selection of old-fashioned, shrub, climbing and species roses, with hardy geraniums, penstemons, shrubby potentillas and other shrubs too. There is a planting advisory service.

Hurrans Garden Centre Ltd

Cheltenham Road East, Churchdown, Gloucester GL3 1AB
☎ 01452 712232   📠 01452 857369

CONTACT   L. Mullen
LOCATION   Between Cheltenham and Gloucester on B4063

OPEN   9 am – 6 pm, Monday – Saturday; 11 am – 5 pm, Sundays
SHOP   Garden products
GARDEN   Display garden
DESIGN SERVICE   Hurrans Garden Centre Ltd

Garden centre selling plants and garden products only. Delivery service and trained staff.

Jardinerie Ltd

Evesham Road, Cheltenham GL50 4SJ
☎ 01242 672560/672153   📠 01242 676135

CONTACT   Peter Ulyatt (Manager)
LOCATION   ½ mile beyond racecourse
OPEN   Opens: 9 am on Monday – Thursday & Saturdays; but 9.30 am on Fridays and 10.30 am on Sundays. Closes: 5 pm, Monday – Saturday, January & February; 6 pm, Monday – Saturday, 1 – 29 March; 8 pm, Monday to Friday, 30 March – 30 June; 6 pm, Bank Holidays & Saturdays, 30 March – 30 June; 6 pm, Monday – Wednesday & Saturdays, 1 July to 31 December; 8 pm on Thursdays & Fridays in July, August & December; 7 pm on Thursdays & Fridays from September to November; 4.30 pm, all Sundays.
SHOP   Gifts, conservatories, garden buildings
REFRESHMENTS   Café

Jardinerie Ltd

Bath Road, Haresfield, Stonehouse GL10 3DP
☎ 01452 721081   📠 01452 724919

CONTACT   Jon Davis (Manager)
LOCATION   South of Gloucester on B4008
OPEN   9.30 am – 6 pm (5 pm in January & February), Monday – Saturday, all year. 10.30 am – 4.30 pm, Sundays in January & February; 11 am – 5 pm, Sundays, March – December
SHOP   Gifts, aquatics, conservatories, garden buildings, countryside centre
REFRESHMENTS   Café

Jekka's Herb Farm

Rose Cottage, Shellards Lane, Alveston, Bristol BS12 2SY
☎ 01454 418878   📠 01454 411988

CONTACT   J. McVicar
OPEN   Mail order only
SPECIALITIES   Herbs; seeds; wild flowers
CATALOGUE   A5 SAE with 36p stamp plus 4 first-class stamps
MAIL ORDER   Yes, no minimum order
DESIGN SERVICE   Yes – new for 1997
SHOWS   RHS Westminster; Malvern (Spring); Malvern (Autumn); Chelsea; BBC GW Live; Hampton Court; Strathclyde

The enthusiastic and knowledgeable Jekka has the best eye of all exhibitors for making attractive compositions with herbs. Her list is comprehensive and the interesting range includes some wild flowers. The business is basically wholesale: retail trade is mail order only. Demonstrations and lectures can be arranged.

Just Phlomis

Sunningdale, Grange Court, Westbury on Severn GL14 1PL

☎ & 📠 01452 760268

CONTACT   J. Mann Taylor
LOCATION   OS Grid reference SO 727 164
OPEN   By appointment
SPECIALITIES   Phlomis
CATALOGUE   2 second-class stamps
MAIL ORDER   Yes
GARDEN   By appointment

The list of Phlomis from the National Collection holder is short by the other nursery's standards, but remarkably long for the interested plantsman – nearly 30 species and cultivars. There is an open day on 21 June, 2 – 5 pm.

Kennedys Garden Centre

Ebley Road, Stonehouse GL10 2LW

☎ 01453 823846   📠 01453 827090

CONTACT   Kevin Brindley (Manager)
OPEN   9 am – 6 pm, Monday – Saturday, April to September, close 5.30 pm, October to March; 10.30 am – 4.30 pm, Sundays
REFRESHMENTS   Café

Kiftsgate Court Gardens

Kiftsgate Court, Chipping Camden GL55 6LW

☎ & 📠 01386 438777

CONTACT   Mr or Mrs Chambers
LOCATION   Adjacent to Hidcote Manor
OPEN   As garden
CATALOGUE   No
MAIL ORDER   No
REFRESHMENTS   Home-made teas
GARDEN   Kiftsgate Court, Gloucestershire, see Gardens section

The nursery sells a seasonally varied range of plants propagated from this well known garden.

Lechlade Garden Centre

Fairford Road, Lechlade GL7 3DP

☎ & 📠 01367 252372

CONTACT   M. Reed (plants) or J. Pitt (shop)
LOCATION   North of Swindon
OPEN   9 am – 6 pm, summer; 9 am – 5 pm, winter
SHOP   Garden machinery
REFRESHMENTS   Coffee shop
DESIGN SERVICE   Lechlade Garden Centre

General garden centre with design and landscaping and delivery services. Agent for Hillier plants. Lots of fuchsias in season.

Marshall's Malmaisons

4 The Damsells, Tetbury GL8 8JA

☎ 01666 502589

CONTACT   Jim Marshall
OPEN   By appointment only
SPECIALITIES   Carnations (Malmaison)
CATALOGUE   On request
MAIL ORDER   Yes

SHOWS   RHS Westminster; Hampton Court
NCCPG   NATIONAL COLLECTIONS   Dianthus (Malmaison)

Not really a nursery: these are Malmaison carnations from the holder of the National Collection. These named varieties can be posted.

Mount Pleasant Trees

Rockhampton, Berkeley GL13 9DU

☎ 01454 260348

CONTACT   G. Locke
LOCATION   Map in catalogue
OPEN   By appointment only
SPECIALITIES   Hedging; trees; Tilia
CATALOGUE   £1 coin or 4 loose second-class stamps (no cheques)
MAIL ORDER   No

Mainly native trees and shrubs for hedging and woodland use. In addition there is an eye-catching selection of specimen trees and shrubs for arboreta. The Tilia range is outstanding, the biggest in Europe. Good Sequoiadendron and Ginkgo collections are other highlights on this enticing list.

Norfields

Lower Meend, St Briavels GL15 6RW

☎ 01594 530134   📠 01594 530113

CONTACT   Andrew Norfield
OPEN   Mail order only
SPECIALITIES   Acers; trees
CATALOGUE   1 first-class stamp
MAIL ORDER   Yes
SHOWS   Malvern (Autumn); BBC GW Live; Hampton Court

Young container-grown trees. Strong on Acer, Betula, Nothofagus and Stewartia.

The Old Manor Nursery

Twyning GL20 6DB

☎ 01684 293516

CONTACT   J. Wilder
LOCATION   Near M50, Jct 1: take Twyning road from A38 (by golf course)
OPEN   2 pm – 5 pm, Mondays, March to October. By appointment at other times. Closed Sundays and Bank Holidays
SPECIALITIES   Alpines
CATALOGUE   Large SAE plus 30p
MAIL ORDER   No
GARDEN   Garden open (£1.50, accompanied children free)

Mainly alpines, but with a changing range of perennials, shrubs and trees also. All are propagated from the garden and can be seen in flower there at the appropriate seasons. Groups of painters and sketchers accepted by arrangement.

Park Garden Centre

Over Lane, Almondsbury, Bristol BS12 4BP

☎ 01454 612247   📠 01454 617559

CONTACT   J. Billings (plants) or J. Parrish (shop)
LOCATION   North of Bristol, off A38

OPEN 9 am – 6 pm, summer; 9 am – 5 pm, winter, Monday – Saturday. 10 am – 4 pm, Sundays
SHOP Garden machinery, conservatory, Park Koi aquatics
REFRESHMENTS Coffee shop
GARDEN Demonstration rose garden and orchard

Garden centre with garden products, and machinery and aquatic centres on site. Agents for Hillier plants. Local delivery and design and landscaping services.

Priory Garden Nursery
The Priory, Kemerton, Tewkesbury GL20 7JN
☎ 01386 725258

CONTACT Mrs Healing
OPEN 2 pm – 7 pm, Fridays only
SPECIALITIES Herbaceous perennials
MAIL ORDER No
REFRESHMENTS On Open Sundays only
GARDEN The Priory, Gloucestershire, see Gardens section

Small nursery selling plants from this Gloucestershire garden which is famous for its late summer borders.

Sherborne Gardens Nursery
Sherborne Gardens, Sherborne, Cheltenham GL54 3DZ
☎ 01451 844522   FAX 01451 844695

CONTACT John Hill
LOCATION Off A40, in Sherborne village
OPEN 8 am – 4.30 pm, Monday – Friday; 8 am – 4 pm, Saturdays. Other times by appointment. Also April to June only, 2 pm – 5 pm, Sundays
SPECIALITIES Hedging; herbaceous perennials; topiary

Nursery based around the working collection of garden designer, John Hill. Specialities include yew hedging, and box topiary. See also his entry in the Services section.

Special Plants
Hill Farm Barn, Greenways Lane, Cold Ashton, Chippenham SN14 8LA
☎ 01225 891686   FAX 01225 852528

CONTACT Derry Watkins
LOCATION Near Bath, junction of A46 & A420
OPEN Most days: phone first
SPECIALITIES Conservatory plants
NEW FOR 1997 Heliotropum 'Midnight', a white hemerocallis, a white diascia and a variegated alstroemeria
CATALOGUE 4 second-class stamps
MAIL ORDER Yes, October to February
SHOWS RHS Westminster; Malvern (Spring); BBC GW Live; Hampton Court

Special Plants concentrates on tender perennials, including Felicia, Osteospermum and Scaevola, and on conservatory climbers and small shrubs with interesting varieties from South Africa. More South African introductions are in the pipeline: the fruit of a three-month plant-hunting trip last year. One-day courses are held at the nursery, and Ms Watkins organises specialist plant sales, including the London Rare Plant Fairs and the Plants & Gardens Festivals in the West.

St Annes Vineyard
Wain House, Oxenhall, Newent GL18 1RW
☎ 01989 720313

CONTACT J. David Jenkins
LOCATION Near Newent
OPEN 10 am – 7 pm, daily, 16 March to 30 September; 10 – 6 pm, Wednesday – Sunday, 1 October to 15 March
SPECIALITIES Vines
CATALOGUE SAE
MAIL ORDER Yes
SHOP Wine
REFRESHMENTS For groups by prior arrangement
SHOWS Malvern (Spring)

Specialist grower of vines for dessert and table wines: they claim to have the largest choice in the United Kingdom. Most of the business is mail order: there are some vines but more wine at the premises.

Thuya Alpine Nursery
Glebelands, Hartpury GL19 3BW
☎ 01452 700548

CONTACT S. W. Bond
LOCATION On A417 north-west of Gloucester
OPEN 10 am – dark, Saturdays and Bank Holidays; 11 am – dark, Sundays; and by appointment
SPECIALITIES Alpines
CATALOGUE 4 second-class stamps
MAIL ORDER Yes
REFRESHMENTS At the Royal Exchange Pub

Alpines in the broadest sense, including bulbs, dwarf conifers and rhododendrons, small ericaceous shrubs, with rarities among them. The nursery plans to attend the AGS shows at Harlow, Exeter, Solihull, Chester and Horsham.

Westonbirt Plant Centre
Westonbirt Arboretum, Tetbury GL8 8QS
☎ 01666 880544   FAX 01666 880559

CONTACT Glyn R. Toplis
LOCATION On A433 3 miles south of Tetbury
OPEN 10 am – 6 pm, daily; 10 am – 5 pm in winter
SPECIALITIES Shrubs; trees
CATALOGUE On request
MAIL ORDER Yes
REFRESHMENTS Courtyard café in arboretum
GARDEN Westonbirt Arboretum, Gloucestershire, see Gardens Section
DESIGN SERVICE Yes
SHOWS Malvern (Spring)

As you would expect, the Plant Centre attached to the famous arboretum specialises in trees and shrubs, including varieties propagated from their collections. Good for Japanese acers.

Wyevale Garden Centre
Shurdington Road, Brockworth GL3 4PU
☎ 01452 862334   FAX 01452 864839

Wyevale Garden Centre
Milbury Heath, Wotton under Edge GL12 8QH
☎ 01454 412247   [FAX] 01454 281502
REFRESHMENTS   Restaurant

GREATER MANCHESTER

Daisy Nook Garden Centre
Daisy Nook, Failsworth, Manchester M35 9WJ
☎ 0161 681 4245   [FAX] 0161 688 0822
CONTACT   P. Tyler
OPEN   9 am – 8 pm, summer; 9 am – 5 pm, winter
SHOP   Landscape materials
REFRESHMENTS   Café

Garden centre including a fish centre.

Fairy Lane Nurseries
Fairy Lane, Sale M33 2JT
☎ 0161 905 1137
CONTACT   Janice A. Coxon
LOCATION   In the Mersey valley, close to M63, Jct 8
OPEN   9 am – 5.30 pm, Monday – Saturday; 10 am – 5.30 pm,
Sundays. Closed over New Year from 21 December and all
Tuesday except April – June
SPECIALITIES   Herbaceous perennials
MAIL ORDER   Yes
SHOP   Garden sundries
GARDEN   Herb garden
DESIGN SERVICE   Fairy Lane Nurseries

A nursery and garden centre which makes an effort to stock
more than just the obvious varieties across its general range.
Worth a return visit because the stock is always changing.
Informal design advice is usually available, and courses are
sometimes run.

Primrose Cottage Nursery & Garden Centre
Ringway Road, Moss Nook, Wythenshawe M22 5WF
☎ 0161 437 1557   [FAX] 0161 499 9932
CONTACT   Caroline Dumville
LOCATION   On B566 1 mile from Manchester airport
OPEN   8.30 am – 6 pm, summer, 8.30 am – 5 pm, winter,
Monday – Saturday; 9.30 am – 5.30 pm, Sundays
SPECIALITIES   Bedding plants; herbaceous perennials; herbs
CATALOGUE   2 first-class stamps
MAIL ORDER   No
REFRESHMENTS   Coffee shop

There are new introductions each year to the choice of
bedding, basket and patio plants, and the range of alpines and
herbaceous plants now includes herbs.

The Vicarage Gardens
Carrington, Urmston M31 4AG
☎ 0161 775 2750   [FAX] 0161 775 3679
CONTACT   Mrs E. M. Haine
LOCATION   Greater Manchester, off M63, Jct 6

OPEN   10 am – 5.30 pm, daily, April to September; 10 am –
5 pm, daily, October to March. Closed Thursdays all year, and
12.30 pm – 1.30 pm, weekdays for lunch
SPECIALITIES   Alpines; herbaceous perennials
CATALOGUE   5 first-class stamps
MAIL ORDER   Yes, minimum order 5 plants
SHOP   Gifts
REFRESHMENTS   Coffee shop
GARDEN   5-acre garden
SHOWS   Malvern (Spring); Harrogate (Spring); Southport;
BBC GW Live; Ayr

Large garden in the hands of a charitable trust. The nursery
sells old-fashioned herbaceous plants and alpines, plus some
water and bog garden plants.

Worsley Hall Nurseries & Garden Centre
Leigh Road, Boothstown, Worsley M28 2LJ
☎ 0161 790 8792
CONTACT   Wayne Broadbent
LOCATION   Near M62, Jct 13: from the south, turn left on
A572 (½ a mile)
OPEN   8 am – 5.30 pm, Monday – Saturday, summer (closes
at dusk in winter); 10.30 am – 4.30 pm, Sundays
SPECIALITIES   Fruit
SHOP   Garden sundries
REFRESHMENTS   Café
GARDEN   Fuchsia Society display bed

Attractively walled garden centre and nurseries with a general
range of plants and products, and a particular interest in fruit
trees and hedging. Delivery service.

HAMPSHIRE

Agars Nursery
Agars Lane, Hordle, Lymington SO41 0FL
☎ 01590 683703
CONTACT   Mrs Diane Tombs
LOCATION   Off Silver Street, Hordle
OPEN   10 am – 5 pm, March to October; 10 am – 4 pm,
February and November. December and January by appoint-
ment. Phone first. Closed Thursdays
SPECIALITIES   Iris; seeds; Penstemon
GARDEN   Display garden
DESIGN SERVICE   Agars Nursery

A family-run nursery which is strong on Penstemon, irises,
osteospermums and salvias. They also stock a range of hardy
trees and shrubs.

Apple Court
Hordle Lane, Hordle, Lymington SO41 0HU
☎ 01590 642130   [FAX] 01590 694220
CONTACT   Diana Grenfell or Roger Grounds
LOCATION   South of New Forest, just north of A337 at
Downton crossroads
OPEN   9.30 am – 1 pm, 2 pm – 5 pm, Thursdays to Mondays,
from February to October; but daily during July and August

SPECIALITIES   Ferns; grasses; South American plants; hostas; *Hemerocallis*
CATALOGUE   4 first-class stamps
MAIL ORDER   Yes
REFRESHMENTS   By prior arrangement for parties
GARDEN   Display gardens open for NGS and NCCPG
DESIGN SERVICE   Apple Court
SHOWS   Southport; Hampton Court
NCCPG NATIONAL COLLECTIONS *Hosta* (small leaved); *Rohdea japonica*; *Woodwardia*

The specialist collections now extend to over 120 hostas and 80 hemerocallis. There is also an interesting selection of ferns and grasses, and a collection of plants for white gardens. Diana Grenfell's book *The Gardener's Guide to Growing Hostas* was published by David & Charles last year.

Blackthorn Nursery
Kilmeston, Alresford SO24 0NL
☎ 01962 771796   📠 01962 771071

CONTACT   S. B. White
LOCATION   1 mile south of Cheriton, off A272
OPEN   9 am – 5 pm, Friday and Saturday only, March to June
SPECIALITIES   Alpines; herbaceous perennials; prunus; *Daphne*; *Epimedium*; hellebores
NEW FOR 1997   *Daphne* 'Fragrant Cloud', *Epimedium latisepalum*
CATALOGUE   3 first-class stamps
MAIL ORDER   No
SHOWS   RHS Westminster

Hellebore breeders and specialists with several strains called Blackthorn. The most striking are semi-doubles called 'Party Dress' hybrids. Otherwise, there is a good range of alpine and rock plants, and a covetable, changing selection of other plants grown at the nursery. There are several new *Epimedium* this year.

C. Fairweather Ltd
Fairweather's Garden Centre, High Street, Beaulieu SO42 7FR
☎ 01590 612307   📠 01590 612519

CONTACT   Christopher Fairweather
LOCATION   At the top of the High Street
OPEN   9 am – 5.15 pm, daily, all year
SPECIALITIES   Bedding plants; shrubs; trees

An all-purpose garden centre with a good line in unusual plants.

Chichester Trees and Shrubs
The Mill Studio, Beaulieu SO42 7YG
☎ 01590 612198   📠 01590 612194

CONTACT   James Chichester
LOCATION   Phone for directions or map in catalogue
OPEN   8 am – 4 pm, Monday – Friday
SPECIALITIES   Shrubs; trees
CATALOGUE   On request
MAIL ORDER   Carriage available for larger quantities

This mainly wholesale nursery has masses of container-grown trees and shrubs, including yew hedging and dwarf box, for landscapers and keen private gardeners. They have larger plants too. The retail side is Pylewell Nursery (01590 626302).

Country Gardens
Salisbury Road, Andover SP11 7DN
☎ 01264 710551   📠 01264 710202

CONTACT   Peter Walker (Manager)
OPEN   9 am – 6 pm, Monday – Saturday; 10.30 am – 4.30 pm, Sundays
SHOP   Garden buildings, machinery

Country Gardens
Winchester Road, North Waltham, Basingstoke PO25 2DJ
☎ 01256 397155   📠 01256 398574

CONTACT   Keith Headland (Manager)
OPEN   9 am – 6 pm, Monday – Saturday; 10.30 am – 4.30 pm, Sundays

Country Gardens
Winchester Road, Fair Oak, Eastleigh SO50 7HD
☎ 01703 600392   📠 01703 601763

CONTACT   Malcolm Martin (Manager)
OPEN   9 am – 6 pm, Monday – Saturday; 10.30 am – 4.30 pm, Sundays

Denmead Geranium Nurseries
Hambledon Road, Denmead, Waterlooville PO7 6PS
☎ 01705 240081

CONTACT   Ivan H. Chance or Mrs K. J. Churcher-Brown
LOCATION   2 miles west of A3, on B2150
OPEN   8 am – 1 pm, 2 pm – 5 pm, Monday – Friday; 8 am – 12.30 pm, Saturdays, except August. Open 2 pm – 5 pm on Saturdays in May and June also. Closed during Christmas and New Year period
SPECIALITIES   Pelargoniums
CATALOGUE   3 second-class stamps
MAIL ORDER   Yes, minimum order 6 plants
GARDEN   Greenhouses open

Specialist growers of pelargoniums, including the following classes: zonal, coloured leaf, ivy leaf, Swiss balcony, miniatures, stellars, angels and regals. Nursery visitors can sometimes buy cultivars which do not appear in the excellent and comprehensive list.

Drysdale Garden Exotics
Bowerwood Road, Fordingbridge SP6 1BN
☎ 01425 653010

CONTACT   David Crampton
OPEN   9.30 am – 5.30 pm, Wednesday – Friday; 10 am – 5.30 pm, Sundays
SPECIALITIES   Bamboos; foliage plants; mediterranean plants
CATALOGUE   3 first-class stamps
MAIL ORDER   Yes
GARDEN   Bamboo garden
DESIGN SERVICE   Drysdale Garden Exotics
NCCPG NATIONAL COLLECTIONS   Bamboos

The plants here are chosen for their dramatic foliage and for use in Mediterranean plantings. The bamboo collection is reflected in the number of species available. Larger, specimen sizes can be collected from the nursery.

Exbury Enterprises Ltd
Exbury, Southampton SO45 1AZ
☎ 01703 898625　　📠 01703 243380
LOCATION　3 miles south of Beaulieu, off B3054
OPEN　9 am – 5.30 pm (dusk if earlier), daily, March to October
SPECIALITIES　Camellias; rhododendrons
CATALOGUE　SAE
MAIL ORDER　Yes
REFRESHMENTS　Restaurant
GARDEN　Exbury Gardens, Hampshire, see Gardens section

Plant centre attached to this famous garden: unsurprisingly they specialise in rhododendrons and azaleas but have camellias and *Pieris* too.

Family Trees
P O Box 3, Botley SO3 2EA
☎ 01329 834812

CONTACT　Philip House
LOCATION　3 miles from Botley, map in catalogue
OPEN　9.30 am – 12.30 pm, Wednesday and Saturday, mid-October to end-April, July and August
SPECIALITIES　Fruit
NEW FOR 1997　10 more old apple varieties
CATALOGUE　On request
MAIL ORDER　Yes, minimum order £35

Many varieties of dessert apples, pears, plums and peaches. They are available field-grown as bushes or trained. They also have old roses, hedging and woodland trees, and can graft to your order.

Hardy's Cottage Garden Plants
Priory Lane, Freefolk, Whitchurch RG28 7NT
☎ 01256 896533　　📠 01256 896572

CONTACT　Mr or Mrs R. K. Hardy
LOCATION　Off B3400 Whitchurch to Overton road
OPEN　9 am – 5.30 pm, Monday – Saturday, March to October; evening visits by appointment
SPECIALITIES　Herbaceous perennials
CATALOGUE　4 first-class stamps
MAIL ORDER　Yes
GARDEN　Display garden being made at new nursery
SHOWS　RHS Westminster; Malvern (Spring); Malvern (Autumn); Harrogate (Spring); Harrogate (Autumn); Southport; Chelsea; BBC GW Live; Hampton Court; Strathclyde

This family-run nursery moves to the address above in March – about ½ mile from its previous site. They have a large range of pretty cottage garden perennials and flowering shrubs. Watch out for their attractive exhibits at shows. They give tours to coach parties and clubs and lectures in the winter months.

Hayward's Carnations
The Chace Gardens, 141 Stakes Road, Purbrook, Waterlooville PO7 5PL
☎ 01705 263047

CONTACT　Sales Office
OPEN　Mail order only
SPECIALITIES　*Dianthus*
CATALOGUE　On request
MAIL ORDER　Yes

This long-established specialist mail-order nursery grows garden pinks, border and perpetual flowering carnations. The plants can be seen flowering in June, by appointment.

Higher End Nursery
Hale, Fordingbridge SP6 2RA
☎ 01725 512243

CONTACT　D. J. Case
LOCATION　Map in catalogue
OPEN　10 am – 5 pm, Wednesday – Saturday; 2 – 5 pm, Sundays; 2 April to 30 August; 9 am – 4 pm, Saturdays in February and March for hellebores
SPECIALITIES　Aquatic plants; hellebores
CATALOGUE　2 first-class stamps
MAIL ORDER　Yes, minimum order £12

Water lilies, aquatics and waterside plants are the main specialities, but there is a good choice of hellebores and other perennials too.

Hillier Garden Centre
Woodhouse Lane, Botley, Southampton SO3 2EZ
☎ 01489 782306　　📠 01489 783763

CONTACT　David Williams (Manager)
OPEN　9 am – 5.30 pm, Monday – Saturday; 10.30 am – 4.30 pm, Sundays

Hillier Garden Centre
Farnham Road, Liss GU33 6LJ
☎ 01730 892196　　📠 01730 893676

CONTACT　Tim Hall (Manager)
LOCATION　By A3, B3006 Liss exit
OPEN　9 am – 5.30 pm, Monday – Saturday; 10.30 am – 4.30 pm, Sundays

Hillier Garden Centre
Botley Road, Romsey SO51 8ZL
☎ 01794 513459　　📠 01794 514750

CONTACT　Andrew Knowles (Manager)
OPEN　9 am – 5.30 pm, Monday – Saturday; 10.30 am – 4.30 pm, Sundays

Hillier Garden Centre
Romsey Road, Winchester SO22 5DL
☎ 01962 842288　　📠 01962 842299

CONTACT　Joy Woods (Manager)
OPEN　9 am – 5.30 pm, Monday – Saturday; 10.30 am – 4.30 pm, Sundays

Hillier Nurseries Ltd

Ampfield House, Ampfield, Romsey SO51 9PA
☎ 01794 368733   [FAX] 01794 368813
SPECIALITIES   Climbers; conifers; shrubs; trees
CATALOGUE   On request or from stockists
MAIL ORDER   No
SHOP   Eleven garden centres
GARDEN   Sir Harold Hillier Gardens and Arboretum, Hampshire See Gardens section
DESIGN SERVICE   Hillier Landscapes
SHOWS   RHS Westminster; Chelsea

Celebrated and long-established wholesale nurseries, best known for their wide range of trees and shrubs, available container or field grown in large sizes. They have eleven garden centres in southern England and the Midlands. Retail customers should contact the Head Office for the name of their nearest Hillier stockist. Hampshire County Council now runs the arboretum built up by Harold Hillier: the Sir Harold Hillier Gardens and Arboretum, Hampshire. There is a free gardening club which produces a magazine with details of events and product discount vouchers (01794 368966).

Hillier Plant Centre

Jermyns Lane, Braishfield, Romsey SO51 9PA
☎ 01794 368407   [FAX] 01794 367947
CONTACT   Chris George (Manager)
OPEN   9 am – 5.30 pm, Monday – Saturday; 10.30 am – 4.30 pm, Sundays

Langley Boxwood Nursery

Rake, Liss GU33 7JL
☎ 01730 894467   [FAX] 01730 894703
CONTACT   Elizabeth Braimbridge
LOCATION   5 miles north of Petersfield, ring for map or directions
OPEN   Monday – Friday. Saturday by appointment
SPECIALITIES   Topiary; boxwood
NEW FOR 1997   *Buxus sempervirens* 'Greenpeace' and *B. s.* 'Blauer Heinz'
CATALOGUE   4 first-class stamps
MAIL ORDER   Yes
GARDEN   Display garden
NCCPG NATIONAL COLLECTIONS *Buxus*

Specialist growers of box with a comprehensive range for hedging, edging, topiary and as specimens. There are over 50 varieties of *Buxus* in their delightful catalogue, and some *Taxus* also.

Longstock Park Nursery

Longstock, Stockbridge SO20 6EH
☎ 01264 810894   [FAX] 01264 810439
CONTACT   D. Stuart
LOCATION   1 mile north of Longstock village
OPEN   8.30 am – 4.30 pm, Monday – Saturday; 2 pm – 5 pm, Sundays, April to September
SPECIALITIES   Aquatic plants; bog plants; herbaceous perennials; primulas; shrubs
CATALOGUE   £1.50
MAIL ORDER   No

REFRESHMENTS   Tea rooms
GARDEN   Longstock Water Gardens, Hampshire, see Gardens section
DESIGN SERVICE   Longstock Park Nursery

A good range of conifers, ferns, perennials and shrubs. The nursery is recommended for its aquatic, moisture-loving and marginal plants, many of which are propagated from the adjacent water gardens. Excellent selection of primulas. The walled garden at the nursery has collections of wall plants, *Clematis viticella*, *Buddleja*, and a 100 metre long herbaceous border. The water gardens, also owned by the John Lewis Partnership, open 2 – 4.30 pm on the first and third Sunday of the month, April to September.

MacGregors Plants

Carters Clay Road, Lockerley, Romsey SO15 0GL
☎ & [FAX] 01794 340256
CONTACT   Mr & Mrs S. Bowron
LOCATION   Ring for directions
OPEN   10 am – 4 pm, Friday – Sunday, March to October
SPECIALITIES   Herbaceous perennials; shrubs
NEW FOR 1997   *Persicaria capitata*, *Lysimachia lichiangensis*, *Teucrium ackermannii*
CATALOGUE   2 first-class stamps
MAIL ORDER   By agreement
NCCPG NATIONAL COLLECTIONS *Phygelius*

This nursery specialises in less-common shrubs and perennials. Its list has some unusual plants for sale and a particularly strong line in *Phygelius* cultivars.

Nine Springs Nursery

24 Winchester Street, Whitchurch RG28 7AL
☎ & [FAX] 01256 892837
CONTACT   Gillian Anderson
OPEN   By appointment
SPECIALITIES   Aquatic plants
CATALOGUE   1 first-class stamp
MAIL ORDER   Yes

Retail and wholesale aquatic plant nursery: small plants by post, and larger sizes on site. They can supply plants in a fibre roll to minimise erosion and wildfowl damage. See also Artscapes, Professional Services section.

Oakleigh Nurseries

Petersfield Road, Monkwood, Alresford SO24 0HB
☎ 01962 773344   [FAX] 01962 772622
CONTACT   Sally Smith
OPEN   10 am – 1 pm, 2 pm – 4.30 pm, Monday – Friday, March to July; 10.30 am – 1 pm, 2 pm – 4 pm, Sundays, March to June
SPECIALITIES   Fuchsias; pelargoniums; epiphyllums
NEW FOR 1997   *Pelargonium* 'Jill Clark'
CATALOGUE   3 first-class stamps
MAIL ORDER   Yes
SHOWS   Chelsea; Hampton Court

Specialists for fuchsias (specimens, bush and standards) and pelargoniums (zonal, regal and ivy leaf). They also have a range of Christmas cacti hybrids and *Epiphyllum*. They publish a number of books, and Periwinkle Productions have filmed videos at the nursery.

Peter Trenear Nurseries
Chequers Lane, Eversley Cross, Hook RG27 0NX
☎ 01734 732300

CONTACT   Peter Trenear
LOCATION   Between Reading and Camberley. 500 yards down lane beside Chequers Inn
OPEN   9 am – 4.30 pm. Closed Sundays
SPECIALITIES   Bonsai; shrubs; trees
NEW FOR 1997   *Crassula* 'Très Bon'
CATALOGUE   1 first-class stamp
MAIL ORDER   Yes, no minimum order

Here is a list of young trees and shrubs, including conifers. They can either be planted out in the garden or cultivated as bonsai specimens.

Pound Lane Nurseries
Ampfield, Romsey SO51 9BL
☎ 01703 739685   [FAX] 01703 740300

CONTACT   T. A. Holmes
LOCATION   Between North Baddesley and Ampfield
OPEN   8.30 am – 5.30 pm, Monday – Friday; 9.30 am – 5 pm, Saturday – Sunday
MAIL ORDER   No
GARDEN   Display gardens
DESIGN SERVICE   Pound Lane Nurseries

Wholesale and retail working nursery offering hardy container-grown stock, including trees, shrubs and heathers.

Rumsey Gardens
117 Drift Road, Clanfield, Waterlooville PO8 0PD
☎ 01705 593367

CONTACT   Norman Giles
LOCATION   Off A3 between Petersfield & Portsmouth: ask for directions
OPEN   9 am – 5 pm, daily, all year. Opens at 10 am on Sundays and Bank Holidays
SPECIALITIES   Cotoneasters
CATALOGUE   Stock list on request
MAIL ORDER   Yes, no minimum charge
REFRESHMENTS   Yes
GARDEN   Five-acre display garden
SHOWS   Southport

A traditional nursery and plant centre with an exceptionally good list of cotoneasters: many species are not available elsewhere. It is always worth asking if they have a particular species coming along.

Southview Nurseries
Chequers Lane, Eversley Cross, Hook RG27 0NT
☎ 01734 732206

CONTACT   Elaine or Mark Treear
LOCATION   Between Camberley and Reading, off B3272

OPEN   9 am – 4.30 pm, Thursday – Saturday. Closed November to January
SPECIALITIES   *Dianthus*; herbaceous perennials
CATALOGUE   On request
MAIL ORDER   Yes, September to May
SHOWS   RHS Westminster; Hampton Court
NCCPG NATIONAL COLLECTIONS   *Dianthus*, old cultivars

Specialists for older varieties of named pinks and herbaceous perennials: they can help with historical plantings. Their own garden opens for the National Gardens Scheme.

Spinners
Boldre, Lymington SO41 5QE
☎ 01590 673347

CONTACT   P. Chappell
LOCATION   Off A337, between Brockenhurst and Lymington
OPEN   10 am – 5 pm, daily. Closed Sundays and Mondays, except by appointment
SPECIALITIES   Herbaceous perennials; shrubs; trees
NEW FOR 1997   Over 150 new items
CATALOGUE   4 first-class stamps
MAIL ORDER   No
GARDEN   Spinners, Hampshire, see Gardens section
DESIGN SERVICE   Spinners

This nursery, attached to a plantsman's garden, is a treasure-house of rare and unusual plants. Some are listed in their catalogue, but many more will be found if you turn up and browse around. The hardy plants are particularly strong, but there are good shrubs and small trees too. Look out for hardy orchids, trilliums (in the green), *Franklinia alatamaha* and an amazing range of magnolias.

Steven Bailey Ltd
Silver Street, Sway, Lymington SO41 6ZA
☎ 01590 682227   [FAX] 01590 683765

CONTACT   S. E. Bailey
LOCATION   Near Hordle: not Sway village
OPEN   8 am – 4.30 pm, Monday – Friday; 9 am – 4.30 pm, Saturdays, March to December. Also 10 am – 4 pm, Sundays, March to June only
SPECIALITIES   Bedding plants; *Dianthus*; *Alstroemeria*
CATALOGUE   2 first-class stamps
MAIL ORDER   Yes
SHOWS   RHS Westminster; Malvern (Spring); Malvern (Autumn); Harrogate (Spring); Harrogate (Autumn); Southport; Chelsea; BBC GW Live; Hampton Court

Long-established specialists for carnations, pinks and alstroemerias. Active on the show circuit, so look out for them. The nursery shop also has a selection of bedding and summer pot plants.

Water Meadow Nursery and Herb Farm
Cheriton, Alresford SO24 0QB
☎ 01962 771895   [FAX] 01962 771985

CONTACT   Sandy Worth

LOCATION Near A272, Winchester to Petersfield road, towards Alresford
OPEN 9 am – 5 pm, Friday – Saturday, and Bank Holidays; 2 pm – 5 pm, Sundays. March to November
SPECIALITIES Aquatic plants; bog plants; herbaceous perennials; herbs
CATALOGUE 3 first-class stamps
MAIL ORDER Yes
REFRESHMENTS Home-made teas on sunny weekends and Bank Holidays
GARDEN Display garden open at the same times
DESIGN SERVICE Water Meadow Design & Landscape
SHOWS RHS Westminster; Malvern (Spring); Malvern (Autumn); Harrogate (Spring); Hampton Court

There is an extensive range of herbs and perennials here, but the main speciality is in plants that grow near water. Strong on *Nymphaea* (70). Other services include design and landscaping, and wholesale. They will be at Parham and Selborne Plant Fairs and the New Forest Show.

Wychwood Waterlilies

Farnham Road (A287), Odiham, Basingstoke RG25 1HS
☎ 01256 702800 [FAX] 01256 701001

CONTACT Ann or Clair Henley
LOCATION On A287 3 miles from M3, Jct 5
OPEN 10 am – 6 pm, daily.
SPECIALITIES Aquatic plants; bog plants; *Nymphaea*
NEW FOR 1997 More varieties of *Nymphaea*
CATALOGUE 1 first-class stamp
MAIL ORDER Yes
REFRESHMENTS Yes
GARDEN Odiham Waterlily Collection, open June – October
DESIGN SERVICE Yes
NCCPG NATIONAL COLLECTIONS *Nymphaea*

The nursery grows water lilies and other aquatics, bog and marginal plants including some rare *Iris ensata* cultivars. The Odiham Water Lily Collection can be visited in summer.

HEREFORD &WORCESTER

Abbey Dore Court Garden

Abbey Dore, Hereford HR2 0AD
☎ 01981 240419 [FAX] 01981 240279

CONTACT Charis Ward
LOCATION Between Hereford and Abergavenny, 3 miles west of A465
OPEN 11 am – 6 pm, Thursday – Tuesday, from first Saturday in March to third Sunday in October
SPECIALITIES Herbaceous perennials
MAIL ORDER No
SHOP Country Gift Gallery
REFRESHMENTS Licensed restaurant, home-made food
GARDEN Abbey Dore Court Garden, Hereford & Worcester, see Gardens section

A small nursery attached to the garden: it is particularly good for perennials. To see the hellebores before the garden season, telephone for an appointment.

Bouts Cottage Nurseries

Bouts Lane, Inkberrow WR7 4HP
☎ 01386 792923

CONTACT Mark Roberts
OPEN Not open to the public
SPECIALITIES Violas
CATALOGUE SAE
MAIL ORDER Yes, no minimum order
SHOWS RHS Westminster; Malvern (Spring); Chelsea; BBC GW Live

Mail-order nursery devoted to old-fashioned violas. The plants can be seen at shows, but the nursery is not open for visiting.

Caves Folly Nurseries

Evendine Lane, Colwall, Malvern WR13 6DU
☎ 01684 540631

CONTACT B. Evans or W. Leaper
LOCATION Near Malvern
OPEN 10 am – 5 pm, Thursday – Saturday
SPECIALITIES Alpines; herbaceous perennials
CATALOGUE On request
GARDEN Garden opens under the NGS
DESIGN SERVICE Caves Folly Nurseries
SHOWS RHS Westminster; Malvern (Spring); Malvern (Autumn); Harrogate (Spring); Harrogate (Autumn); Southport; BBC GW Live; Hampton Court

The nursery sells alpine and herbaceous plants, all of which are organically grown in peat-free compost. A landscaping and garden maintenance service is also offered.

Cooks Garden Centre

26 Worcester Road, Stourport on Severn DY13 5PQ
☎ 01299 826169 [FAX] 01299 824441

CONTACT Paul N. Cook or Millie Bunnett
LOCATION ½ mile from town centre on Worcester road
OPEN 9 am – 6 pm daily
SPECIALITIES Bedding plants
MAIL ORDER Young plant plugs in spring only
SHOWS Malvern (Spring); Malvern (Autumn); Chelsea; BBC GW Live; Hampton Court

Garden centre and nursery specialising in colourful bedding plants, planters and hanging baskets. Their hanging baskets won them a Gold medal at last year's Chelsea.

Cotswold Garden Flowers

1 Waterside, Evesham WR11 6BS
☎ 01386 47337/01386 833849 [FAX] 01386 47337

CONTACT Bob Brown
LOCATION Sands Lane, Badsey, Evesham. Continue ⅓ of a mile after tarmac runs out
OPEN 8 am – 4.30 pm, Monday – Friday. Also open 10 am – 6 pm, Saturday – Sunday, March to September only. Other times by appointment
SPECIALITIES Herbaceous perennials
CATALOGUE On request
MAIL ORDER Yes
GARDEN 1-acre herbaceous display gardens
SHOWS Malvern (Spring); Malvern (Autumn)

The nursery stocks a wide selection of herbaceous perennials, all of which have been chosen on the basis of their garden worthiness. Visitors are advised to bring wellingtons when it's wet.

The Cottage Herbery
Mill House, Boraston, Tenbury Wells WR15 8LZ
☎ 01584 781575   [FAX] 01584 781483

CONTACT K. or R. Hurst
LOCATION Turn off A456 (Worcester to Leominster), at Peacock Inn, 2 miles east of Tenbury Wells
OPEN 10 am – 6 pm, Sundays only; weekdays by appointment, May to July
SPECIALITIES Herbaceous perennials; herbs
NEW FOR 1997 *Teucrium scorodonia* 'Winterdown'
CATALOGUE 4 first-class stamps
MAIL ORDER Seeds only
SHOP Herb products
REFRESHMENTS Teas, Sundays only
GARDEN Garden opens every Sunday
SHOWS RHS Westminster; Malvern (Spring); Malvern (Autumn); BBC GW Live; Hampton Court

A small, specialist nursery whose stock includes herbs and aromatic plants, including *Symphytum*, *Pulmonaria* and *Monarda*. The plants are organically grown in peat-free compost. They will be at specialist Plant Fairs and Shrewsbury Flower Show.

Country Gardens (Burcot)
Alcester Road, Burcot, Bromsgrove B60 1PW
☎ 01527 873470   [FAX] 01527 877806

CONTACT Tony Bryan (Manager)
OPEN 9 am – 6 pm, Monday – Saturday; 10.30 am – 4.30 pm, Sundays
REFRESHMENTS Coffee shop

Country House Hedging
Sunny Bank House, Eaton Bishop HR2 9QP
☎ 01981 250692

CONTACT Elaine Wigg
LOCATION Telephone for directions
OPEN Telephone first
SPECIALITIES Hedging; primulas; topiary
CATALOGUE SAE
MAIL ORDER Yes
GARDEN Under construction
DESIGN SERVICE Yes
SHOWS Malvern (Spring); Malvern (Autumn)

The nursery has recently moved. There is box and yew bare-root hedging as well as topiary. Winter interest shrubs are a new and expanding part of their range. There is a design service which includes landscaping locally.

Cranesbill Nursery
White Cottage, Earls Common Road, Stock Green, Redditch B96 6SZ
☎ 01386 792414

CONTACT J. Bates

LOCATION 9 miles west of Worcester, 1½ miles north of A422
OPEN 10 am – 5 pm, Friday – Tuesday
SPECIALITIES Herbaceous perennials; mediterranean plants; hardy geraniums
CATALOGUE 4 first-class stamps
MAIL ORDER Yes
SHOP Coneybury Plant Centre
GARDEN Customers can visit the 2-acre garden, open under the NGS

Hardy geraniums are the speciality here, nearly 100 of them – hardly surprising given the name. Yet there is a good selection of other perennials, and some interesting shrubs too. They also operate Coneybury Plant Centre, nearby at Dormston, and will do soft landscaping.

D & M Everett
Greenacres Nursery, Bringsty, Worcester WR6 5TA
☎ & [FAX] 01885 482206

CONTACT Daphne Everett
LOCATION A44, 2 miles east of Bromyard
OPEN By appointment
SPECIALITIES Heathers
CATALOGUE On request; separate wholesale and retail lists
MAIL ORDER No
REFRESHMENTS Open days only
GARDEN Owners' garden opens for NGS and Red Cross

A heather specialist, with a mainly wholesale business though a retail list is available. There are upwards of 200 containerised varieties. The garden opens for charity several times each year.

Eastgrove Cottage Garden Nursery
Sankyns Green, Shrawley, Little Witley WR6 6LQ
☎ 01299 896389

CONTACT Malcolm or Carol Skinner
LOCATION Between Shrawley (B4196) and Great Witley (A443)
OPEN 2 – 5 pm, Thursday – Monday, 27 March to July 31; 2 – 5 pm, Thursday – Saturday, 4 September to 18 October; 2 – 5 pm, Sundays 14, 28 September, 12 October. Closed August
SPECIALITIES Herbaceous perennials; New Zealand plants; half-hardy plants
CATALOGUE 5 second-class stamps
MAIL ORDER No
GARDEN Eastgrove Cottage Garden, Hereford & Worcester, see Gardens section

A large and varied range of interesting plants, all of them propagated from this Worcestershire garden. Mainly perennials, but there is a collection of half-hardy plants too.

Frank P Matthews Ltd
Berrington Court, Tenbury Wells WR15 8RS
☎ 01584 810214   [FAX] 01584 811830

CONTACT Janet Powell or Susan Bowen
LOCATION Tenbury Wells
OPEN By appointment only, for collection
SPECIALITIES Fruit; trees
CATALOGUE On request

MAIL ORDER   No

The nursery is mainly a wholesale business, but serious amateurs who are interested in the fruit and ornamental tree ranges are encouraged. The plants are open-ground and container-grown. Order by phone in advance and arrange to collect from the nursery.

Fuchsiavale Nurseries
Worcester Road, Torton, Kidderminster DY11 7SB
☎ 01299 251162   📠 01299 251256
LOCATION   3 miles south of Kidderminster on A449
OPEN   9 am – 5 pm, 2 January to 25 August
SPECIALITIES   Fuchsias
CATALOGUE   3 first-class stamps for mail order catalogue
MAIL ORDER   Yes
SHOWS   Malvern (Spring); Harrogate (Spring); Chelsea; Hampton Court

Fuchsia specialist. Their range of around 300 varieties includes new American cultivars. The full catalogue is available only at the nursery. They attend most large county shows. There is a range of pelargoniums and alpines too.

The Garden at The Elms
The Elms Farm, Frenchlands Lane, Lower Broadheath, Worcester WR2 6QU
☎ 01905 640841   📠 01905 640675

CONTACT   Emma Stewart
LOCATION   Off B4204 4 miles west of Worcester
OPEN   10 am – 5 pm, Tuesdays and Wednesdays, April to September
SPECIALITIES   Herbaceous perennials
CATALOGUE   3 first-class stamps
MAIL ORDER   No
REFRESHMENTS   Teas
GARDEN   Garden opens for NGS
DESIGN SERVICE   Yes
SHOWS   Malvern (Spring); Malvern (Autumn)

An expanding range of cottage garden plants and hardy perennials is available at this developing nursery. They will be attending several shows in Wales and the Midlands this year.

Grange Farm Nursery
Guarlford, Malvern WR13 6NY
☎ 01684 562544

CONTACT   Carol Nicholls
LOCATION   Centre of village on B4211
OPEN   9 am – 5.30 pm, summer; 9 am – dusk, winter.
Closed over Christmas and New Year
SPECIALITIES   Climbers; shrubs; trees
MAIL ORDER   No
SHOWS   Malvern (Spring); Malvern (Autumn)

An all round range of plants, with the emphasis on well-grown hardy trees, climbers and shrubs, sold from the retail plant centre. Some garden ornaments and equipment too.

Hayloft Plants
The Hayloft, Little Court, Radford Road, Rous Lench, Evesham WR11 4UL
☎ & 📠 01386 793361
CONTACT   Yvonne Walker
OPEN   Mail order only
SPECIALITIES   Herbaceous perennials; half-hardy plants
CATALOGUE   On request
MAIL ORDER   Yes
SHOWS   Malvern (Spring); BBC GW Live; Hampton Court

A nursery stocking mainly half-hardy plants – penstemons, osteospermums and gazanias for example – and hardy perennials.

Hergest Croft Gardens
Kington HR5 3EG
☎ & 📠 01554 230160
CONTACT   S. Price
LOCATION   Signed off A44
OPEN   1.30 pm – 6.30 pm, daily, April to October
SPECIALITIES   Shrubs; trees
MAIL ORDER   No
REFRESHMENTS   Yes
GARDEN   Hergest Croft Gardens, Hereford & Worcester, see Gardens section
NCCPG NATIONAL-COLLECTIONS   Acer; Betula; Zelkova

Little-known and rare shrubs and trees propagated from a garden long famed for its trees.

How Caple Court Gardens
How Caple Court, How Caple, Hereford HR1 4SX
☎ 01989 740626   📠 01989 740611
CONTACT   H. M. Lee
LOCATION   On B4224 5 miles north-east of Ross on Wye
OPEN   9 am – 5 pm, Monday – Saturday; 10 am – 5 pm, Sundays, May to October
SPECIALITIES   Fruit; roses
MAIL ORDER   No
REFRESHMENTS   Teas, light snacks
GARDEN   How Caple Court, Hereford & Worcester, see Gardens section

A lovely country house mixture of plants: old apples, old roses, perennials and shrubs.

Jungle Giants
Plough Farm, Wigmore, Leominster HR6 9UW
☎ 01568 770708   📠 01568 770383
CONTACT   Michael Brisbane
LOCATION   In Wigmore village, next to the Compasses Hotel
OPEN   By appointment only – please telephone before visiting
SPECIALITIES   Bamboos
CATALOGUE   Bamboo information pack £5.75
MAIL ORDER   Yes
SHOWS   Malvern (Spring); Hampton Court

Specialist growers of bamboos. They also sell large-diameter canes, bamboo fences, books and artefacts. The information pack and price list make delightful reading.

Kenchester Water Gardens
Church Road, Lyde, Hereford HR1 3AB
☎ 01432 270981   📠 01432 342243
CONTACT   M. R. Edwards
LOCATION   On A49 between Hereford and Leominster
OPEN   9 am – 6 pm, daily, April to September; 9 am – 5.30 pm, daily, October to March. Closed Christmas Day
SPECIALITIES   Aquatic plants
NEW FOR 1997   30 new or reintroduced cultivars, including 15 Perry hybrids
CATALOGUE   Free on request
MAIL ORDER   Yes, payment in advance
SHOP   Fish, pond and pool equipment
REFRESHMENTS   Tea rooms
GARDEN   6-acre water gardens

Retail and wholesale aquatic specialist. Their range includes over 130 varieties of *Nymphaea*. The centre stocks everything needed for ponds and pools.

Marley Bank Nursery
Ivy Croft Plants, Ivington Green, Leominster HR6 0JN
☎ 01568 720344
CONTACT   Sue or Roger Norman
OPEN   By appointment all year
SPECIALITIES   Alpines
CATALOGUE   SAE
MAIL ORDER   No
GARDEN   Under construction

Small, specialist nursery which produces small numbers of a range of alpines and tender perennials. The nursery moved last October.

Marston Exotics
Brampton Lane, Madley, Hereford HR2 9LX
☎ 01981 251140   📠 01981 251649
CONTACT   Paul or Jackie Gardner
LOCATION   7 miles south of Hereford
OPEN   8 am – 4.30 pm, Monday – Friday, all year; 1 pm – 5 pm, Saturday – Sunday, March to October; 11 am – 5 pm, Bank Holidays
SPECIALITIES   Carnivorous plants
CATALOGUE   £1 guide; price list is free
MAIL ORDER   Yes, worldwide
REFRESHMENTS   Light refreshments
GARDEN   *Sarracenia* collection: open times as nursery
DESIGN SERVICE   Yes
SHOWS   RHS Westminster; Malvern (Spring); Malvern (Autumn); Southport; Chelsea; BBC GW Live; Hampton Court

A formidable range of carnivorous plants, the largest public collection in Europe they claim. Their range includes species for the house, greenhouse and garden, as well as appropriate accessories. They are having a Children's Fortnight the last week in July and first week in August.

Merebrook Water Plants
Merebrook Farm, Hanley Swan, Worcester WR8 0DX
☎ 01684 310950   📠 01684 310034
CONTACT   Roger or Biddi Kings
LOCATION   On B4209 near Three Counties showground
OPEN   10 am – 5 pm, Thursday – Tuesday, April to September. Closed Wednesdays
SPECIALITIES   Aquatic plants
NEW FOR 1997   *Nymphaea* 'Joey Tomocick'
CATALOGUE   SAE
MAIL ORDER   Yes
REFRESHMENTS   Tea & coffee
GARDEN   Display pools
SHOWS   Malvern (Spring); Malvern (Autumn)

Water lilies are supplied ready planted in baskets. There are aquatic and marginal plants and a special conservation pack of British native species.

Mrs S M Cooper
Firlands Cottage, Bishops Frome, Worcester WR6 5BA
☎ 01885 490358
CONTACT   Mrs Cooper
LOCATION   Between Hereford and Worcester, off B4214 to Bromyard
OPEN   By appointment
SPECIALITIES   Shrubs; trees
CATALOGUE   Small SAE
MAIL ORDER   Yes, minimum order £20
GARDEN   Being planted

A small, but very interesting list of rare tree and shrub species, all grown from seed. The provenance is named on request.

Old Court Nurseries
Walwyn Road, Colwall, Malvern WR13 6QE
☎ 01684 540416   📠 01684 565314
CONTACT   Meriel Picton
LOCATION   B4218 in Colwall village
OPEN   10 am – 1 pm, 2.15 pm – 5.30 pm, Wednesday – Sunday, April to October
SPECIALITIES   Herbaceous perennials; wild flowers; michaelmas daisies
NEW FOR 1997   *Aster novae-angliae* 'Lou Williams', *Aster* 'Snow Flurry'
CATALOGUE   £2.50 for colour guide, postage included
MAIL ORDER   Yes, asters only
GARDEN   Picton Garden
SHOWS   Malvern (Autumn)
NCCPG NATIONAL COLLECTIONS   *Aster*

Holders of National Collection of Michaelmas daisies. This is their speciality: the extensive collection is fully described in *A Guide to the Asters grown by Old Court Nurseries*. There are also many other interesting perennials and cottage garden type plants here. The garden opens for the National Gardens Scheme, Wednesdays to Sundays, from April to October. Guided tours for groups, by arrangement.

Owen Bros (of Worcs) Ltd
Bevere Nurseries, Bevere Green, Worcester WR3 7RG
☎ 01905 451215   FAX 01905 756804

CONTACT   Mrs J. Owens
LOCATION   Off A449 north of Worcester
OPEN   By appointment only
SPECIALITIES   Conifers; conservatory plants; house plants
CATALOGUE   Yes
MAIL ORDER   No
SHOWS   Malvern (Spring); Malvern (Autumn); Harrogate (Spring); Hampton Court

Conservatory and house plants specialist. Plants are available as individual specimens or arrangements for interior landscaping. They can be rented or bought. Container-grown conifers are the other speciality.

Paul Jasper
The Lighthouse, Bridge Street, Leominster HR6 8DU
☎ 01568 611540   FAX 01568 616499

CONTACT   Paul Jasper
OPEN   By appointment only
SPECIALITIES   Fruit
CATALOGUE   2 first-class stamps
MAIL ORDER   Yes

Trade and retail fruit specialist with over 100 traditional apple varieties among other fruiting and ornamental trees.

Perhill Plants
Worcester Road, Great Witley WR6 6JT
☎ 01299 896329   FAX 01299 896990

CONTACT   D. or S. Straw
LOCATION   At Great Witley, on A443
OPEN   9 am – 5 pm, daily, 1 February to 15 October; by appointment only, 16 October to 31 January
SPECIALITIES   Alpines; herbaceous perennials; herbs
CATALOGUE   6 second-class stamps
MAIL ORDER   Yes

The retail nursery stocks some 2500 different alpines, herbs and perennials. Notable collections include *Dianthus* (100), thymes (40), penstemons (150) and salvias (90). They also operate a wholesale cash-and-carry business and deliver to local garden centres. They will be at several rare plant fairs this year.

R F Beeston
294 Ombersley Road, Worcester WR3 7HD
☎ 01905 453245

CONTACT   R. F. Beeston
LOCATION   Bevere Nurseries, Bevere, Worcester
OPEN   10 am – 1 pm, 2 pm – 5 pm, Wednesday – Friday, March to October. Other times by appointment
SPECIALITIES   Alpines; primulas; *Dionysia*
CATALOGUE   SAE
MAIL ORDER   Yes

Alpine specialist with an emphasis on smaller plants for use in alpine houses, alpine beds and troughs. Strengths include European *Primula* species, *Androsace* and *Dionysia*. They attend most of the AGS shows.

Rickard's Hardy Ferns Ltd
Kyre Park, Tenbury Wells WR15 8RP
☎ 01885 410282   FAX 01885 410398

CONTACT   Hazel or Martin Rickard
LOCATION   Off B4214 Bromyard road, 4 miles south of Tenbury Wells
OPEN   11 am – 5 pm, Wednesday – Monday, April to October; and by appointment. Closed Tuesdays
SPECIALITIES   Tree ferns
CATALOGUE   5 first-class stamps
MAIL ORDER   UK and EC only
REFRESHMENTS   11 am – 6 pm, daily, Easter to October
GARDEN   11 am – 6 pm, April to October, or by appointment, set in Georgian landscape garden undergoing restoration. Admission £1.50
SHOWS   Malvern (Spring); Malvern (Autumn); Chelsea; BBC GW Live; Hampton Court

Specialists in hardy ferns. They have a great number for sale, and over 900 different varieties in their own collection. Half-hardy tree ferns are also sold.

Rileys Chrysanthemums
The Plant Centre, Knowle Hill, Evesham WR11 5EN
☎ 01386 833022   FAX 01386 832915

CONTACT   John Woolman
LOCATION   Off the A46: map in catalogue
OPEN   9 am – 5 pm; daily; all year
SPECIALITIES   Chrysanthemums
CATALOGUE   Yes
MAIL ORDER   Yes
GARDEN   Chrysanthemum fields

A famous firm of chrysanthemum breeders, now owned and managed by John Woolman. The breeding programme continues and new cultivars are introduced every year. The catalogue lists all types: old and new, indoor and outdoor. Cut flowers in season. The fields are open for viewing on Sundays in September.

Rushfields of Ledbury
Ross Road, Ledbury HR8 2LP
☎ 01531 632004

CONTACT   B. Homewood
LOCATION   ½ mile south-west of Ledbury on A449
OPEN   11 am – 5 pm, Wednesday – Saturday, and by appointment
SPECIALITIES   Herbaceous perennials
CATALOGUE   Large SAE (29p) plus £1
MAIL ORDER   No
REFRESHMENTS   By arrangement for prebooked groups
GARDEN   Winter garden opens mid-February
SHOWS   RHS Westminster; Malvern (Spring); Malvern (Autumn); Harrogate (Spring); Southport; BBC GW Live; Hampton Court

A good choice of perennials, including geraniums, hardy osteospermums, hostas and some Helen Ballard hellebore cultivars. They will also be at the Shrewsbury show.

Stone House Cottage Nurseries

Stone, Kidderminster DY10 4BG
☎ & [FAX] 01562 69902

CONTACT   J. F. Arbuthnott
LOCATION   2 miles south-east of Kidderminster, on A448
OPEN   10 am – 5.30 pm, Wednesday – Saturday, 1 March to 18 October. Also some Sundays when garden open for NGS
SPECIALITIES   Climbers; shrubs, wall shrubs
CATALOGUE   SAE
MAIL ORDER   No
GARDEN   Stone House Cottage, Hereford & Worcester, see Gardens section

Wall shrubs and climbers are the speciality here, but there are also some interesting shrubs, old roses (on their own roots) and a constantly changing list of herbaceous plants. The nursery and garden are recommended.

Treasures of Tenbury Ltd

Burford House Gardens, Tenbury Wells, Worcester WR15 8HQ
☎ 01584 810777   [FAX] 01584 810673

CONTACT   Pat Cox or Chris Haydon
LOCATION   Between Tenbury Wells and Ludlow on A456
OPEN   10 am – 6 pm, daily; 10 am – 5 pm, in winter months
SPECIALITIES   Clematis
NEW FOR 1997   Grasses, conservatory plants, bamboos
CATALOGUE   Yes
MAIL ORDER   Clematis only
REFRESHMENTS   Buttery open 10 am – 6pm, daily
GARDEN   Burford House Gardens, Hereford & Worcester, see Gardens section
SHOWS   Malvern (Spring); Malvern (Autumn); BBC GW Live

The nursery specialises in herbaceous plants and especially the clematis which characterise the adjoining garden.

Webbs of Wychbold

Wychbold, Droitwich WR9 0DG
☎ 01527 861777   [FAX] 01527 861284

CONTACT   Boyd J. Douglas-Davies or Claire Hall
LOCATION   1 mile north of M5, Jct 5 on A38. Follow brown signs
OPEN   9 am – 6 pm, Monday – Friday (8 pm April to September), 9 am – 6 pm, Saturdays and Bank Holidays, 10.30 am – 4.30 pm, Sundays
CATALOGUE   £1
MAIL ORDER   No
SHOP   Garden sundries
REFRESHMENTS   Restaurant
GARDEN   Demonstration and display gardens
DESIGN SERVICE   Webbs of Wychbold
SHOWS   Malvern (Spring); Malvern (Autumn)
NCCPG NATIONAL COLLECTIONS   Potentilla fruticosa

Forward-looking garden centre and nursery, with an extensive range of good plants and all sorts of sundries and equipment. Design and landscaping service. The Potentilla collection is housed in a special garden.

Wintergreen Nurseries

Bringsty, Worcester WR6 5UJ
☎ 01886 821858

CONTACT   Stephen Dodd
LOCATION   3 miles east of Bromyard, on A44
OPEN   10 am – 5.30 pm, Wednesday – Sunday, March to October
SPECIALITIES   Alpines; herbaceous perennials
CATALOGUE   2 second-class stamps
MAIL ORDER   Yes
GARDEN   Display garden
SHOWS   Malvern (Spring); Malvern (Autumn); BBC GW Live

A small nursery which specialises in alpines and perennials: there are also some shrubs.

Woolmans Plants Ltd

The Plant Centre, Knowle Hill, Evesham WR11 5EN
☎ 01386 833022   [FAX] 01386 832915

CONTACT   John Woolman
LOCATION   Map in catalogue
OPEN   9 am – 5 pm, daily, all year except Christmas Day & Boxing Day
SPECIALITIES   Chrysanthemums
NEW FOR 1997   Dendranthema 'Woolman's Venture' and several other new cultivars
CATALOGUE   Free
MAIL ORDER   Yes
SHOWS   Harrogate (Autumn); Chelsea

Garden chrysanthemums are the speciality of this nursery, and they have a fine list of cultivars old and new. Many have been bred by members of the Woolman family. They also offer a few dahlias, pelargoniums, osteospermums and similar conservatory plants.

Worcester Garden Centre

Droitwich Road, Worcester WR3 7SW
☎ 01905 451231   [FAX] 01905 755371

CONTACT   Ruth Cullan or any staff member
LOCATION   On A38 north of city centre, before Fernhill Heath
OPEN   9 am – 6 pm, Monday – Saturday; 10 am – 4 pm, Sundays; close at 9 pm, Thursdays
CATALOGUE   Plant lists and leaflets
REFRESHMENTS   Black Pear Café
GARDEN   Yes
DESIGN SERVICE   Yes
SHOWS   Malvern (Spring); Malvern (Autumn); Chelsea; BBC GW Live

Branch of Byrkley Park Centre.

Wyevale Garden Centres plc
Kings Acre Road, Hereford HR4 0SE
☎ 01432 276568   [FAX] 01432 263289
CATALOGUE 99p plant guide
MAIL ORDER No
REFRESHMENTS Yes
SHOWS Malvern (Spring); Chelsea

The country's largest garden centre chain, with 58 centres and another 5 shops. Facilities vary, but all sell the company's illustrated *Good Plant Guide* which covers the Wyevale range. They sell over 2500 trees and shrubs, backed by a substantial wholesale nursery business. In addition the chain operates a plant-finding service for a £5 deposit. Many of the centres also have pet shops and restaurants.

HERTFORDSHIRE

The Abbots House Garden
10 High Street, Abbots Langley WD5 0AR
☎ 01923 264946/443653

CONTACT Dr Peter Tomson or Mrs Joan Gentry
LOCATION 4½ miles north of Watford; 4½ miles south-west of St Albans
OPEN 9 am – 1 pm, 2 pm – 4 pm, Saturdays, March to October; 9 am – 1 pm, Saturdays, November to December; other times by arrangement
SPECIALITIES Conservatory plants
CATALOGUE 3 second-class stamps
MAIL ORDER No
REFRESHMENTS When garden is open
GARDEN Open for NGS: 20 April, 25 May, 22 June, 24 August

A small nursery with a pleasantly mixed range, including shrubs, perennials, half-hardy and conservatory plants. Normally only open Saturdays, but visitors welcome on other days by arrangement.

Aylett Nurseries Ltd
North Orbital Road, London Colney, St Albans AL2 1DH
☎ 01727 822255   [FAX] 01727 823024

CONTACT R. S. Aylett
LOCATION On A414 in Hertfordshire
OPEN 8.30 am – 5.30 pm, Monday – Friday; 8.30 am – 5.30 pm, Saturdays; 9 am – 5 pm, Bank Holidays; 10 am – 4 pm, Sundays
SPECIALITIES Bedding plants; dahlias
CATALOGUE On request
MAIL ORDER No
SHOP Garden sundries
REFRESHMENTS Coffee shop
GARDEN Trial grounds
DESIGN SERVICE Aylett Nurseries Ltd
SHOWS RHS Westminster

A huge (and very busy) general garden centre, in a prime trading position with a vast range of plants and every imaginable sundry. They also offer a design service and delivery. Their award winning speciality is dahlias: they have a large selection of all types, and hold special dahlia weekends in late September.

Chenies Garden Centre
Chenies, Rickmansworth WD3 6EN
☎ 01494 764545   [FAX] 01494 762216
LOCATION Between Rickmansworth and Amersham, on A404
OPEN 9 am – 6 pm, Monday – Saturday, BST; 9 am – 5 pm, Monday – Saturday, winter; 10.30 am – 4.30 pm, Sundays
SHOP Garden buildings, fencing, paving, sundries
GARDEN By arrangement

General garden centre, with a particularly large display of garden buildings. A design service is available through their sister company, Chenies Landscapes (see Services).

Country Gardens
High Street, Codicote SG4 8XA
☎ 01438 820433   [FAX] 01438 821451
CONTACT Julian Simms (Manager)
OPEN 9 am – 6 pm, Monday – Saturday; 10.30 am – 4.30 pm, Sundays
SHOP Machinery
REFRESHMENTS Coffee shop

Country Gardens
Bulbourne Road, Tring HP23 5HF
☎ 01442 891393   [FAX] 01442 828992
CONTACT Martin Andrews (Manager)
OPEN 9 am – 6 pm, Monday – Saturday; 10.30 am – 4.30 pm, Sundays
SHOP Aquatics, conservatories
REFRESHMENTS Coffee shop

Gannock Growers
Gannock Green, Sandon, Buntingford SG9 0RH
☎ 01763 287386
CONTACT Penny Pyle
LOCATION Map in catalogue
OPEN 10 am – 4 pm, Thursday – Saturday, 1 April to mid-October, but please telephone to check times
SPECIALITIES Herbaceous perennials
CATALOGUE 3 first-class stamps
MAIL ORDER Yes
SHOWS RHS Westminster; Malvern (Spring); BBC GW Live; Hampton Court

Herbaceous perennial specialist with a wide selection of the more unusual species and varieties. They visit lots of shows, including Hatfield House Festival of Gardening, Royal Show Stoneleigh and East Anglian Garden Show.

Godly's Roses
Redbourn, St Albans AL3 7PS
☎ 01582 792255   [FAX] 01582 794267
CONTACT Colin or Andy Godly
LOCATION A5183, ½ mile south of M1, Jct 9
OPEN 9 am – 6 pm, daily
SPECIALITIES Roses
CATALOGUE On request

MAIL ORDER   Yes, local orders only for standards
SHOP   Garden sundries
GARDEN   Rose fields

Rose growers with a selection of popular modern varieties. A general range of plants is carried in the garden centre. Godly's have home grown dried flowers available all year round.

Great Gardens of England Ltd

Chipperfield Home & Garden Centre, Tower Hill, Chipperfield WD4 9LH
☎ 01442 834364

CONTACT   The Manager
LOCATION   2 miles west of Kings Langley, off A41
OPEN   9 am – 5.30 pm, Monday – Saturday; 10.30 am – 4.30 pm, Sundays
SHOP   Aquatics, crafts, pets
REFRESHMENTS   Restaurant

This garden centre offers a wide range of plants and sundries for the general gardener.

Hillier Garden Centre (Piccotts End)

Leighton Buzzard Road, Piccotts End, Hemel Hempstead HP1 3BA
☎ 01442 242637   📠 01442 69953

CONTACT   Stephen Williams (Manager)
OPEN   9 am – 5.30 pm, Monday – Saturday; 10.30 am – 4.30 pm, Sundays

Hopleys Plants Ltd

High Street, Much Hadham SG10 6BU
☎ 01279 842509   📠 01279 843784

CONTACT   A. D. Barker
LOCATION   50 yards north of Bull Pub
OPEN   9 am – 5 pm, daily; 2 pm – 5 pm, Sundays. Closed Tuesdays, January and February
SPECIALITIES   Herbaceous perennials; shrubs
CATALOGUE   5 first-class stamps
MAIL ORDER   Yes, autumn only
REFRESHMENTS   Self-service
GARDEN   Garden open at the same time as the nursery
SHOWS   RHS Westminster; Malvern (Spring); Harrogate (Spring); Chelsea; BBC GW Live; Hampton Court

An extensive choice of hardy shrubs and perennials, with many half-hardy varieties too. Strong on diascias, osteospermums, penstemons and salvias. Over the last quarter of a century the nursery has been responsible for numerous introductions, the most famous being *Lavatera* 'Barnsley' and *Potentilla fruticosa* 'Red Ace'. The tradition continues.

LW Plants

23 Wroxham Way, Harpenden AL5 4PP
☎ 01582 768467

CONTACT   Mrs M. Easter
LOCATION   North-east Harpenden, off Ox Lane
OPEN   10 am – 5 pm, most days, phone first
SPECIALITIES   Herbaceous perennials; herbs
CATALOGUE   4 second-class stamps plus A5 SAE
MAIL ORDER   Yes, £15 minimum, September to April
GARDEN   Garden opens for NGS & NCCPG

A selection of plants from a plantsman's garden with perennials and thymes from the National Collection. Group visits can be arranged. The nursery will be at local shows, including NCCPG Capel Manor and Herts Garden Show.

Notcutts Garden Centre (St Albans)

Hatfield Road, Smallford, St Albans AL4 0BR
☎ 01727 853224   📠 01727 847251

CONTACT   Neil Hughes (Manager)
LOCATION   On A1057
OPEN   8.30 am – 5.30 pm, Monday – Saturday; 11 am – 5 pm, Sundays. Closes at 5 pm in winter
SHOP   Garden sundries, furniture
DESIGN SERVICE   Notcutts Landscapes
SHOWS   Chelsea; BBC GW Live; Hampton Court

Paul Bromfield Aquatics

Maydencroft Lane, Gosmore, Hitchin SG4 7QD
☎ 01462 457399   📠 01462 422652

CONTACT   P. Bromfield
LOCATION   1 mile from Hitchin
OPEN   Mail order only; collection by arrangement
SPECIALITIES   Aquatic plants; bog plants; grasses; house plants
CATALOGUE   3 second-class stamps
MAIL ORDER   Yes
SHOP   Maydencroft Aquatic Nurseries
GARDEN   Demonstration gardens

Aquatic, marginal and water-loving plants, available individually or as collections. There is a good choice of water lilies. The nursery is the mail order part of Maydencroft Aquatics.

R Harkness & Co Ltd

The Rose Gardens, Cambridge Road, Hitchin SG4 0JT
☎ 01462 420402   📠 01462 422170

CONTACT   Sales Office
OPEN   9 am – 5.30 pm, Monday – Saturday; 10.30 am – 4 pm, Sundays
SPECIALITIES   Roses
CATALOGUE   On request
MAIL ORDER   Yes, winter despatch
SHOP   Garden centre
REFRESHMENTS   Restaurant
SHOWS   Chelsea; Hampton Court

Rose breeders and growers with an excellent range of Hybrid Teas, floribundas and low-growing varieties. There are also climbers and shrub roses on the list. The medium-sized garden centre is neatly laid out with a fair range of general stock.

Roger Harvey Garden World

The Farm House, Bragbury Lane, Bragbury End, Stevenage SG2 8JJ
☎ 01438 811777

CONTACT   John Morgan
LOCATION   On A602 2 miles east of A1M, Jct 7
OPEN   9 am – 5.30 pm, Monday – Saturday; 10.30 am – 4.30 pm, Sundays
MAIL ORDER   No
SHOP   Fish, silk flowers, gifts, pools, conservatories

REFRESHMENTS   Coffee shop
GARDEN   Monday – Friday
DESIGN SERVICE   Garden Design Centre
SHOWS   Chelsea

Garden centre complex set in old farm buildings. Winners of awards for good garden plants.

Tokonoma Bonsai Nursery
14 London Road, Shenley, Radlett WD7 9EN
☎ 01923 857587   [FAX] 01923 852596

CONTACT   Charlotte Dalampira
LOCATION   Off M25, Jct 22
OPEN   9 am – 5 pm, Monday – Friday; 10 am – 4 pm, Saturday – Sunday
SPECIALITIES   Bonsai
CATALOGUE   SAE
MAIL ORDER   Yes
SHOWS   Chelsea; Hampton Court

Bonsai and Penjing specialist, associated sundries as well. Workshops, lessons and talks can be arranged.

Top Pots
Westmill Farm, Ware SG12 0ES
☎ 01920 465026

CONTACT   Peter or Cris Vigus, Adrian Filipoyitsch
LOCATION   On A602 1 mile north of Ware
OPEN   Times vary according to season, phone to check
SPECIALITIES   Fuchsias
NEW FOR 1997   *Salvia farinacea* 'Alba'
CATALOGUE   Collect at nursery
MAIL ORDER   No
DESIGN SERVICE   Yes

There are 600 varieties of fuchsias, besides hanging baskets and bedding plants. They also supply and install automatic watering systems.

The Van Hage Garden Company
Great Amwell, Ware SG12 9RP
☎ 01920 870811   [FAX] 01920 871861

CONTACT   Sandra Cronin
LOCATION   Off A10
OPEN   9.30 am – 6 pm, Mondays; 9 am – 6 pm, Tuesdays, Wednesdays, Fridays, Saturdays; 9 am – 7.30 pm, Thursdays; 10.30 am – 4.30 pm, Sundays
SPECIALITIES   House plants; seeds
CATALOGUE   Seeds only
MAIL ORDER   Yes
SHOP   Houseplants, furniture, machinery, wholefoods
REFRESHMENTS   Coffee house
GARDEN   Display gardens

Long-established and award-winning garden centre and seed merchants. The garden centre is strong on houseplants, and has a large choice of plants and related products. The seed catalogue covers flowers and vegetables, and includes the record-breaking Carrot 'Flak' as well as some untreated seed which is suitable for organic gardeners. There have a programme of lectures and demonstrations throughout the year.

Wards Nurseries (Sarratt) Ltd
Dawes Lane, Sarratt, Rickmansworth WD3 6BQ
☎ 01923 263237   [FAX] 01923 270930

CONTACT   M. Rawlins
LOCATION   Turn opposite The Boot, in Sarratt
OPEN   8 am – 5 pm, Monday – Saturday; 10 am – 4 pm, Sundays
SPECIALITIES   Shrubs; trees
MAIL ORDER   No

A mixed range which covers shrubs, conifers and herbaceous stock, with the emphasis on scented plants.

Wyevale Garden Centre
Broadwater Garden Centre, Great Gaddesden, Hemel Hempstead HP2 3BW
☎ 01422 231284   [FAX] 01422 68987

Wyevale Garden Centre
North Orbital Road, St Albans AL2 1DL
☎ 01727 825815   [FAX] 01727 825850
REFRESHMENTS   Restaurant

ISLE OF WIGHT

A La Carte Daylilies
Little Hermitage, St Catherine's Down, Ventnor PO38 2PD
☎ 01938 730512

CONTACT   Jan & Andy Wyers
OPEN   By appointment
SPECIALITIES   *Hemerocallis*
CATALOGUE   3 first-class stamps
MAIL ORDER   Yes
GARDEN   NCCPG collection may be viewed by appointment

These daylily specialists now offer over 150 cultivars and are one of the major importers of new hybrids from USA.

Deacon's Nursery
Moor View, Godshill PO38 3HW
☎ 01983 840750/522243 [FAX] 01983 523575

CONTACT   G. D. Deacon or B. H. W. Deacon
LOCATION   Moor View is next to school, off School Crescent
OPEN   8 am – 4 pm, Monday – Friday, 8 am – 2 pm, Saturdays, October to April; 8 am – 6 pm, Monday – Friday, 8 am – 4 pm, Saturdays, April to October
SPECIALITIES   Fruit
CATALOGUE   SAE plus 31p stamp appreciated
MAIL ORDER   Yes, no minimum order
REFRESHMENTS   In village
GARDEN   Public welcome at nursery

Fruit specialist, with tree and soft fruit of every size and variety. The very comprehensive list includes over 250 apple cultivars. All rootstocks are of virus-free origin.

KENT

Alan C Smith
127 Leaves Green Road, Keston BR2 6DG
☎ 01959 572531

CONTACT   Alan C. Smith
OPEN   By appointment only
SPECIALITIES   Alpines; sempervivums
CATALOGUE   50p
MAIL ORDER   Yes
SHOWS   RHS Westminster

An amazing range of sempervivums and jovibarbas, including species, hybrids and cultivars: there are about one thousand on offer, besides a more general selection of rock garden plants. A small selection is also available at Westerham Heights Garden Centre, Hawley Corner, Westerham Hill, Westerham TN16 2AW.

Ashenden Nursery
Cranbrook Road, Benenden, Cranbrook TN17 4ET
☎ 01580 241792

CONTACT   Kevin McGarry
LOCATION   On B2086 between Cranbrook and Benenden
OPEN   By appointment only
SPECIALITIES   Alpines; grasses; herbaceous perennials
NEW FOR 1997   *Thalictrum filamentosum*
CATALOGUE   SAE
MAIL ORDER   Yes

Stocks a range of plants for rock gardens. They exhibit at specialist and local shows, including the Savill Garden Plant Fairs, Hatfield's Festival of Gardening, West Dean and Parham House Garden Weekends.

Bamboo Nursery Ltd
Kingsgate Cottage, Wittersham TN30 7NS
☎ 01797 270607   ☒ 01797 270825

CONTACT   Andy or Fran Sutcliffe
OPEN   By appointment
SPECIALITIES   Bamboos
CATALOGUE   SAE
MAIL ORDER   Yes

Mainly wholesale bamboo specialist with a selection of *Arundinaria*, *Sasa* and *Phyllostachys*. Some are available in large sizes.

Brenda Hyatt
1 Toddington Crescent, Bluebell Hill, Chatham ME5 9QT
☎ 01634 863251

CONTACT   Brenda Hyatt
LOCATION   Phone for directions
OPEN   By appointment
SPECIALITIES   Auriculas
CATALOGUE   SAE plus £1
MAIL ORDER   Yes
SHOWS   Chelsea
NCCPG NATIONAL COLLECTIONS   *Primula auricula* (show)

Auricula specialist and National Collection holder. The superb range includes stripes, doubles, selfs and alpine specimens. Among the show types available are white-edged, green- and grey-flowered plants. Orders are dealt with in rotation, subject to availability. Informative catalogue.

Bybrook Barn Garden Centre
Canterbury Road, Kennington, Ashford TN24 9JZ
☎ 01233 631959   ☒ 01233 662163
LOCATION   M20, Jct 9, first left at roundabout, left at T-junction, then first left again
OPEN   9 am – 5.30 pm, Monday – Saturday; 10.30 am – 4.30 pm, Sundays
SHOP   Garden sundries, gifts, furniture
REFRESHMENTS   Yes

Garden centre stocking garden requirements and indoor plants. A gardening club is run from the premises in spring and summer.

Church Hill Cottage Gardens
Charing Heath, Ashford TN27 0BU
☎ 01233 712522

CONTACT   Mr or Mrs Metianu, Jeremy Metianu
LOCATION   Take Charing Heath road from A20 (Maidstone side of Charing). Turn right at Red Lion, right again after 100 yards, towards church. Garden is 300 yards on right
OPEN   10 am – 5 pm, Tuesday – Sunday, and Bank Holidays. Closed Mondays, and 1 November – 31 January
SPECIALITIES   *Dianthus*; herbaceous perennials; violas
CATALOGUE   3 first-class stamps
MAIL ORDER   Some
REFRESHMENTS   Red Lion nearby
GARDEN   1½-acre garden, admission £1.50 (times as above)

The nursery specialises in hardy herbaceous perennials, but there are many dianthus, alpines, hostas, violas, ferns and shrubs to choose from too. The garden opens as well: park in the nearby pub.

Coblands Garden Centre
Eridge Road, Tunbridge Wells TN4 8HP
☎ 01892 515234   ☒ 01892 528594

CONTACT   Richard McKenna
LOCATION   A26, Tunbridge Wells
OPEN   Daily

Coblands Nursery
Trench Road, Tonbridge TN10 3HQ
☎ 01732 770999   ☒ 01732 770271
LOCATION   Tonbridge
SPECIALITIES   Bamboos; climbers; conifers; ferns; grasses; herbaceous perennials; shrubs; trees
CATALOGUE   Wholesale catalogue only
MAIL ORDER   No

A large wholesale nursery which carries a comprehensive range of all types of plants for landscapers and garden centres. They also supply their own garden centre at Tunbridge Wells and a plant centre at Ightham.

Coblands Plant Centre

Hazeldene Nursery, Sevenoaks Road, Ightham, Sevenoaks

☎ 01732 780816

LOCATION A25

OPEN 8.30 am – 5.30 pm (10 am – 4 pm on Sundays); daily; all year

This plant-oriented garden centre calls itself 'The Gardener's Garden Centre' and offers one of the largest general ranges of plants in the area.

Connoisseurs' Cacti

51 Chelsfield Lane, Orpington BR5 4HG

☎ 01689 837781

CONTACT John Pilbeam

LOCATION Woodlands Farm, Shire Lane, Farnborough, Kent

OPEN 10.30 am – 2 pm, including weekends

SPECIALITIES Cacti and succulents

CATALOGUE SAE

MAIL ORDER Yes, UK and EC only

SHOP Books on cacti

REFRESHMENTS Tea & coffee

SHOWS RHS Westminster; Malvern (Spring); Chelsea; Hampton Court

An extensive range of cacti and succulents (over 20,000 specimens in stock), as well as books on cacti. Particularly strong on *Gymnocalycium*, *Mammillaria*, *Rebutia* and *Sulcorebutia*. The main address is for postal enquiries only.

Country Gardens

Norton Crossroads, Norton, Faversham ME9 9JY

☎ 01795 521549   🖷 01795 522800

CONTACT Stan Knight (Manager)

OPEN 9 am – 6 pm, Monday – Saturday; 10.30 am – 4.30 pm, Sundays

SHOP Bonsai, conservatories, mowers, tools

REFRESHMENTS Coffee shop

Country Gardens

Main Road, Knockholt, Sevenoaks TN14 7LJ

☎ 01959 532187   🖷 01959 532444

CONTACT Charles Smailes (Manager)

OPEN 9 am – 6 pm, Monday – Saturday; 10.30 am – 4.30 pm, Sundays

Country Gardens

Hereson Road, Ramsgate CT11 7ET

☎ 01843 592393   🖷 01843 852535

CONTACT Ross Naulls (Manager)

OPEN 9 am – 6 pm, Monday – Saturday; 10.30 am – 4.30 pm, Sundays

SHOP Aquatics

REFRESHMENTS Coffee shop

Downderry Nursery

649 London Road, Ditton, Aylesford ME20 6DJ

☎ & 🖷 01732 840710

CONTACT Dr Simon J. Charlesworth

LOCATION Telephone for directions

OPEN By appointment only

SPECIALITIES Sweet peas; lavender

CATALOGUE 2 first-class stamps

MAIL ORDER Yes

SHOWS RHS Westminster

Lavender specialist with a fascinating list of species and cultivars, old and new. Many are available as rooted cuttings and liners by post, wholesale and retail. Shows attended include Kent County, South of England and South East Garden Festival.

Forward Nurseries

Borough Green Road, Ightham TN15 9JA

☎ 01732 884726   🖷 01732 886626

CONTACT Paul van Leeuwen

LOCATION A25 and A227 roundabout at Borough Green

OPEN 8 am – 5 pm, daily

SPECIALITIES Hedging; ivies

CATALOGUE Trade catalogue; retail mail order list

MAIL ORDER Yes

This mainly wholesale nursery carries a general range. Their retail section specialises in hedging plants (which are available mail order) and containerised ivy plants.

High Banks Nurseries

Slip Mill Road, Hawkhurst TN18 5AD

☎ & 🖷 01580 753031

CONTACT Jeremy Homewood

LOCATION On A229 north of Hawkhurst

OPEN 8 am – 4.30 pm, winter; 8.30 am – 5 pm, spring and summer

CATALOGUE £1 plus large SAE

MAIL ORDER No

The nursery carries a full, general range of plants and attends local shows. More perennials, including *Knipfhofia*, *Verbascum* and *Viola* will be available this year.

Iden Croft Herbs

Frittenden Road, Staplehurst TN12 0DH

☎ 01580 891432   🖷 01580 892416

CONTACT Rosemary Titterington or Marion Browne

LOCATION Signed from A229, south of Staplehurst

OPEN 9 am – 5 pm, Monday – Saturday, all year; 11 am – 5 pm, Sundays and Bank Holidays, March to September only

SPECIALITIES Herbaceous perennials; herbs; wild flowers

CATALOGUE 6 first-class stamps

MAIL ORDER Yes

SHOP Herb products, seeds, books

REFRESHMENTS Tea room

GARDEN Herb gardens with access for the disabled

DESIGN SERVICE Iden Croft Herbs

NCCPG NATIONAL COLLECTIONS *Origanum; Mentha*

Calls itself a 'total herb centre' with some justification. The range of herbs and aromatic plants is both impressive and extensive. Other herb products are on sale too. The catalogue lists plants by the best-known names. The gardens are designed for disabled access. There are events, workshops and courses throughout the year.

J Bradshaw & Son

Busheyfields Nursery, Herne, Herne Bay CT6 7LJ

☎ & FAX 01227 375415

CONTACT Denis or Martin Bradshaw

LOCATION On A291, 2 miles south of A299 junction

OPEN 10 am – 5 pm, Tuesday – Saturday and Bank Holidays; March to October

SPECIALITIES Clematis; climbers; *Lonicera*, climbing

CATALOGUE A5 SAE plus 2 first-class stamps

MAIL ORDER No

REFRESHMENTS For groups

GARDEN Stock fields of *Clematis* and *Lonicera* open during nursery hours

NCCPG NATIONAL COLLECTIONS *Lonicera* (climbing); *Clematis montana*; *Chrysocoma*

Family nursery. The business was mainly wholesale but they now have a retail climbing and wall plant centre. They specialise in clematis, *Lonicera* and other climbers. The stock fields, with over 100 *Lonicera* species and over 250 *Clematis* are open during nursery hours. They attend local NCCPG plant sales. The annual open day will be 28 June, from 10 am – 5 pm.

Keepers Nursery

Gallants Court, East Farleigh, Maidstone ME15 0LE

☎ & FAX 01622 726465

CONTACT Sima or Hamid Habibi

LOCATION At East Farleigh, 4 miles west of Maidstone, on B2010

OPEN By appointment at all reasonable times

SPECIALITIES Fruit

CATALOGUE 2 first-class stamps

MAIL ORDER Yes

GARDEN Open by arrangement

DESIGN SERVICE Keepers Nursery

A very lengthy list of fruit trees, over 600 varieties. There are apples, pears, plums of all kinds, quinces, medlars, cherries and nuts, including some charmingly named old varieties. They will give advice and offer a grafting service to propagate known and unknown varieties for customers.

Kennedys Garden Centre

Ingles Meadow, Jointon Road, Folkestone CT20 3RS

☎ 01303 258100   FAX 01303 240214

CONTACT Tom Martell (Manager)

OPEN 9 am – 6 pm, Monday – Saturday, April to September, close 5.30 pm, October to March; 10.30 am – 4.30 pm, Sundays

REFRESHMENTS Café

Landscape Plants

Cattamount, Grafty Green, Maidstone ME17 2AP

☎ 01622 850245

CONTACT Tom La Dell

OPEN By appointment

SPECIALITIES Low maintenance shrubs

CATALOGUE 2 first-class stamps

MAIL ORDER Yes

GARDEN Demonstration garden

DESIGN SERVICE Tom La Dell

NCCPG NATIONAL COLLECTIONS *Arbutus unedo*, cultivars

Mainly wholesale shrub nursery. Plants have been selected for interesting mass planting and low maintenance by a knowledgeable plantsman who is also a landscape architect. Helpful catalogue.

Layham Garden Centre

Lower Road, Staple, Canterbury CT3 1LH

☎ 01304 813267   FAX 01304 615349

CONTACT Andrew Marshall (manager)

LOCATION 8 miles south of Canterbury, between Wingham and Ash

OPEN 9 am – 5 pm, Monday – Saturday; 10 am – 5 pm, Sundays

SPECIALITIES Conifers; herbaceous perennials; roses; shrubs; trees

CATALOGUE Rose list on request

MAIL ORDER Yes

REFRESHMENTS Yes

GARDEN Display gardens, open as garden centre

The garden centre carries a general range of plants with a particular accent on roses: the business is backed by its own wholesale nursery, Layham Nurseries (01304 611380). They have a club, which runs workshops on topics including planting and pruning.

Longacre Nursery

Longacre, Perry Wood, Selling, Faversham ME13 9SE

☎ 01227 752254

CONTACT Dr G. Thomas

LOCATION East of Selling village

OPEN 2 pm – 5 pm, April to October

SPECIALITIES Herbaceous perennials

CATALOGUE SAE

MAIL ORDER No

REFRESHMENTS Teas on open days

GARDEN Garden opens under NGS and by appointment

DESIGN SERVICE Longacre Nursery

The nursery sells a wide variety of hardy perennials. The garden can be visited, and the Thomases offer garden design (especially for borders) and lectures. Groups welcome by appointment.

Madrona Nursery

Pluckley Road, Betherden TN26 3DD

☎ 01233 820100

CONTACT Liam MacKenzie

LOCATION Map in catalogue

OPEN 10 am – 5 pm, Saturday – Tuesday, mid-March to end October

SPECIALITIES Ferns; grasses; shrubs; trees

CATALOGUE £1

MAIL ORDER Yes, minimum carriage charge £12

GARDEN Yes

SHOWS RHS Westminster; Hampton Court

The nursery moved to a new site last year. The emphasis is on interesting and attractive trees and shrubs, including new introductions, but there are also perennials, ferns, grasses and bamboos.

Magnolia Gardens
Stodmarsh Road, Canterbury CT3 4AG
☎ 01227 463951

CONTACT Lieselotte Pickard
LOCATION Off A257 just after Golf Club
OPEN 10 am – 5 pm, Tuesdays, Thursdays, Saturdays, Sundays; 1.30 pm – 5 pm, Wednesdays and Fridays. Closed Mondays, except Bank Holidays, Wednesday and Friday am
SPECIALITIES Camellias; rhododendrons; magnolias
MAIL ORDER No

Magnolias, of course, and a selection of other acid-soil loving shrubs: azaleas and rhododendrons, camellias and Pieris.

Notcutts Garden Centre
Newnham Court, Bearsted Road, Maidstone ME14 5LH
☎ 01622 739944   FAX 01622 735887

CONTACT Nigel Coombs (Manager)
LOCATION Near M20, Jct 7
OPEN 9 am – 5.45 pm, Monday – Saturday; 10 am – 5 pm, Sundays
SHOP Garden sundries, furniture, buildings, pets
DESIGN SERVICE Notcutts Landscapes

Notcutts Garden Centre
Tonbridge Road, Pembury, Tunbridge Wells TN2 4QN
☎ 01892 822636   FAX 01892 825251

CONTACT Jean Smith (Manager)
LOCATION From A21, take Pembury Hospital turning
OPEN 8.30 am – 5.30 pm, Monday – Saturday; 11 am – 5 pm, Sundays. Closes at 5 pm in winter
SHOP Garden sundries, furniture, buildings, landscape materials
DESIGN SERVICE Notcutts Landscapes

The Nursery Near Sissinghurst
Biddenden Nurseries, Sissinghurst Road, Biddenden, Ashford TN27 8EJ
☎ 01580 292100   FAX 01580 292097

CONTACT Gerald Bedrich
LOCATION 2 miles from Sissinghurst on A262 to Biddenden
OPEN 9 am (10 am on Saturdays & Sundays) – 5 pm; daily
SPECIALITIES Climbers; shrubs
CATALOGUE 3 first-class stamps
MAIL ORDER Yes

Biddenden Nurseries are long-established wholesalers of bare-root trees and shrubs: they are useful for hedging and landscaping. But their pot-grown retail nursery has a really most interesting list of trees and shrubs: Loropetalum chinense and Philadelphus 'Burkwoodii' are just two of the rarer items.

Oldbury Nurseries
Brissenden Green, Bethersden, Ashford TN26 3BJ
☎ 01233 820416

CONTACT Wendy or Peter Dresman

LOCATION 7 miles south-west of Ashford, off A28
OPEN 9.30 am – 5 pm, daily, February to June
SPECIALITIES Fuchsias; pelargoniums
CATALOGUE 2 first-class stamps
MAIL ORDER Yes
SHOWS Malvern (Spring); Chelsea; BBC GW Live; Hampton Court

Oldbury Nurseries are specialist fuchsia growers with an extensive range. Some pelargoniums too. Groups are catered for by appointment, February to May.

P de Jager & Sons Ltd
Staplehurst Road, Marden TN12 9BP
☎ 01622 831235   FAX 01622 832416
LOCATION Between Maidstone and Staplehurst on A229
OPEN 9 am – 5 pm, Monday – Friday; 9 am – 12 noon, Saturdays
SPECIALITIES Bulbs; daffodils; lilies
CATALOGUE On request; December, May
MAIL ORDER Yes

Bulbs of all kinds, ranging from well known Narcissus and Tulipa varieties to some rare specimen bulbs. All bulbs come from cultivated stocks.

P H Kellett
Laurels Nursery, Benenden, Cranbrook TN17 4JU
☎ 01580 240463

CONTACT P. H. Kellett
LOCATION ¾ mile off Benenden to Rolvenden road, towards Dingleden
OPEN 8 am – 5 pm, Monday – Thursday; 8 am – 4 pm, Fridays; 8.30 am – 12 noon, Saturdays. Other times by appointment
SPECIALITIES Shrubs; trees
CATALOGUE On request
MAIL ORDER No
GARDEN Yes
DESIGN SERVICE P H Kellett

A traditional nursery growing a varied range of trees and shrubs, including roses, conifers, fruit trees and climbers. Plants are both open ground and container-grown: browsers can inspect stock for autumn lifting. Border planning and advice available also. The nursery will be at the Hever Castle Gardeners' Weekend.

Pete & Ken Cactus Nursery
Saunders Lane, Ash, Canterbury CT3 2BX
☎ 01304 812170

CONTACT Ken Burke
LOCATION 10 miles east of Canterbury, off A257
OPEN 9 am – 6 pm, daily
SPECIALITIES Cacti and succulents
CATALOGUE Large SAE
MAIL ORDER Yes

Cacti and succulents specialists, with a particularly good choice of Lithops. Not all the varieties appear in the catalogue. Larger cacti, carnivorous plants, alpines, fuchsias and shrubs are available at the nursery.

Plaxtol Nurseries

The Spoute, Plaxtol, Sevenoaks TN15 0QR

☎ & 📠 01732 810550

CONTACT Donald, Tessa or Jenny Forbes
LOCATION On the east side of Plaxtol, off A227
OPEN 10 am – 5 pm, daily. Closed for a fortnight after Christmas
SPECIALITIES Foliage plants
CATALOGUE 2 first-class stamps
MAIL ORDER Yes, November to March
REFRESHMENTS Available in village
GARDEN Garden open for customers
DESIGN SERVICE Plaxtol Nurseries

Trees, roses, shrubs, heathers, conifers and herbaceous plants: all chosen with the flower arranger in mind. A wide range of talks and courses are available at the nursery. They design and construct Japanese gardens, and their own garden is open to customers.

Rosewood Daylilies

70 Deansway Avenue, Sturry, Canterbury CT2 0NN

☎ 01227 711071

CONTACT Chris Searle
OPEN By appointment
SPECIALITIES *Hemerocallis*
CATALOGUE 2 first-class stamps
MAIL ORDER Yes

There is a good selection of *Hemerocallis*, especially American varieties, with many new introductions this year. Many recent American hybrids are on trial here before being added to the range. Older varieties, especially those with an RHS Award of Garden Merit, are also being added to the list.

Rumwood Nurseries

Langley, Maidstone ME17 3ND

☎ 01622 861477   📠 01622 863123

CONTACT James Fermor
LOCATION On A274 between Maidstone and Headcorn
OPEN 9 am – 5 pm, Monday – Saturday; 10 am – 4 pm, Sundays
SPECIALITIES Roses
CATALOGUE SAE
MAIL ORDER Yes
REFRESHMENTS Hot and cold drinks
GARDEN Rose fields June to October

A family-run retail and wholesale nursery and garden centre. They specialise in roses, of which they grow an all-round range, and other hardy nursery stock. They will be at the Kent County Show. Tours of the rose fields can be arranged from late June to September for groups of 20 or more.

Ruxley Manor Garden Centre Ltd

Maidstone Road, Sidcup DA14 5BQ

☎ 0181 300 0084   📠 0181 302 3879

CONTACT Richard Evans
LOCATION On B2173
OPEN 9 am – 5.30 pm, Monday – Saturday, 10 am – 4 pm, Sundays

SHOP Garden sundries, furniture, conservatories, pools
SHOWS Chelsea

Scalers Hill Nursery

Scalers Hill, Cobham, Gravesend DA12 3BH

☎ 01474 822856

CONTACT Ann Booth
LOCATION South of A2 between Gravesend and Cobham
OPEN 9.30 am – 4.30 pm; Wednesday – Saturday; March to October
SPECIALITIES Alpines; herbaceous perennials
CATALOGUE 2 first-class stamps
MAIL ORDER Yes

This excellent small nursery has a particularly useful selection of perennials and alpines. Good on *Aquilegia*.

Starborough Nursery

Starborough Road, Marsh Green, Edenbridge TN8 5RB

☎ 01732 865614   📠 01732 862166

CONTACT P. Kindley or Colin Tomlin
LOCATION Between Edenbridge and Lingfield on B2028
OPEN 10 am – 4.30 pm, Monday – Saturday. Closed Sundays, and in January and July
SPECIALITIES Rhododendrons; shrubs; trees
CATALOGUE £1.50
MAIL ORDER Yes
SHOWS RHS Westminster

Recently joined forces with G. Reuthe Ltd. They now issue a single catalogue, combining Starborough's trees and shrubs with Reuthe's rhododendrons and azaleas.

Stone Green Nurseries

Pluckley Road, Bethersden, Ashford TN26 3DD

☎ 01233 820998   📠 01233 720147

CONTACT Emma Knox
LOCATION 7 miles from Ashford,
OPEN 4 open weekends per year, phone for details
SPECIALITIES Clematis
NEW FOR 1997 *Lonicera* 'Stone Green', *Clematis* 'Blue Moon' and *C.* 'Blue Ruffles'
CATALOGUE On request
GARDEN Being planted
SHOWS Malvern (Spring); Malvern (Autumn); Southport; Ayr

Nursery with a expanding list of clematis (150 so far) as well as other climbers and shrubs.

Tile Barn Nursery

Standen Street, Iden Green, Benenden TN17 4LB

☎ 01580 240221

CONTACT Peter Moore
LOCATION 2 miles south of Benenden; turn left at crossroads in Iden Green
OPEN 9 am – 5 pm, Wednesday – Saturday
SPECIALITIES Cyclamen
NEW FOR 1997 *Cyclamen mirabile* 'Tilebarn Jan', *Cyclamen coum* 'BSBE'
CATALOGUE SAE
MAIL ORDER Yes

GARDEN   Display garden
NCCPG NATIONAL COLLECTIONS *Cyclamen* on behalf of
the Cyclamen Society

Mail order is restricted to their speciality: *Cyclamen* species.
Plants for sale are raised from seed from stock plants. Nursery
visitors will also find some species *Colchicum, Crocus,
Fritillaria, Leucojum* and *Narcissus*.

Tim Ingram

Copton Ash Gardens, 105 Ashford Road, Faversham
ME13 8XW
☎ 01795 535919

CONTACT   Tim Ingram
LOCATION   On A251, opposite M2 eastbound exit
OPEN   2 pm – 6 pm, Tuesday – Thursday, Saturday – Sunday,
March to October. Other times by appointment
SPECIALITIES   Alpines; fruit; herbaceous perennials; shrubs
CATALOGUE   4 first-class stamps
MAIL ORDER   Yes, fruit trees only
REFRESHMENTS   On NGS days
GARDEN   1½ acre garden

An excellent general list with a preponderance of herbaceous
plants and helpful descriptions based on the owners' experience of growing the plants, not on the usual textbooks. The
1½ acre garden is worth a visit in its own right and is open at
the same times as the nursery.

Westwood Nursery

65 Yorkland Avenue, Welling DA16 2LE
☎ 0181 301 0886

CONTACT   S. Edwards
OPEN   Mail order only
SPECIALITIES   *Pleione;* hardy orchids
CATALOGUE   SAE; summer, winter
MAIL ORDER   Yes

Hardy orchids, including Australian deciduous terrestrial orchids and pleiones: suitable for the garden and frost-free
greenhouse. Some orchid books too.

Wyevale Garden Centre

Romney Marsh Garden Centre, Hamstreet, Ashford TN26
2QF
☎ 01233 732988   FAX 01233 733703

Wyevale Garden Centre

Upper Harbledown, Canterbury CT2 9BE
☎ 01227 454264   FAX 01227 785000
REFRESHMENTS   Restaurant

Wyevale Garden Centre

Elm Court, Capstone Road, Gillingham ME7 3JQ
☎ 01634 813778   FAX 01634 840614
REFRESHMENTS   Restaurant

Wyevale Garden Centre

Oakley Road, Keston Mark, Bromley BR2 6BY
☎ 01689 859419   FAX 01689 862359

Wyevale Garden Centre

Maidstone Road, Paddock Wood, Tonbridge TH12 6QJ
☎ 01892 835777   FAX 01892 834122
REFRESHMENTS   Restaurant

LANCASHIRE

Auldene Nurseries Ltd

338 Southport Road, Ulnes Walton, Leyland PR5 3LQ
☎ 01772 600271   FAX 01772 601483

CONTACT   Richard Iddon
LOCATION   3 miles south of Leyland, on A581
OPEN   9 am – 8 pm (or dusk if earlier), Monday – Friday;
9 am – 5.30 pm, Saturdays; 11 am – 5 pm, Sundays
SHOP   Books, gifts and sundries
REFRESHMENTS   Coffee shop

Family-run garden centre which stocks plants and shrubs,
aquatics, seeds, sundries and conservatories. They deliver free
locally. Monthly gardening seminars are held, and they run
their own gardening club.

Barkers Primrose Nurseries

Whalley Road, Clitheroe BB7 1HT
☎ 01200 423521   FAX 01200 428160

CONTACT   Philip Bradley
LOCATION   Ribble Valley: from M6 Jct 31 follow A59 to
Clitheroe
OPEN   9 am – 5.30 pm, Monday – Saturday; 10 am – 5 pm,
Sundays and Bank Holidays
SPECIALITIES   Acers; herbaceous perennials
CATALOGUE   SAE; ornamental trees, roses, fruit trees and
bushes, herbaceous plants
MAIL ORDER   No
REFRESHMENTS   Ice-cream & soft drinks

Nursery and garden centre with a large and varied range of
plants, including Japanese acers, trees, shrubs and perennials.
Named after the area: they are not *Primula* specialists.

Barton Grange Garden Centre (Bolton)

Wigan Road, Bolton BL3 4RD
☎ 01204 660660   FAX 01204 62525

CONTACT   Jane Stead
LOCATION   ½ mile from M61, Jct 5 on A58 to Bolton
OPEN   9 am – 5.30 pm, Monday – Saturday; 10.30 am – 4.30 pm,
Sundays
SHOP   Garden sundries, gifts
REFRESHMENTS   Café
GARDEN   Display beds and water feature
DESIGN SERVICE   Barton Grange Garden Centre (Bolton)
SHOWS   Southport; Chelsea; BBC GW Live

Large garden centre with a full range of plants and associated garden products. They are stockists for the Hilliers
Premier Plant Collection. Landscaping and garden maintenance service.

Barton Grange Garden Centre (Preston)

Garstang Road, Barton, Preston PR3 5AA

☎ 01772 864242   FAX 01772 863480

CONTACT   N. Gascoyne
LOCATION   Off A6 Garstang road
OPEN   9 am – 5.30 pm, Monday – Saturday; 11 am – 5 pm, Sundays
SHOP   Garden sundries, gifts, furniture, conservatories
REFRESHMENTS   Café
GARDEN   Planned for this year
DESIGN SERVICE   Barton Grange Landscapes
SHOWS   Southport; BBC GW Live

Large garden centre with a full range of plants and products. They have a Halls Conservatory Showcase (01772 865861), and a landscaping and maintenance arm, Barton Grange Landscapes (01772 864242). Weekly talks and demonstrations. They also have a wholesale nursery.

Catforth Gardens

Roots Lane, Catforth, Preston PR4 0JB
☎ 01772 690561/690269

CONTACT   Judith Bradshaw or Chris Moore
LOCATION   From M6, Jct 32 towards Garstang; left at first lights. After 2 miles right at T-junction. Then left into School Lane by Catforth sign. Left again at the end of the road, then first right
OPEN   10.30 am – 5 pm, 15 March – 14 September
SPECIALITIES   Herbaceous perennials
CATALOGUE   5 first-class stamps
MAIL ORDER   No
GARDEN   Three gardens: admission £2, children 50p
NCCPG NATIONAL COLLECTIONS   Geranium

The nursery is sandwiched between three gardens which open at the same times. The list is strongest on hardy geraniums (both species and cultivars): they hold a National Collection. Many other herbaceous perennials are also on offer.

Craig House Cacti

42 Brentwood Court, Southport PR9 9JW
☎ & FAX 01704 545077

CONTACT   George A. McCleod
OPEN   Mail order only
SPECIALITIES   Cacti and succulents
CATALOGUE   Yes
MAIL ORDER   Yes
SHOWS   RHS Westminster; Malvern (Spring); Malvern (Autumn); Harrogate (Spring); Harrogate (Autumn); Southport; Chelsea; BBC GW Live; Hampton Court; Ayr

Mail-order specialists selling cacti, succulents and cycads including Madagascan caudiciform succulents (swollen stemmed). They also exhibit widely, so look out for them at shows, including New Forest, Bath Spring, Holker, Royal Highland and Shrewsbury.

Croston Cactus

43 Southport Road, Eccleston, Chorley PR7 6ET
☎ 01257 452555

CONTACT   John L. Henshaw
LOCATION   On A581, just east of B5253 junction
OPEN   9 am – 5 pm, Wednesday – Sunday; Bank Holidays
SPECIALITIES   Cacti and succulents
CATALOGUE   2 first-class stamps; spring, summer supplement
MAIL ORDER   Yes, no minimum order
GARDEN   Display greenhouse
SHOWS   Southport

Cacti and succulents aimed chiefly at the enthusiast: many mammillarias and some interesting haworthias. Bromeliads and tillandsias are available at the nursery. Society and Plant Group visits are welcomed. They will be at the Royal Lancashire Show.

Eversley Nurseries

10 Granville Avenue, Hesketh Bank, Preston PR4 6AH
☎ 01772 812538

CONTACT   Stan Crabtree
LOCATION   Turn off A59 at Tarleton
OPEN   By appointment, at any time
SPECIALITIES   Heathers
NEW FOR 1997   Calluna 'Rachel Patricia'
CATALOGUE   SAE
MAIL ORDER   Yes
SHOWS   Harrogate (Spring); Southport; BBC GW Live

Specialist growers and exhibitors of heathers (and other ericaceous plants). The large range (over 250 heather varieties) is matched by scale (¼ million heathers grown).

Greenacre Nursery

81 Gorsey Lane, Banks, Southport PR9 8ED
☎ & FAX 01704 26791

CONTACT   H. Armitage
LOCATION   Off A59 near Banks
OPEN   9 am – 5 pm, Monday – Saturday
SPECIALITIES   Dianthus
CATALOGUE   2 first-class stamps
MAIL ORDER   Yes
SHOWS   Malvern (Spring); Malvern (Autumn); Harrogate (Spring); Harrogate (Autumn); Southport; Chelsea; BBC GW Live; Hampton Court; Strathclyde; Ayr

Garden pinks, perpetual flowering carnations and Schizostylis here. They visit lots of shows, including Holker Hall and the Royal Highland this year: look out for their award-winning displays.

Holden Clough Nursery

Holden, Bolton by Bowland, Clitheroe BB7 4PF
☎ & FAX 01200 447615

CONTACT   P. Foley
LOCATION   8 miles north-east of Clitheroe, off A59
OPEN   1 pm – 5 pm, Monday – Thursday; 9 am – 5 pm, Saturdays, all year; 2 pm – 5 pm, Sundays (April and May only); other times by appointment

SPECIALITIES Alpines; conifers; ferns; grasses; herbaceous perennials; shrubs
NEW FOR 1997 Heathers and *Heuchera* from USA
CATALOGUE £1.40
MAIL ORDER Yes, October to March
REFRESHMENTS Available nearby
GARDEN In nursery
SHOWS RHS Westminster; Malvern (Autumn); Harrogate (Spring); Harrogate (Autumn); Southport; BBC GW Live; Courson

A long-established working nursery, with a large and very hardy range of interesting alpines, perennials, dwarf conifers, shrubs, ferns and grasses. Please note that this Pennine nursery only opens for Sundays in April and May, and that the last admission on all days is at 4.30 pm.

Pinks & Carnations

22 Chetwyn Avenue, Bromley Cross, Bolton BL7 9BN
☎ & [FAX] 01204 306273
CONTACT Ruth or Tom Gillies
OPEN By appointment only
SPECIALITIES *Dianthus*
CATALOGUE 1 first-class stamp
MAIL ORDER Yes

This wholesale and retail nursery supplies alpine and garden pinks, perpetual flowering and some Malmaison carnations. Canes and plant-support systems supplied too.

Plantations Perennials

Cicely's Cottage, 43 Elmers Green, Skelmersdale WN8 6SG
☎ 01695 720790/724448
CONTACT Maureen Duncan or Jennifer Madeley
LOCATION M6, Jct 26, M58, Jct 4, further directions given when making appointment
OPEN By appointment
SPECIALITIES Herbaceous perennials; half-hardy perennials
NEW FOR 1997 *Pachyphragma macrophyllum*
CATALOGUE 4 first-class stamps
MAIL ORDER No
REFRESHMENTS Refreshments
SHOWS Harrogate (Spring); Harrogate (Autumn); Southport

Newish nursery with a pleasing mix of perennials, hardy, half-hardy and tender. Lots of penstemons.

Reginald Kaye Ltd

Waithman Nurseries, Silverdale, Carnforth LA5 0TY
☎ 01524 701252
CONTACT Mrs Kaye
LOCATION 4 miles north-west of Carnforth
OPEN 10 am – 5 pm, Wednesday – Saturday; 2.30 pm – 5 pm, Sundays
SPECIALITIES Alpines; ferns; herbaceous perennials
CATALOGUE 60p
MAIL ORDER No
SHOWS Malvern (Spring); Harrogate (Spring); Harrogate (Autumn); BBC GW Live; Hampton Court

Alpine and fern specialists: they will be attending several shows this year.

Stydd Nursery

Stonygate Lane, Ribchester, Preston PR3 3YN
☎ 01254 878797 [FAX] 01254 878254
CONTACT Mrs C. Walker
LOCATION ½ mile from centre of Ribchester village
OPEN 1.30 pm – 5 pm, Tuesday – Friday; 9 am – 5 pm, Saturdays; 2 pm – 5 pm, Sundays; closed Mondays and Sundays 23 December to 1 April
SPECIALITIES Conservatory plants; roses, half-hardy perennials
CATALOGUE £1 or 4 first-class stamps
MAIL ORDER Yes, for roses. Delivery for large orders of other plants can be arranged
GARDEN Yes
SHOWS Harrogate (Spring); Southport

Old-fashioned and some modern shrub and species roses, as well as climbers and ramblers are their speciality. There is a second range of half-hardy perennials and conservatory plants.

Wyevale Garden Centre

Preston New Road, Westby, Kirkham PR4 3PE
☎ 01772 684129 [FAX] 01772 671770
REFRESHMENTS Restaurant

LEICESTERSHIRE

A & A Thorp

Bungalow No 5, Main Street, Theddingworth, Lutterworth LE17 6QZ
☎ 01858 880496
CONTACT Anita Thorp
LOCATION Between Market Harborough and Lutterworth, on A427
OPEN 9 am – 6 pm (dusk in winter)
SPECIALITIES Alpines, woodland plants
CATALOGUE SAE plus 50p
MAIL ORDER No

A small nursery which stocks alpine and herbaceous plants in small quantities. The range is large, though. Personal service rather than help yourself. The garden is open when there are special plant sales

Askew Nurseries

South Croxton Road, Queniborough, Leicester LE7 3RX
☎ 01664 840557
CONTACT J. L. Longland
LOCATION Off A607 2 miles east of Queniborough
OPEN 9 am (10 am at weekends) – 6 pm, Wednesday – Monday, February to September
SPECIALITIES Fuchsias
CATALOGUE 3 first-class stamps
MAIL ORDER Yes
GARDEN Display house

Specialist fuchsia nursery with a large range of cultivars; cuttings by post, larger plants from the nursery. Stock plants in flower during July and August. Tours and talks for groups.

Barnsdale Plants and Gardens

The Avenue, Exton, Oakham LE15 8AH

☎ 01572 813200   [FAX] 01572 813615

CONTACT   Nick Hamilton
LOCATION   Off A606 between Oakham and Stamford
OPEN   10 am – 5 pm, daily, 1 March to 31 October; 10 am – 4 pm, daily, 1 November to 28 February. Closed Christmas and New Year
SPECIALITIES   Herbaceous perennials; shrubs
CATALOGUE   5 second-class stamps and A5 envelope
MAIL ORDER   Yes
GARDEN   Display Gardens open and more being planted; admission £1.50. Barnsdale TV garden £4.50
DESIGN SERVICE   Yes
SHOWS   RHS Westminster; BBC GW Live; Hampton Court

A pleasing selection of perennials, shrubs and trees is grown by the nursery. Many were originally propagated from the BBC TV garden. All are grown in peat-free compost. Barnsdale Garden opens this year.

Fosse Alpines

33 Leicester Road, Countesthorpe LE8 5QU

☎ 0116 2778237

CONTACT   T. West
LOCATION   Phone for directions
OPEN   By appointment only
SPECIALITIES   Alpines
CATALOGUE   2 first-class stamps
MAIL ORDER   Yes, minimum order £8
REFRESHMENTS   Tea & coffee
GARDEN   Display garden

This small nursery is recommended for its range of rare and unusual alpines. They will provide directions when you make an appointment.

Gandy's Roses Ltd

North Kilworth, Lutterworth LE17 6HZ

☎ 01858 880398   [FAX] 01858 880433

CONTACT   Douglas Gandy or Rosemary Gandy
OPEN   Office hours: 9 am – 5 pm, Monday – Saturday; 2 pm – 5 pm, Sundays
SPECIALITIES   Roses
CATALOGUE   On request
MAIL ORDER   Yes
GARDEN   Rose fields open, July – September

Rose growers covering the whole spectrum (600 varieties), with a particularly interesting choice of climbers. The nursery also sells shrubs, fruit trees and conifers. Items need to be ordered in advance for winter collection and mail order.

Goscote Nurseries Ltd

Syston Road, Cossington LE7 4UZ

☎ & [FAX] 01509 812121

CONTACT   D. C. or R. C. Cox
LOCATION   5 miles north of Leicester, on B5328
OPEN   8 am – 5 pm (4.30 pm in winter), Monday – Friday; 9 am – 5 pm, Saturdays; 10 am – 5 pm, Sundays

SPECIALITIES   Conifers; heathers; rhododendrons; shrubs; trees
CATALOGUE   5 second-class stamps
MAIL ORDER   Yes, minimum order £10
GARDEN   Display gardens

An extensive collection of trees and shrubs, including acers, azaleas, clematis, conifers and rhododendrons is available here from the open ground. The nursery centre also stocks container plants.

The Herb Nursery

Thistleton, Oakham LE15 7RE

☎ 01572 767658   [FAX] 01572 768021

CONTACT   Peter Bench
LOCATION   Off A1 north-west of Stamford
OPEN   9 am – 6 pm (or dusk), daily
SPECIALITIES   Herbs; wild flowers
CATALOGUE   A5 SAE
MAIL ORDER   No
GARDEN   Yes

Around 400 herbs and allied plants, including wildflowers, scented leaf pelargoniums plus a range of cottage garden plants. Terracotta pots are available ready planted or can be filled for you.

Hill Farm Herbs

Lubenham Hill, Market Harborough

☎ 01858 469009

OPEN   9.30 am – 5.30 pm, Monday – Tuesday, Thursday – Saturday; 10.30 am – 4.30 pm, Sundays. Closed Wednesdays
SPECIALITIES   Herbs

The second branch of Hill Farm Herbs of Brigstock.

Hill Farmhouse Plants

Hill Farmhouse, Cottingham, Market Harborough LE16 8XS

☎ 01536 770994

CONTACT   Richard Cain
LOCATION   Map in catalogue
OPEN   9.30 am – 6 pm, Saturdays only, 1 March to 31 July and 1 – 30 September
SPECIALITIES   Hardy geraniums
CATALOGUE   2 first-class stamps
MAIL ORDER   No
GARDEN   Garden open as nursery

There is a large and increasing number of hardy geranium species, forms and cultivars – over 150 – which can be seen growing in the garden, with a useful selection of cottage garden plants.

John Smith & Son

Hilltop Nurseries, Thornton, Coalville LE67 1AN

☎ & [FAX] 01530 230331

CONTACT   Nita Smith
LOCATION   3 miles from M1, Jct 22
OPEN   8 am – 5.30 pm; closed Sundays, except in April and May
SPECIALITIES   Fuchsias
CATALOGUE   SAE
MAIL ORDER   Yes

In addition to a general range, the nursery specialises in rooted fuchsia cuttings, including American and other named varieties.

Kayes Garden Nursery

1700 Melton Road, Rearsby, Leicester LE7 4YR
☎ 01664 424578

CONTACT Hazel Kaye
LOCATION On A607 north-east of Leicester
OPEN 10 am – 5.30 pm, Wednesday – Saturday, Bank Holiday Mondays; 10 am – 12 noon, Sundays, March to October; 10 am – 4 pm, Fridays and Saturdays, November, December and February. Closed 16 December to 30 January
SPECIALITIES Climbers; herbaceous perennials
CATALOGUE 2 first-class stamps
MAIL ORDER No
GARDEN Garden during nursery hours
SHOWS Harrogate (Autumn); BBC GW Live

Hardy herbaceous plants and climbers. The owners have a plantsman's eye for quality, and the list includes many of the best forms of a wide range of plants. Half-day courses are run: topics this year include Climbing Plants and Wall Shrubs, Border Design, Shady Endeavours and Colour Theory and Use. The garden is open for the NGS on 5 October.

Linda Gascoigne Wild Flowers

17 Imperial Road, Kibworth Beauchamp, Leicester LE8 0HR
☎ 0116 2793959

CONTACT Linda Gascoigne
LOCATION Between Leicester and Market Harborough, off A6
OPEN By appointment
SPECIALITIES Wild flowers
CATALOGUE 3 first-class stamps
MAIL ORDER Yes, minimum order £5
GARDEN Garden open by appointment

A small nursery with a selection of native flowers and plants which attract wildlife. Linda Gascoigne is also a wildlife artist.

Philip Tivey & Son

28 Wanlip Road, Syston LE7 8PA
☎ 0116 269 2968

OPEN 9 am – 5 pm, Monday – Friday; 9 am – 3 pm, Saturdays
SPECIALITIES Chrysanthemums; dahlias
CATALOGUE SAE plus 25p
MAIL ORDER Yes, minimum order £8.50
SHOWS RHS Westminster; Harrogate (Autumn); Southport; Chelsea; BBC GW Live; Hampton Court

Specialist growers of dahlias, with mixed collections of chrysanthemums, including Korean and hardy border types, available too.

S & S Perennials

24 Main Street, Normanton le Heath LE67 2TB
☎ 01530 262250

CONTACT S. Pierce
OPEN Afternoons and weekends
SPECIALITIES Bulbs; irises
CATALOGUE SAE

MAIL ORDER Yes
This small nursery sells Cyclamen, Erythronium and Fritillaria species, plus a number of Iris cultivars.

Ulverscroft Unusual Plants

Ulverscroft Grange Nursery, Priory Lane, Ulverscroft, Markfield, Leicester LE67 9PB
☎ 01530 243635

CONTACT Ted Brown
LOCATION Near M1, Jct 22
OPEN From 10 am – 5.30 pm, Wednesday – Sunday, and Bank Holiday Mondays and Tuesdays; March to November. Other times by appointment
SPECIALITIES Bamboos; herbaceous perennials; shrubs
MAIL ORDER No

Small nursery with a wide choice of perennials, shrubs and bamboos: particular specialities include Bergenia and Pulmonaria.

Wyevale Garden Centre

1665 Melton Road, East Goscote, Leicester LE7 8YQ
☎ 0116 260 5515   [FAX] 0116 269 5122

LINCOLNSHIRE

Asterby Nurseries

Church Lane, Asterby, Louth LN11 9UF
☎ 01507 343549

CONTACT Elizabeth Aldridge
LOCATION Map in catalogue
OPEN Daily, but phone first
SPECIALITIES Herbaceous perennials; shrubs
CATALOGUE 2 first-class stamps
MAIL ORDER No

This young nursery is beginning to make its presence felt on the show circuit. It offers a good general range, reasonably priced.

Baytree Nurseries

High Road, Weston, Spalding PE12 6JU
☎ 01406 370242   [FAX] 01406 371665

CONTACT Cameron Whitworth
LOCATION 1½ miles east of Spalding, on A151
OPEN 9 am – 6 pm, summer; 9 am – 5.30 pm, winter
SPECIALITIES Roses
MAIL ORDER No
SHOP Garden sundries, machinery, crafts
REFRESHMENTS Restaurant
GARDEN Demonstration gardens
SHOWS Chelsea

Large, award-winning garden centre.

C E & D M Nurseries

The Walnuts, 36 Main Street, Baston, Peterborough PE6 9PB
☎ 01778 560483

CONTACT Colin Fletcher
LOCATION South of Bourne, off A15

OPEN 10 am – 5 pm, Friday – Tuesday. Closed Christmas &
Boxing Day
SPECIALITIES Herbaceous perennials
NEW FOR 1997 *Geranium dalmaticum & others*
CATALOGUE 2 first-class stamps
MAIL ORDER Yes, no minimum order
GARDEN Display gardens

This fenland nursery stocks a dependable selection of hardy
herbaceous perennials. A design service is now available.

Clive Simms
Woodhurst, Essendine, Stamford PE9 4LQ
☎ 01780 55615

CONTACT Clive Simms
OPEN Mail order only
SPECIALITIES Fruit
CATALOGUE 2 first-class stamps
MAIL ORDER Yes

Nut trees and uncommon edible fruits. There are all sorts of
wonderful curiosities on offer here: recommended.

Cottage Nurseries
Thorestthorpe, Alford LN13 0HX
☎ 01507 466968

CONTACT W. H. Denbigh
LOCATION 1 mile from Alford on A1104 Mablethorpe road
OPEN 9 am – 5 pm, daily, March – October; 10 am – dusk,
November – February. Closed Wednesdays, Thursdays in
winter
SPECIALITIES Herbaceous perennials
CATALOGUE 3 first-class stamps
MAIL ORDER Alpines and perennials
GARDEN Demonstration gardens
DESIGN SERVICE Cottage Nurseries

A good choice of garden worthy plants for cottage type
gardens. More perennials and alpines this year.

The Fern Nursery
Grimsby Road, Binbrook, Lincoln LN3 6DH
☎ 01472 398092

CONTACT Neil Timm
LOCATION On B1203
OPEN Saturdays and Sundays, April to September or by
appointment
SPECIALITIES Ferns
CATALOGUE 2 first-class stamps
MAIL ORDER Yes
GARDEN Demonstration garden
DESIGN SERVICE Neil Timm

Hardy ferns and a selection of perennials from this specialist
nursery, small sizes by mail order, larger ones at the nursery.

Glenhirst Cactus Nursery
Station Road, Swineshead, Boston PE20 3NX
☎ 01205 820314

CONTACT N. C. or S. A. Bell
LOCATION Just off A17, near Boston
OPEN 10 am – 5 pm, Thursdays, Fridays and Sundays,
1 April to 30 September

SPECIALITIES Cacti and succulents; seeds
CATALOGUE 2 stamps
MAIL ORDER Yes, all year round
SHOP Books, sundries
GARDEN Desert scree gardens

An extensive range of cacti and succulents, including epiphyllums. They also sell books, seeds and sundries, and are happy
to advise on cultivation and display. Collections available for
beginners, bedding out or conservatory display.

Hall Farm Nursery
Hall Farm, Harpswell, Gainsborough DN21 5UU
☎ 01427 668412

CONTACT Pam or Mark Tatam
LOCATION 7 miles east of Gainsborough on A631
OPEN Open daily. Closed weekends, December to February
SPECIALITIES Herbaceous perennials
CATALOGUE Large SAE
MAIL ORDER No
REFRESHMENTS Charity days only
GARDEN Garden open daily

A nursery with an interesting and expanding range of hardy
roses, shrubs and perennials. The *Nepeta* species and cultivars are worth looking out for.

Hippopottering Nursery
Orchard House, Brackenhill Road, East Lound, Haxey,
Doncaster DN9 2LR
☎ & FAX 01427 752185

CONTACT John or Margaret Gibbons
LOCATION Off A161 at Haxey on Owston Ferry road to
East Lound
OPEN By appointment only
SPECIALITIES Acers
CATALOGUE 2 first-class stamps
MAIL ORDER Yes, after leaf fall, November to mid March
SHOWS Malvern (Spring); Malvern (Autumn); Harrogate
(Spring); Harrogate (Autumn); BBC GW Live; Hampton
Court

True specialists in Japanese maples. The list goes from selected
colourful seedlings and bonsai material to mature specimens.
Cultivars are selected from their collection of over 120; they
also sell rootstocks. Please phone between 8.30 am and
6.30 pm only.

Hurdletree Nurseries
Hurdletree Bank, Holbeach Fen PE12 6SS
☎ 01406 540505/0585 889090 FAX 01406 540505

CONTACT Antony or Alison
LOCATION Off B1168 between Holbeach and Holbeach
St John
OPEN Dawn – dusk, daily
SPECIALITIES Bedding plants
NEW FOR 1997 Trailing *Viola* plants from varieties on
trial
CATALOGUE On request
MAIL ORDER Yes
GARDEN Shrub garden

DESIGN SERVICE Hurdletree Nurseries & Landscape Contractors

All year round bedding, wholesale and retail, general plant range too. They do design, landscaping, clearing and maintenance and will also install automatic watering for hanging baskets.

J Walkers Bulbs
Washway House Farm, Holbeach, Spalding PE12 7PP
☎ 01406 426216 [FAX] 01406 425468
CONTACT J. W. Walkers
OPEN Mail order only
SPECIALITIES Bulbs; daffodils; lilies
CATALOGUE 2 first-class stamps
MAIL ORDER Yes
SHOWS Harrogate (Spring); Chelsea

Specialists in daffodil bulbs of all kinds, fritillaries and lilies, with two Royal Warrants to their credit.

Judy's Country Garden
The Villa, Louth Road, South Somercotes, Louth LN11 7BW
☎ 01507 358487
CONTACT Judy Harry
LOCATION 8 miles east of Louth
OPEN 9 am – 6 pm, most days, mid-March to end September. Phone first to check
SPECIALITIES Herbaceous perennials; herbs
CATALOGUE 3 first-class stamps
MAIL ORDER No
REFRESHMENTS Garden Open days only
GARDEN Garden is open for nursery visitors
DESIGN SERVICE Judy's Country Garden

A small, garden nursery with a range of herbs and perennials, especially the older varieties. The garden opens on 22 June for the NGS. Courses, talks and group visits are held.

Kathleen Muncaster Fuchsias
18 Field Lane, Morton, Gainsborough DN21 3BY
☎ 01427 612329
CONTACT Kathleen Muncaster
LOCATION See catalogue for map
OPEN 10 am – dusk, February to mid-July. Phone first at other times
SPECIALITIES Fuchsias
NEW FOR 1997 Four new cultivars: 'Eric's Majestic', 'Margaret Hazelwood', 'Niula' and 'President George Bartlett'
CATALOGUE 2 first-class stamps
MAIL ORDER Limited mail order
REFRESHMENTS Tea & biscuits for coach parties
GARDEN Garden and stock plants on display

Fuchsia specialist with an extensive range of species, hardy fuchsias and other varieties. The hardy fuchsias can be seen in the garden. They also sell other plants for hanging baskets.

Kathy Wright
Frog Hall Cottage, Wildmore Fen, New York LN4 4XH
☎ 01205 280709
CONTACT Kathy Wright

LOCATION On B1192 between New York and Boston
OPEN 12 noon – 5 pm, Tuesdays and Wednesdays, mid-February to October; 10 am – 5 pm Sundays, mid-February to June, 3rd Sunday July – October
SPECIALITIES Climbers; shrubs
CATALOGUE Large SAE
MAIL ORDER No

Pleasing selection of container-grown shrubs and climbers.

Martin Nest Nurseries
Grange Cottage, Hemswell, Gainsborough DN21 5UP
☎ 01427 668369 [FAX] 01427 668080
CONTACT M. A. Robinson
LOCATION 6 miles east of Gainsborough on A631
OPEN 10 am – 4 pm, daily
SPECIALITIES Alpines; primulas
CATALOGUE 3 second-class stamps
MAIL ORDER Yes
GARDEN Demonstration garden

A good businesslike range of tough pot-grown hardy alpine plants (including an impressive number of primulas and auriculas) for garden centres and individuals.

Mendle Nursery
Holme, Scunthorpe DN16 3RF
☎ 01724 850864
CONTACT A. Earnshaw
LOCATION Holme
OPEN 10 am – 5 pm, daily
SPECIALITIES Alpines; primulas; sempervivums
NEW FOR 1997 20-30 new items every year
CATALOGUE 2 first-class stamps
MAIL ORDER Yes, no minimum order

A broad range of alpines, including primulas, Saxifraga and lots of sempervivums.

Orchard Nurseries
Tow Lane, Foston, Grantham NG32 2LE
☎ & [FAX] 01400 281354
CONTACT R. or J. Blenkinship
LOCATION Near A1
OPEN 10 am – 6 pm, daily, 1 February to 1 October
SPECIALITIES Clematis; climbers; herbaceous perennials
NEW FOR 1997 Lavatera 'Lisanne'
CATALOGUE SAE for information sheet
MAIL ORDER No
GARDEN Display areas
DESIGN SERVICE Orchard Nurseries
SHOWS BBC GW Live

The nursery has a good range of the smaller-flowered Clematis hybrids, and other climbers, as well as many herbaceous plants, including hardy geraniums and hellebores. They offer garden design.

Pennell & Sons Ltd
Garden Centre, Humberston Road, Grimsby DN36 4RW
☎ & [FAX] 01472 694272
CONTACT J. R. Cousins
LOCATION Outskirts of Grimsby

OPEN   8.30 am – 5.30 pm, Monday – Saturday; 10.30 am – 4.30 pm, Sundays; 10 am – 5 pm Bank Holidays
SHOP   Garden sundries

Garden centre with a full range. Delivery available.

The Plant Lovers
Candlesby House, Candlesby, Spilsby PE23 5RU
☎ 01754 850256

CONTACT   Tim Wilson
LOCATION   8 miles west of Skegness on A158
OPEN   Daily, when not away, but phone first
SPECIALITIES   Cacti and succulents; sempervivums
MAIL ORDER   Limited
GARDEN   Display house
SHOWS   Malvern (Spring); Harrogate (Autumn); Southport; Chelsea; BBC GW Live; Hampton Court; Strathclyde; Ayr

Wholesale and retail cacti and succulent specialists. They have a wide selection of reliable varieties and species. The nursery is open most days but you are asked to phone first. They attend lots of shows.

Potterton and Martin
The Cottage Nursery, Moortown Road, Nettleton, Caistor LN7 6HX
☎ & FAX 01472 851792

CONTACT   Mr or Mrs Potterton
LOCATION   On B1205: leave A46 at Nettleton
OPEN   9 am – 5 pm, daily
SPECIALITIES   Alpines; bulbs; carnivorous plants; seeds
CATALOGUE   £1 (for annual set)
MAIL ORDER   Yes
GARDEN   Display gardens
SHOWS   RHS Westminster; Harrogate (Spring); BBC GW Live; Hampton Court

Alpine and rock plant specialist with an interesting and extensive range, running from the easy to the unusual. Bulbs and seeds too. The nursery holds six Chelsea gold medals, and has won the RHS Farrer Trophy (best alpine display) on several occasions.

Southfield Nurseries
Bourne Road, Morton, Bourne PE10 0RH
☎ 01778 570168

CONTACT   Mr or Mrs B. Goodey
LOCATION   On A15, 1 mile north of traffic lights in Bourne
OPEN   10 am – 4 pm, daily
SPECIALITIES   Cacti and succulents
CATALOGUE   1 first-class stamp
MAIL ORDER   Yes
SHOWS   RHS Westminster; Malvern (Spring); Malvern (Autumn); Harrogate (Spring); Harrogate (Autumn); Southport; Chelsea; BBC GW Live; Hampton Court; Strathclyde; Ayr

Cacti and succulent specialist with an extensive choice of plants, all raised from seed at the nursery. Various sizes, including some specimens. Seed sometimes available.

Stephen H Smith's Garden & Leisure
Trent Valley, Doncaster Road, Scunthorpe DN15 8TE
☎ 01724 848950   FAX 01724 271912

CONTACT   Neil Parker
LOCATION   On A18, ½ mile east of M181 junction
OPEN   9 am – 6 pm, summer; 9 am – 5.30 pm, winter; 10.30 am – 4.30 pm, Sundays
SHOP   Garden sundries, furniture, gifts, aquatics
REFRESHMENTS   Coffee shop

Garden centre with plants and garden products, including a Hillier Premier Plants agency. Delivery service.

The Valley Clematis Nursery
Willingham Road, Hainton, Lincoln LN3 6LN
☎ 01507 313396   FAX 01507 313705

CONTACT   Keith or Carol Fair
LOCATION   Off A157 between Louth and Wragby, map in catalogue
OPEN   10 am – 5 pm (dusk in winter), daily. Closed Christmas Eve to New Year's Day
SPECIALITIES   Clematis
CATALOGUE   £1
MAIL ORDER   Yes
GARDEN   Yes
SHOWS   RHS Westminster; Harrogate (Spring); Chelsea; Hampton Court

Clematis specialist with a range of over 350 species and cultivars. Look out for their charming displays at shows, justly rewarded by a string of Gold Medals.

LONDON

Clifton Nurseries
Clifton Villas, Little Venice, London W9 2PH
☎ 0171 289 6851   FAX 0171 286 4215

CONTACT   Simon Haines
LOCATION   50 yards from Warwick Avenue Underground
OPEN   8.30 am – 6 pm, Monday – Saturday; 10.30 am – 4.30 pm, Sundays; March to September. 8.30 am – 5.30 pm, Monday – Saturday; 10 am – 4 pm, Sundays; October to February
SPECIALITIES   Climbers; conservatory plants; house plants; shrubs; topiary
MAIL ORDER   Van delivery in London
DESIGN SERVICE   Clifton Landscape and Design

Smart, stylish source of good plants for Londoners. They concentrate on town gardens, with containers, topiary, statuary, climbers and shrubs in specimen sizes, indoor and conservatory plants.

Country Gardens
Field Heath Road, Hillingdon UB8 3NP
☎ 01895 236141   FAX 01895 811585

CONTACT   Paul Jackson (Manager)
OPEN   9 am – 6 pm, Monday – Saturday; 10.30 am – 4.30 pm, Sundays
SHOP   Aquatics, hydroponics, petfood, turf
REFRESHMENTS   Coffee shop

Country Gardens
Daws Lane, Mill Hill NW7 4SL
☎ 0181 906 4255   📠 0181 959 4696

CONTACT   Richard Fuller (Manager)
OPEN   9 am – 6 pm, Monday – Saturday; 10.30 am – 4.30 pm, Sundays
SHOP   Aquatics

Country Gardens
Windmill Lane, Osterley TW7 5PR
☎ 0181 847 2468   📠 0181 569 8884

CONTACT   Simon Harpin (Manager)
OPEN   9 am – 6 pm, Monday – Saturday; 10.30 am – 4.30 pm, Sundays
SHOP   Aquatics, machinery

CTDA
174 Cambridge Street, London SW1V 4QE
☎ 0171 976 5115

CONTACT   Dr Basil Smith
OPEN   Mail order only
SPECIALITIES   Seeds; sempervivums; hardy cyclamen; hellebores (Ballard strain)
NEW FOR 1997   Cyclamen hederifolium 'Perlenteppich', Helleborus orientalis 'Apricot'
CATALOGUE   On request
MAIL ORDER   Yes

Hardy cyclamen plants by post; named hellebore cultivars, including Ballards; cyclamen seed too, including very good forms of Cyclamen coum.

Derek Lloyd Dean
8 Lynwood Close, South Harrow HA2 9PR
☎ 0181 864 0899

CONTACT   Derek Lloyd Dean
OPEN   Mail order only
SPECIALITIES   Pelargoniums
CATALOGUE   2 first-class stamps
MAIL ORDER   Yes
SHOWS   RHS Westminster; Chelsea; Hampton Court
NCCPG NATIONAL COLLECTIONS Pelargonium 'Angel' cultivars

A pelargonium specialist with an extensive range of rooted cuttings available by mail order only. The list is good on new introductions. The nursery plans to attend the Chelsea Physic Gardens and Middlesex Shows.

Fulham Palace Garden Centre
Bishops Avenue, London SW6 6EE
☎ 0171 736 9820   📠 0171 371 8468

CONTACT   Mrs Taylor
OPEN   9.30 am – 5.30 pm, Monday – Thursday; 9.30 am – 6 pm, Friday – Saturday; 10 am – 5 pm, Sundays

Everything for the town gardener, including specimen size plants, topiary and a good range of containers. They will deliver daily in London. Owned by Fairbridge, the charity which arranges training for inner-city children.

Great Gardens of England (Syon) Ltd
Syon Park, Brentford TW8 8JG
☎ 0181 568 0134/5   📠 0181 847 3865

CONTACT   M. Browne
LOCATION   8 miles west of London on A4
OPEN   9 am – 5.30 pm, Monday – Saturday; 10 am – 4.30 pm, Sundays
MAIL ORDER   Yes, phone for details
REFRESHMENTS   Patio cafeteria
DESIGN SERVICE   See Syon Courtyard

Garden centre with a general stock for indoor and outdoor gardening. A delivery service is available, and they offer landscaping through Syon Courtyard.

Jacques Amand Ltd
The Nurseries, Clamp Hill, Stanmore HA7 3JS
☎ 0181 954 8138   📠 0181 954 6784

CONTACT   Stuart Chapman
OPEN   9 am – 5 pm, Monday – Saturday, all year; Sundays: 10 am – 4 pm, May, June, September, October but 10 am – 2 pm, February, March, April, August, November. Closed on Sundays in January, December and July
SPECIALITIES   Bulbs
CATALOGUE   On request (retail and wholesale)
MAIL ORDER   Yes
REFRESHMENTS   Open day only
GARDEN   Garden open all year round
SHOWS   RHS Westminster; Malvern (Spring); Malvern (Autumn); Harrogate (Spring); Harrogate (Autumn); Southport; Chelsea; BBC GW Live; Hampton Court

Celebrated bulb specialists, whose range includes flower bulbs of all types. There is a wholesale and a retail list. Look out for their displays at shows: they attend many, including the Philadelphia Flower Show.

Notcutts Garden Centre
Bloomingdales, Staines Road, Laleham TW18 2SF
☎ 01784 460832   📠 01784 460831

CONTACT   Colin Dale (Manager)
OPEN   9 am – 6 pm, Monday – Saturday; 11 am – 5 pm, Sundays
SHOP   Gifts, buildings, garden furniture
REFRESHMENTS   Restaurant
DESIGN SERVICE   Notcutts Landscapes

The Palm Centre
563 Upper Richmond Road West, London SW14 7ED
☎ 0181 876 3223   📠 0181 876 6888

CONTACT   Martin Gibbons
OPEN   10 am – 6 pm, daily
SPECIALITIES   Palms; cycads
CATALOGUE   £1.95, palms and cycads
MAIL ORDER   Yes
REFRESHMENTS   Next door

Specialist in ornamental palms, both hardy and indoor varieties. They come in all sizes from seedlings to specimens. There is also a range of cycads. The nursery now has a wholesale division for designers and retailers.

Syon Courtyard

Great Gardens of England (Syon) Ltd, Syon Courtyard,
Syon Park, Brentford TW8 8JG

☎ 0181 568 3114   [FAX] 0181 232 8815

CONTACT   Karl Lawrence
LOCATION   8 miles west of London on A4
OPEN   9 am – 5.30 pm, Monday – Saturday; 9.30 am – 6 pm,
Sundays
CATALOGUE   Lists available
MAIL ORDER   Yes
SHOP   Sheds, paving, fencing
DESIGN SERVICE   Syon Courtyard

Attached to the Great Gardens of England garden centre at
Syon Park. Supplies landscaping materials and offers a design
and landscaping service.

Wolden Nurseries & Garden Centre

Cattlegate Road, Crews Hill, Enfield EN2 9DW

☎ 0181 363 7003   [FAX] 0181 366 2705

CONTACT   Vic Barnard
OPEN   8.30 am – 5.30 pm, Monday – Friday; 8 am – 5 pm,
Saturday; 10 am – 4 pm Sunday
GARDEN   Seasonal displays

North London garden centre. Free advice.

Wyevale Garden Centre

Cattlegate Road, Crews Hill, Enfield EN2 9DX

☎ 0181 367 0422   [FAX] 0181 366 3810

REFRESHMENTS   Restaurant

Wyevale Garden Centre

Headstone Lane, Harrow HA2 6NB

☎ 0181 428 3408   [FAX] 0181 420 1833

Wyevale Garden Centre

Holloway Lane, Harmondsworth, West Drayton UB7 0AD

☎ 0181 897 6075   [FAX] 0181 759 5739

REFRESHMENTS   Restaurant

MERSEYSIDE

Landlife Wildflowers Ltd

The Old Police Station, Lark Lane, Liverpool L17 8UU

☎ 0151 728 7011   [FAX] 0151 728 8413

CONTACT   Gillian Watson
SPECIALITIES   Seeds; wild flowers
CATALOGUE   Large SAE (35p stamp)
MAIL ORDER   Yes

This small nursery sells a range of native wild flowers as seeds,
small plants and bulbs. All profits go to the environmental
charity Landlife, actively involved in the development of the
National Wildflower Centre at Court Hey Park.

Maple Nursery

32 Rivington Road, St Helens WA10 4NE

☎ 01744 29572

CONTACT   Don Vose
LOCATION   Directions by post

OPEN   By appointment between 9 am – 1 pm, Saturdays and
Sundays, April to September
SPECIALITIES   *Hosta*
NEW FOR 1997   *Hosta* 'Whirlwind'
CATALOGUE   No
MAIL ORDER   No
SHOWS   Southport

Hosta specialist. The nursery will be at the Arley Hall and
Holker Hall Garden Festivals.

NORFOLK

African Violet Centre

Station Road, Terrington St Clement, King's Lynn PE34
4PL

☎ 01553 828374   [FAX] 01553 827520

CONTACT   Tony Clements or Maggie Garford
LOCATION   3 miles west of King's Lynn, beside A17
OPEN   10 am – 5 pm, all year, except for Christmas – New
Year period
SPECIALITIES   African violets
NEW FOR 1997   3 new cultivars in the 'Gem' series
CATALOGUE   On request; phone 01553 827281
MAIL ORDER   Yes
REFRESHMENTS   Tea room, Easter to September
GARDEN   Show House opens for groups, May to September
SHOWS   RHS Westminster; Malvern (Spring); Malvern
(Autumn); Harrogate (Spring); Harrogate (Autumn); Chelsea;
BBC GW Live; Hampton Court

The specialists for saintpaulias, with a huge selection on offer.
Weekend shows for other plants are held during the season.

Bawdeswell Garden Centre

Bawdeswell, Dereham NR20 4RZ

☎ 01362 688387   [FAX] 01362 688504

CONTACT   Peter Underwood
LOCATION   Between Norwich and Fakenham on A1067
OPEN   8 am – 5.30 pm, summer; 8 am – 5 pm, winter.
10.30 am – 4.30 pm Sundays
SPECIALITIES   Clematis; trees
CATALOGUE   Plant guide 50p
SHOP   Garden sundries, gifts
REFRESHMENTS   Coffee shop

A traditional garden centre, with a wide range of plants, as
well as furniture, conservatories and greenhouses. They operate a design and landscaping service.

Bressingham Gardens Mail Order

Bressingham, Diss IP22 2AB

☎ 01379 687464   [FAX] 01379 688034

CONTACT   Bill Howard
OPEN   Mail order only
SPECIALITIES   Herbaceous perennials
NEW FOR 1997   *Lewisia* 'Ashwood Carousel' hybrids
CATALOGUE   Mail order catalogue; also available from plant
centres
MAIL ORDER   Yes
SHOWS   Chelsea; BBC GW Live; Hampton Court

The mail order section of Bressinghams. It is run separately from the retail plant centres. The range is similar: an excellent choice of hardy perennials and alpines, and the trademark small conifers and heathers. Border planning service available. The 24-hour telephone orderline number is 01379 687468.

Bressingham Plant Centre

Bressingham, Diss IP22 2AB
☎ 01379 687464   📠 01379 688061

CONTACT   Tony Fry (Manager)
LOCATION   On A1066 3 miles west of Diss
OPEN   9 am – 5.30 pm daily, except Christmas and Boxing Day
SPECIALITIES   Alpines; conifers; herbaceous perennials; shrubs
MAIL ORDER   See Bressingham Mail Order
REFRESHMENTS   Pavilion Tea Room
GARDEN   Bressingham Gardens, Norfolk, see Gardens section
DESIGN SERVICE   Border Planning Service
SHOWS   Chelsea; BBC GW Live; Hampton Court

The plant centre here at Bressingham is a model of its type: there are others at Dorney Court, Berkshire and Elton Hall, Cambridgeshire. The mail order side is called Bressingham Mail Order and is run separately. The retail range is strong on hardy perennials and shrubs, conifers and heathers with a range exceeding 5,000 varieties. Good quality stock. Pick your own fruit also, in season. A border planning service is available. Alan Bloom will lecture on 1 March.

British Wild Flower Plants

23 Yarmouth Road, Ormesby St Margaret, Great Yarmouth NR29 3QE
☎ & 📠 01493 730244

CONTACT   Linda Laxton
LOCATION   4 miles north-east of Great Yarmouth
OPEN   By appointment
SPECIALITIES   Wild flowers
CATALOGUE   SAE
MAIL ORDER   Yes
GARDEN   Garden

Wild flowers grown as plugs or pots from a range of 400 species. The original seed provenance of the stock plants is named, but none of the sale plants were collected in the wild.

Chris Bowers & Son

Whispering Trees Nursery, Wimbotsham PE34 8QB
☎ 01366 388752   📠 01366 386858

CONTACT   Chris Bowers
LOCATION   North of Downham Market
OPEN   9 am – 5 pm; daily; all year. Closed 1 pm – 2 pm at weekends
SPECIALITIES   Fruit
NEW FOR 1997   Raspberry 'Julia'; Gooseberry 'Pax'
CATALOGUE   £1.50
MAIL ORDER   Yes

Although many types of plants are stocked, the attraction here is the fruit. The excellent selection includes purple raspberries,

blueberries and cranberries, and rhubarb cultivars from the National Collection, as well as tree fruits and nuts.

Four Seasons

Forncett St Mary, Norwich NR16 1JT
☎ 01508 488344   📠 01508 488478

CONTACT   J. P. Metcalf or Richard Ball
OPEN   Mail order only
SPECIALITIES   Herbaceous perennials
CATALOGUE   £1
MAIL ORDER   Yes, autumn and spring despatch
SHOWS   RHS Westminster

An outstanding range of herbaceous perennials, both cultivars and species. Highlights include the asters and Monarda. The nursery only trades by mail order, but exhibits regularly at the Westminster shows: Mr Metcalf is well-known at the RHS.

Greens Nurseries Ltd

Norwich Road, Dereham NR20 3AL
☎ 01362 692014   📠 01362 694226

CONTACT   Peter Green
LOCATION   Map in catalogue
OPEN   8 am – 5 pm, Monday – Friday
SPECIALITIES   Soft fruit
CATALOGUE   On request
MAIL ORDER   Yes

Long-established nurseries, now specialising in soft fruit with a range of mouth-watering varieties. They hold a Royal Warrant and supply the fruit farm at Sandringham.

Hickling Heath Nursery

Sutton Road, Hickling, Norwich NR12 0AS
☎ 01692 598513

CONTACT   B. H. Cogan
LOCATION   Off A149 on crossroads to Hickling Broad Staithe
OPEN   9.30 am – 5 pm, Tuesday – Sunday. Closed on Mondays, except Bank Holidays
SPECIALITIES   Shrubs
NEW FOR 1997   Diascia 'Redstart', Heuchera varieties from USA
CATALOGUE   3 first-class stamps
MAIL ORDER   No

Family nursery with a pleasing mix of interesting shrubs and herbaceous plants, both species and cultivars. They will be at the East Anglian and Royal Norfolk Shows.

Hoecroft Plants

Severals Grange, Holt Road, Wood Norton, Dereham NR20 5BL
☎ 01362 684206

CONTACT   Jane M. Lister
LOCATION   2 miles north of Guist on B1110 (not in West Norton village)
OPEN   10 am – 4 pm, Wednesdays, Friday – Sunday, April to September
SPECIALITIES   Foliage plants; grasses
CATALOGUE   £1 or 5 second-class stamps
MAIL ORDER   Yes, no minimum order

GARDEN   Display beds being planted
DESIGN SERVICE   Hoecroft Plants
SHOWS   RHS Westminster; Chelsea; Hampton Court

Well-known specialist for variegated and coloured foliage plants, and especially for decorative grasses – over 200 varieties.

Jenny Burgess' Alpine Nursery

Alpine Nursery, Sisland, Norwich NR14 6EF
☎ 01508 520724

CONTACT   Jenny Burgess
LOCATION   Off A143 between Norwich and Lowestoft
OPEN   By appointment only
SPECIALITIES   Alpines
CATALOGUE   2 first-class stamps
MAIL ORDER   Yes, sisyrinchiums only
GARDEN   Yes
DESIGN SERVICE   Yes
NCCPG NATIONAL COLLECTIONS   Sisyrinchium

An alpine grower, with a strong list of sisyrinchiums, and many campanulas too.

Magpies

Green Lane, Mundford IP26 5HS
☎ 01842 878496

CONTACT   Patricia Cooper
LOCATION   Off A1065
OPEN   9 am – 5 pm, Mondays, Tuesdays, Thursdays, Fridays; 12 noon – 5 pm, Saturdays, Sundays. Closed Wednesdays
SPECIALITIES   Herbaceous perennials
CATALOGUE   4 first-class stamps
MAIL ORDER   No
GARDEN   1½ acre garden opens for NGS

British native plants, grasses, herbaceous perennials and marginals: a personal selection with a simple pricing policy.

Norfolk Lavender Ltd

Caley Mill, Heacham, King's Lynn PE31 7JE
☎ 01485 570384   FAX 01485 571176

CONTACT   Henry Head
LOCATION   North of King's Lynn on A149
OPEN   9.30 am – 6 pm, summer; 10.30 am – 4 pm, winter. Closed 24 December to 13 January inclusive
SPECIALITIES   Lavender
CATALOGUE   2 first-class stamps
MAIL ORDER   Yes, minimum order 6 plants
SHOP   Lavender products
REFRESHMENTS   Yes
GARDEN   Lavender collection
NCCPG NATIONAL COLLECTIONS   Lavandula

They grow and sell hardy and tender Lavandula, bare root and in containers respectively. Lavender products are for sale, and the National Collection is on display.

Norwich Heather and Conifer Centre

54a Yarmouth Road, Thorpe St Andrew, Norwich NR7 0HE
☎ 01603 439434

CONTACT   B. Hipperson

LOCATION   2 miles east of Norwich
OPEN   9 am – 5 pm, Monday – Saturday; 2 – 5 pm, Sundays. Closed Thursdays
SPECIALITIES   Conifers; heathers
CATALOGUE   40p
MAIL ORDER   Yes

Just heathers and conifers, but with about 500 varieties of each the range is very extensive.

Notcutts Garden Centre

Daniels Road, Norwich NR4 6QP
☎ 01603 453155   FAX 01603 507746

CONTACT   Stephen Boon (Manager)
LOCATION   On ring road
OPEN   8.30 am – 5.30 pm, Monday – Saturday; 10 am – 5 pm, Sundays
SHOP   Garden sundries, furniture, pools, pets
REFRESHMENTS   Restaurant
DESIGN SERVICE   Notcutts Landscapes

P W Plants

Sunnyside, Heath Road, Kenninghall NR16 2DS
☎ 01953 888212

CONTACT   Diana Whittaker
LOCATION   South-west of Norwich, just off B1113
OPEN   9 am – 5 pm, Fridays, and last Saturday of the month
SPECIALITIES   Bamboos; climbers; grasses; shrubs
CATALOGUE   5 first-class stamps
MAIL ORDER   Yes, October – December, March – April only
GARDEN   Display gardens
SHOWS   RHS Westminster; Malvern (Spring); Malvern (Autumn); Chelsea; BBC GW Live; Hampton Court

A wide range with the emphasis on garden-worthy plants with interesting foliage and shape, including bamboos and grasses and shrubs. Extensive display gardens.

Peter Beales Roses

London Road, Attleborough NR17 1AY
☎ 01953 454707   FAX 01953 456845

CONTACT   Any staff member
LOCATION   2 miles south of Attleborough: leave A11 at Breckland Lodge
OPEN   9 am – 5 pm, Monday – Friday; 9 am – 4.30 pm, Saturdays; 10 am – 4 pm, Sundays
SPECIALITIES   Roses
CATALOGUE   On request
MAIL ORDER   Yes, no minimum order
GARDEN   Rose garden
DESIGN SERVICE   Peter Beales Roses
SHOWS   Chelsea; BBC GW Live; Hampton Court

Specialist grower and collector of older and classic roses. The extensive list has over 1000 species and varieties, many not available elsewhere. Among the popular and rare items, there is also an interesting selection of early Hybrid Teas. They will design rose gardens, and their own fields can be visited.

The Plantsman's Preference

Lynwood, Hopton Road, Garboldisham, Diss IP22 2QN
☎ 01953 681439

CONTACT   Tim or Jenny Fuller
LOCATION   On B1111, ¼ mile south of junction with A1066
OPEN   9 am – 5 pm; Fridays & Sundays; 1 March to 31 October
SPECIALITIES   Grasses; herbaceous perennials; hardy geraniums
NEW FOR 1997   Euphorbia 'Garblesham Enchanter', E. 'Purple Preference', Geranium × oxonianum 'Red Sputnik', G. × o. 'Lasting Impression', G. × o. 'Breckland Sunset'
CATALOGUE   4 first-class stamps
MAIL ORDER   Yes, no minimum order

Very much a plantsman's nursery, as the name suggests, but limited to hardy herbaceous plants and grasses. Nevertheless, the list is full of rare plants and the nursery has introduced quite a number of new cultivars itself. Worth knowing.

Reads Nursery

Hales Hall, Loddon NR14 6QW
☎ 0150 548395   FAX 0150 548040

CONTACT   Judy Read
LOCATION   Off A146, 1 mile south of Loddon
OPEN   10 am – 1 pm, 2 pm – 5 pm, Tuesday – Saturday
SPECIALITIES   Climbers; conservatory plants; fruit; citrus
CATALOGUE   4 first-class stamps
MAIL ORDER   Yes
NCCPG NATIONAL COLLECTIONS Citrus; Ficus; Vitis vinifera

Long-established family nursery which specialises in citrus and conservatory plants. The mouth-watering list includes excellent collections of both of these, with vines, figs garden and greenhouse fruit trees, and topiary also.

The Romantic Garden Nursery

Swannington, Norwich NR9 5NW
☎ 01603 261488   FAX 01603 871668

CONTACT   John Powles
LOCATION   7 miles north-west of Norwich
OPEN   10 am – 5 pm, Wednesdays, Fridays, Saturdays
SPECIALITIES   Topiary
CATALOGUE   4 first-class stamps
MAIL ORDER   Yes
SHOP   Gifts and presents
GARDEN   Display garden
DESIGN SERVICE   The Romantic Garden Nursery
SHOWS   Chelsea; Hampton Court

Ornamental standards, bobbles and pyramids in Cupressus and Ilex, as well as box in animal and other shapes. Clematis and half-hardy plants are also available. They can design where necessary, and sell topiary packages which include a layout and the necessary plants.

Simpsons Nursery

The Plant Centre, High Street, Marsham, Norwich NR10 5QA
☎ & FAX 01263 733432

CONTACT   Gillian or Jonathan Simpson
LOCATION   2 miles south of Aylsham, off A140
OPEN   Daily in summer; Wednesday – Sunday and Bank Holidays in winter
CATALOGUE   Ask for details
MAIL ORDER   No
GARDEN   Small display garden
DESIGN SERVICE   Simpsons Nursery and Landscaping

Nursery and plant centre which stocks home-grown plants, notably conifers and shrubs. They also have a landscaping and tree surgery department.

Thorncroft Clematis Nursery

The Lings, Reymerston, Norwich NR9 4QG
☎ 01953 850407

CONTACT   Ruth P. Gooch or Dorothy Tolver
LOCATION   Between Dereham and Wymondham on B1135
OPEN   10 am – 4.30 pm, daily, March to October. Closed Wednesdays. By appointment only in winter
SPECIALITIES   Clematis
CATALOGUE   2 first-class stamps
MAIL ORDER   Carriage can be arranged
GARDEN   Display garden

There is a good range of species and cultivars at this Clematis specialist. Free pruning demonstrations take place in late February and early March: phone for details. The nursery will be at the Royal Norfolk Show and the Sandringham Flower Show.

Trevor White Old Fashioned Roses

Bennetts Brier, The Street, Felthorpe, Norwich NR10 4AB
☎ & FAX 01603 755135

CONTACT   Trevor or Vanessa White
OPEN   Mail order only
SPECIALITIES   Roses
CATALOGUE   On request
MAIL ORDER   Yes

Mainly wholesale. An excellent choice of old and species shrub and climbing roses, with some further re-introductions this year. Good quality plants.

Van Tubergen UK

Thetford Road, Bressingham, Diss IP22 2AB
☎ 01379 688282   FAX 01379 687227
OPEN   Mail order only
SPECIALITIES   Bulbs
CATALOGUE   50p
MAIL ORDER   Yes

Long-established and famous specialist in flowering bulbs. Start at Allium aflatunense and continue to Tulipa violacea.

Waveney Fish Farm

Park Road, Diss IP22 3AS

☎ 01379 642697　　FAX 01379 651315

LOCATION　Near Diss town centre, on A1066
OPEN　9.30 am – 5 pm, daily
SPECIALITIES　Aquatic plants
CATALOGUE　On request
MAIL ORDER　Yes, minimum order £10
SHOP　Fish and animals
GARDEN　Display gardens

Aquatic plants for sale: the display gardens are open from March to October.

West Acre Gardens

8 Pretoria Cottages, West Acre, King's Lynn PE32 1UJ

☎ 01760 755562　　FAX 01760 755989

CONTACT　John or Sue Tuite
LOCATION　Off A47 south-east of King's Lynn, map in catalogue
OPEN　10 am – 5 pm, daily, 1 March to 31 October; phone first in winter
SPECIALITIES　Alpines; herbaceous perennials; shrubs
CATALOGUE　Yes
GARDEN　Display beds in walled garden

New nursery with a general range of rarer plants, particularly alpines, but clematis, climbers, herbaceous plants, roses and shrubs as well.

The Wild Flower Centre

Church Farm, Sisland, Norwich NR14 6EF

☎ 01508 520235　　FAX 01508 528294

CONTACT　D. Corne
LOCATION　1½ miles west of Loddon (A146)
OPEN　9 am – 5 pm. Other times by appointment
SPECIALITIES　Wild flowers
CATALOGUE　40p
MAIL ORDER　Yes
GARDEN　Garden open, March to June

This small centre grows a selection of native and naturalised wild flowers and publishes a quarterly magazine about wild plants called 'Flora, Facts and Fables'.

Wyevale Garden Centre

Blue Boar Lane, Sprowston, Norwich NR7 8RJ

☎ 01603 412239　　FAX 01603 402949

REFRESHMENTS　Restaurant

NORTHAMPTONSHIRE

Country Gardens

Harlestone Road, Northampton NN5 6UJ

☎ 01604 751346　　FAX 01604 589841

CONTACT　Alan Green (Manager)
OPEN　9 am – 6 pm, Monday – Saturday; 10.30 am – 4.30 pm, Sundays

E L F Plants, Cramden Nursery

Harborough Road North, Northampton NN2 8LU

☎ 01604 846246

LOCATION　Kingsthorpe, Northampton: leave A508 at Kingsthorpe cemetery
OPEN　10 am – 5 pm, Thursday – Saturday. Closed November to January
SPECIALITIES　Conifers; shrubs; *Daphne*
CATALOGUE　50p plus stamp
MAIL ORDER　No
GARDEN　Garden
SHOWS　RHS Westminster; BBC GW Live

This small nursery specialises in dwarf and small shrubs and conifers that are suitable for rock gardens and borders. Some alpines and heathers too. It's advisable to phone first (evenings only). Garden clubs welcome at any time by arrangement.

F Haynes & Partners

56 Gordon Street, Kettering NN16 0RX

☎ 01536 519836

CONTACT　Nick Maple
LOCATION　Directions in catalogue
OPEN　8.30 am – 4 pm, Mondays – Fridays
SPECIALITIES　Roses
CATALOGUE　On request
MAIL ORDER　Yes
SHOWS　Harrogate (Autumn); Hampton Court

Bare root roses. There is a particularly good selection of varieties for exhibition and miniature roses. The nursery is at Woodford Lane, Lowick. Enquiries and correspondence to 56 Gordon Street, Kettering.

Hill Farm Herbs

Park Walk, Brigstock, Kettering NN14 3HH

☎ 01536 373694　　FAX 01536 373246

CONTACT　Mr or Mrs Simpson
LOCATION　Signed off A6116
OPEN　10.30 am – 5.30 pm daily, but 10.30 am – 4.30 pm in winter
SPECIALITIES　Herbs
CATALOGUE　2 second-class stamps
MAIL ORDER　No
SHOP　Herb products, dried flowers
REFRESHMENTS　Tea shop Easter to September
GARDEN　Display gardens

The nursery and shops are tucked in behind the farm. There is a large range of herbs and cottage garden plants, herb products and seeds, pretty display gardens with a tea shop in summer.

Kennedys Garden Centre

Millers Lane, Wellingborough NN8 2NF

☎ 01933 273728　　FAX 01933 229073

CONTACT　Jim Greenfield (Manager)
OPEN　9 am – 6 pm, Monday – Saturday, April to September, close 5.30 pm, October to March; 10.30 am – 4.30 pm, Sundays
REFRESHMENTS　Café

Mears Ashby Nurseries Ltd
Glebe House, Glebe Road, Mears Ashby NN6 0DL
☎ 01604 811811　　[FAX] 01604 812353

CONTACT Janette E. Gaggini
LOCATION ¼ mile from Sywell aerodrome towards Wellingborough
OPEN 9 am – 5.30 pm; daily; all year
SPECIALITIES Wisteria
NEW FOR 1997 Several new liriopes and agapanthus
CATALOGUE Retail £1 and A5 SAE
MAIL ORDER Yes, retail
REFRESHMENTS Refreshments

Mainly wholesale nursery with a large range of container-grown trees and shrubs. Their retail outlet is Gaggini's Plant Centre. Wisterias are a speciality available at both, and by mail order or carrier.

Podington Garden Centre
High Street, Podington, Wellingborough NN29 7HS
☎ 01933 53656　　[FAX] 01933 410332
LOCATION 2 miles west of A6
OPEN 9 am – 6.30 pm, Monday – Saturday; 10.30 am – 4.30 pm, Sundays. Open until 8 pm, Thursdays. Close at 5.30 pm in winter
SHOP Garden sundries, paving, fencing
REFRESHMENTS Gnomes Kitchen

Plants, aquatic and garden products. Local delivery.

Ravensthorpe Nursery
6 East Haddon Road, Ravensthorpe NN6 8ES
☎ & [FAX] 01604 770548

CONTACT Jean or Richard Wiseman
LOCATION Between Rugby and Northampton, near M1, Jct 18 and A14, Jct 1
OPEN 10 am – 6 pm, Tuesday – Sunday, and Bank Holiday Mondays
SPECIALITIES Herbaceous perennials
CATALOGUE 4 first-class stamps
MAIL ORDER Yes, no minimum order
GARDEN Display garden being made

This nursery has a sound all-round range of plants, much of the material being home-grown.

Wyevale Garden Centre
Newport Pagnell Road, Hardingstone, Northampton NN4 0BN
☎ 01604 765725　　[FAX] 01604 700492
REFRESHMENTS Restaurant

NORTHUMBERLAND

Chipchase Castle Nursery
Wark, Hexham NE48 3NT
☎ 01434 230083　　[FAX] 01434 681312

CONTACT Suzanne Newell or Janet Beakes
LOCATION 2 miles south of Wark, towards Barrasford
OPEN Thursday – Sunday; 28 March to 15 October
SPECIALITIES Herbaceous perennials

NEW FOR 1997 Polemonium reptans 'Alba', Scrophularia sambucifolia
CATALOGUE A5 SAE for plant list
MAIL ORDER No
GARDEN Well-labelled borders & nursery beds to view
SHOWS Harrogate (Autumn); Strathclyde

A newish nursery which raises all its own stock. They are strong in Codonopsis, Dianthus, geraniums, penstemons, salvias and violas, but the list is growing in length and interest all the time.

Halls of Heddon
West Heddon Nurseries, Heddon on the Wall, Newcastle upon Tyne NE15 0JS
☎ 01661 852445

CONTACT J. A. Lockey
OPEN 9 am – 5 pm, Monday – Saturday; 10 am – 5 pm, Sundays
SPECIALITIES Chrysanthemums; dahlias
NEW FOR 1997 New dahlia varieties
CATALOGUE 2 second-class stamps
MAIL ORDER Dahlias and chrysanthemums only
GARDEN Herbaceous borders at Ovington nursery, show fields at Heddon in September
SHOWS Harrogate (Autumn)

Specialists in dahlias and chrysanthemums of all types for showing, the garden and as cut flowers. The garden centre carries a general range. The show fields at Heddon will be open during September.

Heighley Gate Garden Centre
Morpeth NE61 3DA
☎ 01670 513416　　[FAX] 01670 510013

CONTACT G. Humble (Manager)
LOCATION 3 miles north of Morpeth on A697
OPEN 9 am – 5 pm (5.30 pm in summer), Monday – Friday; 9 am – 5 pm Saturdays & Bank Holidays; 10.30 am – 4.30 pm, Sundays
SHOP Garden sundries, gifts, conservatories
REFRESHMENTS Coffee shop
GARDEN Display garden
DESIGN SERVICE Heighley Gate Garden Centre

All-round range of plants and garden sundries, including home-grown bedding, houseplants and pansies.

Herterton House Gardens & Nursery
Hartington, Cambo, Morpeth NE61 4BN
☎ 01670 774278

CONTACT Frank Lawley
LOCATION 2 miles north of Cambo, off B6342
OPEN 1.30 pm – 5.30 pm, daily, April to September, and by appointment. Closed Tuesdays and Thursdays
NEW FOR 1997 Knautia arvensis 'Lawley's White'
MAIL ORDER No
GARDEN Herterton House Gardens & Nursery, Northumberland, see Gardens section

This nursery is one of the best in the north of England. It stocks a range of herbaceous perennials, particularly older varieties, and some herbs. The garden, which is open at the same times, was featured in *The Englishman's Garden*.

Hexham Herbs

Chesters Walled Garden, Chollerford, Hexham NE46 4BQ
☎ 01434 681483
CONTACT   S. White
LOCATION   6 miles north of Hexham, next to Chesters Roman fort
OPEN   10 am – 5 pm, Easter to October. Shorter hours in winter
SPECIALITIES   Herbaceous perennials; herbs; roses; wild flowers
CATALOGUE   £1.50 cheque
MAIL ORDER   No
SHOP   Pots, gifts
GARDEN   Hexham Herbs, Northumberland, see Gardens section
DESIGN SERVICE   Hexham Herbs
NCCPG NATIONAL COLLECTIONS   *Thymus*; *Origanum* (marjoram)

Specialist herb nursery with a wide range of herbs as plants and freshly cut for cooking. They also stock old roses, herbaceous plants, wild flowers, dried flowers and gifts.

Northumbria Nurseries

Castle Gardens, Ford, Berwick upon Tweed TD15 2PZ
☎ 01890 820379   FAX 01890 820594
CONTACT   H. M. Huddleston
LOCATION   10 miles north of Wooler, follow tourist signs off A697 to Ford and Etal
OPEN   9 am – 6 pm, Monday – Friday, all year; 10 am – 6 pm, Saturdays and Sundays from March to October; and by appointment
SPECIALITIES   Herbaceous perennials
CATALOGUE   £2.30 cheque
MAIL ORDER   Yes, (£5 minimum)
GARDEN   Display gardens
DESIGN SERVICE   Hazel M. Huddleston

A wide range of container-grown hardy shrubs and perennials, including groundcover plants and alpines. A design and advisory service is also available. Hazel Huddleston gives garden talks too.

Ryal Nursery

East Farm Cottage, Ryal NE20 0SA
☎ 01661 886562
CONTACT   Ruth Hadden
LOCATION   Map in catalogue
OPEN   1 pm – 5 pm, Tuesdays; 10 am – 5 pm, Sundays; March to July. Other times by appointment
SPECIALITIES   Alpines; primulas; woodland plants
CATALOGUE   SAE
MAIL ORDER   Yes

Woodland and alpine plants, with good primulas, auriculas and some interesting forms of *Ranunculus ficaria*.

NOTTINGHAMSHIRE

The Beeches Nursery

Prospect Farm, Misson Springs, Doncaster DN10 6ET
☎ 01302 772139
CONTACT   Leyland Cox
OPEN   10 am – 4 pm, Friday – Wednesday, 1 March to 30 June; 10 am – 4 pm, Saturdays and Sundays, 1 July to 28 February
SPECIALITIES   Pelargoniums
CATALOGUE   2 first-class stamps
MAIL ORDER   Yes

Pelargonium specialist. A selection of most types and varieties, including species, is available. The plants are grown on to $2\frac{1}{2}$-inch pot size.

Bridgford Garden Centre

Fosse Road, East Bridgford NG13 8LA
☎ 01949 20055   FAX 01949 21155
CONTACT   Edward Tarbatt
LOCATION   On A46 7 miles north-east of Nottingham
OPEN   9 am – 5 pm, October to February; 9 am – 5.30 pm, March to September; 10.30 am – 4.30 pm, Sundays. Closed between Christmas and New Year
SHOP   Gifts

A new addition to the Garden Centres of Excellence group. There is a large pets and aquatics section.

Brinkley Nurseries

Fiskerton Road, Southwell NG24 0TP
☎ 01636 814501
CONTACT   C. Steven
LOCATION   Turn off A612 towards Fiskerton at The White Lion
OPEN   10 am – 5 pm, summer; 10 am – 4 pm, winter
SPECIALITIES   Shrubs; trees
MAIL ORDER   Yes, £10 minimum order
GARDEN   Garden opens under the NGS, or by arrangement. Admission £1.50

Containerised trees and shrubs, both retail and wholesale. The choice is large and interesting, and they also carry herbaceous plants.

Cottage Nurseries

Cross Lane, Collingham, Newark NG23 7NY
☎ 01636 893161
CONTACT   John or Sheila Hipkiss
LOCATION   Off A1133 8 miles north of Newark, 2nd right off Sunderby Road
OPEN   10 am – dusk, daily
SPECIALITIES   Fuchsias
CATALOGUE   2 first-class stamps
MAIL ORDER   Yes

Fuchsia specialist with over 500 varieties. There are also plants for hanging baskets, pots and patios and a range of perennials and shrubs.

Field House Alpines
Leake Road, Gotham, Nottingham NG11 0JN
☎ 0115 9830278

CONTACT   Doug Lochhead or Val Woolley
LOCATION   Near M1, Jct 24 (10 mins)
OPEN   9 am – 5 pm, Friday – Wednesday
SPECIALITIES   Alpines; primulas; seeds; auriculas
CATALOGUE   4 first-class stamps
MAIL ORDER   Yes, primulas, auriculas and seeds
GARDEN   Auricula Theatre at Calke Abbey, Derbyshire, see Gardens section; covered garden at the nursery

A good range of alpines, both as plants and seed. They are particularly strong on primulas and auriculas. As well as maintaining the auricula theatre at Calke Abbey, Derbyshire they are also organising the specialist plant sale there on 20 April.

Greenwood Gardens
Ollerton Road, Arnold, Nottingham NG5 8PR
☎ 0115 920 5757   FAX 0115 920 3100

CONTACT   H. J. Tomlinson
LOCATION   On A614 north of Arnold
OPEN   10 am – 5 pm, Wednesday – Monday. Closed on Tuesdays
SPECIALITIES   Bonsai
NEW FOR 1997   Bonsai from Colombia, Mycaria cauliflora 'Jaboticarpa'
CATALOGUE   SAE and 25p stamp
MAIL ORDER   Books, videos and tools only
SHOP   Pots, crafts and gifts
GARDEN   Open by appointment
DESIGN SERVICE   Yes
SHOWS   BBC GW Live

Bonsai specialist. Everything you are likely to need for bonsai can be found here: books, containers, tools, trees and tuition. Classes are held in spring and autumn. The Summer School will run from 8 – 17 August. Design Service for Bonsai and Japanese gardens.

Hewthorn Herbs & Wild Flowers
82 Julian Road, West Bridgford NG2 5AN
☎ 0115 9812861

CONTACT   Julie Scott
LOCATION   South of Nottingham, near National Water Sports Centre
OPEN   Mail order only
SPECIALITIES   Herbs; wild flowers
CATALOGUE   3 first-class stamps
MAIL ORDER   Yes, no minimum order
GARDEN   Display garden open for groups by arrangement only

The nursery sells organically grown native and naturalised wild flowers, herbs, medicinal, culinary and dye plants. The garden is open for groups by arrangement: talks are also possible.

Mill Hill Plants
Mill Hill House, Elston Lane, East Stoke, Newark NG23 5QJ
☎ 01636 525460

CONTACT   G. M. Gregory
LOCATION   5 miles south-west of Newark. Leave A46 at East Stoke, for Elston; ½ mile down, on right
OPEN   10 am – 6 pm, Wednesday – Sunday, and Bank Holiday Mondays, March to September; Friday – Sunday in October. Closed November to February
SPECIALITIES   Alpines; herbaceous perennials; irises
CATALOGUE   Availability list of irises on request
MAIL ORDER   Yes, irises only
GARDEN   Garden opens for NGS, and when nursery is open
NCCPG NATIONAL COLLECTIONS   Berberis

The nursery stocks a range of hardy perennials and alpines. The speciality is bearded irises, which are available by mail order also. Groups welcome by appointment.

Naturescape
Coach Gap Lane, Langar NG13 9HP
☎ 01949 851045/860592   FAX 01949 850431

CONTACT   Brian Scarborough
LOCATION   Signed off A46 and A52
OPEN   11 am – 5.30 pm daily, 1 April to 30 September
SPECIALITIES   Seeds; wild flowers
CATALOGUE   £1 in stamps
MAIL ORDER   Yes, seeds all year, plants September to April
REFRESHMENTS   Tea room
GARDEN   Wildlife garden and fields

Wild flowers, British native shrubs and trees, pond and marsh species and cottage-garden favourites, available as plants and seeds. The 40 acre growing fields are open. The visitor centre is set in a wildlife garden showing different habitats.

Norwell Nursery
Woodhouse Road, Norwell, Newark NG23 6JX
☎ 01636 636337

CONTACT   Dr Andrew Ward
LOCATION   Off A1, 4 miles north of Newark
OPEN   10 am – 5 pm, Sunday – Thursday, 2 March to 16 October, also Saturdays in May and June. August, 17 October – 1 March, by appointment
SPECIALITIES   Alpines; herbaceous perennials
CATALOGUE   2 first-class stamps
MAIL ORDER   Yes
GARDEN   Display beds

There is an expanding range of perennials, including hardy geraniums, campanulas and alpines. A Dianthus amphitheatre has been created. Plants are grown with Suscon Green to prevent vine weevil. The garden opens for NGS 2 – 5.30 pm 29 June.

Reuben Shaw & Sons
Hollydene Nurseries & Garden Centre, 121 Moorgreen, Newthorpe NG16 2FF
☎ & FAX 01773 714326

CONTACT   James or Reuben Shaw

LOCATION North-west of Nottingham, M1, Jct 27
OPEN 9 am – 5.30 pm, Monday – Saturday; 10.30 am – 4.30 pm, Sunday. Closed at 5 pm, Tuesdays
NEW FOR 1997 New national releases
MAIL ORDER Blooms and Hillier plants only
SHOP Dried and silk flowers
DESIGN SERVICE Yes

Garden centre and nursery, stockists for Blooms of Bressingham and Hillier plants.

Richard Stockwell – Rare Plants
64 Weardale Road, Sherwood, Nottingham NG5 1DD
☎ & FAX 0115 9691063

CONTACT Richard Stockwell
SPECIALITIES Climbers; seeds
CATALOGUE 4 second-class stamps or 2 international reply coupons
MAIL ORDER Mail order only

Climbers and dwarf species available as small plants by post or as seed. An aptly named nursery for plantsmen and collectors.

Salley Gardens
32 Lansdowne Drive, West Bridgford, Nottingham NG2 7FJ
☎ 0115 923 3878

CONTACT Richard Lewin
OPEN By appointment only
SPECIALITIES Seeds; medicinal plants
CATALOGUE On request
MAIL ORDER Yes, no minimum order

Oriental medicinal, aromatic and dye plants, with some culinary herbs and perennial wild flowers. The business is mainly mail order, and they also sell seeds. Telephone first at all times.

Wheatcroft Ltd
Landmere Lane, Edwalton, Nottingham NG12 4DE
☎ 0115 9216060   FAX 0115 9841247
LOCATION On A 606 3 miles south of Trent Bridge
OPEN 9 am – 6 pm (5.30 pm in winter) Monday – Saturday. 11 am – 5 pm (4.30 pm in winter) on Sundays
SPECIALITIES Roses
REFRESHMENTS Yes

Garden centre with roses and a general range.

OXFORDSHIRE

Broadstone Nurseries
13 The Nursery, High Street, Sutton Courtenay, Abingdon OX14 4UA
☎ 01235 847557

CONTACT Broadstone Nurseries
OPEN 2 pm – 5 pm, Tuesdays; 2 pm – 6 pm, Saturdays. Advisable to phone first
SPECIALITIES Alpines
CATALOGUE 3 first-class stamps
MAIL ORDER No
DESIGN SERVICE Broadstone Nurseries

An alpine nursery, with plants for troughs, sinks and screes, as well as a range of perennials. They have a design service, and also supply specialist potting and planting mixtures.

Burford Garden Centre
Shilton Road, Burford OX18 4PA
☎ 01993 823117   FAX 01993 823529

CONTACT Lynne Wainwright
LOCATION Near A40, on B4020 at Burford
OPEN 9 am – 5.30 pm, Monday – Wednesday; 9 am – 7 pm Thursdays & Fridays; 9 am – 6 pm Saturdays; 11 am – 5 pm, Sundays
CATALOGUE Suppliers' catalogues available
SHOP Furniture, fencing, stoneware, Neal's Yard Wholefoods, gifts and pets
REFRESHMENTS Restaurant
SHOWS Malvern (Spring); Malvern (Autumn); Chelsea; Hampton Court

Large garden centre with indoor and outdoor plants, and an extensive clutch of associated product suppliers. Local delivery available; children's play area, and wheelchairs on site.

Country Gardens
Newbury Road, Chilton, Didcot OX11 1QN
☎ 01235 833900   FAX 01235 831266

CONTACT Robin Holmes Smith (Manager)
OPEN 9 am – 6 pm, Monday – Saturday; 10.30 am – 4.30 pm, Sundays
SHOP Garden buildings
REFRESHMENTS Coffee shop

The Cuckoo Pen Nursery
Preston Crowmarsh, Wallingford OX10 4SL
☎ 01491 835971

CONTACT Ian Burles
OPEN By appointment only
SPECIALITIES Herbaceous perennials
MAIL ORDER Limited
GARDEN Yes
SHOWS RHS Westminster; Malvern (Spring); Malvern (Autumn); Harrogate (Spring); Harrogate (Autumn); Southport; BBC GW Live; Hampton Court; Courson

A perennial nursery, specialist planting advice is offered. Most sales are at shows.

Kennedys Garden Centre
Southern Bypass, South Hinksey, Oxford OX1 5AR
☎ 01865 326066   FAX 01865 326137

CONTACT Jim Lilley (Manager)
OPEN 9 am – 6 pm, Monday – Saturday, April to September, close 5.30 pm, October to March; 10.30 am – 4.30 pm, Sundays
REFRESHMENTS Café

Mattocks Roses
Nuneham Courtenay, Oxford OX44 9PY
☎ 01865 343265   FAX 01865 343267

CONTACT Mark W. Mattock
LOCATION On B4015, roundabout Golden Ball (A4074)

OPEN 9 am – 5.30 pm (5 pm in winter), Monday – Saturday; 11 am – 5 pm, Sundays
SPECIALITIES Roses
CATALOGUE On request
MAIL ORDER Yes
SHOP Garden sundries, furniture
REFRESHMENTS Restaurant
GARDEN Rose fields
SHOWS RHS Westminster; Malvern (Autumn); Chelsea; BBC GW Live; Hampton Court

A large choice of all kinds of roses. They are particularly good on ground cover varieties and their own 'County' roses. They are part of Notcutts, and are attached to a Notcutts Garden Centre (01865 343454). The nursery will also be at the New Forest and Taunton shows.

Waterperry Gardens Ltd
Waterperry, Wheatley OX33 1JZ
☎ 01844 339226   [FAX] 01884 339883
LOCATION Near M40, Jct 8
OPEN 10 am – 5.30 pm, Monday – Friday; 10 am – 6 pm, Saturday – Sunday. Closes at 5 pm in winter
SPECIALITIES Saxifrages
CATALOGUE On request
MAIL ORDER No
SHOP Garden sundries
REFRESHMENTS Tea shop
GARDEN Waterperry Gardens, Oxfordshire, see Gardens section

Among a pleasantly laid out general stock there are good alpines, notably the saxifrages, and a useful choice of fruit trees. From 17 – 19 July the nursery will be open only to visitors to Art in Action.

Wyevale Garden Centre
57 London Road, Wheatley OX33 1YJ
☎ 01865 873057   [FAX] 01865 875321

SHROPSHIRE

Applegarth Nursery
The Elms, Maesbrook, Oswestry SY10 8QF
☎ 01691 831577
CONTACT Cathy Preston
LOCATION On B4398 between Knockin and Llanymynech
OPEN 2 pm – 6 pm, Thursday – Saturday, April to September. Phone first
SPECIALITIES Wild flowers
CATALOGUE SAE
MAIL ORDER No
GARDEN Display beds

Herbs, cottage garden plants and wild flowers chosen for their appeal to wild life.

Bucknell Nurseries
Bucknell SY7 0EL
☎ 01547 530606   [FAX] 01547 530699
CONTACT Andrew Coull
LOCATION Off A4113 east of Knighton

OPEN 8 am – 5 pm, Monday – Friday; 10 am – 1 pm Saturdays
SPECIALITIES Hedging; trees
CATALOGUE On request
MAIL ORDER No

Wholesale and retail bare-root tree specialist. The range includes forest trees, hedging plants, ornamental trees and shrubs. The nursery undertakes contract planting, fencing and landscaping.

David Austin Roses
Bowling Green Lane, Albrighton, Wolverhampton WV7 3HB
☎ 01902 373931   [FAX] 01902 372142
CONTACT Sue Webb
LOCATION South of M54, Jct 3
OPEN 9 am – 6 pm, Monday – Friday; 10 am – 6 pm, Saturday – Sunday, April to October. 9 am – 5 pm, Monday – Friday, 10 am – dusk, Saturdays, 12 noon – dusk, Sundays, October to March
SPECIALITIES Irises; paeonies; roses
CATALOGUE On request
MAIL ORDER Yes
REFRESHMENTS Yes
GARDEN Rose and herbaceous gardens
SHOWS Chelsea; BBC GW Live; Hampton Court

Rose grower and breeder, best known for his popular English Roses strain which combines modern performance standards of flowering with an old-fashioned shape. New varieties are introduced each year at Chelsea. There are additional ranges of irises and peonies.

Fron Nursery
Fron Issa, Rhiwlas, Oswestry SY10 7JH
☎ 01691 600605
CONTACT Thoby Miller
LOCATION 6 miles north-west of Oswestry
OPEN By appointment only
SPECIALITIES Conifers; shrubs; trees
NEW FOR 1997 *Abies concolor* 'Swift's Silver', *Abies magnifica*
CATALOGUE SAE
MAIL ORDER Yes, £20 minimum order
GARDEN 2-acre woodland garden

An interesting selection of seed-grown trees and shrubs, including conifers: the smaller sizes are mostly containerised, the larger, open ground. The more choice offerings include *Abies amabilis* and *Taxodium mucronatum*. The setting, 1000 feet up, promises good views as well as hardiness. Many specimens can be seen growing in the woodland planting of native broadleaves with exotics.

Hall Farm Nursery
Kinnerley, Oswestry SY10 8DH
☎ 01691 682135
CONTACT Christine Ffoulkes Jones
LOCATION 2 miles from A5, between Shrewsbury and Oswestry, map in catalogue

OPEN 10 am – 5 pm, Wednesday – Saturday, 1 March to 27 September
SPECIALITIES Grasses; herbaceous perennials
CATALOGUE 4 first-class stamps
MAIL ORDER No
GARDEN Nursery display beds
SHOWS Malvern (Spring); Malvern (Autumn); BBC GW Live; Hampton Court

This expanding nursery carries a good range of fashionable herbaceous perennials, including a great number of geraniums and ornamental grasses. All its plants are grown and propagated on site: nothing is bought in. Requests for cultural advice are therefore welcome. Talks, demonstrations and a garden tour are offered by arrangement for groups.

Hillview Hardy Plants
Worfield, Bridgnorth WV15 5NT
☎ & FAX 01746 716454

CONTACT Ingrid Millington
LOCATION Between Worfield and Albrighton, off B4176
OPEN 9 am – 5 pm, Monday – Saturday, March to October; by appointment, November to March
SPECIALITIES Alpines; herbaceous perennials; primulas
CATALOGUE 4 second-class stamps
MAIL ORDER Yes
GARDEN Display garden
SHOWS RHS Westminster; Malvern (Spring); Malvern (Autumn); Harrogate (Spring); Harrogate (Autumn); Southport; BBC GW Live; Hampton Court; Ayr; Courson

Twin ranges of alpines and hardy perennials. Good list of alpine primulas and auriculas too. As well as a busy show schedule, including Holker Hall, Newby Hall, Kent Garden and NCCPG sales, groups are taken round the nursery.

Lingen Nursery and Gardens
Lingen Alpine Nursery, Lingen, Bucknell SY7 0DY
☎ 01544 267720

CONTACT Kim W. Davis
LOCATION Lingen village is signed off the A4113 & A4362, north-east of Presteigne
OPEN 10 am – 5 pm, February to October
SPECIALITIES Alpines; herbaceous perennials
CATALOGUE 3 first-class stamps
MAIL ORDER Yes, £5 minimum
REFRESHMENTS NGS open days only
GARDEN Gardens open (£1)
SHOWS Malvern (Spring)
NCCPG NATIONAL COLLECTIONS Campanula; Iris sibirica

Good alpine nursery with a growing emphasis on wild collections; an interesting selection of aquilegias, penstemons, irises and campanulas; and a magnificent list of Primula species and hybrids.

Llanbrook Alpine & Wildflower Nursery
3 Llanbrook, Hopton Castle, Clunton SY7 0QG
☎ 01547 530298

CONTACT John Clayfield
LOCATION On B4367
OPEN By appointment, phone first
SPECIALITIES Alpines; wild flowers
MAIL ORDER No
SHOWS Southport

Alpines, wild flowers and other hardy plants, all grown in peat-free compost.

Merton Nurseries
Holyhead Road, Bicton, Shrewsbury SY3 8EF
☎ & FAX 01743 850773

CONTACT Jessica Pannett
LOCATION On B4380 west of Shrewsbury
OPEN 9 am – 5.30 pm, daily
SPECIALITIES Conifers; herbaceous perennials
CATALOGUE Yes
MAIL ORDER Yes
SHOP Sundries, floral art materials
GARDEN Herbert Lewis Hospice Garden
SHOWS Malvern (Spring); Malvern (Autumn)

This family-run nursery carries a wide general range but specialises in conifers and perennials. They give lectures, run day courses, and organise gardening holidays. The show garden opens to support the local hospice.

Nordybank Nurseries
Clee St Margaret, Craven Arms SY7 9EF
☎ 01584 823322

CONTACT Polly Bolton
LOCATION Between Bridgnorth and Ludlow, off B4364
OPEN Mondays, Wednesdays, Sundays, Easter to mid October
SPECIALITIES Herbaceous perennials; herbs; rhododendrons; wild flowers
CATALOGUE Large SAE plus 50p
MAIL ORDER No
REFRESHMENTS Teas
GARDEN Rose and flower display garden

A choice of hardy herbaceous plants, including shade-lovers, with herbs and wild flowers also. Design advice available. The cottage garden opens for the NGS.

Oak Cottage Herb Garden
Nesscliffe, Shrewsbury SY4 1DB
☎ & FAX 01743 741262

CONTACT Edward or Jane Bygott
LOCATION Halfway between Shrewsbury and Oswestry on A5
OPEN Usually 11.30 am – 6.30 pm, daily
SPECIALITIES Herbs; wild flowers
CATALOGUE 3 first-class stamps
MAIL ORDER Yes
SHOP Herb products, books, seeds

GARDEN   Herb garden
DESIGN SERVICE   Oak Cottage Herb Garden

A small nursery propagating and selling wild flowers, herbs and cottage garden plants. Small quantities only, but larger orders by arrangement, and the range is extensive. There's also a small shop, and they offer a design and planting service: knot gardens a speciality. And a new garden is being planted, Oak Cottage Walled Garden at Atcham, east of Shrewsbury; plants for sale there too.

Perrybrook Nursery
Brook Cottage, Wykey, Ruyton XI Towns, Shrewsbury SY4 1JA
☎ & FAX 01939 261120

CONTACT   G. Williams
LOCATION   North Shropshire
OPEN   1 – 6 pm, Tuesday – Friday; other times by appointment
SPECIALITIES   Herbaceous perennials
NEW FOR 1997   Range of *Epimedium* and *Tiarella*
CATALOGUE   4 first-class stamps
MAIL ORDER   No
GARDEN   Garden and display of specialities

Specialist wholesale and retail nursery with a range of hardy perennials. Strong on *Tricyrtis*. There is also a display of agricultural machinery, including a working threshing drum. The nursery will be at Shrewsbury Flower Show.

SOMERSET

Arne Herbs
Limeburn Nurseries, Chew Magna, Bristol BS18 8QW
☎ & FAX 01275 333399

CONTACT   Jenny Thomas
LOCATION   8 miles south of Bristol, just off B3130
OPEN   10 am – 5 pm, usually. Phone first
SPECIALITIES   Herbs; wild flowers
NEW FOR 1997   *Myrica cerifera*, *Withania somnifera*
CATALOGUE   £1.50
MAIL ORDER   Yes, no minimum order
DESIGN SERVICE   Arne Herbs

Twin ranges of herbs and native species which can be used for conservation schemes. Fresh cut herbs available in season too. Advice service for customers. Consultancy for physic gardens.

Avon Bulbs
Burnt House Farm, Mid-Lambrook, South Petherton TA13 5HE
☎ 01460 242177

CONTACT   Chris Ireland-Jones
LOCATION   3 miles north-west of South Petherton, off A303
OPEN   9 am – 4.30 pm, Thursday – Saturday, mid-September to end October, and mid-February to end March
SPECIALITIES   Bulbs
CATALOGUE   4 second-class stamps
MAIL ORDER   Yes
GARDEN   Growing area, open as above

SHOWS   RHS Westminster; Malvern (Spring); Harrogate (Spring); Chelsea

Avon Bulbs offers an impressive variety of bulbs (and close relatives) covering all sizes, seasons and shapes. The nursery is well-run: plants are beautifully grown and immaculately displayed. Well worth a visit early in the year to see a wide range of stocks not listed in the catalogue. Opening hours are limited because of the seasonal nature of the business and their show commitments. It is a good idea to check with them before visiting. The striking show exhibits are recommended.

Blackmore & Langdon
Stanton Nurseries, Pensford, Bristol BS18 4JL
☎ & FAX 01275 332300

CONTACT   Rosemary Langdon
LOCATION   8 miles south of Bristol on B3130, between A37 Wells road and A38
OPEN   9 am – 5 pm, Monday – Saturday; 10 am – 4 pm, Sundays
SPECIALITIES   Begonias; delphiniums; *Phlox*
NEW FOR 1997   Five new begonias: 'Krakatoa', 'Pink Champagne', 'Coppelia', 'Moulin Rouge' and 'Crystal Cascade'.
CATALOGUE   SAE
MAIL ORDER   Yes
SHOWS   Malvern (Spring); Southport; Chelsea; BBC GW Live; Hampton Court

This family business, started in 1901, is still run by the founder's grandchildren. Theirs is a long tradition of showy border plants, notably huge begonias and tall delphiniums. All plants are grown on site. They are regular attenders at shows, especially in the south and west.

Brackenwood Garden Centre
131 Nore Road, Portishead, Bristol BS20 8DU
☎ & FAX 01275 843484

CONTACT   Manager
OPEN   9 am – 5.30 pm, Monday – Saturday; 10 am – 5.30 pm, Sundays. Closed over Christmas
SPECIALITIES   Conifers; herbaceous perennials; shrubs
MAIL ORDER   No
SHOP   Yes
REFRESHMENTS   Restaurant & tea room
GARDEN   8-acre Woodland Garden
DESIGN SERVICE   Brackenwood Garden Centre

Garden centre with a wide and constantly changing all-round range. They have a floristry department which runs regular flower arranging demonstrations and a busy programme of events. See also Brackenwood Plant Centre.

Brackenwood Plant Centre
Leigh Court Estate, Pill Road, Abbots Leigh, Bristol BS8 3RA
☎ 01275 375292

CONTACT   J. Maycock or C. Maycock
OPEN   10 am – 5 pm, spring and summer; 10 am – 4.30 pm, winter
SPECIALITIES   Bamboos; conifers; herbaceous perennials; shrubs
MAIL ORDER   No

SHOP   Yes
REFRESHMENTS   At garden centre
GARDEN   Wildlife lake with native aquatic species planted;
display gardens
DESIGN SERVICE   Brackenwood Nurseries

All-round stock, grown at the site. There's also a lake, and
display gardens. See also Brackenwood Garden Centre.

Broadleigh Gardens

Bishops Hull, Taunton TA4 1AE
☎ 01823 286231   FAX 01823 323646
OPEN   9 am – 4 pm, Monday – Friday. Viewing only, and
collection by prior arrangement
SPECIALITIES   Bulbs; daffodils; herbaceous perennials; irises;
tulip species
CATALOGUE   2 first-class stamps; spring, autumn
MAIL ORDER   Yes
GARDEN   Gardens open
SHOWS   RHS Westminster; Chelsea
NCCPG NATIONAL COLLECTIONS *Narcissus* (miniature)

The nursery is best known as a small-bulb specialist. They now
grow almost as many foliage and woodland perennials. Look
out for the irises, snowdrops, the many miniature narcissus and
species tulips, and a double green *Muscari*. Open for viewing
only. Prior arrangement is essential if you want to collect from
the nursery.

Cannington College

Cannington, Bridgwater TA5 2LS
☎ 01278 652226   FAX 01278 652479
CONTACT·   Mr N. H. Rigden
LOCATION   3 miles west of Bridgwater off A39
OPEN   2 pm – 5 pm, daily, Easter to October
SPECIALITIES   Half-hardy perennials
CATALOGUE   On request
GARDEN   Extensive gardens
SHOWS   Chelsea
NCCPG NATIONAL COLLECTIONS *Abutilon*; *Argyran-
themum*; *Osteospermum*; *Wisteria*

The Somerset county agricultural college at Cannington sells
a range of plants propagated at the college. They are known
particularly for tender perennials including new *Osteospermum* cultivars. The college holds four National Collections.

Elworthy Cottage Garden Plants

Elworthy Cottage, Elworthy, Lydeard St Lawrence,
Taunton TA4 3PX
☎ 01984 656427
CONTACT   J. M. Spiller
LOCATION   10 miles north-west of Taunton, on B3188 in
Elworthy village centre
OPEN   11 am – 6 pm, Tuesdays, Thursdays and Fridays,
mid-March to mid-October; also by appointment
SPECIALITIES   Herbaceous perennials
NEW FOR 1997   *Geranium*   'Elworthy   Dusky',
Polemonium 'Elworthy Amethyst'
CATALOGUE   3 second-class stamps
MAIL ORDER   No
GARDEN   Garden open for NGS

A pleasant selection of perennials and cottage garden plants.
Strong on geraniums, with over 120 varieties, including some
raised here. Will be at the Taunton Flower Show.

Graham's Hardy Plants

Southcroft, North Road, Timsbury, Bath BA3 1JN
☎ 01761 472187
CONTACT   G. E. Nicholls
LOCATION   On B3115 in Timsbury
OPEN   10 am – 4 pm, Tuesday – Thursday, 1 April to 30
September. Telephone first
SPECIALITIES   Alpines
NEW FOR 1997   *Campanula lasiocarpa* 'Talkeetna',
Kelseya uniflora, *Viola cazorlensis*
CATALOGUE   2 first-class stamps
MAIL ORDER   Yes

Small alpine nursery with a short list of rock garden plants,
particularly species from North America. The selection of
Eriogonum and *Penstemon* is interesting for collectors. The
nursery attends most AGS shows and prices are reasonable.
Talks can be arranged.

Hadspen Garden and Nursery

Hadspen Garden, Castle Cary BA7 7NG
☎ & FAX 01749 813707
CONTACT   Nori or Sandra Pope
LOCATION   On A371 2 miles east of Castle Cary
OPEN   9 am – 6 pm, Thursday – Sunday, and Bank Holidays,
6 March to 28 September
SPECIALITIES   Herbaceous perennials; roses
CATALOGUE   3 first-class stamps
MAIL ORDER   No
REFRESHMENTS   Coffee, tea & lunches
GARDEN   Hadspen Garden, Somerset, see Gardens section
NCCPG NATIONAL COLLECTIONS *Rodgersia*

The nursery, which is attached to this well-known garden,
sells the larger garden-worthy herbaceous plants, such as
hostas and rodgersias, as well as clematis and old roses
(many of which are on their own roots).

Halsway Nurseries

Halsway, Crowcombe, Taunton TA4 4BB
☎ 01984 618243
CONTACT   T. A. or D. J. Bushen
LOCATION   ½ mile off A358 between Taunton and Mine-
head
OPEN   10.30 am – dusk, Thursday – Sunday; phone first
SPECIALITIES   Begonias; *Solenostemon* (coleus)
CATALOGUE   SAE for begonias and *Solenostemons*
MAIL ORDER   Summer months

Small nursery with a good choice of foliage begonias and
Solenostemon, besides a wide and varying selection of garden
and house plants. Their greenhouses are Victorian.

Hannays of Bath

Sydney Wharf Nursery, Bathwick, Bath BA2 4ES
☎ 01225 462230
CONTACT   Spencer Hannay
LOCATION   Off A4 ring road, approach along Sydney Mews

OPEN 10 am – 5 pm, Wednesday to Saturday; 2 pm – 5 pm, Sundays and Bank Holiday Mondays; 20 March to 13 October. Closed Mondays and Tuesdays. Winter and other times by appointment
SPECIALITIES Grasses; herbaceous perennials; shrubs
NEW FOR 1997 Plants from Hannay/Kingsbury collection, Bulgaria 1995
CATALOGUE £1.45
MAIL ORDER No
GARDEN Display borders

A rich and always interesting source of herbaceous plants and shrubs, mainly species. Recommended for both gardeners and collectors as a source of well grown grasses, perennials and shrubs. Many plants come from seed collected by the Hannays and the Compton, d'Arcy, Rix expeditions.

Hillier Garden Centre (Bath)
Whiteway Road, Bath BA2 2RG
☎ 01225 421162   FAX 01225 448856

CONTACT Mark Pitman (Manager)
OPEN 9 am – 5.30 pm, Monday – Saturday; 10.30 am – 4.30 pm, Sundays

Hillside Cottage Plants
Gibbet Lane, Whitchurch, Bristol BS14 0BX
☎ 01275 837505

CONTACT Mrs Jo Pike
LOCATION Off A37, 2 miles south of Whitchurch
OPEN Telephone first
SPECIALITIES Herbaceous perennials; Ilex
CATALOGUE 4 first-class stamps
MAIL ORDER No

Hardy geraniums are the speciality of this nursery. Jo Pike grows over 200 cultivars and is trying to get as many of them into her list as possible. She attends many of the West Country shows and fairs.

Kelways Ltd
Barrymore Farm, Langport TA10 9EZ
☎ 01458 250521   FAX 01458 253351

CONTACT Susan Farrell
LOCATION 10 miles east of Taunton
OPEN 9 am – 5 pm, Monday – Friday; 10 am – 4 pm, Saturday – Sunday
SPECIALITIES Herbaceous perennials; irises; peonies
CATALOGUE On request (retail and wholesale)
MAIL ORDER Yes
REFRESHMENTS Tea & coffee
GARDEN Display
SHOWS RHS Westminster; Malvern (Spring); Harrogate (Spring); Chelsea; Hampton Court

Long famous for their herbaceous and tree peonies, Kelways also has a large range of irises and day lilies, and an expanding perennial section. A selection of their plants are now also available through some 150 garden centres. Their catalogue is a handsome publication and a joy to read.

Little Creek Nursery
39 Moor Road, Banwell, Weston super Mare BS24 6EF
☎ 01934 823739

CONTACT Rhys or Julie Adams
LOCATION 3 miles from M5, Jct 21
OPEN Please phone first.
SPECIALITIES Hellebores; cyclamen
CATALOGUE 3 first-class stamps
MAIL ORDER Yes, no minimum order
SHOWS Malvern (Spring); Malvern (Autumn)

A small nursery which specialises in *Cyclamen* species (raised from seed), and *Helleborus*, with some perennials too. This year they attend the Bristol, Royal Bath and West, Taunton and Three Counties shows. They hold part of the Cyclamen Society's NCCPG collection – mainly the early-flowering varieties.

Littelton Nursery
Littleton, Somerton TA11 6NT
☎ 01458 272356

CONTACT Graham or Rosemary Seymour
LOCATION On B3151 between Somerton and Street
OPEN 9 am – 5 pm, daily except Wednesdays; 10 am – 4 pm, Sundays
SPECIALITIES Chrysanthemums; fuchsias; pelargoniums
NEW FOR 1997 *Pelargonium* 'Roller's Pioneer'
CATALOGUE £1 plus SAE (A5)
MAIL ORDER No

These fuchsia and geranium specialists have a good list of fuchsia cultivars, and some very interesting geraniums of every type.

Lower Severalls Herb Nursery
Crewkerne TA18 7NX
☎ 01460 73234   FAX 01460 76105

CONTACT Mary R. Cooper
LOCATION 1 mile east of Crewkerne
OPEN 10 am – 5 pm, Monday – Saturday; 2 pm – 5 pm, Sundays; 1 March to 15 October. Closed Thursdays
SPECIALITIES Herbaceous perennials; herbs
CATALOGUE 4 first-class stamps
MAIL ORDER Yes, minimum order £10 plus p & p
REFRESHMENTS Teas on NGS open days
GARDEN 2½-acre garden
DESIGN SERVICE Lower Severalls Herb Nursery

Herbs of all kinds, as you would expect, but there are also good selections of the hardy geraniums and salvias. A herbaceous border design service is available.

Mallet Court Nursery
Curry Mallet, Taunton TA3 6SY
☎ 01823 480748   FAX 01823 481009

CONTACT David Williamson
OPEN 10 am – 4 pm, Mondays to Fridays. Other days by appointment
SPECIALITIES Acers; trees
CATALOGUE Large SAE (37p stamp)
MAIL ORDER Yes

DESIGN SERVICE　Mallet Court Nursery
SHOWS　RHS Westminster; Malvern (Spring); Malvern (Autumn); Harrogate (Spring); Harrogate (Autumn); Southport; Chelsea; BBC GW Live; Hampton Court; Ayr; Courson

Specialist tree nursery with an excellent list of unusual trees. Particularly good for *Quercus* and *Acer*, and also strong on species from China and Korea. They are currently introducing Japanese maples from the late J. D. Vertrees' collection in the States. The nursery mobile telephone number is 0385 917515. There is an Open Weekend in late October to see the autumn colour.

Margery Fish Plant Nursery
East Lambrook Manor, East Lambrook, South Petherton TA13 5HL
☎ 01460 240328　　[FAX] 01460 242344

CONTACT　Mark Stainer
LOCATION　Signed from A303 at South Petherton
OPEN　10 am – 5 pm, Monday – Saturday, March to October; 10 am – 5 pm, Monday – Friday, November to February
SPECIALITIES　Herbaceous perennials
CATALOGUE　4 first-class stamps
MAIL ORDER　Yes
REFRESHMENTS　Apple juice, coffee & biscuits; pub opposite
GARDEN　East Lambrook Manor, Somerset, see Gardens section
SHOWS　Courson
NCCPG NATIONAL COLLECTIONS *Geranium*

A wide and attractive range mainly devoted to hardy herbaceous perennials. Good for *Artemisia*, *Euphorbia* and *Lavandula*: the *Geranium* list is exceptional. The late Margery Fish's garden needs no recommendation.

Mill Cottage Plants
The Mill, Henley Lane, Wookey BA5 1AP
☎ 01749 676966

CONTACT　Sally Gregson
LOCATION　2 miles from Wells: ring for directions
OPEN　10 am – 5.30 pm, Wednesdays, March to September
SPECIALITIES　Ferns; grasses; herbaceous perennials
CATALOGUE　3 first-class stamps
MAIL ORDER　Yes, minimum order £5; October to March
REFRESHMENTS　Available for groups
GARDEN　Garden open for NGS for groups or by appointment
SHOWS　Malvern (Spring); Malvern (Autumn)

The nursery grows a selection of cottage-garden type plants, including *Dianthus*, ferns, *Geranium* and grasses. Talks and workshops can be arranged, as can design and planting advice. They will be at the Salisbury and the Bristol Flower shows.

Monkton Elm Garden Centre
Monkton Heathfield, Taunton TA2 8QN
☎ 01823 412381　　[FAX] 01823 412745

CONTACT　M. Mills
LOCATION　2½ miles north-east of Taunton
OPEN　9.30 am – 5.30 pm, Monday – Saturday; 11 am – 5 pm, Sundays
SHOP　Garden sundries, greenhouses, buildings, aquatics

REFRESHMENTS　Restaurant
DESIGN SERVICE　Monkton Elm Garden Centre

Large garden centre with a complete range of plants and garden products. They have a design service and can deliver.

Monocot Nursery
Jacklands, Jacklands Bridge, Tickenham, Clevedon BS21 6SG
☎ 01275 810394

CONTACT　Mike Salmon
LOCATION　B3130 Clevedon – Nailsea
OPEN　10 am – 6 pm; Monday – Friday; by appointment
SPECIALITIES　Bulbs; seeds
CATALOGUE　SAE
MAIL ORDER　Yes

Specialist nursery with an amazing collection of bulbous plants (including tubers, rhizomes and corms). The stock is mostly of species, and subspecies, grown from seed, frequently from named collectors and sources. The seed list appears in October. Nursery browsers will find items which are not in the catalogue. Very strongly recommended.

National Collection of Passiflora
Greenholm Nurseries Ltd, Kingston Seymour, Clevedon BS21 6XS
☎ 01934 833350　　[FAX] 01934 877255

CONTACT　R. J. R. Vanderplank
LOCATION　Kingston Seymour
OPEN　9 am – 1 pm, 2 pm – 5 pm, Monday – Saturday
SPECIALITIES　*Passiflora*
CATALOGUE　3 first-class stamps
MAIL ORDER　Yes
SHOP　Gifts
GARDEN　Permanent plant display and exhibition of passion flower prints and history
SHOWS　Malvern (Spring); BBC GW Live; Hampton Court
NCCPG NATIONAL COLLECTIONS *Passiflora*

Passion flowers only. A fascinating proposition for anyone in a position to grow them. The catalogue is detailed, and includes precise temperature requirements. Seeds from the collection are also sold.

Otters' Court Heathers
Back Street, West Camel, Yeovil BA22 7QF
☎ 01935 850285

CONTACT　D. H. Jones
LOCATION　In village centre, 300 yards from shop/PO
OPEN　9 am – 5.30 pm, Wednesday – Sunday. Closed Mondays and Tuesdays
SPECIALITIES　Heathers
CATALOGUE　3 first-class stamps
MAIL ORDER　Yes
GARDEN　Display gardens
DESIGN SERVICE　Otters' Court Heathers

This nursery stocks a selection of hardy, lime-tolerant heathers. They offer a design service, including planting plans, for heather gardens and can give illustrated talks.

P M A Plant Specialities
Lower Mead, West Hatch, Taunton TA3 5RN
☎ 01823 480774   📠 01823 481046

CONTACT Karan Junker
LOCATION Directions given when appointment made
OPEN By appointment only
SPECIALITIES Acers; shrubs; trees; *Cornus; Daphne*
CATALOGUE 5 second-class stamps
MAIL ORDER Yes, no minimum order
GARDEN Demonstration garden
DESIGN SERVICE PMA Plant Specialities

Wholesale growers (with retail trade by mail order) of some interesting container-grown trees and shrubs. Strong on Japanese and snakebark acers, daphnes, magnolias and on tree species of *Cornus*. Some plants are available in larger sizes for instant impact. They also offer design and a specialist pruning service.

Rodney Fuller
Coachman's Cottage, Higher Bratton Seymour, Wincanton BA9 8DA

CONTACT Rodney Fuller
OPEN Mail order only
SPECIALITIES Violas
CATALOGUE SAE
MAIL ORDER Yes, minimum order £25

Very small, and charmingly specialised, viola and violetta cultivars. Dwarf box is a new addition.

Scotts Nurseries Ltd
Merriott TA16 5PL
☎ 01460 72306   📠 01460 77433

CONTACT Sales Desk
LOCATION In middle of village
OPEN 8 am – 5 pm, Monday – Friday; 9 am – 5 pm, Saturdays; 10.30 am – 4.30 pm, Sundays
SPECIALITIES Fruit; roses; trees
CATALOGUE On request; shrubs and perennials; roses and fruit
MAIL ORDER Yes
SHOP Garden sundries
DESIGN SERVICE Scotts Nurseries Ltd

A first-rate, long-established and respected nursery-cum-garden centre, offering a very wide range of field and container-grown plants. It is particularly strong on ornamental trees, top fruit and shrubs. Excellent quality and reasonable prices.

Shepton Nursery Garden
Old Wells Road, Shepton Mallet BA4 5XN
☎ 01749 343630

CONTACT P. W. Boughton
LOCATION Off B3136 Glastonbury road (signed to Shepton Community Hospital)
OPEN 9.30 am – 5.30 pm, Tuesday – Saturday
SPECIALITIES Alpines; herbaceous perennials
CATALOGUE 4 second-class stamps
MAIL ORDER No
GARDEN Display gardens

A mixed stock which includes alpines, herbaceous perennials and many shrubs. The nursery has a collection of *Chaenomeles.*

West Country Geraniums
Staunton Lane, Whitchurch, Bristol BS14 0QL
☎ 01275 832762

CONTACT Alan Pearce
LOCATION Map in catalogue
OPEN 2 pm – 5 pm, Monday – Saturday, 1 April to 30 June; phone first at other times
SPECIALITIES Pelargoniums
SHOWS Malvern (Spring); Southport; Hampton Court

A selection of all types of pelargoniums available both as young plants and in larger sizes at the nursery. They visit most major shows.

West Somerset Garden Centre
Mart Road, Minehead TA24 5BJ
☎ 01643 703612   📠 01643 706470

CONTACT Mrs J. Shoulders
LOCATION Just off Seaward Way
OPEN 8 am – 5 pm, Monday – Saturday; 10 am – 4 pm, Sundays. Some winter variation
SPECIALITIES Bedding plants; shrubs
CATALOGUE On request; roses; fruit; bedding; trees and shrubs
MAIL ORDER Yes, (p & p at cost)
REFRESHMENTS Café – home made food

Bedding plants produced at the nursery, and a good selection of shrubs stand out in a general range. There is a new range of smaller trees this year. Monthly availability lists are produced.

Wyevale Garden Centre
Hicks Gate, Keynsham, Bristol BS18 2AD
☎ 01179 778945   📠 01179 776436
REFRESHMENTS Restaurant

Wyevale Garden Centre
Pen Elm, Norton Fitzwarren, Taunton TA2 6PE
☎ 01823 323777   📠 01823 323773
REFRESHMENTS Restaurant

YSJ Seeds
Kingsfield Conservation Nursery, Broadenham Lane, Winsham, Chard TA20 4JF
☎ & 📠 01460 30070

CONTACT Margaret White
LOCATION Map in catalogue
OPEN Phone first
SPECIALITIES Seeds; trees; wild flowers
CATALOGUE 31p stamp
MAIL ORDER Yes

The nursery specialises in British native trees and shrubs (of British provenance) either open ground or container-grown. Wild flowers are sold as plugs or as seed. Advice or consultations are available.

STAFFORDSHIRE

Barncroft Nurseries

Dunwood Lane, Longsdon, Leek, Stoke on Trent ST9 9QW
☎ & [FAX] 01538 384310
CONTACT   S. Warner
LOCATION   3 miles west of Leek, off A53
OPEN   9 am – 7 pm (dusk if earlier), Friday – Sunday
SPECIALITIES   Conifers; heathers; rhododendrons; shrubs
NEW FOR 1997   *Picea glauca* 'Zucherhut'
MAIL ORDER   No
GARDEN   Display gardens with 400 heather varieties open at weekends

Wholesale nursery open on Fridays and weekends for retail customers. Many varieties of heathers, conifers, shrubs, rhododendrons, trees and some alpines are available, 2000 in all. The display gardens open at the same time. Wholesale only, Monday to Thursday. A design service is available for local customers during winter months.

Bretby Nurseries

Bretby Lane, Burton on Trent DE15 0QS
☎ 01283 703355   [FAX] 01283 704035
CONTACT   David Cartwright
LOCATION   Off A50 Burton to Ashby road
OPEN   9 am – 5 pm, Monday – Saturday; 10.30 am – 4.30 pm, Sundays
CATALOGUE   None
MAIL ORDER   No
SHOP   Gifts
REFRESHMENTS   Tea room

Retail garden centre and wholesale nursery (Barn Farm Nurseries) which specialise in shrubs.

Byrkley Park Centre

Rangemore, Burton on Trent DE13 9RN
☎ 01283 716467   [FAX] 01283 716594
CONTACT   Information Desk
LOCATION   5 miles west of Burton on Trent; leave A38 at Branston
OPEN   9 am – 5 pm, Monday – Saturday, September to March; 9 am – 6 pm, April to August; 9 am – 9 pm, Fridays; 10.30 am – 4.30 pm, Sundays
CATALOGUE   Leaflets
SHOP   Garden products
REFRESHMENTS   Tea room & carvery
DESIGN SERVICE   Byrkley Park Centre
SHOWS   BBC GW Live

Garden centre which has been developed inside a Victorian walled garden. Services include delivery, design and landscaping, play area and farm animals. They run events throughout the year, including a Flower Show on 25 August.

Heldon Nurseries

Asbourne Road, Spath, Uttoxeter ST14 5AD
☎ 01889 563377
CONTACT   J. H. Tate
LOCATION   On B5030 to Rocester 200 yds from A50

OPEN   10 am – sunset, daily
SPECIALITIES   Cacti and succulents; carnivorous plants
CATALOGUE   SAE
MAIL ORDER   Yes
REFRESHMENTS   Yes
SHOWS   Malvern (Spring); Malvern (Autumn); BBC GW Live; Hampton Court

Cactus and succulent specialists, with carnivorous plants too. Coach parties welcome. Shows include the Bath & West, Shrewsbury and the Nottingham.

Intakes Farm Nursery

Intakes Farm, Sandy Lane, Longsden, Stoke on Trent ST9 9QQ
☎ 01538 398452
CONTACT   K. Inman
LOCATION   Map in plant list
OPEN   By appointment only
SPECIALITIES   Herbaceous perennials
CATALOGUE   SAE for plant list
MAIL ORDER   No

A small nursery which concentrates on unusual forms of British native and cottage garden plants; double flowers, variegated or coloured leaves, for example.

Jackson's Nurseries

Clifton Campville, Tamworth B79 0AP
☎ 01827 373307
CONTACT   N. Jackson
LOCATION   3 miles from M42, Jct 11
OPEN   9 am – 5.30 pm, Mondays, Wednesday – Saturday; 10 am – 5 pm, Sundays. Closed Tuesdays
SPECIALITIES   Fuchsias
CATALOGUE   SAE for list
MAIL ORDER   No

Fuchsia specialists, with many cultivars available between March and June. They also have pelargoniums and vegetables, bedding and pot plants in season.

Planters Garden Centre

Woodlands Farm, Freasley, Tamworth B78 2EY
☎ & [FAX] 01827 251511
CONTACT   Gerald Ingram, Christine Ingram or Stewart Milligan
LOCATION   1 mile from M42, Jct 10
OPEN   9 am – 6 pm, Monday – Saturday; 11 am – 5 pm, Sundays
SHOP   Garden sundries, greenhouses, gifts, pets
REFRESHMENTS   Restaurant & coffee shop

Garden centre with outdoor and indoor plant ranges (the plantaria has been greatly enlarged), a large bonsai section, garden products, fish and a toy shop. There are talks and events throughout the year. Delivery service.

Wyevale Garden Centre

Wolseley Bridge, Stafford ST17 0YA
☎ 01889 574884   [FAX] 01889 574881
REFRESHMENTS   Restaurant

SUFFOLK

Brian Sulman Pelargoniums

54 Kingsway, Mildenhall, Bury St Edmunds IP28 7HR
☎ 01638 712297

CONTACT   Brian Sulman
LOCATION   Mildenhall
OPEN   Open weekend 7 – 8 June
SPECIALITIES   Pelargoniums
CATALOGUE   2 first-class stamps
MAIL ORDER   Yes, 6 plants minimum
SHOWS   RHS Westminster; Malvern (Spring); Malvern (Autumn); Harrogate (Spring); Harrogate (Autumn)

Specialist nursery for regal pelargoniums. Only open at the June weekend. Trades from the same address as Pearl Sulman (dwarfs and miniatures) though their businesses are distinct.

Crown Vegetables

Marward House, Stock Corner Farm, Beck Row, Bury St Edmunds IP28 8DW
☎ 01638 712779   FAX 01638 712244

CONTACT   Trevor Sore
OPEN   Mail order only
SPECIALITIES   Vegetables
MAIL ORDER   Yes

Specialist vegetables by post, including asparagus crowns, artichokes and horseradish.

Denbeigh Heathers

All Saints Road, Creeting St Mary, Ipswich IP6 8PJ
☎ & FAX 01449 711220

CONTACT   D. J. Small
LOCATION   Creeting St Mary
OPEN   Phone first
SPECIALITIES   Heathers
NEW FOR 1997   More new bud-blooming varieties of *Calluna vulgaris*
CATALOGUE   On request
MAIL ORDER   Yes

Wholesale and retail hardy heathers, sold as rooted cuttings, mini plants and some larger sizes. There are over 1000 species and cultivars here: they claim to have the largest range in the world, and are the suppliers to the National Collections.

Fisk's Clematis Nursery

Westleton, Saxmundham IP17 3AJ
☎ 01728 648263

CONTACT   E. Collett
LOCATION   On B1125, midway between Yarmouth & Felixstowe
OPEN   9 am – 5 pm, Monday – Friday, March to October; 9 am – 4 pm, Monday – Friday, November to February; 10 am – 1 pm, 2 pm – 5 pm, Saturdays and Sundays, April to October
SPECIALITIES   Clematis
CATALOGUE   4 first-class stamps
MAIL ORDER   Yes
GARDEN   Display garden

Well known clematis breeders and nursery with an extensive list.

Fulbrooke Nursery

Home Farm, Westley, Waterless, Newmarket CB8 0RG
☎ 01638 507124

CONTACT   Paul Lazard
OPEN   By appointment
SPECIALITIES   Bamboos
CATALOGUE   SAE
MAIL ORDER   Yes
GARDEN   Yes

Container-grown bamboos: the list includes some uncommon and tender species. Grasses and *Fatsia* too.

Gardiner's Hall Plants

Gardiner's Hall, Braiseworth, Eye IP23 7DZ
☎ & FAX 01379 678285

CONTACT   R. J. Mayes or J. Stuart
LOCATION   ½ mile off A140 at Stoke Ash
OPEN   10 am to 6 pm; Wednesday – Saturday; April to October
SPECIALITIES   Conservatory plants; fruit; herbaceous perennials
CATALOGUE   £1
MAIL ORDER   Yes, minimum order £15

A small nursery specialising in herbaceous perennials and with a stock of 2,500 varieties. Many genera are well represented by a wide choice of cultivars, some new and others seldom seen.

Goldbrook Plants

Hoxne, Eye IP21 5AN
☎ 01379 668770

CONTACT   Sandra Bond
LOCATION   Map in catalogue
OPEN   10.30 am – 6 pm, Thursday – Sunday. Other days by appointment. Closed January, and around Chelsea and Hampton Court Shows
SPECIALITIES   *Hemerocallis*; hostas
NEW FOR 1997   Hostas 'Chantilly Lace', 'Guacamole', 'Hoosier Harmony', 'Queen Josephine'
CATALOGUE   4 first-class stamps
MAIL ORDER   Yes, winter and spring dispatch
SHOWS   RHS Westminster; Chelsea; Hampton Court

An exceptional collection of *Hosta* (over 400), with a good choice of *Hemerocallis* and shade-loving plants too. As exhibitors they have an impressive run of Chelsea gold medals for each of the last seven years. Help with design sometimes available.

Goldsmith Trees & Landscapes Ltd

Crown Nursery, High Street, Ufford IP13 6EL
☎ 01394 460755   FAX 01394 460142

CONTACT   Anne Raymond
LOCATION   In Ufford village
OPEN   9 am – 5 pm, Monday – Saturday
SPECIALITIES   Hedging; English native trees; outsize trees
CATALOGUE   On request

MAIL ORDER   Yes

Specialists in large trees for special purposes; they also sell fruit trees and offer a design and landscaping service.

Gouldings Fuchsias
Link Lane, Bentley, Ipswich IP9 2DP
☎ 01473 310058

CONTACT   E. J. Goulding
LOCATION   Just off A12, mid-way between Colchester and Ipswich
OPEN   10 am – 5 pm, daily, 7 January to 2 July. Closed Fridays
SPECIALITIES   Fuchsias
CATALOGUE   4 first-class stamps; December
MAIL ORDER   Yes

Smart, efficient fuchsia growers, with about 350 cultivars. The following types are sold: new, foreign, basket, bedding, enclian-dras, triphyllas, species and hardies. Coach parties are welcome, by appointment. Staff can help name unidentified varieties. They also run a service whereby people can have new cultivars named after them or 'in loving memory'. There will be a special Fuchsias in Flower weekend in aid of Multiple Sclerosis 23 – 25 August.

Home Meadows Nursery Ltd
Top Street, Martlesham, Woodbridge IP12 4RD
☎ 01394 382419

CONTACT   S. Denis O'Brien Baker
OPEN   8 am – 5 pm, Monday – Saturday. Closed Sundays
SPECIALITIES   Chrysanthemums
NEW FOR 1997   Several new Korean chrysanthemums
CATALOGUE   SAE
MAIL ORDER   Yes
SHOWS   RHS Westminster; Chelsea
NCCPG NATIONAL COLLECTIONS   Dendranthema (Korean)

As well as a general selection of bedding and herbaceous plants, the main specialities here are Korean and spray Chrysanthemums, and their own Meadhome strain of Iceland Poppies.

Ken Leech Trees
Foxbro, Park Lane, Bulmer Tye, Sudbury CO10 7EQ
☎ & [FAX] 01787 375103

CONTACT   Ken Leech
LOCATION   Off A131, near The Fox in Bulmer Tye
OPEN   For collection of orders only
SPECIALITIES   Fruit
CATALOGUE   Yes
MAIL ORDER   Delivery can be arranged
REFRESHMENTS   Coffee and Biscuits
GARDEN   Yes

Wholesale and retail fruit tree specialist, the immaculate nursery holds a Royal Warrant. Ken Leech is also an orchard judge.

Martins Nursery
Smallwood Green, Bradfield St George, Bury St Edmunds IP30 0AJ
☎ 01449 737698

CONTACT   Richard Martin

LOCATION   6 miles south-east of Bury St Edmunds
OPEN   8.30 am – 5.30 pm, Monday – Friday; 9 am – 4 pm Saturdays; spring & summer
SPECIALITIES   Herbaceous perennials
NEW FOR 1997   Several new grasses
CATALOGUE   SAE
MAIL ORDER   Yes

Hardy herbaceous perennials in useful varieties.

Mickfield Watergarden Centre
Debenham Road, Mickfield, Stowmarket IP14 5LP
☎ 01449 711336   [FAX] 01449 711018

CONTACT   M. C. Burch
OPEN   9.30 am – 5 pm, daily. Closed Christmas, Boxing Day and New Year's Day
SPECIALITIES   Aquatic plants; bog plants
CATALOGUE   50p
MAIL ORDER   Yes
SHOP   Pond products
REFRESHMENTS   Tea room (weekends)
GARDEN   2 acre display gardens
DESIGN SERVICE   Mickfield Watergarden Centre

Plants for in and around water: aquatic, marginal and moisture-loving species. They also sell liners and pumps, and can design and advise on all sorts of water projects.

Mills Farm Plants and Gardens
Norwich Road, Mendlesham IP14 5NQ
☎ 01449 766425

CONTACT   Sue or Peter Russell
LOCATION   On A140, just south of Mendlesham turning
OPEN   9 am – 5.30 pm, daily. Closed Tuesdays, and all January
SPECIALITIES   Dianthus; roses
NEW FOR 1997   Dianthus 'Frank's Frilly', 'Herbert's Pink'
CATALOGUE   5 second-class stamps
MAIL ORDER   Yes, pinks and roses only

Mills Farm specialise in Dianthus (new and old hybrids, species and rock garden types) and roses: there is a list for each genus. The roses are mostly old-fashioned varieties, in a well-chosen selection. Gardening courses are also held at the nursery, spring and summer (SAE for details). Advice is free.

Mrs S Robinson
21 Bederic Close, Bury St Edmunds IP32 7DR
☎ 01284 764310

CONTACT   S. Robinson
LOCATION   Off A14 Bury St Edmunds, Sudbury exit
OPEN   By appointment
SPECIALITIES   Foliage plants
MAIL ORDER   No
GARDEN   Charity garden openings
DESIGN SERVICE   Sue's Garden Designs

Plants on wheels: Sue Robinson lectures to clubs and societies and brings plants to sell with her. A list of lectures is available. Garden design and plant supply also.

Nareys Garden Centre

Bury Road, Stowmarket IP14 3QD

☎ 01449 612559

CONTACT   J. B. Narey, F. Narey or E. Hicks
LOCATION   West of Stowmarket on A14
OPEN   8.30 am – 5.30 pm, summer; 8.30 am – 5 pm, winter; 10.30 am – 4.30 pm, Sundays
SHOP   Garden sundries, above-ground swimming pools
DESIGN SERVICE   Nareys Garden Centre

General garden centre, producing its own bedding and pot plants. Some landscaping and pool and building installation. Delivery service.

North Green Snowdrops

North Green Only, Stoven, Beccles NR34 8DG

CONTACT   John Morley
OPEN   Mail order only
SPECIALITIES   Snowdrops
CATALOGUE   £1.50
MAIL ORDER   Yes

A connoisseur's collection of rare *Galanthus*: some 70 species and cultivars. The nursery only sells mail order – the plants are sold in the green. See also North Green Seeds under Seedsmen.

Notcutts Nurseries (Woodbridge)

Ipswich Road, Woodbridge IP12 4AF

☎ 01394 383344   FAX 01394 385460

CONTACT   Nicholas Budgen
LOCATION.   Woodbridge, and 11 other garden centres
OPEN   8.30 am – 5.45 pm, Monday – Saturday; 11 am – 5 pm, Sundays. Close at 5 pm in winter
SPECIALITIES   Roses; trees
CATALOGUE   £3.25 by post; £2.50 from garden centres
MAIL ORDER   Yes
SHOP   Garden sundries
GARDEN   Demonstration gardens
DESIGN SERVICE   Notcutts Landscapes
SHOWS   RHS Westminster; Chelsea; BBC GW Live; Hampton Court

Large wholesale nurseries with a garden centre chain. They are strongest on flowering shrubs and trees, including roses, but they have more or less everything else too. Quality is first class. They have a design capability through Nottcutts Landscapes who are listed in our Professional Services section. This is the head office: the Woodbridge garden centre is attached (Tel: 01394 445400, Fax 01394 445419).

Paradise Centre

Twinstead Road, Lamarsh, Bures CO8 5EX

☎ & FAX 01787 269449

CONTACT   Hedy J. Stapel-Valk
LOCATION   Map in catalogue
OPEN   10 am – 5 pm, Saturday – Sunday, and Bank Holidays; Easter to October. By appointment at other times
SPECIALITIES   Bulbs; herbaceous perennials; seeds
CATALOGUE   4 first-class stamps
MAIL ORDER   Yes

REFRESHMENTS   In fine weather
GARDEN   5 acre gardens
SHOWS   RHS Westminster; Malvern (Spring); Harrogate (Spring); Chelsea; BBC GW Live; Hampton Court

A garden nursery which specialises in bulbs, herbaceous plants and shade and damp lovers (all grown at the nursery), plus a few seeds.

Park Green Nurseries

Wetheringsett, Stowmarket IP14 5QH

☎ 01728 860139   FAX 01728 861277

CONTACT   Richard or Mary Ford
LOCATION   6 miles north-east of Stowmarket
OPEN   10 am – 5 pm, daily, March to September
SPECIALITIES   Grasses; herbaceous perennials; *Hosta*
NEW FOR 1997   15 more hostas
CATALOGUE   4 first-class stamps
MAIL ORDER   Yes, no minimum order
REFRESHMENTS   Yes
GARDEN   Display garden
SHOWS   RHS Westminster; Malvern (Spring); Malvern (Autumn); Harrogate (Spring); Harrogate (Autumn); Southport; Chelsea; BBC GW Live; Hampton Court; Strathclyde

This nursery specialises in *Hosta* and *Hemerocallis*, with new cultivars each year. Other specialities include astilbes and ornamental grasses and primulas.

Pearl Sulman

54 Kingsway, Mildenhall, Bury St Edmunds IP28 7HR

☎ 01638 712297

CONTACT   Pearl Sulman
OPEN   Mail order only, except for Open weekend, 7 – 8 June
SPECIALITIES   Pelargoniums
CATALOGUE   3 first-class stamps
MAIL ORDER   Yes
REFRESHMENTS   Light refreshments on open day
SHOWS   Southport; Chelsea; BBC GW Live; Hampton Court

A small nursery which specialises in dwarf and miniature pelargoniums (500). Only open on the second weekend in June, otherwise by mail order. Trades from the same address as Brian Sulman.

Potash Nursery

Cow Green, Bacton, Stowmarket IP14 4HJ

☎ 01449 781671

CONTACT   Jim Blythe
LOCATION   On B1113 between Stowmarket and Finningham
OPEN   10 am – 5 pm, Saturday – Monday, mid-February to end June or by appointment
SPECIALITIES   Fuchsias
CATALOGUE   3 first-class stamps
MAIL ORDER   No
GARDEN   Coach parties by appointment
SHOWS   RHS Westminster; Malvern (Spring); Harrogate (Spring); Harrogate (Autumn); Southport; Chelsea; BBC GW Live; Hampton Court

Fuchsia specialist: their range is available as cuttings or larger plants. They are also open from 1 – 24 December for indoor cyclamen, azaleas and poinsettias. No mail order, but they attend lots of shows.

Rougham Hall Nurseries
A14 Rougham, Bury St Edmunds IP30 9LZ
☎ 01359 270577   📠 01359 271149

CONTACT   Ken Harbutt
LOCATION   On A14
OPEN   10 am – 4 pm, daily, March to October
SPECIALITIES   Asters; delphiniums; herbaceous perennials
CATALOGUE   5 first-class stamps
MAIL ORDER   Yes
GARDEN   Yes
SHOWS   RHS Westminster; Malvern (Spring); Malvern (Autumn); Harrogate (Spring); Harrogate (Autumn); Chelsea; BBC GW Live; Hampton Court
NCCPG NATIONAL COLLECTIONS Delphinium;   Ribes (gooseberries)

Breeders, introducers and growers of an extensive and inter-esting range of perennials. The selection of delphiniums and asters is particularly good. Mouthwatering gooseberries.

Siskin Plants
Davey Lane, Charsfield, Woodbridge IP13 7QG
☎ & 📠 01473 737567

CONTACT   C. Wheeler
OPEN   10 am – 5 pm, Tuesday – Saturday
SPECIALITIES   Alpines; dwarf Hebe
CATALOGUE   £1
MAIL ORDER   Yes
DESIGN SERVICE   Yes
SHOWS   BBC GW Live; Hampton Court

Alpines and dwarf shrubs, with a good choice of hebes from the National Collection.

The Walled Garden
Park Road, Benhall, Saxmundham IP17 1JB
☎ & 📠 01728 602510

CONTACT   J. R. Mountain
LOCATION   Map in catalogue
OPEN   9.30 am – 5 pm, Tuesday – Sunday and Bank Holi-days. Closed on Sundays from December to February
SPECIALITIES   Herbaceous perennials
CATALOGUE   2 first-class stamps
MAIL ORDER   No
GARDEN   Yes, planting continues

The nursery has a useful range of good garden plants, climbers, shrubs, perennials and annuals in season. The walled garden itself has been restored. Replanting continues.

Wyevale Garden Centre
Rougham Road, Bury St Edmunds IP33 2RN
☎ 01284 755818   📠 01284 706184

Wyevale Garden Centre
Newton Road, Chilton, Sudbury CO10 0PZ
☎ 01787 373628   📠 01787 373714

Wyevale Garden Centre
Grundisburgh Road, Woodbridge IP13 6HX
☎ 01394 380022   📠 01394 380740

REFRESHMENTS   Restaurant

SURREY

Beechcroft Nursery
127 Reigate Road, Ewell KT17 3DE
☎ & 📠 0181 393 4265

CONTACT   C. Kimber
LOCATION   On A240
OPEN   10 am – 5 pm, summer; 10 am – 4 pm, winter, and Sundays and Bank Holidays
SPECIALITIES   Alpines; bedding plants; conifers
CATALOGUE   On request
MAIL ORDER   No
GARDEN   Display garden

A mainly wholesale nursery specialising in the supply of alpines and conifers to nurseries and garden centres. Some retail trade also, and they have bedding plants in season.

Brian & Heather Hiley
25 Little Woodcote Estate, Wallington SM5 4AU
☎ 0181 647 9679

CONTACT   Brian or Heather Hiley
LOCATION   Send SAE for directions
OPEN   9 am – 5 pm, Wednesday – Saturday
SPECIALITIES   Conservatory plants; half-hardy plants
CATALOGUE   3 first-class stamps
MAIL ORDER   Yes, £10 minimum order
GARDEN   Display gardens open for NGS
SHOWS   RHS Westminster; Malvern (Spring); Malvern (Autumn); Harrogate (Spring); Chelsea; BBC GW Live; Hampton Court; Strathclyde

A stylish collection of tender perennials and shrubs: the salvias are particularly good. Among the hardy perennials the pen-stemons stand out. The Hileys are regulars at RHS shows where their brilliant exhibits have gained the recognition they deserve.

Clay Lane Nursery
3 Clay Lane, South Nutfield, Redhill RH1 4EG
☎ 01737 823307

CONTACT   K. W. Belton
OPEN   9 am – 5 pm, Tuesday to Sunday, 25 January – 31 March; daily, 1 April to 31 August. Closed September to end January
SPECIALITIES   Fuchsias
CATALOGUE   2 first-class stamps
MAIL ORDER   No
GARDEN   Fuchsia garden: June to August

This fuchsia specialist sells a wide range of cultivars and species, including hardy varieties and varieties which are suitable for baskets. The centre will operate in three stages: rooted cuttings (to mid-April); containerised plants (from May); and a full garden display (June to August).

Country Gardens
Horsham Road, Alfold, Cranleigh GU6 8JE
☎ 01403 752359   📠 01403 753301
CONTACT   David Snell (Manager)
OPEN   9 am – 6 pm, Monday – Saturday; 10.30 am – 4.30 pm, Sundays

Country Gardens
Wickham Road, Shirley, Croydon CR9 8AG
☎ 0181 654 3720   📠 0181 656 4755
CONTACT   Jay Rangdale (Manager)
OPEN   9 am – 6 pm, Monday – Saturday; 10.30 am – 4.30 pm, Sundays

Country Gardens
Reigte Road, Dorking RH4 1WP
☎ 01306 884845   📠 01306 740379
CONTACT   Neil Evans (Manager)
OPEN   9 am – 6 pm, Monday – Saturday; 10.30 am – 4.30 pm, Sundays

Country Gardens
London Road, Windlesham GU20 6LL
☎ 01344 21411   📠 01344 873146
CONTACT   John Hart (Manager)
OPEN   9 am – 6 pm, Monday – Saturday; 10.30 am – 4.30 pm, Sundays
SHOP   Aquatics, conservatories, petfood
REFRESHMENTS   Coffee shop

D N Bromage & Co Ltd
St Mary's Gardens, Worplesdon, Guildford GU3 3RS
☎ 01483 232893
CONTACT   D. N. Bromage or Mrs R. Tizard
LOCATION   On A322 Guildford to Bagshot road, next to White Lyon
OPEN   10 am – 4 pm, Thursday – Tuesday. Closed Wednesdays
SPECIALITIES   Bonsai
CATALOGUE   Brochure on request
MAIL ORDER   Yes
SHOP   Bonsai accessories

Bonsai trees and all accessories. Other services include offering a holiday home and repotting.

Foliage Scented & Herb Plants
Walton Poor Cottage, Ranmore Common, Dorking RH5 6SX
☎ & 📠 01483 282273
CONTACT   Prudence Calvert
LOCATION   From A246 take Greendene Shere turning outside East Horsley. Turn first left at Crocknorth Road. Nursery and garden 1 mile on right (near Ranmore Arms pub)
OPEN   Wednesday – Sundays, and Bank Holidays, March to September
SPECIALITIES   Aromatic and scented plants; herbs
CATALOGUE   Yes
MAIL ORDER   No
REFRESHMENTS   Nearby pub and restaurant
GARDEN   Herb gardens and new potager

DESIGN SERVICE   Foliage Scented & Herb Plants
The nursery stocks a range of aromatic herbs and shrubs. The herb gardens and potager open at the same times as the nursery. Talks on herbs and cookery demonstrations can be arranged.

Forest Lodge Garden Centre
Holt Pound, Farnham GU10 4LD
☎ & 📠 01420 23275
LOCATION   On A325 2 miles south of Farnham
OPEN   8.30 am – 5.30 pm, Monday – Saturday; 10.30 am – 4.30 pm, Sundays
SHOP   Gardening products, Gifts
REFRESHMENTS   Coffee shop
GARDEN   Demonstration gardens

Large garden centre. Previous winner GCA 'Garden Centre of the Year' Award.

Garden Style
68 Wrecclesham Hill, Farnham GU10 4JX
☎ 01252 735331   📠 01252 735269
CONTACT   John Hanson, Ben Cox
LOCATION   On A325 1 mile south of Farnham
OPEN   8.30 am – 5.30 pm, Monday – Friday; 8.30 am – 12.30 pm, Saturday
SPECIALITIES   Large sizes
CATALOGUE   On request
MAIL ORDER   No

Wholesale and retail nursery which specialises in specimen sizes in containers. They have climbers, conifers, shrubs and trees from 1m – 6m high. The largest container is 1,500 litres.

Garson Farm
Thompson Bros (Esher) Ltd, Garson Farm, Winterdown Road, Esher KT10 8LS
☎ 01372 460181   📠 01372 470410
CONTACT   Garson Farm
LOCATION   Off A307 or A244 via West End Lane
OPEN   9 am – 5 pm, Monday – Saturday; 11 am – 5 pm, Sundays. Extended hours in summer
SHOP   Farm shop
REFRESHMENTS   Restaurant

A garden centre, with plants and garden products, and a pick-your-own farm, including a farm shop.

Green Farm Plants
Bentley, Farnham GU10 5JX
☎ 01420 23202   📠 01420 22382
CONTACT   John Coke or Marina Christopher
LOCATION   North-east Hampshire
OPEN   10 am – 6 pm, Wednesday – Saturday, mid-March to mid-October
SPECIALITIES   Herbaceous perennials
CATALOGUE   3 first-class stamps
MAIL ORDER   No
REFRESHMENTS   Yes
GARDEN   New garden designed by Piet Oudlof
SHOWS   RHS Westminster

This nursery is full of interesting plants, including the results of recent collecting trips. It moved to a new, more spacious site last autumn. The main groups are hardy and half-hardy perennials, with an increasing number of woodland plants and sun-loving shrubs. Check before visiting.

Herons Bonsai Ltd
Herons Bonsai Nursery, Wire Mill Lane, Newchapel, Lingfield RH7 6HJ
☎ 01342 832657   📠 01342 832025
CONTACT   Peter or Dawn Chan
LOCATION   Newchapel
OPEN   9 am – 6 pm, daily
SPECIALITIES   Bonsai; Japanese plants
CATALOGUE   SAE plus £1
MAIL ORDER   Yes
SHOP   Bonsai accessories, Japanese items
GARDEN   Display
DESIGN SERVICE   Herons Bonsai Ltd
SHOWS   Chelsea; Hampton Court

Bonsai nursery, with a string of Chelsea golds. As well as trees for indoors and outdoors, there are pots, tools and accessories (retail and wholesale). Bonsai classes (SAE for details) and design available.

Hillier Garden Centre (Sunningdale)
London Road, Windlesham GU20 6LN
☎ 01344 23166   📠 01344 27904
CONTACT   Russell Winteridge (Manager)
OPEN   9 am – 5.30 pm, Monday – Saturday; 10.30 am – 5.30 pm, Sundays

Hydon Nurseries
Clock Barn Lane, Hydon Heath, Godalming GU8 4AZ
☎ 01483 860252   📠 01483 419937
CONTACT   A. F. George or Mrs A. M. George
LOCATION   2 miles east of A3, Milford exit. Near Cheshire Home
OPEN   8 am – 5 pm, Monday – Friday, and Saturdays in season. Closed for lunch 12.45 pm – 2 pm
SPECIALITIES   Rhododendrons
CATALOGUE   £2
MAIL ORDER   Yes, p & p at cost
DESIGN SERVICE   Hydon Nurseries
SHOWS   RHS Westminster

Rhododendron and azalea specialists. The extensive range covers all types, among them some tender species and their own *Rhododendron yakushimanum* hybrids. They also stock companion trees and shrubs. They can advise on design and planting. There will be special open weekends at Easter and during May.

Kaytie Fisher Nursery
South End Farm, Long Reach, Ockham GU23 6PF
☎ & 📠 01483 282304
CONTACT   Kaytie Fisher
LOCATION   Map in catalogue
OPEN   10 am – 4.30 pm, daily, May – July; Wednesday – Sunday, April, August, September; Wednesday – Friday, March and October; by appointment, November – February
SPECIALITIES   Herbaceous perennials; roses

CATALOGUE   5 second-class stamps
MAIL ORDER   Yes
GARDEN   Small cottage garden, open on request
DESIGN SERVICE   Kaytie Fisher

Older varieties for cottage-garden planting unite a pleasing mix of perennials, roses and shrubs. The design service specialises in Victorian and cottage gardens. They also have a stand at Ham House, Surrey every afternoon except Friday from April to October.

Kennedys Garden Centre
Oaken Lane, Claygate KT10 0RH
☎ 0181 398 0047   📠 0181 398 9559
CONTACT   Peter Harber (Manager)
OPEN   9 am – 6 pm, Monday – Saturday, April to September, close 5.30 pm, October to March; 10.30 am – 4.30 pm, Sundays

Kennedys Garden Centre
Rockinghams Garden Centre, Waddon Way, Purley Way, Croydon CR0 4HY
☎ 0181 688 5117   📠 0181 681 2208
CONTACT   Peter Hill (Manager)
OPEN   9 am – 6 pm, Monday – Saturday, April to September, close 5.30 pm, October to March; 10.30 am – 4.30 pm, Sundays
REFRESHMENTS   Café

Knap Hill Nursery Ltd
Barrs Lane, Knaphill, Woking GU21 2JW
☎ 01483 481214/5   📠 01483 797261
CONTACT   Joy West
LOCATION   2½ miles west of Woking, off A322
OPEN   9 am – 5 pm, Monday – Friday
SPECIALITIES   Rhododendrons
CATALOGUE   50p plus postage
MAIL ORDER   Yes
SHOP   Garden centre
REFRESHMENTS   Coffee shop & carvery
SHOWS   RHS Westminster

Garden and nursery which specialises in rhododendrons and azaleas. Their extensive list includes hybrids, dwarf, semi-dwarf and *R. yakushimanum* cultivars, as well as deciduous and evergreen azaleas.

Knights Garden Centre
Limpsfield Road, Chelsham CR6 9DZ
☎ 01883 622340   📠 01883 627252
CONTACT   Mr David Knight
OPEN   8 am – 5.30 pm, Monday – Saturday; 10.30 am – 4.30 pm, Sundays
REFRESHMENTS   Pantry Coffee Shop
SHOWS   Chelsea

One of four Knights garden centres.

Knights Garden Centre
Nag's Hall Nursery, Godstone RH9 8DB
☎ 01883 742275   📠 01883 744429
OPEN   8 am – 5.30 pm, Monday – Saturday; 10.30 am – 4.30 pm, Sundays

General garden centre, including garden sundries and house plants.

Knights Garden Centre
Rosedene Nursery, Woldingham Road, Woldingham CR3 7LA

☎ 01883 653142   📠 01883 652221

CONTACT   Mrs B. Butler
LOCATION   Near M25, Jct 6
OPEN   8 am – 5.30 pm, Monday – Saturday; 10.30 am – 4.30 pm, Sundays
SHOP   Garden sundries, pond equipment, gifts
REFRESHMENTS   Conservatory Coffee Shop
GARDEN   Woldingham Dene
SHOWS   Chelsea

The head office of the four Surrey garden centres in the Knights chain. Events are held in the adjacent Woldingham Dene.

Knights Garden Centres (Head Office)
Ivy Mill Nursery, Godstone RH9 8NB

☎ 01883 563142   📠 01883 743564

CONTACT   Berry Butler
LOCATION   West of Godstone
OPEN   8 am – 5.30 pm, Monday – Saturday; 10.30 am – 4.30 pm, Sundays

Little Brook Fuchsias
Ash Green Lane West, Ash Green, Aldershot GU12 6HL

☎ 01252 29731

CONTACT   Carol Gubler
LOCATION   1 mile from A31, just off White Lane
OPEN   9 am – 5 pm, Wednesday – Sunday and Bank Holidays, 1 January to 1 July. Closed Mondays and Tuesdays
SPECIALITIES   Fuchsias
CATALOGUE   SAE plus 30p
MAIL ORDER   No
GARDEN   Open as nursery

Old and new *Fuchsia* varieties in abundance, as well as selected bedding and container plants at the nursery in spring.

Merrist Wood College Plant Shop
Merrist Wood College, Worplesdon, Guildford GU3 3PE

☎ 01483 235122   📠 01483 236518

CONTACT   Danny O'Shaughnessy
LOCATION   On campus, off A322 or A323
OPEN   8 am – 5 pm, Monday – Friday. Selected weekends too: phone first
SPECIALITIES   Conifers; shrubs; trees
MAIL ORDER   No
REFRESHMENTS   Mornings (during term)
SHOWS   Chelsea

Plants of all descriptions, from bedding to semi-mature trees. Most of it is produced by the students as part of their training.

Millais Nurseries
Crosswater Lane, Churt, Farnham GU10 2JN

☎ 01252 792698   📠 01252 792526

CONTACT   David Millais

LOCATION   From A287, ½ mile north of Churt, take Jumps Road, and follow signs
OPEN   10 am – 1 pm, 2 pm – 5 pm, Tuesday – Friday. Also Saturdays, March, April, October November; and daily, May only
SPECIALITIES   Rhododendrons
NEW FOR 1997   *Rhododendron* 'Gloria', 'Lady Romsey'
CATALOGUE   5 second-class stamps
MAIL ORDER   Yes, minimum order £25; October to March
REFRESHMENTS   NGS days only, 24 – 26 May
GARDEN   10-acre woodland garden, 1 May to 7 June
SHOWS   RHS Westminster; Malvern (Spring); Hampton Court

A rhododendron and azalea specialist. The extensive range of species and hybrids includes some new Himalayan species. The garden is open in May and early June.

Nettletons Nursery
Ivy Mill Lane, Godstone RH9 8NF

☎ & 📠 01883 742426

CONTACT   Jonathan Nettleton
LOCATION   Near M25, Jct 6: beside the green
OPEN   9 am – 1 pm, 2 pm – 5 pm, Monday – Saturday. Sundays in spring by appointment only. Closed Wednesdays
SPECIALITIES   Acers; conifers; shrubs; *Wisteria*
CATALOGUE   2 first-class stamps
MAIL ORDER   No

Acers in great variety (100), as well as many wisterias, 18 this year. There are other good trees and shrubs here too, all produced at the nursery. Telephone to check availability for rare plants.

Notcutts Garden Centre
Waterers Nurseries, London Road, Bagshot GU19 5DG

☎ 01276 472288   📠 01276 453570

CONTACT   Nicholas Chandler (Manager)
LOCATION   On A30
OPEN   9 am – 5.30 pm, Monday – Saturday; 11 am – 5 pm, Sundays. Closes at 5 pm in winter
SPECIALITIES   Rhododendrons; shrubs
SHOP   Garden sundries, furniture, pools, aquatics
REFRESHMENTS   Restaurant
DESIGN SERVICE   Notcutts Landscapes
SHOWS   BBC GW Live

Famous old nursery (including a wholesale division). Now part of the Notcutts empire.

Notcutts Garden Centre
Guildford Road, Cranleigh GU6 8LT

☎ 01483 274222   📠 01483 267247

CONTACT   Mark Vaughan (Manager)
LOCATION   On B2128
OPEN   8.30 am – 5.30 pm, Monday – Saturday; 11 am – 5 pm, Sundays. Closes at 5 pm in winter
SHOP   Garden sundries, furniture, machinery
REFRESHMENTS   Restaurant
DESIGN SERVICE   Notcutts Landscapes
SHOWS   Chelsea; BBC GW Live; Hampton Court

Pantiles Plant & Garden Centre

Almners Road, Lyne, Chertsey KT16 0BJ

☎ 01932 872195   FAX 01932 874030

CONTACT   Brendan Gallagher
OPEN   8.30 am – 5.30 pm, Monday – Saturday; 9 am – 5 pm, Sundays
SPECIALITIES   Bedding plants, large specimen trees and shrubs
CATALOGUE   SAE for availability list
MAIL ORDER   No
REFRESHMENTS   Coffee shop
DESIGN SERVICE   Pantiles Plant & Garden Centre
SHOWS   Chelsea; Hampton Court

The nursery specialises in outsize container-grown specimens (up to 8 metres), including *Dicksonia antarctica* (tree fern). There is also a good bedding range and a full landscaping service.

Planta Vera

Lyne Hill Nursery, Lyne Crossing Road, Chertsey KT16 0AT

☎ & FAX 01932 563011

CONTACT   Morris May
LOCATION   Map in catalogue
OPEN   9 am – 5 pm, last weekend of month and Bank Holidays, April to October; other times by appointment
SPECIALITIES   Violas
NEW FOR 1997   *Viola* 'Anna Leyns', 'Judy Goring', *Viola cornuta* 'Katie Grayson'
CATALOGUE   £1
MAIL ORDER   Yes
GARDEN   Display beds
NCCPG NATIONAL COLLECTIONS   *Viola*

Mr May took over the collection of *Viola* built up by Richard Cawthorne and continues his work. Visitors to the nursery can see the collection growing in the display beds. Plants are propagated from autumn cuttings and dispatched in spring.

RHS Plant Centre, Wisley

RHS Garden, Wisley, Woking GU23 6QB

☎ 01483 211113   FAX 01483 212372

LOCATION   RHS Garden, Wisley near Jct 10, M25 (A3 intersection)
OPEN   10 am – 6 pm (6.30 pm on Saturdays), Monday – Saturday; April to August. 10 am – 5.30 pm; Monday – Saturday; October to March. Also Sundays, 10 am – 4 pm, November to February, 11 am – 5 pm, March to October
CATALOGUE   No
MAIL ORDER   No
SHOP   Garden sundries, seeds, books
REFRESHMENTS   Restaurants in RHS Garden
GARDEN   RHS Garden, Wisley, Surrey, see Gardens section

Wisley's plant centre carries a very wide and interesting selection of most kinds of plants: one of the best in the country. Over 10,000 different cultivars are offered in the course of the year, including some rare and unusual plants. The bookshop has over 7,000 gardening titles for sale and a quality range of gifts. The adjacent garden is an obvious draw.

Rupert Bowlby

Gatton, Reigate RH2 0TA

☎ & FAX 01737 642221

CONTACT   Rupert Bowlby
LOCATION   Near M25, Jct 8: see catalogue for map
OPEN   Saturdays and Sunday afternoons, March, September and October. By appointment at other times
SPECIALITIES   Bulbs; *Allium*
CATALOGUE   2 first-class stamps
MAIL ORDER   Yes
SHOWS   RHS Westminster; Chelsea; Hampton Court

Bulb specialist, including *Narcissus, Tulipa* and *Fritillaria*. The *Allium* collection which has formed such striking displays in recent years continues to grow, stimulated by increasing public interest.

Secretts Garden Centre

Old Portsmouth Road, Milford, Godalming GU8 5HL

☎ 01483 426633   FAX 01483 426855

CONTACT   Manager
LOCATION   On A3100 on Milford/Godalming boundary
OPEN   9 am – 5.30 pm, Monday – Saturday; 10.30 am – 4.30 pm, Sundays; 9 am – 5 pm, Bank Holidays
SPECIALITIES   Conservatory plants; house plants
SHOP   Farm shop, flowers
REFRESHMENTS   Coffee shop
GARDEN   Yes, all year
NCCPG NATIONAL COLLECTIONS   *Cornus florida; Kalmia latifolia*

Plant orientated garden centre, including a flower nursery and pick-your-own shop.

Toobees Exotics

Blackhorse Road, Woking GU22 0QT

☎ 01483 797534   FAX 01483 751995

CONTACT   Bob Potter
LOCATION   On A324 between Woking and Brookwood
OPEN   10 am – 5 pm, Wednesday – Sunday, April to October. Phone first from November to March
SPECIALITIES   Cacti and succulents; carnivorous plants; palms
CATALOGUE   SAE
MAIL ORDER   Yes
REFRESHMENTS   Yes
GARDEN   Private collection on view
SHOWS   RHS Westminster; Malvern (Spring); Malvern (Autumn); Harrogate (Spring); Harrogate (Autumn); Southport; BBC GW Live; Hampton Court; Strathclyde; Courson

Succulents from Africa and Madagascar, including rare species of *Euphorbia*, besides carnivorous plants, palms and cycads. The address for correspondence is 20 Inglewood, Woking, Surrey GU21 3HX; evening telephone number 01483 722600.

V H Humphrey – Iris Specialist

Westlees Farm, Logmore Lane, Westcott, Dorking RH4 3JN

☎ 01306 889827   FAX 01306 889371

CONTACT   P. J. Brown
OPEN   By appointment only, and at May open days

SPECIALITIES Irises
CATALOGUE Large SAE or 3 first-class stamps
MAIL ORDER Yes
REFRESHMENTS Open days only
GARDEN 11 am – 3 pm, 17 – 18 May, only
SHOWS RHS Westminster; Chelsea

Irises only, and in abundance. Most of this list consists of bearded irises, but there are also species, pacific coast hybrids, *spuria* and *sibirica* cultivars too, with new named *ensata* hybrids this year. The business is mainly mail order, but there are two open days in May, at flowering time.

The Vernon Geranium Nursery
Cuddington Way, Cheam, Sutton SM2 7JB
☎ 0181 393 7616 FAX 0181 786 7437

CONTACT Philip James
LOCATION South-west of Cheam, map in catalogue
OPEN 9.30 am – 5.30 pm, Monday – Saturday; 10 am – 4 pm, Sundays; 1 February to 27 July
SPECIALITIES Fuchsias; pelargoniums
CATALOGUE £2, refundable on orders over £15
MAIL ORDER Yes, no minimum order
GARDEN Fuchsia display area

Specialist growers of pelargoniums (1100) and fuchsias (100). Plants are available as rooted cuttings by post, and pot-grown plants can be had from the nursery. The number of pelargonium varieties speaks for itself. Some patio plants available at the nursery. Open days, 12 – 27 July. Group visits (minimum of 12) are by appointment.

Wyevale Garden Centre
Lower Morden Lane, Morden SM4 4SJ
☎ 0181 337 7781 FAX 0181 335 3326
REFRESHMENTS Restaurant

EAST SUSSEX

Axletree Nursery
Starvecrow Lane, Peasmarsh, Rye TN31 6XL
☎ & FAX 01797 230470

CONTACT Dr D. J. Hibberd
LOCATION 2 miles south-west of Peasmarsh, off A268. Send SAE for map and directions
OPEN 10 am – 5 pm, Wednesday – Saturday, 10 March to 27 September
SPECIALITIES Hardy geraniums
CATALOGUE 4 first-class stamps, available in March; SAE for autumn mail-order list, available in August
MAIL ORDER Hardy geraniums only, in autumn
GARDEN 1-acre woodland garden, containing 3000 varieties: open same time as nursery

Best known for their substantial list of hardy geraniums: still more new cultivars are being introduced this year. There is a good range of other herbaceous perennials too, with an emphasis upon the unusual.

Coghurst Nursery
Ivy House Lane, Three Oaks, Hastings TN35 4NP
☎ 01424 756228

CONTACT J. Farnfield, Mr or Mrs Edgar
LOCATION Near Hastings – map in catalogue
OPEN 12 noon – 4.30 pm, Monday – Friday; 10 am – 4.30 pm, Sundays. Closed Saturdays
SPECIALITIES Camellias; rhododendrons
NEW FOR 1997 Range of *Camellia sasanqua*
CATALOGUE 2 second-class stamps
MAIL ORDER Yes, no minimum order
SHOWS RHS Westminster

Camellia and *Rhododendron* specialists. They stock all types of camellias and rhododendrons, and have a good selection of hydrangeas, eucryphias and other shrubs. A range of autumn flowering Sasanqua Camellias, including some scented varieties is being introduced. The nursery welcomes visitors and will give advice.

Country Gardens
Warren Road, Brighton BN2 2XX
☎ 01273 607888 FAX 01273 607799

CONTACT Andrew Turlington (Manager)
OPEN 9 am – 6 pm, Monday – Saturday; 10.30 am – 4.30 pm, Sundays
SHOP Aquatics, pets
REFRESHMENTS Restaurants

Country Gardens
Bexhill Road, St Leonards-on-Sea TN38 8AR
☎ 01424 443414 FAX 01424 428733

CONTACT Ian Dixon (Manager)
OPEN 9 am – 6 pm, Monday – Saturday; 10.30 am – 4.30 pm, Sundays
SHOP Garden buildings
REFRESHMENTS Coffee shop

Great Dixter Nurseries
Great Dixter, Northiam, Rye TN31 6PH
☎ 01797 253107 FAX 01797 252879

CONTACT K. Leighton
LOCATION Off A28, ½ mile north of Northiam
OPEN 9 am – 12.30 pm, 1.30 pm – 5 pm, Monday – Friday; 9 am – 12 noon, Saturdays; and when Great Dixter Gardens are open
SPECIALITIES Clematis; herbaceous perennials; shrubs
CATALOGUE 4 first-class stamps or £1
MAIL ORDER Yes, minimum order £10; not in May to August
SHOP Books
REFRESHMENTS Cold drinks when gardens open
GARDEN Great Dixter, East Sussex, see Gardens section

The nursery is attached to Christopher Lloyd's famous garden, and copies of his books are on sale here. The nursery specialises in clematis, but the rest of the general range includes perennials, shrubs and many other plants which can be seen in the garden.

Harvest Nurseries

Harvest Cottage, Boonshill Farm, Iden, Rye TN31 7QA
☎ 0181 325 5420

CONTACT D. A. Smith
OPEN Mail order only
SPECIALITIES Cacti and succulents
CATALOGUE 2 first-class stamps
MAIL ORDER Yes, no minimum order

A mail order only cacti and succulent nursery. They specialise in *Epiphyllum* hybrids. All the plants are propagated at the nursery.

Just Roses

Beales Lane, Northiam, Rye TN31 6QY
☎ 01797 252355

CONTACT J. H. Banham
OPEN 9 am – 5 pm, Tuesday – Friday; 10 am – 4 pm, Saturday – Sunday. Closed Mondays
SPECIALITIES Roses
CATALOGUE On request
MAIL ORDER Yes, November to February
GARDEN Display garden

Specialist rose growers, covering the whole spectrum of the genus. Container roses can be bought from mid-March, while stocks last. Most of the business is bare root, from November on.

Kennedys Garden Centre

Lower Dicker, Hailsham BN27 4BJ
☎ 01323 844834   FAX 01323 442922

CONTACT John Phillips (Manager)
LOCATION On A22
OPEN 9 am – 6 pm, Monday – Saturday, April to September, close 5.30 pm, October to March; 10.30 am – 4.40 pm, Sundays
REFRESHMENTS Café

Kent Street Nurseries

Sedlescombe, Battle TN33 0SF
☎ 01424 751134

CONTACT D. Downey
LOCATION 5 miles from Hastings, on A21
OPEN 9 am – dusk, daily
SPECIALITIES Bedding plants; fuchsias; pelargoniums
CATALOGUE SAE plus 2 first-class stamps per list

A general plant range is complemented by over 800 *Fuchsia* and *Pelargonium* varieties, including some older ones. They have separate lists for fuchsias and pelargoniums: specify which one you want.

Lime Cross Nursery

Herstmonceux, Hailsham BN27 4RS
☎ 01323 833229

CONTACT Louise Newman or Bob Bryant
LOCATION East of Herstmonceux, on A271
OPEN 8.30 am – 5 pm; daily
SPECIALITIES Conifers; shrubs; trees
CATALOGUE On request
MAIL ORDER No

Specialist conifer growers with some 300 varieties and more. There is also a useful choice of trees and shrubs among a general plant range.

Long Man Gardens

Lewes Road, Wilmington, Polegate BN26 5RS
☎ 01323 870816

CONTACT O. Menzel
LOCATION On A27 between Wilmington and Milton Gate
OPEN By appointment
SPECIALITIES Conservatory plants
CATALOGUE On request
MAIL ORDER No

The nursery specialises in unusual plants for conservatory and greenhouse culture, including an attractive choice of *Hoya* and *Bougainvillea*.

Merriments Gardens

Hawkhurst Road, Hurst Green TN19 7RA
☎ 01580 860666   FAX 01580 860324

CONTACT Mark Buchele
LOCATION Signed from A21 at Hurst Green
OPEN 10 am – 5.30 pm, daily
SPECIALITIES Herbaceous perennials
NEW FOR 1997 *Heliopsis* 'Benzigold'
CATALOGUE £1
MAIL ORDER No
SHOP Garden sundries
REFRESHMENTS Tea room
GARDEN 4-acre show garden, admission £1.50

Retail nursery growing a range of hardy plants. They also sell garden products and have their own garden club.

Norman Bonsai

3 Westdene Drive, Brighton BN1 5HE
☎ 01273 506476   FAX 01273 389724

CONTACT Ken Norman
LOCATION Leonardslee Gardens, Lower Beeding, West Sussex
OPEN 10.30 am – 6 pm, 1 April to 31 October, at Leonardslee Gardens
SPECIALITIES Bonsai
MAIL ORDER No
SHOP Bonsai accessories
REFRESHMENTS Restaurant & tea room
GARDEN Leonardslee Gardens, West Sussex, see Gardens section
SHOWS Chelsea

Imported and British-grown bonsai trees and accessories. There is a permanent display at Leonardslee Gardens of part of Mr Norman's personal bonsai collection. Demonstrations and tuition can be arranged, and a bonsai design and a mainte-nance service is also offered.

Oakhurst Nursery

Oakhurst, Mardens Hill, Crowborough TN6 1XL
☎ & FAX 01892 653273

CONTACT Stephanie Colton

LOCATION Between A26 and B2188 north-west of Crow-borough
OPEN 11 am – 5.30 pm, most days, mid-April to mid-September. Please phone first
SPECIALITIES Herbaceous perennials
CATALOGUE 2 first-class stamps
MAIL ORDER No

Small garden nursery with a constantly changing selection of useful perennials.

Perryhill Nurseries

Hartfield TN7 4JP
☎ 01892 770377   [FAX] 01892 770929

CONTACT Peter Chapman
LOCATION 1 mile north of Hartfield on B2026
OPEN 9 am – 5 pm, March to October; 9 am – 4.30 pm, November to February
SPECIALITIES Herbaceous perennials; roses
NEW FOR 1997 × Halimiocistus 'Ice Dancer', Rosa 'White Flower Carpet'
CATALOGUE £1.65
MAIL ORDER No; delivery for large orders
DESIGN SERVICE Perryhill Nurseries

No real specialities, except for the width of the range. Trees, shrubs, herbaceous perennials and roses are all available in quantity, and the varieties are well-chosen. A design and landscaping service is available.

Stone Cross Nurseries & Garden Centre

Rattle Road, Pevensey BN24 5EB
☎ 01323 763250   [FAX] 01323 763195

CONTACT C. Barker
LOCATION On old A27 between Polegate and Pevensey
OPEN 8.30 am – 5.30 pm, Monday – Saturday; 10 am – 4 pm, Sundays
CATALOGUE Trade catalogue only
MAIL ORDER No
SHOP Sundries

Wholesale and retail nursery and garden centre with an all-round plant range, including plants for chalky soils and coastal positions, mainly home-produced. They also have a PYO farm.

Usual & Unusual Plants

Onslow House, Magham Down, Hailsham BN27 1PL
☎ 01323 840967   [FAX] 01323 844725

CONTACT Jennie Maillard
LOCATION On A271
OPEN 9.30 am – 5.30 pm, daily; but Saturdays and Sundays only during August. Please phone first
SPECIALITIES Herbaceous perennials
CATALOGUE SAE plus 1 first-class stamp
MAIL ORDER No

Small herbaceous nursery: its specialities include hardy geraniums, Erysimum, Penstemon and Euphorbia.

Wyevale Garden Centre

Newhaven Road, Kingston, Lewes BN7 3NE
☎ 01273 473510   [FAX] 01273 477135
REFRESHMENTS Restaurant

WEST SUSSEX

Allwood Bros

Mill Nursery, Hassocks BN6 9NB
☎ 01273 844229   [FAX] 01273 846022

CONTACT D. James
OPEN 9 am – 4 pm, Monday – Friday
SPECIALITIES Dianthus
CATALOGUE 2 first-class stamps
MAIL ORDER Yes
SHOWS Malvern (Spring); Malvern (Autumn); Harrogate (Spring); Harrogate (Autumn); Southport; Chelsea; BBC GW Live; Hampton Court; Strathclyde; Ayr

The nursery lists 30 of the allwoodii hybrids which made its name, as well as old-fashioned laced pinks, alpine Dianthus, perpetual and border carnations.

Anthony Archer-Wills Ltd

Broadford Bridge Road, West Chiltington RH20 2LF
☎ 01798 813204   [FAX] 01798 815080

OPEN By appointment
SPECIALITIES Aquatic plants; bog plants
CATALOGUE On request
MAIL ORDER Yes, limited
DESIGN SERVICE Anthony Archer-Wills Ltd
SHOWS Chelsea

Water nursery belonging to a garden designer: see his entry in Professional Services for more details. The nursery stocks aquatic, marginal and waterside plants. They also sell liners and pumps. Anthony Archer-Wills's The Water Gardener is published by Frances Lincoln.

Apuldram Roses

Apuldram Lane, Dell Quay, Chichester PO20 7EF
☎ 01243 785769   [FAX] 01243 536973

CONTACT D. Sawday
LOCATION 1 mile south-west of Chichester
OPEN 9 am – 5 pm, Monday – Saturday; 10.30 am – 4.30 pm, Sundays and Bank Holidays
SPECIALITIES Roses
NEW FOR 1997 Roses 'Especially for You', 'Marguerite Anne', 'Poetry in Motion', 'Sunset Boulevard'
CATALOGUE On request
MAIL ORDER Yes
REFRESHMENTS Coffee machine, cold drinks, ice-cream and biscuits
GARDEN Rose fields
DESIGN SERVICE Apuldram Roses

Apuldram sell a mixed range of mainly modern roses. The pruning week is 4 – 9 March, and the open evenings in the rose fields are 6.30 pm – 8.30 pm, 19 & 26 June.

Architectural Plants
Cooks Farm, Nuthurst, Horsham RH13 6LH
☎ 01403 891772   📠 01403 891056
CONTACT Angus White or Sarah Chandler
LOCATION 3 miles south of Horsham, behind the Black Horse pub in Nuthurst
OPEN 9 am – 5 pm, Monday – Saturday
SPECIALITIES Foliage plants; trees; hardy exotics
CATALOGUE On request
MAIL ORDER Yes, minimum carriage £14
GARDEN Display garden

Somewhat out of the ordinary: they specialise in exotic-looking, evergreen foliage plants, often with stylish, architectural shapes. We particularly like their catalogue: breezily written and easy to use. Larger sizes are available for immediate impact, and they deliver anywhere. They also sell terracotta pots and wheelbarrows of their own design.

Cheals Garden Centre
Horsham Road, Crawley RH11 8LY
☎ 01293 522101   📠 01293 524255
LOCATION Junction of A264 with A23
OPEN 9 am – 5 pm, daily
SHOP Garden sundries

General garden centre.

Coombland Gardens
Coneyhurst, Billingshurst RH14 9DY
☎ 01403 741549   📠 01403 741079
CONTACT Rosemary Lee or David Browne
LOCATION Off A272 between Billingshurst and Haywards Heath
OPEN 2 pm – 4 pm, Monday – Friday, March to October. Bank Holidays and other times by appointment
SPECIALITIES Herbaceous perennials; seeds; hardy geraniums
CATALOGUE 5 first-class stamps for plants, £1 for seeds
MAIL ORDER Yes, minimum order £10
REFRESHMENTS Open days only
GARDEN Open in June, Saturdays or by appointment for groups
NCCPG NATIONAL COLLECTIONS Geranium, hardy

There are masses of hardy geraniums here, nearly 200, besides a general herbaceous range. They now also have an international seed list.

Cottage Garden Plants of Cuckfield
Mytten Twitten, High Street, Cuckfield RH17 5EN
☎ & 📠 01444 456067
CONTACT David or Pat Clarke
SPECIALITIES Herbaceous perennials

An appropriately named nursery. Their range is mostly herbaceous, but they sell shrubs and climbers too.

Country Gardens
Bognor Road, Merston, Chichester PO20 6EG
☎ 01243 789276   📠 01243 788708
CONTACT Colin Butler (Manager)
OPEN 9 am – 6 pm, Monday – Saturday; 10.30 am – 4.30 pm, Sundays
SHOP Aquatics, garden buildings, pets, farm shop
REFRESHMENTS Coffee shop

Country Gardens
London Road, Handcross RH17 6BA
☎ 01444 400725   📠 01444 400909
CONTACT Richard Dougal (Manager)
OPEN 9 am – 6 pm, Monday – Saturday; 10.30 am – 4.30 pm, Sundays
SHOP Aquatics, pets, reptile house

Country Gardens
Stopham Road, Pulborough RH20 1DS
☎ 01798 872961   📠 01798 874046
CONTACT David Williams (Manager)
OPEN 9 am – 6 pm, Monday – Saturday; 10.30 am – 4.30 pm, Sundays

Country Gardens
Littlehampton Road, Ferring, Worthing BN12 6PG
☎ 01903 242003   📠 01903 507486
CONTACT Steve Baker (Manager)
OPEN 9 am – 6 pm, Monday – Saturday; 10.30 am – 4.30 pm, Sundays
SHOP Aquatics, crafts, equestrian
REFRESHMENTS Coffee shop

Croftway Nursery
Yapton Road, Barnham, Bognor Regis PO22 0BH
☎ 01243 552121   📠 01243 552125
CONTACT Graham Spencer
LOCATION Between Yapton and Barnham, on B2233
OPEN 9 am – 5.30 pm, daily. Closed 27 November to 28 January
SPECIALITIES Herbaceous perennials; irises; hardy geraniums
CATALOGUE 4 first-class stamps
MAIL ORDER Bearded Iris sent August and September, Geranium sent April to October
REFRESHMENTS Picnic area available
GARDEN Display garden and iris fields
DESIGN SERVICE Keymer Landscapes
SHOWS Chelsea

This family business specialises in bearded irises, of which they have a very large selection. But they also sell other Iris types, and herbaceous perennials, including hardy geraniums. There will be a hardy geranium weekend 3 – 5 May and an Iris picnic weekend 31 May – 1 June.

Denmans Garden Plant Centre
Clock House, Denmans, Fontwell, Arundel BN18 0SU
☎ 01243 542808   📠 01243 544064
CONTACT Michael J. Neve
LOCATION 6 miles east of Chichester, just off westbound A27
OPEN 9 am – 5 pm, daily
CATALOGUE £2.50
REFRESHMENTS Café

GARDEN Denmans, West Sussex, see Gardens section
DESIGN SERVICE John Brookes Ltd

Part of this 1940s garden which is now under designer John Brookes's care. The plant centre, which can be visited separately, sells a good choice of shrubs and other plants, many of them propagated from the garden.

Fleur de Lys
The Lodge, Upperton Farm, Petworth GU28 9BE
☎ & FAX 01798 343742

CONTACT Lisa Rawley
OPEN By appointment
SPECIALITIES Conservatory plants
CATALOGUE On request
MAIL ORDER No
DESIGN SERVICE Yes

Home visits to advise on and supply conservatory owners with interesting plants. Planting service and maintenance available as well.

Hellyer's Garden Plants
Orchards (off Wallage Lane), Rowfant, Crawley RH10 4NJ
☎ 01342 718280

CONTACT Penelope Hellyer
LOCATION Map in catalogue
OPEN 10 am – 4 pm, Friday – Sunday, March to July and September; August and other times by appointment
SPECIALITIES Herbaceous perennials
NEW FOR 1997 Lots of hardy geraniums
CATALOGUE 3 first-class stamps and A5 SAE
MAIL ORDER No
REFRESHMENTS NGS days only
GARDEN Garden opens for NGS and by prior appointment

A selection of hardy and half-hardy perennials, including geraniums and salvias propagated from the garden made by the late Arthur and Grace Hellyer. The garden is now being restored. It opens for the NGS and can also be visited privately by appointment.

Hillier Garden Centre
Brighton Road, Horsham RH13 6QA
☎ 01403 210113 FAX 01403 275144

CONTACT Terry Clarke (Manager)
OPEN 9 am – 6 pm, Monday – Saturday; 10.30 am – 4.30 pm, Sundays

Holly Gate Cactus Nursery
Billingshurst Road, Ashington RH20 3BA
☎ 01903 892930

CONTACT T. M. Hewitt
LOCATION ½ mile from Ashington, on B2133 to Billingshurst
OPEN 9 am – 5 pm, daily. Closed 25 – 26 December
SPECIALITIES Cacti and succulents; seeds
CATALOGUE 4 second-class stamps
MAIL ORDER Yes
SHOP Garden sundries
REFRESHMENTS Yes
GARDEN Cactus garden

One of the largest of the cacti and succulent specialists. The extensive retail and wholesale lists includes all types of cacti, with over 50,000 specimens in stock, fascinating for cognoscenti and an eye-opener for the uninitiated. There is a cactus garden, and monthly special events are held in the spring and summer. They also issue an extensive seed list, and supplementary plant lists: £2 covers all mailings.

Houghton Farm Plants
Houghton Farm, Arundel BN18 9LW
☎ 01798 831100 FAX 01798 831183

CONTACT R. Lock
LOCATION In Houghton village, on B2139
OPEN 10 am – 5 pm, Monday – Friday; 10 am – 12 noon, Saturdays, March to October. Closed Sundays
SPECIALITIES Herbaceous perennials
CATALOGUE 3 first-class stamps
MAIL ORDER Yes
GARDEN Display garden

An interesting range of perennials and shrubs with the emphasis on the best available forms and some promising novelties. Cut flowers too.

Mephams Nursery
Chapel Lane, West Wittering PO20 8QG
☎ 01243 511132

CONTACT Mr or Mrs F. W. Mepham
LOCATION 6 miles south of Chichester
OPEN 10 am – 5 pm, Good Friday to early June. Closed Mondays, except Bank Holidays
SPECIALITIES Pelargoniums
CATALOGUE 2 first-class stamps
MAIL ORDER Yes
SHOWS BBC GW Live; Hampton Court

The nursery specialises in dwarf, fancy leaf and scented pelargoniums, but carries many other members of the genus too.

Peter J Smith
Chanctonbury Nursery, Rectory Lane, Ashington RH20 3AS
☎ 01903 892870 FAX 01903 893036

LOCATION On A24 between Horsham & Worthing
OPEN Mail order only
SPECIALITIES Alstroemeria
NEW FOR 1997 Four new miniatures: 'Princess Ragna', 'Princess Angela', 'Princess Sissi' & 'Princess Charlotte'
CATALOGUE 1 first-class stamp
MAIL ORDER Yes
SHOWS RHS Westminster; Malvern (Spring); Harrogate (Spring); Southport; Chelsea; BBC GW Live; Hampton Court; Ayr

Hybridist of Limonium, Freesia and Alstroemeria, which bear the 'Princess' prefix. They have a long flowering season, and last well as cut flowers.

Roundstone Garden Centre Ltd
Roundstone Bypass, Angmering BN16 4BD
☎ 01903 776481 FAX 01903 785433

CONTACT Alan Cureton

LOCATION   On A259 at Angmering
OPEN   9 am – 5.30 pm, summer and weekends; 11 am – 5 pm, winter
CATALOGUE   On request
SHOP   Garden sundries, buildings, machinery, gifts, aquatics
REFRESHMENTS   Coffee shop

Garden hypermarket with a large choice of plants, garden and more general products including foods. Delivery service.

Vesutor Airplants
The Bromeliad Nursery, Marringdean Road, Billingshurst RH14 9EH
☎ 01403 784028   FAX 01403 785373
CONTACT   Sharon Hanley
LOCATION   Telephone for directions
OPEN   By appointment. 9 am – 3 pm, Monday – Friday
SPECIALITIES   Air plants; bromeliads
CATALOGUE   £1 handbook; SAE for list
MAIL ORDER   Yes

Specialist grower and retailer of bromeliads, with an outstanding range of Tillandsia. They also have orchids and some carnivorous plants ('microplants'). Their wholesale business supplies these plants to many garden centres.

W E Th Ingwersen Ltd
Birch Farm Nursery, Gravetye, East Grinstead RH19 4LE
☎ 01342 810236
CONTACT   Paul Ingwersen
LOCATION   Sussex/Surrey borders
OPEN   9 am – 1 pm, 1.30 pm – 4 pm, daily, March to September. Closed Saturdays and Sundays from October to February
SPECIALITIES   Alpines; bulbs; conifers; seeds
CATALOGUE   2 first-class stamps
MAIL ORDER   Can be arranged. Orders can also be collected from shows, except Chelsea
GARDEN   Display garden
DESIGN SERVICE   Yes
SHOWS   RHS Westminster; Malvern (Spring); Malvern (Autumn); Harrogate (Spring); Harrogate (Autumn); Southport; Chelsea; BBC GW Live; Hampton Court; Strathclyde

Long-established alpine nursery with an excellent range of popular and less common rock garden plants, including dwarf shrubs and conifers. There is an annual plant sale in late September, but the nursery is worth a browse at any season. Excellent value.

Wyevale Garden Centre
Rogers Lane, Findon BN14 0RE
☎ 01903 874111   FAX 01903 877256
REFRESHMENTS   Restaurant

TYNE & WEAR

Birkheads Cottage Garden Nursery
Birkheads Lane, Sunniside, Newcastle upon Tyne NE16 5EL
☎ & FAX 01207 232262
CONTACT   Christine Liddle

LOCATION   5 miles from A1(M) Birtley Services, via A692 or A693, and then A6076: ½ mile south of Tanfield Steam Railway
OPEN   10 am – 6 pm; Saturdays, Sundays & Bank Holidays; April to October; other times by appointment
SPECIALITIES   Alpines; herbaceous perennials
MAIL ORDER   No
GARDEN   Two-acre display gardens: including topiary, pond, herbaceous borders and alpine rockeries
DESIGN SERVICE   Birkheads Cottage Garden Nursery

Small nursery with a varied and informed selection of cultivar and species alpines, perennials and shrubs. Worth a browsing visit. A professional design service is available, and plants can also be supplied from stock. Courses are held throughout the year on the professional use and maintenance of horticultural machinery and pesticides.

Cowells Garden Centre
Main Road, Woolsington, Newcastle upon Tyne NE13 8BW
☎ 0191 286 3403   FAX 0191 271 2597
CONTACT   John Taylor
LOCATION   1 mile south of Newcastle airport
OPEN   9 am – 6 pm, summer; 9 am – 5 pm, winter
SPECIALITIES   Prunus
REFRESHMENTS   Coffee room
GARDEN   Demonstration gardens

Award-winning garden centre, which stocks Blooms of Bressingham plants and is also a Hilliers Premier Plant stockist. They have a special emphasis on hanging baskets, in season, and won first prize for their hanging basket at Chelsea in 1996.

Peter Barratt's Garden Centres
Gosforth Park, Newcastle upon Tyne NE3 5EN
☎ 0191 236 7111   FAX 0191 236 5496
CONTACT   Sheila Caisley
OPEN   9 am – 5.30 pm. Monday – Saturday; 10.30 am – 4.30 pm, Sundays
SHOP   Garden sundries, aquatics
REFRESHMENTS   Yes
GARDEN   Demonstration gardens

Garden centre with a range of garden and leisure products. Delivery service.

Wyevale Garden Centre
The Peel Centre, District 10 (A1231), Washington NE37 2PA
☎ 0191 4177777   FAX 0191 4154787
REFRESHMENTS   Restaurant

WARWICKSHIRE

A D & N Wheeler
Pye Court, Willoughby, Rugby CV23 8BZ
☎ 01788 890341
CONTACT   Tony Wheeler
LOCATION   Map in catalogue
OPEN   10 am – 4.30 pm, daily, January to June. Phone first at other times

SPECIALITIES Fuchsias; pelargoniums
CATALOGUE 2 first-class stamps
MAIL ORDER Yes
SHOWS Malvern (Spring); Southport; BBC GW Live;
Hampton Court

Fuchsia and pelargonium specialists, with a good range of both
as well as hardy geraniums. They exhibit at shows in the
Midlands besides Capel Manor and Hatfield.

Collectors Corner Plants
33 Rugby Road, Clifton-upon-Dunsmore, Rugby CV23 0DE
☎ 01788 571881

CONTACT Pat Neesam
LOCATION Just off A5
OPEN By appointment
NEW FOR 1997 Lavatera 'Lisanne', Geranium lanugi-
nosum, Geranium sanguineum var. striatum 'Splish
Splash'
CATALOGUE 4 first-class stamps
MAIL ORDER Yes, no minimum order

This nursery has a most interesting list. It tries to acquire and
sell every worthwhile new garden plant. This quest for novelty
and rarity is matched by reasonable prices.

Diana Hull
Fog Cottages, 178 Lower Street, Hillmorton, Rugby
CV21 4NX
☎ 01788 536574

CONTACT Diana Hull
LOCATION Directions given when making appointment
OPEN By appointment only
SPECIALITIES Pelargonium (species)
CATALOGUE SAE
MAIL ORDER Yes

This small and very specialised nursery concentrates on species pelargoniums: the list gets yearly more enticing. Seed of
many species is available.

Fibrex Nurseries Ltd
Honeybourne Road, Pebworth, Stratford upon Avon
CV37 8XT
☎ 01789 720788   📠 01789 721162

CONTACT R. L. Godard-Key
OPEN 12 noon – 5 pm, Monday – Friday, January to March,
September to November; 12 noon – 4 pm, Tuesday – Sunday,
April to August
SPECIALITIES Ferns; pelargoniums; Hedera
NEW FOR 1997 Pelargonium 'Alys Collins'
CATALOGUE 2 first-class stamps
MAIL ORDER Yes
GARDEN Display gardens
SHOWS RHS Westminster; Malvern (Spring); Malvern
(Autumn); Harrogate (Spring); Southport; Chelsea; BBC GW
Live; Hampton Court
NCCPG NATIONAL COLLECTIONS Hedera; Pelargonium

Specialists for pelargoniums. They hold the national collection,
but plants are for sale from April to August only. The collec-

tion is open then too. Hardy ferns and Hedera are available
all year round. There is a fern garden, and a new ivy garden.

The Hiller Garden and Plant Centre
Dunnington Heath Farm, Dunnington, Alcester B49 5PD
☎ 01789 490991   📠 01789 490439

CONTACT David R. Carvill
LOCATION On B4088 (formerly the A435) 3 miles south of
Alcester, near A46 junction
OPEN 10 am – 5 pm, daily
SPECIALITIES Herbaceous perennials; roses
CATALOGUE 2 first-class stamps
MAIL ORDER No
REFRESHMENTS Garden tea rooms
GARDEN 2-acre demonstration garden

The Hiller Garden Centre is expanding the range of old-
fashioned, species and English roses it offers alongside the
perennials which remain the mainstay of their business. All
may be seen in their excellent display garden.

Hillier Garden Centre
Henley Road, Mappleborough Green, Studley B80 7DR
☎ 01527 852266   📠 01527 853124

CONTACT Donna Melbourne (Manager)
OPEN 9 am – 5.30 pm, Monday – Saturday; 10.30 am –
4.30 pm, Sundays

Kennedys Garden Centre
Kings Newnham Road, Church Lawford, Rugby CV23 9EP
☎ 01203 542319   📠 01203 545524

CONTACT Alan Jones (Manager)
OPEN 9 am – 6 pm, Monday – Saturday, April to September,
close 5.30 pm, October to March; 10.30 am – 4.30 pm, Sundays
REFRESHMENTS Café

Woodfield Bros
Wood End, Clifford Chambers, Stratford on Avon CV37
8HR
☎ 01789 205618

CONTACT Brian Woodfield
LOCATION On B4632 between Stratford and Broadway
OPEN 9.30 am – 4.30 pm, daily. Closed Sunday afternoons
SPECIALITIES Delphiniums; carnations (exhibition); lupins
CATALOGUE SAE
MAIL ORDER Yes, carnations and seeds only
SHOWS Chelsea; BBC GW Live

They specialise in perpetual flowering carnations, delphiniums
and lupins. Phlox, Hosta and Begonia cultivars are usually
available also. Mail order is restricted to carnations, delphinium and lupin seeds.

WEST MIDLANDS

Ashwood Nurseries Ltd
Greensforge, Kingswinford DY6 0AE
☎ 01384 401996   📠 01384 401108

CONTACT P. D. Baulk
LOCATION 2 miles west of Kingswinford, near A449

OPEN   9 am – 6 pm, Monday – Saturday; 9.30 am – 6 pm, Sundays. Closed 25 & 26 December
SPECIALITIES   Seeds; sempervivums; *Lewisia*; *Cyclamen*; Hellebores
NEW FOR 1997   *Lewisia* hybrids 'Ashwood Carousel'
CATALOGUE   4 first-class stamps
MAIL ORDER   Seeds only
SHOP   Gifts
REFRESHMENTS   Tea room
GARDEN   Display gardens
SHOWS   RHS Westminster
NCCPG NATIONAL COLLECTIONS *Lewisia*; *Cyclamen*, hardy

This large nursery carries a wide general range as well as a particularly good selection of hardy cyclamen and hellebores. *Lewisia*, *Cyclamen*, *Helleborus* and *Primula auricula* seeds are on sale, as well as lewisias from the National Collection.

Country Gardens
Brownshill Green Road, Allesley, Coventry CV5 9BB
☎ 01203 333998   FAX 01203 336815

CONTACT   Steve Walton (Manager)
OPEN   9 am – 6 pm, Monday – Saturday; 10.30 am – 4.30 pm, Sundays

Jardinerie Ltd
Kenilworth Road, Hampton-in-Arden, Solihull B92 0LP
☎ 01675 442866   FAX 01675 443326

CONTACT   Roger Smith (Manager)
LOCATION   On A452 north-west of Balsall Common
OPEN   9 am – 6 pm (but 5 pm in January & February), Monday – Saturday (but open until 8 pm on Wednesdays & Thursdays in May & June); all year. 11 am – 5 pm, Sundays
SHOP   Gifts, conservatories, garden buildings, hydroponics centre
REFRESHMENTS   Café

Notcutts Garden Centre
Stratford Road, Shirley, Solihull B90 4EN
☎ 0121 744 4501   FAX 0121 744 4867

CONTACT   Julian Ranson (Manager)
LOCATION   Near M42, Jct 4 on Stratford Road
OPEN   9 am – 6 pm, Monday – Saturday; 11 am – 5 pm, Sundays. Closes at 8 pm, Thursdays and Fridays in spring and summer; 5.30 pm closing in winter
SHOP   Garden sundries, buildings, furniture
REFRESHMENTS   Restaurant
DESIGN SERVICE   Notcutts Landscapes

Oscroft's Dahlias
Woodside, Warwick Road, Chadwick End, Solihull B93 0BP
☎ 01564 782450

CONTACT   Mrs Nash or Mr Oscroft
LOCATION   On A4177 between Knowle and Warwick, 1½ miles north of town centre
OPEN   9 am – 6 pm, daily
SPECIALITIES   Dahlias

CATALOGUE   SAE
MAIL ORDER   Yes
GARDEN   Yes, always open

Dahlia specialist. Their wide range is available both as tubers and mini plants. Cut flowers are for sale in season. They have made a series of videos on dahlias.

Wyevale Garden Centre
Hampton Road, Eastcote, Hampton in Arden, Solihull B92 0JJ
☎ 01675 442031   FAX 01675 443859

WILTSHIRE

Barters Farm Nurseries Ltd
Chapmanslade, Westbury BA13 4AL
☎ 01373 832294   FAX 01373 832677

CONTACT   Duncan Travers
LOCATION   At the Westbury end of the village, on A3098
OPEN   9 am – 5 pm, Monday – Saturday; 10 am – 5 pm, Sundays and Bank Holidays
SPECIALITIES   Ferns; ground cover plants; hedging; trees; half-hardy plants
CATALOGUE   On request
MAIL ORDER   No
GARDEN   The Potter's Garden
DESIGN SERVICE   Barters Farm Nurseries Ltd

A retail plant centre operates in conjunction with a wholesale nursery. The range runs from trees, conifers and shrubs (mostly container-grown) to half-hardy and ground cover plants. There are many ferns on offer. Open weekends are held in May, for container gardening, in September, when the nurseries are opened, and for National Tree Week at the end of November.

Botanic Nursery
Bath Road, Atworth, Melksham SN12 8NU
☎ 01225 706597   FAX 01225 700953

CONTACT   Terence or Mary Baker
LOCATION   On A365 in Atworth, behind the clock tower
OPEN   10 am – 5 pm, daily. Closed for lunch 1 pm – 2 pm; also closed Tuesdays and all of January
SPECIALITIES   Herbaceous perennials; shrubs
NEW FOR 1997   *Campanula trachelium* 'Flore Plena'
CATALOGUE   £1
MAIL ORDER   No
GARDEN   Occasional displays
DESIGN SERVICE   The Botanic Nursery
SHOWS   RHS Westminster; Malvern (Spring); Malvern (Autumn); Harrogate (Spring); Harrogate (Autumn); Southport; Chelsea; BBC GW Live; Hampton Court; Courson
NCCPG NATIONAL COLLECTIONS *Digitalis*

Specialists for lime-tolerant plants, including foxgloves, of which they have the National Collection. There is much else of interest here. No mail order, but you can arrange to collect from shows. The landscape company offers design and construction services for larger gardens in southern England.

Broadleas Gardens Charitable Trust Ltd

Broadleas, Devizes SN10 5JQ
☎ 01380 722035

CONTACT Lady Anne Cowdray
LOCATION 1½ miles south-west of Devizes, on A360
OPEN 2 pm – 6 pm, Wednesday – Thursday, Sunday, April to October
SPECIALITIES Salvias
NEW FOR 1997 Emmenopterys henryii
MAIL ORDER No
REFRESHMENTS Home-made teas on summer Sundays
GARDEN Broadleas, Wiltshire, see Gardens section

The nursery sells a varied selection of plants propagated from this plantswoman's garden. The emphasis is on salvia species and cultivars, but includes magnolias and the very rare Emmenopterys henryii.

Jardinerie Ltd

Hay Lane, Wroughton, Swindon SN4 9QT
☎ 01793 852736   FAX 01793 852746

CONTACT Bob Sawyer (Manager)
LOCATION On B4005 towards Wroughton, just off M4, Jct 16
OPEN 9 am – 6 pm, Monday – Saturday; 10.30 am – 4.30 pm, Sundays
SHOP Gifts, aquatics, conservatories, garden buildings
REFRESHMENTS Café

Kennedys Garden Centre

Hyde Road, Swindon SN2 6SE
☎ 01793 822224   FAX 01793 832934

CONTACT Helen Taylor (Manager)
OPEN 9 am – 6 pm, Monday – Saturday April to September, closes 5.30 pm, October to March; 10.30 am – 4.30 pm, Sundays
REFRESHMENTS Café

Landford Trees

Landford Lodge, Landford, Salisbury SP5 2EH
☎ 01794 390808   FAX 01794 390037

CONTACT C. D. Pilkington
LOCATION 10 miles south-east of Salisbury
OPEN 8 am – 5 pm, Monday – Friday
SPECIALITIES Hedging; trees
CATALOGUE On request
MAIL ORDER Yes, minimum order £15
GARDEN Display plantings
SHOWS Courson

An interesting range of ornamental, deciduous, field-grown trees – some 600 varieties. In addition many species are now available in containers, and they stock hedging and conifers too. On a different tack they sell stone urns. Group visits by arrangement.

Longhall Nursery

Stockton, Warminster BA12 0SE
☎ 01985 850914

CONTACT Helen or James Dooley

LOCATION 7 miles south-east of Warminster, off A36. Near Stockton church
OPEN 9.30 am – 5.30 pm, Wednesday – Saturday, 20 March to 28 September. Other times by appointment
SPECIALITIES Herbaceous perennials
CATALOGUE 3 first-class stamps
MAIL ORDER Yes
REFRESHMENTS Teas at Longhall, when open
GARDEN Longhall
DESIGN SERVICE Yes

Next door to Longhall Gardens. There's a good choice of chalk tolerant perennials, many propagated from the garden.

The Mead Nursery

Brokerswood, Westbury BA13 4EG
☎ 01373 859990

CONTACT Emma Lewis-Dale
LOCATION Near Rudge, off A36 or A361
OPEN 9 am – 5 pm, Wednesday – Saturday, and Bank Holiday Mondays; 12 noon – 5 pm, Sundays, 1 February to 31 October
SPECIALITIES Alpines; herbaceous perennials
CATALOGUE 5 first-class stamps
MAIL ORDER No
GARDEN Display gardens

A mixed range of alpines and herbaceous perennials, including varieties suitable for trough plantings. Pot-grown bulbs and hypatufa sinks are also on sale.

Natural Selection

1 Station Cottages, Hullavington, Chippenham SN14 6ET
☎ 01666 837369

CONTACT Martin Cragg-Barber
LOCATION Off A429 south of Malmesbury
OPEN By appointment
NEW FOR 1997 Bellis perennis 'Monstrosa'
CATALOGUE 2 first-class stamps
MAIL ORDER Yes
GARDEN Opening Easter this year
DESIGN SERVICE Yes

The nursery seeks out rare British native plants and strange forms of commoner ones. Some species and scented-leaf pelargoniums too. They run courses and have a design service. An occasional newsletter links those who share their interest in recording odd plant forms.

Sherston Parva Nursery Ltd

Malmesbury Road, Sherston SN16 0NX
☎ 01666 841066   FAX 01666 841132

CONTACT Martin Rea
LOCATION On B4040 west of Malmesbury
OPEN 10 am – 5 pm, daily, all year
SPECIALITIES Clematis; climbers
CATALOGUE 4 first-class stamps
MAIL ORDER Yes
SHOWS RHS Westminster; Malvern (Spring); Malvern (Autumn); BBC GW Live; Hampton Court

There are around 100 clematis at the nursery besides climbers and shrubs suitable for wall planting and conservatory plants. The mail-order list is shorter.

Wessex Nurseries

Great Hinton, Trowbridge BA14 6BY
☎ 01380 870427

CONTACT　Tony Whatley
LOCATION　Between Trowbridge and Devizes
OPEN　8.30 am – 4.30 pm, daily
SPECIALITIES　Miniature roses
SHOWS　Malvern (Spring); Southport; Hampton Court

Miniature rose specialists. No mail order but they attend lots of shows.

West Kington Nurseries

West Kington, Chippenham SN14 7JG
☎ 01249 782822　　FAX 01249 782953

CONTACT　Barbara Stockitt
LOCATION　Off A420 8 miles west of Chippenham
OPEN　10 am – 5 pm, Tuesday – Sunday, plus Bank Holiday Mondays
SPECIALITIES　Alpines; herbaceous perennials; roses
CATALOGUE　On request (wholesale)
REFRESHMENTS　Coffee & home-made cakes
GARDEN　Pound Hill Garden, Wiltshire, see Gardens section
DESIGN SERVICE　West Kington Nurseries
SHOWS　RHS Westminster; Malvern (Spring); Hampton Court; Courson

Wholesale nursery which deals in alpine and herbaceous plants. The attached retail plant centre also has a selection of old-fashioned and English roses, and topiary plants.

Westdale Nurseries

3 Westdale Nurseries, Holt Road, Bradford on Avon BA15 1TS
☎ & FAX 01225 863258

CONTACT　C. W. or P. A. Clarke
OPEN　9 am – 6 pm, daily. Closed Christmas Day
SPECIALITIES　Pelargoniums; Bougainvillea
NEW FOR 1997　Pelargonium 'Westdale Apple Blossom'
CATALOGUE　Bougainvillea leaflet 2 first-class stamps plus SAE
MAIL ORDER　Bougainvillea
GARDEN　Greenhouse display of Bougainvillea
SHOWS　RHS Westminster; Malvern (Spring); Malvern (Autumn); Southport; Chelsea; BBC GW Live; Hampton Court

A West Country source of Bougainvillea in numerous varieties. The nursery also stocks pelargoniums. Talks can be arranged for groups of 12 and above. Coaches by appointment.

Whitehall Garden Centre Ltd

Lacock, Chippenham SN15 2LZ
☎ 01249 730204　　FAX 01249 730755
LOCATION　Between Chippenham and Melksham on A350
OPEN　9 am – 6 pm, Monday – Saturday (5.30 pm in winter); 10.30 am – 4.30 pm, Sundays
SHOP　Garden sundries, conservatories, pools, gifts

REFRESHMENTS　Restaurant
GARDEN　5-acre gardens
DESIGN SERVICE　Whitehall Garden Centre

Large family-run garden centre with outdoor and indoor plants, conservatories and greenhouses. Extensive landscaped gardens, and a landscaping service in association with a local landscaping firm. There are demonstrations and talks most Wednesday afternoons.

Wilton House Garden Centre

Wilton SP2 0BJ
☎ 01722 742280　　FAX 01722 743330

CONTACT　The Manager
LOCATION　On A30 west of Salisbury
OPEN　9 am – 5.30 pm, Monday – Saturday; 11 am – 5 pm, Sundays, summer; 10 am – 4 pm, Sundays, winter
REFRESHMENTS　Coffee shop

Well-run garden centre with a good range of plants.

Woodborough Garden Centre

Nursery Farm, Woodborough, Pewsey SN9 5PF
☎ & FAX 01672 851249

CONTACT　Els Brewin
LOCATION　3 miles west of Pewsey
OPEN　9 am – 5 pm, Monday – Saturday; 11 am – 5 pm, Sundays
SPECIALITIES　Clematis
MAIL ORDER　No
REFRESHMENTS　Coffee shop
GARDEN　Demonstration gardens

A garden centre on a large daffodil farm, and old flower nursery – the variety 'Fortune' was bred here. The garden centre specialises in clematis and spring bulbs. Pick your own fruit, vegetables and flowers. A varied programme of demonstrations is planned.

EAST YORKSHIRE

California Gardens

Howden, Goole DN14 7TF
☎ 01430 430824　　FAX 01430 432023
LOCATION　On A614, near M62, Jct 37
OPEN　9 am – 5 pm, daily
MAIL ORDER　No
SHOP　Greenhouses, garden buildings, sundries
REFRESHMENTS　Coffee lounge

Proud of a history going back to 1879, this garden centre carries an all-round range of plants and sundries. They stock Blooms' perennials, and organise demonstrations and garden workshop days.

The Cottage Garden Plant Centre

Thorn Road, Hedon, Hull HU12 8HN
☎ 01482 891434

CONTACT　Mr P. N. Pinnock
LOCATION　Off Hedon Bypass, map in catalogue
OPEN　9 am – 6 pm, daily
SPECIALITIES　Herbaceous perennials; herbs
CATALOGUE　50p

MAIL ORDER Yes
REFRESHMENTS Yes
GARDEN Large garden

Herbs and perennials grown without chemicals and over-cosseting to flourish anywhere. Courses in horticulture are run here for Hull College of Education.

J & D Marston

Culag, Green Lane, Nafferton, Driffield YO25 0LF
☎ 01377 254487

CONTACT J. or D. Marston
LOCATION Off A166 2 miles from Driffield
OPEN 1.30 pm – 4.30 pm, Saturday – Sunday, Easter to mid-September, and by appointment
SPECIALITIES Ferns
CATALOGUE £1.25
MAIL ORDER Yes

Excellent list of ferns for all growing conditions: hardy, cold greenhouse, temperate and warm.

Mires Beck Nursery

Low Mill Lane, North Cave, Brough HU15 2NR
☎ 01430 421543

CONTACT Martin Rowland or Irene Tinklin
LOCATION Access is via Mires Lane, off road between North Cave and South Cave
OPEN 10 am – 4 pm, Wednesday – Saturday, 1 March to 30 September; 10 am – 3 pm, Wednesday – Friday, 1 October to 28 February
SPECIALITIES Herbaceous perennials; wild flowers
CATALOGUE 3 first-class stamps
MAIL ORDER Yes

This nursery grows herbaceous perennials and wild flowers of Yorkshire provenance. They can give advice on wildflower planting. It is run to provide horticultural training and work experience for the disabled and is now a registered charity.

White Cottage Alpines

Sunnyside Nurseries, Hornsea Road, Sigglesthorne HU11 5QL
☎ 01964 542692   FAX 01964 642692

CONTACT S. E. Cummins
LOCATION On B1244 between Beverley and Hornsea
OPEN 10 am – 5 pm, Thursday – Sunday, and Bank Holiday Mondays. Closed December and January
SPECIALITIES Alpines
CATALOGUE 4 first-class stamps
MAIL ORDER Yes
GARDEN Display garden and troughs

The nursery has moved to a more spacious site which will allow it to expand an already interesting range. Among the plants for alpine houses and rock gardens are some American species, and species under collectors' numbers. Shows include the Gateshead Spring and Summer shows, and several AGS shows.

NORTH YORKSHIRE

Arcadia Nurseries Ltd

Brasscastle Lane, Nunthorpe, Middlesbrough TS8 9EB
☎ 01642 310782(Mail order) FAX 01642 300817

CONTACT P. Middleton
LOCATION On B1365 between Middlesbrough and Stokesley
OPEN Daily: 9 am – 7 pm in summer; 9 am – 5 pm in winter; 10.30 am – 4.30 pm on Sundays
SPECIALITIES Fuchsias
CATALOGUE 3 first-class stamps
MAIL ORDER Yes
REFRESHMENTS Coffee shop
GARDEN Demonstration gardens
SHOWS Harrogate (Spring); Harrogate (Autumn)

Specialist grower whose huge range of fuchsias – some 1,200 different cultivars – is the biggest in England. Visit between June and September to see them in flower.

Battersby Roses

Peartree Cottage, Old Battersby, Great Ayton, Cleveland TS9 6LU
☎ 01642 723402

CONTACT Eric Stainthorpe
LOCATION Between Kildale and Ingleby Greenhow, on the edge of the North Yorkshire moors
OPEN During flowering and planting season
SPECIALITIES Roses
NEW FOR 1997 Rose 'Brave Heart'
CATALOGUE SAE
MAIL ORDER Yes
SHOWS Harrogate (Autumn)

A family-run specialist growing only roses. They are mainly modern types, with a particular emphasis on exhibition roses. Other interests include northern roses. They will attend Gateshead, Rosecarpe (Belsay Hall), Rotherham and RNRS Northern Shows.

Cruck Cottage Cacti

Cruck Cottage, Cliff Road, Wrelton, Pickering YO18 8PJ
☎ 01751 472042

CONTACT Ronald or Dorothy Wood
LOCATION 3 miles west of Pickering, just off A170
OPEN 9 am – 12 noon, 1 am – 6 pm
SPECIALITIES Cacti and succulents
NEW FOR 1997 Range of *Euphorbia* species
MAIL ORDER No
GARDEN Gardens of ½ an acre surround the nursery

The nursery sells both large and small specimens of cacti and succulents, especially caudiciforms, and has special collections for beginners. Advice is on hand from the owners, and the nursery is accessible for disabled visitors.

Daleside Nurseries

Ripon Road, Killinghall, Harrogate HG3 2AY
☎ 01423 506450   FAX 01423 527872
LOCATION 4 miles north of Harrogate (A61)

OPEN 9 am – 5 pm, Monday – Saturday; 10 am – 12 noon, 1.30 pm – 4.30 pm, Sundays
CATALOGUE Lists available
MAIL ORDER No

A general plant range, including clematis, conifers and shrubs. They are happy to provide free advice on garden planning.

Deanswood Plants
Deanswood, Potteries Lane, Littlethorpe, Ripon HG4 3LF
☎ 01765 603441

CONTACT Jacky Barber
OPEN 10 am – 5 pm, April to September. Closed Mondays
SPECIALITIES Bog plants
CATALOGUE 4 first-class stamps for list
MAIL ORDER No
GARDEN 2-acre garden opens for NGS and Northern Horticultural Society

A nursery in a streamside garden, specialising in moisture-loving plants. Open in the summer only, from April to September. The garden is open for nursery visitors (donation to NGS), and for groups by appointment. Also a flower-arranging service with trained florists.

Fir Trees Pelargonium Nursery
Stokesley, Middlesbrough TS9 5LD
☎ & [FAX] 01642 713066

CONTACT Helen Bainbridge
LOCATION On A172 1 mile from Stokesley
OPEN 10 am – 4 pm, daily (please phone first in winter)
SPECIALITIES Pelargoniums
NEW FOR 1997 Pelargonium 'Fir Trees Fire Star'
CATALOGUE £1 or 3 first-class stamps
MAIL ORDER Large plants sent by carrier
SHOWS RHS Westminster; Malvern (Spring); Malvern (Autumn); Harrogate (Spring); Harrogate (Autumn); Southport; Chelsea; BBC GW Live; Hampton Court; Strathclyde; Ayr

They specialise in fancy leaf varieties at this nursery, part of a range of over 400 pelargoniums.

Gardenscape
Fairview, Smelthouses, Summerbridge, Harrogate HG3 4DH
☎ 01423 780291/0374 918582 [FAX] 01423 780291

CONTACT Michael D. Myers
LOCATION 12 miles north of Harrogate
OPEN By appointment only, and on open days
SPECIALITIES Bulbs; primulas; Hepaticas
CATALOGUE 3 second-class stamps
MAIL ORDER Yes
GARDEN Garden opens under NGS and by appointment
NCCPG NATIONAL COLLECTIONS Anemone nemorosa; Hepatica; Primula marginata

This specialist nursery is based around the three national collections held: Anemone nemorosa, Primula marginata and Hepatica. Other specialities include Galanthus and dwarf bulbs. They also sell hand made stone troughs and ornaments.

Kettlesing Nurseries
The Old Post Office, Kettlesing, Harrogate HG3 2LB
☎ 01423 770831

CONTACT Andrew or Angela Durance
LOCATION Off A59 6 miles west of Harrogate
OPEN 9 am – 5 pm, Thursday – Monday, March to October
SPECIALITIES Alpines, woodland plants
SHOWS Harrogate (Spring); Harrogate (Autumn)

Alpine and rock plant nursery, with lots of gentians, lewisias and primulas.

Norden Alpine Nursery
Hirst Road, Carlton, Selby DN14 9PX
☎ 01405 861348

CONTACT N. Walton
LOCATION Between Selby and Goole
OPEN March – September; winter by appointment
SPECIALITIES Alpines; primulas
CATALOGUE 3 second-class stamps
MAIL ORDER Yes
REFRESHMENTS B & B
GARDEN Garden

A large range of alpines, including Campanula, Oxalis, Primula and Saxifraga, propagated from a stock of some 2,000 plants. Bed and Breakfast is available at the nursery.

Oak Tree Nursery
Mill Lane, Barlow, Selby YO8 8EY
☎ 01757 618409

CONTACT C. G. or G. M. Plowes
LOCATION 14 miles south of York
OPEN 10 am – 4.30 pm, Tuesday – Sunday. Closed Mondays
SPECIALITIES Herbaceous perennials
CATALOGUE 2 first-class stamps
MAIL ORDER No
DESIGN SERVICE Acorn Landscapes
SHOWS Harrogate (Autumn)

A range of cottage-garden type plants, mainly herbaceous perennials. Full garden design and construction service. School visits to the nursery can be arranged. The nursery will be at the Great Yorkshire Show.

Orchard House Nursery
Orchard House, Wormald Green, Harrogate HG3 3PX
☎ & [FAX] 01765 677541

CONTACT Brian Corner
LOCATION 4 miles south of Ripon on A61
OPEN 9 am – 5 pm, Monday – Saturday; closed Sundays & Bank Holidays
SPECIALITIES Ferns; herbaceous perennials
CATALOGUE £1 or 4 first-class stamps
MAIL ORDER No
GARDEN Yes
DESIGN SERVICE Orchard House Nursery
SHOWS Harrogate (Spring); Harrogate (Autumn)

A fairly new nursery with a mixed range of hardy perennials, ferns and traditional favourites.

Perry's Plants

River Garden, Sleights, Whitby YO21 1RR
☎ 01947 810329

CONTACT Patricia Perry or Richard Perry
LOCATION 2 miles south-west of Whitby, on B1410 (near A169)
OPEN 10 am – 5 pm, daily, Easter to end of October
SPECIALITIES Herbaceous perennials
NEW FOR 1997 *Malva* 'Perry's Blue', *Erysimum* 'Gingernut'
CATALOGUE 60p in stamps
MAIL ORDER No
REFRESHMENTS Licensed café
GARDEN Riverside gardens

Herbaceous plants, particularly *Anthemis*, *Erysimum* and *Malva*, including their own new cultivars and others which originated here (e.g. *Osteospermum* 'Stardust'). Boats, putting and croquet in the old Victorian gardens.

R V Roger Ltd

The Nurseries, Pickering YO18 7HG
☎ 01751 472226   ☎ 01751 476749

CONTACT Ian Roger
LOCATION 1 mile south of Pickering, on A169 (The Roger Plant Centre)
OPEN 9 am – 5 pm, Monday – Saturday; 1 pm – 5 pm, Sundays
SPECIALITIES Bulbs; fruit; roses
CATALOGUE £1.50
MAIL ORDER Yes
SHOWS RHS Westminster; Malvern (Spring); Malvern (Autumn); Harrogate (Spring); Harrogate (Autumn); Southport; Chelsea; BBC GW Live; Hampton Court; Strathclyde; Ayr
NCCPG NATIONAL COLLECTIONS *Erodium; Erythronium*

The nurseries have a good all-round range including alpines, bulbs, conifers, perennials, roses, and trees and shrubs. They are especially good on fruit trees and bushes, including apples and gooseberries. They will be at all major shows this year.

Rivendell Nursery

1 Menagerie Cottages, Escrick, York YO4 6EH
☎ 01904 728690

CONTACT Dave Fryer
LOCATION 1½ miles down the Skipworth road, off the A19 York-Selby road
OPEN 10 am – 5 pm, Sundays. Other times by appointment
SPECIALITIES Conifers; shrubs
CATALOGUE 2 second-class stamps
MAIL ORDER No
GARDEN Organic vegetable plot
DESIGN SERVICE Rivendell Nursery

A small wholesale nursery which opens for retail customers on Sundays. The range includes alpines, conifers, heathers and shrubs. The nursery is one of the most respected organic nurseries in the country and takes part in the HDRA garden opening days.

Stillingfleet Lodge Nurseries

Stillingfleet, York YO4 6HW
☎ & FAX 01904 728506

CONTACT Vanessa Cook
LOCATION 7 miles south of York: turn opposite the church
OPEN 10 am – 4 pm, Tuesday – Wednesday, Friday – Saturday, 1 April to 18 October
SPECIALITIES Clematis; grasses; herbaceous perennials
CATALOGUE 5 first-class stamps
MAIL ORDER Yes, winter only
REFRESHMENTS In aid of Church on open Sundays
GARDEN Garden opens for NGS, 1 – 4 pm Wednesday afternoons, May and June, and 1.30 – 5.30 pm Sundays 18 May, 29 June
NCCPG NATIONAL COLLECTIONS *Pulmonaria*

Excellent herbaceous list with a high proportion of unusual plants from a nursery on top form. The catalogue changes each year. Particularly good for geraniums and pulmonarias. The *Pulmonaria* collection is open 1.30 – 5 pm, 20 April.

Strikes Garden Centre

York Road, Knaresborough HG5 0SP
☎ 01423 865351   FAX 01423 860155
LOCATION ½ mile east of Knaresborough
OPEN 9 am – 6 pm, Monday – Saturday; 10.30 am – 4.30 pm, Sundays
SHOP Gifts

Strikes Garden Centre

Boroughbridge Road, Northallerton DL7 8BN
☎ 01609 773694   FAX 01609 780604

CONTACT John Bailey (Manager)
LOCATION 1 mile from town centre, beyond the station
OPEN 9 am – 6 pm, Monday – Saturday; 10.30 am – 4.30 pm, Sundays
SHOP Gifts

Strikes Garden Centre

Meadowfields, Stokesley TS9 5HJ
☎ 01642 710419   FAX 01642 712831

CONTACT Pat Drummond (Manager)
OPEN 9 am – 6 pm, Monday – Saturday; 10.30 am – 4.30 pm, Sundays
SHOP Gifts

Whitestone Gardens Ltd

Sutton under Whitestone Cliffe, Thirsk YO7 2PZ
☎ & FAX 01845 597467

CONTACT Roy Mottram
LOCATION 4 miles east of Thirsk on A170
OPEN Dawn till dusk, daily. Closed Fridays
SPECIALITIES Cacti and succulents
CATALOGUE 4 second-class stamps
MAIL ORDER Yes
SHOP Books, sundries

A lengthy list of cacti and succulents is available at this specialist nursery, which holds the National Collection of the Borzicactinae section of the Cactaceae. They also sell relevant books and sundries.

Woodlands Cottage Nursery

Woodlands Cottage, Summerbridge, Harrogate HG3 4BT
☎ & FAX 01423 780765

CONTACT   A. Stark
LOCATION   On B6165 between Harrogate and Pateley Bridge
OPEN   10.30 am – 6 pm, Wednesday, Friday – Monday, 1 April to 30 September; or by appointment
SPECIALITIES   Herbaceous perennials; herbs
CATALOGUE   3 first-class stamps
MAIL ORDER   No
GARDEN   Garden opens for NGS
DESIGN SERVICE   Ann Stark

This small nursery specialises in herbs, cottage and rock garden plants, particularly shade lovers. There is a full design service.

Wyevale Garden Centre

Boroughbridge Road, Poppleton, York YO2 6QE
☎ 01904 795920   FAX 01904 794987
REFRESHMENTS   Restaurant

Yorkshire Garden World

Main Road, West Haddesley, Selby YO8 8QA
☎ 01757 228279

CONTACT   Carole Atkinson
LOCATION   6 miles south of Selby, off A19
OPEN   9.30 am – 5.30 pm, daily. In winter, closed at dusk
SPECIALITIES   Heathers; herbs
CATALOGUE   £1.50 'Herbs and Heathers'
MAIL ORDER   Yes
SHOP   Gifts, dried flowers
REFRESHMENTS   Tea room
GARDEN   Display garden
DESIGN SERVICE   Yorkshire Garden World
SHOWS   Harrogate (Spring); Harrogate (Autumn)
NCCPG NATIONAL COLLECTIONS   Santolina

The nursery changed its name last year from Herb and Heather Gardens Centre, but its main line remains herbs and heathers, with lots to choose from. Conifers, evergreen shrubs, wild flowers and cottage garden plants are stocked too. The display gardens cover several acres.

SOUTH YORKSHIRE

Brambling House Alpines

119 Sheffield Road, Warmsworth, Doncaster DN4 9QX
☎ 01302 850730

CONTACT   Jane McDonagh
LOCATION   West of Doncaster on A630; near A1M Rotherham exit
OPEN   10 am – 6 pm, spring and autumn. Closed Mondays except Bank Holidays. Phone first in summer
SPECIALITIES   Alpines; sempervivums; Diascia
CATALOGUE   Large SAE
MAIL ORDER   Yes, spring and autumn
GARDEN   Garden

A small nursery concentrating on alpines. Look out for their saxifrages and a wide range of Sempervivum species and cultivars, as well as auriculas, and Diascia from the National Collection holder. They visit a number of local shows, including Gateshead Spring and the Great Yorkshire.

Ferndale Nursery and Garden Centre Ltd

Dyche Lane, Coal Aston, Sheffield S18 6AB
☎ 01246 412763

CONTACT   Neil Grant
LOCATION   On Sheffield's southern boundary, off the A61
OPEN   9 am – 5.30 pm (6 pm, March to September), daily. 11 am – 5 pm on Sundays
SHOP   Florists, conservatories, greenhouses and garden buildings
REFRESHMENTS   Light lunches & coffee shop
DESIGN SERVICE   Ferndale Nursery and Garden Centre Ltd

A garden centre with a wide general range: stockists of both Hillier and Blooms' plants. They have a garden design service, and can advise on plant ailments too. The 'Expert in Your Garden' service is very popular. Talks, demonstrations and classes are also held, especially in spring and autumn.

Oscroft's Dahlias

Sprotborough Road, Doncaster DN5 8BE
☎ 01302 785026

LOCATION   North of Doncaster town centre
OPEN   9 am – 6 pm, daily
SPECIALITIES   Dahlias
CATALOGUE   SAE
MAIL ORDER   Yes
GARDEN   End June – end October

See their main entry under West Midlands.

Scott's Nurseries

Denaby Lane, Old Denaby, Doncaster DN12 4LD
☎ 01709 589906

CONTACT   M. Scott
LOCATION   Off A6023 west of Doncaster
OPEN   9 am – 6 pm, daily
SPECIALITIES   Dahlias
NEW FOR 1997   More new releases from the Barbarry collection
CATALOGUE   SAE
MAIL ORDER   Yes

Dahlia specialist: still more new varieties are due this year.

WEST YORKSHIRE

Armitage's Garden Centre

Pennine Garden Centre, Huddersfield Road, Shelley, Huddersfield HD8 8LG
☎ 01484 607248   FAX 01484 608673

CONTACT   A. Harper
LOCATION   Between Shelley and Skelmanthorpe on the B6116
OPEN   9 am – 5.30 pm, daily. Closes at 8 pm in the summer
SPECIALITIES   Garden Machinery
SHOP   Garden sundries; cut flowers
REFRESHMENTS   Café

Long-established garden centre, stocking trees and shrubs, alpines, house plants, aquatics, greenhouses and garden machinery. Their specialist garden machinery outlet, Mower World, is at the garden centre in Birchencliffe (off the A629).

Cravens Nursery
1 Foulds Terrace, Bingley BD16 4LZ
☎ 01274 561412

CONTACT   Steven or Marlene Craven
LOCATION   Ring for details
OPEN   By appointment, Thursdays – Sundays
SPECIALITIES   Dianthus; primulas; seeds
CATALOGUE   £1 each; £1.50 both (seed & plant)
MAIL ORDER   Yes, minimum order £10
SHOWS   RHS Westminster; Malvern (Spring); Harrogate (Spring); Harrogate (Autumn); Southport; Chelsea; Courson

A solid nursery with a reliable line in *Primula* species and named varieties, show auriculas and pinks, old and new. They also issue a separate seed catalogue devoted to primulas and auriculas: the Cravens are active breeders and are developing several good strains with their own prefix.

Greenslacks Nurseries
Ocot Lane, Scammonden, Huddersfield HD3 3FR
☎ 01484 842584

CONTACT   V. K. Tuton
LOCATION   Off A640: see catalogue for map
OPEN   10 am – 4 pm, March to October. Closed Mondays and Tuesdays
SPECIALITIES   Alpines; primulas; sempervivums; *Saxifraga*
CATALOGUE   4 first-class stamps
MAIL ORDER   Yes
GARDEN   Display garden
DESIGN SERVICE   Greenslacks Nurseries

An impressive and interesting list of alpines and hardy succulents. Strengths include Kabschia saxifrages (now Porpophyllum section) sedums and sempervivums. Their ready-made collections are good value.

Hedgerow Nursery
24 Braithwaite Edge Road, Keighley BD22 6RA
☎ 01535 606531

CONTACT   Nigel Hutchinson
LOCATION   Map in catalogue
OPEN   9 am – 5 pm, Wednesday – Sunday, March to October. Closed Mondays and Tuesdays except Bank Holidays.
SPECIALITIES   Alpines; conifers; rhododendrons; *Hebe*, dwarf
CATALOGUE   4 first-class stamps
MAIL ORDER   Yes
REFRESHMENTS   Open day only
GARDEN   Opens during nursery hours
NCCPG NATIONAL COLLECTIONS   Dwarf *Hebe*

Alpine specialists with an excellent list, particularly good for primulas, saxifrages, dwarf rhododendrons and hebes, of which they hold a NCCPG National Collection. Reasonably prices. Strongly recommended.

Mansell & Hatcher Ltd
Cragg Wood Nurseries, Woodlands Drive, Rawdon, Leeds LS19 6LQ
☎ 0113 2502016

CONTACT   Allan Long
LOCATION   Leave A658 at Apperley Bridge: follow signs to Carlton Rest Home
OPEN   9 am – 5 pm, Monday – Friday. Closed Bank Holidays. Open some weekends: phone for details
SPECIALITIES   Orchids
CATALOGUE   On request
MAIL ORDER   Yes
SHOWS   RHS Westminster; Southport

Long-established orchid growers and hybridisers, with a large range of many genera, species and cultivars, including *Odontoglossum* and *Masdevallia*. They will be at a number of Orchid shows.

Newton Hill Alpines
335 Leeds Road, Newton Hill, Wakefield WF1 2JH
☎ 01924 377056

CONTACT   Sheena Vigors
LOCATION   3 miles east of M1, Jct 41
OPEN   9 am – 5 pm, daily. Closed Thursdays
SPECIALITIES   Alpines
CATALOGUE   50p by post
MAIL ORDER   No
GARDEN   Garden opens, as nursery

This mainly wholesale alpine nursery welcomes retail customers too. They are good for saxifrages especially, and also have dwarf conifers and heathers. There is an additional list of plants available in small numbers.

Slack Top Alpines
Hebden Bridge HX7 7HA
☎ 01422 845348

CONTACT   Michael or Ron Mitchell
LOCATION   ¾ mile beyond Heptonstall, on an unclassified road between Hebden Bridge and Colne
OPEN   10 am – 6 pm, Wednesday – Sunday and Bank Holidays, 1 March to 31 October; closed Mondays and Tuesdays
SPECIALITIES   Alpines
NEW FOR 1997   Some 50 new items
CATALOGUE   SAE
MAIL ORDER   No
GARDEN   Display garden

This traditional family nursery set high in the Pennines produces all its own stock of alpine and rock garden plants. There are troughs for sale, and a large show garden. Prices are very reasonable.

Springwood Pleiones
35 Heathfield, Adel, Leeds LS16 7AB
☎ 0113 2611781

CONTACT   K. Redshaw
OPEN   By appointment
SPECIALITIES   *Pleione*

CATALOGUE   SAE
MAIL ORDER   Yes
SHOWS   Harrogate (Spring); Chelsea

There is a selection of *Pleione* species and varieties; smaller size bargain lots and bulbils also available.

Stephen H Smith's Garden & Leisure
Aire Valley, Wilsden Road, Harden, Bingley BD16 1BL
☎ 01535 274653   ℻ 01535 271912
CONTACT   Richard Coggill
LOCATION   Take Wilsden road from B6429 in Harden: the nursery is on the right after 1 mile
OPEN   9 am – 6 pm, summer; 9 am – 5.30 pm, winter. 11 am – 5 pm, Sundays
SHOP   Garden sundries, furniture, aquatics, gifts
REFRESHMENTS   Coffee shop

Garden centre with plants and garden products: Hillier stockists. The range of indoor plants has been extended. Delivery service.

Stephen H Smith's Garden & Leisure
Wharfe Valley, Pool Road, Otley LS21 1DY
☎ 01943 462195   ℻ 01943 850074
CONTACT   Peter Scott
LOCATION   1 mile east of Otley on A659
OPEN   9 am – 6 pm, summer; 9 am – 5.30 pm, winter. 11 am – 5 pm, Sundays
SHOP   Garden sundries, furniture, aquatics, gifts
REFRESHMENTS   Coffee shop

This garden centre has been greatly enlarged. It sells a good range of both indoor and outdoor plants and garden products: agents for both Hillier and Blooms. Delivery service.

Strikes Garden Centre
Selby Road, Swillington Common, Leeds LS15 4LQ
☎ 0113 286 2981   ℻ 0113 287 0663
CONTACT   Adam Ratcliffe (Manager)
LOCATION   Between Leeds and Selby
OPEN   9 am – 6 pm, Monday – Saturday; 10.30 am – 4.30 pm, Sundays
SHOP   Gifts

Strikes Garden Centre
Red Hall Lane, Wellington Hill, Leeds LS17 8NA
☎ 0113 265 7839   ℻ 0113 273 2935
CONTACT   Eric Snowden (Manager)
LOCATION   Weatherby Road, Leeds
OPEN   9 am – 6 pm, Monday – Saturday; 10.30 am – 4.30 pm, Sundays
SHOP   Gifts

Totties Nursery
Greenhill Bank Road, Totties, Holmfirth, Huddersfield HD7 1UN
☎ 01484 683363
CONTACT   David A. Shires
LOCATION   On the edge of the Pennines
OPEN   9 am – 5 pm, daily
MAIL ORDER   No

The wide range here includes shrubs, conifers, alpines and herbaceous plants.

Zephyrwude Irises
48 Blacker Lane, Crigglestone, Wakefield WF4 3EW
☎ 01924 252101
CONTACT   Richard L. Brook
LOCATION   1 mile south-west of M1, Jct 39, off A636
OPEN   Viewing and ordering: 9 am – dusk, daily, May and June; collection of pre-booked orders: by appointment August to October
SPECIALITIES   Irises
CATALOGUE   1 first-class stamp (between April and September)
MAIL ORDER   Yes
GARDEN   Display garden open 9 am – dusk, daily, May and June

Specialist growers and importers of modern bearded irises. The range concentrates on miniature and standard dwarf, intermediate, and miniature tall types, mostly post-1970 American cultivars. There is a selection of border and tall bearded irises too. The list appears in April, for collection or despatch in August and September. The trial fields are open in May and June, 9 am till dusk, but check first.

WALES

CLWYD

Aberconwy Nursery
Graig, Glan Conwy, Colwyn Bay LL28 5TL
☎ 01492 580875
CONTACT   Dr Keith Lever
LOCATION   South of Glan Conwy, 2nd right off A470. Turn right at top of hill: nursery is on the right
OPEN   10 am – 5 pm, Tuesday – Sunday. Closed Mondays, except Bank Holidays
SPECIALITIES   Alpines
NEW FOR 1997   *Dianthus* 'Alice Lever', *Gentiana* 'Serenity'
CATALOGUE   2 second-class stamps
MAIL ORDER   No
GARDEN   Their own garden, Bryn Meifod, opens under the National Gardens Scheme, by appointment

Mainly alpines, including some interesting primulas, but there are also trees, shrubs and herbaceous plants, including plants for acid soils.

Bodnant Garden Nursery Ltd
Tal-y-Cafn, Colwyn Bay LL29 6DG
☎ 01492 650731   ℻ 01492 650863
CONTACT   Ms Sian Grindley
LOCATION   Next to Bodnant Garden, signed from A55
OPEN   9.30 am – 5.30 pm, daily

SPECIALITIES   Camellias; rhododendrons; seeds; shrubs; magnolias
CATALOGUE   3 first-class stamps
MAIL ORDER   Yes
REFRESHMENTS   Yes
GARDEN   Bodnant Garden, Clwyd, see Gardens section

The nursery specialises in those plants for which the garden is renowned — rhododendrons, azaleas, magnolias and camellias. There is much else of interest in the wide choice of trees and shrubs here. They publish regular availability lists and a specialist seed list.

C & K Jones

Halghton Nursery, Whitchurch Road, Halghton, Bangor on Dee SY14 7LX
☎ 0194 830685

CONTACT   Paula Woolley
LOCATION   Between Whitchurch and Bangor on Dee, on A525
OPEN   9 am – 5 pm, daily, March to September; 9 am – 4 pm, Friday – Monday, October to February
SPECIALITIES   Roses
CATALOGUE   £1
MAIL ORDER   Yes
SHOWS   Harrogate (Autumn); Southport; BBC GW Live; Hampton Court; Ayr

C & K Jones's plant centre. The rose crop is produced here. There are shrubs and conifers on sale too. They will also be at the Shrewsbury Show. See C & K Jones, Cheshire for more details.

Celyn Vale Nurseries

Allt-y-Celyn, Carrog, Corwen LL21 9LD
☎ & FAX 01490 430671

CONTACT   Andrew McConnell
LOCATION   3 miles east of Corwen, near A5
OPEN   9 am – 4 pm, Monday – Friday, March to October
SPECIALITIES   Trees; Eucalyptus; Acacia
CATALOGUE   1 first-class stamp
MAIL ORDER   Yes, minimum order 3 plants; p & p is included
GARDEN   Extensive Eucalyptus plantings

Specialist growers of eucalyptus and acacias: they use seed from high altitude specimens to maximise hardiness and will advise, preferably by telephone, on suitable species. Retail and wholesale.

Deva Orchids

Littlebrook Farm, Stryt Isa, Pen-y-ffordd CH4 0JY
☎ 01978 762454

CONTACT   Chris Channon
LOCATION   7 miles west of Chester
OPEN   By appointment and on Open Weekends
SPECIALITIES   Orchids
CATALOGUE   List free on request
MAIL ORDER   Yes
SHOWS   RHS Westminster; Southport

Orchid breeder and grower with a range of species and hybrids, including new introductions. There are plants for both beginners and experienced growers.

Dibleys

Efenechtyd Nurseries, Llanelidan, Ruthin LL15 2LG
☎ 01978 790677   FAX 01978 790668

LOCATION   Directions in catalogue
OPEN   9 am – 5 pm, daily, April to September
SPECIALITIES   Begonias; house plants; mediterranean plants; Prunus; gesneriads
NEW FOR 1997   New varieties of Streptocarpus
CATALOGUE   SAE
MAIL ORDER   Yes
SHOWS   RHS Westminster; Malvern (Spring); Malvern (Autumn); Harrogate (Spring); Harrogate (Autumn); Southport; Chelsea; BBC GW Live; Hampton Court; Strathclyde; Ayr

Varieties and species of Streptocarpus are the main speciality here, but the choice extends to other gesneriads, coleus and foliage begonias. Active on the show circuit: they attend more than 50 each year.

Paul Christian Rare Plants

P O Box 468, Wrexham LL13 9XR
☎ & FAX 01978 366399

CONTACT   Dr P. J. Christian
OPEN   Mail order only
SPECIALITIES   Bulbs
NEW FOR 1997   Tender bulbs for greenhouse cultivation
CATALOGUE   3 first-class stamps; May, December
MAIL ORDER   Yes

Bulb, corm and tuber specialist. An exciting range of rare and enticing small, hardy bulbs and greenhouse subjects. The list changes annually according to the availability of new and rediscovered items. There is an illustrated book which goes into more detail than the catalogues.

DYFED

Cilwern Plants

Cilwern, Talley, Llandeilo SA19 7YH
☎ 01558 685526

CONTACT   Anne Knatchbull-Hugessen
LOCATION   6 miles north of Llandeilo on B4302, before Talley village
OPEN   11 am – 6 pm (4 pm from October to March), daily
SPECIALITIES   Herbaceous perennials
NEW FOR 1997   Grasses
CATALOGUE   SAE for list
MAIL ORDER   No
GARDEN   1½-acre garden of trees, shrubs and herbaceous plants

The nursery sells a range of hardy perennials, particularly hardy geraniums and is making a collection of grasses. There are also shrubs and conifers. The 1½-acre garden is open for the NGS on 22 June: it has been charmingly made out of the surrounding scrub and swamp over the last 15 years.

Exotic Fuchsias

Pen-y-Banc Nursery, Crwbin, Pontyberem, Kidwelly SA17 5DP

☎ 01269 870729

CONTACT　Terry or Susie Evans
LOCATION　Map in catalogue
OPEN　10 am – 5 pm, daily, 1 March to 1 September; and by appointment
SPECIALITIES　Fuchsias
NEW FOR 1997　New Dutch fuchsias, including 'Super Sport'
CATALOGUE　On request
MAIL ORDER　Yes
SHOWS　Malvern (Spring)

Fuchsia specialist growing around 600 varieties.

Farmyard Nurseries

Llandysul SA44 4RL

☎ 01559 363389

CONTACT　Richard Bramley
LOCATION　Take road opposite Llandysul petrol station for 1 mile
OPEN　9 am – 6 pm, daily except 25 & 26 December
SPECIALITIES　Hellebores
NEW FOR 1997　50 new plants
CATALOGUE　SAE
MAIL ORDER　Yes
SHOP　9 am – 5.30 pm, Mansell Street, Carmarthen
REFRESHMENTS　Coffee shop
GARDEN　Two show gardens, open by appointment only

This is a traditional nursery, where 90% of the plants are grown and raised on site. Herbaceous perennials are its speciality, with some alpines and shrubs as well: some 2,500 varieties in all.

John Shipton (Bulbs)

Y Felin, Henllan Amgoed, Whitland SA34 0SL

☎ 01994 240125

CONTACT　John Shipton
OPEN　By appointment
SPECIALITIES　Bulbs
CATALOGUE　SAE
MAIL ORDER　Yes

This wholesale and retail bulb nursery specialises in British native bulbs, which they guarantee are not taken from wild sources. There are also older daffodil cultivars and perennials for naturalising. The catalogue includes *Galanthus elwesii* propagated in Turkey as part of a Flora and Fauna International conservation project.

Manorbier Garden Centre

Station Road, Manorbier, Tenby SA70 7SN

☎ 01834 871206　　FAX　01834 871678

CONTACT　Roger Thompson
OPEN　9.30 am – 5.30 pm, daily. Closed Christmas and Boxing Day
SPECIALITIES　Shrubs
NEW FOR 1997　*Camellia sinensis*

MAIL ORDER　No
REFRESHMENTS　Restaurant
DESIGN SERVICE　Manorbier Garden Centre

Garden centre and nurseries with a general range. New shrub varieties are their speciality. There is a local delivery service.

St Ishmaels Nurseries and Garden Centre

St Ishmaels, Haverfordwest SA62 3SX

☎ & FAX　01646 636343

CONTACT　Mr or Mrs Phippen
LOCATION　Between Milford Haven and Dale
OPEN　9 am – 5.30 pm, daily, summer; 9 am – 5 pm, daily, winter. Closed 5 days at Christmas and New Year
SPECIALITIES　Shrubs; trees
MAIL ORDER　No
SHOP　Florist, silk and dried flowers, gifts, pots, tools, sundries, pond and pool equipment
REFRESHMENTS　Coffee shop
DESIGN SERVICE　St Ishmaels Nurseries

Large garden centre with a general range, especially trees and shrubs.

Wyevale Garden Centre

Myrtle Hill, Pensarn, Carmarthen SA31 2NG

☎　01267 221363　　FAX　01267 221316

REFRESHMENTS　Restaurant

Wyevale Garden Centre

Bynea, Llanelli SA14 9SR

☎　01554 772189　　FAX　01554 777938

MID GLAMORGAN

Wyevale Garden Centre

Village Farm Industrial Estate, Pyle CF33 6NU

☎　01656 741443　　FAX　01656 744693

REFRESHMENTS　Restauran

SOUTH GLAMORGAN

Fisher Fuchsias

Brynawel Garden Centre Ltd, Sully Road, Penarth CF64 3UU

☎ & FAX　01222 702660

CONTACT　J. Anderson
LOCATION　Map in catalogue
OPEN　9 am – 6 pm, daily, spring and summer; 9 am – dusk, winter; 10 am – 4 pm, Sundays
SPECIALITIES　Fuchsias
CATALOGUE　2 first-class stamps
MAIL ORDER　Yes, cuttings, from September to May
SHOP　Garden centre
GARDEN　Exhibition house open February to September

Fuchsias specialists with a range of over 700 varieties. Part of Brynawel Garden Centre. There are pelargoniums and a full range of summer and winter bedding.

Jardinerie Ltd
Newport Road, St Mellons, Cardiff CF3 9XH
☎ 01222 777977   [FAX] 01222 793351

CONTACT   Malcolm Jones (Manager)
OPEN   9 am – 6 pm, Monday – Saturday; 10.30 am – 4.30 pm, Sundays
SHOP   Gifts, pets
REFRESHMENTS   Cafét

WEST GLAMORGAN
Wyevale Garden Centre
Siemens Way, Swansea Enterprise Park, Llansamlet, Swansea SA7 9FT
☎ 01792 310052   [FAX] 01792 310608

REFRESHMENTS   Restaurant

GWENT
Waterwheel Nursery
Bully Hole Bottom, Usk Road, Shirenewton, Chepstow NP6 6SA
☎ 01291 641577

CONTACT   Desmond or Charlotte Evans
LOCATION   Turn off B4235 (Chepstow to Usk road), to Bully Hole Bottom, 1½ miles north-west of Huntsman Hotel, to bottom of valley on right
OPEN   9 am – 6 pm, Tuesday – Saturday plus Bank Holiday Mondays
SPECIALITIES   Climbers; herbaceous perennials; trees
CATALOGUE   2 first-class stamps
MAIL ORDER   Yes, winter only
REFRESHMENTS   At Huntsman Hotel
GARDEN   Garden around mill buildings

A wide and interesting choice of perennials, trees and shrubs for different situations. Most of the plants can be seen in the garden: many are rare and unusual. You are advised to phone for directions.

Wye Valley Herbs
The Nurtons, Tintern NP6 7NX
☎ 01291 689253

CONTACT   A. or E. Wood
LOCATION   7 miles north of M4, Jct 22, opposite 'Old Station Tintern' on A466
OPEN   10.30 am – 5 pm, daily
SPECIALITIES   Herbaceous perennials; herbs
CATALOGUE   3 first-class stamps
MAIL ORDER   No
REFRESHMENTS   At 'Old Station Tintern'
GARDEN   Herb garden, herbaceous beds and wildlife pond

A large collection of organically grown herbs, with an expanding selection of perennials and shrubs. All carry the Soil Association symbol.

Wyevale Garden Centre
Newport Road, Castleton, Cardiff CF3 8UQ
☎ 01633 680002   [FAX] 01633 680769

REFRESHMENTS   Restaurant

GWYNEDD
Crûg Farm Plants
Griffith's Crossing, Caernarfon LL55 1TU
☎ & [FAX] 01248 670232

CONTACT   Sue Wynn-Jones
LOCATION   2 miles north-east of Caernarfon, off A487, follow signs to Bethel
OPEN   10 am – 6 pm, Thursday – Sunday, and Bank Holidays
SPECIALITIES   Climbers; shade-loving plants
CATALOGUE   SAE plus 1 second-class stamp
MAIL ORDER   No
GARDEN   Garden opens for NGS

The nursery is unusual in specialising in plants for shade: perennials, shrubs and climbers. The range is extensive and interesting. Their selection of hardy geraniums equals many specialists in the genera. The fruits of recent collecting expeditions to Korea, Sikkim and Taiwan are now being released.

Gwydir Plants
Plas Muriau, Betws-y-coed LL24 0HD
☎ 01690 710201   [FAX] 01690 750379

CONTACT   L. Schärer
LOCATION   ¼ mile north of Waterloo Bridge, towards Llanrwst on A470
OPEN   10 am – 5.30 pm, Tuesday – Saturday, and Bank Holidays, 2 – 5.30 pm, Sundays, March to October
SPECIALITIES   Herbs; wild flowers
CATALOGUE   2 first-class stamps
MAIL ORDER   No
GARDEN   Plas Muriau garden is open under the NGS

This small nursery specialises in herbs, wild flowers and cottage garden plants. They can supply collections for school projects.

Henllys Lodge Plants
Henllys Lodge, Beaumaris, Anglesey LL58 8HU
☎ 01248 810106

CONTACT   E. Lane
LOCATION   Turn left, ½ mile after Beaumaris Castle, and then first left again
OPEN   11 am – 5 pm, daily. Closed Tuesdays and Thursdays
SPECIALITIES   Herbaceous perennials
CATALOGUE   2 first-class stamps
MAIL ORDER   No
REFRESHMENTS   Cream teas
GARDEN   Cottage-style garden open under NGS and by appointment
DESIGN SERVICE   Henlly's Lodge Plants

The nursery stocks a selection of cottage garden type perennials including many hardy geraniums and plants for shade. They run half day workshops for small groups on planning and planting a garden, and their own garden is also open.

The Herb Garden & Plant Hunters Nursery

Pentre Berw, Gaerwen, Anglesey LL60 6LF
☎ 01248 421064

CONTACT   Mr or Mrs D. R. Tremaine-Stevenson
LOCATION   Map in catalogue
OPEN   9 am – 6 pm, Wednesday – Sunday and Bank Holidays. Phone first out of season
SPECIALITIES   Herbs; wild flowers
CATALOGUE   £1 and A5 SAE
MAIL ORDER   Yes
GARDEN   Yes

Herbs of all kinds and British native species are the specialities; there are perennials and old roses too.

Holland Arms Garden Centre

Gaerwen, Isle of Anglesey LL60 6LA
☎ 01248 421655

CONTACT   Susan Knock
LOCATION   On A5 in central Anglesey
OPEN   9 am – 5.30 pm, Monday – Saturday; 11 am – 5 pm, Sundays; 10 am – 5.30 pm, Bank Holidays
REFRESHMENTS   Restaurant
GARDEN   Demonstration gardens

Large, family-run garden centre, with indoor and outdoor plants. Hilliers Premier collection agent. The very large Christmas display includes a bilingual Santa, and there are lots of lectures and events throughout the year.

Ty'r Orsaf Nursery

Maentwrog Road Station, Ty Nant, Gellilydan, Blaenau Ffestiniog LL41 4RB
☎ 01766 590233

CONTACT   Tony or Molly Faulkner
LOCATION   Between Trawsfynydd and Ffestiniog on A470
OPEN   9 am – 6 pm, summer; 9 am – dusk, winter
SPECIALITIES   Herbaceous perennials
CATALOGUE   3 second-class stamps
MAIL ORDER   No
GARDEN   Garden open daily

A pleasantly mixed collection of garden-worthy hardy perennials: specialities include *Astilbe*, *Potentilla* and a large range of *Sidalcea*.

Wild Seeds

Branas, Llandderfel LL23 7RF

CONTACT   Mike Thorne
OPEN   Mail order only
SPECIALITIES   Seeds; wild flowers
CATALOGUE   On request
MAIL ORDER   Yes

Native plants, including bulbs and trees, available as seed and as plants. All are available in quantity. Special flower mixtures for different habitats.

POWYS

Blooming Things

Y Bwthyn, Cymerau, Glandyfi, Machynlleth SY20 8SS
☎ 01654 781256

CONTACT   Wyn or Dale Garnes
OPEN   Mail order only
SPECIALITIES   Herbs; wild flowers
CATALOGUE   SAE
MAIL ORDER   Yes

Organically grown herbs, vegetables, wild flowers and plants for hanging baskets are sent as young plant plugs from this Welsh nursery, retail and wholesale if ordered in advance. They have a club which entitles members to discounts on advance orders. The nursery will be at the Royal Welsh Show.

Welsh Fruit Stocks

Bryngwyn, via Kington, Hereford HR5 3QZ
☎ & FAX 01497 851209

CONTACT   S. Fromant
LOCATION   Phone for directions
OPEN   By appointment for collection only
SPECIALITIES   Soft fruit
CATALOGUE   SAE
MAIL ORDER   Yes, cash with order

Strawberries, raspberries, black, red and white currants, jostaberry, gooseberries and rhubarb grown in healthy isolated conditions.

SCOTLAND

BORDERS

Edrom Nurseries

Coldingham, Eyemouth TD14 5TZ
☎ & FAX 018907 71386

CONTACT   Jim Jermyn
LOCATION   A1107, 5 minutes from A1
OPEN   10 am – 4.30 pm; Monday – Friday; 1 March to 1 October
SPECIALITIES   Alpines
CATALOGUE   SAE (9" × 5")
MAIL ORDER   Yes
SHOWS   RHS Westminster; Malvern (Spring); Malvern (Autumn); Harrogate (Spring); Harrogate (Autumn); Southport; Hampton Court; Strathclyde

This well-known alpine nursery specialises in primulas, gentians and *Meconopsis*. The list of these three genera is particularly comprehensive, and includes many forms that are not available elsewhere. As with the other alpines it lists, many are new to commerce or grown under collectors' numbers.

Lilliesleaf Nursery

Garden Cottage, Linthill, Lilliesleaf TD6 9HU

☎ & FAX 01835 870415

CONTACT   T. de Bordes

LOCATION   On B6359 between Midlem and Lilliesleaf

OPEN   9 am – 5 pm, Monday – Saturday; 10 am – 4 pm, Sundays. December to March, phone first

SPECIALITIES   Herbaceous perennials

MAIL ORDER   No

GARDEN   Walled garden

General plant range, with the emphasis on perennials. Good for *Epimedium*.

CENTRAL

Klondyke Garden Centre

Beancross Road, Polmont FK2 0XS

☎ 01324 717035   FAX 01324 714999

CONTACT   Alan Yardley (Manager)

Klondyke Garden Centre

Glasgow Road, Whins of Milton, Stirling FK7 8ER

☎ 01786 816167   FAX 01786 813730

CONTACT   Les Croy (Manager)

Plantings Garden Nursery

Main Street, Thornhill, By Stirling FK8 3PP

☎ 01786 850683

CONTACT·   Robin Price

LOCATION   Map in catalogue

OPEN   9.30 am – 5.30 pm, Wednesday to Saturday; Bank Holidays, March to October

SPECIALITIES   Herbaceous perennials; roses

CATALOGUE   2 first-class stamps

GARDEN   Norrieston House

A useful range of herbaceous plants available wholesale and retail, as well as container-grown roses. The garden at Norrieston House opens for Scotland's Garden Scheme.

DUMFRIES & GALLOWAY

Bridge End Nurseries

Gretna Green DG16 5HN

☎ 01461 800612

CONTACT   Robin Bird

LOCATION   Signed from Gretna Green to Chapelknowle and Bridge End Nurseries

OPEN   9 am – dusk, daily

SPECIALITIES   Herbaceous perennials

MAIL ORDER   No

GARDEN   Display gardens

SHOWS   Malvern (Spring); Southport; BBC GW Live; Hampton Court; Strathclyde; Ayr

Lots of cottage garden plants, both well known and rarer varieties. Talks given for groups and societies.

British Wild Plants

Stockerton Nursery, Kirkcudbright, Galloway DG6 4XS

☎ 01557 31226

CONTACT   Martin Gould

LOCATION   3½ miles from Kirkcudbright on the Dalbeattie road

OPEN   By arrangement

SPECIALITIES   Wild flowers

CATALOGUE   2 first-class stamps for guide to garden use of plants

MAIL ORDER   Yes

GARDEN   Display garden

A small nursery with a range of native wild plants for a variety of habitats, including aquatic, coastal, meadow and hedgerow, and woodland. Their stock includes bulbs, trees and shrubs.

Cally Gardens

Gatehouse of Fleet, Castle Douglas DG7 2DJ

FAX 01557 815029

CONTACT   Michael Wickenden

LOCATION   12 miles west of Castle Douglas, on Gatehouse road off A75

OPEN   10 am – 5.30 pm, Saturday – Sunday only, Easter to early October

SPECIALITIES   Herbaceous perennials

NEW FOR 1997   Plants from the 1996 expedition to eastern Russia

CATALOGUE   3 first-class stamps; November

MAIL ORDER   Yes, £15 minimum order; spring despatch

GARDEN   18th-century walled garden

A nursery for the horticultural avant-garde. It specialises in perennials from collected and botanic garden seed. Culled from a collection of over 3500 varieties, the catalogue changes by as much as half each year. Plants from an expedition trip to eastern Russia in 1996 will be included this year.

Charter House Hardy Plant Nursery

2 Nunwood, Dumfries DG2 0HX

☎ 01387 720363

CONTACT   John Ross

LOCATION   Between Terregles and Newbridge

OPEN   9 am – 5 pm, daily, March to October. By appointment only November to February

SPECIALITIES   Alpines; herbaceous perennials

CATALOGUE   3 first-class stamps

MAIL ORDER   Yes

GARDEN   Demonstration gardens.

SHOWS   Strathclyde; Ayr

NCCPG NATIONAL COLLECTIONS   *Erodium*

Here are hardy geraniums and erodiums in abundance, plus a selection of other herbaceous and alpine plants. The demonstration gardens are getting larger. Advice on planting and design. They will be at Dundee and Gateshead Spring and Autumn and the Royal Highland Show this year.

Craig Lodge Nurseries
Craig Lodge, Balmaclellan, Castle Douglas DG7 3QR
☎ 01644 420661

CONTACT   Michael or Sheila Northway
LOCATION   Directions in catalogue
OPEN   10 am – 5 pm, Wednesdays – Mondays, late March to 31 October
SPECIALITIES   Alpines; primulas
CATALOGUE   4 second-class stamps and A5 SAE
MAIL ORDER   Yes
GARDEN   Rock gardens, raised beds, two alpine houses

This young nursery grows all kinds of alpines, including bulbs and dwarf shrubs. They specialise in plants from wild collected seed, and say they have interesting plants from recent germinations. The cyclamen collection continues to develop.

Craigieburn Classic Plants
By Moffat DG10 9LF
☎ & 📠 01683 221250

CONTACT   Janet Wheatcroft or Bill Chudziak
LOCATION   2½ miles east of Moffat, on A74. On the left, beyond Craiglochan signs
OPEN   12.30 pm – 7 pm, Tuesday – Sunday, 12 April to 27 October. Open on Public Holidays
SPECIALITIES   Herbaceous perennials; primulas; half-hardy plants; *Meconopsis*
CATALOGUE   £1; October
MAIL ORDER   Yes, minimum order £10; delivery service available
GARDEN   Craigieburn Woodland Garden, admission £1.50

The nursery carries an attractive range of perennials, with an emphasis on woodlanders. *Meconopsis* and primulas are among the specialities. An 8-acre garden is being developed alongside the nursery.

Elizabeth MacGregor
Ellenbank, Tongland Road, Kirkcudbright DG6 4UU
☎ 01557 330620   📠 01557 330620

CONTACT   Elizabeth or Alasdair MacGregor
LOCATION   On A711 1 mile north of Kirkcudbright
OPEN   10.30 am – 5.30 pm, Fridays and Saturdays, May to October
SPECIALITIES   Herbaceous perennials; violas
CATALOGUE   4 first-class stamps
MAIL ORDER   Yes, a speciality
GARDEN   Walled garden
SHOWS   Strathclyde; Ayr

Violas – over 100 of them – are the speciality at this excellent nursery, complemented by a lively selection of perennials and shrubs for cottage garden and mixed border planting.

J Tweedie Fruit Trees
Maryfield Road Nursery, Maryfield, Terregles DG2 9TH
☎ 01387 720880

CONTACT   John Tweedie
LOCATION   3 miles from Dumfries, between Newbridge and Terregles

OPEN   9.30 am – 2 pm, Saturdays, 21 October to March. Other times by appointment
SPECIALITIES   Fruit
NEW FOR 1997   Dwarf cherries on Edabriz rootstocks, Gooseberry 'Pax', 'Rokula', Rhubarb 'Canada Red'
CATALOGUE   SAE
MAIL ORDER   Yes

A good, wide choice of fruit trees and bushes and rhubarb in new varieties, with old ones also in the list. During the season fresh soft fruits can be bought.

Whitehills Nurseries
Minnigaff, Newton Stewart DG8 6SL
☎ 01671 402049   📠 01671 403106

CONTACT   C. A. Weston
LOCATION   1 mile north of A75, on east bank of Cree
OPEN   9 am – 4.30 pm, by appointment
SPECIALITIES   Rhododendrons; shrubs
NEW FOR 1997   *Rhododendron* species from wild collected seed
CATALOGUE   50p
MAIL ORDER   Yes, minimum order £25 + VAT
GARDEN   Woodland and water garden open 1 June for SGS
DESIGN SERVICE   Yes

Specialists for rhododendrons and azaleas: they have a wide choice of other trees and shrubs also. The garden admission of £1.50 is refundable against nursery purchases.

FIFE

Dalgety Bay Garden Centre
Western Approach Road, Dalgety Bay KY11 5XP
☎ 01383 823841   📠 01383 821874

CONTACT   Laura Hastie (Manager)
OPEN   9 am – 6 pm, Monday – Saturday; 10 am – 6 pm, Sundays. Closes at 5 pm in winter
SPECIALITIES   South American plants
SHOP   Aquatics, books, gifts, pets
REFRESHMENTS   Tea room

A Dobbies garden centre. There will be a hanging basket demonstration in May.

Roots Garden Centre Ltd
1 Caskieberran Road, Glenrothes KY6 2NR
☎ 01592 756407   📠 01592 758973

CONTACT   Jim McGregor
LOCATION   Opposite Saltire Centre
OPEN   8.30 am – 5.30 pm, Monday – Friday; 9 am – 5.30 pm, Saturdays; 10 am – 5.30 pm, Sundays
SHOP   Garden sundries, furniture, buildings, florist
DESIGN SERVICE   Roots Garden Centre Ltd

Garden centre with a full range of plants and products. They offer design and landscaping (interior and exterior) and daily delivery.

GRAMPIAN

Aultan Nursery

Newton of Cairnhill, Cuminestown, Turriff AB53 5TN

☎ & [FAX] 01888 544702

CONTACT Richard King
LOCATION Take A947 from Turriff towards Banff, first right to Cuminestown and after two miles follow signs to nursery
OPEN 11 am – 4 pm, Mondays; 1.30 pm – 6 pm, Saturdays; 10 am – 6 pm, Sundays. Closed Tuesdays – Fridays. Other times please ring first
SPECIALITIES Herbaceous perennials; shrubs
CATALOGUE 2 first-class stamps
MAIL ORDER Yes

Organically grown herbaceous perennials and shrubs.

Ben Reid & Co

Pinewood Park Nurseries, Countesswells Road, Aberdeen AB9 2QL

☎ 01224 318744   [FAX] 01224 310104

CONTACT Mr Shand
LOCATION Aberdeen
OPEN Garden Centre open 9 am – 5 pm, Monday – Saturday; 10 am – 5 pm, Sundays
SPECIALITIES Hedging; trees
CATALOGUE On request
MAIL ORDER Yes, £10 minimum order
REFRESHMENTS Hot drinks

Large wholesale nursery which specialises in coniferous and deciduous forest trees, hedging, ornamental trees and shrubs. Their retail plant centre carries a good general range.

Christie Elite Nurseries

Forres, Moray IV36 0TW

☎ 01309 672633   [FAX] 01309 676846

CONTACT Dr S. Thompson
LOCATION Bogton Road, Forres (off bypass)
OPEN 8 Am – 5.30 pm, Monday – Saturday; 10 am – 5.30 pm, Sundays
SPECIALITIES Hedging; shrubs; trees
CATALOGUE On request (FREEPOST)
MAIL ORDER Yes

Large and long-established nursery and garden centre. A wide range of trees and shrubs, from woodland and hedging species to ornamental varieties. Some fruit trees also.

Findlay Clark (Aberdeen)

Hazeldene Road, Hazlehead, Aberdeen AB9 2QU

☎ 01224 318658

LOCATION Off Queen's Road
OPEN 9 am – 5.30 pm, daily
SHOP Gifts, books, conservatories
REFRESHMENTS Coffee shop

James Cocker & Sons

Whitemyres, Lang Stracht, Aberdeen AB15 6XH

☎ 01224 313261   [FAX] 01224 312531

OPEN 9 am – 5 pm, daily

SPECIALITIES Roses
CATALOGUE On request; May
MAIL ORDER Yes, no minimum order
SHOP Garden centre
REFRESHMENTS Yes

A famous firm of rose breeders and growers, with a garden centre too. They have an all-round range of roses, but the emphasis is on the modern, shorter varieties. The firm holds a royal warrant.

Tough Alpine Nursery

Westhaybogs, Tough, Alford, Aberdeenshire AB33 8DU

☎ 019755 62783   [FAX] 019755 63561

CONTACT Fred Carrie
OPEN 10 am – 4 pm, February to October
SPECIALITIES Alpines
CATALOGUE 3 second-class stamps
MAIL ORDER Yes, minimum order £10

Retail and wholesale alpine nursery producing a wide range of very hardy alpines in this chilly area.

HIGHLAND

Abriachan Gardens & Nursery

Abriachan Nurseries, Loch Ness Side, Inverness-shire IV3 6LA

☎ & [FAX] 01463 861232

CONTACT Mr or Mrs Davidson
LOCATION 9 miles south-west of Inverness, on A82
OPEN 9 am – 6 pm (or dusk if earlier), daily, February to November
SPECIALITIES Herbaceous perennials; primulas
CATALOGUE 3 first-class stamps
MAIL ORDER Yes, no minimum order
REFRESHMENTS At hotel 1 mile away
GARDEN Three-acre garden open under SGS

Mainly perennials, with a large choice of primroses particularly the Barnhaven strains. Other interesting ranges including helianthemums and hebes. The garden walk is mapped and labelled. The exuberant catalogue is a joy to read.

Ardfearn Nursery

Bunchrew, Inverness IV3 6RH

☎ 01463 243250/223607   [FAX] 01463 7117133

CONTACT Alasdair Sutherland
LOCATION Off A862 west of Inverness
OPEN 9 am – 5.30 pm, daily
SPECIALITIES Alpines; primulas
CATALOGUE 4 second-class stamps
MAIL ORDER Yes, from October to March
GARDEN Demonstration garden

Alpines and small ericaceous shrubs in quantity are produced at this nursery in a lovely Highland setting. Particularly good for celmisias, gentians and, above all, primulas. The sales area has easy wheelchair access.

Evelix Daffodils

Aird Asaig, Evelix, Dornoch, Sutherland IV25 3NG
☎ 01862 810715

CONTACT D. C. MacArthur
LOCATION Off A9 at Evelix filling station
OPEN By appointment
SPECIALITIES Daffodils
CATALOGUE 3 first-class stamps
MAIL ORDER Yes, minimum order £5

Daffodil breeder with an interesting small range of novelty, exhibition and garden varieties. Watch out for new varieties. Sutherland Soil Services operates from the same address.

Garden Cottage Nursery

Tournaig, Poolewe, Achnasheen, Ross-shire IV22 2LH
☎ 01445 781339

CONTACT R. B. J. Rushbrooke or L. E. Rushbrooke
LOCATION 1½ miles north of Inverewe Gardens
OPEN 12 noon – 7 pm, Monday – Saturday, mid-March to mid-October
SPECIALITIES Herbaceous perennials; primulas
CATALOGUE 4 second-class stamps; September
MAIL ORDER Yes, minimum order £10

Specialises in those plants which thrive in the mild, moist climate: Asiatic primulas, damp-loving perennials and *Meconopsis*. Not all their stock is shown in the catalogue.

Island Plants

The Old Manse, Knock, Point, Isle of Lewis HS2 0BW
☎ 01851 870281

CONTACT D. Ferris
OPEN 2 pm – 5 pm, Monday – Saturday
SPECIALITIES New Zealand plants
CATALOGUE 1 first-class stamp
MAIL ORDER Yes

Mail-order nursery specialising in New Zealand plants, including 150 species and varieties of *Hebe*, as well as those which tolerate wind and sea spray. All plants very reasonably priced: excellent value for money.

Jack Drake

Inshriach Alpine Nursery, Aviemore, Inverness-shire PH22 1QS
☎ 01540 651287   FAX 01540 651656

CONTACT J. C. Lawson
LOCATION From B9152 take B970 (ski road) to Inverdruie, outside Aviemore. Turn right, ¾ mile after the Spey Bridge
OPEN 9 am – 5 pm Monday – Friday; 9 am – 4 pm, Saturdays. Closed Sundays
SPECIALITIES Alpines; seeds
CATALOGUE £1
MAIL ORDER Yes, no minimum order
GARDEN Yes

This famous Highland nursery is Mecca for devotees of alpine and rock garden plants. Its catalogue has a large number of selected or collected forms. True alpines rub shoulders with species for wild and bog gardens. An excellent seed list is also available, containing about 300 items.

Poyntzfield Herb Nursery

Black Isle, By Dingwall, Ross and Cromarty IV7 8LX
☎ & FAX 01381 610352

CONTACT Duncan Ross
LOCATION 5 miles west of Cromarty, on B9163
OPEN 1 pm – 5 pm, Monday – Saturday, March to September; Sundays, June to August
SPECIALITIES Herbs
NEW FOR 1997 *Stevia rebaudiana*
CATALOGUE SAE plus 3 first-class stamps
MAIL ORDER Yes
GARDEN Display garden
DESIGN SERVICE Poyntzfield Herb Nursery

This range of herbs and aromatic plants from the north of Scotland is grown with an eye on hardiness and vigour as well as scent and flavour. They specialise in native species and medicinal plants from all over the world. Two new cultivars of chives have recently won AGMs from the RHS: *Allium* 'Black Isle Blush' and A. 'Pink Perfection'.

Speyside Heather Centre

Dulnain Bridge, Inverness-shire PH26 3PA
☎ 01479 851359   FAX 01479 851396

CONTACT David or Betty Lambie
LOCATION Between Aviemore and Grantown on Spey, off A95
OPEN 9 am – 6 pm, Monday – Saturday; 10 am – 5.30 pm, Sundays
SPECIALITIES Heathers
CATALOGUE £2.25 booklet
MAIL ORDER Yes
SHOP Crafts, garden sundries
REFRESHMENTS Restaurant
GARDEN Gardens

Garden centre which specialises in heathers and heather gardening. They have other plants, a design service, sundries, crafts and a restaurant (Clootie Dumpling Restaurant) where 21 dumpling dishes are on offer.

Uzumara Orchids

9 Port Henderson, Gairloch, Ross-shire IV21 2AS
☎ 01445 741228

CONTACT I. F. La Croix
LOCATION 8 miles south-west of Gairloch
OPEN By appointment
SPECIALITIES African and Madagascar orchids
CATALOGUE SAE
MAIL ORDER Yes

A highly specialised nursery offering species orchids from Africa and Madagascar, most of them seed raised.

LOTHIAN

Belwood Nurseries Ltd

Mauricewood Mains, Penicuik, Midlothian EH26 0NJ
☎ 01968 673621   FAX 01968 678354

CONTACT Ron Low (Sales Manager)
LOCATION Dalkeith (Midlothian) and Meigle (Tayside)

OPEN By appointment only: 8 am – 5 pm, Monday – Friday
SPECIALITIES Conifers; shrubs; trees
CATALOGUE On request
MAIL ORDER Carriage arranged anywhere in mainland UK
REFRESHMENTS Tea & coffee
GARDEN Nursery (300 acres) open by arrangement

A large and expanding wholesale nursery, with some 300 acres under production. Retail customers must make an appointment before visiting. Trees, shrubs and conifers are available root-balled or container-grown in various sizes. They specialise in semi-mature specimens, and stock for special projects. Trade shows attended include SALTEX and SCOTGROW.

Binny Plants

Binny Estate (Sue Ryder), Ecclesmachan Road, Broxburn EH52 6NL
☎ & FAX 01506 858931

CONTACT Billy Carruthers
LOCATION 2 miles north of Uphall
OPEN 11 am – 5 pm, Friday – Sunday, Easter to Halloween
SPECIALITIES Grasses; herbaceous perennials; shrubs
CATALOGUE First-class SAE
MAIL ORDER Yes, minimum £25

Newish nursery with an expanding range which specialises in *Euphorbia*, grasses, perennials and shrubs. The catalogue has good, helpful plant descriptions, with some shrewd observations that give the reader confidence.

Dobbies Gardening World

Melville Nursery, Lasswade, Midlothian EH18 1AZ
☎ 0131 663 1941   FAX 0131 654 2548

CONTACT J. Oliver
LOCATION On A7 by Edinburgh Butterfly Farm
OPEN 9 am – 6 pm, Monday – Friday; 9 am – 6 pm, Saturdays; 10 am – 6 pm, Sundays. Closes at 5 pm in winter
CATALOGUE No
SHOP Aquatics, books, gifts
REFRESHMENTS Tea room
GARDEN Yes

Large garden centre, headquarters of the Dobbies chain.

Klondyke Garden Centre

Mortonhall Park, Frogston Road East, Edinburgh EH16 6TK
☎ 0131 664 8698   FAX 0131 658 1757

CONTACT Nick Thompson (Manager)

Klondyke Garden Centre

Campus Roundabout, Livingston EH54 7AW
☎ 01506 410053   FAX 01506 460575

CONTACT Sheena Elliot (Manager)

STRATHCLYDE

Ardencaple Garden Centre

Rhu Road Higher, Helensburgh G84 8JT
☎ 01436 671202   FAX 01436 671291

CONTACT A. P. O'Connor
LOCATION Just west of Helensburgh on the A84

OPEN 9 am – 6 pm, Monday – Saturday; 10 am – 6 pm, Sundays. Closes at 5 pm in winter
SPECIALITIES Rhododendrons
SHOP Books, gifts
REFRESHMENTS Tea room

A Dobbies garden centre.

Ballagan Nursery

Gartocharn Road, Alexandria, Dunbartonshire G83 8NB
☎ 01389 752947   FAX 01389 711288

CONTACT Mr Wilson
LOCATION Between Balloch and Gartocharn on A811
OPEN 9 am – 6 pm, daily
SPECIALITIES Bedding plants
SHOP Garden centre

Garden centre and nursery dealing in bedding plants, unusual hardy shrubs and trees (including feathered specimens).

Barwinnock Herbs

Barrhill, Girvan KA26 0RB
☎ & FAX 01465 821338

CONTACT Mon or Dave Holtom
LOCATION Map in catalogue
OPEN 10 am – 6 pm, daily, April to October
SPECIALITIES Herbs
CATALOGUE 3 first-class stamps
MAIL ORDER Yes
GARDEN Display garden
SHOWS Strathclyde; Ayr

Organically grown culinary, medicinal, aromatic herbs and plants with scented foliage. There is a new garden and farm walks to see wild flowers and rare breeds. Wellies advised.

Burnside Nursery

By Girvan KA26 9JH
☎ 01465 714290

CONTACT C. Walker
LOCATION On A77 halfway between Girvan and Turnberry
OPEN 10 am – dusk, Thursday – Tuesday, 1 April to 31 October. Closed Wednesdays
SPECIALITIES Herbaceous perennials; seeds
NEW FOR 1997 30 more hardy geraniums
CATALOGUE SAE
MAIL ORDER Yes, spring and summer, hardy geraniums only
SHOWS Ayr

The nursery is enthusiastic about their range of *Dicentra* – there is a increasing selection of hardy geraniums and other perennials as well.

Chatelherault Garden Centre

The Country Park, Ferniegair, Hamilton ML3 7UE
☎ 01698 457700   FAX 01678 458382

CONTACT R. O. F. Mackenzie
LOCATION On Lanark road out of Hamilton
OPEN 9 am – 6 pm, Monday – Saturday; 10 am – 6 pm, Sundays. Closes at 5 pm in winter
SHOP Aquatics, books, gifts
REFRESHMENTS Restaurant/tea room

A Dobbies garden centre offering hardy plant stock, aquatics, pot plants and sundries. Good access for the disabled.

Dobbies Westerwood Garden Centre
Eastfield Road, Westerwood, Cumbernauld G68 0EB
☎ 01236 736100   [FAX] 01236 737660
LOCATION   Off A80 at Cumbernauld
OPEN   9 am – 6 pm, Monday – Saturday; 10 am – 6 pm, Sundays. Closes at 5 pm in winter
SHOP   Aquatics, books, gifts, pets
REFRESHMENTS   Tea room

Hillier's Premier agents. Open until 8 pm, Thursdays in summer.

Duncans of Milngavie
Flower & Garden Centre, 101 Main Street, Milngavie, Glasgow G62 6JJ
☎ 0141 956 2377   [FAX] 0141 956 6649
CONTACT   Andrew N. Duncan
LOCATION   North of Glasgow, on A81
OPEN   8.30 am – 5.30 pm, Monday – Saturday; 10 am – 5 pm, Sundays
SHOP   Florist, garden sundries and furniture
REFRESHMENTS   Tea room

Garden centre and florists with a comprehensive choice of indoor and outdoor plants and associated products.

Findlay Clark Ltd
Boclair Road, Milngavie, Glasgow G62 6EP
☎ 01360 620721   [FAX] 01360 622833
LOCATION   At Allander Toll roundabout, on B8049
OPEN   9 am – 9 pm, summer; 9 am – 6 pm, winter
SHOP   Gifts, books, garden buildings, saddlery
REFRESHMENTS   Coffee shop

Findlay Clark's Head Office.

Kinlochlaich House Gardens
Appin, Argyll PA38 4BD
☎ 01631 730342   [FAX] 01631 730482
CONTACT   D. E. Hutchison
LOCATION   On A828 halfway between Oban and Fort William
OPEN   9.30 am – 5.30 pm, Monday – Saturday,
10.30 am – 5.30 pm, Sundays, April to mid-October;
9.30 am – 4.45 pm, Monday – Saturday, mid-October to March
CATALOGUE   No
MAIL ORDER   No
GARDEN   Kinlochlaich House Gardens
DESIGN SERVICE   Lorne Landscapers

The largest garden centre in the West Highlands, with a range of hardy garden plants across the whole spectrum from alpines to trees. Design service through Lorne Landscapers.

Klondyke Garden Centre
Kilsyth Road, Kirkintilloch G66 1QF
☎ 0141 776 2001   [FAX] 0141 776 2137
CONTACT   Douglas Blythe (Manager)

Kittoch Mill Hosta Garden
Kittoch Mill, Carmunnock, Glasgow G76 9BJ
☎ 0141 644 4712
CONTACT   P. A. Jordan
LOCATION   Off B759 Busby to Carmunnock road
OPEN   By appointment only: phone first
SPECIALITIES   Herbaceous perennials; Hosta
NEW FOR 1997   New varieties of Hosta and Ligularia
MAIL ORDER   No
REFRESHMENTS   By arrangement
GARDEN   Display gardens open 2 – 5 pm, 22 June, 6 July

They specialise in hostas, including new American cultivars. Some other perennials too, including Ligularia. The nursery usually has plants for sale at NCCPG events in Strathclyde.

Tree Shop
Ardkinglas Estate Nurseries, Cairndow PA26 8BH
☎ & [FAX] 01499 600263
CONTACT   Mark Sands
LOCATION   On A83 at head of Loch Fyne
OPEN   9.30 am – 6 pm, daily, April to September; 9.30 am – 5 pm, daily, October to March. Closed 25 December – 31 January
SPECIALITIES   Rhododendrons; shrubs; trees
CATALOGUE   On request
MAIL ORDER   Yes
SHOP   Woodwork
REFRESHMENTS   Light refreshments, April to September

This neat and welcoming nursery at the top of Loch Fyne offers an interesting and varied selection of specimen trees and unusual plants, including azaleas and rhododendrons. There is also a range of woodwork, including toys and garden furniture.

TAYSIDE

Angus Heathers
Crosston Farm, By Letham DD8 2NZ
☎ 01307 818504   [FAX] 01307 818055
CONTACT   David Sturrock
LOCATION   On main road from Forfar to Letham
OPEN   9 am – 5 pm, daily
SPECIALITIES   Heathers; rhododendrons; gentians
CATALOGUE   On request
MAIL ORDER   No
GARDEN   Demonstration garden

As well as over 130 heathers they stock a range of gentians, and a number of dwarf and slow-growing conifers which make good companions for the heathers.

Bonhard Nursery
Murrayshall Road, Scone, Perth PH2 7PQ
☎ & [FAX] 01738 552791
CONTACT   C. Hickman
LOCATION   Between Perth and New Scone. Turn right off A94; continue for 1 mile
OPEN   10 am – 6 pm (or dusk if sooner)
SPECIALITIES   Fruit; roses
CATALOGUE   Rose and fruit tree lists only

MAIL ORDER   No
REFRESHMENTS   Tea room with home baking
GARDEN   Yes, demonstration garden in part of walled garden and spring flowers in woodland garden

Just outside Perth, this family-run nursery stocks a general range of plants, with an emphasis on old shrub roses and fruit trees.

Christie's Nursery
Downfield, Westmuir, Kirriemuir DD8 5LP
☎ & 🗐 01575 572977

CONTACT   Ian or Ann Christie, Ian Martin
LOCATION   On A926 1 mile west of Kirriemuir
OPEN   10 am – 5 pm, daily. November to January by appointment only
SPECIALITIES   Alpines
NEW FOR 1997   *Corydalis solida* 'Blushing Girl', *Dactylorhiza fuchsii* 'Cruickshank'
CATALOGUE   2 first-class stamps
MAIL ORDER   Yes
GARDEN   Demonstration garden
SHOWS   Harrogate (Autumn); Ayr

This Alpine nursery in the Highlands has an impressive list, particularly strong on gentians, hardy orchids, corydalis and lewisias. Not all their plants can be sent by courier, but they go to Scottish Rock Garden Club and some AGS shows.

Dobbie & Co Ltd
Crieff Road, Perth PH1 2NR
☎ 01738 638555   🗐 01738 633005
LOCATION·   Beside Tesco superstore
OPEN   9 am – 6 pm, Monday – Saturday; 10 am – 6 pm, Sundays. Closes at 5 pm in winter
SHOP   Aquatics, books, gifts, pets
REFRESHMENTS   Tea room

Garden centre, with a Hilliers Premier Plants agency.

Findlay Clark (Kinross)
Kinross Garden Centre, Turfhills, Kinross KY13 7NQ
☎ 01577 863327
LOCATION   Off M90, Jct 6, next to Granada Services
OPEN   9 am – 5.30 pm, daily
SHOP   Gifts, books, craft centre, golf shop, falconry
REFRESHMENTS   Coffee shop

Glendoick Garden Centre
Glendoick, Perth PH2 7NS
☎ 01738 860260   🗐 01738 860735
CONTACT   Mrs Cox or Mr Meldrum
LOCATION   7 miles from Perth, on A90 (old A85)
OPEN   9 am – 5 pm, winter; 9 am – 6 pm, summer
SPECIALITIES   Primulas; rhododendrons
NEW FOR 1997   *Rhododendron* 'Oban'
CATALOGUE   £1.50 in stamps
MAIL ORDER   Yes
REFRESHMENTS   Coffee shop, light lunches, home baking
GARDEN   Glendoick Gardens, Tayside

The garden centre is open daily at the times shown: the nursery is only open by prior arrangement. Glendoick are specialist

growers of rhododendrons and other ericaceous shrubs, with a large and impressive collection, including new hybrids. Among the short list of other plants there are a number of interesting Asiatic primulas from collected seed and *Meconopsis*.

NORTHERN IRELAND

CO. ANTRIM

Carncairn Daffodils
Carncairn Grange, Broughshane, Ballymena BT43 7HF
☎ 01266 861216
CONTACT   Mrs R. H. Reade
LOCATION   5 miles from Ballymena, just outside Broughshane
OPEN   10 am – 5 pm, by appointment
SPECIALITIES   Daffodils
CATALOGUE   On request; March
MAIL ORDER   Yes
GARDEN   Visitors welcome, by appointment

Important breeders of new hybrids: they introduced six novelties last year, the same number as in 1995, almost all of their own raising. The catalogue lists some 350 cultivars from every division of the genus *Narcissus*, with an emphasis on daffodils for exhibition use and garden display. Callers are requested to make a prior appointment.

Colemans Nurseries
6 Old Ballyclare Road, Templepatrick, Ballyclare BT39 0BJ
☎ 01849 432513   🗐 01849 432151
CONTACT   The Manager
LOCATION   Templepatrick: also at Bangor
OPEN   Summer: 9 am – 8 pm, Monday – Friday; 9 am – 5.30 pm, Saturdays; 12.30 pm – 5.30 pm, Sundays. Winter: closes at 5.30 pm. Winter Sundays 2 pm – 5.30 pm
CATALOGUE   Yes
MAIL ORDER   Yes
SHOP   Garden sundries
REFRESHMENTS   Yes
DESIGN SERVICE   Yes

Nursery and garden centre (the head office is Templepatrick). As well as a general range of plants and sundries they sell cuttings and young plants. They will be at the Northern Ireland Flower Festival in June.

Landscape Centre
24 Donegore Hill, Dunadry BT41 2QU
☎ 01849 432175   🗐 01849 432051
CONTACT   Mark Davis or Kaye Campbell
OPEN   9 am – 6 pm, Monday – Saturday; 12.30 pm – 6 pm, Sundays. Late closing, 8 pm, Wednesdays and Thursdays, April to August
SHOP   Sundries, gifts

REFRESHMENTS Coffee shop
GARDEN Demonstration gardens
DESIGN SERVICE Landscape Centre

General garden centre with a range of plants and garden products. Run in conjunction with a landscape design office: see Professional Services section.

CO. DOWN

Ballydorn Bulb Farm
Ballydorn Hill, Killinchy, Newtownards BT23 6QB
☎ 01238 541250

CONTACT Sir Frank Harrison
OPEN By invitation only
SPECIALITIES Daffodils
CATALOGUE £1
MAIL ORDER Yes

Narcissus breeders and hybridisers since 1946. The unique collection consists solely of their own cultivars, bred for either the show bench or the garden. They were awarded a gold medal in 1993 by the American Daffodil Society for hybridising. They will be at the Northern Ireland Daffodil Group Show.

Ballyrogan Nurseries
The Grange, Ballyrogan, Newtownards BT23 4SD
☎ 01247 810451 (evenings)

CONTACT Gary Dunlop
LOCATION Map on request
OPEN Collection only, by prior arrangement
SPECIALITIES Grasses; herbaceous perennials; *Celmisia*; *Crocosmia*; *Euphorbia*
CATALOGUE 2 first-class stamps
MAIL ORDER Yes, £10 minimum order
GARDEN By appointment
NCCPG NATIONAL COLLECTIONS *Celmisia*; *Crocosmia*; *Euphorbia*

A small part-time nursery selling stock derived from their own large collections. The plants are mostly herbaceous: the celmisias, crocosmias and euphorbias are from the National Collections and look particularly interesting. There are more *Agapanthus*, *Dierama* and *Kniphofia* coming.

Dickson Nurseries Ltd
Milecross Road, Newtownards BT23 4SS
☎ 01247 812206   ☎ 01247 813366

CONTACT Linda Stewart
OPEN 8 am – 12.30 pm, 1.15 – 5 pm, Monday – Thursday; 8 am – 12.30 pm, Fridays. Closed Saturdays and Sundays
SPECIALITIES Roses
CATALOGUE On request
MAIL ORDER Yes
GARDEN Rose fields open, as above

Modern rose breeders, with some distinguished introductions to their credit. They only sell their own roses, and those of Jackson & Perkins and Interplant.

Donaghadee Garden Centre
34 Stockbridge Road, Donaghadee BT21 0PN
☎ 01247 883603   ☎ 01247 883030

LOCATION Between Bangor and Donaghadee, off B21
OPEN 9.30 am – 5.30 pm, Monday – Saturday; 12.30 pm – 5.30 pm, Sundays
SHOP Gifts
REFRESHMENTS Coffee shop
DESIGN SERVICE Donaghadee Garden Centre

Garden centre with a range of hardy plants. They offer a landscaping and design service, and can deliver. There is also a customer club and discount scheme.

Lisdoonan Herbs
98 Belfast Road, Saintfield BT24 7HF
☎ 01232 813624

CONTACT Barbara Pilcher
LOCATION Between Carryduff and Saintfield, 6 miles south of Belfast on A7
OPEN Wednesday and Saturday mornings, and by appointment
SPECIALITIES Herbs
CATALOGUE 2 first-class stamps
MAIL ORDER No
REFRESHMENTS By prior arrangement for groups and workshops
GARDEN Demonstration gardens
DESIGN SERVICE Lisdoonan Herbs

The nursery sells culinary and aromatic herbs, salad plants and unusual vegetables, as well as cut herbs. One-day workshops are held during the season and visits to the garden can be arranged. Design advice, planting plans and a booklet on growing herbs available.

Seaforde Gardens
Seaforde, Downpatrick BT30 8PG
☎ 01396 811225   ☎ 01396 811370

CONTACT Patrick Forde
LOCATION Between Belfast and Newcastle
OPEN 10 am – 5 pm, Monday – Saturday; 1 pm – 6 pm, Sundays. Open Monday – Friday only, November to February
SPECIALITIES Rhododendrons; trees
NEW FOR 1997 *Dicksonia antarctica & D. squarrosa*
CATALOGUE On request
MAIL ORDER Yes
REFRESHMENTS Tea-rooms
GARDEN Gardens, maze and butterfly house
NCCPG NATIONAL COLLECTIONS *Eucryphia*

An important nursery for trees and shrubs, including Irish specialities (*Eucryphia* × *intermedia* 'Rostrevor') and tender taxa. The list now includes a growing number of rhododendrons grown from Patrick Forde's own collecting expeditions to Bhutan, Yunnan, Tibet and Vietnam. The gardens, maze and tropical butterfly house are also worth seeing.

Timpany Nurseries
77 Magheratimpany Road, Ballynahinch BT24 8PA
☎ 01238 562812
CONTACT   Susan Tindall
LOCATION   2½ miles from Ballynahinch
OPEN   10 am – 6 pm, Monday – Saturday. Closed Sundays and Mondays during winter. Phone for an appointment at other times
SPECIALITIES   Alpines; herbaceous perennials; New Zealand plants; primulas
NEW FOR 1997   *Meconopsis*, named auriculas
CATALOGUE   75p
MAIL ORDER   Yes
GARDEN   Garden

A selection of alpine and rock garden plants, including specimens raised from collected seed. There are 12 *Celmisia*, nearly 90 *Primula* and 70 *Saxifraga*. The garden is open to groups by arrangement.

CO. TYRONE

Baronscourt Nurseries
Abercorn Estates, Newtownstewart BT78 4EZ
☎ 016626 61683   [FAX] 016626 62059
CONTACT   Mrs Dawn Pinkerton
OPEN   Garden centre: 10 am – 4.30 pm, Monday – Saturday; 2 pm – 4.30 pm, Sundays; 17 March to 31 October. Wholesale enquiries at any time
SPECIALITIES   Trees
CATALOGUE   Trade catalogues only
MAIL ORDER   No
SHOP   Garden centre

Retail garden centre and a wholesale nursery. They specialise in large trees, and container-grown conifers and shrubs.

Brian Duncan Daffodils
Knowehead, 15 Ballynahatty Road, Omagh BT78 1PN
☎ & [FAX] 01662 242931
CONTACT   Elizabeth Ann Duncan
OPEN   August and September only
SPECIALITIES   Daffodils
NEW FOR 1997   Range of new hybrids
MAIL ORDER   Yes, cash with order for new customers
SHOWS   RHS Westminster

Breeder and grower of novelty and exhibition daffodils.

CHANNEL ISLANDS

GUERNSEY

Martel's Garden World
Route des Blicqs, St Andrews GY6 8YD
☎ 01481 36888   [FAX] 01481 35542
CONTACT   D. de la Rue
OPEN   9 am – 5.30 pm, daily

SHOP   General garden centre
REFRESHMENTS   Cold drinks and ices

JERSEY

Jersey Lavender Ltd
Rue du Pont Marquet, St Brelade JE3 8DS
☎ 01534 42933   [FAX] 01534 845613
CONTACT   David Christie
LOCATION   Between St Aubin's Bay and Red Houses, on B25
OPEN   10 am – 5 pm, Monday – Saturday, 19 May to 20 September
SPECIALITIES   Lavender
CATALOGUE   On request
MAIL ORDER   Products only: not plants
SHOP   Lavender products
REFRESHMENTS   Tea room
GARDEN   Herb garden, conifers, bamboo collection and lavender farm
NCCPG NATIONAL COLLECTIONS   *Lavandula*

Jersey Lavender is a working lavender farm, growing and distilling lavender and rosemary. The distillery and bottling room can be visited. A range of *Lavandula* species and cultivars is also for sale.

Ransoms Garden Centre
St Martin JE3 6UD
☎ 01534 856699   [FAX] 01534 853779
CONTACT   Barry Webb
LOCATION   Between St Martin's Church and Gorey village
OPEN   8.30 am – 5.30 pm, Monday – Saturday
CATALOGUE   Lists free
MAIL ORDER   No
SHOP   Gifts
REFRESHMENTS   Restaurant

Garden centre with licensed restaurant: lunch bookings (01534 853668).

St Peters Garden Centre
Airport Road, St Peter JE3 7BP
☎ 01534 45903   [FAX] 01534 46774
CONTACT   Mark Berresford
LOCATION   On main airport road
OPEN   8.30 am – 6 pm, summer; 8.30 am – 5.30 pm, winter
REFRESHMENTS   Bay Tree Tea Room
SHOWS   Harrogate (Spring)

Delivery service available.

ISLE OF MAN

Ballalheannagh Gardens
Glen Roy, Lonan IM4 7QO
☎ & [FAX] 01624 861875
CONTACT   Cliff or Maureen Dadd

OPEN 10 am – 1 pm, 2 pm – 5 pm daily, but subject to alteration November – March
SPECIALITIES Australian plants; New Zealand plants; rhododendrons; shrubs
NEW FOR 1997 *Pieris japonica* 'Glenroy Goblin'
CATALOGUE £1.50
MAIL ORDER Yes, limited
GARDEN Ballalheannagh Gardens
DESIGN SERVICE Ballalheannagh Gardens

There is an extensive range of ericaceous shrubs, including rhododendrons and many plants from the southern hemisphere. The woodland garden covers 23 acres.

P & S Allanson
Rhendhoo, Jurby IM7 3HB
☎ 01624 880766   📠 01624 880649

CONTACT Paul Allanson
OPEN By appointment only
SPECIALITIES Australian plants; New Zealand plants
CATALOGUE £1.50
MAIL ORDER Yes

This shrub nursery has a remarkable list of Australian and New Zealand plants including a wide choice of *Hebe*, *Callistemon*, *Melaleuca*, *Correa* and *Olearia*, besides plants for coastal and windy positions.

REPUBLIC OF IRELAND

CO. CORK

Deelish Garden Centre
Deelish, Skibbereen
☎ & 📠 00 353 28 21374

CONTACT Rain Chase or Bill Chase
LOCATION 1 mile from Skibbereen: signed from Skibbereen to Ballydehob road, N71
OPEN 10 am – 1 pm, 2 pm – 6 pm, Monday – Saturday; 2 pm – 6 pm, Sundays and Bank Holidays
SPECIALITIES Conservatory plants
NEW FOR 1997 *Acacia podalyriifolia*, *Beschorneria yuccoides*, *Callistemon pallidus*,
CATALOGUE Yes: specialist range only
MAIL ORDER Delivery in Irish republic
DESIGN SERVICE Deelish Garden Centre

The nursery carries a general range of most types of plants, and – among some more unusual varieties – specialises in plants for mild coastal situations and conservatories.

Hosford's Geraniums & Garden Centre
Cappa, Enniskeane
☎ 00 353 23 39159   📠 00 353 23 39300
CONTACT John or David Hosford
LOCATION On N71 5 miles west of Bandon

OPEN 9 am – 6 pm, Monday – Saturday, January to June, October to December; 9 am – 6 pm, Tuesday – Saturday, July to September; 2 pm – 5.30 pm, Sundays, March to Christmas only. Closed Mondays July to September
SPECIALITIES Pelargoniums; roses
CATALOGUE Lists for pelargoniums, roses, perennials, hedging etc.
MAIL ORDER Yes, credit cards accepted
REFRESHMENTS For groups by prior arrangement
DESIGN SERVICE Hosford's Geranium & Garden Centre

Hosford's has moved to a new site about a mile from the old one. A general garden centre which also makes a speciality of pelargoniums. The rose list is good, and there are regular talks and demonstrations, including rose pruning on 16 February. The lively and helpful catalogue doubles as a tourist guide to the area.

CO. DONEGAL

Crocknafeola Nursery
Killybegs
☎ 00 353 73 51018

CONTACT Andy McKenna
LOCATION 3 miles from Killybegs
OPEN 9 am – 7 pm, Monday – Saturday; 12 noon – 6 pm, Sundays; March to November
SPECIALITIES Topiary; coastal plants
NEW FOR 1997 More perennials
MAIL ORDER No
DESIGN SERVICE Yes

The nursery produces a range of hardy plants which are particularly suitable for exposed and coastal positions. All stock is properly hardened off before sale.

CO. DUBLIN

Flower Centre
754 Howth Road, Blackbanks, Dublin 5
☎ 00 353 1 832 7047   📠 00 353 1 832 7251

CONTACT Eugene Higgins
LOCATION 5 miles east of Dublin
OPEN 10 am – 1 pm, 2.30 pm – 6 pm (5 pm, winter); 2.30 pm – 6 pm, Sundays (5 pm, winter)
CATALOGUE Occasional lists
MAIL ORDER No
SHOP Garden sundries

Well-established Dublin garden centre with a full range of plants.

Mackey's Garden Centre
Castlepark Road, Sandycove
☎ 00 353 280 7385   📠 00 353 284 1922
CONTACT Breda Roseingrave
LOCATION 5 miles south of Dublin
OPEN 9 am – 5.30 pm, Monday – Saturday; 2 pm – 5.30 pm, Sundays and Holidays
SPECIALITIES Australian plants; seeds

CATALOGUE   On request; bulbs, seeds, old roses, modern roses

MAIL ORDER   Yes

SHOP   Garden centre and city shop

The garden centre outlet of a famous old seed merchants (founded in 1777). There are many interesting plants in the all-round range, most notably the Australian collection. Mackey's Seed Ltd is at 22 St Mary Street, Dublin.

Malahide Nurseries Ltd

Mabestown, Malahide

☎ 00 353 845 0110   FAX 00 353 845 0872

CONTACT   Ann Nutty

LOCATION   7 miles north of Dublin, opposite Malahide Castle

OPEN   9.30 am – 1 pm, 2 pm – 5.30 pm, Monday – Friday; 9.30 am – 5.30 pm, Saturdays; 2 pm – 5.30 pm, Sundays and Bank Holidays

SPECIALITIES   Aquatic plants

NEW FOR 1997   Betula utilis var. jacquemontii 'Trinity College'

SHOP   Garden products, seeds

GARDEN   2 model gardens

This nursery, trading from a thatched building, carries a general range of plants and sundries. The aquatic plants are home grown – as is their own Pittosporum tenuifolium 'Nutty's Leprechaun'.

CO. GALWAY

Seaside Nursery and Garden Centre

Claddaghduff

☎ 00 353 95 44687   FAX 00 353 95 44761

CONTACT   Charles Dÿck

LOCATION   Claddaghduff (near Clifden)

OPEN   9 am – 1 pm, 2 pm – 6 pm, Monday – Saturday; 2 pm – 6 pm, Sundays

SPECIALITIES   Coastal plants

CATALOGUE   I£1

MAIL ORDER   No

SHOP   Pots

DESIGN SERVICE   Seaside Nursery and Garden Centre

The nursery specialises in plants for seaside locations, including phormiums, and in plants for containers. They also import and sell Italian pots.

CO. KERRY

Liscahane Nursery and Garden Centre

Ardfert, Tralee

☎ 00 353 66 34222   FAX 00 353 66 34600

CONTACT   Don Nolan or Bill Cooley

LOCATION   3½ miles north-west of Tralee

OPEN   9 am – 6 pm (or dusk), Tuesday – Saturday; 2 pm – 6 pm (or dusk) Sundays

MAIL ORDER   No

General plant range; particularly those suitable for shelter belts and coastal gardening. A new garden is under development to exhibit the salt-resistant species which are one of the nursery's specialities.

Muckross Garden Centre

Muckross, Killarney

☎ 00 353 64 34044   FAX 00 353 64 31114

CONTACT   John Fuller

LOCATION   3 miles from Killarney, on Kenmare road

OPEN   10 am – 6 pm, Tuesday – Saturday; 2 pm – 6 pm, Sundays. Closed Mondays. Restricted opening hours in January and February

CATALOGUE   Available in September

MAIL ORDER   Yes, minimum charge I£15 plus postage

DESIGN SERVICE   Muckross Garden Centre

Garden centre with a general range: a new shrub nursery is being developed. They have a design and maintenance capacity. The garden centre is opposite the Killarney National Park, and you can stay in their B & B, Friar's Glen.

Ryans Nurseries

Lissivigeen, Killarney

☎ & FAX 00 353 64 33507

CONTACT   Tadhg Ryan

LOCATION   1½ miles from Killarney

OPEN   9 am – 6 pm, Monday – Saturday; 2 pm – 6 pm, Sundays and Bank Holidays

SPECIALITIES   Camellias; shrubs

MAIL ORDER   No

DESIGN SERVICE   Ryans Nurseries

Shrubs for the mild climate and acid soil of Kerry, including Arbutus and Dicksonia.

CO. KILDARE

Johnstown Garden Centre

Naas

☎ & FAX 00 353 458 79138

CONTACT   Jim Clarke

LOCATION   On N7

OPEN   9.30 am – 6 pm, Monday – Saturday; 12 noon – 6 pm, Sundays and Bank Holidays

MAIL ORDER   No

GARDEN   Yes

Garden centre with general range, Hillier stockists, emphasis on colourful foliage plants.

CO. LEITRIM

Eden Plants

Rossinver

☎ 00 353 72 54122

CONTACT   Rod Alston

LOCATION   25 miles north-east of Sligo

OPEN   2 pm – 6 pm, daily

SPECIALITIES   Herbs

CATALOGUE   I£1 plus SAE

MAIL ORDER Yes, SAE for price list
GARDEN Herb garden

An organic herb nursery: all stock is grown at the nursery under organic conditions.

CO. TIPPERARY

Clonmel Garden Centre Ltd

Glenconnor House, Clonmel

☎ 00 353 52 23294 FAX 00 353 52 29196

CONTACT Beth or Terry Hanna
OPEN 9 am – 6 pm, Monday – Saturday; 12 noon – 6 pm, Sundays and Bank Holidays
SPECIALITIES Trees
MAIL ORDER No
GARDEN Surrounding gardens
DESIGN SERVICE Clonmel Garden Centre

This garden centre is set in the grounds of a country house: there are also antique showrooms on the site. The emphasis is on trees and shrubs.

CO. WATERFORD

Orchardstown Nurseries

Cork Road, Waterford

☎ 00 353 51384273 FAX 00 353 51384422

CONTACT Ron Dool
LOCATION 4 miles from Waterford, towards Cork
OPEN 9 am – 6 pm, Monday – Saturday; 2 pm – 6 pm, Sundays
SPECIALITIES Rhododendrons; trees
CATALOGUE £1.50
MAIL ORDER Yes
REFRESHMENTS Yes
DESIGN SERVICE Orchardstown Landscapes

Irish nursery, with a wide choice of plants and trees, including magnolias, rhododendrons and other ericaceous shrubs.

9

Nursery Specialities

ACERS
Altoona Nurseries, Devon
Andrew Norfield Seeds, Gloucestershire
Barkers Primrose Nurseries, Lancashire
Barthelémy & Co Nurseries, Dorset
Hippopottering Nursery, Lincolnshire
Mallet Court Nursery, Somerset
Nettletons Nursery, Surrey
Norfields, Gloucestershire
P M A Plant Specialities, Somerset

AFRICAN VIOLETS
African Violet Centre, Norfolk

AIR PLANTS
Tamarisk Nurseries, Buckinghamshire
Vesutor Airplants, West Sussex

ALPINES
A & A Thorp, Leicestershire
Aberconwy Nursery, Clwyd
Alan C Smith, Kent
Ardfearn Nursery, Highland
Ashenden Nursery, Kent
Beechcroft Nursery, Surrey
Birkheads Cottage Garden Nursery, Tyne & Wear
Blackthorn Nursery, Hampshire
Brambling House Alpines, South Yorkshire
Bressingham Plant Centre, Cambridgeshire
Bressingham Plant Centre, Norfolk
Bressingham Plant Centre, Berkshire
Broadstone Nurseries, Oxfordshire
Brownthwaite Hardy Plants, Cumbria
Caves Folly Nurseries, Hereford & Worcester
Charter House Hardy Plant Nursery,
    Dumfries & Galloway
Chris Pattison (Nurseryman), Gloucestershire

Christie's Nursery, Tayside
Craig Lodge Nurseries, Dumfries & Galloway
DHE Plants, Derbyshire
Edrom Nurseries, Borders
Field House Alpines, Nottinghamshire
The Firs Nursery, Cheshire
Fosse Alpines, Leicestershire
Foxgrove Plants, Berkshire
Glen Chantry, Essex
Graham's Hardy Plants, Somerset
Greenslacks Nurseries, West Yorkshire
Hartside Nursery Garden, Cumbria
Hedgerow Nursery, West Yorkshire
Highgates Nursery, Derbyshire
Hillview Hardy Plants, Shropshire
Holden Clough Nursery, Lancashire
Hoo House Nursery, Gloucestershire
Jack Drake, Highland
Jenny Burgess' Alpine Nursery, Norfolk
Kettlesing Nurseries, North Yorkshire
Lingen Nursery and Gardens, Shropshire
Llanbrook Alpine & Wildflower Nursery, Shropshire
Marley Bank Nursery, Hereford & Worcester
Martin Nest Nurseries, Lincolnshire
The Mead Nursery, Wiltshire
Mendle Nursery, Lincolnshire
Mill Hill Plants, Nottinghamshire
Newton Hill Alpines, West Yorkshire
Nicky's Rock Garden Nursery, Devon
Norden Alpine Nursery, North Yorkshire
Norwell Nursery, Nottinghamshire
The Old Manor Nursery, Gloucestershire
One House Nursery, Cheshire
Perhill Plants, Hereford & Worcester
Potterton and Martin, Lincolnshire
R F Beeston, Hereford & Worcester
Reginald Kaye Ltd, Lancashire

Robert W & R Bewley, Co. Durham
Rookhope Nurseries, Co. Durham
Ryal Nursery, Northumberland
Scalers Hill Nursery, Kent
Shepton Nursery Garden, Somerset
Siskin Plants, Suffolk
Slack Top Alpines, West Yorkshire
Southcombe Gardens, Devon
Thuya Alpine Nursery, Gloucestershire
Tim Ingram, Kent
Timpany Nurseries, Co. Down
Tough Alpine Nursery, Grampian
Town Farm Nursery, Co Durham
The Vicarage Gardens, Greater Manchester
W E Th Ingwersen Ltd, West Sussex
West Acre Gardens, Norfolk
West Kington Nurseries, Wiltshire
White Cottage Alpines, East Yorkshire
Wintergreen Nurseries, Hereford & Worcester

AQUATIC PLANTS
Anthony Archer-Wills Ltd, West Sussex
Bennetts Water Lily Farm, Dorset
Higher End Nursery, Hampshire
Honeysome Aquatic Nursery, Cambridgeshire
Kenchester Water Gardens, Hereford & Worcester
Longstock Park Nursery, Hampshire
Malahide Nurseries Ltd, Co. Dublin
Merebrook Water Plants, Hereford & Worcester
Mickfield Watergarden Centre, Suffolk
Nine Springs Nursery, Hampshire
Paul Bromfield Aquatics, Hertfordshire
Rowden Gardens, Devon
Stapeley Water Gardens Ltd, Cheshire
The Water Garden Nursery, Devon
Water Meadow Nursery and Herb Farm, Hampshire
Waveney Fish Farm, Norfolk
Wychwood Waterlilies, Hampshire

AROMATIC AND SCENTED PLANTS
Foliage Scented & Herb Plants, Surrey

ASTERS
Rougham Hall Nurseries, Suffolk

AUSTRALIAN PLANTS
Ausfern Nurseries UK Ltd, Essex
Ballalheannagh Gardens, Isle of Man
County Park Nursery, Essex
Mackey's Garden Centre, Co. Dublin
Marwood Hill Gardens, Devon
P & S Allanson, Isle of Man
The Seed House, Hampshire

BAMBOOS
Bamboo Nursery Ltd, Kent
Brackenwood Plant Centre, Somerset
Coblands Nursery, Kent
Drysdale Garden Exotics, Hampshire
Fulbrooke Nursery, Suffolk
Jungle Giants, Hereford & Worcester
P W Plants, Norfolk
Simply Plants, Cambridgeshire
Ulverscroft Unusual Plants, Leicestershire

BEDDING PLANTS
Aylett Nurseries Ltd, Hertfordshire
Ballagan Nursery, Strathclyde
Beechcroft Nursery, Surrey
C Fairweather Ltd, Hampshire
Cooks Garden Centre, Hereford & Worcester
Elmridge Gardens Ltd, Co. Durham
Harold Walker, Cheshire
Henry Street Garden Centre, Berkshire
Hurdletree Nurseries, Lincolnshire
Kent Street Nurseries, East Sussex
Pantiles Plant & Garden Centre, Surrey
Primrose Cottage Nursery & Garden Centre,
    Greater Manchester
Steven Bailey Ltd, Hampshire
West Somerset Garden Centre, Somerset

BEGONIAS
Blackmore & Langdon, Somerset
Dibleys, Clwyd
Halsway Nurseries, Somerset
Rhodes & Rockliffe, Essex

BOG PLANTS
Anthony Archer-Wills Ltd, West Sussex
Bennetts Water Lily Farm, Dorset
Deanswood Plants, North Yorkshire
Honeysome Aquatic Nursery, Cambridgeshire
Longstock Park Nursery, Hampshire
Marwood Hill Gardens, Devon
Mickfield Watergarden Centre, Suffolk
Paul Bromfield Aquatics, Hertfordshire
Rowden Gardens, Devon
Stapeley Water Gardens Ltd, Cheshire
The Water Garden Nursery, Devon
Water Meadow Nursery and Herb Farm, Hampshire
Wychwood Waterlilies, Hampshire

BONSAI
D N Bromage & Co Ltd, Surrey
Greenwood Gardens, Nottinghamshire
Herons Bonsai Ltd, Surrey

Norman Bonsai, East Sussex
Peter Trenear Nurseries, Hampshire
Tokonoma Bonsai Nursery, Hertfordshire

BROMELIADS
Vesutor Airplants, West Sussex

BULBS
Avon Bulbs, Somerset
Bloms Bulbs Ltd, Bedfordshire
Broadleigh Gardens, Somerset
Cambridge Bulbs, Cambridgeshire
Gardenscape, North Yorkshire
J Walkers Bulbs, Lincolnshire
Jacques Amand Ltd, London
John Shipton (Bulbs), Dyfed
Knightshayes Garden Trust, Devon
Monocot Nursery, Somerset
P de Jager & Sons Ltd, Kent
Paradise Centre, Suffolk
Paul Christian Rare Plants, Clwyd
Potterton and Martin, Lincolnshire
R V Roger Ltd, North Yorkshire
Rupert Bowlby, Surrey
S & S Perennials, Leicestershire
Van Tubergen UK, Norfolk
W E Th Ingwersen Ltd, West Sussex

CACTI AND SUCCULENTS
Abbey Brook Cactus Nursery, Derbyshire
Alan Phipps Cacti, Gloucestershire
Connoisseurs' Cacti, Kent
Craig House Cacti, Lancashire
Croston Cactus, Lancashire
Cruck Cottage Cacti, North Yorkshire
Glenhirst Cactus Nursery, Lincolnshire
Harvest Nurseries, East Sussex
Heldon Nurseries, Staffordshire
Holly Gate Cactus Nursery, West Sussex
Pete & Ken Cactus Nursery, Kent
The Plant Lovers, Lincolnshire
Southfield Nurseries, Lincolnshire
Tamarisk Nurseries, Buckinghamshire
Toobees Exotics, Surrey
Westfield Cacti, Devon
Whitestone Gardens Ltd, North Yorkshire

CAMELLIAS
Bodnant Garden Nursery Ltd, Clwyd
Burncoose Nurseries, Cornwall
Coghurst Nursery, East Sussex
Exbury Enterprises Ltd, Hampshire
Lodge Lane Nursery, Cheshire

Magnolia Gardens, Kent
Marwood Hill Gardens, Devon
Porthpean House Gardens, Cornwall
Ryans Nurseries, Co. Kerry
Trehane Camellia Nursery, Dorset
Trewithen Nurseries, Cornwall

CARNIVOROUS PLANTS
Flora Exotica, Essex
Heldon Nurseries, Staffordshire
Marston Exotics, Hereford & Worcester
Potterton and Martin, Lincolnshire
Tamarisk Nurseries, Buckinghamshire
Toobees Exotics, Surrey

CHRYSANTHEMUMS
Collinwood Nurseries, Cheshire
Halls of Heddon, Northumberland
Harold Walker, Cheshire
Home Meadows Nursery Ltd, Suffolk
Littelton Nursery, Somerset
Lower Icknield Farm Nurseries, Buckinghamshire
Philip Tivey & Son, Leicestershire
Rileys Chrysanthemums, Hereford & Worcester
Woolmans Plants Ltd, Hereford & Worcester

CLEMATIS
Bawdeswell Garden Centre, Norfolk
Beamish Clematis Nursery, Co. Durham
Caddick's Clematis Nursery, Cheshire
Fisk's Clematis Nursery, Suffolk
Great Dixter Nurseries, East Sussex
J Bradshaw & Son, Kent
Orchard Nurseries, Lincolnshire
Peveril Clematis Nursery, Devon
Pounsley Plants, Devon
Scotts Clematis, Devon
Sheila Chapman Clematis, Essex
Sherston Parva Nursery Ltd, Wiltshire
Stillingfleet Lodge Nurseries, North Yorkshire
Stone Green Nurseries, Kent
T H Barker & Son, Cumbria
Thorncroft Clematis Nursery, Norfolk
Treasures of Tenbury Ltd, Hereford & Worcester
The Valley Clematis Nursery, Lincolnshire
Woodborough Garden Centre, Wiltshire

CLIMBERS
Beamish Clematis Nursery, Co. Durham
Cherry Tree Nursery (SWOP), Dorset
Churchills Garden Nursery, Devon
Clifton Nurseries, London
Coblands Nursery, Kent

Crûg Farm Plants, Gwynedd
Grange Farm Nursery, Hereford & Worcester
Hillier Nurseries Ltd, Hampshire
Hollington Nurseries, Berkshire
J Bradshaw & Son, Kent
Kathy Wright, Lincolnshire
Kayes Garden Nursery, Leicestershire
The Nursery Near Sissinghurst, Kent
Orchard Nurseries, Lincolnshire
P W Plants, Norfolk
The Plantsman Nursery, Devon
Reads Nursery, Norfolk
Richard Stockwell - Rare Plants, Nottinghamshire
Roseland House Nursery, Cornwall
Sherston Parva Nursery Ltd, Wiltshire
Stone House Cottage Nurseries,
    Hereford & Worcester
Trewithen Nurseries, Cornwall
Waterwheel Nursery, Gwent

CONIFERS
Barncroft Nurseries, Staffordshire
Beechcroft Nursery, Surrey
Belwood Nurseries Ltd, Lothian
Brackenwood Garden Centre, Somerset
Brackenwood Plant Centre, Somerset
Bressingham Plant Centre, Cambridgeshire
Bressingham Plant Centre, Norfolk
Bressingham Plant Centre, Berkshire
Cherry Tree Nursery (SWOP), Dorset
Coblands Nursery, Kent
The Conifer Garden, Buckinghamshire
Duchy of Cornwall Nursery, Cornwall
E L F Plants, Cramden Nursery, Northamptonshire
Fron Nursery, Shropshire
Goscote Nurseries Ltd, Leicestershire
Hedgerow Nursery, West Yorkshire
Hillier Nurseries Ltd, Hampshire
Holden Clough Nursery, Lancashire
Hull Farm Conifer Centre, Essex
Kenwith Nursery, Devon
Layham Garden Centre, Kent
Lime Cross Nursery, East Sussex
Merrist Wood College Plant Shop, Surrey
Merton Nurseries, Shropshire
Nettletons Nursery, Surrey
Norwich Heather and Conifer Centre, Norfolk
Owen Bros (of Worcs) Ltd, Hereford & Worcester
Rivendell Nursery, North Yorkshire
W E Th Ingwersen Ltd, West Sussex

CONSERVATORY PLANTS
The Abbots House Garden, Hertfordshire

Brian & Heather Hiley, Surrey
Brockings Exotics, Cornwall
Burncoose Nurseries, Cornwall
Clifton Nurseries, London
Deelish Garden Centre, Co. Cork
Fleur de Lys, West Sussex
Four Counties Nursery, Gloucestershire
Gardiner's Hall Plants, Suffolk
Hardy Exotics Nursery, Cornwall
Long Man Gardens, East Sussex
Lower Icknield Farm Nurseries, Buckinghamshire
Owen Bros (of Worcs) Ltd, Hereford & Worcester
The Plantsman Nursery, Devon
Reads Nursery, Norfolk
Secretts Garden Centre, Surrey
Special Plants, Gloucestershire
Stydd Nursery, Lancashire
Tamarisk Nurseries, Buckinghamshire
Trebah Nursery, Cornwall

DAFFODILS
Ballydorn Bulb Farm, Co. Down
Brian Duncan Daffodils, Co. Tyrone
Broadleigh Gardens, Somerset
Carncairn Daffodils, Co. Antrim
Evelix Daffodils, Highland
J Walkers Bulbs, Lincolnshire
P de Jager & Sons Ltd, Kent
R A Scamp, Cornwall

DAHLIAS
Aylett Nurseries Ltd, Hertfordshire
Butterfields Nursery, Buckinghamshire
Halls of Heddon, Northumberland
Oscroft's Dahlias, West Midlands
Oscroft's Dahlias, South Yorkshire
Philip Tivey & Son, Leicestershire
Scott's Nurseries, South Yorkshire

DELPHINIUMS
Blackmore & Langdon, Somerset
Rougham Hall Nurseries, Suffolk
Woodfield Bros, Warwickshire

DIANTHUS
Allwood Bros, West Sussex
Church Hill Cottage Gardens, Kent
Cravens Nursery, West Yorkshire
Greenacre Nursery, Lancashire
Hayward's Carnations, Hampshire
Mills Farm Plants and Gardens, Suffolk
Pinks & Carnations, Lancashire
Southview Nurseries, Hampshire

Steven Bailey Ltd, Hampshire
Three Counties Nurseries, Dorset

FERNS
Apple Court, Hampshire
Ausfern Nurseries UK Ltd, Essex
Barters Farm Nurseries Ltd, Wiltshire
Coblands Nursery, Kent
The Fern Nursery, Lincolnshire
Fibrex Nurseries Ltd, Warwickshire
Hartside Nursery Garden, Cumbria
Holden Clough Nursery, Lancashire
J & D Marston, East Yorkshire
Madrona Nursery, Kent
Mill Cottage Plants, Somerset
Orchard House Nursery, North Yorkshire
Reginald Kaye Ltd, Lancashire

FOLIAGE PLANTS
Architectural Plants, West Sussex
Decorative Foliage, Devon
Dingle Plants & Gardens, Cambridgeshire
Drysdale Garden Exotics, Hampshire
Eggleston Hall Gardens, Co. Durham
Hoecroft Plants, Norfolk
Mrs S Robinson, Suffolk
Plaxtol Nurseries, Kent

FRUIT
Bonhard Nursery, Tayside
Chris Bowers & Son, Norfolk
Clive Simms, Lincolnshire
Deacon's Nursery, Isle of Wight
Family Trees, Hampshire
Frank P Matthews Ltd, Hereford & Worcester
Gardiner's Hall Plants, Suffolk
Highfield Nurseries, Gloucestershire
How Caple Court Gardens, Hereford & Worcester
J Tweedie Fruit Trees, Dumfries & Galloway
Keepers Nursery, Kent
Ken Leech Trees, Suffolk
Ken Muir Nurseries, Essex
Paul Jasper, Hereford & Worcester
R V Roger Ltd, North Yorkshire
Reads Nursery, Norfolk
Scotts Nurseries Ltd, Somerset
Thornhayes Nursery, Devon
Tim Ingram, Kent
Worsley Hall Nurseries & Garden Centre,
    Greater Manchester

FUCHSIAS
A D & N Wheeler, Warwickshire

Arcadia Nurseries Ltd, North Yorkshire
Askew Nurseries, Leicestershire
B & H M Baker, Essex
Beacon Fuchsias, Dorset
C S Lockyer, Gloucestershire
Clay Lane Nursery, Surrey
Cottage Nurseries, Nottinghamshire
Exotic Fuchsias, Dyfed
Fisher Fuchsias, South Glamorgan
Fuchsiavale Nurseries, Hereford & Worcester
Gouldings Fuchsias, Suffolk
Jackson's Nurseries, Staffordshire
John Smith & Son, Leicestershire
Kathleen Muncaster Fuchsias, Lincolnshire
Kent Street Nurseries, East Sussex
Littelton Nursery, Somerset
Little Brook Fuchsias, Surrey
Meadowcroft Fuchsias, Cambridgeshire
Oakleigh Nurseries, Hampshire
Oldbury Nurseries, Kent
Potash Nursery, Suffolk
Silver Dale Nurseries, Devon
Top Pots, Hertfordshire
The Vernon Geranium Nursery, Surrey
Ward Fuchsias, Cheshire
White Veil Fuchsias, Dorset

GRASSES
Apple Court, Hampshire
Ashenden Nursery, Kent
Ballyrogan Nurseries, Co. Down
Binny Plants, Lothian
Birchdale Plants, Dorset
C M Dickinson, Cheshire
Coblands Nursery, Kent
Hall Farm Nursery, Shropshire
Hannays of Bath, Somerset
Hoecroft Plants, Norfolk
Holden Clough Nursery, Lancashire
John Chambers' Wild Flower Seeds,
    Northamptonshire
Madrona Nursery, Kent
Mill Cottage Plants, Somerset
P W Plants, Norfolk
Park Green Nurseries, Suffolk
Paul Bromfield Aquatics, Hertfordshire
The Plantsman's Preference, Norfolk
Simply Plants, Cambridgeshire
Southcombe Gardens, Devon
Stillingfleet Lodge Nurseries, North Yorkshire
Trevor Scott Ornamental Grasses, Essex

GROUND COVER PLANTS
Barters Farm Nurseries Ltd, Wiltshire
Growing Carpets, Cambridgeshire

HEATHERS
Abbey Brook Cactus Nursery, Derbyshire
Angus Heathers, Tayside
Barncroft Nurseries, Staffordshire
D & M Everett, Hereford & Worcester
Denbeigh Heathers, Suffolk
Eversley Nurseries, Lancashire
Goscote Nurseries Ltd, Leicestershire
Naked Cross Nurseries, Dorset
Norwich Heather and Conifer Centre, Norfolk
Okell's Nurseries, Cheshire
Otters' Court Heathers, Somerset
Speyside Heather Centre, Highland
Yorkshire Garden World, North Yorkshire

HEDGING
Barters Farm Nurseries Ltd, Wiltshire
Ben Reid & Co, Grampian
Buckingham Nurseries and Garden Centre,
    Buckinghamshire
Bucknell Nurseries, Shropshire
Christie Elite Nurseries, Grampian
Country House Hedging, Hereford & Worcester
Forward Nurseries, Kent
Goldsmith Trees & Landscapes Ltd, Suffolk
Landford Trees, Wiltshire
Mount Pleasant Trees, Gloucestershire
Perrie Hale Forest Nursery, Devon
Sherborne Gardens Nursery, Gloucestershire
Weasdale Nurseries, Cumbria

HERBACEOUS PERENNIALS
Abbey Dore Court Garden, Hereford & Worcester
Abriachan Gardens & Nursery, Highland
Archangel Plants, Dorset
Arley Hall Nursery, Cheshire
Ashenden Nursery, Kent
Ashford Garden Centre, Devon
Asterby Nurseries, Lincolnshire
Aultan Nursery, Grampian
Ballyrogan Nurseries, Co. Down
Barkers Primrose Nurseries, Lancashire
Barnsdale Plants and Gardens, Leicestershire
Bellhouse Nursery, Cheshire
Bents Garden Centre and Nurseries, Cheshire
The Beth Chatto Gardens Ltd, Essex
Binny Plants, Lothian
Birchwood Farm Nursery, Derbyshire
Birkheads Cottage Garden Nursery, Tyne & Wear

Blackthorn Nursery, Hampshire
Bosvigo Plants, Cornwall
Botanic Nursery, Wiltshire
Boyton Nursery, Cornwall
Brackenwood Garden Centre, Somerset
Brackenwood Plant Centre, Somerset
Bregover Plants, Cornwall
Bressingham Gardens Mail Order, Norfolk
Bressingham Plant Centre, Cambridgeshire
Bressingham Plant Centre, Norfolk
Bressingham Plant Centre, Berkshire
Bridge End Nurseries, Dumfries & Galloway
Broadleigh Gardens, Somerset
Brownthwaite Hardy Plants, Cumbria
Buckingham Nurseries and Garden Centre,
    Buckinghamshire
Burnside Nursery, Strathclyde
C E & D M Nurseries, Lincolnshire
C M Dickinson, Cheshire
Cally Gardens, Dumfries & Galloway
Catforth Gardens, Lancashire
Caves Folly Nurseries, Hereford & Worcester
Charter House Hardy Plant Nursery,
    Dumfries & Galloway
Chipchase Castle Nursery, Northumberland
Church Hill Cottage Gardens, Kent
Churchills Garden Nursery, Devon
Cilwern Plants, Dyfed
Coblands Nursery, Kent
Coombland Gardens, West Sussex
Cotswold Garden Flowers, Hereford & Worcester
The Cottage Garden, Essex
The Cottage Garden Plant Centre, East Yorkshire
Cottage Garden Plants of Cuckfield, West Sussex
The Cottage Herbery, Hereford & Worcester
Cottage Nurseries, Lincolnshire
Craigieburn Classic Plants, Dumfries & Galloway
Cranesbill Nursery, Hereford & Worcester
Croftway Nursery, West Sussex
The Cuckoo Pen Nursery, Oxfordshire
Dingle Plants & Gardens, Cambridgeshire
Duchy of Cornwall Nursery, Cornwall
Eastgrove Cottage Garden Nursery,
    Hereford & Worcester
Elizabeth MacGregor, Dumfries & Galloway
Elworthy Cottage Garden Plants, Somerset
Fairy Lane Nurseries, Greater Manchester
The Firs Nursery, Cheshire
Four Seasons, Norfolk
Frances Mount Perennial Plants, Essex
Gannock Growers, Hertfordshire
The Garden at The Elms, Hereford & Worcester
Garden Cottage Nursery, Highland

Gardiner's Hall Plants, Suffolk
Glebe Cottage Plants, Devon
Glen Chantry, Essex
Goldenfields Nursery, Cheshire
Great Dixter Nurseries, East Sussex
Green Farm Plants, Surrey
Hadspen Garden and Nursery, Somerset
Halecat Garden Nurseries, Cumbria
Hall Farm Nursery, Lincolnshire
Hall Farm Nursery, Shropshire
Hannays of Bath, Somerset
Hardy's Cottage Garden Plants, Hampshire
Hayloft Plants, Hereford & Worcester
Hellyer's Garden Plants, West Sussex
Henllys Lodge Plants, Gwynedd
Hexham Herbs, Northumberland
The Hiller Garden and Plant Centre, Warwickshire
Hillside Cottage Plants, Somerset
Hillview Hardy Plants, Shropshire
Holden Clough Nursery, Lancashire
Hoo House Nursery, Gloucestershire
Hopleys Plants Ltd, Hertfordshire
Houghton Farm Plants, West Sussex
Iden Croft Herbs, Kent
Intakes Farm Nursery, Staffordshire
Judy's Country Garden, Lincolnshire
Kayes Garden Nursery, Leicestershire
Kaytie Fisher Nursery, Surrey
Kelways Ltd, Somerset
Kittoch Mill Hosta Garden, Strathclyde
Knightshayes Garden Trust, Devon
Langthorns Plantery, Essex
Layham Garden Centre, Kent
Lilliesleaf Nursery, Borders
Lingen Nursery and Gardens, Shropshire
Little Treasures Nursery, Cornwall
Lodge Lane Nursery, Cheshire
Longacre Nursery, Kent
Longhall Nursery, Wiltshire
Longstock Park Nursery, Hampshire
Lower Severalls Herb Nursery, Somerset
LW Plants, Hertfordshire
MacGregors Plants, Hampshire
Magpies, Norfolk
Margery Fish Plant Nursery, Somerset
Martins Nursery, Suffolk
Marwood Hill Gardens, Devon
The Mead Nursery, Wiltshire
Merriments Gardens, East Sussex
Merton Nurseries, Shropshire
Mill Cottage Plants, Somerset
Mill Hill Plants, Nottinghamshire
Mill Race Nursery, Essex

Milton Garden Plants, Dorset
Mires Beck Nursery, East Yorkshire
Monksilver Nursery, Cambridgeshire
Nordybank Nurseries, Shropshire
Northumbria Nurseries, Northumberland
Norwell Nursery, Nottinghamshire
Oak Tree Nursery, North Yorkshire
Oakhurst Nursery, East Sussex
Old Court Nurseries, Hereford & Worcester
One House Nursery, Cheshire
Orchard House Nursery, North Yorkshire
Orchard Nurseries, Lincolnshire
Otter Nurseries Ltd, Devon
Paradise Centre, Suffolk
Park Green Nurseries, Suffolk
Perhill Plants, Hereford & Worcester
Perry's Plants, North Yorkshire
Perrybrook Nursery, Shropshire
Perryhill Nurseries, East Sussex
Plantations Perennials, Lancashire
Plantings Garden Nursery, Central
The Plantsman's Preference, Norfolk
Pounsley Plants, Devon
Primrose Cottage Nursery & Garden Centre,
    Greater Manchester
Priory Garden Nursery, Gloucestershire
R D Plants, Devon
Ravensthorpe Nursery, Northamptonshire
Reginald Kaye Ltd, Lancashire
Rookhope Nurseries, Co. Durham
Roseland House Nursery, Cornwall
Rougham Hall Nurseries, Suffolk
Rowden Gardens, Devon
Rushfields of Ledbury, Hereford & Worcester
Sampford Shrubs, Devon
Scalers Hill Nursery, Kent
Shepton Nursery Garden, Somerset
Sherborne Gardens Nursery, Gloucestershire
Southcombe Gardens, Devon
Southview Nurseries, Hampshire
Spinners, Hampshire
Stillingfleet Lodge Nurseries, North Yorkshire
Thyme House Nursery, Cambridgeshire
Tim Ingram, Kent
Timpany Nurseries, Co. Down
Tissington Nurseries, Derbyshire
Town Farm Nursery, Co Durham
Ty'r Orsaf Nursery, Gwynedd
Ulverscroft Unusual Plants, Leicestershire
Usual & Unusual Plants, East Sussex
Veryans Plants, Devon
The Vicarage Gardens, Greater Manchester
The Walled Garden, Suffolk

Water Meadow Nursery and Herb Farm, Hampshire
Waterwheel Nursery, Gwent
West Acre Gardens, Norfolk
West Kington Nurseries, Wiltshire
Westwinds Perennial Plants, Co Durham
Wintergreen Nurseries, Hereford & Worcester
Withleigh Nurseries, Devon
Woodlands Cottage Nursery, North Yorkshire
Wye Valley Herbs, Gwent

HERBS
Arne Herbs, Somerset
Barwinnock Herbs, Strathclyde
Blooming Things, Powys
Cheshire Herbs, Cheshire
The Cottage Garden Plant Centre, East Yorkshire
The Cottage Herbery, Hereford & Worcester
Eden Plants, Co. Leitrim
Elly Hill Herbs, Co. Durham
Elsworth Herbs, Cambridgeshire
Foliage Scented & Herb Plants, Surrey
Gwydir Plants, Gwynedd
The Herb Garden, Derbyshire
The Herb Garden & Plant Hunters Nursery, Gwynedd
The Herb Nursery, Leicestershire
Hewthorn Herbs & Wild Flowers, Nottinghamshire
Hexham Herbs, Northumberland
Hill Farm Herbs, Northamptonshire
Hill Farm Herbs, Leicestershire
Hollington Nurseries, Berkshire
Iden Croft Herbs, Kent
Jekka's Herb Farm, Gloucestershire
Judy's Country Garden, Lincolnshire
Lisdoonan Herbs, Co. Down
Lower Severalls Herb Nursery, Somerset
LW Plants, Hertfordshire
Nordybank Nurseries, Shropshire
Oak Cottage Herb Garden, Shropshire
The Old Mill Herbary, Cornwall
Parkinson Herbs, Cornwall
Perhili Plants, Hereford & Worcester
Poyntzfield Herb Nursery, Highland
Primrose Cottage Nursery & Garden Centre,
    Greater Manchester
Water Meadow Nursery and Herb Farm, Hampshire
Woodlands Cottage Nursery, North Yorkshire
Wye Valley Herbs, Gwent
Yorkshire Garden World, North Yorkshire

HOUSE PLANTS
B & H M Baker, Essex
Boonwood Garden Centre, Cumbria
Clifton Nurseries, London

Dibleys, Clwyd
Owen Bros (of Worcs) Ltd, Hereford & Worcester
Paul Bromfield Aquatics, Hertfordshire
Secretts Garden Centre, Surrey
The Van Hage Garden Company, Hertfordshire

IRISES
Agars Nursery, Hampshire
Broadleigh Gardens, Somerset
Croftway Nursery, West Sussex
David Austin Roses, Shropshire
Kelways Ltd, Somerset
Mill Hill Plants, Nottinghamshire
Rowden Gardens, Devon
S & S Perennials, Leicestershire
V H Humphrey - Iris Specialist, Surrey
Zephyrwude Irises, West Yorkshire

LILIES
Flora Exotica, Essex
J Walkers Bulbs, Lincolnshire
P de Jager & Sons Ltd, Kent

MEDITERRANEAN PLANTS
Cranesbill Nursery, Hereford & Worcester
Dibleys, Clwyd
Drysdale Garden Exotics, Hampshire

NEW ZEALAND PLANTS
Ausfern Nurseries UK Ltd, Essex
Ballalheannagh Gardens, Isle of Man
County Park Nursery, Essex
Eastgrove Cottage Garden Nursery,
    Hereford & Worcester
Flora Exotica, Essex
Island Plants, Highland
Marwood Hill Gardens, Devon
P & S Allanson, Isle of Man
Timpany Nurseries, Co. Down

ORCHIDS
Burnham Nurseries, Devon
Deva Orchids, Clwyd
Equatorial Plant Co, Co. Durham
Mansell & Hatcher Ltd, West Yorkshire
Tamarisk Nurseries, Buckinghamshire
Woodstock Orchids and Automations,
    Buckinghamshire

PAEONIES
David Austin Roses, Shropshire
Kelways Ltd, Somerset
Phedar Nursery, Cheshire

PALMS

Ausfern Nurseries UK Ltd, Essex
The Palm Centre, London
Toobees Exotics, Surrey
Trebah Nursery, Cornwall

PELARGONIUMS

A D & N Wheeler, Warwickshire
The Beeches Nursery, Nottinghamshire
Brian Sulman Pelargoniums, Suffolk
Denmead Geranium Nurseries, Hampshire
Derek Lloyd Dean, London
Fibrex Nurseries Ltd, Warwickshire
Fir Trees Pelargonium Nursery, North Yorkshire
Hosford's Geraniums & Garden Centre, Co. Cork
Kent Street Nurseries, East Sussex
Littelton Nursery, Somerset
Meadowcroft Fuchsias, Cambridgeshire
Mephams Nursery, West Sussex
Oakleigh Nurseries, Hampshire
Oldbury Nurseries, Kent
Pearl Sulman, Suffolk
Three Suns Nursery, Essex
Trebah Nursery, Cornwall
The Vernon Geranium Nursery, Surrey
West Country Geraniums, Somerset
Westdale Nurseries, Wiltshire

PRIMULAS

Abriachan Gardens & Nursery, Highland
Ardfearn Nursery, Highland
Country House Hedging, Hereford & Worcester
Craig Lodge Nurseries, Dumfries & Galloway
Craigieburn Classic Plants, Dumfries & Galloway
Cravens Nursery, West Yorkshire
Field House Alpines, Nottinghamshire
Garden Cottage Nursery, Highland
Gardenscape, North Yorkshire
Glendoick Garden Centre, Tayside
Greenslacks Nurseries, West Yorkshire
Hartside Nursery Garden, Cumbria
Hillview Hardy Plants, Shropshire
Lingholm Gardens, Cumbria
Longstock Park Nursery, Hampshire
Martin Nest Nurseries, Lincolnshire
Mendle Nursery, Lincolnshire
Norden Alpine Nursery, North Yorkshire
One House Nursery, Cheshire
R F Beeston, Hereford & Worcester
Ryal Nursery, Northumberland
Surrey Primroses, Surrey
Timpany Nurseries, Co. Down

PRUNUS

Blackthorn Nursery, Hampshire
Cowells Garden Centre, Tyne & Wear
Dibleys, Clwyd

RHODODENDRONS

Angus Heathers, Tayside
Ardencaple Garden Centre, Strathclyde
Ballalheannagh Gardens, Isle of Man
Barncroft Nurseries, Staffordshire
Bodnant Garden Nursery Ltd, Clwyd
Burncoose Nurseries, Cornwall
Coghurst Nursery, East Sussex
Exbury Enterprises Ltd, Hampshire
F Morrey & Son, Cheshire
Glendoick Garden Centre, Tayside
Goscote Nurseries Ltd, Leicestershire
Hedgerow Nursery, West Yorkshire
The High Garden, Devon
Highgates Nursery, Derbyshire
Hydon Nurseries, Surrey
Knap Hill Nursery Ltd, Surrey
Lanhydrock Gardens, Cornwall
Lea Gardens, Derbyshire
Lingholm Gardens, Cumbria
Magnolia Gardens, Kent
Millais Nurseries, Surrey
Muncaster Plants, Cumbria
Nordybank Nurseries, Shropshire
Notcutts Garden Centre (Bagshot), Surrey
Orchardstown Nurseries, Co. Waterford
Sampford Shrubs, Devon
Seaforde Gardens, Co. Down
Starborough Nursery, Kent
Tree Shop, Strathclyde
Trewithen Nurseries, Cornwall
Wall Cottage Nursery, Cornwall
Whitehills Nurseries, Dumfries & Galloway

ROSES

A J Palmer & Son, Buckinghamshire
Abbey Plants, Dorset
Apuldram Roses, West Sussex
Battersby Roses, North Yorkshire
Baytree Nurseries, Lincolnshire
Bents Garden Centre and Nurseries, Cheshire
Bonhard Nursery, Tayside
Boyton Nursery, Cornwall
Burrows Roses, Derbyshire
C & K Jones, Cheshire
C & K Jones, Clwyd
Cants of Colchester, Essex
Cranborne Manor Garden Centre, Dorset

David Austin Roses, Shropshire
Dickson Nurseries Ltd, Co. Down
F Haynes & Partners, Northamptonshire
F Morrey & Son, Cheshire
Fryer's Roses Ltd, Cheshire
Gandy's Roses Ltd, Leicestershire
Godly's Roses, Hertfordshire
Hadspen Garden and Nursery, Somerset
Henry Street Garden Centre, Berkshire
Hexham Herbs, Northumberland
The Hiller Garden and Plant Centre, Warwickshire
Hosford's Geraniums & Garden Centre, Co. Cork
How Caple Court Gardens, Hereford & Worcester
Hunts Court Garden & Nursery, Gloucestershire
James Cocker & Sons, Grampian
Just Roses, East Sussex
Kaytie Fisher Nursery, Surrey
Layham Garden Centre, Kent
Mattocks Roses, Oxfordshire
Mills Farm Plants and Gardens, Suffolk
Notcutts Nurseries (Woodbridge), Suffolk
Perryhill Nurseries, East Sussex
Peter Beales Roses, Norfolk
Plantings Garden Nursery, Central
R Harkness & Co Ltd, Hertfordshire
R V Roger Ltd, North Yorkshire
Rumwood Nurseries, Kent
Scotts Nurseries Ltd, Somerset
Stydd Nursery, Lancashire
Thyme House Nursery, Cambridgeshire
Trevor White Old Fashioned Roses, Norfolk
West Kington Nurseries, Wiltshire
Wheatcroft Ltd, Nottinghamshire

SEMPERVIVUMS
Alan C Smith, Kent
Ashwood Nurseries Ltd, West Midlands
Bennetts Water Lily Farm, Dorset
Brambling House Alpines, South Yorkshire
CTDA, London
Greenslacks Nurseries, West Yorkshire
H & S Wills, Devon
Mendle Nursery, Lincolnshire
One House Nursery, Cheshire
The Plant Lovers, Lincolnshire

SHRUBS
Abbey Plants, Dorset
Asterby Nurseries, Lincolnshire
Aultan Nursery, Grampian
Ballaheannagh Gardens, Isle of Man
Barncroft Nurseries, Staffordshire
Barnsdale Plants and Gardens, Leicestershire

Beechcroft Nurseries, Cumbria
Beetham Nurseries, Cumbria
Bellhouse Nursery, Cheshire
Belwood Nurseries Ltd, Lothian
Bents Garden Centre and Nurseries, Cheshire
Binny Plants, Lothian
Bluebell Nursery, Derbyshire
Bodnant Garden Nursery Ltd, Clwyd
Botanic Nursery, Wiltshire
Brackenwood Garden Centre, Somerset
Brackenwood Plant Centre, Somerset
Bressingham Plant Centre, Norfolk
Bressingham Plant Centre, Berkshire
Brinkley Nurseries, Nottinghamshire
C Fairweather Ltd, Hampshire
Cherry Tree Nursery (SWOP), Dorset
Chichester Trees and Shrubs, Hampshire
Chris Pattison (Nurseryman), Gloucestershire
Christie Elite Nurseries, Grampian
Churchills Garden Nursery, Devon
Clifton Nurseries, London
Coblands Nursery, Kent
Duchy of Cornwall Nursery, Cornwall
E L F Plants, Cramden Nursery, Northamptonshire
F Morrey & Son, Cheshire
Fron Nursery, Shropshire
Goscote Nurseries Ltd, Leicestershire
Grange Farm Nursery, Hereford & Worcester
Great Dixter Nurseries, East Sussex
Hannays of Bath, Somerset
Hergest Croft Gardens, Hereford & Worcester
Hickling Heath Nursery, Norfolk
Hillier Nurseries Ltd, Hampshire
Holden Clough Nursery, Lancashire
Hopleys Plants Ltd, Hertfordshire
Hunts Court Garden & Nursery, Gloucestershire
Kathy Wright, Lincolnshire
Knightshayes Garden Trust, Devon
Langthorns Plantery, Essex
Lanhydrock Gardens, Cornwall
Layham Garden Centre, Kent
Lime Cross Nursery, East Sussex
Little Treasures Nursery, Cornwall
Longstock Park Nursery, Hampshire
MacGregors Plants, Hampshire
Macpennys Nurseries, Dorset
Madrona Nursery, Kent
Manorbier Garden Centre, Dyfed
Merrist Wood College Plant Shop, Surrey
Monksilver Nursery, Cambridgeshire
Mrs S M Cooper, Hereford & Worcester
Nettletons Nursery, Surrey
Notcutts Garden Centre (Bagshot), Surrey

The Nursery Near Sissinghurst, Kent
P H Kellett, Kent
P M A Plant Specialities, Somerset
P W Plants, Norfolk
Peter Barratt's Garden Centres (Stockton),
    Co Durham
Peter Trenear Nurseries, Hampshire
Phedar Nursery, Cheshire
Pleasant View Nursery & Garden, Devon
Rivendell Nursery, North Yorkshire
Ryans Nurseries, Co. Kerry
Sampford Shrubs, Devon
Spinners, Hampshire
St Ishmaels Nurseries and Garden Centre, Dyfed
Starborough Nursery, Kent
Stone House Cottage Nurseries,
    Hereford & Worcester
Tim Ingram, Kent
Tissington Nurseries, Derbyshire
Town Farm Nursery, Co Durham
Tree Shop, Strathclyde
Ulverscroft Unusual Plants, Leicestershire
Wards Nurseries (Sarratt) Ltd, Hertfordshire
Weasdale Nurseries, Cumbria
West Acre Gardens, Norfolk
West Somerset Garden Centre, Somerset
Westonbirt Plant Centre, Gloucestershire
Whitehills Nurseries, Dumfries & Galloway
Withleigh Nurseries, Devon

SOUTH AMERICAN PLANTS
Apple Court, Hampshire
Dalgety Bay Garden Centre, Fife
Feebers Hardy Plants, Devon
Peter Barratt's Garden Centres (Stockton), Co. Durham

SWEET PEAS
Downderry Nursery, Kent
S & N Brackley, Buckinghamshire

TOPIARY
Brockings Exotics, Cornwall
Clifton Nurseries, London
Country House Hedging, Hereford & Worcester
Crocknafeola Nursery, Co. Donegal
Langley Boxwood Nursery, Hampshire
The Romantic Garden Nursery, Norfolk
Sherborne Gardens Nursery, Gloucestershire

TREES
Architectural Plants, West Sussex
Baronscourt Nurseries, Co. Tyrone
Barters Farm Nurseries Ltd, Wiltshire

Bawdeswell Garden Centre, Norfolk
Beechcroft Nurseries, Cumbria
Beetham Nurseries, Cumbria
Belwood Nurseries Ltd, Lothian
Ben Reid & Co, Grampian
Bluebell Nursery, Derbyshire
Brinkley Nurseries, Nottinghamshire
Buckingham Nurseries and Garden Centre,
    Buckinghamshire
Bucknell Nurseries, Shropshire
C Fairweather Ltd, Hampshire
Celyn Vale Nurseries, Clwyd
Chichester Trees and Shrubs, Hampshire
Christie Elite Nurseries, Grampian
Churchills Garden Nursery, Devon
Clonmel Garden Centre Ltd, Co. Tipperary
Coblands Nursery, Kent
Duchy of Cornwall Nursery, Cornwall
Dulford Nurseries, Devon
F Morrey & Son, Cheshire
Four Counties Nursery, Gloucestershire
Frank P Matthews Ltd, Hereford & Worcester
Fron Nursery, Shropshire
Goscote Nurseries Ltd, Leicestershire
Grange Farm Nursery, Hereford & Worcester
Hergest Croft Gardens, Hereford & Worcester
Hillier Nurseries Ltd, Hampshire
Knightshayes Garden Trust, Devon
Landford Trees, Wiltshire
Layham Garden Centre, Kent
Lime Cross Nursery, East Sussex
Macpennys Nurseries, Dorset
Madrona Nursery, Kent
Mallet Court Nursery, Somerset
Marwood Hill Gardens, Devon
Merrist Wood College Plant Shop, Surrey
Mill Race Nursery, Essex
Mount Pleasant Trees, Gloucestershire
Mrs S M Cooper, Hereford & Worcester
Norfields, Gloucestershire
Notcutts Nurseries (Woodbridge), Suffolk
Orchardstown Nurseries, Co. Waterford
P H Kellett, Kent
P M A Plant Specialities, Somerset
Perrie Hale Forest Nursery, Devon
Peter Trenear Nurseries, Hampshire
Scotts Nurseries Ltd, Somerset
Seaforde Gardens, Co. Down
Spinners, Hampshire
St Ishmaels Nurseries and Garden Centre, Dyfed
Starborough Nursery, Kent
Thornhayes Nursery, Devon
Thyme House Nursery, Cambridgeshire

Tree Shop, Strathclyde
Wards Nurseries (Sarratt) Ltd, Hertfordshire
Waterwheel Nursery, Gwent
Weasdale Nurseries, Cumbria
Westonbirt Plant Centre, Gloucestershire
YSJ Seeds, Somerset

VIOLAS

Bouts Cottage Nurseries, Hereford & Worcester
C W Groves & Son, Dorset
Church Hill Cottage Gardens, Kent
Elizabeth MacGregor, Dumfries & Galloway
Planta Vera, Surrey
Rodney Fuller, Somerset

WILD FLOWERS

Applegarth Nursery, Shropshire
Arne Herbs, Somerset
Blooming Things, Powys
British Wild Flower Plants, Norfolk
British Wild Plants, Dumfries & Galloway
CN Seeds, Cambridgeshire

Gwydir Plants, Gwynedd
The Herb Garden & Plant Hunters Nursery,
    Gwynedd
The Herb Nursery, Leicestershire
Hewthorn Herbs & Wild Flowers, Nottinghamshire
Hexham Herbs, Northumberland
Iden Croft Herbs, Kent
Jekka's Herb Farm, Gloucestershire
John Chambers' Wild Flower Seeds,
    Northamptonshire
Landlife Wildflowers Ltd, Merseyside
Linda Gascoigne Wild Flowers, Leicestershire
Llanbrook Alpine & Wildflower Nursery, Shropshire
Mires Beck Nursery, East Yorkshire
Naturescape, Nottinghamshire
Nordybank Nurseries, Shropshire
Oak Cottage Herb Garden, Shropshire
Old Court Nurseries, Hereford & Worcester
The Wild Flower Centre, Norfolk
Wild Seeds, Gwynedd
YSJ Seeds, Somerset

Seedsmen

10

Andrew Norfield Seeds

Lower Meend, St Briavels, Gloucestershire GL15 6RW
☎ 01594 530134　　FAX 01594 530113

CONTACT　Andrew Norfield
OPEN　Mail order only
SPECIALITIES　Acers; seeds
CATALOGUE　1 first-class stamp
MAIL ORDER　Yes
SHOWS　Malvern Spring

Pre-germinated seed of trees, shrubs, houseplants, bulbs and herbaceous plants. Here you pay a premium on the ordinary seed price, but do not have to wait for lengthy or difficult germination conditions to be fulfilled.

Ashwood Nurseries Ltd

See West Midlands, Nurseries section

B & T World Seeds

Whitnell House, Fiddington, Bridgwater, Somerset TA5 1JE
☎ & FAX 01278 733209

CONTACT　David Sleigh
OPEN　Mail order only
SPECIALITIES　Seeds
CATALOGUE　Master list £10 (£14 beyond Europe); sub lists 50p
MAIL ORDER　Yes

Specialists in exotic seeds supplied from (and to) most of the world. The system is based on a computerised master list, and 150 specialist lists (say Californian natives or Salt tolerant) derived from it. Seed lists don't come any longer than this one: the range is phenomenal. Be aware that many species will be ordered specially for you and that this may take time.

Bodnant Garden Nursery Ltd

See Clwyd, Nurseries section

Carters Tested Seeds Ltd

Hele Road, Torquay, Devon TQ2 7QJ
☎ 01803 616156　　FAX 01803 615747
OPEN　From stockists only
SPECIALITIES　Seeds
MAIL ORDER　From stockists only

Long-established seed company in the Suttons group. The flower and vegetable range is sold through garden centres and some supermarkets. Details of stockists from the company.

Cheshire Herbs

See Cheshire, Nurseries section

Chiltern Seeds

Bortree Stile, Ulverston, Cumbria LA12 7PB
☎ 01229 581137　　FAX 01229 584549

CONTACT　P. A. Burns
OPEN　Mail order only
SPECIALITIES　Seeds
CATALOGUE　On request
MAIL ORDER　Yes
GIFT TOKENS　Own

The distinctive long, tall catalogue is uniquely comprehensive. Last year's edition had 288 pages and listed 4,500 species and cultivars from around the world including garden flowers and vegetables. A good proportion of novelties (455 last year) means that there is always something to interest the adventurous or the armchair gardener. The careful descriptions make it useful for reference too. Orders can be phoned through 24 hrs a day.

Chris Chadwell – Freelance Botanist

See Berkshire, Nurseries section

CN Seeds

Denmark House, Pymoor, Ely, Cambridgeshire CB6 2EG
☎ 01353 699413　　FAX 01353 698806

CONTACT　Chris Nye
SPECIALITIES　Seeds; wild flowers
CATALOGUE　Trade, on request
MAIL ORDER　Yes

Wholesale herb and flower seed merchants, but retail customers are welcome. Prices are quoted by weight and quantities given. There is a wide range, from British wild flowers to exotic trees but they are particularly good on herbaceous plants. Try them for *Fritillaria meleagris* to naturalise: 1 gr will cost you £3 plus VAT, and yield about 800 seeds.

Coombland Gardens

See West Sussex, Nurseries section

Cravens Nursery

See West Yorkshire, Nurseries section

CTDA

See London, Nurseries section

D T Brown & Co Ltd

Station Road, Poulton le Fylde, Lancashire FY6 7HX
☎ 01253 882371   FAX 01253 890923
OPEN   Mail order only
SPECIALITIES   Seeds
CATALOGUE   On request
MAIL ORDER   Yes
GIFT TOKENS   Own

Flower and vegetable seed merchants, with some young plants, grass seed and horticultural sundries. A large range is sold from their clear and concise catalogue. They issue a separate seed catalogue for commercial growers and florists.

Edwin Tucker & Sons

Brewery Meadow, Stonepark, Ashburton, Devon
TQ13 7DG
☎ 01364 652403   FAX 01364 654300
CONTACT   Mrs G. Heath
LOCATION   Asburton and Crediton
OPEN   Ashburton: 8 am – 5 pm, Monday – Friday; 8 am – 4 pm, Saturday. Crediton: 8.30 am – 5 pm, Monday – Saturday
SPECIALITIES   Seeds
CATALOGUE   On request
MAIL ORDER   Yes
SHOP   Seeds, garden sundries, plants
REFRESHMENTS   Yes
GIFT TOKENS   HTA

Long-established seed merchants, with a retail and agricultural catalogue. They have over 70 seed potatoes, including continental varieties, as well as vegetables and garden flowers and grass seed. Some garden products are also available mail order. There is a country store at the above address and at Commercial Road, Crediton (01363 772202). Their working malthouse (near Newton Abbot railway station) can be visited daily, except Saturdays, from Easter to October (01626 334734).

Emorsgate Seeds

The Pea Mill, Market Lane, Terrington St Clement, King's Lynn, Norfolk PE34 4HR
☎ 01553 829028   FAX 01553 829803
CONTACT   Mark Schofield
OPEN   Mail order only
SPECIALITIES   Seeds
CATALOGUE   On request
MAIL ORDER   Yes

Wild flowers, wild grasses and mixtures for retail and wholesale customers. The seed stocks are based on native collected seed which is then grown at the farm: the source county is given and stocks are regularly replenished. A good choice of wild and amenity grasses. Flower and grass mixtures are available for different soil types, and some are derived (with permission) from specified nature reserves.

Field House Alpines

See Nottinghamshire, Nurseries section

Glenhirst Cactus Nursery

See Lincolnshire, Nurseries section

Holly Gate Cactus Nursery

See West Sussex, Nurseries section

J E Martin

4 Church Street, Market Harborough, Leicestershire
LE16 7AA
☎ 01858 462751   FAX 01858 434544
LOCATION   Town centre
OPEN   Monday to Saturday. Closed Wednesday afternoons
SPECIALITIES   Seeds
CATALOGUE   On request
MAIL ORDER   Yes
GIFT TOKENS   HTA

Seed potatoes in variety, including 'Pink Fir Apple' and 'Stroma' and 'Kestrel' as well as onion sets and some vegetable seeds. Mainly wholesale: they operate in the Midlands, with another shop in Lutterworth.

J W Boyce

Bush Pasture, Lower Carter Street, Fordham, Ely, Cambridgeshire CB7 5JU
☎ & FAX 01638 721158
CONTACT   Roger Morley
OPEN   9 am – 1 pm, 2 – 5 pm, Monday – Friday; 9 am – 12 noon, Saturdays. Closed Sundays
SPECIALITIES   Seeds
CATALOGUE   On request
MAIL ORDER   Yes
GIFT TOKENS   Own

Specialists for Pansy seed, including their Surprise strain (developed over the last 80 years). Many other fresh flower and vegetable seeds, which are sold packeted and by weight. Free help and advice.

Jack Drake

See Highland, Nurseries section

James Henderson & Sons

Kingholm Quay, Dumfries, Dumfries & Galloway DG1 4SU
☎ 01387 252234   FAX 01387 262302
CONTACT   Richard or James Henderson
OPEN   Mail order only
SPECIALITIES   Seeds
CATALOGUE   SAE
MAIL ORDER   Yes

Seed potato merchants with a wholesale and retail business. They supply many garden centres but you can also order direct. This family firm currently lists 38 varieties including 'Duke of York', and a special potato fertiliser.

Jim & Jenny Archibald

Bryn Collen, Ffostrasol, Llandysul, Dyfed SA44 5SB
CONTACT   Jim or Jenny Archibald
OPEN   Mail order only
SPECIALITIES   Seeds
NEW INTRODUCTIONS FOR 1997   Fresh seed from Greece and South Africa
CATALOGUE   On request
MAIL ORDER   Yes

Serious alpine seed list for serious alpine enthusiasts. The Archibalds are professional collectors, and the list is based on their extensive trips. It includes detailed collection, cultivation and historical notes. Many species will be unavailable elsewhere. This year's catalogue is particularly strong on South African monocots.

John Chambers' Wild Flower Seeds

15 Westleigh Road, Barton Seagrave, Kettering, Northamptonshire NN15 5AJ
☎ 01933 652562   📠 01933 652576
OPEN   Mail order only
SPECIALITIES   Grasses; seeds; wild flowers
CATALOGUE   On request
MAIL ORDER   Yes
SHOP   Books
SHOWS   Chelsea, BBC GW Live
GIFT TOKENS   Own

Biggest and best-known of the wild flower merchants, with everything from British natives and butterfly plants to mixtures and ornamental grass seeds. There's also a good choice of books in the somewhat frenetic catalogue.

John Drake Aquilegias

Hardwicke House, Fen Ditton, Cambridge, Cambridgeshire CB5 8TF
☎ 01223 292246
CONTACT   L. J. Drake
SPECIALITIES   Seeds; aquilegias
CATALOGUE   70p
MAIL ORDER   Yes, minimum order £12
GARDEN   Hardwicke House, Fen Ditton, Cambridge, Cambridgeshire
NCCPG NATIONAL COLLECTIONS   *Aquilegia; Semi-aquilegia*

Seeds of *Aquilegia* species and forms (and not just columbines but other genera too), from an enthusiast and collector. Plants available when garden opens for NGS. Garden Design and Garden Restoration Design Service.

Johnsons Seeds

W W Johnson & Son Ltd, London Road, Boston, Lincolnshire PE21 8AD
☎ 01205 365051   📠 01205 310148
CONTACT   Richard Johnson
LOCATION   On A52, 1 mile north of Boston town centre
SPECIALITIES   Seeds; grass seed
CATALOGUE   On request
MAIL ORDER   Yes
GARDEN   July and August
SHOWS   BBC GW Live
GIFT TOKENS   HTA

Founded in 1820 and still run by the Johnson family. Large collection of general flower and vegetable seed available by post. Flower packets contain an illustrated plastic label. The company's products, including its grass seed range, are also sold in shops and garden centres: Johnsons are probably the leading UK breeders of new turf grass cultivars. There's also a wholesale division.

Kings

Monks Farm, Pantlings Lane, Coggeshall Road, Kelvedon, Essex CO5 9PG
☎ 01376 570000   📠 01376 571189
OPEN   Mail order only
SPECIALITIES   Seeds
CATALOGUE   On request
MAIL ORDER   Yes

Good value retail seed list. All the seed is untreated, so suitable for organic gardeners too. Strong on herbs and sweet peas. They also have a large wholesale flower and vegetable seed business aimed at growers.

Landlife Wildflowers Ltd

See Merseyside, Nurseries section

Mackey's Garden Centre

See Co. Dublin, Nurseries section

Marshalls

S E Marshall & Co Ltd, Wisbech, Cambridgeshire PE13 2RF
☎ 01945 583407   📠 01945 588235
CONTACT   Val Green
OPEN   Mail order
SPECIALITIES   Seeds; potatoes
NEW INTRODUCTIONS FOR 1997   Pre-chitted seed potatoes
CATALOGUE   On request
MAIL ORDER   Yes
GIFT TOKENS   Own

Fenland seed company which specialises in vegetables and seed potatoes: they have a range of popular flowers too, and own Elm House Nursery (which supplies young plants). Like the other major seed firms they place great emphasis on looking after their customers: there are free seeds for larger orders. Regular opportunities to trial (and report) on varieties before they are properly introduced.

Monocot Nursery

See Somerset, Nurseries section

Mr Fothergill's Seeds Ltd

Gazeley Road, Kentford, Newmarket, Suffolk CB8 7QB
☎ 01638 751161   📠 01638 751624
CONTACT   Catalogues: 01638 751887; Orders: 01638 552512
OPEN   Mail order only
SPECIALITIES   Seeds; 'heritage' seed potatoes
NEW INTRODUCTIONS FOR 1997   50 exclusive new varieties
CATALOGUE   On request
MAIL ORDER   Yes
GIFT TOKENS   Own

General seed company selling flowers, vegetables and some sundries from a colourful catalogue. High standard of service and information: they also publish a supplementary 'Enthusiast's Catalogue.' Catalogues can be requested 24 hours of the day; the mail order line is manned 9 am – 4.30 pm, Monday – Friday.

Naturescape

See Nottinghamshire, Nurseries section

North Green Seeds

16 Witton Lane, Little Plumstead, Norwich, Norfolk
NR13 5DL

CONTACT   John Morley and Richard Hobbs
OPEN   Mail order only
SPECIALITIES   Seeds
CATALOGUE   4 first-class stamps
MAIL ORDER   Yes

A pleasantly eclectic range of good things from around the world. Order in summer for autumn sowing. See also North Green Snowdrops, in Nurseries & Garden Centres section.

Paradise Centre

See Suffolk, Nurseries section

Peter Grayson – Sweet Pea Seedsman

34 Glenthorne Close, Brampton, Chesterfield, Derbyshire
S40 3AR
☎ 01246 278503   📠 01246 566918

CONTACT   Peter Grayson
OPEN   Mail order only
SPECIALITIES   Seeds
CATALOGUE   On request
MAIL ORDER   Yes

An enticing list which includes unrivalled collections of *Lathyrus* species, and pre-Spencer Grandifloras (or Heirlooms), and some of Mr Grayson's introductions. There will be hollyhocks this year. Seed is produced on site. Wholesale and retail.

Phedar Nursery

See Cheshire, Nurseries section

Plant World Botanic Gardens

See Devon, Nurseries section

Potterton and Martin

See Lincolnshire, Nurseries section

Richard Stockwell – Rare Plants

See Nottinghamshire, Nurseries section

Roy Young Seeds

23 Westland Chase, West Winch, King's Lynn, Norfolk
PE33 0QH
☎ & 📠 01553 840867

CONTACT   Roy or Sheila Young
OPEN   Mail order only
SPECIALITIES   Seeds
CATALOGUE   On request (retail and wholesale)
MAIL ORDER   International Mail Order

A vast range of cacti and succulent seeds by post, for retail and wholesale customers. Much of the seed is harvested from their own plants. The *Lithops* range is especially notable, with a great number of different forms listed under collectors' numbers. Many items are in short supply, and so telephone orders are not accepted.

S & N Brackley

117 Winslow Road, Wingrave, Aylesbury,
Buckinghamshire HP22 4QB
☎ 01296 681384

CONTACT   S. Brackley
LOCATION   Between Aylesbury and Leighton Buzzard, off A418
OPEN   For plant collection in April only; seeds at all times
SPECIALITIES   Seeds; sweet peas; vegetables
CATALOGUE   On request
MAIL ORDER   Yes
SHOWS   RHS Westminster, Malvern Spring, Malvern Autumn, Harrogate (Spring), Harrogate (Autumn), Southport, Chelsea, BBC GW Live, Hampton Court

Sweet pea specialists, both as seeds and as young plants: garden and exhibition varieties. You can see their displays at the many – mainly southern – shows which they attend. They also produce exhibition vegetable seeds, with leek and onion plants available in April.

S M McArd

39 West Road, Pointon, Sleaford, Lincolnshire NG34 0NA
☎ & 📠 01529 240765

CONTACT   S. McArd
OPEN   Mail order only
SPECIALITIES   Seeds; vegetables
CATALOGUE   On request
MAIL ORDER   Yes

Carefully selected vegetable seeds divided into such headings as 'Connoisseur's Choice' and 'Oriental vegetables.' Some bulbs and flower seeds too, plus soft fruit and unusual vegetable plants.

Salley Gardens

See Nottinghamshire, Nurseries section

Samuel Dobie & Son Ltd

Broomhill Way, Torquay, Devon TQ2 7QW
☎ 01803 616281   📠 01803 615150

CONTACT   Customer services
OPEN   Mail order only
SPECIALITIES   Seeds
CATALOGUE   On request
MAIL ORDER   Yes
REFRESHMENTS   On open days
GARDEN   2 open days, in August
GIFT TOKENS   Own

General seed company with a catalogue of flower and vegetable varieties. They specialise in young annual plants also, and have a decent range of garden equipment too.

The Seed House

9a Widley Road, Cosham, Portsmouth, Hampshire
PO6 2DS
☎ 01705 325639

CONTACT   Richard Spearing
OPEN   Mail order only
SPECIALITIES   Australian plants; seeds

CATALOGUE   4 first-class stamps or 4 international reply coupons
MAIL ORDER   Yes, £5 minimum order

Interesting list of Australian native plants, including *Callistemon* and *Eucalyptus* as well as less common genera. The species are chosen with regard to suitability for a European climate.

Seeds-by-Size
45 Crouchfield, Boxmoor, Hemel Hempstead, Hertfordshire HP1 1PA
☎ 01442 251458

CONTACT   John Robert Size
OPEN   Mail order only
SPECIALITIES   Seeds
CATALOGUE   On request; SAE appreciated
MAIL ORDER   Yes

Over 1400 vegetable strains, and around 4200 flower varieties. Seeds are sold by weight in any quantity from ½ gram up: the pricing system looks more daunting than it really is. Mr Size is a good source for many old and hard to obtain varieties. Take your pick from 64 carrots, 57 lettuces, 222 sweet peas or 52 asters for example.

Simpson's Seeds
27 Meadowbrook, Old Oxted RH8 9LT
☎ & [FAX] 01883 715242

CONTACT   Colin Simpson
SPECIALITIES   Seeds
NEW FOR 1997   Hundreds of old or re-introduced cultivars
CATALOGUE   On request
MAIL ORDER   Yes

Quite the most unusual seedsman in the world. Colin Simpson runs his operation as a society (see *The Tomato Growers' Club*) which enables him to import and export seeds much more easily than he would as a nurseryman. His specialities are tomatoes, peppers and seed potatoes: his descriptive list has a fascinating number of these and other vegetables from all over the world. His own garden is open in early autumn for fellow-fans of unusual varieties to see them growing.

Surrey Primroses
Merriewood, Sandy Lane, Milford, Godalming GU8 5BJ
☎ 01483 416747

CONTACT   G. J. E. Yates
OPEN   Mail order only
SPECIALITIES   Primulas
CATALOGUE   SAE
MAIL ORDER   Yes, no minimum order

Specialist source of old, named single primrose and polyanthus cultivars. Some 30 varieties of delightful and garden-worthy survivors.

Stewarts (Nottm) Ltd
The Garden Shop, 3 George Street, Nottingham NG1 3BH
☎ 0115 9476338

CONTACT   Brenda Lochhead
LOCATION   Nottingham city centre
OPEN   9 am – 5.30 pm

SPECIALITIES   Seeds
CATALOGUE   On request
MAIL ORDER   Yes
SHOP   Seeds and bulbs, chemicals, fertilisers, sundries
GIFT TOKENS   HTA

Long-established seed and bulb merchant. Seeds and bulbs, including potatoes and their own grass seed mixtures. Their Economy collections of flowers and vegetables are packaged by them.

Suttons Seeds
Hele Road, Torquay, Devon TQ2 7QJ
☎ 01803 614455   [FAX] 01803 615747

CONTACT   Customer Services
OPEN   Mail order only
SPECIALITIES   Seeds
CATALOGUE   On request
MAIL ORDER   Yes
REFRESHMENTS   On open days
GARDEN   2 open days in August
GIFT TOKENS   Own

Famous old seed house with a strong catalogue of flowers and vegetable varieties as well as a useful range of garden sundries, young plants and bulbs.

Thompson & Morgan
Poplar Lane, Ipswich, Suffolk IP8 3BU
☎ 01473 688588   [FAX] 01473 680199

OPEN   See below
SPECIALITIES   Seeds
NEW INTRODUCTIONS FOR 1997   *Brachycome* 'Strawberry Mousse', *Dianthus* 'Fenbows Nutmeg Clove'
CATALOGUE   On request
MAIL ORDER   Yes
GARDEN   Trial grounds
SHOWS   Malvern Autumn, Southport, Chelsea, BBC GW Live, Hampton Court
GIFT TOKENS   Own

Established in 1855. The T & M list is the world's largest illustrated seed catalogue. It combines a tradition of good new introductions with a wide choice of less easily attainable plants. Like all the major seed companies, they pride themselves on their service to customers. The trial grounds will be open to the public on 2 – 3 August.

Unwins Seeds Ltd
Histon, Cambridge, Cambridgeshire CB4 4LE
☎ 01223 236236   [FAX] 01223 237437

CONTACT   Order Department
OPEN   Mail order and retailers nationwide
SPECIALITIES   Seeds
CATALOGUE   On request; October
MAIL ORDER   Yes

Long-famous as breeders of sweet peas. Unwins also have a full choice of flowers and vegetables, including mixtures, new introductions and established varieties.

The Van Hage Garden Company
See Hertfordshire, Nurseries section

W E Th Ingwersen Ltd

See West Sussex, Nurseries section

W Robinson & Sons Ltd

Sunny Bank, Forton, Preston, Lancashire PR3 0BN
☎ 01524 791210   📠 01524 791933
LOCATION   17 miles north of Preston on A6
OPEN   Phone first
SPECIALITIES   Seeds
CATALOGUE   On request
MAIL ORDER   Yes
SHOWS   RHS Westminster, Malvern Autumn, Harrogate
(Autumn), Southport

Home of the 'Mammoth' seed strain: exhibition and garden
vegetable seeds, including the 'Mammoth Improved Onion'
and their new climbing French Bean 'Kingston Gold'. Seedlings
and small plants are also available. Their show exhibits are
superb. They will be at Kings Heath and Shrewsbury as well.

Westfield Cacti

See Devon, Nurseries section

Wild Seeds

See Gwynedd, Nurseries section

YSJ Seeds

See Somerset, Nurseries section

11

Importing & Exporting Plants

Thanks to the EC's Single Market, plants can now in general be moved freely between all the countries of the European Community. This is very good news for British gardeners. To see why, browse through the section of European nurseries in this book. There are some exceptionally good lists there, opening up access to many cultivars that are unavailable in the UK. We think many gardeners will find this prospect exciting. For this reason, this chapter concentrates on private individuals who want to bring plants into the UK, although we also touch on the more complicated situation for exporters and the wholesale trade.

Some controls remain, and it is necessary to understand how these work in order to take full advantage of what has been a significant relaxation in import controls. There are three overlapping systems of control.

The first distinguishes between the status of the importer. Individuals bringing plants in for their own use face the least restriction. Plants which are imported ready for immediate retail sale are more tightly controlled, but have a number of exemptions from the stricter régime which is applied to plants passing between wholesalers.

There are distinctions based on origin. A generally permissive régime applies within the EC, with the exception of particular protected zones (usually designated to protect disease-free areas). For the rest of the world, more restrictions exist, although these are relaxed sometimes for other European and Mediterranean countries. Where diseases are localised, especially for economic species, very complex and specific regulations can apply.

Species which are considered to be endangered are subject to CITES. The Convention on International Trade in Endangered Species of wild fauna and flora. Permits are required to move species covered by CITES. Wild plants may also be covered by national protection legislation.

Private individuals: moving plants within the EC

As a general rule, there are no restrictions on private individuals buying plants for their personal use anywhere in the EC. That is a direct result of the coming of the Single Market: Europe is one country now. Plants must be carried in your personal baggage (e.g. in your car) and be for your own household use. They must also be free from signs of pests or diseases.

People who live in protected zones will have to comply with the higher plant health standards which exist there. Protected zones are exceptions to the free movement policy which have been negotiated by individual member states. They are areas (usually countries) which are substantially free from a particular harmful pest or disease and where, as a result, a higher level of plant health control is required to keep them free. If in doubt contact MAFF. It is not possible, for example, to import poinsettia cuttings from elsewhere in the EU because the UK is a protected zone for *Euphorbia pulcherrima*: this was imposed to protect British crops from infection with a pest called *Bemisia tabaci*. The main application of protected zones to the UK are to seed potatoes, conifers and potential carriers of fireblight.

Private individuals: the rest of the world

Contrary to widespread belief, individuals are free to bring back small quantities of plants and propagating material from anywhere in the world. Again, they must be for personal use, be carried in your baggage and be free from pests and diseases. 'Small quantities' means:

Up to 2kg of fruit and raw vegetables (no potatoes)
One bouquet of cut flowers or parts of plants
Five packets of retail seed (not potatoes)
These can be imported from any part of the world.

In addition, two extra categories may be imported from 'non-EC countries of the Euro-Mediterranean area':

2kg of bulbs, corms tubers and/or rhizomes

Five plants

This applies to all European countries, plus Algeria, Cyprus, Egypt, Israel, Jordan, Lebanon, Libya, Malta, Morocco, Tunisia and Turkey.

These allowances extend to children as well as to adults. The regulations make no distinction between wild-collected and cultivated plants, but see the note on CITES and conservation below. Nor is there any restriction on the import of flower seeds from any part of the world: the 'five packets' rule therefore applies only to non-flower seeds.

Similar rules apply in the rest of the EC and in Northern Ireland (they derive from the same EC directive), but it is always worth checking first before taking plants from the UK to other parts of the EC in case protective zones apply.

Further advice on personal allowances is available from the Plant Health Division, MAFF, Room 340, Foss House, 1 – 2 Peasholme Green, Kings Pool, York YO1 2PX. MAFF also publishes a leaflet entitled *Travellers: Plants brought back to Britain from abroad could carry serious pests and diseases* (Contact: 0645 556000).

Wholesale Material in the EC

Free movement is permitted provided that the plants have been inspected at the place of production and are accompanied by a plant passport. Plant passports are effectively phytosanitary certificates for internal EC use only. Introduced in 1993, these plant passports are issued by the selling nursery and the procedures are easily accommodated within the routines of a well-run nursery. Any nursery may apply to MAFF for authority to issue plant passports.

Plant passports are needed even within a single member state, for any sale or transport of certain economic plants: hops, potatoes, vines, citrus fruits and all those fruit trees or berried ornamentals which are members of the Rosaceae and susceptible to fungal and bacterial diseases – *Amelanchier, Chaenomeles* (Japanese quince), *Cotoneaster, Crataegus, Cydonia* (common quince), *Eriobotrya* (loquat), *Malus* (apple), *Mespilus* (medlar), *Prunus* (plum, cherry, peach, almond & apricot), *Pyracantha, Pyrus* (pear), *Sorbus* and *Stranvaesia*. The plant passport is required at all stages down to the retailer.

In many instances, the requirement to issue a plant passport is waived if the plants are intended and ready

for immediate retail sale. Those plants include the following families and genera: Araceae, *Argyranthemum* (chrysanthemums), *Aster, Brassica, Castanea* (chestnuts), *Cucumis* (cucumbers), *Dendranthema* (chrysanthemums), *Dianthus, Exacum, Fragaria* (strawberries), *Gerbera, Gypsophila, Impatiens, Lactuca* (lettuces), *Larix* (larches), *Leucanthemum* (chrysanthemums), *Lupinus*, Marantaceae, Musaceae, *Pelargonium, Persea* (avocado pears), *Picea* (spruces), *Pinus* (pines), *Platanus* (plane trees), *Populus* (poplars), *Pseudotsuga* (Douglas firs), *Quercus* (oaks), *Rubus* (blackberries & raspberries), Solanaceae (except potatoes) *Spinacia* (spinach), Strelitzaceae, *Tanacetum* (tansy), *Tsuga* (hemlock trees) and *Verbena*. To these should be added bulbs and seeds of onions, leeks and chives; and bulbs and corms of: *Camassia, Chionodoxa, Crocus flava, Galanthus, Galtonia candicans, Gladiolus, Hyacinthus, Iris, Ismene, Muscari, Narcissus, Ornithogalum, Puschkinia, Scilla, Tigridia* and *Tulipa*.

This is only an outline of a complex system. More detailed information and assistance is available from MAFF offices or from the Scottish Office or the Department of Agriculture for Northern Ireland.

The EC and the Rest of the World

For plants moving between the EC and the rest of the world, the phytosanitary certificate (issued after inspection by government scientists to certify that produce is free from disease) still holds sway. Certificates are needed for the export of a large number of types of plants to many countries and for their import into the EC. The legislation is complicated and precise and we do not attempt a summary here. Anyone who is likely to be affected by it should seek the assistance of their local MAFF Plant Health and Seeds Inspector. Note that private individuals wishing to import plants from outside the Euro-Mediterranean countries may also require phytosanitary certificates.

Even with a phytosanitary certificate, not all genera may be imported. As an indication, the rules are most readily relaxed for those countries nearest to us. The following genera, for example, can be imported into the EC from all non-EC European countries: *Abies* (firs), *Castanea* (sweet chestnuts), *Cedrus* (cedars); *Chaenomeles* (Japanese quinces), *Chamaecyparis* (false cypresses); *Cydonia* (true quinces); *Juniperus* (junipers); *Larix* (larches); *Malus* (apples); *Photinia; Picea* (spruces); *Pinus* (pines); *Prunus* (plum, cherry, peach, almond & apricot), *Pseudotsuga* (Douglas firs), *Pyrus* (pears); *Quercus* (oaks), *Rosa* (roses) and *Tsuga* (hemlock trees).

There is still an absolute ban on their import from outside Europe, subject to certain concessions.

Some types of plants are banned from entering the EC from whatever source. These include two major economic genera: *Vitis* (grape vines) and *Citrus*.

CITES

CITES regulates the trade in wild plants which are listed in its schedules: the UK is among its 120 signatories. 'Trade' is not limited to commerce: any movement of specimens across international frontiers constitutes trade for CITES purposes. Failure to comply with the rules is a criminal offence. CITES is administered in the UK by the Department of the Environment, Wildlife Licensing Branch, Tollgate House, Houlton Street, Bristol BS2 9DJ (0117 9878168).

The list of species is regularly revised. It forbids the import or export of those species which are listed as endangered (Appendix 1) and restricts trade in those which are at risk of becoming endangered (Appendix 2). The principal genera protected by CITES are *Aloe, Cyclamen, Galanthus, Nepenthes, Sternbergia* and all orchids, cycads and cacti, but it is essential that anyone wishing to buy, sell or collect plants should know what is protected and what is not. That said, you can assume that any plant offered by a reputable nurseryman may legitimately be bought.

As far as most international conservation controls are concerned, there is no distinction between wild and cultivated plants. Many species have been endangered by careless or unscrupulous collectors in the past, and we suggest that plant collecting is best left to the experts. If you do collect, the guiding principles are: do not touch anything unless (i) you are sure it is not protected and (ii) you have the permission of the owner. Moreover, you should never endanger the plant community from which you collect, nor take material which you will not be able to grow or use. To avoid introducing pests and diseases from foreign countries, remember that seed is generally the best way of bringing back plants because it can be cleaned, although some viruses are seed-borne. The recent infestation of gypsy moths in South Norwood is thought to have entered the country as eggs laid on the underside of a vehicle. But there is no danger of introducing gypsy moths or Colorado beetles with a packet of seeds.

Further reading

The basis of all the rules about importing and exporting plants is *The Plant Health (Great Britain) Order 1993* (SI 1993 No. 1320) and its amending instruments.

12

European Nurseries

In July 1994, the member states of the European Union scrapped all their old national controls on the import and export of plants. Europe is one country now. Gone are the days when holidaymakers on the Spanish costas smuggled back cuttings in their sponge bags. Now we are free to order plants and seeds anywhere in the European Union. Why should you wish to do so? Quite simply, because there are more and better nurseries in Europe as a whole than in any part of it.

The British (and particularly the English) are accustomed to suppose that foreigners have nothing to teach them about gardening. Nothing could be further from the truth. There are excellent nurseries in every country in Europe. Indeed, certain genera are much better served abroad than at home: among them are *Iris*, *Paeonia* and *Rosa*. The same is true of fruit trees and of many popular Mediterranean plants like oleanders and hibiscus. In fact, almost every foreign nursery will have at least some plants which are not grown at all on this side of the Channel. And you will be amazed by the range and variety of what the best European nurseries have to offer.

European nurseries tend to make a charge for their catalogue. Sometimes it is a substantial publication – glossy paper, lots of colour, and full of advice on how to choose and cultivate the different types of plants. It follows that the charge may be considerably higher than one would expect to pay in the UK – as much as £20 for a top German nursery. Our description of what the nursery offers should help you to decide whether you should ask for one. But the money is usually well spent and sometimes the cost of the catalogue is remitted against your first order. Most nurseries intend their catalogue to last several years, with annual updates, pricing or availability lists. If you forget, or decline to pay the price, you are unlikely to receive the catalogue. Nurserymen will not be pleased by Britiish correspondents who neither pay for the catalogue nor buy

from it, so readers are urged to remember that the good name of Britiish gardeners is at stake on this matter of principle.

It pays to shop around. Currency movements affect value for money. We have found that the only limitation on spending a fortune at French nurseries is the strength of the French franc. This is more than balanced by the cheapness of plants in Italy and the reasonable prices (as well as excellent quality) to be found in Germany and the Netherlands. All this may change, of course, as currencies harden or ease. It is worth noting that credit cards are not as widely used in some countries as in England, and that Visa is accepted more than Access. We find the best way to pay is with Eurocheques.

Most of the entries in this chapter are nurseries, rather than garden centres. Large garden centres are as ubiquitous on the continent as in Britain and Ireland. They are usually modern and well planned, but not designed as places to take the family for a day out: there are no cafés or loos. Almost all the nurseries we list offer mail order: the few that sell only to callers are listed because their stock is so good that they are worth a long journey to buy from. We also find that many smaller nurserymen who say they do mail order may not actually have posted plants to Britain before. There is just as much of a learning curve abroad as there is at home. Some nurseries may need to be convinced that plants can be sent to you without a phytosanitary certificate issued by the local competent authority. There is confusion and disbelief even at official levels. It is worth remembering, however, that the basic law is the same now throughout the EU and we have always found that, once people make enquiries locally, they are persuaded that plants can be sent abroad and indeed become excited by the prospect of doing so. See our chapter on Importing and Exporting for guidance.

English is the second language throughout the European Union. In countries like Denmark and the Netherlands, you may be certain that almost everyone will speak English, and speak it well. We have in any event given the name of an English-speaking contact in each nursery, where this information is available. Sometimes this will be a younger member of the family whose school English is only marginally better than your own children's school French. If in doubt, write to the nursery in English, rather than telephoning. Fax numbers are often a different length to telephone numbers. There is no logic to this: we have, however, checked both numbers as carefully as possible. All are given as for dialling from the UK.

You may wish to know more about just what is available in European nurseries. There are several plant finders. France has two and, if you wish to know as much as possible about French nurseries, you will need both although they are unfortunately rather out-of-date now. The larger of the two is *Où trouver vos plantes* by Anita Pereire & Philippe Bonduel. (Hachette, 1992. Price 98FF). It lists 30,000 plants and 600 nurseries, including a few selected nurseries in GB & Belgium. The second plant finder is *25,000 Plantes – où et comment les acheter*, promoted by La Société Nationale d'Horticulture de France (Maison Rustique, 1993. Price 98FF). Based on 300 nurseries, it lists 500 varieties of *Prunus*, 700 fuchsias, 1400 irises and 1700 roses. The Dutch *Planten Vinder voor de Lage Landen* by Sarah Hart (Terra, 1994. HFl. 17.50) is closely modelled on the English one – the type, the paper even the colour of the cover are all familiar – but lists only a small number of Dutch nurseries and fewer Belgian. Its 80 nurseries account for some 30,000 different plant varieties. The first Italian plantfinder came out last year: *Il Cercapiante* (Ed. Tiziana Volta. Mondadori. Lit. 25,000). It lists some 15,000 plants in 400 nurseries and shows just how many new cultivars await our gardens once we begin to import them from southern Europe. However, our strongest recommendation is for the German PPP by Walter Erhardt, published by Eugen Ulmer, which comes with a CD-Rom that carries the entire book. Written in English, French and German, it comes as close as anyone has been able to get to a truly European plantfinder. PPP, by the way, stands for *Pflanzen, Plantes, Plants*. The next edition due later this year or early in 1998, promises to incorporate the national plantfinders of every European country except Britain. This will make PPP the most authoritative of all plantfinders. Every gardener should look forward to its publication, when the best nurseries of every country in Europe are listed in a single book, so that we can see at a glance just what is in cultivation and who has it for sale.

AUSTRIA

Baumschule Alfred Weber
Linke Bahnzeile 15, A-2486 Pottendorf-Landegg
☎ 00 43 2623 72282   📠 00 43 2623 73526
SPECIALITIES Herbaceous perennials; shrubs
CATALOGUE ÖS 80
MAIL ORDER No

A good general nurseryman, with a few rarities e.g *Rosa* 'Hermann Schmidt', and a fine list of fruit cultivars. And remember: if it's hardy in Austria it's hardy anywhere in the UK.

Baumschule Franz Praskac
Praskacstr. 101–108, Postfach 242, A-3430 Tulln
☎ 00 43 2272 62460   📠 00 43 2272 63816
ENGLISH-SPEAKING CONTACT Wolfgang Praskac
SPECIALITIES Herbaceous perennials; shrubs; trees
CATALOGUE ÖS 50
MAIL ORDER Yes

The most famous Austrian nursery, with an excellent general range and high quality plants. They also have a garden centre in Vienna. They grow all types of perennials, shrubs and trees, including conifers and fruit. Their highly illustrated catalogue is invaluable to anyone who needs to know what will survive the bitter winters of Central Europe and thrive.

Fuchsien Kulturen Lakonig
Niederdorf 37, A-9591 Treffen
☎ 00 43 4248 3685   📠 00 43 4248 3688
ENGLISH-SPEAKING CONTACT Harald or Caroline Lakonig
SPECIALITIES Fuchsias
CATALOGUE ÖS 30
MAIL ORDER Yes

The range at this fuchsia nursery extends to some 1,000 cultivars with 200 new introductions this year. A nursery to watch.

Grumer Rosen
Raasdorferstr. 28–30, A-2285 Leopoldsdorf im Marchfelde
☎ 00 43 2216 2223   📠 00 43 2216 222333
SPECIALITIES Roses
CATALOGUE Free
MAIL ORDER Yes

A cheerful list of trees, shrubs and roses. The roses are almost all post-war, but include some one-time favourites which are no longer available in Britain and several Kordes and Tantau hybrids that have never been released here. And remember: anything that grows in Austria will be hardy throughout the UK.

Sarastro
Christian Kreß, A-4974 Ort im Innkreis
☎ 00 43 7751 424   📠 00 43 7751 424
ENGLISH-SPEAKING CONTACT Christian or Fritzi Kreß
SPECIALITIES Alpines; herbaceous perennials
CATALOGUE 1 International reply coupon
MAIL ORDER Yes

Young nursery being built up by enthusiastic plantsman to specialise in species perennials and forms. Christian Kre also writes and lectures on perennials.

Silvia Tunkl
Hauptplatz 8A, A-2242 Prottes
☎ 00 43 2282 3958   FAX 00 43 2282 5178
ENGLISH-SPEAKING CONTACT Frau Silvia Tunkl
SPECIALITIES Mediterranean plants; seeds; citrus; tropical fruit
CATALOGUE ÖS 20
MAIL ORDER Yes

Tropical, subtropical and Mediterranean plants and seeds. There are *Passiflora*, *Citrus* in both small and specimen sizes up to 2 metres, including such varieties as *Citrus medica* and 'Lipo', *Ficus* 'White Adriatic' and 'San Pedro'. Some plants which require protection in Austria would probably be hardy in milder parts of Britain.

Stauden Feldweber
im Innkreis 139, A-4974 Ort
☎ 00 43 7751 320   FAX 00 43 7751 7223
ENGLISH-SPEAKING CONTACT Mrs Suzanne Platz
SPECIALITIES Alpines; herbaceous perennials
CATALOGUE ÖS 85 for main catalogue and collectors' list
Founded in 1896, this nursery lists a wide range of alpines and perennials in two catalogues, one their general list and the other for plantsmen. They are particularly good for paeonies, irises, hostas and grasses, of which they stock large numbers. There are also some interesting *Primula* hybrids and cultivars e.g. *P. × seriana* 'Oberschlesien'. Coming from Austria, everything is extremely hardy, and the list contains a good number of cultivars not grown in the UK. Recommended.

Wirth Dahlien
Leschetitzkygasse 11, A-1100 Wien
☎ 00 43 222 479 5383   FAX 00 43 222 479 1083
SPECIALITIES Dahlias
CATALOGUE Free
MAIL ORDER Yes

Every serious dahlia-grower should know this important nursery, founded in 1929. Dr Wirth is the leading breeder of new dahlias in Austria, and a useful source of interesting new material, both for showing and for garden use. He lists over 200 cultivars, and indicates which have won prizes at the international trials in several countries.

BELGIUM

Arboretum Waasland
Kriekelaarstraat 29, B-9100 Nieuwkerken-Waas
☎ 00 32 3 775 93 09   FAX 00 32 3 755 36 50
ENGLISH-SPEAKING CONTACT Michel Decalut
SPECIALITIES Shrubs; trees
CATALOGUE BFr 300
MAIL ORDER Yes

The best tree and shrub nursery in Belgium, perhaps in all Europe. The sheer number of forms and varieties they offer is amazing – some 10,000 taxa, and chosen for their hardiness

down to –20°C. Obviously it includes hundreds which have never been grown in the UK, let alone offered for sale. The rarer ones are propagated to order, so you may have to wait a while for delivery. The catalogue is essential reading for any serious dendrophile, National Collection holder, or seeker after novelty. Among last year's introductions were *Fagus sylvatica* 'Montefiore' and *Quercus cerris* 'Waasland'.

Boomkwekerij De Linde
Nieuwstraat 70, B-8956 Kemmel
☎ 00 32 57 44 63 49   FAX 00 32 57 44 82 94
ENGLISH-SPEAKING CONTACT Bart Dequidt
SPECIALITIES Fruit
CATALOGUE BFr 50

This nursery has a good list of tree fruit and soft fruit, and a particularly interesting selection of apples. Many are indigenous varieties of Flanders and the Pas de Calais, obtained from the Belgian *Ressources Génétiques Fruitières* and the French *Espace Naturel Régional*: they should do well in southern England. Collection only.

Fuchsia's Michiels-De Smedt
Kruisstraat 51, B-2500 Lier-Koningshooikt
☎ 00 32 3 482 25 62   FAX 00 32 3 482 02 14
ENGLISH-SPEAKING CONTACT Yes
SPECIALITIES Fuchsias
CATALOGUE BFr 140

The best *Fuchsia* nursery we know, with a remarkable list of over 3,315 varieties. Not only do they seek to be comprehensive, and grow every new variety, but they actively seek out old hybrids to propagate and preserve. Every year the new additions total some 200 items. There is no mail order, but it is worth a special journey to Antwerp to collect. Open daily, except Sunday afternoons and public holidays. Strongly recommended.

Kawana
Wijnegembaan, B-2520 Ranst
☎ 00 32 3 3540270   FAX 00 32 3 3530158
ENGLISH-SPEAKING CONTACT Koen Engelen
SPECIALITIES Iris
CATALOGUE Free

Iris mega-nursery, with an amazing list of all the main groups: hundreds of tall bearded, c.80 remontant, over 100 dwarf bearded, hundreds of Japanese irises (*Iris Ensata* and so on). Essential reading for anyone interested in irises, and a fascinating read for any keen plantsman They also list about 120 Japanese paeony varieties. Their new catalogue comes out in April.

Lens Roses
Redinnestraat 11, B-8460 Oudenburg
☎ 00 32 59 267 830   FAX 00 32 59 265 614
ENGLISH-SPEAKING CONTACT Yes
SPECIALITIES Roses
CATALOGUE BFr 50
MAIL ORDER Yes

Probably the best-known rose-breeders in Belgium, Lens have also been responsible for reviving interest in the old and shrub roses. Their list is impressive, and essential reading for all keen rosarians. Its 700 cultivars include many that are not known in Britain. Among the most exciting are the wonderful series of modern hybrid musks which they have bred over the last 15 years, updating the work of Rev. Pemberton 80 years ago.

DENMARK

Arne Kr Jorgensen
Kirkebjergvej 22, Roerslev, DK-5466 Asperup
☎ 00 45 6448 1073

ENGLISH-SPEAKING CONTACT Arne Kr Jorgensen
SPECIALITIES Alpines; herbaceous perennials
CATALOGUE Free
MAIL ORDER Yes

Alpine and perennial nursery. The closely printed catalogue lists 1,800 species but up to 4,500 are available from the nursery in small quantities.

Assens Planteskole
Fáborgvej 10, DK-5610 Assens
☎ 00 45 64 71 16 99   [FAX] 00 45 7 06 46 59

ENGLISH-SPEAKING CONTACT Ole Madsen
SPECIALITIES Alpines; bog plants; fruit; herbaceous perennials; roses; shrubs; trees
CATALOGUE Yes, five separate catalogues
MAIL ORDER Yes

A first-rate all-round nursery, particularly strong on roses, fruit trees (200 apples), irises and shrubs. Here are a few of the hundreds of cultivars which are not available in UK: *Rosa* 'Thor', 'Wilhelm Hansman' & 'Président Dutailley'; *Anemone nemorosa* 'Italica', *Armeria maritima* 'Arvi' and *Aster alpinus* 'Blue Star'; *Maddenia hypoleuca, Malus ioensis* 'Fimbriata', and *Menziesia pilosa*. Strongly recommended.

Caroline Mathildestiens Stauder
v/ Birgit Reimer, Caroline Mathildestien 51, DK-2950 Vedb'k
☎ 00 45 45 66 03 32   [FAX] 00 45 45 66 01 60

ENGLISH-SPEAKING CONTACT Birgit Reimer
SPECIALITIES Herbaceous perennials
CATALOGUE Free
MAIL ORDER Yes

A traditional-style herbaceous perennial nursery about 20 kms north of Copenhagen. There is an excellent selection of English and German plants, and a few Danish-raised varieties are beginning to find their way into the catalogue. A nursery of great charm.

Horning Fuchsiari: v/ H og B Hojer
Alléen 2, DK-8362 Horning
☎ 00 45 869222230

ENGLISH-SPEAKING CONTACT Troels Have Kristensen
(Tel 00 45 40568664, 6 pm – 8 pm)
SPECIALITIES Fuchsias
CATALOGUE DKr.20
MAIL ORDER Yes

Fuchsia specialist with a range of over 1,000 cultivars. There are new introductions every year.

Lynge Staudegartneri
Lynge Mellevej 4, DK-3540 Lynge
☎ 00 45 4218 7248   [FAX] 00 45 4218 8126

ENGLISH-SPEAKING CONTACT Grethe Petersen
SPECIALITIES Herbaceous perennials
CATALOGUE DKr.25
MAIL ORDER Yes

Perennial nursery with a range of 1,800 different kinds. Collection preferred, but mail order is possible.

Majlands Stauder
Simmelbrovej 36, DK-7260 Sdr. Omme
☎ 00 45 75341285   [FAX] 00 45 75341085

ENGLISH-SPEAKING CONTACT Leif Rahbeck
SPECIALITIES Alpines; herbaceous perennials
CATALOGUE DKr.15

A promising list of alpines and perennials with some interesting cultivars such as *Thalictrum delavayi* 'Sternhimmel' and *Trollius* 'Kerstin'. Collection only.

Rhododendron-Haven Planteskole
Viborg Hovedvej 114, Hammer, DK-7160 Torring
☎ 00 45 7580 0555   [FAX] 00 45 7580 0333

ENGLISH-SPEAKING CONTACT Claus Jorgensen
SPECIALITIES Rhododendrons
CATALOGUE DKr.50
MAIL ORDER Yes

A first-rate rhododendron nursery with one of the best collections of species in Europe (second only to Muncaster Plants) and a good list of rhododendron and azalea hybrids, many of them unknown and ungrown in the UK. The highly informative catalogue is in Danish only, but beautifully illustrated.

Rosenplanteskolen i Love
Plantevej 3, Love, DK-4270 Hong
☎ 00 45 53569313   [FAX] 00 45 53569019

ENGLISH-SPEAKING CONTACT All staff
SPECIALITIES Roses
CATALOGUE DKr.120
MAIL ORDER Yes

The most important plants at this nursery (previously Petersen) are the vast collection of roses. There is a long list of all types, with a bias towards older and rare kinds. Species roses are especially good – several forms are listed according to provenance in some cases. Rosarians should study it carefully: the list is longer than any rose nursery's in UK and there is an impressive number of cultivars unavailable from other sources.

Sonderborg Planteskole
Spang, DK-6400 Sonderborg
☎ 00 45 74425080

ENGLISH-SPEAKING CONTACT Jorgen Thagaard Jensen
SPECIALITIES Rhododendrons; shrubs; trees
CATALOGUE DKr.52
MAIL ORDER Yes

A good nursery, especially for trees and shrubs, including conifers – some of them quite unusual. The main speciality, however, is ericaceous plants: the excellent long list of hardy *Rhododendron* and azalea varieties contains many German and Danish hybrids not available in Britain.

FRANCE

Arboretum National des Barres

F-45290 Nogent-sur-Vernisson
☎ 00 33 2 38 95 02 74 [FAX] 00 33 2 38 95 02 78

ENGLISH-SPEAKING CONTACT Jean-Christophe Reuter or Thierry Lamant
SPECIALITIES Shrubs; trees
CATALOGUE FF 10

The Nurseries attached to the National Arboretum divide their catalogue into two parts: plants grown from seed, grafts or cuttings taken at the arboretum (or other botanical collection), and those grown from seed collected in the wild. Provenance is listed in the latter section. Both parts contain much to interest the dendrologist, including *Syringa henryi*, *Fagus sylvatica* 'Faux de Versy', and *Alnus trabeculosa*. Collection only; orders must be placed at least 8 days ahead.

Bambous de Planbuisson

Rue Montaigne, F-24480 Le Buisson
☎ & [FAX] 00 33 5 53 22 01 03

ENGLISH-SPEAKING CONTACT Michel Bonfils
SPECIALITIES Bamboos; grasses
CATALOGUE FF 25
MAIL ORDER Yes

Youngish nursery stocking bamboos and grasses. The first-class collection consists of about 150 varieties of each: 20 more were added last year. They have an enthusiastic approach to their speciality which they like to convey to customers.

Bernard Boureau

28 bis, rue du Maréchal Galliéni B P 8, F-77166 Grisy-Suisnes
☎ 00 33 1 64 05 91 83 [FAX] 00 33 1 64 05 97 66
SPECIALITIES Roses
CATALOGUE Yes
MAIL ORDER Yes

The collection of old roses here now extends to more than 500 different varieties, especially shrubs. More are added each year. Recent introductions include 'Menja', 'Princesse Lise Troubetzkoy' and 'Thor'. Roses are available bare root for collection and by mail order. From the last weekend in May to the last weekend in June they can be bought in containers at the nursery, on Friday afternoons, Saturdays and Sundays. The display gardens, with some 400 varieties of old roses grown with other shrubs and perennials, are open at the same times.

Bonsaï Rémy Samson

25, rue de Chateaubriand, F-92290 Châtenay-Malabry
☎ 00 33 1 47 02 91 99 [FAX] 00 33 1 47 02 61 75
ENGLISH-SPEAKING CONTACT Mr or Mrs Samson
SPECIALITIES Bonsai
MAIL ORDER Yes

Bonsai for indoors, outdoors and conservatories as well as accessories, pots and books. There is a second shop at 10 rue de la Comète, 75007 Paris.

Bulbes d'Opale

Cedex 528, F-59285 Buysscheure
☎ 00 33 3 28 43 04 67 [FAX] 00 33 3 28 43 02 65

ENGLISH-SPEAKING CONTACT Patrice Blary
SPECIALITIES Bulbs; *Allium*
CATALOGUE 3 first-class stamps
MAIL ORDER Yes

Nursery opens by appointment only. It is conveniently close to the Channel ports and tunnel and has a range of the less common bulbs and is particular strong on *Allium*. They introduced a hybrid called 'Beauregard' last year.

Cactus Esterel

Chemin de Maupas, F-83600 Bagnols en Fôret
☎ 00 33 4 94 40 66 73 [FAX] 00 33 4 94 40 69 11

ENGLISH-SPEAKING CONTACT Vincent Cerutti
SPECIALITIES Cacti and succulents
CATALOGUE FF 25 or 5 International reply coupons
MAIL ORDER Yes

Remarkably comprehensive list of cacti and succulents with a large proportion of unusual species and varieties.

Cayeux SA

La Carcaudière, F-45500 Poilly-Lèz-Gien
☎ 00 33 2 38 67 05 08 [FAX] 00 33 2 38 67 84 98

ENGLISH-SPEAKING CONTACT Mr Richard Cayeux
SPECIALITIES Iris; *Hemerocallis*
CATALOGUE FF 14
MAIL ORDER Mail order only

This distinguished old nursery was founded in 1892 and now specialises in the highly popular *Iris* and *Hemerocallis*. Their iris fields are a breathtaking sight towards the end of May: they grow and test many more than the 350 bearded cultivars offered in their excellent catalogue. Sibiricas, japonicas and water-irises are other specialities. Recommended.

Delbard

16, quai de la Mégisserie, F-75054 Paris Cedex 01
☎ 00 33 1 44 88 80 10 [FAX] 00 33 1 40 26 36 25

ENGLISH-SPEAKING CONTACT Christian Ledeux
SPECIALITIES Fruit; roses
CATALOGUE Free
MAIL ORDER Yes, France and EU countries

To many people Delbard means roses, and rightly so, but they are equally accomplished breeders of fruit trees. They introduce a new cultivar most years: this year it is an apple called 'Tentation' ('une pomme secrète, un peu timide mais qui contient tous les plaisirs'), which follows on 'Delbard Jubilé' and 'Papi Delbard'. Their new roses include a line of striped HTs named after artists ('Camille Pissarro', 'Claude Monet' etc.), scented roses ('Dioressence', 'Crêpe de Chine' etc.), shrub roses, climbers and many others. Few, if any, are known and grown in Britain: we cannot think why.

Dino Pellizzaro
290, chemin de Léouse, F-06220 Vallauris
☎ 00 33 4 93 64 18 43 FAX 00 33 4 93 64 40 14

ENGLISH-SPEAKING CONTACT Dino Pellizzaro
SPECIALITIES Mediterranean plants
CATALOGUE FF 20 in stamps or notes
MAIL ORDER No

Dino Pellizzaro does not offer mail order, but his remarkable list merits a special journey.

EARL des Cailloux Vivants
F-46360 Saint-Cernin
☎ 00 33 5 65 31 31 51 FAX 00 33 5 65 31 32 66

ENGLISH-SPEAKING CONTACT Jean-Luc Marcénac
SPECIALITIES Fuchsias; shrubs
CATALOGUE FF 15
MAIL ORDER Yes

Fuchsias for collectors: there are about 500 cultivars in this catalogue, stylishly printed on hand-made paper. The list of species is particularly impressive. Recommended.

EARL Ribanjou
Zone Horticole du Rocher, Briollay, F-49125 Tiercé
☎ 00 33 2 41 42 65 19 FAX 00 33 2 41 42 66 45
SPECIALITIES Soft fruit
MAIL ORDER Yes

Soft fruit. The nursery has many cultivars that are not known in England. One example is a raspberry called 'Bois Blanc' from the Savoy, said to have superb flavour, if disease prone. They also stock many unusual minor fruits, including forms of elderberry, *Aronia* and *Amelanchier* selected for their fruit. Good blueberries and blackberries.

Éts Hort Hodnik
Le Bourg, F-45700 St Maurice s/Fessard
☎ 00 33 2 38 97 84 59 FAX 00 33 2 38 97 89 39
SPECIALITIES Conservatory plants; Mediterranean plants
CATALOGUE FF 30
MAIL ORDER Yes

Mediterranean, half-hardy and conservatory plants. There is a wide choice, but they have two impressive specialities. One is species and hybrid *Begonia*, of which they list about 100. The other is *Hibiscus rosa-sinensis* cultivars, which they have introduced to cultivation in France in large numbers: they now list over 100 cultivars. They say they are happier with written than spoken English.

Éts Jean-Pierre Tourly
17, rue Danton, Asnières, F-18000 Bourges
☎ 00 33 2 48 24 44 21 FAX 00 33 2 48 69 09 54

ENGLISH-SPEAKING CONTACT Mme Edith Tourly
SPECIALITIES Fuchsias; pelargoniums
CATALOGUE FF 20 (stamps or cash)
MAIL ORDER Yes

Wholesalers and retailers who have made a name for themselves as collectors of old varieties of fuchsias and pelargoniums which have disappeared from other nurserymen's catalogues. They also breed and introduce pelargoniums.

Éts Kuentz: Monde des Cactus
327, rue du Général-Brosset, F-83600 Fréjus
☎ 00 33 4 94 51 48 66 FAX 00 33 4 94 95 49 31
SPECIALITIES Cacti and succulents
CATALOGUE FF 30
MAIL ORDER Yes

One of the best nurseries for cacti and succulents in Europe. The range is impressive: 39 haworthias, 55 euphorbias, 20 agaves, 29 aloes, and nearly 80 opuntias as well as hundreds of lesser genera. Large specimens, at least ten years old, are also available for the impatient, though here the range is smaller.

Gaec de Champagne M Bourdillon
B P 2, F-41230 Soings-en-Sologne
☎ 00 33 2 54 98 71 06 FAX 00 33 2 54 98 76 76
SPECIALITIES Iris; *Hemerocallis*
CATALOGUE FF 10
MAIL ORDER Yes

Iris and *Hemerocallis* are still not as popular in Britain as they deserve. It is different in France where people visit iris gardens in the same spirit as we flock to Mottisfont. There is a splendid selection of bearded iris and dramatic day lilies to tempt possible converts in this catalogue. And although sales are by mail order at the appropriate time of year they have a show garden which can be visited. Best around 20 May, they say.

Iris de Thau
Route de Villeveyrac, F-34140 Mèze
☎ 00 33 4 67 43 59 54
SPECIALITIES Iris
CATALOGUE Free
MAIL ORDER Yes

This excellent iris nursery sells the latest hybrids from all over the world. Tall bearded hybrids are their speciality and prices range between FF 15 and FF 80, but most are in the region of FF 20. Their instructive catalogue lists about 800 cultivars, of which some 100 are illustrated in colour.

Iris en Provence
B P 53, Route de l'Appie
☎ 00 33 4 94 65 98 30 FAX 00 33 4 94 35 24 91
SPECIALITIES Iris; *Hemerocallis*
CATALOGUE FF 14
MAIL ORDER Mail order only

Iris and *Hemerocallis* in profusion. They are breeders as well as growers of both. The brilliantly coloured catalogue lists a huge variety of their own and American cultivars with regular new introductions. Besides the tall bearded iris so popular in France, there also hybrids of *I. spuria*, *I. sibirica* and *I. louisiana*. Mail order only, but the gardens can be visited in late April and May.

Jardin Aquatique
Chemin de Maupas, F-83600 Bagnols en Fôret
☎ 00 33 4 94 40 62 32 FAX 00 33 4 94 40 69 11
SPECIALITIES Aquatic plants
CATALOGUE FF 25
MAIL ORDER Yes

Specialists in waterlilies with over 100 from which to choose, including 30 tropical hybrids and 8 night-flowering varieties, (*Nelumbo*) and aquatics: two new lotuses last year were 'Shirokunshi' and 'Sharon'.

La Bambouseraie de Prafrance

Générargues, F-30140 Anduze
☎ 00 33 4 66 61 70 47 [FAX] 00 33 4 66 61 64 15

ENGLISH-SPEAKING CONTACT Martine Bouret
SPECIALITIES Bamboos
CATALOGUE FF 40
MAIL ORDER No

The Bambouseraie is the sort of place which needs superlatives. Everything is immensely stylish and done on a large scale: the catalogue (there are English and French editions), the bamboo nursery (the biggest in Europe), the gardens and the bamboos themselves. An impressive selection is available container-grown, ranging from rare varieties for collectors to those suitable for massed planting. If you have a chance to visit the garden (strongly recommended) you can see established plantations and examples of how to use bamboo for everything and anything, from all-bamboo houses to tiny ornaments.

Latour Marliac SA

F-47110 Temple s/Lot
☎ 00 33 5 53 01 08 05 [FAX] 00 33 5 53 01 02 30

ENGLISH-SPEAKING CONTACT Mr Chris Farmer
SPECIALITIES Aquatic plants
CATALOGUE Free
MAIL ORDER Yes

Proud of being the oldest water lily nursery in the world, Latour Marliac can boast of supplying Monet at Giverny. The current catalogue lists some 120 hardy varieties, besides tropical kinds, *Nelumbo* and a range of other aquatic plants.

Les Jardins de Cotelle

Avenue Gabriel de Clieu, F-76370 Derchigny-Graincourt
☎ 00 33 2 35 83 61 38 [FAX] 00 33 2 35 04 06 00

ENGLISH-SPEAKING CONTACT Frédéric or Catherine Cotelle
SPECIALITIES Heathers; herbaceous perennials
CATALOGUE FF 25
MAIL ORDER Yes

Nursery and gardens with a large perennial range, besides heathers, clematis, roses and shrubs.

Les Roses Anciennes d'André Eve

Morailles, F-45300 Pithiviers-le-Vieil
SPECIALITIES Roses
CATALOGUE Yes
MAIL ORDER Yes

André Eve's catalogue lists a tempting selection of old roses plus a few modern varieties and some good climbers bred by him. His selection of old climbers and ramblers is particularly attractive and includes such varieties as 'Alexandre Tremouillet', 'Château de la Juvenie' and 'Primevère'. Mail order only. His own garden can be visited during the rose season.

Lumen

Les Coutets, F-24100 Creysse Bergerac
☎ 00 33 5 53 57 62 15 [FAX] 00 33 5 53 58 54 88

ENGLISH-SPEAKING CONTACT Bernadette Cross or Michel Lumen
SPECIALITIES Ferns; grasses; herbaceous perennials
CATALOGUE FF 20
MAIL ORDER Yes

This nursery near Bergerac has an extensive range of garden-worthy perennials, ferns and grasses and lots of *Sempervivum*. Most plants are open-ground but a container selection is always available. Useful for Dordogne dwellers who want an English border or cottage garden.

Marcel Lecoufle

5 Rue de Paris, F-94470 Boissy St Léger
☎ 00 33 1 45 95 25 25 [FAX] 00 33 1 45 98 34 19

ENGLISH-SPEAKING CONTACT Isabelle Bert
SPECIALITIES Orchids
CATALOGUE FF 24
MAIL ORDER Yes

This old-established firm (founded in 1888) is one of the leading orchid breeders and propagators in Europe. They also trade under the name Vacherot & Lecoufle. Popular hybrids are their main line but these include novelties of their own raising and they also have a collection of 2,000 different taxa which may be visited most days of the year.

Meilland Richardier

B P 2, F-69815 Tassin-la-Demi-Lune Cedex
☎ 00 33 4 78 34 46 52 [FAX] 00 33 4 72 38 09 97

SPECIALITIES Roses
MAIL ORDER Yes

Roses bred by the Meilland dynasty form the bulk of the catalogue: an interesting way of seeing how rose breeding has moved since the war. The newest varieties are very floriferous, and open flat to give an abundance of colour. Three modern climbers are among them: 'César', 'Tchin Tchin' and 'Domaine de Courson'. The catalogue also includes companion plants and sundries.

Nature et Paysages

F-32360 Peyrusse-Massas
☎ 00 33 5 62 65 52 48 [FAX] 00 33 5 62 65 50 44

SPECIALITIES Carnivorous plants
CATALOGUE 10 International reply coupons
MAIL ORDER Yes

This name, with its echoes of Rousseau, belongs to a carnivorous plant nursery. The catalogue is informative and clear, the range impressive. It includes such curiosities as *Brocchina reducta*, *Roridula dentata*, some 30 *Pinguicula* species and a good selection of *Sarracenia*. The minimum value for mail order outside France is FF1,000.

Pép Botanique Jean Thoby

Château de Gaujacq, F-40330 Amou
☎ 00 33 5 58 89 24 22 [FAX] 00 33 5 58 89 06 62

ENGLISH-SPEAKING CONTACT Jean Thoby (a little)

SPECIALITIES Camellias; shrubs; trees; *Hosta*; *Hydrangea*; *Wisteria*
CATALOGUE FF 55
MAIL ORDER Yes

This is one of the most dynamic plantsman's nurseries in Europe. The catalogue alone is a collectors' piece, stylishly produced on handmade paper bound with raffia, quite apart from the treasures it contains. Jean Thoby summarises the contents as 'Camellias (550), Hydrangeas (240), Hosta (220), Wisteria (40) as well as 4,000 other taxa, trees, shrubs, climbers and perennials.

Pép Brochet Lanvin
Lieu-dit 'La Presle', F-51480 Nanteuil-la-Forêt
☎ 00 33 3 26 59 43 39 ［FAX］ 00 33 3 26 59 42 20

ENGLISH-SPEAKING CONTACT Mr Brochet (school English)
SPECIALITIES Alpines; herbaceous perennials; roses; shrubs
CATALOGUE FF 10
MAIL ORDER Yes

The nursery says it specialises in lime-tolerant plants and those which tolerate cold and drought. The range is spread across all plant types from trees to alpines. Among the familiar names are some rarities: their lists of saxifrages, roses, spiraeas and willows are particularly long and interesting.

Pép Charentaises
Route de Beauregarde, F-16310 Montemboeuf
☎ 00 33 5 46 65 02 61 ［FAX］ 00 33 5 45 65 14 40

ENGLISH-SPEAKING CONTACT Roland Meynet
SPECIALITIES Climbers; conifers; fruit; roses; shrubs; trees
CATALOGUE FF 40 (1995)
MAIL ORDER Mainland France only

Long-established and very big nurseries. The large glossy catalogue lists an extensive and well chosen range of trees and shrubs, conifers, roses, climbers and fruit trees, from the familiar favourite to the collectors' rarity, such as *Rosa* 'Lorenzo Pahissa'. Indeed, a fair number of their plants are available from no other source. Recommended if you can visit them or have a house in France.

Pép Christophe Delay
Les Combes, F-38780 Estrablin
☎ 00 33 4 74 57 14 42 ［FAX］ 00 33 4 74 57 14 29
SPECIALITIES Fruit
CATALOGUE FF 10
MAIL ORDER Yes

Here are old cultivars of tree fruits, mainly of French origin, apples, plums, pears, cherries and peaches, chosen for their good flavour. Organic methods of cultivation are used.

Pép Claude Thoby
B P 113, Route de Paris, F-44471 Carquefou Cedex
☎ 00 33 2 40 50 88 48 ［FAX］ 00 33 2 40 77 91 92
SPECIALITIES Camellias
CATALOGUE FF 50
MAIL ORDER Yes

Quite simply, the best camellia nursery in Europe. Thoby grows hundreds of different varieties, from the newest species to the oldest *japonica* hybrids. His beautiful catalogue lists

and re-lists them, first alphabetically, then according to their time of flowering and their colour and finally botanically, according to their species and groups. Compulsory reading for all camellia-lovers.

Pép Côte Sud des Landes
route départ. 12, F-40230 Saint Geours de Maremme
☎ & ［FAX］ 00 33 5 58 57 33 30
SPECIALITIES Shrubs; trees
CATALOGUE FF 30
MAIL ORDER Yes

This excellent nursery in the south-west of France specialises in ornamental trees and shubs for acid soils. They have a particularly long list of *Acer*, *Camellia*, *Cornus*, *Hydrangea*, *Rhododendron* and *Viburnum*. Among 67 new items this year are *Ampelopsis seyaniaefolia* and 15 forms of *Hydrangea macrophylla* including 'Bergfink' and 'Buntspech'.

Pép de la Foux
Chemin de la Foux, F-83220 Le Pradet
☎ 00 33 4 94 75 35 45 ［FAX］ 00 33 4 94 08 17 13
SPECIALITIES Salvias
CATALOGUE Yes
MAIL ORDER No

Best known for their national collection of *Salvia*, which is growing fast and now dominates their list. It has over 160 of them: this year's list will see the number greatly increased. They also have a good general stock of plants suitable for the south of France or English conservatories. They only deliver locally and do not do mail order, but they attend many of the best garden fairs in France like Courson, St Jean de Beauregard and Gaujacq, and are willing to bring plants for collection.

Pép de la Vallée de l'Huveaune
CD 2, Route de Gémenos, F-13400 Aubagne
☎ 00 33 4 42 82 36 00 ［FAX］ 00 33 4 42 82 97 55
ENGLISH-SPEAKING CONTACT Robert Pélissier
SPECIALITIES Conservatory plants
CATALOGUE FF 35
MAIL ORDER Yes

This nursery east of Marseilles specialises in plants for a Mediterranean climate. This means (to English eyes) a mixture of the familar and the exotic. *Eleagnus* and *Cupressus* rub along with palms, cycads and fruiting cultivars of jujube. The catalogue lists almost all the staple plants of traditional gardens, together with some good modern additions. New this year are a collection of *Agapanthus* and more cycads from South Africa and Australia.

Pép Eric Dumont
42, avenue des Martyrs, F-10800 Buchères
☎ 00 33 3 25 41 84 87 ［FAX］ 00 33 3 25 41 96 59
ENGLISH-SPEAKING CONTACT Eric Dumont or Christine Mangin
SPECIALITIES Fruit
MAIL ORDER Delivery can be arranged

Fruit trees in old and new varieties. They specialise in producing specimens which are ready to fruit, trained in traditional styles, fans, cordons, espaliers, and pyramids. Rare varieties can be grafted to order. There is a general nursery on site too. Eric Dumont comes from a long tradition of nurserymen: he is the 13th generation.

Pép Filippi
RN 113, F-34140 Mèze
☎ 00 33 4 67 43 88 69   [FAX] 00 33 4 67 43 84 59

ENGLISH-SPEAKING CONTACT Olivier Filippi
SPECIALITIES Mediterranean plants; *Nerium oleander*
CATALOGUE FF 40
MAIL ORDER Yes

This catalogue set out to inspire drought-conscious gardeners everywhere, as well as those who garden around the Mediterranean. And it succeeds. There is a wealth of plant material for dry gardens, including over 100 *Nerium oleander* cultivars (the best collection in Europe), all of which are fully described. More *Cistus, Artemisia, Teucrium,* and *Callistemon* have just been added to the range. Highly recommended, particularly to lovers of conservatory plants.

Pép Gautier et Fils
F-13670 Saint Andiol
☎ 00 33 4 90 95 02 55   [FAX] 00 33 4 90 95 47 02

ENGLISH-SPEAKING CONTACT Louis Gaultier
SPECIALITIES Fruit; vines
MAIL ORDER Yes

Wholesale nurseries which specialise in fruit trees, understocks and vines, though there is a general range as well.

Pép Jean Rey
Route de Carpentras, F-84150 Jonquières
☎ 00 33 4 90 70 36 00   [FAX] 00 33 4 90 70 35 21

ENGLISH-SPEAKING CONTACT J. Paul Charvin
SPECIALITIES Conservatory plants; Mediterranean plants
MAIL ORDER Wholesale only

Wholesale nursery specialising in Mediterranean and conservatory plants – everything from cistus to palms. They introduced several new cultivars of *Nerium oleander* this year. Retail sales are from their garden centre on RN98 83250 La Londe les Maures.

Pép Marie-Pierre Fournier
Patrie, F-32110 Magnan
☎ 00 33 5 62 69 01 15

ENGLISH-SPEAKING CONTACT Marie-Pierre Fournier
SPECIALITIES *Salvia*
CATALOGUE Free
MAIL ORDER Yes

Small nursery offering a collection of nearly 150 *Salvia* species and forms from all over the world.

Pép Minier
Les Fontaines de l'Aunay, BP 79, F-49250 Beaufort-en-Vallée
☎ 00 33 2 41 79 48 25   [FAX] 00 33 2 41 47 50 13
SPECIALITIES Shrubs
CATALOGUE FF 100

Wholesale nursery with a range of container-grown plants. They have a small retail section for rare plants open twice a week from September to May. Last year they introduced three new lilacs, *Syringa vulgaris* 'Comtesse d'Harcourt', 'Prince Wolkonsky' and 'Princesse Sturdza'.

Pép Remy Viala
F-20290 Borgo-Revinco
☎ 00 33 4 95 36 07 65
SPECIALITIES Citrus trees
CATALOGUE Free
MAIL ORDER No

Citrus fruit are the speciality of this Corsican nursery: they offer large sizes in traditional pots.

Pép Rhône-Alpes A Gayraud
3549, route de Paris, F-01440 Viriat
☎ 00 33 4 74 25 36 55
SPECIALITIES Fruit; hedging; shrubs; trees
CATALOGUE FF 30
MAIL ORDER Yes

The main catalogue lists the nursery's specialities of ornamental trees and shrubs, hedging and a good range of roses of all types, old and new. The collections of *Cornus* and *Magnolia* include some good varieties. But separately, in a special catalogue called *Fruits Oubliés* (FF 40), are listed and described with clarity and Gallic charm many old kinds of fruit trees: apples, pears, plums, cherries, figs and peaches. Recipes, some in rhyme, will help customers to enjoy the crop.

Pép Yves Dupont
B P 8148, F-45081 Orléans Cedex 2
☎ 00 33 2 38 66 39 29   [FAX] 00 33 2 38 56 49 88

ENGLISH-SPEAKING CONTACT Yves or Catherine
SPECIALITIES Ferns
CATALOGUE FF 30
MAIL ORDER Mail order only

Enthusiastic specialist fern grower. The beautifully produced catalogue is particularly helpful, with good illustrations, lists of hardy ferns suitable for different aspects and positions, and suggestions for companion plantings.

Pépinière de l'Arboretum de Balaine
Château de Balaine, F-03460 Villeneuve-sur-Allier
☎ 00 33 4 70 43 50 07   [FAX] 00 33 4 70 43 36 91

ENGLISH-SPEAKING CONTACT Louise Courteix-Adanson
SPECIALITIES Rhododendrons; shrubs; trees
CATALOGUE FF 15
MAIL ORDER Yes

The nursery attached to this world-famous arboretum specialises in ericaceous shrubs and rare trees, many of them not available in Britain. The list of *Magnolia* species and *Quercus* is quite exceptional. Among this year's novelties are *Quercus* 'Warburgii' and *Fagus sylvatica* 'Brocklesby'. The arboretum, 17 kms north of Moulins on the N7, is open from 9 am – 12 noon and 2 pm to 7 pm from April to November.

Pépinières et Roseraies Vizier
11 rue des Prés, F-77482 Provins
☎ 00 33 1 64 00 02 42 📠 00 33 1 60 67 86 07
SPECIALITIES Roses

General nurserymen and rose-growers from the great rose-growing town of Provins. Their general list is run-of-the-mill but the list of modern roses includes a good selection of older varieties, some of which are not available in the UK. 'Armentières', 'Léopold Shengor' and 'Climbing Dr Débat' are some of the more unusual names.

Pépinières Travers
Rue Cour-Charette, F-45650 Saint-Jean-le-Blanc
☎ 00 33 2 38 66 37 53 📠 00 33 2 38 51 90 18
ENGLISH-SPEAKING CONTACT Arnaud Travers
SPECIALITIES Clematis; climbers
CATALOGUE Leaflet free on request for France only
MAIL ORDER France only

This nursery specialises in climbing plants and soft fruit. Its list of clematis is particularly good: some 200 cultivars, including a regular supply of new introductions. 'Golden Tiara' is their latest, a new form of C. tangutica.

Pivoines Michel Rivière
La Plaine, F-26400 Crest
☎ 00 33 4 75 25 44 85 📠 00 33 4 75 76 77 38
ENGLISH-SPEAKING CONTACT Jean-Luc Rivière
SPECIALITIES Paeonies
CATALOGUE FF 25
MAIL ORDER Yes

Famous paeony nursery. They still breed and introduce new varieties besides continuing to seek out older cultivars. Their collection of over 600 varieties is recognised as a French national collection. The list also includes plants bred by Sir Peter Smithers.

Plantbessin
F-14490 Castillon
☎ 00 33 2 31 92 56 03 📠 00 33 2 31 22 70 09
ENGLISH-SPEAKING CONTACT Hubert Sainte Beuve
SPECIALITIES Herbaceous perennials
CATALOGUE FF 38
MAIL ORDER Yes

An excellent herbaceous nursery with a wide range – many plants will be familiar to English readers. There is a good selection of hardy geraniums.

Pommiers du Pays d'Auge
La Redoute, St Germain de Livet, F-14100 Lisieux
☎ 00 33 2 31 31 68 65
ENGLISH-SPEAKING CONTACT Denis Jacques
SPECIALITIES Fruit
CATALOGUE FF 15
MAIL ORDER Yes

Apple trees only, new and old, dessert and cider varieties. New cultivars last year were 'Faras', 'Belle Joséphine' and 'Verité'.

Roseraies Pierre Guillot
Domaine de la Plaine, F-38460 Chamagnieu
☎ 00 33 4 74 90 27 55 📠 00 33 4 74 90 27 17
ENGLISH-SPEAKING CONTACT Martine Guillot
SPECIALITIES Roses
CATALOGUE Free
MAIL ORDER Yes

Rose breeders and growers with a proud tradition stretching back to 1829, who introduced the first polyantha and the first hybrid tea, Guillot specialises in old roses, especially those bred by his ancestors, such as 'Emotion' (before 1862), and 'Renée Danielle' (1913). There are modern introductions now too, in the old fashioned style: 'Sonia Rykiel' and 'Manuel Canovas', his answer to David Austin.

Roses Anciennes du Lot
Pépinières Prayssacoises, sarl Horti-d'Olt, Route du Collège, F-46220 Prayssac
☎ 00 33 2 65 22 40 30 📠 00 33 2 65 22 40 50
SPECIALITIES Roses
CATALOGUE Free
MAIL ORDER Yes

Old-fashioned roses. The list is not exhaustive but includes some cultivars that are not available in the UK: for instance, 'Maurice Lepellier' and 'Souvenir d'Adolphe Turc'.

Santonine
Tout y Faut, F-17260 Villars en Pons
☎ 00 33 5 46 94 26 94 📠 00 33 5 46 94 62 36
ENGLISH-SPEAKING CONTACT Christine Verneuil
SPECIALITIES Herbaceous perennials
CATALOGUE FF 5
MAIL ORDER Yes

A charming list of herbaceous plants. Most are varieties popular in England but adapted to the climate of south-west France. The list is strong on Salvia species, of which they have the French national collection: SS. nevadensis, moelleri, trijuga and tubifera are recent additions to their list. Worth investigating.

Schryve Jardin
1.315, route du Steentje, F-59270 Bailleul
☎ 00 33 3 28 49 27 40 📠 00 33 3 28 49 27 42
ENGLISH-SPEAKING CONTACT Delphine Quilliot (00 33 20 54 32 02)
SPECIALITIES Bulbs
CATALOGUE FF 30
MAIL ORDER Yes

All types of flowering bulbs are catalogued according to time of flowering. You can start with Colchicum 'Attlee' in the autumn and continue until Eremurus × isabellinus 'Cleopatra' flowers in July. There is a new display garden, open from 2 pm – 6 pm on Thursday and 10 am – 6 pm at weekends from 16 May to 12 September. Roses and perennials stocked too.

GERMANY

Albrecht Hoch

Potsdamerstr. 40, D-14163 Berlin/Zehlendorf

☎ 00 49 30 8026251   📠 00 49 30 8026222

ENGLISH-SPEAKING CONTACT Frau Irene Hoch
SPECIALITIES Bulbs; iris; lilies; paeonies; prunus
CATALOGUE DM 10
MAIL ORDER Yes

Not producers, but importers and suppliers of lilies, bulbs, irises, tree and herbaceous paeonies, Hemerocallis from the USA and all kinds of bulbs. Proud of a tradition which stretches back a century, they have extended the list to include perennials.

Alpengarten Pforzheim

Auf dem Berg 6, D-75181 Pforzheim-Würm

☎ 00 49 7231 70590   📠 00 49 7231 788626

ENGLISH-SPEAKING CONTACT M. Carl
SPECIALITIES Alpines; shrubs

Alpine nursery in a hillside garden, worth seeking out and visiting for its interesting collection of alpines, particularly Primula, rock garden plants and dwarf shrubs.

Alpine Staudengärtnerei Siegfried Geißler

OT Gorschmitz Nr 14, D-04703 Leisnig/Sachsen
SPECIALITIES Alpines
CATALOGUE Yes
MAIL ORDER Yes

Really rare alpines from a collector turned professional. There is a pretty, small display garden, arranged geographically. Stock changes constantly.

Alpiner Garten Dieter Kaufmann

Roseggerstr. 20, D-08060 Zwickau

☎ 00 49 375 527748

SPECIALITIES Alpines
CATALOGUE Free
MAIL ORDER Yes

This alpine specialist has a small list, but it contains some very interesting plants, some of them more herbaceous perennials than true alpines. We noticed Iris sintenisii brandzae, Pulsatilla flavescens and Saxifraga montenegrina among other rarities on his latest list.

Arboretum Altdorf

Sachsenstr. 6, D-91052 Erlangen

☎ & 📠 00 49 9131 301004

ENGLISH-SPEAKING CONTACT Gisela Dönig
SPECIALITIES Trees
CATALOGUE Free
MAIL ORDER Yes

Specialists in just one genus, Fagus. Arboretum Altdorf grows every form of common beech known to man, and offers them all for sale. There are over 60 of them: we particularly recommend the prostrate-growing 'Suntalensis', but Altdorf sells dozens of cultivars not yet grown in the UK.

Bambuschulen Janssen

Stöckheimerstr. 11, D-50259 Pulheim

☎ 00 49 2238 965530   📠 00 49 2238 9655355

SPECIALITIES Bamboos
CATALOGUE DM 5
MAIL ORDER Yes

An excellent list of bamboos: nearly 300 of them, most of them unknown to bamboo-enthusiasts in Britain. Strongly recommended.

Bambuszentrum Niederbayern

Spanberg 60, D-84332 Hebertsfelden/Eggenfelden

☎ 00 49 8721 2288   📠 00 49 8721 2295

SPECIALITIES Bamboos
CATALOGUE Free
MAIL ORDER Yes

A good list of bamboos, nearly 100 different taxa, some of them for greenhouse culture only and many of them not grown in the UK. Recommended.

Baumschule Böhlje

Oldenburgerstr. 9, D-26655 Westerstede

☎ 00 49 4488 2203   📠 00 49 4488 71286

ENGLISH-SPEAKING CONTACT G. D. Böhlje
SPECIALITIES Conifers; rhododendrons; shrubs; trees
CATALOGUE DM 10
MAIL ORDER Yes

Large wholesale nurseries (though retail customers can be seen by appointment) with an impressive list of trees and shrubs, including some good conifers. New introductions last year included Tsuga canadensis 'Wintergold', Prunus spinosa 'Pendula' and Chaenomeles japonica 'Cido'.

Baumschule H Hachmann

Brunnenstr. 68, D-25355 Barmstedt in Holstein

☎ 00 49 4123 2055/2470   📠 00 49 4123 6626

ENGLISH-SPEAKING CONTACT Holger Hachmann
SPECIALITIES Rhododendrons
CATALOGUE DM 32
MAIL ORDER Yes

Baumschule Hachmann is a serious rhododendron nursery and has been responsible for the recent surge of interest in the genus in Germany and central Europe. Hans Hachmann has been breeding new cultivars for over 40 years: he specialises in hybrids that are low-growing and very hardy. The magnificent catalogue offers over 500 cultivars, together with a good range of conifers. It will be of interest to every rhododendron enthusiast.

Baumschule Herr

Baumschulenweg 19-25, D-53340 Meckenheim

☎ 00 49 2225 92080   📠 00 49 2225 15884

ENGLISH-SPEAKING CONTACT Theo Wiesel & Gunter Herr
SPECIALITIES Fruit; fruit bushes
CATALOGUE Free
MAIL ORDER Yes

Soft and tree fruit – apples, pears, plums, sweet and sour cherries, apricots, red and black currants, gooseberries, raspberries, blueberries, table grapes and nuts – in both modern and old varieties.

Baumschule Röhler
Auf der Bult 20, D-31700 Heuerßen – OT Kobbensen
☎ 00 49 5725 5065   FAX 00 49 5725 5879
SPECIALITIES   Shrubs; trees; *Fagus*; *Quercus*
CATALOGUE   DM 3 in stamps

Wholesale and retail nursery with a range of container grown trees and shrubs. The special list of *Fagus* and *Quercus* contains many rare forms and species such as *Fagus* × *moesiaca*, *Fagus sylvatica* 'Süntelensis', *Quercus petraea* 'Giesleri', and 'Spessart'.

Baumschule-Heidepark Jürgen Krebs
D-27318 Hoyerhagen 130
☎ 00 49 4251 2993   FAX 00 49 4251 7785
SPECIALITIES   Heathers
CATALOGUE   Free
MAIL ORDER   Yes

Heath garden specialists, including dwarf rhododendrons, azaleas, gaultherias and other small ericaceous shrubs besides heathers.

blattgrün
Willstätterstr. 1, D-38116 Braunschweig
☎ 00 49 531 512529   FAX 00 49 531 515364
ENGLISH-SPEAKING CONTACT   Gaby Braun-Nauerz
SPECIALITIES   Hostas
CATALOGUE   Free
MAIL ORDER   Yes

One of the great *Hosta* nurseries, which specialises in sending young plants by mail order. They also have a nursery which is open from 8 am to 12 noon from Monday to Friday and between 6 pm and 8 pm on Wednesdays from May to September: the address is Am Bülten, 38176-Wendeburg. They will be bringing out about 25 new cultivars in April this year: hostamaniacs, please note.

Bonsai Centrum
Mannheimerstr. 401, D-69123 Heidelberg
☎ 00 49 6221 84910   FAX 00 49 6221 849130
SPECIALITIES   Bonsai
CATALOGUE   Free
MAIL ORDER   Yes

A splendid centre for good bonsai, including some unconventional types: *Crassula arborescens* and *Portulaca afra* for example. The centre also offers a wide range of accessories and Japanese garden ornaments. The nursery is open every day except Sunday.

Botanische Raritäten
Oberkohlfurth, D-42349 Wuppertal-Cronenberg
☎ 00 49 202 470443   FAX 00 49 202 4780119
ENGLISH-SPEAKING CONTACT   Bernd Wetzel
SPECIALITIES   Alpines; bulbs; herbaceous perennials; orchids
CATALOGUE   DM 7
MAIL ORDER   Yes

An extensive list of alpines, herbaceous plants, bulbs and terrestrial orchids. Almost all are species, forms and natural varieties – few hybrids. A high percentage of what they offer is unavailable in the UK. Seriously interesting.

Eberhard Schuster (Wasserpflanzen)
D-19089 Augustenhof
☎ & FAX 00 49 3863 222705
ENGLISH-SPEAKING CONTACT   Eberhard Schuster
SPECIALITIES   Aquatic plants; bog plants
CATALOGUE   DM 3
MAIL ORDER   Yes

Aquatic, bog and marginal plant specialist. The definition is generous: the range covers all plants which like damp conditions. New introductions last year included *Carex aurea* and *Carex fascicularis*.

Erdbeerzuchtbetrieb Hummel
Köstlinstr. 121/1, D-70499 Stuttgart/Weilimdorf
☎ 00 49 771 864279   FAX 00 49 771 861450
SPECIALITIES   Strawberries
CATALOGUE   Free
MAIL ORDER   Yes

Well-known (in Germany) breeder, wholesaler and mail-order retailer of strawberries. They offer about 15 cultivars, chosen for their suitability for different soils, seasons and tastes.

Fa Treffinger-Hofmann
Am Stadion 20, D-75038 Oberderdingen
☎ 00 49 7045 2214   FAX 00 49 7045 90237
SPECIALITIES   Roses
CATALOGUE   Free
MAIL ORDER   Yes

This firm is the main outlet for roses bred by Hetzel, who has begun to revolutionise German rose breeding in the same way that David Austin has in England. Most of the list consists of Hetzel hybrids, including 'Super Dorothy' and 'Super Excelsa', the repeat-flowering ramblers which have been so successful on the continent.

Flora Mediterranea
Königsgütler 5, D-84072 Au/Hallertau
☎ 00 49 8752 1238   FAX 00 49 8752 9930
ENGLISH-SPEAKING CONTACT   Christoph or Maria Köchel
SPECIALITIES   Conservatory plants; Mediterranean plants; specimen sizes
CATALOGUE   DM 8
MAIL ORDER   To German speaking countries only

This is a substantial nursery, with five enormous glasshouses, each maintained with different climatic conditions. They produce an extensive range of container-grown half-hardy and sub-tropical plants for conservatories and interior landscapes. Many are available in specimen sizes. Christoph and Maria Köchel's book *Wintergärten – vom Traum zur Wirklichkeit* was published last year.

Gartenbau F Westphal

Peiner Hof 7, D-25497 Prisdorf

☎ 00 49 4101 74104   📠 00 49 4101 781113

ENGLISH-SPEAKING CONTACT Mr Manfred or Mrs Sabine
Westphal

SPECIALITIES Clematis

CATALOGUE Free

MAIL ORDER Yes, throughout Europe

The nursery lists some 350 Clematis species, hybrids and
cultivars in both large and small flowered varieties. Many
originated in the Baltic States and former USSR. These are
identified in the list of varieties and are particularly interesting.
Examples include 'Maerjamaa', 'Mefistofel', 'Roogoja' and
'Sakala'. Strongly recommended.

Gartenbaubetrieb Engelhardt

Güterbahnhofstr. 53, D-01809 Heidenau bei Dresden

☎ 00 49 5329 512069

SPECIALITIES Dahlias

CATALOGUE Free

MAIL ORDER Yes

Long-established (founded in 1914) nursery specialising in
dahlias. They have introduced a large number of their own
seedlings over the years, specialising in pompon and cactus
types. Their current lists offers over 200 cultivars, many of
which are not known in the UK. Thoroughly recommended.

Gärtnerei Hermann Ermel

Kurpfalzstr. D-67308 Zellertal-Harxheim

☎ 00 49 6355 639   📠 00 49 6355 3462

SPECIALITIES Fuchsias

CATALOGUE DM 10

MAIL ORDER Yes

An excellent fuchsia nursery, with a list of some 2,500 varieties. They are particularly good at introducing new cultivars
bred by German hybridisers. Their catalogue is strongly recommended to any fuchsia enthusiast who is looking for new
and unusual stock.

Georg Arends

Monschaustr. 76, D-42369 Wuppertal-Ronsdorf

☎ 00 49 202 464610   📠 00 49 202 464957

ENGLISH-SPEAKING CONTACT Anja Maubach

SPECIALITIES Herbaceous perennials; Astilbe

CATALOGUE DM 10

MAIL ORDER Yes

A famous name, but did you know that Georg Arends worked
in England over 100 years ago? He exhibited at Chelsea a plant
which he raised and which is still deservedly popular today
Sedum telephium 'Herbstfreude' ('Autumn Joy'). Now run
by the fourth generation, the nursery continues to be an
excellent source of good perennials including Astilbe and
Phlox raised here.

Grübele Baumschulen

Martin-Luther-Weg 14, D-71554 Weissach im
Tal-Unterweissach

☎ 00 49 7191 51234   📠 00 49 7191 52513

SPECIALITIES Acers; conifers; trees

CATALOGUE DM 10

MAIL ORDER Yes

This nursery has an excellent list of unusual trees:
dendrologists, please note. One of their specialities is Ginkgo
(14 cultivars); another is Acer (150 cultivars, including 100
palmatum). But every part of their list has rare taxa. Take
Syringa × prestoniae, for instance: they offer 'Coral',
'Donald Wymann', 'Nocturne' and 'Royalty', none of them
available from UK nurseries.

Hagemann Staudenkulturen

Walsroder Str. 324, D-30855 Langenhagen

☎ 00 49 511 73 76 44   📠 00 49 511 73 64 65

ENGLISH-SPEAKING CONTACT Clas Frese

SPECIALITIES Ferns; herbaceous perennials

CATALOGUE DM 10

MAIL ORDER Yes

This nursery specialises in supplying herbaceous plants for
naturalising. This means creating those natural plants communities which include 'steppe' plantings and rock gardens. It also
explains why such unusual choices as Urtica dioica and
Rumex acetosa turn up in its catalogue alongside the more
conventional exotics. In fact the list is particularly good for
Aster, Delphinium and Phlox.

Ingwer J Jensen GmbH

Am Schloßpark 2b, D-24960 Glucksberg

☎ 00 49 4631 60100

SPECIALITIES Roses

CATALOGUE Yes, several, costing between DM 17.50 and
DM 27.50

MAIL ORDER Yes

Long list of old and new roses, besides clematis, climbers,
rhododendrons and azaleas. The list of varieties of old roses
available from Jensen is one of the most extensive anywhere.
There is a good selection of modern roses too, including many
English roses from David Austin. Efficient mail order.

Johann Wieting

Omorikastr. 6, Gießelhorst, D-26655 Westerstede

☎ 00 49 4488 3588   📠 00 49 4488 71211

SPECIALITIES Rhododendrons

CATALOGUE Yes

MAIL ORDER DM 10

Long-established rhododendron nurserymen from the heart of
Germany's nursery area. They make a speciality of the smaller
modern hybrids, many bred in Germany to survive the cold
winters, but they are also well-known for their azaleas and
Pieris.

Kakteen Haage

Blumenstr. 68, D-99092 Erfurt

☎ 00 49 361 2261014   📠 00 49 361 2119320

ENGLISH-SPEAKING CONTACT Ulrich Haage

SPECIALITIES Cacti and succulents; hoyas; tillandsias

CATALOGUE Free

MAIL ORDER Yes

Haage is the oldest cactus nursery in Europe, dating from 1822.
The present head of the family, H-F Haage has a distinguished

collection, in the best German tradition of scholar-nurserymen. The excellent list of cacti and succulents includes over 100 *Mammillaria* and more than 50 succulent *Euphorbia*, as well as a vast selection of epiphytic cacti, some 70 hoyas and 60 tillandsias. The nursery is a focus for cactophiles throughout Europe, and hosts such events as an annual 'Hoyafest'. They sell seeds, too.

Kakteengärtnerei Max Schleipfer

Sedlweg 71, D-86356 Neusäß bei Augsburg
☎ 00 49 821 464450
SPECIALITIES Alpines; cacti and succulents; herbaceous perennials
CATALOGUE Cacti list free; perennials DM 3
MAIL ORDER Yes, all year round for cacti. Other plants collection only.

Combined specialities of cacti and perennials, each listed separately. Cacti are of garden origin, not imported. The range is extensive. They list 70 named varieties of *Echinopsis* among their specialities, with more available in small quantities. In the list of alpines and perennials enthusiasts should note named forms of *Geranium cinerarium* (sub-caulescens) 'Glühwein', 'Signa' and 'Giuseppina', an improved 'Giuseppe'.

Karl Foerster-Stauden GmbH

Am Raubfang 6, D-14469 Potsdam-Bornim
☎ 00 49 331 520294   ☒ 00 49 331 520124
SPECIALITIES Herbaceous perennials

This famous wholesale nursery has been responsible for many good introductions and well-known for its influence on the history of garden design and planting over the last 100 years. Post-war introductions are now being introduced here by discerning nurseries.

Klaus Oetjen

Oberbühlhof, D-78337 Schienen/Bodensee
☎ 00 49 7735 2247   ☒ 00 49 7735 3734
ENGLISH-SPEAKING CONTACT Klaus Oetjen (written English preferred)
SPECIALITIES Alpines; herbaceous perennials
CATALOGUE DM 3
MAIL ORDER Yes

Alpine and herbaceous plants are the specialities of this owner-run nursery, particularly campanulas, geraniums and paeonies. Among their recent introductions are *Campanula persicifolia* 'Duett', *Rosmarinus officinalis* 'Blaulippe', *Lavandula angustifolia* 'Siesta', *Campanula cochlearifolia* 'Seekampf' and *Geranium himalayense* 'Larissa': enough to show that this is an excellent source of new and interesting forms of popular herbaceous genera. Recommended.

Kurt Kernstein

Blumenzwiebel-Versand, Am Kirchenfeld 8, D-86316 Friedberg
☎ 00 49 821 783275   ☒ 00 49 821 279890
SPECIALITIES Bulbs
CATALOGUE Free
MAIL ORDER Yes

An attractive list of small bulbs, useful to know if you want a German supplier.

Lacon GmbH

J-S-Piazolostr. 4a, D-68759 Hockenheim
☎ 00 49 62 05 40 01   ☒ 00 49 62 05 185 74
ENGLISH-SPEAKING CONTACT Lioba Riedel-Laule
SPECIALITIES Roses
MAIL ORDER Yes

Agents for John Scarman, who has a rose nursery in Staffordshire and apparently trades in Germany as *Roses du Temps Passé*. They also sell companion plants and prairie wildflower mixes.

Naturwuchs

Bardenhorst 15, D-33739 Bielefeld
☎ 00 49 521 8751500   ☒ 00 49 521 85356
ENGLISH-SPEAKING CONTACT Th. Reichelt
SPECIALITIES Fruit; herbaceous perennials; roses; shrubs; trees
CATALOGUE DM 5 or £2
MAIL ORDER Yes, Germany only

This nursery specialises in native plants, forms and hybrids for habitat planting as well as old and traditional varieties of fruit, shrubs, bulbs and perennials for cottage garden planting. They will advise, design and plant these for you too, and offer an intriguing roof planting kit.

Osnabrücker Staudenkulturen P und B zur Linden

Linner Kirchweg 2, D-49143 Bissendorf – Linne
☎ 00 49 5402 5618   ☒ 00 49 5402 4706
ENGLISH-SPEAKING CONTACT P. and B. zur Linden
SPECIALITIES Herbaceous perennials; *Phlox*
CATALOGUE DM 5 in stamps

Perennial breeders and growers with a particular interest in introducing and popularising new species and cultivars. Their breeding work with such genera as *Aster* and *Phlox* has resulted in the introduction of some 20 new named cultivars in recent years. Definitely a nursery to watch. Collection only.

Röllke Orchideenzucht

Fößweg 11, Stukenbrock, D-33758 Schloß Holte-Stukenbrock
☎ 00 49 5207 6647   ☒ 00 49 5207 6697
ENGLISH-SPEAKING CONTACT Lutz Röllke
SPECIALITIES Orchids
CATALOGUE Free
MAIL ORDER Yes

Orchid breeder and grower. There is range of species and hybrids with lots of regular new introductions. They also sell companion plants and accessories.

Rosen von Schultheis

Rosenhof, D-61231 Bad Nauheim Steinfurth
☎ 00 49 6032 81013   ☒ 00 49 6032 85890
SPECIALITIES Roses
CATALOGUE DM 10
MAIL ORDER Yes

Schultheis is one of the most famous rose nurseries in Germany, and still run by the family after 125 years. It specialises in old and rare roses, although the long and interesting list includes a representative selection of modern ones too.

Rosenschule Martin Weingart
Hirtengasse 16, D-99947 Bad Langensalza-Ufhoven
☎ 00 49 3603 813926

ENGLISH-SPEAKING CONTACT Martin Weingart
SPECIALITIES Roses
CATALOGUE Yes
MAIL ORDER Yes

Martin Weingart's list of old, rare and species roses includes many unobtainable elsewhere. He has a good selection of varieties bred by the Austro-Hungarian Rudolf Geschwind such as 'Freya', 'Ernst G. Dörell' and 'Gilda'. Much of his budwood comes from the great Rosarium at Sangerhausen. Strongly recommended.

Rudolf u Klara Baum (Fuchsienkulturen)
Scheffelrain 1, D-71229 Leonberg
☎ 00 49 7152 27558   [FAX] 00 49 7152 28965

ENGLISH-SPEAKING CONTACT Frau Woller speaks some English
SPECIALITIES Conservatory plants; fuchsias; house plants
CATALOGUE DM 13
MAIL ORDER Germany only

Fuchsias and exotic conservatory and house plants. Very basic descriptions for the true plantsman seeking to enlarge his collection from the 1,000 Fuchsia, over 100 Brugmansia (daturas), nearly 200 Passiflora and other species offered. A remarkable list, which gets better every year, and worth the journey to collect.

Schimana Staudenkulturen und Wassergärten
Waldstr. 21, D-86738 Deiningen bei Nördlingen
☎ & [FAX] 00 49 9081 28074

ENGLISH-SPEAKING CONTACT Eckhard & Walter Schimana
SPECIALITIES Aquatic plants; ferns; grasses; herbaceous perennials
CATALOGUE DM 8
MAIL ORDER Yes

Good all-round list of aquatic plants, ferns, grasses and perennials with an impressive list of 13 named forms of Yucca filamentosa. New introductions last year included Helictotrichon sempervirens 'Robust' and Veronica longifolia 'Rosenkerze'.

Schmidt der Gärtner
Ringstr. 84, D-91555 Feuchtwangen
☎ 00 49 9852 67750   [FAX] 00 49 9852 677575

ENGLISH-SPEAKING CONTACT Hans Martin Schmidt
SPECIALITIES Alpines; herbaceous perennials
CATALOGUE DM 2
MAIL ORDER Yes

Alpine and perennial nursery. Troughs are a speciality. The number of saxifrages has been greatly increased in recent years. Good.

Schöppinger Irisgarten (Werner Reinermann)
Bürgerweg 8, D-48624 Schöppingen
☎ 00 49 2555 1851   [FAX] 00 49 2861 85145

SPECIALITIES Iris; Hemerocallis; Hosta
MAIL ORDER Mail order

Well known breeder of Hemerocallis who also specialises in Hosta and Iris. Each year the list includes a number of his introductions. Mail order only, but there are two open weekends each year. Open 9 am – 5 pm, Saturday, 9 am – 2 pm, Sunday.

Staudengarten M. & W Urban
Obere Kirchstr. 3, D-96271 Grub am Forst
☎ & [FAX] 00 49 2560 765

ENGLISH-SPEAKING CONTACT Monika or Wolfgang Urban
SPECIALITIES Herbaceous perennials; herbs
CATALOGUE DM 8
MAIL ORDER Yes

Perennial nursery with an additional range of organically grown herbs, especially mints, and scented pelargoniums.

Staudengärtner Klose
Rosenstr. 10, D-34253 Lohfelden bei Kassel
☎ 00 49 561 515555   [FAX] 00 49 561 515120

ENGLISH-SPEAKING CONTACT Heinz Richard Klose
SPECIALITIES Delphiniums; herbaceous perennials; paeonies; Hosta
CATALOGUE DM 18
MAIL ORDER Yes

A large nursery, best-known as a breeder and grower of hostas, paeonies and other perennials: their paeony fields are a marvellous sight in June. Last year's new introductions included Delphinium 'Gewitterstimmung', Hosta 'Schwarzer Ritter' and 'Violetta' all bred here.

Staudengärtnerei Dieter Gaissmayer
Jungvielweide 3, D-89257 Illertissen
☎ 00 49 7303 7258   [FAX] 00 49 7303 42181

ENGLISH-SPEAKING CONTACT Mr Gaimayer or Mr Mayer
SPECIALITIES Herbaceous perennials
CATALOGUE DM 5
MAIL ORDER Yes

The general catalogue is stylish and helpful, indicating whether a plant can be used in cookery, is attractive to bees and butterflies, can be cut and dried as well as details of size, height, colour, cultural conditions and delightful descriptions of a plant's special peculiarities. There is an extra herbaceous list, with a wide range and many varieties not available in the UK – particularly Astilbe ´ arendsii and Phlox paniculata forms. Recommended.

Staudengärtnerei Gräfin von Zeppelin

Laufen am Südschwarzwald, D-79295 Sulzburg (Baden)

☎ 00 49 7634 69716   [FAX] 00 49 7634 6599

ENGLISH-SPEAKING CONTACT Cai von Rumohr
SPECIALITIES Herbaceous perennials; iris; paeonies; sempervivums; *Papaver orientalis*
CATALOGUE DM 10
MAIL ORDER Yes, worldwide

Famous nursery in pretty setting on the southern edge of the Black Forest now run by Gräfin von Zeppelin's daughter and son-in-law Aglaia and Cai von Rumohr who speak excellent English. The well-produced and informative catalogue lists around 3,000 species and cultivars. The best times to visit are mid-May to mid-June, July and September. Their open weekend at the end of May features guided tours and lectures on their specialities. New introductions raised by them last year include: *Clematis heracleifolia* 'Cassandra', *Papaver orientale* 'Abu Hassan', 'Aslahan', 'Effendi', 'Khedive' and 'Prinz Eugen'.

Staudengärtnerei Hügin

Zähringerstr. 281, D-79108 Freiburg i. Br

☎ 00 49 761 553725

SPECIALITIES Herbaceous perennials

Staudengärtnerei Rolf Peine

Industriestr. 51, D-82194 Gröbenzell

☎ 00 49 8142 57990   [FAX] 00 49 8142 579999

SPECIALITIES Herbaceous perennials
CATALOGUE Free
MAIL ORDER No

An excellent nursery for herbaceous plants, with a particularly good line in delphiniums, phlox and miscanthus. They also have a garden centre on the B471 at Schöngeising, just west of Munich.

Staudengärtnerei Schöllkopf

Postfach 7137, D-72735 Reutlingen

☎ 00 49 7121 54971   [FAX] 00 49 7121 580912

ENGLISH-SPEAKING CONTACT Herr Schöllkopf or Frau Peter
SPECIALITIES Herbaceous perennials
CATALOGUE Free
MAIL ORDER Yes

The nursery lists perennials in the widest sense and includes culinary herbs, grasses, ferns, bog and aquatic plants too. Asters, delphiniums, phlox and chrysanthemums, popular in Germany, are well represented.

Staudengärtnerei Wolfgang Sprich

Papierweg 20, D-79400 Kandern

☎ 00 49 7626 6855/7443

SPECIALITIES Grasses; herbaceous perennials
CATALOGUE DM 10
MAIL ORDER Yes

Perennial nursery. Grasses and hardy geraniums are the main specialities. New varieties introduced last year included *Geranium renardii* 'Tschelda', and *Geranium* × *cantabrigiense* 'Vorjura'.

Staudengärtnerei Zinser

Burgwedelerstr. 48, D-30916 Isernhagen HB

☎ 00 49 511 732385

ENGLISH-SPEAKING CONTACT Irene, Petra & Dr R. Zinser
SPECIALITIES Grasses; herbaceous perennials
MAIL ORDER No

Perennial nursery with a good range, including lots of cultivars not well known here. No mail order.

Staudenkulturen Stade

Beckenstrang 24, D-46325 Borken-Marbeck

☎ 00 49 2861 2604

SPECIALITIES Grasses; herbaceous perennials
MAIL ORDER Yes

Stade offers coloured catalogues for their water-plants and perennials, but it is best to ask for the Price List, which has a very wide range of alpines, perennials and grasses. Among some 4,000 different lines, there are particularly good lists of asters, astilbes, delphiniums, phlox and saxifrages. Recommended.

Südflora Baumschulen

Stutsmoor 42, D-22607 Hamburg

☎ 00 49 40 8991698   [FAX] 00 49 40 8901170

ENGLISH-SPEAKING CONTACT Peter Klock
SPECIALITIES Fruit; Mediterranean plants; *Citrus*; subtropical fruit
CATALOGUE Free
MAIL ORDER Yes

This nursery specialises in Mediterranean plants, citrus and subtropical fruit, understocks and fruit trees: the list of oranges and tangerines is particularly interesting. There is a range of fruit selected for growing in containers, on a balcony, terrace or in a garden.

T J Rud Seidel

Gärtnereiweg 1, D-01936 Grüngräbchen

☎ 00 49 35797 73542

SPECIALITIES Rhododendrons

Wholesale *Rhododendron* grower. The range is mainly hardy hybrids and includes 17 *yakushimanum* hybrids hardy to −26°C.

Tropen Express

Familie Steininger, Dr Winklhofer Straße 22, D-94036 Passau

☎ 00 49 851 81831   [FAX] 00 49 851 87687

ENGLISH-SPEAKING CONTACT Hubert & Gudrun Steininger
SPECIALITIES Palms, tropical plants
CATALOGUE DM 3 and international reply coupon
MAIL ORDER Yes

Palms and tropical plants. An amazing list of tender tropical plants, including palms, bananas and gingers. The list is in two parts: plants available from stock and the real rarities which are available only by special advance order. Tucked in at the end of their catalogue is a list of the *Crinum* species and cultivars which they offer: a mere 28 of them! Strongly recommended.

Versuchsgärtnerei Simon

Staudenweg 2, D-97823 Marktheidenfeld

☎ 00 49 9391 3516   📠 00 49 9391 2183

ENGLISH-SPEAKING CONTACT Werner & Dr Hans Simon
SPECIALITIES Bamboos; herbaceous perennials; shrubs
CATALOGUE DM 20
MAIL ORDER Yes

Bamboos, species perennials and shrubs. Recent introductions have included *Geranium gracile* 'Sirak', *Aster trinervius ageratoides* and *Solidago rugosa* 'Fireworks'.

W Linnemann Strauchpäonien

Rheindorferstr. 49, D-53225 Bonn

☎ 00 49 228 471488   📠 00 49 228 471247

ENGLISH-SPEAKING CONTACT Wolfgang Linnemann
SPECIALITIES Paeonies
CATALOGUE 3 International reply coupons
MAIL ORDER Yes

Wolfgang Linnemann imports tree paeonies from Japan, China, USA and Europe. The range extends to nearly 300 cultivars. Recent introductions include winter-flowering tree paeonies to grow in a cool greenhouse and *Paeonia delavayi* Potaninii group 'Alba'.

W Kordes' Söhne

D-25365 Klein Offenseth-Sparrieshoop

☎ 00 49 4121 48700   📠 00 49 4121 84745

SPECIALITIES Roses
CATALOGUE Yes
MAIL ORDER Yes

An important firm of breeders and growers, one of the largest in Europe. They sell mainly modern roses and maintain a regular stream of new introductions. Their sumptuous catalogue suggests a large and efficient mail-order service, which we can vouch for. Their plants are exceptionally healthy and well-grown.

Wolff's Pflanzen

Hauptstr. 19, D-74541 Vellberg-Großaltdorf

☎ 00 49 7907 89792   📠 00 49 7907 23865

SPECIALITIES Herbaceous perennials; roses, general range
CATALOGUE Free
MAIL ORDER Yes

An nursery for herbaceous plants, with a useful sideline in old-fashioned roses. Most of the roses are available in UK, but there a few which are not: 'Zoë', 'Tom Wood' and 'La Reine Rosarien', for example. Among the herbaceous plants, however, are many good cultivars which have yet to be introduced to UK: pink-flowered *Lychnis chalcedonica* 'Morgenrot', pale pink *Geranium sanguineum* 'Apfelblüte' and *Veronica spicata* 'Spielarten', for instance.

ITALY

Arquebuse

Borgata Serre Marchetto, 53, I-10060 Pinasca Val Chisone (TO)

☎ & 📠 00 39 121 804949

SPECIALITIES Alpines; herbaceous perennials

CATALOGUE Lit. 10,000
MAIL ORDER Yes

This nursery is at 1,200m in the hills above Turin, and specialises in alpine plants, both the rock-clingers and the herbaceous ones from alpine meadows. The list is not long, but many of the plants are grown from wild-collected seed and there are one or two rarities like *Draba sibirica*.

Azienda Agricola Fiorella Gilli

Strada Buttigliera, 300, I-14019 Villanova d'Asti (AT)

☎ 00 39 141 937335   📠 00 39 141 947562

ENGLISH-SPEAKING CONTACT Enrico Cattilino
CATALOGUE Free
MAIL ORDER Yes

Much of this nursery's stock is familiar to English gardeners, but it is also worth looking out for the unusual varieties tucked in between them: *Rosa bracteata* for example, *Cornus florida* 'Cherokee Sunset', two species of *Ptelea* (PP. *baldwinii & polyadenia*), and three forms of *Hydrangea quercifolia* ('Harmony', 'Snowflake' and 'Tennessee').

Bassi Vivai

Via Tonello 17, I-12100 Cuneo

☎ 00 39 171 402149   📠 00 39 171 634351

ENGLISH-SPEAKING CONTACT Dr Guido Bassi
SPECIALITIES Fruit
CATALOGUE Free
MAIL ORDER Yes

Specialists in old fruit cultivars, with one of the best lists of apples, pears, peaches & plums in Italy. Dr Bassi is a champion of the local varieties of fruit and his catalogue offers a wonderful choice of names which are unknown in UK. Minor crops are not forgotten: there are apricots, cherries, walnuts, Japanese chestnuts, and some 20 Italian chestnuts as well as fungal spawn for boletus and truffle species. Strongly recommended to anyone interested in traditional varieties.

Calvisi Manlio

I-33040 Perteole (UD), Via Verdi, 74

☎ 00 39 431 99413   📠 00 39 431 99413

ENGLISH-SPEAKING CONTACT Calvisi Manlio (written English only)
SPECIALITIES Aquatic plants
CATALOGUE Free
MAIL ORDER Yes

A first-class nursery for aquatics, Calvisi lists more than 90 hardy waterlilies and 15 forms of the lotus lily *Nelumbo nucifera*. The list of bog plants and marginals is likewise excellent. Highly recommended.

Camelie Borrini snc

Via della Torre, I-55065 Sant'Andrea di Compito (LU)

☎ 00 39 583 977066   📠 00 30 586 501920

ENGLISH-SPEAKING CONTACT Giulio Cattolica
SPECIALITIES Camellias
CATALOGUE Free
MAIL ORDER In special circumstances

This camellia nursery specialises in pot-grown cultivars, old and new. They are busy breeding new hybrids, the first of which may find their way into the catalogue later this year. They are also experimenting with the cultivation of tea-plants. Guido Cattolica is the joint author of the modern classic *Camelie dell'800 in Italia* (Pacini, Pisa) and organiser of the annual Old Camellias Show at Pieve di Compito.

Capitanio Stefano
Contrada Conghia, 298, I-70043 Monopoli (BA)
☎ 00 39 80 801720   [FAX] 00 39 80 801720
CATALOGUE Lit. 5,000, plus postage
MAIL ORDER Yes

Specialises in Mediterranean and aromatic plants, especially unusual ones. Among last year's novelties were *Galvezia speciosa* and *Rouellia amoena*. The list is forever changing and improving as Sig. Capitanio travels around looking for new plants.

Cellarina di Maria Luisa Sotti
Via Montà, 65, I-14100 Cellarengo (AT)
☎ & [FAX] 00 39 141 935258

ENGLISH-SPEAKING CONTACT Dr Carola Lodari (00 39 11 8127267)
SPECIALITIES Aromatic and scented plants; grey-leaved perennials
CATALOGUE Two: aromatic plants & grey-leaved
MAIL ORDER Yes

Maria Luisa Sotti is the *grande dame* of Italian plantsmen. She trained first as a botanist, and is still one of the experts on the flora of Piemonte, but her great love is aromatic plants and her expertise as a tutor is sought by gardens and gardeners throughout Italy. Recent introductions include *Chenopodium umbrosum*, *Micromeria juliana*, *M. dalmatica* and *Satureja thymbra*. Maria Luisa Sotti is the author of *Le Piante Perenni* (Mondadori, 1991) the classic Italian book on herbaceous plants which is based entirely upon her own experiences and has none of the regurgitated Graham Stuart Thomas you normally get in Italian gardening books.

Centro Bambù Italia di Eberts Wolfgang
Via Conturli, 20, I-16042 Carasco (GE)
☎ 00 39 185 351049   [FAX] 00 39 185 351115

ENGLISH-SPEAKING CONTACT Dieter Reiss
SPECIALITIES Bamboos

Italian branch of the great Eberts bamboo nursery in Baden-Baden, particularly good for species that are not hardy in colder climates.

Coltivazione Riviera del Conero di Oste Lucio
Via G Pascoli, 12, I-60020 Loreto (AN)
☎ & Fax 00 39 71 978384

ENGLISH-SPEAKING CONTACT Federico Oste
SPECIALITIES Palms
CATALOGUE Free
MAIL ORDER Palms only

This is a traditional general nursery which sells a good selection of trees, shrubs and herbaceous plants, including some 120 irises. However, it is also the centre for an amazing collection of palm trees, the largest selection in Europe. As well as trialling some 80 species for hardiness in eastern Italy, where winter temperatures descend to $-15\,^{\circ}$C, they broker some 900 different palm species from all over the world, and a long list of cycads too. It is essential reading for anyone who is interested in palms. Naturally the nursery also acts as a European centre of knowledge and research.

Flora 2000
Via Zenzalino Sud, 19/A, I-40054 Budrio (BO)
☎ 00 39 51 800406   [FAX] 00 39 51 808039

ENGLISH-SPEAKING CONTACT Andrea Pagani (evenings)
SPECIALITIES Fruit; paeonies; roses
CATALOGUE Lit. 5,000
MAIL ORDER Yes

Specialists in old varieties of roses, paeonies and fruit. New last year were the downy cherry *Prunus tomentosa* and a giant jujube *Ziziphus* 'Lee'.

Floricultura Coccetti Aldo e Bruno
Via Crocera, 23, I-21018 Lisanza di Sesto Calende (VA)
☎ 00 39 331 977183   [FAX] 00 39 331 977183

ENGLISH-SPEAKING CONTACT Antonella Coccetti
SPECIALITIES Alpines; herbaceous perennials
CATALOGUE Lit. 3,000
MAIL ORDER Yes, just starting

This excellent list from a nurseryman in the temperate climate of the Italian Lakes will be of particular interest to Brits abroad who are looking for a good source of herbaceous and rock plants. They also sell shrubs, roses and climbers. Among a fair number of plants not grown in the UK are *Rhodohypoxis* 'Tetra Helen' and *Viola cornuta* 'Roem van Aalsmeer'.

Floricultura Hillebrand
Viale Azari, 95, I-28048 Verbania Pallanza (NO)
☎ & [FAX] 00 39 323 503802

ENGLISH-SPEAKING CONTACT Piero Hillebrand
SPECIALITIES Camellias; rhododendrons; shrubs; trees
CATALOGUE Free
MAIL ORDER Yes

This tree and shrub nursery specialises in ericaceous and calcifuge taxa. Their list of camellias is particularly good, with many modern US hybrids alongside traditional 19th-century Italian cultivars. Among their recent introductions are *Arbutus unedo* 'Quercifolia' and *Stewartia pteropetiolata*. One of the most botanically-minded of Italian nurseries.

Floricultura Lago Maggiore di Piffaretti Giovanni
Via Verdi, 22, I-21036 Gemonio (VA)
☎ & [FAX] 00 39 332 610059

ENGLISH-SPEAKING CONTACT Roberto Piffaretti
SPECIALITIES Camellias; rhododendrons
CATALOGUE Free
MAIL ORDER Yes

One of the best nurseries on Lake Maggiore, an area which has always been famous for its ornamental plants. Piffaretti's main specialities are camellias, rhododendrons, azaleas and similar acid-loving shrubs. He is introducing a long list of new camellias later this year.

Gardenland di Giacomasso R & C

Strada Chieri, 59, I-10025 Pino Torinese (TO)
☎ 00 39 11 8111554   📠 00 39 11 8111186

ENGLISH-SPEAKING CONTACT Riccardo Giacomasso
SPECIALITIES Fruit; Mediterranean plants; shrubs; trees
CATALOGUE Lit. 10,000
MAIL ORDER Yes

Gardenland's handsome and helpful catalogue makes it clear that they offer everything that the Italian climate will allow, from the hardiest trees for alpine regions to the palms and cycads of the southern coast. The selection is conservative but reliable, and the extensive list of fruit varieties is particularly impressive.

Il Giardino delle Delizie

Fraz. Mezzano, I-27039 Sannazzaro dei Burgondi (PV)
☎ & 📠 00 39 382 997386

ENGLISH-SPEAKING CONTACT Dr Franca Tacchini
CATALOGUE Lit. 6,000

Rather an English catalogue of roses, based on David Austin's wholesale list, attached to a display garden, the Garden of Delights. About 250 roses and 200 herbs and perennials, with a good line in irises and hemerocallis. New plants for 1996 included *Clerodendron tricotomum* and *Vitex agnus-castus*. Their new list should be out by the time we are published.

Il Giardino delle Higo

Via Jerago, 18, I-21010 Besnate (VA)
☎ & 📠 00 39 331 274096

ENGLISH-SPEAKING CONTACT Dr Franco Ghirardi
SPECIALITIES Camellias
CATALOGUE In 1998
MAIL ORDER In due course

Dr Ghirardi is an amateur with the largest collection of Higo camellias in Europe. He grows some 80 of the 109 cultivars which the Japanese authorities recognise. He has begun to propagate them, partly to make them available to fellow-enthusiasts and partly to encourage more people to grow them.

Il Giardino delle Rose

Via Palastra, 27, I-50020 Chiesanuova (FI)
☎ & 📠 00 39 55 8242388

ENGLISH-SPEAKING CONTACT Dr Maria Giulia Cimarelli Nenna
SPECIALITIES Roses
CATALOGUE Lit. 19,000 (posted)
MAIL ORDER Yes, but Italy only

This nursery specialises in the classic roses of Peter Beales and Jean Pierre Guillot. Among the more recent novelties introduced from Guillot are 'Mozabito', 'Manuel Canova' and 'Sonia Rykel'. The display garden has about 450 varieties.

L'Antico Pomario (Vivai Dalmonte)

Via Casse, 9, I-48013 Brisighella
☎ 00 39 546 81037   📠 00 39 546 80061

ENGLISH-SPEAKING CONTACT Carlo Dalmonte
SPECIALITIES Fruit
CATALOGUE Free
MAIL ORDER Yes

Dalmonte is a large modern nursery with a wide choice of all fruit varieties. It has, for example, almost a complete collection of minor Italian wine grapes. L'Antico Pomario is a small undertaking within the whole company, devoted to ancient (pre-1850) and old (pre-1900) varieties, many with evocative names. The list has about 40 apples (e.g. 'Gambafina Piatta', 'Sasso' and 'Decio'), 20 pears (e.g. 'Brutti e Buoni' and 'Volpino') and 10 peaches (e.g. 'Poppa di Venere'). Their hardiness, disease resistance and ability to survive makes such varieties of special interest to bio-friendly growers.

L'Oasi del Geranio di Giorgio Carlo

Via Aurelia, 312, I-17023 Ceriale (SV)
☎ 00 39 182 990280
SPECIALITIES Pelargoniums
CATALOGUE Cost of postage
MAIL ORDER Only in Italy

This small nursery is founded on the enthusiasm for pelargoniums of a husband and wife who have a magnificent list of over 200 species and 700 cultivars for sale. They are keen to help people to understand the enormous diversity of the genus – not just the zonals and ivy-leaved hybrids but also the climbers, succulents and geophytes among them. Recently introduced species include *caledonicum*, *fissifolium* and *parvipetalum*: among the newer cultivars are 'Meriblu' and 'Gen. Rena'. No mail order, but worth a visit for any visitor to the Riviera.

La Montà di Susanna Tavallini

Via Vittorio Veneto, 8, I-13060 Roasio (VC)
☎ & 📠 00 39 163 87212

ENGLISH-SPEAKING CONTACT Susanna Tavallini
SPECIALITIES Paeonies
CATALOGUE Lit. 10,000
MAIL ORDER Yes

Susanna Tavallini specialises in paeony hybrids. She lists 26 *Paeonia lactiflora*, 12 *P. suffruticosa* and 6 *P. lutea* varieties, among others. They are mainly French in origin and raised by the great breeders of yesteryear. The stylish catalogue is beautifully illustrated, with a helpful essay on planting, cultivating and positioning paeonies.

Mati Piante Az Agr di Cesare Mati

Via Bonellina, 49, I-51100 Pistoia
☎ 00 39 573 380051   📠 00 39 573 382361

ENGLISH-SPEAKING CONTACT Paolo, Andrea or Cristina Mati
SPECIALITIES Shrubs; trees
CATALOGUE Lit. 12,000
MAIL ORDER Yes

One of the biggest and best of the Pistoia nurseries with a large range of trees and shrubs. They specialise in the supply and transplantation of outsize trees.

Mini-Arboretum di Guido Piacenza

I-13057 Pollone (BI)

☎ 00 39 15 61693   FAX 00 39 15 61498

ENGLISH-SPEAKING CONTACT Guido Piacenza
SPECIALITIES Roses; shrubs; trees; unusual plants
CATALOGUE Lit. 7,000
MAIL ORDER Yes

Modern plantsman's nursery which has been responsible for introducing many English plants to Italy, particularly shrubs and roses: Harold Hillier was Guido Piacenza's mentor. Recent introductions are *Prunus* × *yedoensis* 'Ivensii' and *Aucuba japonica* 'Rozannie'. Guido Piacenza owns Villa Boccanegra, Ellen Willmott's Riviera garden. His latest list includes some old Piedmontese apple varieties.

Montivivai dei F.lli Monti

Picciorana per Tempagnano, I-55010 Picciorana (LU)

☎ 00 39 583 998115   FAX 00 39 583 998117

ENGLISH-SPEAKING CONTACT Signora Arianna Monti
SPECIALITIES Camellias; fruit
CATALOGUE Free
MAIL ORDER Yes

Garden designers and maintainers, with a good basic catalogue of every kind of plant but also an interest in old varieties of roses, camellias and fruit trees. They have set to rediscovering old varieties from the Lucca region and have made a success of finding, naming and propagating some 20 old camellias, including 'General Coletti', 'Prof. Giovanni Santarelli' and 'Rosa Risorta'. Their classic collection of roses offers nothing new to UK gardeners, but their fruit tree list has some unusual names.

Oscar Tintori Vivai

Via Tiro a Segno, 55, I-51012 Castellare di Pescia (PT)

☎ 00 39 572 429191   FAX 00 39 572 429605

ENGLISH-SPEAKING CONTACT Alberto Tintori
SPECIALITIES Citrus fruits
CATALOGUE Free
MAIL ORDER Collection only

Oscar Tintori has the best citrus nursery in Italy. His extensive glasshouses are geared mainly to the wholesale trade, but direct retail sale is also available at the nursery. He publishes an extremely handsome catalogue in English and German. Among this year's novelties are *Citrus* 'Kucle', a cross between a kumquat and a clementine. All their plants are sold in pots: they have a good line in large specimens growing in traditional Tuscan terracotta vases.

Piante Esotiche Marsure

Via Cividina, 10, I-33040 Povoletto (UD)

☎ & FAX 00 39 432 679443

ENGLISH-SPEAKING CONTACT Furio Ersetti
SPECIALITIES Aquatic plants; carnivorous plants
CATALOGUE Lit. 2,500
MAIL ORDER Yes

Carnivorous plants, aquatics, bog plants and bamboos: this nursery offers seeds and plants of a limited number of species. But they include 22 species or forms of *Drosera*.

Rose & Rose Emporium

Contrada Fossalto, 9, I-05015 Fabro (TR)

☎ 00 39 763 82812   FAX 00 39 763 82828

SPECIALITIES Roses
MAIL ORDER Yes

A comprehensive list of roses, stylishly designed and based on Peter Beales' collection, with a number of Italian oldies added. 'Clementina Carbonieri', 'Gartendirektor O. Linne' and 'Guglielmo Betto' are among the rarer items. The nursery is just off the main A1 motorway, one hour north of Rome, and has a very pretty demonstration garden.

Rose Barni

Via Autostrada, 5, I-51100 Pistoia

☎ 00 39 573 380464   FAX 00 39 573 382072

ENGLISH-SPEAKING CONTACT Piero or Enrico Barni
SPECIALITIES Roses
CATALOGUE Free
MAIL ORDER Yes

This famous old firm of rose breeders, introducers and growers was founded in 1882 and is now the largest in Italy. Their catalogue is highly colourful and middle-market. They list every type of rose, from gallicas to David Austin's 'English' roses, but the heart of their business is the wonderful choice of traditional HTs and floribundas which Barni themselves have bred for the Italian climate. These open slowly and keep their colours in strong sunlight: worth trying in southern England.

Venzano

Loc. Venzano, Mazzolla, I-56048 Volterra (PI)

☎ & FAX 00 39 588 39095

ENGLISH-SPEAKING CONTACT Don Leevers
SPECIALITIES Aromatic and scented plants; herbs; shrubs
CATALOGUE Free
MAIL ORDER Yes

This nursery in the heart of Tuscany is English-owned and English-run. Don Leevers has a plantsman's catalogue with an excellent mixture of English plants that do well in Italy and plants that he has acquired from his years in the Mediterranean. He has a particularly comprehensive list of herbs, old pinks and scented pelargoniums. He is happy to advise expats on making and planting a garden in Italy and he is also an acute observer of the Italian gardening scene.

Vivai F.lli Bindi

Via Cristoforo Colombo Km 21, I-00124 Casalpalacco (Roma)

☎ 00 39 6 5090840   FAX 00 39 6 50912355

ENGLISH-SPEAKING CONTACT Maria Cherubini or Simona Bindi

A large garden centre with good stock, well-known for its displays. Every May it hosts a week-long show devoted to such themes as herbal plants, bog gardens and how to use rock plants. Their list is largely familiar to English gardeners but includes some cultivars which have not yet made it into commerce here e.g. Hebe 'Wiri Mist' and Hibiscus syriacus 'Mauve Queen'.

Vivai Fratelli Tusi
Via Sorbara, 40, I-46013 Canneto sull'Oglio (MN)
☎ 00 39 376 723460   [FAX] 00 39 376 723632
ENGLISH-SPEAKING CONTACT Signora Daniela Manuini
CATALOGUE   Lit. 12,000
MAIL ORDER   Yes

Principally garden designers who work both for private clients and for professionals. Outsize trees are a speciality, and among the new plants they have recently stocked for the first time are Clethra alnifolia and Malus transitoria.

Vivai Isola del Sole
Cda. San Biagio, I-95013 Fiumefreddo (CT)
☎ & [FAX] 00 39 95 641854
ENGLISH-SPEAKING CONTACT Jan Petiet
SPECIALITIES   Hibiscus rosa-sinensis; Bougainvillea
CATALOGUE   Free
MAIL ORDER   No

This Sicilian nursery lists over 400 varieties of Hibiscus rosa-sinensis and over 100 varieties of Bougainvillea. Both are available as standards. Jan Petiet is keen to grow his collections still further: definitely worth a journey.

Vivai Nord
Via Brianza, 1/A, I-22040 Lurago d'Erba (CO)
☎ 00 39 31 699749   [FAX] 00 39 31 699804
ENGLISH-SPEAKING CONTACT Francis Milner
SPECIALITIES   Herbaceous perennials; shrubs; trees
CATALOGUE   Free
MAIL ORDER   Yes

A consortium of four nurseries, one producing liners, another shrubs, the third trees and the fourth herbaceous plants. Among their exclusives are Pinus cembra 'Sartori' and a wonderful fastigiate oak Quercus 'Mauri' which is thought to be a cross between Q. rubra and either Q.coccinea or Q. palustris.

Vivai Piante Armato
Via Marinella, SS 115, I-91022 Castelvetrano (TP)
☎ 00 39 924 902096   [FAX] 00 39 924 89480
ENGLISH-SPEAKING CONTACT Giacomo Armato
SPECIALITIES   Palms; outsize trees
CATALOGUE   Free
MAIL ORDER   Yes

Big collection of trees, shrubs and climbers.

Vivai Pierluigi Priola
Via Acquette, 4, I-31100 Treviso (TV)
☎ 00 39 422 304096   [FAX] 00 39 422 301859
ENGLISH-SPEAKING CONTACT Please write
SPECIALITIES   Alpines; herbaceous perennials
CATALOGUE   Free
MAIL ORDER   Yes

An excellent herbaceous and alpine nursery whose main business is now wholesale. They have a stock of 4,000 plants, of which a selection is always available for purchase, while the rest may be ordered for later delivery. Many of their plants come originally from English, German, Dutch and East European nurseries, but they have also hybridised, selected and named plants themselves. Among their many recent introductions are Delphinium 'Dämmerung', Sedum cauticola 'Robustum' and Myosotis palustris 'Perle von Ronnenberg'. Strongly recommended.

Vivai Pietro Vanetti
Via Patrioti, 24, I-21020 Inarzo (VA)
☎ 00 39 332 964250   [FAX] 00 39 332 964228
ENGLISH-SPEAKING CONTACT Eleonora Vanetti
SPECIALITIES   Aquatic plants; bog plants
CATALOGUE   Lit. 5,000
MAIL ORDER   Yes

Specialists in water gardens. A recent introduction is Nymphaea 'Escarboucle'.

Vivai Torsanlorenzo Srl
Via Campo di Carne, 51, I-00040 Ardea (Roma)
☎ 00 39 6 91019005   [FAX] 00 39 6 91011602
SPECIALITIES   Shrubs

The biggest nursery in Italy, where you can buy almost anything you want, except herbaceous perennials. The scale is enormous: over 100 hectares – we were driven through their polytunnels in a Range Rover. Big trees are one of their many specialities, including 100-year-old olives and palms. But there are vast areas of camellias, citrus fruit, oleanders and hundreds of other desirable plants. Highly recommended to all landscapers, Brits abroad and visitors to Rome.

Vivaibambù di Mario Branduzzi
Via Dosso di Mattina, 19, I-26010 Credera/Rubbiano
☎ & [FAX] 00 39 373 61009
ENGLISH-SPEAKING CONTACT Dr Mario Brandazzi
SPECIALITIES   Aquatic plants; bamboos
CATALOGUE   Lit. 10,000
MAIL ORDER   Yes

This nursery offers a remarkable selection of 120+ bamboos, 100+ aquatics and many tropical plants. Among last year's introductions are: Bambusa ventricosa 'Kimmei', Bambusa balcooa, Phyllostachys bambusoides, Dendrocalamus asper, Tricomanthes kirilowii 'Japonica' and Rhus javanica.

Vivaio Anna Peyron
Cascina La Custodia (Fraz. San Genésio), I-10090 Castagneto Po (TO)
☎ 00 39 11 912982   [FAX] 00 39 11 912590
ENGLISH-SPEAKING CONTACT Saskia Pellion or Nicola Bocca
SPECIALITIES   Bulbs; roses
CATALOGUE   Roses Lit. 12,000; Bulbs Lit. 9,000
MAIL ORDER   Yes

Anita Peyron established her reputation among Italian nurserymen by her consistent promotion of the best old-fashioned roses. Her list plumps for quality rather than quantity: 170 varieties of old and not-so-old roses from gallica 'Officinalis' to 'Graham Thomas'. There are no great surprises among the selection, which is made with the highly variable Italian climate in mind, but UK fans of Italian breeders should note 'Purezza' among the otherwise rather English choice. Peyron has now moved into bulbs and dahlias – hydrangeas are next in line – and here again the choice is safe and trustworthy rather than imaginative: but that is what one would expect of a Piedmontese nurseryman.

Vivaio Cooperativa CREA
Via XXV Aprile, I-41012 Cibeno di Carpi (MO)
☎ & 〔FAX〕 00 39 59 651408
SPECIALITIES   Ecological species

This eco-friendly nursery – CREA stands for *Centro Riproduzione Essenze Autoctone* – offers native southern European species for landscaping in the natural way.

Vivaio Guido degl'Innocenti
Via Colle Ramole, 7 – Loc. Bottai, I-50029 Tavarnuzze (FI)
☎ 00 55 237 45 47   〔FAX〕 00 55 202 06 76
ENGLISH-SPEAKING CONTACT Mrs Elisabeth or Mrs Fiorella
SPECIALITIES   Iris
CATALOGUE   Lit. 10,000
MAIL ORDER   Yes

A large nursery with a distinguished history. Innocenti means irises, and they list 400+ varieties, most of them tall bearded, but there are some interesting *oncocyclus* hybrids too. Almost all are gloriously illustrated in their spectacular catalogue. Prices vary from Lit. 3,000 for popular lines to Lit. 35,000 for the latest American hybrids, but the most common prices are Lit. 4,000 and Lit. 5,000, so they are not expensive. They have a useful second line in *Hemerocallis* and herbaceous plants and last year they introduced 30 new aquatics.

Vivaio Luciano Noaro
Via Vittorio Emanuele, 151, I-18033 Camporosso (IM)
☎ & 〔FAX〕 00 39 184 288225
ENGLISH-SPEAKING CONTACT Signora Linda Noaro
SPECIALITIES   Mediterranean plants; exotic fruit; variegated plants
CATALOGUE   Lit. 6,000
MAIL ORDER   Yes

This excellent list is widely spread among trees, shrubs, climbers, and herbaceous plants, mainly Mediterranean or tropical. There are some interesting palms and large specimens of such exotic flowering plants as *Doryanthes palmeri*, as well as a fine selection of salvias, jasmines, tropical thunbergias, and edible species of *Eugenia*. The stock is always changing as Noaro winkles out new rarities from his frequent forays abroad. Recommended.

Vivaio Pegoraro Francesco
Via Marconi, 31 (SS Postumia), I-35101 San Pietro in Gù (PD)
☎ & 〔FAX〕 00 39 49 5991658
SPECIALITIES   Bog plants
CATALOGUE   Yes
MAIL ORDER   No

Not so much a nursery as water-garden specialists: design and planting for Italian gardens.

Vivai-Fattoria 'La Parrina'
Località La Parrina, I-58010 Albinia (GR)
☎ 00 39 564 865060   〔FAX〕 00 39 564 862636
ENGLISH-SPEAKING CONTACT Fabio Fusari
SPECIALITIES   Australian plants; Mediterranean plants; oleanders
CATALOGUE   Lit. 3,500
MAIL ORDER   No

Among the novelties introduced by this plantsman's nursery last year were *Coleonema album* and a pink-flowered form of *Westringia fruticosa* called 'Wynabbie Gem'.

Walter Branchi
Le Rose, Corbara, 55, I-05019 Orvieto (TR)
ENGLISH-SPEAKING CONTACT Prof Walter Branchi
SPECIALITIES   Roses
CATALOGUE   Free
MAIL ORDER   Yes

A niche nursery with a very comprehensive list of Tea roses (c.60), China roses (40+) and Noisettes (c.25), both bush and climbing varieties. This is probably the most complete list in the world of these fashionable 19th century roses. Walter Branchi is a delightful retired Professor of Music and speaks fluent American.

SWEDEN
Cedergren & Co Plantskola
Box 16016, S-25016 Råå
☎ 00 46 42 260052   〔FAX〕 00 46 42 260890
ENGLISH-SPEAKING CONTACT Krister Cedergren
SPECIALITIES   Clematis; roses
CATALOGUE   SKr.20
MAIL ORDER   Yes

Old roses and clematis.

Impecta Handels
S-640 25 Julita
☎ 00 46 150 923 31   〔FAX〕 00 46 150 923 16
ENGLISH-SPEAKING CONTACT Veronica Karlsson
SPECIALITIES   Herbaceous perennials; herbs; shrubs
CATALOGUE   £1
MAIL ORDER   Yes

This nursery is excellent for herbaceous plants and herbs, but is even better for seeds. They offer a wide choice of varieties: conservatory plants are one of their specialities, as well as annual plants and old varieties of vegetables.

Örtagårdens Plantskole
PL. 3460, S-28890 Vinslöv
☎ 00 46 44 81934   〔FAX〕 00 46 44 81934
ENGLISH-SPEAKING CONTACT Rune Brand
SPECIALITIES   Herbaceous perennials; herbs
CATALOGUE   £2
MAIL ORDER   Yes

Specialists in herbs and medicinal plants. Their stylish catalogue has helpful descriptions and a dozen charming recipes at the end.

THE NETHERLANDS

Belle Epoque Rozenkwekerij

Oosteinderweg 489, NL-1432 BJ Aalsmeer

☎ 00 31 297 342546   [FAX] 00 31 297 340597

SPECIALITIES Roses
CATALOGUE HFl.8
MAIL ORDER Yes

The best rose-list in Holland, handsomely illustrated and offering some 750 cultivars, from the oldest gallicas to the most modern English roses. Among a fair number which are not available in the UK, we noted 'White Dorothy', 'Orange Morsdag' and 'Royal Queen', which is a climbing sport of 'White Queen Elizabeth'. They also sell wholesale under the trading name 'J D Maarse & Zonen B V'. Worth investigating.

Boomkwekerij André van Nijnatten BV

Meirseweg 26a, NL-4881 DJ Zundert

☎ 00 31 76 597 2605   [FAX] 00 31 76 597 5360

SPECIALITIES Shrubs; trees
CATALOGUE Free to trade
MAIL ORDER Yes

This firm of wholesalers has an interesting list of ornamental trees. It specialises in new introductions. We particularly recommend *Acer campestre* 'Nanum' among five cultivars of the fields maple not yet grown in this country. Other exciting novelties include *Carpinus betulus* 'Fastigiata Nana', *Malus* 'Pom Zai', *Ligustrum japonicum* 'Grace' and five new cultivars of *Tilia cordata*. Every adventurous nurseryman or garden centre owner should investigate further.

Coen Jansen

Ankummer Es 15, NL-7722 RD Dalfsen

☎ 00 31 5294 34086

SPECIALITIES Herbaceous perennials
CATALOGUE HFl.7.50

This nursery offers a good list of herbaceous plants, and the catalogue (in Dutch) has particularly long and helpful plant descriptions. Coen Jansen are good at tracking down and introducing new cultivars from other countries. Among many familiar plants are a good number of names that do not appear in *The Plant Finder* – four named cultivars of *Salvia nemorosa*, for example, half-a-dozen delphiniums, three cultivars of *Helenium*, several geraniums and many others. Worth investigating.

De Gentiaan

P O Box 51, NL-9620 AB Slochteren

☎ & [FAX] 00 31 59 8421380

ENGLISH-SPEAKING CONTACT John – after 7 pm Dutch time
SPECIALITIES Bulbs
CATALOGUE 2 International reply coupons
MAIL ORDER Yes

Bulb specialists, particularly rare species and bulk orders for naturalising. *Agapanthus*, *Allium* and cyclamen are their main lines: new last year was a long-leaved form of *Cyclamen*

hederifolium with pale lilac flowers and an *Allium giganteum* × *schubertii* hybrid.

De Grienê Hân

Weaze 29, NL-8495 HE Aldeboarn (Frl.)

☎ 00 31 566 631226

ENGLISH-SPEAKING CONTACT Auke R. Kleefstra
SPECIALITIES Fruit
CATALOGUE Free
MAIL ORDER Yes

Specialists in old fruit tree varieties; about 60 apples, 45 pears, 20 plums and 10 cherries. Some are familiar, but there is a good sprinkling of Dutch names and local varieties. A new catalogue is planned.

Fa C Esveld

Rijneveld 72, NL-2771 XS Boskoop

☎ 00 31 172 213289   [FAX] 00 31 172 215714

ENGLISH-SPEAKING CONTACT All staff
SPECIALITIES Herbaceous perennials; shrubs; trees
CATALOGUE £5
MAIL ORDER Yes

One of the biggest nurseries in Europe – over 7,000 different varieties of trees, shrubs and hardy plants. This year's novelties alone number several hundreds. Their list is a fat handbook, like a spiral-bound version of Hillier's *Guide* without the detailed descriptions. The number of unusual varieties which are not grown in the UK is enormous – almost every genus seems to have at least one new name. Every keen plantsman needs this catalogue.

Fa Jac Verschuren-Pechtold BV

Kalkhofseweg 6A, NL-5443 NA Haps

☎ 00 32 485 316258   [FAX] 00 32 485 322300

ENGLISH-SPEAKING CONTACT Koen Verschuren
SPECIALITIES Roses

Long established rose nurserymen (founded in 1875) who produce over one million bushes a year. Their current list contains over 700 varieties: 'White Dorothy' and 'Abbaye de Cluny' are among those that are not available in the UK. Collection only.

Fuchsia-Kwekerij Spek

1e Hoornerveensewg 7, NL-8181 LW Heerde

☎ 00 31 578 693604   [FAX] 00 31 578 696052

ENGLISH-SPEAKING CONTACT Yes
SPECIALITIES Fuchsias; pelargoniums
CATALOGUE HFl.5
MAIL ORDER Yes

One of the great European *Fuchsia* nurseries, with more than 2,000 varieties. These include about 60 species (and forms of species), 50 hardy forms (hardy in The Netherlands means hardy anywhere in the UK) and a long list of hybrids old and new. They also have a video on fuchsia growing.

Gebr van 't Westeinde: Kwekerij 'Westhof'

Westhofsezandweg 3, NL-4444 SM 's-Heer Arendskerke
☎ 00 31 113 561219   📠 00 31 113 563399
ENGLISH-SPEAKING CONTACT Peter van 't Westeinde
SPECIALITIES Fuchsias; walnuts
CATALOGUE HFl.5 (fuchsias)
MAIL ORDER Yes

The specialities are grafted walnuts and fuchsias. They do small plants by mail order, but say collection is better.

Jan Spek Rozen

Zijde 155, NL-2771 EV Boskoop
☎ 00 31 172 212120   📠 00 31 172 214455
ENGLISH-SPEAKING CONTACT Mr Helle Spek
SPECIALITIES Roses
CATALOGUE Free
MAIL ORDER Yes

Famous old firm of rose breeders, who act as agents for overseas breeders like Sam McGredy, Louis Lens and Jackson & Perkins. Their current list is quite small, but has a number of varieties which we do not have in Britain. They also sell shrubs wholesale for public amenity planting.

Jos Frijns en Zonen BV

Groot-Welsden 30, NL-6269 EV Margraten
☎ 00 31 43 4581246   📠 00 31 43 4582734
ENGLISH-SPEAKING CONTACT Mr J. M. H. Frints
SPECIALITIES Fruit
CATALOGUE Free

Fruit tree specialists with an excellent list of around 250 apples, 110 pears, 60 cherries and a very wide range of everything else. A good proportion of the names does not appear in The Plant Finder, especially varieties bred in Germany and the Netherlands. Very interesting.

Kwekerij Oudolf

Broekstraat 17, NL-6999 DE Hummelo
☎ 00 31 314 38 11 20   📠 00 31 314 38 11 99
ENGLISH-SPEAKING CONTACT Piet Oudolf
SPECIALITIES Herbaceous perennials
CATALOGUE Free
MAIL ORDER No

Piet Oudolf is best known (and very highly regarded) as one of the pioneers of the new style of planting perennials. It comes as no surprise, therefore, to discover that his catalogue is stocked with plants both familiar and unfamiliar: all are chosen for their excellence in planting schemes. Cultivars unknown in England rub shoulders with the commonplace. Worth careful study.

Kwekerij Th Ploeger en Zn BV

Blauwkapelsenweg 73, NL-3731 EB De Bilt
☎ 00 31 30 2202602   📠 00 31 30 2204494
SPECIALITIES Herbaceous perennials

CATALOGUE Yes
MAIL ORDER Yes

This long-established and first-rate herbaceous nursery has a steady stream of introductions. Last year, for example, they introduced some 130 new plants, many of them already known in the UK but some of them not, including Salvia nemorosa 'Schneehügel', Sanguisorba tenuifolia 'Pink Elephant' and Aubrieta 'Sauerland'.

M M Bömer Boomkwekerij

Vagevuurstraat 6, NL-4882 NK Zundert
☎ 00 31 76 5972735   📠 00 31 76 5974585
ENGLISH-SPEAKING CONTACT J. Bömer
SPECIALITIES Trees
CATALOGUE Free
MAIL ORDER Yes

This remarkable nursery has a niche market in rare oaks, beeches, horse chestnuts and hazels. There are some 65 cultivars of Fagus sylvatica, 130 Quercus and an amazing 99 cultivars of Corylus. It goes without saying that many are unknown in England. Essential reading for all dendrophiles.

Moerheim Plantenwinkel

Moerheimstraat 78, NL-7701 CG Dedemsvaart
☎ 00 31 523 612345   📠 00 31 523 617140
ENGLISH-SPEAKING CONTACT Most staff
SPECIALITIES Herbaceous perennials
CATALOGUE HFl.15
MAIL ORDER Yes

Famous old herbaceous nursery (Helenium 'Moerheim Beauty') with a sound all-round catalogue. Their range includes trees, shrubs, alpines, roses (from Meilland), aquatics and fruit and there are a number of unusual varieties among them.

Pieter Zwijnenburg

Halve Raak 18, NL-2771 AD Boskoop
☎ 00 31 172 216232   📠 00 31 172 218474
ENGLISH-SPEAKING CONTACT Pieter Zwijnenburg
SPECIALITIES Conifers; shrubs; trees
CATALOGUE £2
MAIL ORDER Yes

This is one of the best all-round nurseries in Europe. Its herbaceous list alone is better than most UK nurseries. But it really scores with the sheer number of trees and shrubs it offers. There are, for example, more than 20 Quercus robur cultivars, over 50 Fagus sylvatica and 20 Liquidamber styraciflua. But page after page, genus after genus, Zwijnenburg shows that it is comprehensive and has an eye for new forms and cultivars. This is an essential source for anyone in search of the unusual.

13

European Nursery Specialities

ACERS
Grübele Baumschulen, Germany

ALPINES
Alpengarten Pforzheim, Germany
Alpine Staudengärtnerei Seigfried Geiler, Germany
Alpiner Garten Dieter Kaufmann, Germany
Arne Kr. Jorgensen, Denmark
Arquebuse, Italy
Assens Planteskole, Denmark
Botanische Raritäten, Germany
Floricultura Coccetti Aldo e Bruno, Italy
Kakteengärtnerei Max Schleipfer, Germany
Klaus Oetjen, Germany
Majlands Stauder, Denmark
Pép. Brochet Lanvin, France
Sarastro, Austria
Schmidt der Gärtner, Germany
Stauden Feldweber, Austria
Vivai Pierluigi Priola, Italy

AQUATIC PLANTS
Calvisi Manlio, Italy
Eberhard Schuster (Wasserpflanzen), Germany
Jardin Aquatique, France
Latour Marliac SA, France
Piante Esotiche Marsure, Italy
Schimana Staudenkulturen und Wassergärten, Germany
Vivai Pietro Vanetti, Italy
Vivaibambù di Mario Branduzzi, Italy

AROMATIC AND SCENTED PLANTS
Cellarina di Maria Luisa Sotti, Italy
Venzano, Italy

AUSTRALIAN PLANTS
Vivai-Fattoria 'La Parrina', Italy

BAMBOOS
Bambous de Planbuisson, France
Bambuschulen Janssen, Germany
Bambuszentrum Niederbayern, Germany
Centro Bambù Italia di Eberts Wolfgang, Italy
La Bambouseraie de Prafrance, France
Versuchsgärtnerei Simon, Germany
Vivaibambù di Mario Branduzzi, Italy

BOG PLANTS
Assens Planteskole, Denmark
Eberhard Schuster (Wasserpflanzen), Germany
Vivaio Pegoraro Francesco, Italy

BONSAI
Bonsai Centrum, Germany
Bonsaï Rémy Samson, France

BULBS
Albrecht Hoch, Germany
Botanische Raritäten, Germany
Bulbes d'Opale, France
De Gentiaan, The Netherlands
Kurt Kernstein, Germany
Schryve Jardin, France
Vivaio Anna Peyron, Italy

CACTI AND SUCCULENTS
Cactus Esterel, France
Éts. Kuentz: Monde des Cactus, France

Kakteen Haage, Germany
Kakteengärtnerei Max Schleipfer, Germany

CAMELLIAS
Camelie Borrini snc, Italy
Floricultura Hillebrand, Italy
Floricultura Lago Maggiore di Piffaretti Giovanni, Italy
Il Giardino delle Higo, Italy
Montivivai dei F.lli Monti, Italy
Pép. Botanique Jean Thoby, France
Pép. Claude Thoby, France

CARNIVOROUS PLANTS
Nature et Paysages, France
Piante Esotiche Marsure, Italy

CLEMATIS
Cedergren & Co. Plantskola, Sweden
Gartenbau F. Westphal, Germany
Pépinières Travers, France

CLIMBERS
Pép. Charentaises, France
Pépinières Travers, France

CONIFERS
Baumschule Böhlje, Germany
Grübele Baumschulen, Germany
Pép. Charentaises, France
Pieter Zwijnenburg, The Netherlands

CONSERVATORY PLANTS
Éts. Hort. Hodnik, France
Flora Mediterranea, Germany
Pép. de la Vallée de l'Huveaune, France
Pép. Jean Rey, France
Rudolf u. Klara Baum (Fuchsienkulturen), Germany

DAHLIAS
Gartenbaubetrieb Engelhardt, Germany
Wirth Dahlien, Austria

DELPHINIUMS
Staudengärtner Klose, Germany

FERNS
Hagemann Staudenkulturen, Germany
Lumen, France
Pép. Yves Dupont, France
Schimana Staudenkulturen und Wassergärten, Germany

FRUIT
Assens Planteskole, Denmark
Bassi Vivai, Italy
Baumschule Herr, Germany

Boomkwekerij De Linde, Belgium
De Grienê Hân, The Netherlands
Delbard, France
Flora 2000, Italy
Fratelli Ingegnoli, Italy
Gardenland di Giacomasso R. & C., Italy
Jos Frijns en Zonen BV, The Netherlands
L'Antico Pomario (Vivai Dalmonte), Italy
Montivivai dei F.lli Monti, Italy
Naturwuchs, Germany
Pép. Charentaises, France
Pép. Christophe Delay, France
Pép. Eric Dumont, France
Pép. Gautier et Fils, France
Pép. Rhône-Alpes A. Gayraud, France
Pommiers du pays d'Auge, France
Südflora Baumschulen, Germany

FUCHSIAS
E.A.R.L. des Cailloux Vivants, France
Éts. Jean-Pierre Tourly, France
Fuchsia's Michiels-De Smedt, Belgium
Fuchsia-Kwekerij Spek, The Netherlands
Fuchsien Kulturen Lakonig, Austria
Gebr. van 't Westeinde: Kwekerij 'Westhof',
    The Netherlands
Gärtnerei Hermann Ermel, Germany
Horning Fuchsiari: v/ H. og B. Hojer, Denmark
Rudolf u. Klara Baum (Fuchsienkulturen), Germany

GRASSES
Bambous de Planbuisson, France
Lumen, France
Schimana Staudenkulturen und Wassergärten, Germany
Staudengärtnerei Wolfgang Sprich, Germany
Staudengärtnerei Zinser, Germany
Staudenkulturen Stade, Germany

HEATHERS
Baumschule-Heidepark Jürgen Krebs, Germany
Les Jardins de Cotelle, France

HEDGING
Pép. Rhône-Alpes A. Gayraud, France

HERBACEOUS PERENNIALS
Arne Kr. Jorgensen, Denmark
Arquebuse, Italy
Assens Planteskole, Denmark
Baumschule Alfred Weber, Austria
Baumschule Franz Praskac, Austria
Botanische Raritäten, Germany
Caroline Mathildestiens Stauder, Denmark

Coen Jansen, The Netherlands
Fa. C. Esveld, The Netherlands
Floricultura Coccetti Aldo e Bruno, Italy
Georg Arends, Germany
Hagemann Staudenkulturen, Germany
Impecta Handels, Sweden
Kakteengärtnerei Max Schleipfer, Germany
Karl Foerster-Stauden GmbH, Germany
Klaus Oetjen, Germany
Kwekerij Oudolf, The Netherlands
Kwekerij Th. Ploeger en Zn. bv, The Netherlands
Les Jardins de Cotelle, France
Lumen, France
Lynge Staudegartneri, Denmark
Majlands Stauder, Denmark
Moerheim Plantenwinkel, The Netherlands
Naturwuchs, Germany
Örtagårdens Plantskole, Sweden
Osnabrücker Staudenkulturen P. und B. zur Linden,
  Germany
Pép. Brochet Lanvin, France
Plantbessin, France
Santonine, France
Sarastro, Austria
Schimana Staudenkulturen und Wassergärten, Germany
Schmidt der Gärtner, Germany
Stauden Feldweber, Austria
Staudengarten M. & W. Urban, Germany
Staudengärtner Klose, Germany
Staudengärtnerei Dieter Gaissmayer, Germany
Staudengärtnerei Gräfin von Zeppelin, Germany
Staudengärtnerei Hügin, Germany
Staudengärtnerei Rolf Peine, Germany
Staudengärtnerei Schöllkopf, Germany
Staudengärtnerei Wolfgang Sprich, Germany
Staudengärtnerei Zinser, Germany
Staudenkulturen Stade, Germany
Versuchsgärtnerei Simon, Germany
Vivai Nord, Italy
Vivai Pierluigi Priola, Italy
Wolff's Pflanzen, Germany

HERBS
Impecta Handels, Sweden
Örtagårdens Plantskole, Sweden
Staudengarten M. & W. Urban, Germany
Venzano, Italy

HOUSE PLANTS
Rudolf u. Klara Baum (Fuchsienkulturen), Germany

IRIS
Albrecht Hoch, Germany

Cayeux SA, France
Gaec de Champagne M. Bourdillon, France
Iris de Thau, France
Iris en Provence, France
Kawana, Belgium
Schöppinger Irisgarten (Werner Reinermann), Germany
Staudengärtnerei Gräfin von Zeppelin, Germany
Vivaio Guido degl'Innocenti, Italy

LILIES
Albrecht Hoch, Germany

MEDITERRANEAN PLANTS
Dino Pellizzaro, France
Éts. Hort. Hodnik, France
Flora Mediterranea, Germany
Gardenland di Giacomasso R. & C., Italy
Pép. Filippi, France
Pép. Jean Rey, France
Silvia Tunkl, Austria
Südflora Baumschulen, Germany
Vivaio Luciano Noaro, Italy
Vivai-Fattoria 'La Parrina', Italy

ORCHIDS
Botanische Raritäten, Germany
Marcel Lecoufle, France
Röllke Orchideenzucht, Germany

PAEONIES
Albrecht Hoch, Germany
Flora 2000, Italy
La Montà di Susanna Tavallini, Italy
Pivoines Michel Rivière, France
Staudengärtner Klose, Germany
Staudengärtnerei Gräfin von Zeppelin, Germany
W Linneman Strauchpäonien, Germany

PALMS
Coltivazione Riviera del Conero di Oste Lucio, Italy
Tropen Express, Germany
Vivai Piante Armato, Italy

PELARGONIUMS
Éts. Jean-Pierre Tourly, France
Fuchsia-Kwekerij Spek, The Netherlands
L'Oasi del Geranio di Giorgio Carlo, Italy

PRUNUS
Albrecht Hoch, Germany

RHODODENDRONS
Baumschule Böhlje, Germany

Baumschule H. Hachmann, Germany
Floricultura Hillebrand, Italy
Floricultura Lago Maggiore di Piffaretti Giovanni, Italy
Johann Wieting, Germany
Pépiniere de l'Arboretum de Balaine, France
Rhododendron-Haven Planteskole, Denmark
Sonderborg Planteskole, Denmark
T. J. Rud. Seidel, Germany

ROSES
Assens Planteskole, Denmark
Belle Epoque Rozenkwekerij, The Netherlands
Bernard Boureau, France
Cedergren & Co. Plantskola, Sweden
Delbard, France
Fa. Jac Verschuren-Pechtold b.v., The Netherlands
Fa. Treffinger-Hofmann, Germany
Flora 2000, Italy
Grumer Rosen, Austria
Il Giardino delle Rose, Italy
Ingwer J. Jensen GmbH, Germany
Jan Spek Rozen, The Netherlands
Lacon GmbH, Germany
Lens Roses, Belgium
Les Roses Anciennes de André Eve, France
Meilland Richardier, France
Mini-Arboretum di Guido Piacenza, Italy
Naturwuchs, Germany
Pép. Brochet Lanvin, France
Pép. Charentaises, France
Pépinières et Roseraies Vizier, France
Rose & Rose Emporium, Italy
Rose Barni, Italy
Rosen von Schultheis, Germany
Rosenplanteskolen i Love, Denmark
Rosenschule Martin Weingart, Germany
Roseraies Pierre Guillot, France
Roses Anciennes du Lot, France
Vivaio Anna Peyron, Italy
W. Kordes' Söhne, Germany
Walter Branchi, Italy
Wolff's Pflanzen, Germany

SEMPERVIVUMS
Staudengärtnerei Gräfin von Zeppelin, Germany

SHRUBS
Alpengarten Pforzheim, Germany
Arboretum National des Barres, France
Arboretum Waasland, Belgium
Assens Planteskole, Denmark
Baumschule Alfred Weber, Austria
Baumschule Böhlje, Germany

Baumschule Franz Praskac, Austria
Baumschule Röhler, Germany
Boomkwekerij André van Nijnatten B.V.,
    The Netherlands
E.A.R.L. des Cailloux Vivants, France
Fa. C. Esveld, The Netherlands
Floricultura Hillebrand, Italy
Gardenland di Giacomasso R. & C., Italy
Impecta Handels, Sweden
Mati Piante Az. Agr. di Cesare Mati, Italy
Mini-Arboretum di Guido Piacenza, Italy
Naturwuchs, Germany
Pép. Botanique Jean Thoby, France
Pép. Brochet Lanvin, France
Pép. Charentaises, France
Pép. Côte Sud des Landes, France
Pép. Minier, France
Pép. Rhône-Alpes A. Gayraud, France
Pépiniere de l'Arboretum de Balaine, France
Pieter Zwijnenburg, The Netherlands
Sonderborg Planteskole, Denmark
Venzano, Italy
Versuchsgärtnerei Simon, Germany
Vivai Nord, Italy
Vivai Torsanlorenzo S.r.l., Italy

TREES
Arboretum Altdorf, Germany
Arboretum National des Barres, France
Arboretum Waasland, Belgium
Assens Planteskole, Denmark
Baumschule Böhlje, Germany
Baumschule Franz Praskac, Austria
Baumschule Röhler, Germany
Boomkwekerij André van Nijnatten B.V.,
    The Netherlands
Fa. C. Esveld, The Netherlands
Floricultura Hillebrand, Italy
Gardenland di Giacomasso R. & C., Italy
Grübele Baumschulen, Germany
M M Bömer Boomkwekerij, The Netherlands
Mati Piante Az. Agr. di Cesare Mati, Italy
Mini-Arboretum di Guido Piacenza, Italy
Naturwuchs, Germany
Pép. Botanique Jean Thoby, France
Pép. Charentaises, France
Pép. Côte Sud des Landes, France
Pép. Rhône-Alpes A. Gayraud, France
Pépiniere de l'Arboretum de Balaine, France
Pieter Zwijnenburg, The Netherlands
Sonderborg Planteskole, Denmark
Vivai Nord, Italy

14

Foreign Seedsmen

This chapter lists seedsmen of every kind, in Europe and further afield. One of the excitements of writing this chapter has been to discover just how excellent and comprehensive are some of the wildflower seed merchants, especially the Australian and South African ones. All have fascinating lists. Most of the Australian seedsmen are wholesalers, but many sell sample packets too: useful quantities at affordable prices. We have only included a selection of them in *The Gardener's Yearbook*, but the Australian Tree Seed Centre also publishes a complete list of Australian tree seed suppliers, some thirty of them, which is available on the internet.

The American lists divide into two types. First there are the plantsman's lists, which offer many choices and vie with each other for rarity. Second, there are the ecological wildflower mixes - some of them containing genera from all over the world. These appeal more to the suburban enthusiast for natural beauty than to the botanist or gardener. Some of the best lists come from alpine specialists who concentrate on small plants from higher altitudes but also offer seed of some herbaceous plants and shrubs.

Remember that unusual and exotic seeds are also available from many of the specialist societies. We particularly commend: The Alpine Garden Society; The Scottish Rock Garden Club; Gesellschaft der Staudenfreunde; Wildflower Society of Australia; and the American Rock Garden Society.

There is no restriction on the import and export of seeds within the EU. Indeed, the regulations do not even talk of 'import' and 'export' nowadays, but merely of movement within the European Union.

The position is however different when dealing with the import into Europe (including the UK) from outside the EU. Here the rules are as follows:

1. There is a complete ban on the import of potato seed, i.e. true seed of *Solanum tuberosum*.

2. A phytosanitary certificate is needed for the import of the following: *Allium cepa* (onions), *Allium porrum* (leeks), *Allium schoenoprasum* (chives), *Capsicum*, *Helianthus annuus* (sunflowers), *Lycopersicon esculentum* (tomatoes), *Medicago sativa* (lucerne), *Oryza* (rice), *Phaseolus* (beans), *Prunus, Rubus, Zea mays* (sweetcorn).

3. A phytosanitary certificate is needed for all members of the Cruciferae, Gramineae and the genus Trifolium if they are imported from Argentina, Australia, Bolivia, Chile, New Zealand or Uruguay.

MAFF publishes a Guide for Importers which is intended mainly for retailers and is available from the Plant Health Division, MAFF, Peaseholme, York, YO1 2PX. If readers are in any doubt as to whether a particular seed may be brought in, they should speak in the first instance to the Plant Health Inspector at their local branch of MAFF.

Some seedsmen may need to be convinced that plants can be sent to you without a phytosanitary certificate issued by the local competent authority. We were told by an American supplier that she would not send us a copy of her seed list because the UK authorities forbade her to export to us. It took considerable persuasion before she was willing to accept an order. Remember too that many seedsmen accept Visa or Mastercard, and a telephone call is often the quickest, if not the cheapest, way to order.

AUSTRALIA

D. Orriell – Seed Exporters
45 Frape Avenue, Mt. Yokine, Perth, WA 6060
☎ 00 61 9 344 2290   [FAX] 00 61 9 344 8982

SPECIALITIES   Seeds

One of the leading Australian native seed merchants but primarily wholesale, since their minimum quantity is 25gr. As well as a general list, they offer several special lists: hardy eucalypts; Australian everlastings for dried flowers; Australian conifers; proteaceae; palms, cycads, pandanus and palm-like species. The scope is impressive: 75 *Banksia* species, nearly 50 *Grevillea* and 75 *Hakea*. Trade packets are available of most items for A$3.50.

Ellison Horticultural Pty Ltd
P O Box 365, Nowra, NSW 2541
☎ 00 61 44 21 4255   📠 00 61 44 23 0859

SPECIALITIES   Seeds
MAIL ORDER   Yes

Wholesalers of Australian tree, shrub and palm seeds. Not the longest list, but it contains some taxa not found elsewhere and others collected from interesting locations. Minimum order is A$30.

Harvest Seeds Co
325 McCarrs Creek Road, Terrey Hills, NSW 2084
☎ 00 61 29 450 2699   📠 00 61 29 450 2750

SPECIALITIES   Seeds
MAIL ORDER   Yes

Strictly wholesale, but what a list! The company majors on Australian native seeds, many from specific provenances: over 200 *Eucalyptus* and 30 *Melaleuca*, for example. Minimum quantities are 25gr: the 22 *Callistemon* species cost between A$4 and A$15 – and 25gr goes a very long way.

M L Farrar Pty Ltd
P 0 Box 1046, Bomaderry, NSW 2541
☎ 00 61 44 217966   📠 00 61 44 210051

SPECIALITIES   Seeds
CATALOGUE   Free
MAIL ORDER   Yes

A good list for trees and shrubs, most of them Australian, but not all. There are, for example, about 40 *Pinus* species alongside the 150 species of *Acacia* and endless *Eucalyptus*. Strictly wholesale, but in practice (like most Australian wholesalers) they offer trial packets at A$3.50. Recommended.

CZECH REPUBLIC

Euroseeds
P O Box 95, 741 01 Novy Jicin

SPECIALITIES   Seeds
CATALOGUE   US$2
MAIL ORDER   Yes

This excellent alpine and herbaceous list is written in English and payment may be made in any major currency. The owner, Mojmír Pavelka, collects every year in a different mountain region and receives wild seed from correspondents elsewhere, notably the USA. The list therefore changes, but the Turkish and Balkan collections are particularly good at the moment. Strongly recommended to plantsmen.

FRANCE

Catros Gérand
1, avenue de la Gardette, F-33560 Carbon Blanc
☎ 00 33 5 57 80 90 90   📠 00 33 5 56 06 80 11

SPECIALITIES   Seeds
CATALOGUE   Free
MAIL ORDER   Yes

A good middle-range French catalogue, handsomely printed with helpful descriptions. The list of vegetable seeds will be of particular interest to UK readers: most of the items offered are traditional French strains. The lists of peas and beans are particularly long and varied.

Sanrival
793, rue Augustin Bay, F-59690 Vieux-Condé
☎ 00 33 3 27 25 20 30   📠 00 33 3 27 25 28 28

SPECIALITIES   Seeds

Sanrival offers a wide range of seeds: annuals and bedding plants, perennials and vegetables. They sell through shops throughout France. There is a fair range of peas and beans, in particular.

Vilmorin
B P 37, F-38291 St Quentin F. Cedex
☎ 00 33 4 74 82 10 10   📠 00 33 4 74 82 11 11

ENGLISH-SPEAKING CONTACT   Claude Battu
SPECIALITIES   Seeds
CATALOGUE   FF 20
MAIL ORDER   Yes

Now part of the Oxadis group, Vilmorin is the most famous seed house in France, with a reputation that goes back 250 years. They offer some interesting bedding plants – strains not grown in UK – but the joy of Vilmorin's list is that it open the door to the world of French vegetables – 30 varieties of lettuce, 26 haricot beans, 9 types of turnip and even 5 strains of *mâche*.

GERMANY

Albert Schenkel GmbH
Postfach 1304, D-22872 Wedel
☎ 00 49 4103 601088   📠 00 49 4103 601089

SPECIALITIES   Seeds
CATALOGUE   Free
MAIL ORDER   Yes

Albert Schenkel was founded in Tenerife in 1862 and specialises to this day in seeds of exotic plants from warm climates. Its list is a good source of seeds for plants for the conservatory or for homes abroad. It has a fair selection of Australian and South African plants, including a separate list for *Protea*) but it is also worth looking out for *Drosera*, *Sarracenia* and *Musa*. Their cacti and succulents list is good all-round, but particularly strong on *Gymnocalycium*, *Mamillaria*, *Opuntia* and *Lithops*.

Carl Sperling & Co
Postfach 2640, D-21316 Lüneburg
☎ 00 49 4131 30170   ☒ 00 49 4131 301745

SPECIALITIES Seeds
CATALOGUE Free
MAIL ORDER Yes

This seedsman operates in the middle market and produces a cheerful catalogue. There is a good list of novelties and longish sections devoted to annuals, wild flowers and vegetables. It is hard to know how many of their lines are unique to their list, but they offer a large number of F1 hybrids.

Exotische Sämereien
Postfach 1348, D-72074 Tübingen
☎ & ☒ 00 40 7071 73141

SPECIALITIES Seeds
MAIL ORDER Yes

An excellent list, in the best tradition of German glasshouse horticulture. Most of the seeds it offers are of subtropical and Mediterranean plants, with a good proportion of rarities. It is particularly good for palms, cycads and Australian plants, most of them unknown in the UK. Recommended.

Jelitto Staudensamen GmbH
Postfach 1264, D-29685 Schwarmstedt
☎ 00 49 5071 4085   ☒ 00 49 5071 4088

SPECIALITIES Seeds
CATALOGUE Free
MAIL ORDER Yes

Jelitto is one of the greatest seedhouses in Europe and a good source of unusual herbaceous material for keen plantsmen, gardening clubs and small nurserymen. Strictly speaking Jelitto deal only with the trade, in wholesale quantities, but they also offer seeds in packets, subject to a minimum order of DM 80. The list includes more than 50 campanulas, 20 gentians and 20 silenes, as well as a number of species which have been pre-treated to break seed dormancy. Thoroughly recommended.

Manfred Meyer
D-60435 Frankfurt/M
☎ 00 49 69 546552   ☒ 00 49 69 5483798

SPECIALITIES Seeds
CATALOGUE DM 10
MAIL ORDER Yes

Wholesalers and retailers of flower seeds, plus some bulbs and sundries for orchids, which they propagate in vitro. The seed list is very comprehensive and has all the latest strains of popular bedding plants. Take Viola for example: there are 11 'Fama', 7 'Première', 5 'Joker', 9 'Weseler', 4 'Polaris' and 15 'Riesen Verbote' items – all of them registered trade marks – as well as examples from the 'Princess', 'Velour' and 'Imperial' strains.

Samen & Töpfe
Peter u. Monika Klock, Postfach 520604, D-22596 Hamburg
☎ 00 49 40 8991698   ☒ 00 49 40 8901170

SPECIALITIES Seeds

CATALOGUE Free
MAIL ORDER Yes

This is the seed division of Südflora Baumschulen. The list is particularly good for house plants and conservatory plants: 30+ Passiflora for example. Seeds come in three packet sizes, containing 12, 50 and 100 seeds respectively.

ITALY

Fratelli Ingegnoli
Corso Buenos Aires, 54, I-20124 Milano
☎ 00 39 2 29513167   ☒ 00 39 2 29529759

ENGLISH-SPEAKING CONTACT Mr Calenzani
SPECIALITIES Fruit; seeds
CATALOGUE Free
MAIL ORDER Yes

This famous old firm was founded in 1817 and is still one of the leading Italian seedsmen and growers. Their glossy catalogue sells everything from Hybrid Tea roses to clever grafting tools that match a scion to its stock. But it is the best list we know for Italian vegetable seeds – chicory, radicchio, red onions, yellow beans, aubergines and tomatoes – and very good for melons, zucchini and squashes too.

NEW ZEALAND

Kings Seeds
1660 Great North Road – P O Box 19.084, Avondale, Auckland
☎ & ☒ 00 64 9 828 7588

SPECIALITIES Seeds
CATALOGUE NZ$6
MAIL ORDER Yes

A good general seed catalogue of the English type: lots of annuals and perennials, plus vegetables, herbs and dried flowers seeds. What makes it so interesting is the number of un-English varieties, many from Australia, south east Asia and the USA. The heirloom tomatoes (black, pink and purple as well as red and yellow) are particularly fascinating.

Southern Seeds
The Vicarage, Sheffield, Canterbury
☎ & ☒ 00 64 3 318 3814

CONTACT Dr Ena Patterson
SPECIALITIES Seeds
CATALOGUE NZ$5 or UK Cheque for £2
MAIL ORDER Yes

This list consists almost entirely of New Zealand alpine species, hardy in the UK. The contents differ according to the season but are always impressive for their range and comprehensiveness. Last year's list offered 10 Aciphylla species, 16 coprosmas, 7 forget-me-nots and 8 Ranunculus among many other genera. All items cost NZ$5 and there is a minimum order is NZ$25. Highly recommended.

SOUTH AFRICA

Rust-en-Vrede Nursery
P O Box 753, Brackenfell, 7560
☎ 00 27 21 9814515   [FAX] 00 27 21 9810050

SPECIALITIES   Seeds
CATALOGUE   Free
MAIL ORDER   Yes

Specialist in native South African bulb seeds, with a good list of *Gladiolus*, *Moraea* and *Lachenalia* among others.

Silverhill Seeds
P O Box 53108, Kenilworth 7745
☎ 00 27 21 762 4245   [FAX] 00 27 21 797 6609

ENGLISH-SPEAKING CONTACT   Rachel Saunders
SPECIALITIES   Seeds
CATALOGUE   £1
MAIL ORDER   Yes

An excellent list of South African native seeds, most of them collected in the wild. Annuals, perennials, bulbs, shrubs and trees: the list extends to about 2,000 names, including long lists of *Aloe*, *Erica*, *Leucodendron* and *Pelargonium*. Highly recommended.

USA

Alplains
P O Box 489, Kiowa, CO 80117-0489
☎ 00 1 303 621 2247   [FAX] 00 1 303 621 2864

SPECIALITIES   Seeds
CATALOGUE   US$2
MAIL ORDER   Yes

Alplains specialise in species native to the North American West, though the list does include a good range of taxa from other parts of the world. That said, many of the items they list are uncommon in cultivation because they have not received much horticultural exposure. Alplains actively seeks out wild flowers with good potential and the results are impressive: 16 *Eriogonum* species, 25 *Astragalus* and over 60 *Penstemon*. The helpful catalogue has good descriptions of the plants and the growing conditions they require. Strongly recommended.

Carter Seeds
475 Mar Vista Drive, Vista, California 92083
☎ 00 1 619 724 5931   [FAX] 00 1 619 724 8832

SPECIALITIES   Seeds
MAIL ORDER   Yes

American wholesalers, who sell by the ounce and the pound. They are particularly good for trees and shrubs, especially tropical taxa, and palms (which they list separately).

Fred & Jean Minch
4329 Chrisella Road East, Puyallup, WA 98372
☎ 00 1 206 845 8045   [FAX] 00 1 206 845 1678

SPECIALITIES   Seeds
CATALOGUE   Free
MAIL ORDER   Yes

Fred & Jean Minch are rhododendromaniacs and much loved in north-west gardening circles. They offer seeds of over 400 different species, forms, hybrids and made-to-measure crosses. Packets contain a minimum of 50 seeds and cost US$2.50 each. Unique.

Native Gardens
5737 Fisher Lane, Greenback, Tennessee 37742
☎ 00 1 615 856 0220

SPECIALITIES   Seeds
CATALOGUE   US$2
MAIL ORDER   Yes

Primarily a native plant nursery, but they also offer a good selection of native seeds from Tennessee and some other parts of the eastern USA. About 200 taxa, including 5 *Aster* and 7 *Solidago*, and lists of those suitable for drought or attractive to butterflies.

Northwest Native Seed
4441 S. Meridian St, 363, Puyallup, WA 98373

CONTACT   Ron Ratko
SPECIALITIES   Seeds
CATALOGUE   Free
MAIL ORDER   Yes

Seeds of native plants of the western United States, much of it collected in the wild. The catalogue is impressive, and contains over 600 items. There is an emphasis on bulbs and herbaceous species and, as you would expect, there are long lists of *Allium*, *Astragalus*, *Calochortus*, *Eriogonum* and *Penstemon*. But shrubs are not forgotten: Ron Ratko offers, for example, three species of *Ribes* and three of *Rubus*.

Rocky Mountain Rare Plants
1706 Deerpath Road, Franktown, Colorado 80116-9462
☎ & [FAX] 00 1 303 660 6498

SPECIALITIES   Seeds
MAIL ORDER   Yes

A good list, but not confined to north-west USA: many items are collected in Turkey too. The provenance is always given, and the year of collection. There are 34 penstemons, 12 eriogonums and some interesting rarities like *Townsendia incana*, *Polemonium grayanum* and *Oxytropis parryana*.

Southern Exposure Seed Exchange
P O Box 170, Earlysville, VA 22936
☎ 00 1 804 973 4703   [FAX] 00 1 804 973 8717

SPECIALITIES   Seeds
CATALOGUE   US$5
MAIL ORDER   Yes

This is a fascinating list with long historical descriptions: it makes for compulsive reading. Heritage varieties are the main line, most of them edible plants. Varieties come from all over the world. Take tomatoes, for example. There are over 70 listed. They include original species from South America; a hybrid developed for the Siberian summer; a pickling tomato; tiny wild ones like redcurrants; strains from Italy, Germany, Hungary, Czechoslovakia, Bulgaria and every part of the USA; tomatoes in red, pink, purple, yellow, white and stripes. Highly recommended.

Southwestern Native Seeds
Box 50503, Tucson, AZ 85703

SPECIALITIES Seeds
CATALOGUE $2
MAIL ORDER Yes

Long established plant-hunters and native seed suppliers with over 400 species, most of them collected in the wild. About half come from Arizona and New Mexico and most of the rest from California, Utah, Mexico and Montana. They are divided according to habitat and type: desert or mountain and trees, shrubs, wildflowers and succulents. Most are wildflowers, meaning herbaceous, and the list is very impressive, but we like it (and have bought from it for twenty years) because there is no better source for American trees and shrubs. There are 9 *Agastache*, 14 *Aquilegia*, 21 *Calochortus* and so on down to 14 *Yucca* species. Highly recommended.

15

Gardening Sites on the Internet

The Internet provides links from a suitably equipped computer to horticultural and botanical sources all over the world. The best of these sites tend to be connected to academic or public institutions, and many have an American bias. This reflects the historical development of the Internet. As more and more users gain access to it, though, this is changing and more and more European and private sites are being set up. This has already started happening. Users of the Internet will be aware that the quality, quantity and currency of information accessible through the Net is very variable. Sites also tend to change their address or disappear for one reason or another. A small collection of sites is listed below: many have connections to other horticultural sites so starting from these pages an astonishingly diverse range of information is at your fingertips. A version of this page is stored on the Royal Horticultural Society's new internet site (http://www.rhs.org.uk/yearbook.html). In that electronic version a click of the mouse should take you straight to all the sites listed below.

Some of our readers may have no idea what we are talking about: we suggest they turn this (printed) page and continue.

http://www.rhs.org.uk
Royal Horticultural Society: their trial page describes a range of publications, events and services organised by the RHS

http://www.helsinki.fi/kmus/botmenu.html
The Internet directory for Botany: the outstanding collection of links to botany and horticulture sites, some of them very specialised

General

http://www.maff.gov.ukMAFF
Ministry of Agriculture, Fisheries and Food

http://www.compulink.co.uk/~museumgh
Museum of Garden History

http://www.open.gov.uk/niab/niabhome.htm
National Institute of Agricultural Botany

http://www.ukindex.co.uk/nationaltrust/index.html
National Trust: information county by county on the Trust's many properties

http://www.nhm.ac.uk
Natural History Museum

http://www.waterstones.co.uk
Waterstones' searchable book database

Gardens

http://www.mobot.org/AABGA
The American Association of Botanic Gardens and Arboreta: useful links to its member gardens throughout the USA

http://www.engref.fr/barres.htm
Arboretum National des Barres: quite a short site, with a link to ENGREF (Ecole Nationale du Génie Rural des Eaux et des Fôrets)

http://arboretum.harvard.edu
Arnold Arboretum, Harvard University: includes an inventory of the Arboretum's living collection

http://155.187.10.12/anbg.html
Australian National Botanic Gardens: a wealth of information about Australian plants and botany, with links to other botanic gardens in Australia

http://www.bordehill.co.uk
Borde Hill Garden: this Sussex garden has its own page with useful information and photographs from the garden. Expect to see more sites like this in the future

http://www.stadt-frankfurt.de/
palmengarten
Palmengarten, Frankfurt

http://www.rbge.org.uk
Royal Botanic Garden, Edinburgh: includes a searchable version of the Flora Europaea database

http://www.rbgkew.org.uk
Royal Botanic Gardens, Kew: searchable databases of plant names; information about the gardens and a useful page of links to other botanical sites

http://www.nybg.org
New York Botanical Garden

Societies

http://www.eskimo.com/~mcalpin/
soc.html
List of Alpine Garden societies: societies from around the world, with links where available to contact mailboxes or internet sites

http://www.pacificrim.net/~bydesign
/acs.html
American Conifer Society: suitably green homepage with some links to other conifer sites and general information about growing and choosing conifers

http://www2.trop-hibiscus.com/
trop-hibiscus
American Hibiscus Society

http://eMall.com/ahs/ahs.html
American Horticultural Society

http://www.isomedia.com/homes/AIS
American Iris Society

http://pathfinder.com/vg/Gardens/AOS
American Orchid Society: the OrchidWeb site is a model of its type: well worth visiting

http://www.eskimo.com/~mcalpin/aps.
html
American Primrose Society

http://www.ars.org
American Rose Society: includes lists of rose societies all over the USA

http://rbge-sun1.rbge.org.uk/bss
Botanical Society of Scotland

http://www.rls.ox.ac.uk/users/djh/ebs/
ebsindex.htm
European Bamboo Society: includes link to the American Bamboo Society

http://www.med-rz.uni-sb.de/med_fak/
physiol2/camellia/home.htm#topics
International Camellia Society

http://www.h2olily.rain.com
International Water Lily Society

http://www.linnean.org.uk
Linnean Society of London

http://www.mobot.org/NARGS
North American Rock Garden Society

http://www.roses.co.uk/harkness/
rnrs/rnrs.htm
Royal National Rose Society: information about the society and its Rose 2000 appeal is hosted on the Harkness rose nursery site (http://www.roses.co.uk)

http://www.ozemail.com.au:80/~sgap
Society for Growing Australian Plants: much useful information and a blinking yellow "G'day" for a welcome

Magazine sites

http://trine.com/GardenNet/home.htm
GardenNet "The Garden Center on the Net": It's American, and its good. Societies, gardens, catalogues – you name it

http://www.prairienet.org/
garden-gate
Garden Gate

http://www.gardenweb.com
GardenWeb: magazine-style site including information about gardens and societies; an on-line magazine; and the GardenWeb forums in which gardeners swap and seek advice on a range of topics and plants

16

Garden Supplies

A E Headen Ltd
218 High Street, Potters Bar, Hertfordshire EN6 5BJ
☎ 01707 652688   FAX 01707 645372

CONTACT A P Johnson
PRODUCTS Greenhouses
NEW PRODUCTS Low-threshold model with wheelchair ramp
CATALOGUE On request
MAIL ORDER Yes

Makers of Aluminium greenhouses and accessories. Delivery is included for most of UK.

A T Lee & Co Ltd
32 New Broadway, Tarring Road, Worthing, West Sussex BN11 4HP
☎ 01903 210225   FAX 01903 821936

CONTACT Doreen Teale
PRODUCTS Plant hangers; hanging bags
CATALOGUE On request
MAIL ORDER Yes

Suppliers of plant-pot hangers and hanging growing bags.

Access Garden Products
17 Yelvertoft Road, Crick, Northampton, Northamptonshire NN6 7XS
☎ 01788 822301   FAX 01788 824256

CONTACT Sales Department
PRODUCTS Mini greenhouses; frames; watering systems
CATALOGUE On request
MAIL ORDER Yes

Established family firm supplying high quality aluminium frames and mini-greenhouses. They also have a complete range of watering and irrigation systems. Access Irrigation Ltd (01788 823811) supplies sprinkler systems to nurseries and garden centres.

Agralan
The Old Brickyard, Ashton Keynes, Swindon, Wiltshire SN6 6QR
☎ 01285 860015   FAX 01285 860056
PRODUCTS Non-chemical plant protection; sprayers

NEW PRODUCTS New pheromone trap for carnation tortrix and cyclamen moth
CATALOGUE SAE
MAIL ORDER Yes, 75p handling charge per order

Fleece, mesh and mulches for crop protection, non-chemical pest controls including pheromone traps, and the Birchmeier range of sprayers and accessories.

Agriframes
Charlwood Road, East Grinstead, West Sussex RH19 2HT
☎ 01342 328644   FAX 01342 327198

CONTACT Customer Services
PRODUCTS Frames; pergolas; cages
CATALOGUE On request
MAIL ORDER Yes

Practical and decorative metal products including fruit cages, frames, arches, pergolas and gazebos. They also sell horticultural fleece for frost protection. Trade customers should contact them on 01342 318181.

Alitex Ltd
Station Road, Alton, Hampshire GU34 2PZ
☎ & FAX 01420 82860

CONTACT Chris Sawyer
PRODUCTS Greenhouses
CATALOGUE On request
MAIL ORDER No

Top-quality aluminium glasshouses and greenhouses in Victorian styles and models for professional and amateur users. All are individually and stylishly designed.

Allen Power Equipment Ltd
The Broadway, Didcot, Oxfordshire OX11 8ES
☎ 01235 813936   FAX 01235 811491

CONTACT Lance Bassett
PRODUCTS Garden machinery
NEW PRODUCTS Ascender wheelbarrows; patriot vacuum blowers
CATALOGUE On request
MAIL ORDER Yes

Manufacturers of sprayers, brush- and hedge-cutters, shredders, hover-mowers, rotary and cylinder garden tractors. They also sell the Echo GB range of powered hand-tools.

Alton Greenhouses
Station Works, Fenny Compton, Leamington Spa, Warwickshire CV33 0XB
☎ 01295 770795   FAX 01295 770819
CONTACT   Grahame Lester
PRODUCTS   Greenhouses
NEW PRODUCTS Cedar summerhouse
CATALOGUE On request (0800 269850)
MAIL ORDER Yes

Long-established firm producing traditional greenhouses in red cedarwood. They claim superior strength and heat retention over aluminium products.

Amdega
Faverdale, Darlington, Co. Durham DL3 0PW
☎ 01325 468522   FAX 01325 489209
CONTACT   Amdega Marketing
PRODUCTS   Amdega and Machin conservatories; Amdega summerhouses
CATALOGUE Ring 0800 591523
MAIL ORDER No

Designers, suppliers and installers of conservatories and wooden summerhouses. One of the leading companies: established in 1874.

Anderson & Firmin Ltd
43-44 Hirwaun Industrial Estate, Hirwaun, Aberdare, Mid Glamorgan CF44 9UP
☎ 01685 814000   FAX 01685 814057
CONTACT   Mandy Davis
PRODUCTS   Garden gloves and footwear; garden sundries; irrigation systems
NEW PRODUCTS Range of sprayers
CATALOGUE On request from sales office
MAIL ORDER No

Garden gloves, shoes and boots, garden twine and masses of garden sundries. Distributors of Claber hoses and irrigation systems.

Andreas Stihl Ltd
Stihl House, Stanhope Road, Camberley, Surrey GU15 3YT
☎ 01276 20202   FAX 01276 670502
PRODUCTS   Garden machinery; lawn mowers and tractors; power tools
CATALOGUE Yes

Stihl manufactures a comprehensive range of chain saws, brushcutters and hedgetrimmers. Viking, its garden division, makes lawnmowers, ride-on mowers, shredders, sweepers and cultivators.

Andrew Crace Designs
90 Bourne Lane, Much Hadham, Hertfordshire SG10 6ER
☎ 01279 842685   FAX 01279 843646
PRODUCTS   Plant labels; garden furniture; terracotta pots; garden statuary; teak hanging baskets; wind chimes

CATALOGUE On request
MAIL ORDER Yes

The eclectic collection includes 'Alitag' aluminium plant labels, stylish wooden garden furniture and gazebos. Also bronze sculptures, terracotta pots and bamboo cloches.

Architectural Heritage Ltd
Taddington Manor, Taddington, Cutsdean, Cheltenham, Gloucestershire GL54 5RY
☎ 01386 584414   FAX 01386 584236
CONTACT   Nina Ziegler
PRODUCTS   Garden statuary
NEW PRODUCTS Composition stone heron, two-tier fountain, and a seated Mercury in bronze
CATALOGUE On request
MAIL ORDER No

Suppliers of antique garden statuary and reproduction statues. They ship worldwide and can also provide insurance valuations (£75 plus VAT).

Atco-Qualcast
Suffolk Works, Stowmarket, Suffolk IP14 1EY
☎ 01449 742000   FAX 01449 675444
CONTACT   Gary King
PRODUCTS   Lawnmowers; garden machinery
NEW PRODUCTS Atco Quiet Shredder 2000
MAIL ORDER No

Long-established manufacturer of lawnmowers, hedgetrimmers and other garden machinery, now part of the giant German Bosch empire. Sold through garden centres and DIY stores, Atco-Qualcast has one third of the UK market.

B J Crafts
17 Coopers Wood, Crowborough, East Sussex TN6 1SW
☎ 01892 655899
CONTACT   B R or I J Welbury
PRODUCTS   Watercolours of flowers
NEW PRODUCTS Free-style paintings on black with gouache
CATALOGUE On request
MAIL ORDER Yes

Original watercolours and gouaches of flowers from miniatures to larger compositions.

Backwoodsman Horticultural Products
Barcaldine, Oban, Strathclyde PA37 1SL
☎ & FAX 01631 720539
CONTACT   Andrew McIntyre
PRODUCTS   Greenhouses; frames
CATALOGUE On request
MAIL ORDER Yes

Manufacturers of an eye-catching pyramidal rotating mini-greenhouse: the 'GrowMate'. Sold by mail, the standard and mini models are for self-assembly. The micro model is pre-assembled.

Barnsley House Garden & Decorative Furnishings

Barnsley House, Cirencester, Gloucestershire GL7 5EE
☎ 01285 740561   [FAX] 01285 740628

CONTACT   Amanda Jamieson
PRODUCTS   Garden furniture
CATALOGUE   Yes
MAIL ORDER   Yes

Handsome teak garden furniture designed by Charles Verey. Planter tubs also supplied.

Bel Mondo Garden Features

11 Tatnell Road, Honor Oak Park, London SE23 1JX
☎ 0181 291 1920

CONTACT   Jamie Ripman
PRODUCTS   Fountains; decorative taps and water spouts
CATALOGUE   On request
MAIL ORDER   Yes

Attractive cast-iron fountains, wall basins and decorative taps and spouts.

Biotal Industrial Products Ltd

5 Chiltern Close, Cardiff CF4 5DL
☎ 01222 747414   [FAX] 01222 747140

CONTACT   Eileen Dowdie
PRODUCTS   Biological compost makers, insect controls and pond products
CATALOGUE   Leaflets
MAIL ORDER   No

Biological compost-makers with a general range including pond products.

The Birdtable Company

1 Evendine Corner, Colwall, Malvern, Hereford & Worcester WR1 6DY
☎ & [FAX] 01684 540370

CONTACT   Suzanne Wilesmith
PRODUCTS   Dovecotes and bird-tables; nesting boxes
CATALOGUE   On request
MAIL ORDER   Yes

Makers of bird-tables, nesting-boxes and dovecotes. Letter- and paper-boxes are a new addition.

Blackwall Ltd

10 Glover Way, Parkside, Leeds LS11 5JP
☎ 0113 276 1646   [FAX] 0113 271 3083

CONTACT   Carol Gough
PRODUCTS   Compost bins; cloches; garden sundries; water butts
CATALOGUE   On request
MAIL ORDER   Yes

Manufacturers and suppliers of compost-making bins, water-butts, propagating aids and other garden supplies.

Bob Andrews Ltd

1 Bilton Industrial Estate, Lovelace Road, Bracknell, Berkshire RG12 8YT
☎ 01344 862111   [FAX] 01344 861345

CONTACT   Roy or Joan
PRODUCTS   Garden machinery; sprayers
NEW PRODUCTS   Giant-Vac & IBEA outdoor vacuum-sweepers
CATALOGUE   On request
MAIL ORDER   Yes, if no local dealer

Powered and wheeled garden-machinery for amateurs and professionals, including vacuums, leaf sweepers, scarifiers, sprayers, spreaders and trimmers.

Bonnington Plastics Ltd

Trent Lane, Castle Donington, Derbyshire DE7 2NP
☎ 01332 811811   [FAX] 01332 811421

CONTACT   James Bloomfield
PRODUCTS   Hoses; hose fittings
NEW PRODUCTS   Aquarius hose, Aquareel hose reels & trolley
CATALOGUE   On request
MAIL ORDER   Yes

Manufacturers of garden-hoses, hose-reels, irrigation fittings, sprinklers and tree-ties.

Boughton Loam Ltd

Telford Way, Telford Way Industrial Estate, Kettering, Northamptonshire NN16 8UN
☎ 01536 510515   [FAX] 01536 510691

CONTACT   Mike Franklin or Richard Chinn
PRODUCTS   Composts; turf-dressings
MAIL ORDER   No

Suppliers of specialist turf-dressings, general horticultural composts and landscaping mixes to the trade and the public.

Brettell & Shaw Ltd

West Street, Quarry Bank, Brierly Hill, West Midlands DY5 2DT
☎ 01384 566838   [FAX] 01384 569123

CONTACT   W A Hobbis
PRODUCTS   Greenhouse heater; compost bins; incinerators; watering cans
NEW PRODUCTS   Eltex 3000 Propane Gas heater
CATALOGUE   Leaflets on request

Makers of 'Eltex' paraffin and LP-gas greenhouse heaters. The range has recently been redesigned and extended. Watering-cans, composters and incinerators are also available.

The British Museum Company

46 Bloomsbury Street, London WC1B 3QQ
☎ 0171 323 1234   [FAX] 0171 636 7186

CONTACT   Carey Wells
PRODUCTS   Garden statuary
CATALOGUE   On request
MAIL ORDER   Yes

Replica classical statues, reliefs and busts from the museum's collection: the reconstituted marble items can be placed outside.

Bulbeck Foundry
Reach Road, Burwell, Cambridgeshire CB5 0AH
☎ 01638 743153   [FAX] 01638 743374
CONTACT   H Smith
PRODUCTS   Garden ornaments; statuary; fountains
CATALOGUE   On request
MAIL ORDER   Yes

A lead foundry which produces fountains, tanks, statues, urns and planters. Cisterns can be designed to commission, as can leadwork for rainwater systems. They also restore antique leadwork.

Burgon & Ball Ltd
La Plata Works, Holme Lane, Sheffield S6 4JY
☎ 0114 233 8262   [FAX] 0114 285 2518
CONTACT   Brian Marson
PRODUCTS   Shears; scythes; grasshooks; knives
NEW PRODUCTS   Multifunctional 'Til 'n Hoe' tool; Trompe l'oeil cut-outs of flowers and animals
CATALOGUE   On request
MAIL ORDER   Yes

Beautifully made, handsome garden tools, including sheep shears for trimming topiary, scythes, hooks, knives and stones to sharpen them with. The company was established in 1730: the 'trompe l'oeil' range is new – and fun!

Burton McCall Ltd
163 Parker Drive, Leicester, Leicestershire LE4 0JP
☎ 0116 2340800   [FAX] 0116 2358031
CONTACT   Sue Isaac
PRODUCTS   Hand tools; gloves
CATALOGUE   On request

Suppliers of hand-tools and clothing, including pruning saws, Victorinox horticultural knives and the top-of-the-range secateurs 'Felco'.

C H Whitehouse Ltd
Buckhurst Works, Bells Yew Green, Frant, Tunbridge Wells, Kent TN3 9BN
☎ & [FAX] 01892 750247
PRODUCTS   Greenhouses; garden buildings; summerhouses; frames
CATALOGUE   On request
MAIL ORDER   Yes

Attractive traditional red-cedar greenhouses, summerhouses and frames made to order. They have specialist models for alpine growers and orchidists.

Cambridge Glasshouse Co Ltd
Barton Road, Comberton, Cambridge, Cambridgeshire CB3 7BY
☎ 01223 262395   [FAX] 01223 262713
CONTACT   Teresa Snazle
PRODUCTS   Glasshouses
NEW PRODUCTS   Custom-made Victorian-style greenhouses

CATALOGUE   On request
MAIL ORDER   Direct supply

Professional-quality greenhouses, made to order in almost any size. For the amateur as well as for nurseries and botanic gardens.

Capital Garden Products Ltd
Gibbs Reed Barn, Pashley Road, Ticehurst, East Sussex TN5 7HE
☎ 01580 201092   [FAX] 01580 201093
PRODUCTS   Architectural features; fountains; plant containers
CATALOGUE   On request
MAIL ORDER   Yes, if no local retailer

Tanks, urns, tubs and planters in glass fibre, wood, cast lead and faux-lead; pedestals, urns, fountains, steel furniture and garden edging tiles.

Chempak Products
Geddings Road, Hoddesdon, Hertfordshire EN11 0LR
☎ 01992 441888   [FAX] 01992 467908
CONTACT   W Richardson
PRODUCTS   Fertilisers; pesticides; garden sundries; water-storing granules; peat alternatives
CATALOGUE   On request
MAIL ORDER   Yes, (£10 minimum)

A very wide range of garden chemicals and fertilisers, as well as general garden products. Mail order is available through the Garden Direct catalogue.

Chillington Manufacturing Ltd
Camden Street, Walsall Wood, West Midlands WS9 9BJ
☎ 01543 376441   [FAX] 01543 373030
CONTACT   Jeanette Brown
PRODUCTS   Wheelbarrows
CATALOGUE   On request
MAIL ORDER   No

Manufacturers of garden and multi-purpose wheelbarrows in galvanised steel and polypropylene.

Connoisseur Sun Dials
Lane's End, Strefford, Craven Arms, Shropshire SY7 8DE
☎ & [FAX] 01588 672126
CONTACT   Silas Higgon
PRODUCTS   Sun dials; armillary spheres
NEW PRODUCTS   11"- and 22"-diameter brass horizontal dials
CATALOGUE   On request
MAIL ORDER   Yes

A range of accurate brass and bronze sun dials for both northern and southern hemispheres: equatorial, horizontal, polar, vertical, and analemmatic, as well as indoor models. They take commissions: dials can be inscribed to order.

Cookson Plantpak Ltd
Burnham Road, Mundon, Maldon, Essex CM9 6NT
☎ 01621 740140   [FAX] 01621 742400
CONTACT   Chris Breed
PRODUCTS   Plastic plant pots; plastic plant containers
CATALOGUE   Trade

MAIL ORDER No

A very wide range of plastic pots, seed trays, hanging baskets and other plastic items. Sold through garden centres.

Cooper Pegler Ltd
4-5 Watling Close, Sketchley Meadows Business Park, Hinckley, Leicestershire LE10 3EX
☎ 01455 233811 📠 01455 233815
CONTACT Nick Wood
PRODUCTS Garden sprayers
CATALOGUE On request
MAIL ORDER No

Leading suppliers of spraying equipment for amateur gardeners and professionals. The range includes hand-held, knapsack and wheeled sprayers with a full choice of nozzles and appropriate safety equipment.

Courtyard Designs
Suckley, Worcester, Hereford & Worcester WR6 5EH
☎ 01886 884640 📠 01886 884444
CONTACT Ursula Mason
PRODUCTS Summerhouses; garden buildings
NEW PRODUCTS Studios & offices for gardens
CATALOGUE On request
MAIL ORDER No

Manufacturers and suppliers of traditional wooden summer-houses and pavilions. Complete service, including installation, offered. They can design to order too.

Cowbridge Compost
Penllyn Estate Farm, Llwynhelig, Cowbridge, South Glamorgan CF71 7AQ
☎ 01446 772600 📠 01446 774825
CONTACT John Homfray
PRODUCTS Fertilisers and soil conditioner
NEW PRODUCTS High-nitrogen composts
MAIL ORDER Yes

Fertiliser and compost based on farmyard manure and made in the traditional way but weed-free and odour-free.

Cranborne Antiques
13b Thurleigh Road, London SW12 8UB
☎ & 📠 0181 675 4699
CONTACT Deborah Cutler
PRODUCTS Botanical prints

Antiquarian botanical and Natural History prints and greeting cards. There is a search service for prints.

Cranborne Stone
West Orchard, Shaftesbury, Dorset SP7 0LJ
☎ 01258 472685 📠 01258 471251
PRODUCTS Cast stone garden ornaments
CATALOGUE On request
MAIL ORDER Delivery arranged

Formerly trading as 'Knight Terrace Pots', Cranborne Stone is best-known for its reconstituted stone garden ornaments. These range from simple pots and troughs to elaborate vases, finials and balustrades. The works can be visited by appointment, and they can design or copy originals to order.

Crowther of Syon Lodge
Busch Corner, London Road, Isleworth, London TW7 5BH
☎ 0181 560 7978 📠 0181 568 7572
CONTACT Tricia Snell
PRODUCTS Antique garden statuary; garden ornaments; architectural stonework
NEW PRODUCTS Hand-carved stonework from Italy; timber-framed summerhouses in Georgian or Gothic styles
CATALOGUE Photographs available of all stock
MAIL ORDER No

This family-owned business is the oldest specialist for architectural antiques in the country. If you have a specific request they can supply a photograph of appropriate items in stock. Armillary spheres are made on site; the display garden is worth a visit.

CSM Lighting Ltd
Unit 8, Malmesbury Business Park, Tetbury Hill, Malmesbury, Wiltshire SN16 9JU
☎ 01666 825450 📠 01666 825436
CONTACT Peter Harding
PRODUCTS Garden lighting
CATALOGUE Leaflets on request
MAIL ORDER Yes

Lighting for gardens, ponds and patios: solar lighting.

Darlac Products
PO Box 996, Slough, Berkshire SL3 9JF
☎ 01753 547790 📠 01753 580524
CONTACT Peter Darban
PRODUCTS Garden tools
CATALOGUE On request
MAIL ORDER Yes

Garden tools including secateurs and a fruit picker: some items feature innovative designs. They attend about 50 flower, garden and county shows.

David Bell Ltd
Eastfield Drive, Penicuik, Lothian EH26 8BA
☎ 01968 678480 📠 01968 678878
CONTACT Mark Sinclair
PRODUCTS Fertilisers; grass seed
CATALOGUE Lawngrass brochure
MAIL ORDER Yes

Scottish seed wholesalers who supply grass mixtures and specialised lawn fertilisers. They also supply bird feed.

Dax Products Ltd
PO Box 119, Nottingham, Nottinghamshire NG3 5ED
☎ 0115 960 9996 📠 0115 966 1173
CONTACT Amanda Roberts
PRODUCTS Herbicides; fungicides; algaecides
MAIL ORDER Yes

Makers of 'Root Out', a herbicide for trees, stumps, brushwood and weeds. 'Fungo' kills moss, algae, lichen and slime.

Defenders Ltd
Occupation Road, Wye, Ashford, Kent TN25 5EN
☎ 01233 813121　　FAX 01233 813633

CONTACT　Dale Mitchell
PRODUCTS　Biological controls
NEW PRODUCTS　Delphastus pucillus beetles to control whitefly
CATALOGUE　On request
MAIL ORDER　Yes

Biological controls for professional and amateur gardeners for the following organisms: whitefly, red spider mite, aphids, thrips, caterpillars, mealy bugs, soft scale, sciardids, slugs and vine weevils. Thursday despatch ensures they arrive by the weekend. A sister company of Biological Crop Protection.

Dennis
Ashbourne Road, Kirk Langley, Derby, Derbyshire DE6 4NJ
☎ 01332 824777　　FAX 01332 824525

CONTACT　Ian Howard
PRODUCTS　Cylinder mowers; grass care equipment
NEW PRODUCTS　Ride-on powered barrow
CATALOGUE　On request
MAIL ORDER　Yes

Manufacturers of high-quality cylinder grass-cutting equipment for amenity use and large gardens. Their new cylinder mowers have removable cassettes to brush, scarify, spike and cut lawns.

Diddybox
132-134 Belmont Road, Astley Bridge, Bolton, Lancashire BL1 7AN
☎ 01204 595610　　FAX 01204 592405

CONTACT　Kath White
PRODUCTS　Dried flowers; flower arrangers' sundries
CATALOGUE　£1
MAIL ORDER　Yes

Supplies for flower arrangers, including containers, accessories and dried flowers by mail order. Fresh flowers and occasional day-courses at the shop.

Diplex Ltd
P O Box 172, Watford, Hertfordshire WD1 1BX
☎ 01923 231784　　FAX 01923 243791

CONTACT　Ernest Danzig, Barbara Leach, Sheila Rodel
PRODUCTS　Thermometers; rain gauges; weather equipment; hygrometers
NEW PRODUCTS　High-temperature conservatory thermometer; frost-resistant rain-guage; pocket pH meter
CATALOGUE　On request
MAIL ORDER　Yes

Manufacturers of an extensive range of thermometers, rain-gauges, frost-predictors, and other meteorological measuring equipment for amateur and professional use. Models include inexpensive, decorative and scientific devices.

DIY Plastics (UK) Ltd
Regal Way, Faringdon, Oxfordshire SN7 7XD
☎ 01367 242932　　FAX 01367 242200

CONTACT　Mrs J Russen
PRODUCTS　Plastic sheeting
NEW PRODUCTS　Twin-wall, safe-glaze greenhouse
CATALOGUE　2 first class stamps
MAIL ORDER　Yes

Plastic sheeting for house and garden use including netting, shading, pond liners and horticultural acrylic sheets.

Drummonds of Bramley Architectural Antiques
Birtley Farm, Horsham Road, Bramley, Guildford, Surrey GU5 0LA
☎ 01483 898766　　FAX 01483 894393

CONTACT　J A Swayne
PRODUCTS　Architectural antiques

Architectural antiques, including antique garden furniture and well-heads.

Dupre Vermiculite
Tamworth Road, Hertford, Hertfordshire SG13 7DL
☎ 01992 582541　　FAX 01992 553436

CONTACT　Freya Rymer
PRODUCTS　Vermiculite
NEW PRODUCTS　Veri-Gro horticultural vermiculite
CATALOGUE　On request
MAIL ORDER　No

Suppliers of horticultural vermiculite, through trade wholesalers. High water-retaining and nutrient-absorbing characteristics.

Durston Peat Products
Avalon Farm, Sharpham, Street, Somerset BA16 9SE
☎ 01458 442688　　FAX 01458 448327

CONTACT　Tony Jones
PRODUCTS　Peat-based and alternative growing media and mulches
CATALOGUE　On request
MAIL ORDER　No

Manufacturer of peat-based composts and growing media, with alternative products including bark, vegetable waste and coir.

E H Thorne (Beehives) Ltd
Louth Road, Wragby, Lincoln, Lincolnshire LN3 5LA
☎ 01673 858555　　FAX 01673 857004

CONTACT　Sales Dept
PRODUCTS　Beekeeping equipment
CATALOGUE　On request
MAIL ORDER　Yes

A complete range of beekeeping equipment. There is a new branch at Oakley Green, Windsor, SL4 4PZ (Tel. 01753 830256)

E J Godwin (Peat Industries) Ltd
Batch Farm, Meare, Glastonbury, Somerset BA6 9SP
☎ 01458 860644 ☐ 01458 860587
CONTACT Simon Stock
PRODUCTS Growing media; peat alternatives
CATALOGUE On request
MAIL ORDER No

Suppliers of composts and peat products under the 'Godwin's' and 'Fruit of the Earth' brand names. Organic alternatives as well as peat-based mixes.

E P Barrus Ltd
Launton Road, Bicester, Oxfordshire OX6 0UR
☎ 01869 363636 ☐ 01869 363620
CONTACT Martin Wasley
PRODUCTS Garden machinery
NEW PRODUCTS MTD Cub Cadet, Yardman & Lawnlite
CATALOGUE On request
MAIL ORDER No

Makers and distributors of the Lawnflite range of lawn-mowers, garden tractors, brush-cutters, hedge-trimmers, cultivators and chipper/shredders.

The English Garden Collection
3 Langley Business Centre, Station Road, Langley, Berkshire SL3 8DS
☎ 0800 203000 (orders) ☐ 01753 817815
PRODUCTS Sundries
CATALOGUE Free
MAIL ORDER Yes

Up-market mail order firm with a wide range of top-quality gardening products.

English Hurdle
Curload, Stoke St Gregory, Taunton, Somerset TA3 6JD
☎ 01823 698418 ☐ 01823 698859
CONTACT James Hector
PRODUCTS Traditional willow-hurdles; sundries
NEW PRODUCTS Cylindrical plant-support for climbers in willow
CATALOGUE Free
MAIL ORDER Yes

Makers of traditional garden features in woven willow: hurdles fences, seats, arches, bowers and frames for climbing plants.

English Woodlands Biocontrol
Hoyle, Graffham, Petworth, West Sussex GU28 0LR
☎ & ☐ 01798 867574
CONTACT Sue Cooper
PRODUCTS Biological controls
CATALOGUE On request
MAIL ORDER Yes

Biological controls for whitefly, red spider mite, aphids, mealy bugs, caterpillars, vine weevils and leafhoppers. Larger quantities are available at professional prices, and they produce a useful guide to the compatibility of biological controls with garden chemicals.

Exmouth Garden Products
Units 7/8 Salterton Workshops, Budleigh Salterton, Devon EX9 6RJ
☎ 01395 442796 ☐ 01395 442851
CONTACT D J Redfern
PRODUCTS Greenhouse equipment; netting
CATALOGUE On request
MAIL ORDER Yes

Greenhouse shelving, staging and other accessories, insulation film and netting.

F Peart & Co Ltd
Baltic Works, Baltic Street, Hartlepool, Co Durham TS25 1PW
☎ 01429 263331 ☐ 01429 262179
CONTACT G Ridden
PRODUCTS Garden furniture
NEW PRODUCTS Several new designs and additions to their range
CATALOGUE On request

Hand-crafted garden furniture, benches, chairs and tables, made of teak from sustainable sources.

Fairweather Sculpture
Hillside House, Starston, Norfolk IP20 9NN
☎ & ☐ 01379 852266
CONTACT Dennis Fairweather
PRODUCTS Ceramic sculpture
CATALOGUE On request
MAIL ORDER Carrier

Hand-made ceramic sculptures – heads and birds, including several owls. Each piece is an original.

Ferrum Dried Flowers
Love Hill Farm, Trotton, Petersfield, West Sussex GU31 5ER
☎ & ☐ 01730 817277
CONTACT A Ferrier
PRODUCTS Dried flowers; silk flowers
NEW PRODUCTS Leaf-ware
CATALOGUE Yes
MAIL ORDER Yes

Suppliers of dried flower and foliage arrangements, dyed and silk flowers, preserved foliage, leaves and nuts.

The Finch Conservatory Company Ltd
Unit 1 Leylands Park, Nobs Crook, Golden Common, Winchester, Hampshire SO21 1TH
☎ 01703 696001 ☐ 01703 695890
CONTACT Colin Gentles
PRODUCTS Conservatories; blinds
CATALOGUE Freephone 0800 378168

Designers, manufacturers and installers of timber and PVC conservatories.

Fiskars UK Ltd
Bridgend Business Centre, Bridgend, Mid Glamorgan CF31 3XJ
☎ 01656 655595   [FAX] 01656 659582

CONTACT Sara Webber
PRODUCTS Hand and garden tools
CATALOGUE On request
MAIL ORDER No

Wide range of hand and garden tools carrying the Wilkinson Sword brand name. The UK market leader.

The Flower Arrangers Show Shop
PO Box 38, Stratford upon Avon, Warwickshire CV37 6WJ
☎ 01789 266318

CONTACT S E Grant
PRODUCTS Floral accessories; containers; figurines
CATALOGUE SAE
MAIL ORDER Yes

Flower-arranging accessories, verdigris figurines and dried plant material. Only the figurines and containers are available mail order: look out for the stand at shows. They will be at NAFAS at Telford this year.

Forsham Cottage Arks
Goreside Farm, Great Chart, Ashford, Kent TN26 1JU
☎ 01233 820229   [FAX] 01233 820157

CONTACT Cindy Pellett
PRODUCTS Dovecotes
CATALOGUE On request
MAIL ORDER Yes

Decorative and functional dovecotes and small poultry units for the garden.

Frolics of Winchester
82 Canon Street, Winchester, Hampshire SO23 9JQ
☎ 01962 856384   [FAX] 01962 844896

CONTACT Robert Dick-Read
PRODUCTS Garden furniture; ornamental trellis
CATALOGUE On request
MAIL ORDER Yes

Manufacturers of wooden garden furniture and of painted trellis-work cut to intricate shapes, including perspective arches. Individual pieces made to order as well. Trade and garden designer discounts.

Frost & Co
The Old Forge, Tempsford, Sandy, Bedfordshire SG19 2AG
☎ 01767 640808   [FAX] 01767 640561

CONTACT Charles Frost
PRODUCTS Hardwood conservatories
CATALOGUE On request
MAIL ORDER No

Manufacturers of high-quality hardwood conservatories: their brochure is particularly informative.

The Fyba Pot Company Ltd
Malvern Road, Knottingley, West Yorkshire WF11 8EG
☎ 01977 677676   [FAX] 01977 607138

CONTACT Joan Foster
PRODUCTS Horticultural sundries and plant pots
CATALOGUE On request
MAIL ORDER Yes

Manufacturers of biodegradable plant pots, hanging baskets and planters.

Gardena
Dunhams Lane, Letchworth, Hertfordshire SG6 1BD
☎ 01462 475000   [FAX] 01462 686789

CONTACT Sales/Spares/Service
PRODUCTS Watering systems; garden tools
NEW PRODUCTS Microdrip products
CATALOGUE On request
MAIL ORDER No

Manufacturers of watering systems, lighting, pumps and electrical tools. Also a range of interchangeable tool heads.

Gardencast Ltd
Rosemount Tower, Wallington Square, Wallington, Surrey SN6 8RG
☎ 0181 669 8265   [FAX] 0181 669 8281

CONTACT V Allison
PRODUCTS Garden furniture; pots; gazebo
NEW PRODUCTS Traditional garden lighting
CATALOGUE Leaflets free
MAIL ORDER No

Makers of cast-aluminium, hardwood and resin garden furniture, pots and troughs, gazebos and a mini-marquee. They also produce architectural metalwork such as friezes, balusters and decorative panels.

Gardenglow Cocoa Shell
Clay Lane, South Nuffield, Redhill, Surrey RH1 4EG
☎ 01737 822562   [FAX] 01737 822472

CONTACT Carina Glanville
PRODUCTS Mulches
NEW PRODUCTS Composted manure; garden furniture
CATALOGUE On request
MAIL ORDER Yes

Fertilising and soil-conditioning mulches made from cocoa-shell and coir. Delivery within seven days of order.

Gay Ways Lawn Mower Centre
213 – 217 Watford Road, Harrow, London HA1 3UA
☎ 0181 908 4744   [FAX] 0181 904 6520

CONTACT Michael Fey
PRODUCTS Lawnmowers; garden machinery; hand tools; spare parts
MAIL ORDER Yes, nationwide distribution

Garden machinery sales and spares. You can order by telephone for nationwide delivery.

Gaze Burvill

Plain Farm Old Dairy, East Tisted, Alton, Hampshire
GU34 3RT
☎ 01420 587467   FAX 01420 587354

CONTACT   Simon Burvill
PRODUCTS   Oak garden furniture
CATALOGUE   On written request
MAIL ORDER   Yes

Handsome garden furniture made in British oak from managed woodlands.

Geeco Limited

Gore Road Industrial Estate, New Milton, Hampshire
BH25 6SE
☎ 01425 614600   FAX 01425 619463

CONTACT   Joyce King
PRODUCTS   Containers; watering cans and accessories; planters and hanging baskets
NEW PRODUCTS   Micro-irrigation systems
CATALOGUE   On written request
MAIL ORDER   No

Manufacturers of watering cans and accessories, hanging baskets, plant-containers, brushware and storage systems.

Gerhardt Pharmaceuticals Ltd

PO Box 777, London SW19 5DY
☎ 0181 944 0505

CONTACT   Carolyn Archer
PRODUCTS   Insecticides

Makers of Dethlac insecticidal lacquer and Dethtrap whitefly catcher for greenhouses and conservatories.

Globe Organic Services

163A Warwick Road, Solihull, West Midlands B92 7AR
☎ 0121 707 4120   FAX 0121 707 4934

CONTACT   Tom Raitt
PRODUCTS   Shredders; chippers; composters
CATALOGUE   On request
MAIL ORDER   Yes, price includes delivery

Suppliers of equipment to recycle garden waste, shredder/chippers, composters and two-wheeled barrows.

Good Directions Ltd

15 Talisman Business Centre, Duncan Road, Park Gate, Southampton, Hampshire SO31 7GA
☎ 01489 577828   FAX 01489 577858

CONTACT   Rosalie Bulmer
PRODUCTS   Architectural features; weathervanes; sundials; garden taps
NEW PRODUCTS   Brass/copper windchimes
CATALOGUE   On request
MAIL ORDER   Yes

Cupolas, clock turrets, weather vanes, sundials, decorative garden taps and sprinklers. Garden temples and gazebos are a recent addition.

Green Gardener Products

41 Strumpshaw Road, Brundall, Norfolk NR13 5PG
☎ 01603 715096

CONTACT   John Manners
PRODUCTS   Biological controls
NEW PRODUCTS   New treatment for scale insect
CATALOGUE   On request
MAIL ORDER   Yes

Suppliers of biological pest-controls for whitefly, red spider mite, vine weevil, aphids and mealy bug. There is a daytime helpline (on the number above); they can advise on integrated pest control using a combination of traps, sprays and controls.

Greenacres Horticultural Supplies

P O Box 1228, Iver, Buckinghamshire SL0 0EH
☎ 01895 835235   FAX 01753 672906

CONTACT   I Ludford
PRODUCTS   Pre-germinated grass seed; fertilisers; lawn products; water storage granules; liquid and granular sulphur
CATALOGUE   On request
MAIL ORDER   Yes

Suppliers of commercial and amenity products to the amateur gardener. Mail order, local delivery and collection from yard.

GWS Ltd

The Walnuts, Pinfold Lane, Harby, Melton Mowbray, Leicestershire LE14 4BU
☎ 01949 861379   FAX 01949 861487

CONTACT   Chris Tetley
PRODUCTS   Conservatories; sunrooms
CATALOGUE   On request
MAIL ORDER   No

Family firm selling UPVC Georgian sun rooms direct to the public. Designed for easy installation and maintenance. Their Pyramid roof goes well with bungalows.

H₂0

The Stables, Winwick Warren, West Haddon, Northampton, Northamptonshire NN6 7NS
☎ 01788 510529   FAX 01788 510728

CONTACT   Gillian Ingman-Jones
PRODUCTS   Irrigation systems
CATALOGUE   On request
MAIL ORDER   Yes

These suppliers and installers of automatic watering systems offer individual service. Site visits and estimates are free of charge, and service contracts can be arranged.

Haddonstone Ltd

The Forge House, East Haddon, Northampton, Northamptonshire NN6 8DB
☎ 01604 770711   FAX 01604 770027

CONTACT   Sales Department
PRODUCTS   Garden ornaments; architectural stonework
NEW PRODUCTS   Jubilee urn, launched to commemorate Haddonstone's silver jubilee
CATALOGUE   Full colour 120 pages £5
MAIL ORDER   Delivery

Leading manufacturers and suppliers of garden ornaments, statuary and architectural stonework in the reconstituted stone material 'Haddonstone'. The range is exceptionally large, but they can also design to order. Antique finishes available.

Hartley Botanic
Greenfield, Oldham, Lancashire OL3 7AG
☎ 01457 873244   〔FAX〕 01457 870151

CONTACT   John Aston
PRODUCTS   Clearspan and Hartley Botanic glasshouses and greenhouses
NEW PRODUCTS   Victorian-style glasshouses
CATALOGUE   On request
MAIL ORDER   Greenhouses & accessories

Manufacturers and designers of residential and commercial greenhouses and Victorian glasshouses, including Hartley, Chelsea and Clearspan ranges. Structures can be custom-built to any design.

Haws Watering Cans
120 Beakes Road, Smethwick, Warley, West Midlands B67 5RN
☎ 0121 420 2494   〔FAX〕 0121 429 1668

CONTACT   John Massey
PRODUCTS   Watering cans; sprayers
CATALOGUE   On request – new brochure
MAIL ORDER   Yes

Watering cans that look like watering cans from this well-known company. They also sell other watering equipment, and supply spares – and cans if necessary – by mail order.

Hayters plc
Spellbrook, Bishop's Stortford, Hertfordshire CM23 4BU
☎ 01279 723444   〔FAX〕 01279 600338

CONTACT   Barbara Garton
PRODUCTS   Lawnmowers
CATALOGUE   On request (01279 600919)

Well-known manufacturers of handsome lawnmowers and garden tractors: most of their products are rotary cutting.

Heritage Woodcraft
Unit 5, Shelley Farm, Ower, Romsey, Hampshire SO51 6AS
☎ 01703 814145

CONTACT   David Finch
PRODUCTS   Garden furniture; wooden wheelbarrows
CATALOGUE   Free leaflets
MAIL ORDER   Yes

Traditionally crafted wooden garden furniture made from iroko (derived from managed sources) and English oak.

The Heveningham Collection
Weston Down, Weston Colley, Micheldever, Winchester, Hampshire SO21 3AQ
☎ 01962 774990   〔FAX〕 01962 774790

CONTACT   Annie Eadie
PRODUCTS   Wrought-iron garden furniture
CATALOGUE   £2.50, refundable
MAIL ORDER   Yes

Expanding range of wrought-iron furniture with clean lines.

Hillhout (UK) Ltd
Unit 3, Salmon Road, Great Yarmouth, Norfolk NR30 3QS
☎ 01493 332226   〔FAX〕 01493 332228

CONTACT   W Durrant
PRODUCTS   Fencing; wooden garden products; garden buildings
CATALOGUE   On request
MAIL ORDER   No

Suppliers and manufacturers of wooden fencing, trellis, pergolas, garden furniture, sand pits and garden buildings.

Homer Pressings
Charles Street, Walsall, West Midlands WS2 9NB
☎ 01922 720111   〔FAX〕 01922 29781

CONTACT   Pat Jenkins
PRODUCTS   Garden and hand tools
CATALOGUE   Leaflets from agents

Manufacturers of a range of traditional garden and hand tools.

The Hop Shop
Castle Farm, Shoreham, Sevenoaks, Kent TN14 7UB
☎ 01959 523219   〔FAX〕 01959 524220

CONTACT   Caroline Alexander
PRODUCTS   Dried flowers; grasses; hop bines
CATALOGUE   4 first class stamps
MAIL ORDER   Yes

Dried-flower producers and suppliers: trade and retail. Their range includes grasses, wheatsheaves and autumnal hop bines. Group tours by arrangement in season. They also offer a programme of courses and demonstrations on the art of arranging dried flowers.

Hotbox Heaters Ltd
7 Gordleton Industrial Park, Sway Road, Lymington, Hampshire SO41 8JD
☎ 01590 683788   〔FAX〕 01590 683511

CONTACT   Marketing department
PRODUCTS   Greenhouse heaters; propagators; lighting; circulation fans; foot-warming panels
CATALOGUE   Leaflets
MAIL ORDER   Yes

Electric and gas heaters and air-circulation fans for small greenhouses and larger units for professional users and hobbyists. There is also a range of propagating benches, foot-warming panels and horticultural lighting.

Hozelock Ltd
Haddenham, Aylesbury, Buckinghamshire HP17 8JD
☎ 01844 291881   〔FAX〕 01844 290344

CONTACT   Consumer Services (01844 291820)
PRODUCTS   Watering equipment; garden lighting; sprayers; aquatic products
CATALOGUE   Trade catalogue on request
MAIL ORDER   No

Manufacturers and suppliers of a wide range of products and accessories for watering, lighting, spraying and pond care.

Husqvarna Forest & Garden UK

Oldends Lane Industrial Estate, Stonehouse Lane,
Stonehouse, Gloucestershire GL10 3SY

☎ 01453 822382 　 [FAX] 01453 826936

CONTACT Heather Gardner
PRODUCTS Garden machinery; lawnmowers and tractors;
chainsaws
CATALOGUE On request
MAIL ORDER No

A full range of machinery from domestic lawn mowers and
lawn tractors to professional brushcutters and chainsaws.

Interval Systems Ltd

PO Box 40, Woking, Surrey GU22 7YU

☎ 01483 727888 　 [FAX] 01483 727828

CONTACT Sarah Ford
PRODUCTS Wooden garden features; trellis; wheelbarrows
CATALOGUE On request
MAIL ORDER Yes, see below

Distributors of 'Ultra' wooden arches, trellis, ornamental
fences and bridges; 'FORT' wheelbarrows. Mail order: for
'Ultra' products contact the address above; 'FORT' mail order
through Boulder Barrows, 99 Westfield Road, Woking, Surrey, GU22 9QR. (Tel. 01482 730658).

J G S Weathervanes

Unit 6, Broomstick Estate, High Street, Edlesborough,
Dunstable, Bedfordshire LU6 2HS

☎ 01525 220360 　 [FAX] 01525 222786

CONTACT J Sayer
PRODUCTS Weather-vanes
CATALOGUE On request, please send stamp
MAIL ORDER Yes

Makers of metal weather-vanes in traditional and modern
designs. They offer over 180 designs and also do commissions.

Jemp Engineering

Canal Estate, Station Road, Langley, Berkshire SL3 6EG

☎ 01753 548327 　 [FAX] 01753 580137

CONTACT Mansford
PRODUCTS Propagators; greenhouse heaters; greenhouse
equipment
CATALOGUE On request
MAIL ORDER Yes

Manufacturers of heaters and electric propagators, as well as
shading and other greenhouse equipment.

Jiffy Products (UK) Ltd

14 – 16 Commercial Road, March, Cambridgeshire
PE15 8QP

☎ 01354 652565 　 [FAX] 01354 651891

CONTACT Sandy Shepherd
PRODUCTS Propagation pellets and pots
NEW PRODUCTS Professional trays for the keen amateur
gardener
CATALOGUE Available from Johnsons Seeds
MAIL ORDER Yes: Freephone 0880 614323

Manufacturers and suppliers of peat and fibre pots and propagation trays for commercial growers and retail customers. No
direct retail trade.

John Deere Ltd

Harby Road, Langar, Nottingham, Nottinghamshire
NG13 9HT

☎ 01949 860491 　 [FAX] 01949 860490

CONTACT Graham Williams
PRODUCTS Lawn mowers; lawn tractors
CATALOGUE Leaflets

Manufacturers of lawn and groundsmanship machinery from
garden and commercial lawn mowers, through to lawn tractors
and large tractor units.

John McLauchlan Horticulture

50a Market Place, Thirsk, North Yorkshire YO7 1LH

☎ 01845 525585 　 [FAX] 01845 523133

CONTACT John McLauchlan
PRODUCTS Fertilisers; growing media
NEW PRODUCTS Viresco micro-organisms for suppressing
disease; Aquifer turf-wetting agent
CATALOGUE On request
MAIL ORDER Yes

Specialist suppliers of growing media to trade and retail customers, including vermiculite, perlite, pumice and biosorb.
They also sell fertilisers and some sundries. Mail order service.

Joseph Bentley

Beck Lane, Barrow on Humber, Lincolnshire DN19 7AQ

☎ 01469 532000 　 [FAX] 01469 532111

CONTACT Paul Knott
PRODUCTS Composts; fertilisers; garden sundries
CATALOGUE On request
MAIL ORDER Yes

Suppliers of a wide range of general and specialist composts
and fertilisers including straight fertilisers, organic granules
and compost mixes for chrysanthemum and fuchsia growers.

Julian Chichester Designs

Unit 12, 33 Parsons Green Lane, London SW6 4HH

☎ 0171 371 9055 　 [FAX] 0171 371 9066

PRODUCTS Garden furniture
CATALOGUE Yes, phone or write
MAIL ORDER Yes, with credit card by phone

Handsome teak garden furniture, benches, chairs and tables in
classical 18th-century styles based on the designs of Sheraton,
Chippendale and J P White.

King Easton Ltd

The Green, Station Road, Winchmore Hill, London
N21 3NB

☎ 0181 886 8783 　 [FAX] 0181 882 2685

CONTACT Brian Easton
PRODUCTS Garden furniture; parasols; gazebos
CATALOGUE On request

A stylish collection of traditional French metal outdoor furniture.

Knowle Nets
20 East Road, Bridport, Dorset DT6 4NX
☎ 01308 424342　　📠 01308 458186
CONTACT　Mrs B Scorey
PRODUCTS　Fruit cages; garden netting; plant supports
NEW PRODUCTS　Vegetable cages
CATALOGUE　On request, with samples
MAIL ORDER　Yes

Manufacturers of fruit cages, protective netting and woven sheeting for plant support, and windbreak. They also produce sports nets.

Kubota (UK) Ltd
Dormer Road, Thame, Oxfordshire OX9 3UN
☎ 01844 214500　　📠 01844 216685
CONTACT　Stuart Ellis
PRODUCTS　Lawn mowers; lawn tractors; garden machinery
NEW PRODUCTS　Super B series tractors (18hp, 21hp & 24hp)

Garden machinery range including lawn mowers, lawn tractors, compact tractors, hedgetrimmers, brushcutters and generators. The range extends to professional and amenity machines.

Labelplant
Unit F2, Duck Farm, Tincleton Road, Bockhampton, Dorchester, Dorset DT2 8QL
☎ 01305 849089　　📠 01305 849042
CONTACT　Tony Palmer
PRODUCTS　Labels; markers; sundries
NEW PRODUCTS　Three new types of label
CATALOGUE　Free on request
MAIL ORDER　Yes

Range of plant labels, pens and markers, gardeners' and growers' sundries. Mail order only, but they attend lots of shows.

Lady Muck
Marshwood House, Whitegate, Forton, Chard, Somerset TO20 4HL
☎ 01460 220822　　📠 01460 67768
CONTACT　Jane Down
PRODUCTS　Organic composts
CATALOGUE　On request
MAIL ORDER　Yes

User-friendly manure-based compost which is clean to use and odour-free.

Larch-Lap Ltd
Units 291-296, Hartlebury Trading Estate, Crown Lane, Hartlebury, Hereford & Worcester DY10 4JB
☎ 01299 251725　　📠 01299 251017
CONTACT　Linda Phillips
PRODUCTS　Garden buildings; fencing; trellis
NEW PRODUCTS　New range of gates and decorative trellis
CATALOGUE　On request
MAIL ORDER　No

Manufacturers of timber and metal garden buildings, fencing and trellis.

Leaky Pipe Systems Ltd
Frith Farm, Dean Street, East Farleigh, Maidstone, Kent ME15 0PR
☎ 01622 746495　　📠 01622 745118
CONTACT　Chris Fermor
PRODUCTS　Irrigation systems
CATALOGUE　Leaflets
MAIL ORDER　Yes

This company specialises in the supply and installation of porous rubber hose irrigation systems. The pipes are actually made from recycled car tyres. Leaky Pipe can be used for horticultural, amenity and agricultural situations.

Levington Horticulture Ltd
Paper Mill Lane, Bramford, Ipswich, Suffolk IP8 4BZ
☎ 01473 830492　　📠 01473 830386
CONTACT　Consumer Relations Dept
PRODUCTS　Composts; fertilisers; garden chemicals; growing media
NEW PRODUCTS　Levington compost with Stimulex bio-stimulant; evergeen grass seed
CATALOGUE　Trade only
MAIL ORDER　No

Fisons Horticulture was bought out by its managers and now trades as Levington. The range has not changed and includes 'Levington' composts, 'Evergreen' fertilisers and 'Murphy' products. Available from garden centres. Consumer advice line: Freecall 0500 888558.

Lindum Seeded Turf
West Grange, Thorganby, North Yorkshire YO4 6DJ
☎ 01904 448675　　📠 01904 448713
CONTACT　David Snowden
PRODUCTS　Turf
NEW PRODUCTS　Blocks of instant-use turf
CATALOGUE　On request
MAIL ORDER　No

Growers and suppliers nationwide of cultivated turf for sporting, garden and landscaping uses. The new drop-in repair range can be used immediately.

Link-Stakes Ltd
30 Warwick Road, Upper Boddington, Daventry, Northamptonshire NN11 6DH
☎ 01327 260329　　📠 01327 262428
CONTACT　Madeline Knowles
PRODUCTS　Plant supports; stakes
CATALOGUE　On request
MAIL ORDER　Yes

Suppliers of interlocking wire plant-supports and single stakes. The stakes adapt to a variety of shapes and uses. There is also a range of wire cloches.

Lister Lutyens Ltd
South Road, Hailsham, East Sussex BN27 3DT
☎ 01323 840771　　📠 01323 440109
CONTACT　Rachel Breen
PRODUCTS　Garden furniture

CATALOGUE On request
MAIL ORDER No

Founded over 100 years ago, Lister teak garden furniture in a variety of styles is well known. The iroko range is called 'Country'.

Lizzard & Co Ltd/Le Blanc Fine Art
Manor House, Saxby, Melton Mowbray, Leicestershire LE14 2RR
☎ 01572 787503   📠 01572 787688

CONTACT J Le Blanc or H Warner
PRODUCTS Bronze fountains and sculptures
NEW PRODUCTS New fountains; life-sized bronze horses, swans and gateway lions.
CATALOGUE £5, apply by post or fax
MAIL ORDER Pro-forma

They specialise in limited-edition and specially commissioned bronze fountains and sculptures.

Lucas Garden Statuary
Firsland Park Estate, Henfield Road, Albourne, Henfield, West Sussex BN6 9JJ
☎ 01273 494931   📠 01273 495125

CONTACT M S Lucas
PRODUCTS Garden ornaments and antiqued stone statuary
NEW PRODUCTS New Victorian-style pieces and mythical statues
CATALOGUE Yes, from retailers, or £3 direct
MAIL ORDER No

Garden statuary, classical figures, mythical beasts, sundials, fountains, urns, planters, and benches made from reconstituted stone with an aged finish.

Marion Smith
The Studio, Farm Cottage, Puttenham, Guildford, Surrey GU3 1AJ
☎ 01483 810352

CONTACT Marion Smith
PRODUCTS Bronze and bronze/resin sculpture
NEW PRODUCTS Bronze horses in editions of 10 or 12, suitable for offices, conservatories and small gardens
CATALOGUE On request
MAIL ORDER Yes, 50% on ordering, balance when work cast

Bronze and bronze/resin sculptures of children and animals for gardens, conservatories and interiors in limited editions. Marion Smith shows regularly at Chelsea.

Marston & Langinger Ltd
192 Ebury Street, London SW1W 8UP
☎ 0171 823 6829   📠 0171 824 8757
PRODUCTS Conservatories; conservatory furniture
CATALOGUE On request

Individually designed conservatories with an excellent reputation: the showroom which also displays their range of conservatory fittings is in London. The factory is in Norfolk.

Matthew Eden
Pickwick End, Corsham, Wiltshire SN13 0JB
☎ 01249 713335   📠 01249 713644

CONTACT Matthew Eden
PRODUCTS Garden furniture
NEW PRODUCTS Wrought-iron garden daybeds
CATALOGUE Free
MAIL ORDER Yes

Well-respected supplier of wirework pergolas, obelisks and chairs; wrought iron garden furniture; and wooden benches to Lutyens and earlier designs. They also undertake individual commissions to order.

Maxicrop International Ltd
Weldon Road, Corby, Northamptonshire NN17 5US
☎ 01536 402182   📠 01536 204254

CONTACT Jenny Paxton
PRODUCTS Fertilisers
NEW PRODUCTS Flower fertiliser
CATALOGUE On request
MAIL ORDER Yes (10 litres minimum)

Liquid seaweed extract and fertilisers.

Melcourt
Eight Bells House, Tetbury, Gloucestershire GL8 8JG
☎ 01666 503919   📠 01666 504398

CONTACT Rosemary Latter or Elaine Rose
PRODUCTS Mulches; soil conditioners
MAIL ORDER No

Bark and wood-based mulches and soil conditioners, compost additives, play and walk surfaces. No direct retail, telephone for local stockists.

Mellors Garden Ceramics
Rosemead, Marshwood, Bridport, Dorset DT6 5QB
☎ 01297 678217

CONTACT Kate Mellors
PRODUCTS Garden ornaments; fountains; planters; lanterns, birdbaths
CATALOGUE Large SAE
MAIL ORDER Yes

Hand-made waterproof and frost-proof ceramic planters, fountains and garden ornaments in glazed stoneware clay.

Metpost Ltd
Mardy Road, Cardiff, South Glamorgan CF3 8EX
☎ 01222 777877   📠 01222 779295

CONTACT R Kindred
PRODUCTS Fencing; trellis
CATALOGUE On request
MAIL ORDER Yes

Manufacturers of the 'Metpost' fence-fixing stake, and a range of maintenance-free trellis made from recycled polystyrene ('Timbron').

Miracle Garden Care
Salisbury House, Weyside Park, Catteshall Lane,
Godalming, Surrey GU7 1XE
☎ 01483 410210   [FAX] 01423 421220

CONTACT   Consumer Services Help Desk
PRODUCTS   Pesticides; fertilisers; herbicides; growing media; house plant care products; biological controls
MAIL ORDER   No

Manufacturers and suppliers of a wide range of chemicals and gardening sundries, many of them household names.

Monsanto Garden Care
Garden Division, PO Box 53, Lane End Road, High
Wycombe, Buckinghamshire HP12 4HL
☎ 01494 474918   [FAX] 01494 474920

CONTACT   Richard Garnett
PRODUCTS   Pesticides; herbicides
CATALOGUE   Trade catalogue only
MAIL ORDER   No

Suppliers of horticultural and agricultural chemicals: they make the herbicide 'Roundup' the multi-purpose insecticide 'Polysect' and such brands as 'Weedatak' and 'Ant-Stop'.

Mukaluk
Ian Landless Farming Partnership, Hill Farm, Duns Tew,
Bicester, Oxfordshire OX6 4JJ
☎ 01869 347532   [FAX] 01869 347701

CONTACT   Caroline Landless
PRODUCTS   Growing media; soil improvers
NEW PRODUCTS   Ericaceous compost
CATALOGUE   Leaflet
MAIL ORDER   No

Peat-free composts, mulches and soil-improvers based on farmyard manure.

Nehra Cookes Chemicals Ltd
16 Chiltern Close, Warren Wood, Arnold,
Nottinghamshire NG5 9PX
☎ 01159 203839   [FAX] 01159 671734

CONTACT   David Nehra
PRODUCTS   Garden sundries and herbicides; wrought-iron garden features
NEW PRODUCTS   Lawn-moss killer
MAIL ORDER   Wrought-iron garden products only

Garden products and chemicals.

Netlon Sentinel Partnership
P O Box 119, Shepcote Lane, Sheffield, South Yorkshire
S9 1TY
☎ 0114 256 2020   [FAX] 0114 261 0157

CONTACT   Dawn Staniland
PRODUCTS   Netting; mesh; film; timber; wire
NEW PRODUCTS   New range of pot-holders
CATALOGUE   On request

A wide range of netting, timber, wire, film, fabric and mesh products for plant support and protection. They also sell bubble insulation and ties.

Nortene
Linenhall House, Stanley Street, Chester, Cheshire
CH1 2LR
☎ 01244 346193   [FAX] 01244 320054

CONTACT   Miss K Mason
PRODUCTS   Netting; sheeting; trellis; garden sundries
NEW PRODUCTS   Mini-greenhouse and gazebo
CATALOGUE   On request
MAIL ORDER   No

Originally known for netting, the range now includes protective films and mulches, plant supports, garden furniture-covers, and trellis.

Nutscene Garden Products Ltd
Old Brechin Road, Forfar, Tayside DD8 3DX
☎ 01307 468589   [FAX] 01307 467051

CONTACT   Murray Anderson
PRODUCTS   Garden twine and plant supports
NEW PRODUCTS   Economy range of twines & accessories
CATALOGUE   SAE
MAIL ORDER   Yes

Manufacturers of garden twines (traditional jute and modern polypropylene), tree ties, labels and plant-support accessories.

The Oak Barrel Company
Old NCB Workshop, Pipers Lane, Ansley Common,
Nuneaton, Warwickshire CV10 0RH
☎ 01203 392700   [FAX] 01203 395995

CONTACT   R Hill
PRODUCTS   Barrels and pumps
CATALOGUE   Brochure & price list free
MAIL ORDER   Yes, cheque or card with order

Manufacturers and suppliers of a wide range of oak barrels and pumps.

Oak Leaf Conservatories
Kettlestring Lane, Clifton Moor, York, North Yorkshire
YO3 4XF
☎ 01904 690401   [FAX] 01904 690945

CONTACT   Tracey Sanders
PRODUCTS   Conservatories
CATALOGUE   On request

Made to measure conservatories noted for imaginative designs: recent commissions have included domes and two storeys. Their exhibits at Chelsea and Hampton Court in recent years have been the talk of the shows.

Organic Concentrates Ltd
3 Broadway Court, Chesham, Buckinghamshire HP5 1EN
☎ 01494 792229   [FAX] 01494 792199

CONTACT   C J P Green
PRODUCTS   Organic fertilisers; pesticides; sundries
NEW PRODUCTS   6X The 100% Natural Fertiliser Easy-Spread Pellets
CATALOGUE   On request
MAIL ORDER   Yes

Suppliers of the concentrated, dried and sterilised poultry manure '6X', a non-toxic slug killer and 'Sunshine of Africa', a cocoa shell mulch.

The Organic Gardening Catalogue
Coombelands House, Adlestone, Surrey KT15 1HY
☎ 01932 820958   📠 01932 829322
PRODUCTS   Organic supplies; seeds; manures
NEW PRODUCTS   More seed potato cultivars; Victorian seed collection; rain forest house plants
CATALOGUE   On request
MAIL ORDER   Yes

The Organic Gardening Catalogue is produced in association with the HDRA and offers a magnificent range of organic supplies and untreated seed. Many items are stocked at Ryton Organic Gardens too. 10% discounts are available to HDRA and RHS members. Recommended.

Ornate Products
26-27 Clivemont Road, Cordwallis Industrial Estate, Maidenhead, Berkshire SL6 7BZ
☎ 01628 25414   📠 01628 23409
CONTACT   Mandy Clamp
PRODUCTS   Garden ornaments
CATALOGUE   On request
MAIL ORDER   Yes

Finely ornamental stoneware and terracotta in classical and contemporary styles.

Oxley's Garden Furniture
Lapstone Barn, Westington Hill, Chipping Campden, Gloucestershire GL55 6UR
☎ 01386 840466   📠 01386 840855
CONTACT   Simon Hudson
PRODUCTS   Garden furniture
CATALOGUE   On request
MAIL ORDER   Yes

Distinctive, solid, cast-aluminium garden furniture with maintenance-free finishes. Also attractive oak Versailles tubs.

P J Bridgman & Co Ltd
Barnbridge Works, Lockfield Avenue, Brimsdown, Enfield, London EN3 7PX
☎ 0181 804 7474   📠 0181 805 0873
CONTACT   Sales Office
PRODUCTS   Garden furniture
NEW PRODUCTS   Folding and reclining armchair; new table designs
CATALOGUE   On request and from stockists
MAIL ORDER   No

Wide range of solidly built Iroko garden furniture in period styles: many include carved details. Wood is derived from sustainable sources.

Pamal
The Cottage, Sproxton, Melton Mowbray, Leicestershire LE14 4QS
☎ 01476 860266   📠 01476 860523
CONTACT   Pamela Graham or Malise Graham

PRODUCTS   Garden furniture
CATALOGUE   On request
MAIL ORDER   Yes

Manufacturers and suppliers of hardwood garden furniture, including benches and Versailles tubs.

Pan Britannica Industries Ltd
Britannica House, Waltham Cross, Hertfordshire EN8 7DY
☎ 01992 623691   📠 01992 626452
CONTACT   David Coop
PRODUCTS   Composts; fertilisers; herbicides; garden sundries
NEW PRODUCTS   Baby Bio Patio Plant Food; Bio Multi-sprayers
CATALOGUE   Trade only
MAIL ORDER   No

Large garden group with a best-selling range of growing media, garden chemicals and plant-care products, including 'Baby Bio'.

Park Forge
Units CB1/CB2, Hayedown Industrial Estate, Hayedown, Tavistock, Devon PL19 0NN
☎ & 📠 01822 810623
CONTACT   Dave Russell
PRODUCTS   Metal pergolas and bowers; arches; weathervanes; hanging baskets
CATALOGUE   On request
MAIL ORDER   Yes

Manufacturers and suppliers of traditionally made wire arches and pergolas, weather-vanes and hanging basket trees: bespoke work is a speciality.

Patricia Dale
Court Lodge, West Meon, Petersfield, Hampshire GU32 1JG
☎ & 📠 01730 829473
CONTACT   Patricia Dale
PRODUCTS   Botanical watercolours; associated stationery
NEW PRODUCTS   New note-cards & paintings; new RHS Collectors' Plate No 7
CATALOGUE   Information on request

This well-known botanical artist painted the 1995 Chelsea Flower Show plate. Her main work is with original watercolour paintings, cards and paper. She also works on commission and opens her garden for the NGS.

Peta (UK) Ltd
Mark's Hall, Mark's Hall Lane, Margaret Roding, Chelmsford, Essex CM6 1QT
☎ 01245 231118   📠 01245 231811
CONTACT   Genny Crockett
PRODUCTS   Ergonomic garden tools
NEW PRODUCTS   'Magic' weeding wand, a controlled applicator to eliminate bending and stooping
CATALOGUE   Free on request
MAIL ORDER   Yes, cash with order, no cards

Makers of 'Peta' fist-grips garden tools with the handle at right-angles to the head. The range is designed to alleviate strain for gardeners with weak hands and poor grip. It now includes arm supports and extension handles.

Phostrogen
28 Parkway, Deeside Industrial Estate, Deeside, Clwyd
CH5 2NS
☎ 01244 280800   FAX 01244 281784
CONTACT Julie Bryde
PRODUCTS Fertilisers; house plant care; irrigation equipment
CATALOGUE On request
MAIL ORDER No

Manufacturers of soluble and slow-release fertilisers, hose-end dilutors and irrigation equipment.

Platipus Anchors Ltd
Perrywood Business Park, Honeycrock Lane, Salfords, Redhill, Surrey RH1 5DZ
☎ 01737 762300   FAX 01737 773395
CONTACT Adam Lacey
PRODUCTS Tree anchoring systems
CATALOGUE On request
MAIL ORDER Yes

'Platipus' systems for securing newly planted standard and semi-mature trees: above-ground guy-fixing and rootball-fixing.

PLM Power Products
Units 5&6, The Shires Industrial Estate, Essington Close, Birmingham Road, Lichfield, Staffordshire WS14 9AZ
☎ 01543 414477   FAX 01543 414541
CONTACT Diane Cooper
PRODUCTS Horticultural, garden and forest machinery and tools
CATALOGUE Free on request
MAIL ORDER Yes

Importers and distributors of 'Corona' tools, 'Little Wonder', 'Mantis', 'Brill', 'Shindawa' and 'Kees' machinery for amateur and professional use.

Plysu Housewares Ltd
Wolseley Road, Kempston, Bedfordshire MK42 7UD
☎ 01234 841771   FAX 01234 841037
CONTACT Peter Fraser/Kate Beal
PRODUCTS Watering can; plastic plant containers; water butts; composters
CATALOGUE On request
MAIL ORDER No

Best-known for their household products, Plysu also make plastic watering cans, water butts, composters and plant containers.

Porous Pipe Ltd
PO Box 2, Colne, Lancashire BB8 7BY
☎ 01282 871778   FAX 01282 871785
CONTACT Martin Flitton
PRODUCTS Watering systems
NEW PRODUCTS 'Water Wizard' hanging basket and Grow-bag Waterer

CATALOGUE On request
MAIL ORDER Yes

Manufacturers of porous pipe system of garden watering. They also visit garden shows in France and Germany.

Portland Conservatories Ltd
Portland House, Ouse Street, Salford, Greater Manchester M5 2EW
☎ 0161 745 7920   FAX 0161 745 8813
CONTACT Irene Cairns
PRODUCTS Conservatories
CATALOGUE Freephone 0800 269126 for brochure

Manufacturers and installers of a range of hardwood and UPVC conservatories. They have local representation, including Sainsburys Homebase at Croydon.

The Potting Shack
Smart's Centre, Dry Hill Lane, Sundridge, Sevenoaks, Kent TN14 6ED
☎ 01959 561243   FAX 01959 565604
CONTACT E F Di Bona
PRODUCTS Terracotta pots
NEW PRODUCTS Wooden pot stands; new terracotta patterns
CATALOGUE Trade only

Very large selection of frost-resistant terracotta and oriental earthenware.

Power Garden Products
3 Daytona Drive, Allesley, Coventry, West Midlands CV5 9QG
☎ 01676 523062
CONTACT J Fallon
PRODUCTS Plant supports; cloches
CATALOGUE First class stamp
MAIL ORDER Yes

Mail-order garden supplies including 'Power' plant supports and 'Chase Barn' cloches, both of which are only available from Power.

Practicality Brown Ltd
Iver Stud, Swan Road, Iver, Buckinghamshire SL0 9LA
☎ 01753 652022   FAX 01753 653007
CONTACT David Middleton
PRODUCTS Mulches
CATALOGUE On request
MAIL ORDER No

Mulches and bark products in various grades for horticultural and amenity use. Tree-moving, landscaping and chipping services available.

Precise Irrigation (UK) Ltd
Unit 1, The Warehouse, Reading Road, Wantage, Oxfordshire OX12 8HP
☎ 01235 763760   FAX 01235 765467
CONTACT Jeremy Browning and Monica Lumsden
PRODUCTS Irrigation systems
CATALOGUE On request
MAIL ORDER Yes

Designers, suppliers and installers of irrigation systems for domestic and commercial customers. No charge for evaluations and quotations. Starter and hanging-basket kits available.

Pumps 'n' Tubs
Unit H1-H3, Holly Farm Business Park, Honiley,
Warwickshire CV8 1NP
☎ 01926 484244   [FAX] 01926 484194
CONTACT   I J Eborall
PRODUCTS   Rustic tubs and barrels; water features
CATALOGUE   On request
MAIL ORDER   Yes

Wooden tubs, cast-iron pumps and water features which combine the two. Rustic garden furniture is a recent addition to the range.

Raffles – Thatched Garden Buildings
Laundry Cottage, Prestwold Hall, Prestwold,
Loughborough, Leicestershire LE12 5SQ
☎ & [FAX] 01509 881426
CONTACT   Andrew V Raffle
PRODUCTS   Summer-houses
CATALOGUE   On request
MAIL ORDER   No

Suppliers of thatched summer-houses and garden buildings built with traditional materials to old designs. Besides their standard range, there is a custom-design service and they can also restore existing buildings.

Ransomes Consumer Ltd
Bell Close, Newnham Industrial Estate, Plympton,
Plymouth, Devon PL7 4JH
☎ 01752 346555   [FAX] 01752 340851
PRODUCTS   Garden machinery
NEW PRODUCTS   Complete new range
CATALOGUE   On request: 0800 378699
MAIL ORDER   Yes

Extensive range of garden machinery including the best-selling Westwood lawn tractor, Mountfield lawnmowers, shredders, cultivators and garden generators. They also sell an alarm to protect garages and garden sheds.

Rapitest
London Road, Corwen, Clwyd, Wales LL21 0DR
☎ 01490 412804   [FAX] 01490 412716
CONTACT   Madeline Lowe
PRODUCTS   Soil-test kits; plant supports
NEW PRODUCTS   Link-ups plant supports
CATALOGUE   On written request

Manufacturers of a wide range of soil-test kits and plant support systems, sold through garden centres and B&Q.

Rayment Wirework
The Forge, Durlock, Minster, Thanet, Kent CT12 4HE
☎ 01843 821628   [FAX] 01843 821635
CONTACT   Ron or Adrian Rayment
PRODUCTS   Wirework planters; arches; gazebos; furniture
CATALOGUE   Large SAE
MAIL ORDER   Yes

Hand-painted wirework structures for the garden and conservatory, from plant-holders to furniture and intricate gazebos and temples. They accept commissions.

Record Bulldog Tools Holdings Ltd
Parkway Works, Sheffield, South Yorkshire S9 3BL
PRODUCTS   Hand tools
NEW PRODUCTS   New 'Premier' range of tools
CATALOGUE   On request

Manufacturer of hand-tools and other horticultural implements.

Redwood Stone Ltd
46 North Road, Wells, Somerset BA5 2TL
☎ 01749 673601   [FAX] 01749 675701
CONTACT   Tim or Martin Redwood
PRODUCTS   Ornamental stonework
NEW PRODUCTS   Mediterranean statuary
CATALOGUE   Yes
MAIL ORDER   Yes

Redwood's main line is classical ornamental stonework, but they also have an interesting range of oriental ornaments in hand-carved granite.

Regency Garden Buildings
Barugh Green Road, Barugh Green, Barnsley, South
Yorkshire S75 1JU
☎ 01226 390000   [FAX] 01226 388886
CONTACT   K J Lodge
PRODUCTS   Timber garden buildings
NEW PRODUCTS   Traditional greenhouses in cedar or deal
CATALOGUE   On telephone request
MAIL ORDER   No

Makers of chalets, summer-houses, garden-rooms, workshops, sheds and playhouses.

Rehau Ltd
Hill Court, Walford, Ross-on-Wye, Hereford & Worcester
HR9 5QN
☎ 01989 702700
CONTACT   Cliff Wheatley on 01753 588519
PRODUCTS   Hoses
CATALOGUE   Trade only
MAIL ORDER   No

Range of garden hoses and fittings.

Remanoid
Unit 44, Number One Industrial Estate, Medomsley Road,
Consett, Co. Durham DH8 6SZ
☎ 01207 591089   [FAX] 01207 502512
CONTACT   Susan Breen
PRODUCTS   Aquatic products
CATALOGUE   On request
MAIL ORDER   Yes

Suppliers of a wide range of pumps and accessories for water-gardens and ponds.

Renaissance Bronzes
79 Pimlico Road, London SW1W 8PH
☎ 0171 823 5149   📠 0171 730 4598
CONTACT   Simon Jacques
PRODUCTS   Garden statuary
CATALOGUE   On request
MAIL ORDER   No

Classical and classically-styled bronzes – statuary, urns and fountains – for indoor and outdoor positions.

Robinsons Greenhouses Ltd
Robinsons House, First Avenue, Millbrook, Southampton, Hampshire SO15 0LG
☎ 01703 703355   📠 01703 705588
CONTACT   Sales Office
PRODUCTS   Greenhouses; benching & shelving
NEW PRODUCTS   Toughened safety glass (BS6206A); new range of 'Bearchair' garden furniture
CATALOGUE   Yes
MAIL ORDER   Yes

These well-established manufacturers of greenhouses and greenhouse accessories have a good reputation. Two of their models are at Wisley, one in the model fruit garden and the other in the model vegetable garden.

Roebuck Eyot Limited
7A Hatfield Way, South Church Enterprise Park, Bishop Auckland, Co Durham DL14 6XF
☎ 01388 772233   📠 01388 775233
CONTACT   Howard Marshall
PRODUCTS   Animal repellent
CATALOGUE   Leaflet

Makers of 'Renardine' animal repellent for cats, dogs and rabbits. 'Renardine' 72/2 repels foxes, badgers and moles.

Roffey Ltd
Throop Road, Bournemouth, Hampshire BH8 0DF
☎ 01202 537777   📠 01202 532765
CONTACT   Robert Parsons or Marcus Newberry
PRODUCTS   Commercial composts; fertilisers ; grass seeds
NEW PRODUCTS   Slow-release turf fertiliser; peat-free composts based on coir/sylvafibre
CATALOGUE   On request
MAIL ORDER   No

Composts and materials for commercial growers and garden retailers, including bark, sterilised loam, coir, grit and leca.

Roger Platts Garden Design & Nurseries
Stick Hill, Edenbridge, Kent TN8 5NH
☎ & 📠 01732 863318
CONTACT   Roger Platts
PRODUCTS   Garden furniture; pergolas; plants; garden design
NEW PRODUCTS   New nursery opened in September last year
CATALOGUE   On request
MAIL ORDER   Yes

Roger Platts is a garden designer who diversified into garden furniture, including seats and tables made from cast iron and wood, and oak pergolas. The nursery is a new venture, and worth investigating. Work will shortly begin on show gardens.

Ruardean Garden Pottery
Ruardean, Forest of Dean, Gloucestershire GL17 9TP
☎ 01594 543577   📠 01594 544536
CONTACT   John Huggins
PRODUCTS   Terracotta pots; garden ornaments
CATALOGUE   SAE
MAIL ORDER   Yes

Hand-made terracotta pots, decorative planters, pot feet, edging tiles and forcing domes. The pots are frost-proof and come in all sizes; commissions are accepted.

Ryobi Lawn & Garden (UK) Ltd
Pavilion 1, Olympus Park Industrial Estate, Quedgeley, Gloucestershire GL2 4NF
☎ 01542 724777   📠 01452 727400
CONTACT   Mrs Val Smith
PRODUCTS   Powered garden tools
NEW PRODUCTS   Lightweight garden vacuum cleaner
CATALOGUE   On request
MAIL ORDER   No

Manufacturers of powered garden machinery including hedge trimmers, vacuum sweepers, cultivators, chainsaws, trimmers and brush cutters.

Samsons
Edwin Avenue, Hoo Farm Industrial Estate, Kidderminster, Hereford & Worcester DY11 7RA
☎ 01562 825252   📠 01562 820380
CONTACT   Sales Office
PRODUCTS   Wrought-iron garden features
NEW PRODUCTS   'Gardenframes' patio planter for hanging baskets and pots
CATALOGUE   On request
MAIL ORDER   Yes

Decorative wrought-iron garden features including arches, obelisks, bowers, gates and panels which can be combined to form pergolas and screens.

Samuel Parkes & Co Ltd
New Road, Willenhall, West Midlands WV13 2BU
☎ 01902 366481   📠 01902 633789
CONTACT   Michelle Robins or Sue Lander
PRODUCTS   Garden tools
CATALOGUE   On request
MAIL ORDER   No

Long-established manufacturers of a wide range of hand and garden tools.

Sarah Burgoyne Revivals
Old Whyly, East Hoathly, East Sussex BN8 6EL
☎ 01825 840738
CONTACT   Sarah Burgoyne
PRODUCTS   Garden furniture

CATALOGUE   On request
MAIL ORDER   Yes

Old-fashioned garden furniture in beech, including a traditional steamer chair with an elegant fringed canopy.

The Secret Garden Company of Ware Limited
Ware, Hertfordshire SG12 0YJ
☎ & FAX 01920 462081

CONTACT   Susan King
PRODUCTS   Gazebos; pavilions; summerhouses
CATALOGUE   Free on request

Upmarket makers of stylish garden buildings, made from iroko and cedar and finished with shingled roofs and leaded lights.

Shamrock Horticulture Ltd
The Crescent Centre, Temple Back, Bristol BS1 6EZ
☎ 0117 921 1666   FAX 0117 922 5501

CONTACT   Anne Pearse
PRODUCTS   Peat; peat-based composts; peat-free composts
MAIL ORDER   No

Major peat supplier with an extended range which includes compost mixes, conditioners and coconut fibre products. Ring for details of your nearest supplier.

Sheen Developments Ltd
11 Earl Road, East Sheen, London SW14 7JH
☎ & FAX 0181 878 8842

CONTACT   John Hockley
PRODUCTS   Labels for botanic and display gardens
CATALOGUE   On request
MAIL ORDER   Yes

Professionally engraved plant labels and holders. Used by RBG Kew.

Shire
Brigstock Road, Wisbech, Cambridgeshire PE13 3JJ
☎ 01945 465295   FAX 01945 582673

CONTACT   Mike Ward
PRODUCTS   Garden buildings; greenhouses
CATALOGUE   Yes

Manufacturers of a splendid range of wooden garden sheds, workshops, summerhouses and cedar greenhouses.

Sim and Coventry
Eastham House, Copse Road, Fleetwood, Lancashire FT7 7NY
☎ 01253 778888   FAX 01253 878711

CONTACT   Lesley Pritchard
PRODUCTS   Garden furniture, fencing, bamboo canes and tree stakes
NEW PRODUCTS   Log rolls, 'big hand' garden scoops, bird feeders
CATALOGUE   On request
MAIL ORDER   No

A division of David Halsall plc. Suppliers of bamboo canes, trellis and jardinaires; timber trellis and tree stakes; plastic trellis and lawn edging.

Somerset Postal Flowers
Carew Cottage, Crowcombe, Taunton, Somerset TA4 4AD
☎ 01984 618314   FAX 01984 618611

CONTACT   Rosalind Gill
PRODUCTS   Fresh flowers
CATALOGUE   On request
MAIL ORDER   Yes

This firm specialises in sending fresh flowers by post to addresses in the United Kingdom and much of Europe. They also offer their flower arrangement skills nationwide and run classes to learn their art.

Spear & Jackson Garden Products
Neill Tools Ltd, Handsworth Road, Sheffield, South Yorkshire S13 9BR
☎ 0114 244 9911   FAX 0114 256 1545

CONTACT   Linda Collins
PRODUCTS   Hand tools; garden tools
CATALOGUE   On request
MAIL ORDER   No

Manufacturers of a wide range of hand and garden tools under this well-known brand name.

The Standard Manufacturing Co
55 Woods Lane, Derby, Derbyshire DE3 3UD
☎ 01332 343369   FAX 01332 381531

CONTACT   G Mahaffey
PRODUCTS   Garden tools; cloches
CATALOGUE   No
MAIL ORDER   Yes

Makers of a range of garden tools, including tree pruners, fruit-pickers, sweepers, spreaders and cloches.

Stangwrach Leisure Products
Stangwrach, Llanfynydd, Camarthen, Dyfed SA32 7TG
☎ & FAX 01558 668287

CONTACT   Terry or Grace Maidment
PRODUCTS   Garden furniture
NEW PRODUCTS   Benches for bad backs; new swing-benches
CATALOGUE   £1
MAIL ORDER   Yes

Hardwood garden furniture in strong designs, made to individual requirements. The timber is sourced only from managed forests. They also undertake repairs and refurbishment.

Starkie & Starkie Ltd
39 The Heathers Industrial Park, Freemen's Common, Leicester, Leicestershire LE2 7SQ
☎ 0116 2854772   FAX 0116 2854884

CONTACT   R A Starkie
PRODUCTS   Tool-sharpening systems
CATALOGUE   On request
MAIL ORDER   Yes

Suppliers of diamond whetstones and tool-sharpening systems.

Store More Garden Buildings

Store More House, Latham Close, Bredbury Industrial Park, Stockport, Cheshire SK6 2SD

☎ 0161 430 3347   📠 0161 406 6054

CONTACT   Chris Downes or Sharon Winch
PRODUCTS   Garden buildings; greenhouses
CATALOGUE   On request
MAIL ORDER Yes

Zinc-coated steel sheds and garden buildings which are maintenance-free; aluminium glasshouses; garden and storage buildings in logwood or ship-lap. All items are available mail-order, flat-packed for DIY assembly.

Stratford Power Garden Machinery

4 Marsh Road, Wilmcote, Stratford on Avon, Warwickshire CV37 9XR

☎ 01789 294839   📠 01789 261119

CONTACT   Arnold Coffee
PRODUCTS   Garden machinery
NEW PRODUCTS Earth auger
CATALOGUE   On request
MAIL ORDER Yes

Distributors of the 'Texas' range of garden cultivators, 'Ikra' electric hedgecutters, 'Bertolini' sickle mowers and 'Zenoah' chainsaws.

Stuart Garden Architecture

Burrow Hill Farm, Wiveliscombe, Somerset TA4 2RN

☎ 01984 667458   📠 01984 667455

CONTACT   Melanie Harris
PRODUCTS   Trellis; wooden garden features; garden furniture
NEW PRODUCTS Colony dining table
CATALOGUE   £2
MAIL ORDER Yes

Stylish range of trellis work, gazebos, pergolas, bridges and garden furniture. All constructed from hardwoods from sustainable sources. Custom design and build available.

Studio Forge

The Forge, Offham, Lewes, Sussex BN7 3QD

☎ 01273 474173   📠 01273 480069

CONTACT   Richard Heanley
PRODUCTS   Ironwork furniture; garden ornaments
CATALOGUE   On request
MAIL ORDER Yes

Makers of wrought-iron garden furniture, arches, gazebos, obelisks, plant stands and tunnels. Pieces can also be made to customers' specifications.

Sunshine of Africa (UK) Ltd

The Coach House, Gatcombe Park, Newport, Isle of Wight PO30 3EJ

☎ 01983 721010   📠 01983 721117

CONTACT   Karen Bland
PRODUCTS   Mulches
NEW PRODUCTS New bag sizes
MAIL ORDER No

Wholesalers of garden mulch and lawn-care products made from cocoa shell, Sunshine of Africa (UK) Ltd is the UK brand leader.

Super Natural Ltd

Bore Place Farm, Chiddingstone, Edenbridge, Kent TN8 7AR

☎ 01732 463255   📠 01732 740264

CONTACT   Caroline Dunmall
PRODUCTS   Organic composts and mulches; organic plant food
CATALOGUE   On request

Organic composts, plant foods and soil conditioners. Also available in commercial sizes.

Supersheds Ltd

Coppice Road, Willaston, Nantwich, Cheshire CW5 6QH

☎ 01270 668121   📠 01270 669280

CONTACT   John Partington
PRODUCTS   Garden buildings; garden furniture
NEW PRODUCTS Barbecues, racking, chalets, summerhouses
CATALOGUE   Yes

Manufacturers of a range of garden sheds and garden furniture. Metal garden sheds are supplied too.

Sussex Trugs Ltd

Thomas Smith's Trug Shop, Hailsham Road, Herstmonceux, East Sussex BN27 4LH

☎ 01323 832137   📠 01323 833801

CONTACT   Robin or Sue Tuppen
PRODUCTS   Garden trugs
CATALOGUE   On request
MAIL ORDER Yes

Makers of the traditional Sussex trug basket.

Terrace & Garden Ltd

Orchard House, Patmore End, Ugley, Bishops Stortford, Hertfordshire CM22 6JA

☎ 01799 543289   📠 01799 543586

CONTACT   Sandra Burrows
PRODUCTS   Decorative taps; wind-chimes; weather-vanes; sundials
NEW PRODUCTS Patio furniture; Gardener's pouch-type aprons
CATALOGUE   On request
MAIL ORDER Yes

Decorative and amusing sundials, animal-shaped tap heads, bird-houses, trellises, weather-vanes, path signs, and wind-chimes for garden and home. The range is expanding and continues to show the inventiveness which has characterised all their products.

Thames Valley Wirework Co Ltd

792 Weston Road, Slough Trading Estate, Slough, Berkshire SL1 4HR

☎ 01753 521992   📠 01753 574160

CONTACT   Sales Office
PRODUCTS   Plant supports
CATALOGUE   SAE

MAIL ORDER Yes

Manufacturers of 'Gro-Thru' plant supports for herbaceous plants and a range of other supports for indoor and outdoor use.

Thermoforce Ltd
Wakefield Road, Cockermouth, Cumbria CA13 0HS
☎ 01900 823231   FAX 01900 825965
CONTACT L Kitchen
PRODUCTS Greenhouse equipment
NEW PRODUCTS Heaters and air-circulation products
CATALOGUE On request
MAIL ORDER Yes

Manufacturers of greenhouse equipment including soil cables, mist units, automatic vents, thermostats and lighting.

Tildenet Ltd
Longbrook House, Ashton Vale Road, Bristol BS3 2HA
☎ 0117 966 9684   FAX 0117 923 1251
CONTACT Angie Bunce
PRODUCTS Netting
NEW PRODUCTS Extruded plastic range of crop protectors
CATALOGUE On request
MAIL ORDER No

Manufacturers of netting for perimeters, wind-breaks and ground cover.

Town and Country Products
Whitwick Business Park, Stenson Road, Whitwick, Leicestershire LE67 4JP
☎ 01530 830990   FAX 01530 830877
CONTACT Nick Page
PRODUCTS Tool holders; gloves
CATALOGUE On request

Manufacturers and suppliers of pouches and tool holders, and suppliers of 'Wells Lamont' garden and work gloves.

Tracmaster Ltd
Teknol House, Victoria Road, Burgess Hill, West Sussex RH15 9LH
☎ 01444 247689   FAX 01444 871612
CONTACT Chris Trull
PRODUCTS Garden machinery
NEW PRODUCTS Hay rake
CATALOGUE On request
MAIL ORDER Yes

Suppliers of heavy-duty, two-wheeled tractors which handle tasks from grass-cutting and cultivating, to trailer-towing and snow-blowing. Shredder-chippers are a recent addition.

Trade and DIY Products Ltd
The Pump House, Hazelwood Road, Duffield, Belper, Derbyshire DE56 4DQ
☎ 01332 842685   FAX 01332 842806
CONTACT R Barlow
PRODUCTS Sheeting; weed suppressants; fleece; capillary matting; cloches
NEW PRODUCTS Plantex Gropax; Q-mat mulch
CATALOGUE On request

MAIL ORDER Yes

Suppliers of horticultural fleece and 'Plantex' weed suppressant fabric (as used by RBG Kew) to retail and trade customers.

The Traditional Garden Supply Company Ltd
Unit 12, Hewitts Industrial Estate, Elmbridge Road, Cranleigh, Surrey GU6 8LU
☎ 01249 447000   FAX 01249 448137
CONTACT General sales staff
PRODUCTS Garden supplies, garden furniture, cold frames, tool stores
CATALOGUE On request: 3 a year
MAIL ORDER Yes

Mail-order suppliers of carefully selected garden products: some practical, some decorative, some both. They have a shop, too.

The Trailer Barrow
Elsan Ltd, Bellbrook Park, Uckfield, East Sussex TN22 1QF
☎ 01825 748200   FAX 01825 761212
CONTACT Karen Isted
PRODUCTS Wheelbarrows; garden trailers
CATALOGUE On request
MAIL ORDER Yes, if no local stockist

Two-wheeled barrows for pulling and larger models for towing.

Trident Water Garden Products
Carlton Road, Foleshill, Coventry, West Midlands CV6 7FL
☎ 01203 638802   FAX 01203 638775
CONTACT Marian Ryan
PRODUCTS Water gardening and aquatic products
CATALOGUE SAE
MAIL ORDER No

Pumps, pre-formed pools and pond liners, filtration systems, fountains, lighting and water garden accessories.

Two Chapel Yard
2 Chapel Yard, Holt, Norfolk NR25 6HX
☎ & FAX 01263 713933
CONTACT Karen Macdonald Thomas
PRODUCTS Floral sundries; baskets; trugs
CATALOGUE Free
MAIL ORDER Yes

Suppliers of floral sundries, including trugs and baskets. They also run day-workshops in creative flowers.

Two Wests and Elliott Ltd
Unit 4, Carrwood Road, Sheepbridge Industrial Estate, Chesterfield, Derbyshire S41 9RH
☎ 01246 451077   FAX 01246 260115
CONTACT J M West
PRODUCTS Greenhouse fittings and equipment; propagators; cold frames and mini-greenhouses; fruit cages
CATALOGUE On request
MAIL ORDER Yes

Manufacture and sell a wide range of greenhouse and conservatory equipment including staging, heating, ventilators, watering, propagation equipment and mini-greenhouses. For amateur and professional use. Elliott is the dog.

Tyrite
PO Box 61, Alton, Hampshire GU34 3YU
☎ & [FAX] 01420 588546
CONTACT   Janet Brighton
PRODUCTS   Plant supports
CATALOGUE   Leaflets
MAIL ORDER   Yes

The 'wires with loops' for training and supporting plants. Can be used on walls, posts or fences.

Vale Garden Houses Ltd
Melton Road, Harlaxton, Grantham, Lincolnshire
NG32 1HQ
☎ 01476 564433   [FAX] 01476 578555
CONTACT   Lisa Morton
PRODUCTS   Conservatories, orangeries and pavilions
CATALOGUE   On request
MAIL ORDER   No

Individually designed conservatories in period styles for domestic use. Vale Conservatories Ltd handles larger and commercial projects.

Verdigris Ltd
Walkern Hall Farm, Walkern, Stevenage, Hertfordshire
SG2 7HZ
☎ 01438 869346   [FAX] 01438 869370
CONTACT   D N C De Boinville
PRODUCTS   Copper plant labels
CATALOGUE   On request
MAIL ORDER   Yes

Copper plant labels, tags and markers. These can be embossed to order.

Vitax Ltd
Owen Street, Coalville, Leicestershire LE67 3DE
☎ 01530 510060   [FAX] 01530 510299
CONTACT   Ana Rawling
PRODUCTS   Composts; fertilisers and soil improvers; herbicides
CATALOGUE   On request
MAIL ORDER   No

Makers of a range of composts, lawn-care products, fertilisers and plant foods, soil-improvers and herbicides.

Wartnaby Gardens
Melton Mowbray, Leicestershire LE14 3HY
☎ 01664 822549   [FAX] 01664 822231
CONTACT   Tel 01664 822296
PRODUCTS   Plant labels
CATALOGUE   On request
MAIL ORDER   Yes

Practical zinc plant labels either as tie-ons or with stems; 14-inch stands are available for the tie-on variety and they also sell marking and engraving equipment. The labels will be on Wells & Winter's stand at shows.

Wells & Winter
Mereworth, Maidstone, Kent ME18 5NB
☎ 01622 813267
CONTACT   Sir John Wells
PRODUCTS   Labels; tree ties; apron; clamp for aerial layering
NEW PRODUCTS   Garden hurdles
CATALOGUE   On request
MAIL ORDER   Yes

Good quality plastic, aluminium, zinc and copper labels, tags, and marking equipment. Labels can be pre-engraved to your order. Mail order and shows only. Some other products, and books (at shows only).

Wessex Horticultural Products Ltd
South Newton, Salisbury, Wiltshire SP2 0QW
☎ 01722 742500   [FAX] 01722 742571
CONTACT   Rosemary Henderson
PRODUCTS   Growing media; organic products
NEW PRODUCTS   Decorative stones in six colours/grades
CATALOGUE   On request
MAIL ORDER   Yes

Manufacturers and suppliers of peat-free and traditional growing media. Their sister company Growing Success Organics Ltd sells slug killer, hanging basket liners and insect traps.

West Meters Ltd
Western Bank Industrial Estate, Wigton, Cumbria CA7 9SJ
☎ 016973 44288   [FAX] 016973 44616
CONTACT   John Fisher
PRODUCTS   Thermometers; measuring equipment; clocks
CATALOGUE   On request
MAIL ORDER   Yes

A large choice of thermometers, rain gauges, hygrometers, soil-test meters and barometers, as well as some household measuring instruments. They also trade as Taylor Instruments.

Westland Horticulture
97 Moy Road, Dungannon, Co. Tyrone
☎ & [FAX] 018687 84007
CONTACT   Seamus McGrane
PRODUCTS   Growing media; mulches
NEW PRODUCTS   John Innes composts made to the original specification & others with farmyard manure
CATALOGUE   On request

Manufacturers and suppliers of Westland composts and growing media including mulches and chipped bark.

Whichford Pottery
Whichford, Shipston on Stour, Warwickshire CV36 5PG
☎ 01608 684416   [FAX] 01608 684833
CONTACT   Jane Lancia
PRODUCTS   Terracotta pots
NEW PRODUCTS   New designs and glazes
CATALOGUE   6 first class stamps
MAIL ORDER   Yes, £15.50 delivery charge

Hand-made, frost-free terracotta pots in plain and decorated designs. The pottery, which can be visited, handles some very large pieces.

William Sinclair Horticulture

Firth Road, Lincoln, Lincolnshire LN6 7AH
☎ 01522 537561   [FAX] 01522 513609

CONTACT   Advisory Service
PRODUCTS   Composts; fertilisers; aggregates; lawn care
MAIL ORDER   No

Horticultural conglomerate whose range includes composts, fertilisers and soil conditioners from J. Arthur Bowers; 'Silvaperl' aggregates including sand, gravel and perlite; the 'Garotta' brand compost equipment; and peat-free composts and conditioners.

Wiltshire Summerhouses

137 High Street, Littleton Panell, Devizes, Wiltshire SN10 4EU
☎ & [FAX] 01380 818967

CONTACT   Sally or Steve Peake
PRODUCTS   Summerhouses; garden buildings
CATALOGUE   On request
MAIL ORDER   Yes, personal delivery

Rotating wooden summerhouses in kit form or ready-assembled. All are made to order. Other styles include potting sheds and there is a bespoke service.

WOLF Garden

Alton Road, Ross on Wye, Hereford & Worcester HR9 5NE
☎ 01989 767600   [FAX] 01989 765589

CONTACT   Sales Office

PRODUCTS   Hand tools; lawn-mowers; garden machinery; garden lights
NEW PRODUCTS   Ride-on mini-mower
CATALOGUE   From Wolf and their stockists
MAIL ORDER   No

An extensive range of tools for the gardener from this well-known company. Products include garden tools with interchangeable heads, cultivating tools, pruning equipment, lawn-mowers, powered machinery, barbecues and garden lighting. Shredders, hedge-trimmers and Malibu garden lights are recent additions to their range.

Woodgrow Horticulture Ltd

84 Burton Road, Findern, Derby, Derbyshire DE65 6BE
☎ 01332 516392/517600 [FAX] 01332 511481

CONTACT   Arnold, Martin or Philip Woodhouse
PRODUCTS   Landscaping materials
CATALOGUE   Brochures & product sheets
MAIL ORDER   Some items

Landscape materials, especially bark and other mulches, for the trade and retail users.

Woodside Horticulture Ltd

Woodside Farm, Dearham, Maryport, Cumbria CA15 7LD
☎ 01900 816579   [FAX] 01900 876019

CONTACT   J Cox
PRODUCTS   Composts; fertilisers; bark
CATALOGUE   Yes
MAIL ORDER   Yes

Suppliers and manufacturers of peat and peat-free composts, bark and fertilisers. They also attend the commercial shows at Four Oaks and Scotgrow.

17

Professional
Services

For even the most enthusiastic gardener there comes a time to call on professional help. Others may turn to the experts more often – for large and demanding jobs, for knowledge and expertise, or for their ideas and inspiration. The good news is that there is no shortage of assistance available out there. Choosing the right person for the right task, however, and making sure that what you get is what you actually want are more tricky. The information in this section is designed to help you on your way.

Employing a professiotnal

The most important job is to decide what you want. You don't have to make all the decisions yourself, but the nature and extent of the work which you are prepared to pay for must be laid out at the start. For small and well-defined tasks such as the removal of a tree limb this should be straightforward enough. For anything more extensive it's vital to discuss and agree the brief with the professional concerned. Many professionals produce detailed information on the way they carry out their business and what clients can expect. Then you need to spell out your requirements on such matters as time scale, the budget, and the degree of finish. It has to be absolutely clear that the professional understands your terms and is able to fulfil them. This process can be time-consuming. Avoid the temptation to rush it. This will avoid many costly misunderstandings and potential disappointments. Among the questions to ask, satisfy yourself on the following:

What are your qualifications? Do you belong to an appropriate professional body?

What levels of third party insurance and public liability insurance do you carry? This is very important for heavy or hazardous work such as tree surgery or construction.

Can I see a portfolio, inspect completed work or contact previous clients to see whether I like your work?

Will you use your own staff or employ outside contractors? Can a designer recommend contractors?

Notes on the lists

Suppliers of professional services are listed alphabetically, by name. In each entry you will find details of the services which the firm offers, the geographical area they operate in, and examples of the kind of projects of which they have experience. The main divisions are Garden Design, Landscape Architecture, Horticultural Consultancy, Arboricultural Services and Landscape Contractors. A number of the nurseries and garden centres we list also offer garden design and landscaping, ranging in degree from informal (but expert) advice to full design, construction or consultancy services. Such nurseries are indicated here by a cross-reference to their main entry in the Nurseries section.

Professional bodies and qualifications

Many of the entries include details of the main professional bodies and organisations to which they belong. This information is not definitive, and not everyone has supplied full details, yet it is a useful guide to the sort of service you can expect to find. Firms and practitioners are strictly vetted before they can join these bodies, and this vetting may include inspection of their work and a requirement to carry specified levels of insurance. For more details about these bodies see the Organisations section. Academic qualifications in horticulture and related disciplines are something of a minefield. There remains scope for confusion: a diploma in landscape architecture, for instance, is a postgraduate qualification involving years of study, whereas a diploma in garden design may be attained in a matter of weeks. It is up to you to decide on what level of technical competence or experience – not to mention artistry and imagination – is appropriate.

FHort   Fellow of the Institute of Horticulture
MIHort   Member of the Institute of Horticulture
AIHort   Associate of the Institute of Horticulture
FSGD   Fellow of the Society of Garden Designers
MSGD   Member of the Society of Garden Designers

Affiliates of the Society of Garden Designers are entitled to mention their affiliation in brochures and promotional material, but they may not use the Society's initials after their name. Do not read too much into the designation Corresponding Member: anyone can become one for £25.

ALI   Associate of the Landscape Institute
AAAC   Arboricultural Association Approved Contractor
FAA   Fellow of the Arboricultural Association
BALI   British Association of Landscape Industries
APL   Association of Professional Landscapers

Further information

The Institute of Horticulture produces a list of horticultural consultants: to receive a free copy write to the institute at 14/15 Belgrave Square, London SW1X 8PS. *The Society of Garden Designers* also produces a list of its membership with notes about their careers: free of charge from the Hon. Secretary, Society of Garden Designers, 23 Reigate Road, Ewell, Surrey KT17 1PS. If you contact the *British Association of Landscape Industries* (BALI) at Landscape House, Henry Street, Keighley, West Yorkshire BD21 3DR they can provide a list of BALI members in your area. *The Arboricultural Association*, at Ampfield House, Romsey, Hampshire SO51 9PA can send you a copy of their directory of approved contractors and consultants on request. A *Directory of Registered Landscape Practices*, which includes all the *Landscape Institute*'s members, can be obtained from RIBA shops (£10) and by post (£11) from the Royal Institute of British Architects.

Caveat Emptor

Our list is based on information which the firms themselves have supplied. Accordingly, the presence in or absence from this list of a firm should not be taken as a judgement on the firm or any sort of recommendation. It's your decision whom you employ in the end – and, as so often, the motto is *Buyer Beware*.

Ace of Spades Postal Garden Design
16 Cranley Road, Guildford, Surrey GU1 2JE
☎ 01483 572716
CONTACT Sue Howson
WORKING AREA UK
SERVICES Garden design

STARTED TRADING 1993
PROJECTS Small private gardens
Garden designer. Plans and planting guides by post to provide an inexpensive service.

Acorn Landscapes, North Yorkshire
For full details see Nurseries section

Acres Wild (Landscape & Garden Design)
45a High Street, Billingshurst, West Sussex RH14 9PP
☎ 01403 785385
CONTACT Ian Smith or Debbie Roberts
WORKING AREA Surrey & Sussex
ASSOCIATIONS MSGD
SERVICES Garden design
STARTED TRADING 1988
PROJECTS School garden at Hazlewick School, Crawley; seaside garden, Rottingdean; meditation/Feng shui garden, Virginia Water
Garden design. Both partners have degrees in landscape architecture and like their schemes to blend in with the natural environment.

Agars Nursery, Hampshire
For full details see Nurseries section

Alan Sargent
8 Willow Walk, Petworth, West Sussex GU28 0EY
☎ & ✉ 01798 342388
CONTACT Alan Sargent
WORKING AREA Southern England
ASSOCIATIONS MIHort, MILAM
SERVICES Garden design; contractors
STARTED TRADING 1968
PROJECTS Construction of Gold Medal garden, Chelsea 1996
Garden and landscape design and construction. Specialists in paving and walling.

All Seasons Tree Service
Paradise Cottage, Sandy Lane, Chew Magna, Somerset BS18 8RT
☎ 01275 333401/01225 429996 ✉ 01275 333125
CONTACT Kit or Penny Hogg
WORKING AREA South-west England
ASSOCIATIONS AAAC
SERVICES Contractors; arboricultural services
STARTED TRADING 1984
Tree surgeons specialising in amenity trees. They also sell woodchip mulch.

Allan Hart Associates
Orchard House, 61 Christchurch Road, East Sheen, London SW14 7AN
☎ 0181 878 2017   ✉ 0181 878 1638
CONTACT Allan Hart
WORKING AREA UK & Europe, Middle & Far East, USA
ASSOCIATIONS ALI, MIHort, MILAM

SERVICES   Garden design; horticultural consultancy; landscape architecture; sport and recreation facilities
STARTED TRADING 1968
PROJECTS   Renovation at Radnor Gardens, Twickenham; cricket ground at Hornetye, Hastings, Sussex; public open space for recreation and nature conservation, Hanworth

Landscape architecture practice with particular horticultural expertise. Allan Hart's training includes the Kew diploma. Work includes company headquarters, hospitals, estates and landscape restoration.

Allseasons Landscapes
Prospect House, The Green, Ninfield, Battle, East Sussex
TN33 9JE
☎ 01424 893222/01273 562160   [FAX] 01424 893485
CONTACT   Philip Boast
WORKING AREA   East & West Sussex
ASSOCIATIONS   BALI
SERVICES   Garden design; contractors; interior landscaping and maintenance
STARTED TRADING 1982

Andrea Parsons – The Parsons Garden
15a Rawsthorn Road, Colchester, Essex CO3 3JH
☎ 01206 570440   [FAX] 01206 763408
CONTACT   Andrea Parsons
WORKING AREA   Nationwide
SERVICES   Garden design; contractors
STARTED TRADING 1989
PROJECTS   Garden in Eaton Square, London; Chelsea Show gardens, 1996, 1997

Distinction at College of Garden Design. Garden design and construction for private clients.

Ann Stark, North Yorkshire
For full details see Nurseries section

Annabel Allhusen
Capstitch House, Compton Abbas, Shaftesbury, Dorset
SP7 0NB
☎ 01747 811622   [FAX] 01747 850004
CONTACT   Annabel Allhusen
WORKING AREA   Devon, Dorset, Hampshire, Somerset, Wiltshire
SERVICES   Garden design; horticultural consultancy
STARTED TRADING 1989
PROJECTS   Water project at Manor House, Dorset

Trained at the College of Garden Design. Garden design, including drawings and planting schedules. Consultancy advice and individual border planning also available.

Anthea Sokell
Rickleden, Maddox Lane, Bookham, Leatherhead, Surrey
KT23 3BS
☎ & [FAX] 01372 452052
CONTACT   Anthea Sokell
WORKING AREA   Southern England
SERVICES   Garden design
STARTED TRADING 1990

PROJECTS   New town house garden; period cottage garden; garden on steep slope
Garden design for private gardens. Trained at the College of Garden Design.

Anthony Archer-Wills Ltd
Broadford Bridge Road, West Chiltington, West Sussex
RH20 2LF
☎ 01798 813204   [FAX] 01798 815080
CONTACT   Lynn Archer-Wills
SERVICES   Garden design; contractors
STARTED TRADING 1965

Garden designer with particular expertise in water gardens: he can supply the plants and associated products too. See also the Nurseries section.

Anthony du Gard Pasley
3 The Homestead, Corseley Road, Groombridge, Kent
TN3 9RN
☎ 01892 864548
CONTACT   A du Gard Pasley
WORKING AREA   Home Counties, south-west Scotland & Borders, Europe
ASSOCIATIONS   FLI, FSA(Scot), FSDG
SERVICES   Garden design; horticultural consultancy; landscape architecture
STARTED TRADING 1972
PROJECTS   Hedsor Wharf, Berkshire; Wadhurst Park, Sussex

Landscape architect and garden designer with particular expertise in restoring and altering historic gardens for easier maintenance without loss of character. Lectures and writes. His Scottish address is: Roseburn, Haywood Road, Moffat, Dumfries & Galloway DG10 9BU (01683 220146).

Anthony George & Associates
The Old Brick House, Village Road, Dorney, Windsor, Berkshire SL4 6QJ
☎ 01628 604224   [FAX] 01628 604401
CONTACT   Anthony George
WORKING AREA   London, Midlands & southern England
ASSOCIATIONS   ALI
SERVICES   Garden design; arboricultural services; landscape architecture; architectural consultants
STARTED TRADING 1982

Architectural consultants, planners and landscape architects.

Anthony Johns
Norton Nursery and Garden Centre, Norton Lane, Whitchurch, Bristol BS14 0BT
☎ 01275 832834
CONTACT   Anthony Johns
WORKING AREA   Dorset, Gloucestershire, Somerset, Wiltshire

SERVICES   Garden design; horticultural consultancy; contractors
STARTED TRADING 1994

Garden Designer for mainly private gardens. Trained at Pershore. Works in association with family nursery.

Anthony Short & Partners
34 Church Street, Ashbourne, Derbyshire DE6 1AE
☎ 01335 342345   [FAX] 01335 300624
CONTACT   Anthony Short
WORKING AREA   50-mile radius
ASSOCIATIONS   ALI, RIBA
SERVICES   Landscape architecture; chartered architects
STARTED TRADING 1966

Architectural and landscape architectural practice.

Anthos Design
47 Bennerley Road, London SW11 6DR
☎ 0171 228 2288   [FAX] 0171 978 4148
CONTACT   Ian David Dougill
WORKING AREA   South-east England
ASSOCIATIONS   ALI
SERVICES   Garden design; landscape architecture
STARTED TRADING 1976
PROJECTS   Garden projects in the London area, including wildlife habitats and meadows

Landscape architect and garden designer with a diploma in town planning.

Antony Young
Ridleys Cheer, Mountain Bower, Chippenham, Wiltshire SN14 7AJ
☎ 01225 891204   [FAX] 01225 891139
CONTACT   Antony Young
WORKING AREA   UK & Europe
SERVICES   Garden design; horticultural consultancy; contractors
STARTED TRADING 1990
PROJECTS   Lucknam Park Hotel, Bath

Full garden design service.

Apple Court, Hampshire
For full details see Nurseries section

Apuldram Roses, West Sussex
For full details see Nurseries section

Arabella Lennox-Boyd
45 Moreton Street, London SW1V 2NY
☎ 0171 931 9995   [FAX] 0171 821 6585
CONTACT   Tommaso del Buono
WORKING AREA   UK, Western Europe, USA, Caribbean
ASSOCIATIONS   MSGD, ALI
SERVICES   Garden design; horticultural consultancy; landscape architecture
STARTED TRADING 1971
PROJECTS   Roof garden, No 1 Poultry, City of London; The Ritz; private gardens and estates in Western Europe and Barbados

Undertakes projects of all sizes, including historical gardens. Equal emphasis on architectural design and planting. Specialities include roof and Mediterranean gardens. Arabella Lennox-Boyd is also a trustee of RBG Kew, a council member of the Painshill Park Trust, and has written books on traditional English gardens and London gardens.

Architectural Landscape Design Ltd
3–5 Kelsey Road, Beckenham, Kent BR3 2LH
☎ 0181 658 4455   [FAX] 0181 658 2785
CONTACT   Chris Coope
WORKING AREA   One hour's drive from M25
ASSOCIATIONS   BALI, MIHort
SERVICES   Garden design; contractors
STARTED TRADING 1978

Complete landscape service from site-clearance through to design, planting and construction.

Arne Herbs, Somerset
For full details see Nurseries section

Arrow Tree Services
102 Quebec Road, St Leonards on Sea, East Sussex TN38 9HT
☎ 01424 714376
CONTACT   David Archer
WORKING AREA   Kent, London, Surrey, Sussex
ASSOCIATIONS   AAAC
SERVICES   Arboricultural services
STARTED TRADING 1976
PROJECTS   Restoration of Victorian pleasure gardens; management of plane trees along South Bank, London

Arboricultural consultant and contractor.

Artscapes & Theseus Maze Designs
Silk Mill House, 24 Winchester Street, Whitchurch, Hampshire RG28 7DD
☎ & [FAX] 01256 892837
CONTACT   Graham Burgess
WORKING AREA   UK & overseas
ASSOCIATIONS   FHort
SERVICES   Garden design; horticultural consultancy; water and riparian services; maze and labyrinth design
STARTED TRADING 1981

Kew-trained garden designer whose work includes symbolic and historic designs, with a special expertise in mazes and multi-media work.

ASH Consulting Group
15 Carlton Court, Glasgow, Strathclyde G5 9JP
☎ 0141 420 3131   [FAX] 0141 420 3020
CONTACT   Ross Anderson
WORKING AREA   UK & overseas
ASSOCIATIONS   ALI
SERVICES   Garden design; landscape architecture
STARTED TRADING 1979
PROJECTS   Management & restoration plan for gardens designed by Adam and Bruce, Hopetoun House

Substantial landscape design and planning group formed by the merger of ASH and Cousins Stephens. There are other branches in Scotland and England. The practice includes landscape architects, ecologists, foresters, town planners, environmental scientists and economists.

Aylett Nurseries Ltd, Hertfordshire
For full details see Nurseries section

Aylmer Addison Associates
Walnut Tree Farm, Kirstead, Brooke, Norwich, Norfolk NR15 1EG
☎ 01508 50402   [FAX] 01508 50110
CONTACT   Mr Aylmer or Mr Addison
WORKING AREA   Cambridgeshire, Norfolk, Suffolk
ASSOCIATIONS   AAAC
SERVICES   Arboricultural services
STARTED TRADING   1979

Arboricultural work including amenity planting, surgery, the conservation and maintenance of small woodlands, heathland restoration and advice on safety for Local Authorities.

Ballalheannagh Gardens, Isle of Man
For full details see Nurseries section

Barbara Hunt
91 Church Street, Staines, Surrey TW18 4XS
☎ & [FAX] 01784 452919
CONTACT   Barbara Hunt
WORKING AREA   London, Surrey, Buckinghamshire, Berkshire, Oxfordshire
ASSOCIATIONS   MIHort, MSGD
SERVICES   Garden design
STARTED TRADING   1980

Has a diploma in 3-D design. Landscape design and consultancy for private and commercial clients. Winner of Tudor Rose Award at Hampton Court in 1992, 1993, 1994.

Barrell Treecare
8 Linnet Close, Ringwood, Hampshire BH24 3RE
☎ 01425 461633   [FAX] 01425 472269
CONTACT   Jeremy Barrell
WORKING AREA   UK
ASSOCIATIONS   AAAC, FAA
SERVICES   Arboricultural services
STARTED TRADING   1980

Tree consultancy specialising in reports for insurance and mortgage uses and expert witness.

Barters Farm Nurseries Ltd, Wiltshire
For full details see Nurseries section

Barton Grange Garden Centre (Bolton), Lancashire
For full details see Nurseries section

Barton Grange Landscapes, Lancashire
For full details see Nurseries section

Beechcroft Nurseries, Cumbria
For full details see Nurseries section

Berrys Garden Company Ltd
6 Hodford Road, London NW11 8NP
☎ 0181 209 0194   [FAX] 0181 458 6442
CONTACT   Brian Berry
WORKING AREA   Buckinghamshire, Hertfordshire, Middlesex, London north of the Thames
ASSOCIATIONS   BALI
SERVICES   Garden design; horticultural consultancy; contractors; lighting and irrigation systems
STARTED TRADING   1980
PROJECTS   Hampstead Garden Suburb Trust; Harlesden City Challenge

Landscape design and build, including garden electrics, carpentry and irrigation and drainage.

Birkheads Cottage Garden Nursery, Tyne & Wear
For full details see Nurseries section

Boonwood Garden Centre, Cumbria
For full details see Nurseries section

Brackenwood Garden Centre, Avon
For full details see Nurseries section

Brackenwood Nurseries, Somerset
For full details see Nurseries section

Branchline Tree Services
23 Charlestown Cottages, Glossop, Derbyshire SK13 8LF
☎ & [FAX] 01457 862954
CONTACT   Paul Turkentine
WORKING AREA   North-west England & Greater Manchester
ASSOCIATIONS   AAAC
SERVICES   Arboricultural services
STARTED TRADING   1988

Approved local and county council contractors.

Brent Surveys & Designs
158a Edenvale Road, Westbury, Wiltshire BA13 3QG
☎ 01373 827331   [FAX] 01373 777148
CONTACT   Mike Osborne
WORKING AREA   Nationwide
ASSOCIATIONS   MIHort
SERVICES   Horticultural consultancy; contractors; house and garden building design
STARTED TRADING   1985
PROJECTS   Italian-style garden in Trowbridge

Garden design, surveys and construction. Husband and wife team combine design and estate management experience. The business is based on a postal service: design and planting plans are created from your sketch, photographs and soil test. Site visits are available as an additional service.

Brian Jones Garden Design
Tree Cottage, 3 High Street, East Harptree, Bristol,
Somerset BS18 6AY
☎ 01761 221588

CONTACT   Brian Jones
WORKING AREA   South-west
ASSOCIATIONS   RIBA
SERVICES   Garden design
STARTED TRADING   1994
PROJECTS   Private gardens near Bristol and Portsmouth

Architect turned garden designer and artist.

Broadstone Nurseries, Oxfordshire
For full details see Nurseries section

Brockings Exotics, Cornwall
For full details see Nurseries section

Bunny Guinness
Sibberton Lodge, Thornhaugh, Peterborough,
Cambridgeshire PE8 6NH
☎ & 𝗙𝗔𝗫 01780 782518

CONTACT   Bunny Guinness
WORKING AREA   England & France
ASSOCIATIONS   ALI
SERVICES   Garden design; horticultural consultancy;
landscape architecture
STARTED TRADING   1985
PROJECTS   Holywell Hall, Lincolnshire

Landscape architect with a degree in Horticulture. Wide
experience in public and private practice. Commissions can be
phased over several years and an initial free consultation is
offered. Gold Medal winner at Chelsea in 1994, 1995 and
1996. Her book, 'Family Gardens' was published by David &
Charles last year.

Burncoose & South Down Nurseries, Cornwall
For full details see Nurseries section

Byrkley Park Centre, Staffordshire
For full details see Nurseries section

Cabbages & Kings
Wilderness Farm, Wilderness Lane, Hadlow Down, East
Sussex TN22 4HU
☎ 01825 830552   𝗙𝗔𝗫 01825 830736

CONTACT   Andrew or Ryl Nowell
WORKING AREA   UK & overseas (design and planting)
ASSOCIATIONS   FSGD
SERVICES   Garden design; horticultural consultancy;
contractors
STARTED TRADING   1989

Over 30 years experience designing gardens. They will supply
and plant too. Demonstration garden. They also run courses
all through the year.

Canopy Tree Care
The Meal House, Iscoyd Park, Whitchurch, Shropshire
SY13 3AW
☎ 01948 780512   𝗙𝗔𝗫 01948 780412

CONTACT   B Kearsley
WORKING AREA   Wales, Midlands, north-west England
ASSOCIATIONS   AAAC
SERVICES   Arboricultural services
STARTED TRADING   1953

Part of Flintshire Woodlands, a large group whose activities
include woodland management, tree care and environmental
consultancy.

Capital Gardens Landscapes
Highgate Garden Centre, Townsend Yard, Highgate Village,
London N6 5JF
☎ 0181 342 8977   𝗙𝗔𝗫 0181 341 5032

CONTACT   John Edwards
WORKING AREA   London, home counties & Europe
SERVICES   Garden design; horticultural consultancy;
contractors; arboricultural services
STARTED TRADING   1969
PROJECTS   Chinese garden in London

This practice, specialising in design and construction services,
now incorporates Mark Enright Landscapes.

Caves Folly Nurseries, Hereford & Worcester
For full details see Nurseries section

Channel Island Tree Service
Frenchmans Cottage, Beechvale, St John, Jersey, Channel
Islands JE3 4FL
☎ 01534 862343

CONTACT   Ian Averty
WORKING AREA   Channel Islands
ASSOCIATIONS   AAAC
SERVICES   Arboricultural services
STARTED TRADING   1987
PROJECTS   Remedial tree works at Trinity Manor and
Avranche Manor; woodland management for Jersey Tree
Council

The only Arboricultural Association approved contractor in
the islands. The mobile number is 0979 718459.

Charles Hogarth
Wissellii House, Dunsley Place, Tring, Hertfordshire
HP23 6JL
☎ 01442 890985   𝗙𝗔𝗫 01442 823817

CONTACT   Charles, Deb or Sandy
WORKING AREA   Southern England
SERVICES   Garden design; contractors; water and riparian
services
STARTED TRADING   1989

Garden designer and contractor. Specialises in schemes using
water.

Chenies Landscapes Limited
Bramble Lane, London Road East, Amersham,
Buckinghamshire HP7 9DH
☎ 01494 728004   [FAX] 01494 721403
CONTACT   Neil Denton or Kevin Copping
WORKING AREA   London & south-east England & south
Midlands
ASSOCIATIONS   BALI
SERVICES   Garden design; contractors; arboricultural serv-
ices; interior landscapes
STARTED TRADING   1961

A large firm with specialist construction, maintenance and
landscape architecture divisions. Chenies Interiorscape designs and maintains interior schemes, and the group also owns
a garden centre and a horticultural machinery outlet.

Cheryl Cummings
Holly Tree House, Green Pastures, Penallt, Monmouth,
Gwent NP5 4SB
☎ & [FAX] 01600 716296
CONTACT   Cheryl Cummings
WORKING AREA   South Wales, Herefordshire, Gloucester-
shire, North Somerset
SERVICES   Garden design
STARTED TRADING   1992
PROJECTS   Private gardens in traditional and modern styles

Garden designer. Aims to combine environmental awareness
with clients' needs. Trained at College of Garden Design,
Pershore.

Chris Yarrow & Associates
Wilderness Wood, Hadlow Down, Uckfield, East Sussex
TN22 4HJ
☎ 01825 830509   [FAX] 01825 830977
CONTACT   Chris Yarrow
WORKING AREA   Nationwide
ASSOCIATIONS   FAA
SERVICES   Arboricultural services; recreation and tourism
advisory service
STARTED TRADING   1972
PROJECTS   Tree survey for SAGA HQ

Comprehensive forestry advisory service specialising in recreational and tourism aspects. Tree surveys, planning appeals
and advice on subsidence claims.

Christopher Bradley-Hole
20 Fitzgerald Avenue, London SW14 8SZ
☎ & [FAX] 0181 241 8056
CONTACT   Christopher Bradley-Hole
WORKING AREA   London & nationwide
ASSOCIATIONS   RIBA, MSGD
SERVICES   Garden design; Architect
STARTED TRADING   1989
PROJECTS   The Daily Telegraph garden, Chelsea 1997;
restoration of historic garden, Suffolk; walled kitchen garden,
Sussex; town gardens, London

Garden designer and architect. Likes to link gardens to their
houses and surroundings. Also designs garden buildings and
lectures on garden design.

Christopher Maguire
15 Harston Road, Cambridge, Cambridgeshire CB2 5PA
☎ 01223 872800
CONTACT   Christopher Maguire
WORKING AREA   Cambridge, Essex, Hertfordshire,
Bedfordshire
ASSOCIATIONS   RIBA, MSGD
SERVICES   Garden design; Architecture
STARTED TRADING   1987
PROJECTS   Designs for private gardens

Qualified architect and garden designer. Services available
combine both disciplines.

Christopher Pickard Garden &
Landscape Design Consultancy
The Lyme House, Castle Street, Eccleshall, Staffordshire
ST21 6DP
☎ 01785 850240   [FAX] 01785 851665
CONTACT   Christopher Pickard
WORKING AREA   UK, Europe, North America
ASSOCIATIONS   APLD, MSGD
SERVICES   Garden design; Landscape design
STARTED TRADING   1975
PROJECTS   Garden in Eaton Square, London; Old Hall
Whitington, Lichfield; regional centre of horticultural excel-
lence at Rosemoor Garden, Devon

Garden and landscape designer and consultant. Services include complete design and project management. Christopher
Pickard is the principal of the School of Garden Design.

Claire Gregory
41 Riverside Gardens, Henley-in-Arden, Warwickshire
B95 5JX
☎ & [FAX] 01564 794049
CONTACT   Claire Gregory
WORKING AREA   Midlands
ASSOCIATIONS   AIHort
SERVICES   Garden design
STARTED TRADING   1994

Garden design for private clients.

Clifton Landscape and Design, London
For full details see Nurseries section

Clonmel Garden Centre, Co. Tipperary
For full details see Nurseries section

Colin White Tree Surgeon and
Forestry Contractor
The Manor House, Colwell, Hexham, Northumberland
NE46 4TL
☎ & [FAX] 01434 681598
CONTACT   Colin White
WORKING AREA   North-east England
ASSOCIATIONS   BALI, AAAC

SERVICES Arboricultural services
STARTED TRADING 1978
PROJECTS MoD Health and Safety Arboricultural Programme; Tyne and Wear Metro Arboricultural and Environmental Maintenance Programme

Full arboricultural service including planting, maintenance and chipping.

Colvin & Moggridge
Filkins, Lechlade, Gloucestershire GL7 3JQ
☎ 01367 860225   📠 01367 860564
CONTACT David McQuitty
WORKING AREA UK & overseas
ASSOCIATIONS FLI, ALI, FIHort, RIBA
SERVICES Garden design; horticultural consultancy; water and riparian services; landscape architecture
STARTED TRADING 1922

Landscape consultancy which provides a full range of landscape planning and design services for up to very large scale landscapes. Experienced in designing public and private gardens of all sizes. Past commissions have included work at Knole and Blenheim, pipeline restoration on Dartmoor, landscaping industrial and commercial headquarters, as well as private gardens.

Complete Tree Services
Wayside, Kingston Stert, Chinnor, Oxfordshire OX9 4NL
☎ & 📠 01844 351488
CONTACT Steven Burkitt
WORKING AREA Thames Valley & home counties
ASSOCIATIONS AAAC
SERVICES Arboricultural services
STARTED TRADING 1982
PROJECTS Treescape restoration, Littlemore Hospital, Oxford

Full range of services including 24-hour emergency call-out. Recommended by councils and have worked for the National Trust.

Conservatory Gardens
17 Hartington Road, Chiswick, London W4 3TL
☎ & 📠 0181 994 6109
CONTACT Joan Phelan
WORKING AREA Nationwide
ASSOCIATIONS PhD (Botany)
STARTED TRADING 1991

Help on all aspects of conservatory plants and planting design from a botanist and garden designer team. Pre-building advice and schemes for small gardens are also available, as is a postal service.

Cottage Nurseries, Lincolnshire
For full details see Nurseries section

Crowther Landscapes
Ongar Road, Abridge, Essex RM4 1AA
☎ 01708 688581   📠 01708 688677
CONTACT Ken Crowther
WORKING AREA East Anglia, London, home counties

ASSOCIATIONS ALI, BALI
SERVICES Garden design; horticultural consultancy; contractors
STARTED TRADING 1966

Complete landscape service including design and maintenance and irrigation. Have worked in Europe. Crowthers has a retail nursery in Essex, where Ken Crowther is well known as a local broadcaster.

Crowther Nurseries and Landscapes, Essex
For full details see Nurseries section

D Wells Landscaping
The Cottage, 15 Park Avenue, Eastbourne, East Sussex BN21 2XG
☎ 01323 502073
CONTACT D Wells
WORKING AREA 50-mile radius
ASSOCIATIONS BALI
SERVICES Garden design; contractors
STARTED TRADING 1970
PROJECTS Water features in private gardens

Landscape firm which specialises in water gardens and natural stonework. They won a BALI award for design and build in 1995.

Dagenham Landscapes Ltd
Redcrofts Farm, Ockendon Road, Upminster, Essex RM14 2DJ
☎ 01708 222379   📠 01708 221050
CONTACT Colin Byrne
WORKING AREA Essex & North London
ASSOCIATIONS BALI
SERVICES Garden design; contractors; turf suppliers
STARTED TRADING 1968

Garden design and landscape construction service. They also undertake garden maintenance for private and commercial customers, install swimming pools and supply grassland turf.

Dalrymple Ltd
1 Charlwood Place, Charlwood, Surrey RH6 0EB
☎ 01293 863119   📠 01293 863167
CONTACT Jason Dalrymple
WORKING AREA 100-mile radius from Gatwick
ASSOCIATIONS AAAC, FAA
SERVICES Arboricultural services
STARTED TRADING 1959

As well as arboricultural work, Dalrymple supply professional forestry machines and winches, including chippers to the National Trust.

David Brown Landscape Design
10 College Road, Impington, Cambridge, Cambridgeshire CB4 4PD
☎ 01223 232366   📠 01223 235293
CONTACT David Brown or Alistair Huck
WORKING AREA Nationwide
ASSOCIATIONS ALI, FAA, MIHort

SERVICES   Garden design; arboricultural services; landscape architecture
STARTED TRADING 1988
PROJECTS   St Andrews Park, Norwich; Ipswich Business Park

Landscape architects whose work ranges from business parks to garden design. Experienced at tree and vegetation surveys, and can undertake historical research and expert witness work.

David R Sisley
Straight Mile Nursery Gardens, Ongar Road, Brentwood, Essex CM15 9SA
☎ 01277 374439

CONTACT   David Sisley
WORKING AREA   UK
ASSOCIATIONS   BALI, FSGD
SERVICES   Garden design; horticultural consultancy; contractors
STARTED TRADING 1976
PROJECTS   Several private gardens on severely sloping sites

Garden designer based at Straight Mile Nurseries. Services include design and construction within a 40-mile radius or design and supervision nationwide.

David Stevens International Ltd
Corner Cottage, Thornton, Buckinghamshire MK17 0HE
☎ & FAX 01280 821097

CONTACT   David Stevens
WORKING AREA   UK & worldwide
ASSOCIATIONS   FLI, FIHort, FSGD
SERVICES   Garden design; horticultural consultancy; contractors; landscape architecture; lectures on garden design
STARTED TRADING 1972

Undertakes domestic and commercial work all over the UK and abroad. David Stevens is one of the country's best-known garden designers, and is professor of garden design at Middlesex University. He is also a broadcaster and writer. He has won 11 Gold Medals at Chelsea.

Debbie Jolley Garden Design
Maycotts, Matfield, Tonbridge, Kent TN12 7JU
☎ 01892 722203   FAX 01892 723222

CONTACT   Debbie Jolley
SERVICES   Garden design
STARTED TRADING 1992

Garden designer for private and small commercial projects. Trained at the English Gardening School and now lectures there.

Deelish Garden Centre, Co. Cork
For full details see Nurseries section

Design, Construction and Maintenance, Devon
For full details see Nurseries section

Diana Baskervyle-Glegg
2 High Street, Fletching, East Sussex TN22 3SS
☎ 01825 723128

CONTACT   Diana Baskervyle-Glegg
WORKING AREA   UK (mainly Kent & Sussex)
SERVICES   Garden design; horticultural consultancy
STARTED TRADING 1964

Garden designer who also writes, lectures and runs courses on garden design.

Diana Eldon, Garden Designer
27 Parsons Lane, Bierton, Aylesbury, Buckinghamshire HP22 5DF
☎ 01296 24138

CONTACT   Diana Eldon
WORKING AREA   30-mile radius
SERVICES   Garden design
STARTED TRADING 1991

Larger- or smaller-scale private garden design, including garden features such as arches and ponds. Will produce planting plans and maintenance notes. Holds classes at local Adult Education Centre. Gives talks.

Dolwin & Gray
Alpha House, Crowborough Hill, Crowborough, East Sussex TN6 2EG
☎ 01892 664612   FAX 01862 663636

CONTACT   F Noakes or C Goss
WORKING AREA   South-east England
ASSOCIATIONS   AAAC, BALI
SERVICES   Contractors; arboricultural services; Woodland management
STARTED TRADING 1969

The firm provides a wide range of arboricultural contracting and consultancy services.

Donaghadee Garden Centre, Co. Down
For full details see Nurseries section

Down to Earth – Garden Design by Gail Mackey
28 Westone Avenue, Westone, Northampton, Northamptonshire NN3 3JJ
☎ & FAX 01604 402764

CONTACT   G Mackey
WORKING AREA   Northampton & nationwide by post
SERVICES   Garden design; horticultural consultancy
STARTED TRADING 1995
PROJECTS   Town gardens; water gardens; gardens on sloping sites

Garden designer offering a postal service. Personal visits locally only.

Druid Designs, Cheshire
For full details see Nurseries section

Drysdale Garden Exotics, Hampshire
For full details see Nurseries section

Duncan Heather
Garden Design, 142 Reading Road, Henley on Thames, Oxfordshire RG9 1EA
☎ 01491 573577   📠 01491 411161

CONTACT   Duncan Heather
WORKING AREA   Nationwide & overseas
SERVICES   Garden design; garden design courses
STARTED TRADING   1987

Duncan Heather is also the director of the Oxford College of Garden Design. In 1995 he won the George Cook Award at Hampton Court for innovative design.

Eachus Huckson
7 Church Street, Kidderminster, Hereford & Worcester DY10 2AD
☎ 01562 825825   📠 01562 829860

CONTACT   Andrew Huckson
WORKING AREA   Europe & Middle East
ASSOCIATIONS   ALI
SERVICES   Garden design; horticultural consultancy; landscape architecture
STARTED TRADING   1981

Landscape architects. Services include feasibility studies, detailed designs and contract administration.

Eastern Landscape Service
27 High Street, Cottenham, Cambridge, Cambridgeshire CB4 4SA
☎ 01954 250338   📠 01954 252559

CONTACT   K Hewitt
WORKING AREA   50-mile radius
ASSOCIATIONS   AAAC
SERVICES   Horticultural consultancy; contractors; arboricultural services
STARTED TRADING   1972

Landscape, forestry and tree-surgery contractors, including tree and shrub identification and advice on pests and diseases.

Eastern Tree Surgery
71b High Street, Teversham, Cambridgeshire CB1 5AG
☎ & 📠 01223 292110

CONTACT   Paul Cole
WORKING AREA   East Anglia
ASSOCIATIONS   AAAC
SERVICES   Arboricultural services
STARTED TRADING   1974

Care and preservation of ornamental trees.

Elizabeth Banks Associates Ltd
13 Abercorn Place, London NW8 9EA
☎ 0171 624 5740   📠 0171 372 0964

CONTACT   Elizabeth Banks, Tom Stuart-Smith, Todd Longstaffe-Gowan
WORKING AREA   UK & abroad
ASSOCIATIONS   AIHort, ALI
SERVICES   Garden design; landscape architecture
STARTED TRADING   1987

PROJECTS   Landscape design for Fidelity Investments, Kent; conservation advice and landscape strategy plan for Octagon Developments Limited, Berkshire; garden and park designs in England, Italy and France

Landscape practice which has made a name for its work on historical restoration projects. Also active in designing new gardens and advising on land use and garden management. Its varied and impressive client list is matched by EBA's well-qualified personnel, including director Tom Stuart-Smith (ALI), and Dr Todd Longstaffe-Gowan.

Elizabeth Huntly Francis
86 Beechwood Drive, St Albans, Hertfordshire AL1 4XZ
☎ 01727 810849   📠 01727 841219

CONTACT   Elizabeth Huntly Francis
WORKING AREA   Home Counties & south-east England
SERVICES   Garden design
STARTED TRADING   1994

Garden designer with a degree in Horticulture.

Elizabeth Whateley
48 Glossop Road, Sanderstead, South Croydon, Surrey CR2 0PU
☎ 0181 651 0226

CONTACT   Elizabeth Whateley
WORKING AREA   Kent, London, Surrey, Sussex
ASSOCIATIONS   MSGD
SERVICES   Garden design
STARTED TRADING   1986

PROJECTS   Layout and planting schemes for rural gardens near Ewhurst and Meopham, Surrey; water garden, East Malling, Kent

A full garden design service, including surveys, plans, and planting schemes. Elizabeth Whateley will liaise with contractors, and can provide maintenance schedules and a follow-up consultancy visit when required.

Endsleigh Garden Centre, Devon
For full details see Nurseries section

Euro Tree Service
Caxton Lodge Farm, Lodge Lane, Cronton, Widnes, Cheshire WA8 9QA
☎ 0151 424 0333   📠 0151 430 7836

CONTACT   Simon Walton
WORKING AREA   North-west England & Wales
ASSOCIATIONS   AAAC
SERVICES   Arboricultural services
STARTED TRADING   1980

Full arboricultural service, including stump grinding and woodland maintenance. Suppliers of timber, logs, mulch and chippings.

Fairy Lane Nurseries, Greater Manchester
For full details see Nurseries section

Ferndale Nursery and Garden Centre Ltd, South Yorkshire

For full details see Nurseries section

FMG Garden Designs

21 Crescent Gardens, London SW19 8AJ
☎ 0181 879 3168   [FAX] 0181 944 1977

CONTACT Nilla Gallanzi
WORKING AREA London & home counties
SERVICES Garden design; horticultural consultancy
STARTED TRADING 1987
PROJECTS Private gardens in London and West Sussex

Trained in garden design. Create and supervise the construction and maintenance of gardens with a special expertise in perennial borders.

The Focus Group of Garden Designers

17 Millcroft Road, Streetly, Sutton Coldfield, West Midlands B74 2EE
☎ 0121 353 7367

CONTACT Pat Jordan
WORKING AREA Central England & Wales
ASSOCIATIONS MSGD
SERVICES Garden design
STARTED TRADING 1992

The members are Alison Broady, Cheryl Cummings, Pat Dickinson, Pam Freeman, Barry Hunt, Michael Jackson, Pat Jordan, Mike Lewis, Rosemary Tebbett and Ron Thursfield.

Foliage Scented & Herb Plants, Surrey

For full details see Nurseries section

Fountain Forestry Ltd

Mollington House, Mollington, Banbury, Oxfordshire OX17 1AX
☎ 01295 750000   [FAX] 01295 750001

CONTACT T P Rose
WORKING AREA Nationwide
ASSOCIATIONS AAAC, BALI
SERVICES Arboricultural services; forestry and woodland maintenance
STARTED TRADING 1957
PROJECTS Arboricultural projects for Waddesdon Estate (NT); planting and maintenance of trees on A14 dual carriageway

The largest privately owned independent forestry and land use company in the country. Through ten district offices (and another in New England) their range includes woodland services, timber harvesting, tree care, vegetation control and fencing.

Garden Creation Co

Manor Farm, Main Street, Scarrington, Nottinghamshire NG13 9BQ
☎ 01949 851485   [FAX] 01949 851486

CONTACT Hugh Frost
WORKING AREA Midlands & East Anglia
SERVICES Garden design; contractors

STARTED TRADING 1979

Design and construction of large gardens and country house gardens. Design service available independently.

Garden Design

The Urn Cottage, Station Road, Charfield, Wotton-under-Edge, Gloucestershire GL12 8SY
☎ 01453 843156

CONTACT Lesley Rosser
WORKING AREA Gloucestershire, Gwent, Somerset, Wiltshire
ASSOCIATIONS BSc, PhD (Botany), MSGD
SERVICES Garden design; horticultural consultancy; contractors
STARTED TRADING 1983

Design, construction and planting for private gardens.

Garden Design Centre, Hertfordshire

For full details see Nurseries section

Gardens by Graham Evans

20 Grandfield Avenue, Radcliffe on Trent, Nottinghamshire NG12 1AL
☎ 0115 9335737

CONTACT Graham or Alison Evans
WORKING AREA East Midlands
ASSOCIATIONS BALI
SERVICES Garden design; contractors
STARTED TRADING 1986
PROJECTS 40 private gardens landscaped 1995/6

Garden design and construction.

Geoff Moring Garden Design

Five Gables, Bury Rise, Bovingdon, Hemel Hempstead, Hertfordshire HP3 0DN
☎ 01442 833164

CONTACT Geoff Moring
WORKING AREA Buckinghamshire, Hertfordshire, London
SERVICES Garden design; horticultural consultancy; contractors
STARTED TRADING 1993
PROJECTS 2 acre garden including walled garden with sunken croquet lawn, formal garden and informal areas

Garden designer offering full service. Trained at English Gardening School.

Geoffrey Coombs

47 Larcombe Road, Petersfield, Hampshire GU32 3LS
☎ 01730 267417

CONTACT Geoffrey Coombs
WORKING AREA 30-mile radius
ASSOCIATIONS FSGD
SERVICES Garden design; horticultural consultancy; arboricultural services
PROJECTS Private gardens in Hampshire and West Sussex

Formerly garden adviser for the RHS at Vincent Square, now retired. Garden design and consultancy: the latter specialises in trees, shrubs and hardy plants.

Geoffrey Whiten
19 St Nicholas Place, Emerald Quay, Harbour Way,
Shoreham-by-Sea, West Sussex BN43 5JR
☎ & 𝔽𝔸𝕏 01273 455097
CONTACT   Geoffrey Whiten
WORKING AREA   UK & Europe
ASSOCIATIONS   FSGD, MIHort
SERVICES   Garden design; horticultural consultancy;
Lasndscape design
STARTED TRADING   1970
PROJECTS   Refurbishment of gardens, Lambeth Palace

Garden designer, consultant and writer. Frequent Gold
Medallist at Chelsea.

Gillian Temple Associates
15 Woodside Avenue, Weston Green, Esher, Surrey
KT10 8JQ
☎ 0181 339 0323   𝔽𝔸𝕏 0181 339 0335
CONTACT   Gillian Temple
WORKING AREA   UK & overseas
ASSOCIATIONS   MIHort, MSGD
SERVICES   Garden design; horticultural consultancy; Interior
landscape design
STARTED TRADING   1991
PROJECTS   Landscape design for Victoria Embankment
Gardens and Bessborough Gardens, Westminster; Hindu
Temple, Neasden, private gardens and landscapes

Landscape and garden design for both private and commercial
clients. Special expertise in interior design projects.

Golden Landscapes
St Anne, Tuckey Grove, Send Marsh, Ripley, Woking,
Surrey GU2 6JG
☎ 01483 225412
CONTACT   R F Golding
WORKING AREA   Design, nationwide; Construction, 50-mile
radius
ASSOCIATIONS   AIHort
SERVICES   Garden design; contractors
STARTED TRADING   1993
PROJECTS   Rock and water garden; Japanese style courtyard
garden

Design and construction service.

Grace Landscapes Ltd
Nunbrook Farm, 7 Leeds Road, Mirfield, West Yorkshire
WF14 0BY
☎ 01924 481200   𝔽𝔸𝕏 01924 491180
CONTACT   Tim Grace or Hugh Pawsey
WORKING AREA   Midlands & northern England
ASSOCIATIONS   BALI
SERVICES   Garden design; horticultural consultancy;
contractors; landscape architecture
STARTED TRADING   1978
PROJECTS   Country park, Horton Bank Reservoir, Bradford;
car park planting, factory outlets, Doncaster

Specialists in design-and-build contracts for both the
commercial and the domestic garden sectors.

Graham A Pavey & Associates
11 Princes Road, Bromham, Bedfordshire MK43 8QD
☎ 01234 823860
CONTACT   Chris or Graham Pavey
WORKING AREA   Nationwide
SERVICES   Garden design; horticultural consultancy
STARTED TRADING   1988

Trained at the English Gardening School. Services include
garden and landscape design, planting plans and advice. In
addition to their detailed comprehensive service, they offer
special design packages for smaller gardens.

Graham King Arboricultural Consultant
Ridgeways, Oakley Road, Battledown, Cheltenham,
Gloucestershire GL52 6PA
☎ & 𝔽𝔸𝕏 01242 522051
CONTACT   Graham King
WORKING AREA   Southern Britain
ASSOCIATIONS   FAA
SERVICES   Arboricultural services
STARTED TRADING   1981

Arboricultural consultancy.

Green Man Landscapes
The Pines, 18 Church Close, Whittlesford, Cambridgeshire
CB2 4NY
☎ 01223 832725
CONTACT   Michael or Ann Hood
WORKING AREA   East Anglia & Hertfordshire
ASSOCIATIONS   AIHort, BALI
SERVICES   Garden design; contractors
STARTED TRADING   1982

Small firm of knowledgeable plantsmen, specialising in soft
landscaping and maintenance for private clients.

Greenslacks Nurseries, West Yorkshire
For full details see Nurseries section

Greenstone Landscapes
18 Woodmancott Close, Forest Park, Bracknell, Berkshire
RG12 0XU
☎ & 𝔽𝔸𝕏 01344 59042
CONTACT   Bob Mattei
WORKING AREA   Berkshire, Buckinghamshire
ASSOCIATIONS   BALI
SERVICES   Garden design; contractors
STARTED TRADING   1989
PROJECTS   Construction and planting of private gardens,
working with designer

Trained at Glasnevin. Garden design and construction
particularly with water features.

Hambrook Landscapes Ltd
Wangfield Lane, Curdridge, Southampton, Hampshire
S03 2DA
☎ 01489 780505   𝔽𝔸𝕏 01489 785396
CONTACT   Norman Hambrook

WORKING AREA   South Hampshire
ASSOCIATIONS   BALI, Assoc Professional Landscapers
SERVICES   Garden design; horticultural consultancy; con-
tractors; arboricultural services; water and riparian services
STARTED TRADING   1969

Landscaping and maintenance for private and commercial
customers, carried out by full-time professionals. Their garden
centre is at 135 Southampton Road, Titchfield, Fareham,
Hampshire PO14 4PR.

Hardy Exotics, Cornwall

For full details see Nurseries section

Hayes Garden World, Cumbria

For full details see Nurseries section

Hazel M. Huddleston, Northumberland

For full details see Nurseries section

Heath Garden

Heath Hill, Sheriffhales, Shifnal, Shropshire TF11 8RR
☎ 01952 691341

CONTACT   Gordon Malt
WORKING AREA   Shropshire & Staffordshire
ASSOCIATIONS   MIHort
SERVICES   Garden design; horticultural consultancy;
contractors; arboricultural services
STARTED TRADING   1989

Trained at RBG Edinburgh, with 25 years of varied experience
in horticulture. Comprehensive range of services includes
garden design, landscaping work and tree and shrub care.

Heather Godsmark Partnership

Swallowfield, Eastergate Lane, Eastergate, Chichester,
West Sussex PO20 6SJ
☎ 01243 543834   [FAX] 01243 543708

CONTACT   Heather Godsmark
WORKING AREA   Midlands & southern England
ASSOCIATIONS   ALI, MIHort
SERVICES   Garden design; horticultural consultancy;
landscape architecture
STARTED TRADING   1986
PROJECTS   Adventurous water-feature using pots and pithois

Landscape architects and horticultural consultants, handling
design-and-build contracts, landscape-planning advice and all
forms of development work and horticultural and environmental consultancy for commercial and private clients.

Heighley Gate Garden Centre, Northumberland

For full details see Nurseries section

Henlly's Lodge Plants, Gwynedd

For full details see Nurseries section

Heritage Tree Services

Redwood Meadow, Stoke Row, Henley on Thames,
Oxfordshire RG9 5QR
☎ 01491 681185   [FAX] 01491 680077

CONTACT   Hugo Loudon

WORKING AREA   Berkshire, Buckinghamshire, Oxfordshire
ASSOCIATIONS   AAAC
SERVICES   Arboricultural services
STARTED TRADING   1985

This firm offers a wide range of arboricultural services. As
well as designs for arboreta and advice on every aspect of
tree-planting, they also sell semi-mature trees.

Herons Bonsai Ltd, Surrey

For full details see Nurseries section

Hexham Herbs, Northumberland

For full details see Nurseries section

Hillier Landscapes

Ampfield House, Ampfield, Romsey, Hampshire SO51 9PA
☎ 01794 368733   [FAX] 01794 368813

CONTACT   Richard Barnard
WORKING AREA   UK & overseas
ASSOCIATIONS   ALI, BALI, FAA, MIHort, MSGD
SERVICES   Garden design; horticultural consultancy;
contractors; arboricultural services; landscape architecture
STARTED TRADING   1864

Landscape architects offering garden design, consultancy, commercial and industrial landscaping and contract management.
Plants are supplied by their own nurseries. Construction and
maintenance are available in the Hillier heartland of southern
and western England. They also offer a postal design and
planning service for private clients.

Hoecroft Plants, Norfolk

For full details see Nurseries section

Hollington Nurseries, Berkshire

For full details see Nurseries section

Hosford's Geranium & Garden Centre, Co. Cork

For full details see Nurseries section

Hugh O'Connell

108 Yonder Street, Ottery St Mary, Devon EX11 1HH
☎ 01404 812986

CONTACT   Hugh O'Connell
WORKING AREA   UK & Europe
SERVICES   Garden design; horticultural consultancy; water
and riparian services
STARTED TRADING   1988
PROJECTS   Garden for 17th century thatched longhouse,
Devon

Garden designer and horticultural consultant. Aims to
combine low maintenance with good display.

Hurdletree Nurseries & Landscape Contractors, Lincolnshire

For full details see Nurseries section

Hurrans Garden Centre Ltd, Gloucestershire
For full details see Nurseries section

Hydon Nurseries, Surrey
For full details see Nurseries section

Iain Tavendale Arboricultural Consultant
High Bank Farm, Stoney Bank Road, Earby, Colne, Lancashire BB8 6LD
☎ & 🖷 01282 844191
CONTACT   Iain Tavendale
WORKING AREA   Lancashire & Yorkshire
ASSOCIATIONS   AAAC, FAA
SERVICES   Arboricultural services
STARTED TRADING   1980

Arboricultural consultant and approved contractor.

Iden Croft Herbs, Kent
For full details see Nurseries section

J & D Clark Treework Specialists
28 Frances Street, Chesham, Buckinghamshire HP5 3EQ
☎ 01494 783536
CONTACT   John Clark
WORKING AREA   40-mile radius
ASSOCIATIONS   AAAC
SERVICES   Arboricultural services
STARTED TRADING   1953

Full tree service including stump-grinding, reports and emergency service. Wood chippings supplied.

Jack's Patch, Devon
For full details see Nurseries section

Jacqui Stubbs Associates
24 Duncan Road, Richmond, Surrey TW9 2JD
☎ & 🖷 0181 948 0744
CONTACT   Jacqui Stubbs
WORKING AREA   London & south-east England
ASSOCIATIONS   MSGD
SERVICES   Garden design
STARTED TRADING   1986
PROJECTS   Large gardens in Surrey and Eire

Garden designer for mainly private clients. Consultation, design, advice on construction and/or planting schemes.

Jakobsen Landscape Architects
Mount Sorrel, West Approach Drive, Pittville, Cheltenham, Gloucestershire GL52 3AD
☎ 01242 241501   🖷 01242 520693
CONTACT   Preben Jakobsen or Lorraine du Feu
WORKING AREA   UK & Europe mainly
ASSOCIATIONS   ALI, AAC, FSGD, MIHort
SERVICES   Garden design; horticultural consultancy; water and riparian services; landscape architecture; arboricultural consultancy
STARTED TRADING   1969

Landscape architects with a Kew-trained principal. The practice has won numerous awards, including the Landscape Institute's Gold Medal, for landscape, garden and urban-design projects for public, commercial and private clients. Experienced in historic restoration but with a particular aptitude for modern and futuristic design.

James Tregelles
The Garden Shop (Kingsbridge) Ltd, 59 Fore Street, Kingsbridge, Devon TQ7 1PG
☎ 01548 852541   🖷 01548 550338
CONTACT   James Tregelles
WORKING AREA   Landscaping, South Hams, Devon; Design, nationwide
SERVICES   Garden design; contractors
STARTED TRADING   1981
PROJECTS   Several landscape contracts for design-and-build projects in his working area.

The complete service – design, construction and maintenance – is available in the South Hams area only, but gardens can be designed elsewhere using the postal service.

Jan Martinez
Everden Farmhouse, Alkham, Dover, Kent CT15 7EH
☎ 01303 893462
CONTACT   Jan Martinez
WORKING AREA   London & south-east England mainly
SERVICES   Garden design; horticultural consultancy; contractors
STARTED TRADING   1968
PROJECTS   Continuing development at Eastern Docks, Dover; terraces and water features for private gardens

Garden and commercial designer, now operating as a solo designer. All forms of exterior design undertaken. Plants can be supplied. Own garden opens for NGS.

Jane Fearnley-Whittingstall
Merlin Haven House, Wotton-under-Edge, Gloucestershire GL12 7BA
☎ 01453 843228   🖷 01453 521433
CONTACT   Jane Fearnley-Whittingstall
WORKING AREA   Britain, Europe, USA
ASSOCIATIONS   Dip LA
SERVICES   Garden design; horticultural consultancy; lectures
STARTED TRADING   1980
PROJECTS   New garden at Bradfield College, Berkshire; landscaping in Luxembourg and north Wales; private garden in Provence

Garden designer and landscape architect who has worked on some well-known gardens. Chelsea gold medallist. Her book *Plants and Planting Made Easy* will be published in February this year.

Jean Bishop & Partner
Wood Farm, Dunston, Norwich, Norfolk NR14 8QD
☎ 01508 470649
CONTACT   Jean Bishop & Partner
WORKING AREA   Design, nationwide; construction, home counties & East Anglia

SERVICES Garden design; horticultural consultancy; contractors
STARTED TRADING 1984

Both partners hold diplomas from Merrist Wood and work either separately or together on design and construction.

Jean Goldberry Garden Design
Garden Cottage, Vicarage Road, Blackawton, Totnes. Devon TQ9 7AY
☎ & [FAX] 01803 712611
CONTACT Jean Goldberry
WORKING AREA Worldwide by post, site visits nationally
SERVICES Garden design
STARTED TRADING 1982
PROJECTS Designs for BBC 2 programmes

Garden designer. Operates a special postal service: you supply a plan and photographs prepared to her instructions.

Jeffrey Wright Landscapes
3 Knott Park House, Wrens Hill, Oxshott, Surrey KT22 0HW
☎ & [FAX] 01372 843824
CONTACT Jeffrey Wright
WORKING AREA Surrey
ASSOCIATIONS BALI
SERVICES Garden design; horticultural consultancy; contractors
STARTED TRADING 1991
PROJECTS Private gardens in Surrey

Trained at Merrist Wood. Design, construction and planting of private gardens with a consultancy scheme for regular advisory visits.

Jennifer Gayler Garden Design
Mallorn, Ladygate Drive, Grayshott, Hindhead, Surrey GU26 6DR
☎ 01428 606885   [FAX] 01428 607941
CONTACT Jennifer Gayler
WORKING AREA UK & France
SERVICES Garden design
STARTED TRADING 1989
PROJECTS City garden designed as tropical retreat; courtyard for listed building; romantic country garden

Trained at Inchbald School of Design. Complete design service from planning to construction for mainly private clients.

Jill Billington Garden Design
100 Fox Lane, London N13 4AX
☎ & [FAX] 0181 886 0898
CONTACT Jill Billington
WORKING AREA UK & overseas
ASSOCIATIONS MSGD
SERVICES Garden design
STARTED TRADING 1983
PROJECTS Large private garden, Hampshire; competition success at Floréales d'Angers, France

Degree in Fine Art (sculpture). Has designed at Chelsea, written books on garden design and also lectures at Middlesex

University and Inchbald School of Garden Design. Her book *Companion Planting* is published by Rylands, Peters & Small this year.

Jill Fenwick
Friars, 14 Knoll Road, Dorking, Surrey KT4 3EW
☎ & [FAX] 01306 889465
CONTACT Jill Fenwick
WORKING AREA London & south-east England
SERVICES Garden design; horticultural consultancy

Garden designer.

Joanna Stay Garden Design & Consultancy
67 Dalton Street, St Albans, Hertfordshire AL3 5QH
☎ & [FAX] 01727 869765
CONTACT Joanna Stay
WORKING AREA Home counties; nationwide & abroad
ASSOCIATIONS MSGD
SERVICES Garden design; horticultural consultancy
STARTED TRADING 1981

Garden designer for mainly private clients. Trained at Pershore and Oaklands College. Specialises in low-maintenance gardens, country estates and gardens for wildlife.

John A Davies Landscape Consultants
11 Heol Ffinant Quarry, Ffinant, Newcastle Emlyn, Dyfed SA38 9QL
☎ 01239 711443
CONTACT John Davies
WORKING AREA International
ASSOCIATIONS MIHort
SERVICES Garden design; horticultural consultancy; landscape architecture
STARTED TRADING 1967

Chelsea gold medallists. Landscape and garden designers with a subsidiary office in Bahrain, working for private and corporate clients. Bahrain address: P O Box 15560, State of Bahrain. (00 973 710122)

John Akeroyd
Lawn Cottage, Fonthill Gifford, Tisbury, Wiltshire SP3 6SG
☎ & [FAX] 01747 871507
CONTACT Dr John Akeroyd
WORKING AREA Nationwide
STARTED TRADING 1989

Highly qualified professional botanist, writer and lecturer. Advises on conservation and plant identification with a special interest in weeds. Editor of the plant conservation magazine *Plant Talk*. Author of 'Collins Wild Guide: Flowers of Britain and Ireland' (Harper Collins 1996).

John Brookes, Landscape Designer
Clock House, Denmans, Fontwell, Arundel, West Sussex BN18 0SU
☎ 01243 542808   [FAX] 01243 544064
CONTACT John Brookes or Michael Zinn
WORKING AREA UK & overseas
ASSOCIATIONS FSGD

SERVICES   Garden design
PROJECTS   Consultancy at Westminster Abbey; landscape for hotel near Vilnius, Lithuania; wildlife ponds by natural brooks, West Sussex; Restoration of 17th century garden, West Sussex

One of the country's best-known garden designers. They aim to work with you rather than for you. The practice covers a full service, including specifications and implementation. John Brookes also teaches landscape and garden design, and writes and lectures on the subject.

John Brookes Ltd, West Sussex
For full details see Nurseries section

John H Lucas
Lansdowne House, 320 Chessington Road, West Ewell, Surrey KT19 9XG
☎ 0181 393 9946
CONTACT   John Lucas
WORKING AREA   Nationwide
ASSOCIATIONS   AIHort, FIDiagE, MSGD
SERVICES   Garden design; horticultural consultancy; landscape design; lectures; writing & broadcasting
STARTED TRADING   1976
PROJECTS   Consultant to Parham House Gardens in West Sussex

Provides a landscape and garden design service, and will oversee contractors' work. A postal service is also offered. John Lucas writes and lectures on gardening topics: his book *A Comprehensive Guide to Specification Writing for Garden Designers* was published last year.

John Medhurst Landscape Consultant
77 Harold Road, Upper Norwood, London SE19 3SP
☎ & ᖴᴬˣ 0181 653 0921
CONTACT   John Medhurst
WORKING AREA   London & south-east England
ASSOCIATIONS   ALI, AIHort, AA Dipl. Cons.
SERVICES   Garden design; horticultural consultancy; landscape architecture
STARTED TRADING   1981
PROJECTS   Consultancy work for: British Film Institute; London Borough of Enfield; Territorial Army; Wing Yip Supermarkets

Trained in horticulture and conservation, as well as landscape design. Worked for the GLC Architect's department, and is the landscape design tutor at RBG Kew. Offers a complete service for private and public projects of all sizes.

John Moreland
11 Morrab Place, Penzance, Cornwall TR18 4 DG
☎ 01736 67525
CONTACT   John Moreland
WORKING AREA   UK & Europe
ASSOCIATIONS   Dip LA, FSGD
SERVICES   Garden design; landscape architecture; woodland and estate management
STARTED TRADING   1970
PROJECTS   Tregenna Castle; Land's End

Landscape architect and garden designer: works in Britain and abroad on large and small gardens in modern or traditional styles. Director of the Garden Design School at Capel Manor. A Gold Medal winner at Chelsea in 1990, 1993 and 1996.

Josephine Hindle, Garden Designer and Lecturer
11 Beechfield, Newton Tony, Salisbury, Wiltshire SP4 0HQ
☎ 01980 629323
CONTACT   Josephine Hindle
WORKING AREA   Wiltshire, Hampshire, Dorset, Somerset
SERVICES   Garden design; horticultural consultancy
STARTED TRADING   1992

Trained at the English Gardening School. Garden designer with a fine arts degree.

Joy Jardine, Garden Designer
Heath House, Alldens Lane, Munstead, Godalming, Surrey GU8 4AP
☎ & ᖴᴬˣ 01483 416961
CONTACT   Joy Jardine
WORKING AREA   Nationwide
SERVICES   Garden design
STARTED TRADING   1989
PROJECTS   Creating a stream & waterfall in a Surrey garden

Garden design, including planting plans, maintenance schedules and project supervision.

Judith Walton
The Corner House, Foxcombe Lane, Boars Hill, Oxford, Oxfordshire OX1 5DH
☎ 01865 735179   ᖴᴬˣ 01865 736604
CONTACT   Judith Walton
WORKING AREA   Southern England
SERVICES   Garden design
STARTED TRADING   1990

Trained at the College of Garden Design. Part of Oxford Garden Design Associates.

Judy's Country Garden, Lincolnshire
For full details see Nurseries section

Julia Fogg, Landscape Architect/Garden Designer
St Osyth's, Parsons Fee, Aylesbury, Buckinghamshire HP20 2QZ
☎ 01296 87502/01850 381730ᖴᴬˣ 01296 392825
CONTACT   Julia Fogg
WORKING AREA   UK & Europe
ASSOCIATIONS   ALI, BA, Dip LA, MSGD
SERVICES   Garden design; horticultural consultancy; landscape architecture
STARTED TRADING   1989
PROJECTS   Many current projects, in London and the country as well as abroad

Julia Fogg is both a landscape architect and a Council Member of the Society of Garden Designers. She teaches at Middlesex University and the Oxford College of Garden Design.

Julian and Isabel Bannerman
Hanham Court, Hanham Abbots, Bristol, Gloucestershire
BS15 3NT
☎ 01272 610593   📠 01272 611202
CONTACT   Isabel or Julian Bannerman
WORKING AREA   Worldwide
SERVICES   Garden design; contractors; water and riparian services
STARTED TRADING   1987

Garden designers with a flair for romantic landscapes. Construction service too.

Julian Dowle Partnership
The Old Malt House, High Street, Newent, Gloucestershire
GL18 1AY
☎ 01531 820512   📠 01531 822421
CONTACT   Jacquie Gordon or Julian Dowle
WORKING AREA   UK & Europe
ASSOCIATIONS   ALI, BALI, FSGD
SERVICES   Garden design; horticultural consultancy; landscape architecture
STARTED TRADING   1979
PROJECTS   Gold Medal at Chelsea 1996

Well-established partnership which undertakes all kinds of garden and landscape projects. They have won 7 Gold Medals at Chelsea. The partnership covers various disciplines and offers a wide range of experience. Construction work is now done by a separate company, Peter Dowle Plants and Gardens.

Julian Treyer-Evans
Magnolia House, 26 Cuckfield Road, Hurstpierpoint,
West Sussex BN6 9SA
☎ & 📠 01273 834833
CONTACT   Julian Treyer-Evans
WORKING AREA   Southern England & Australia
ASSOCIATIONS   MIHort
SERVICES   Garden design
STARTED TRADING   1977
PROJECTS   Private gardens in Canada and Switzerland; tree planting schemes for golf courses, UK

Garden and landscape designer. A Chelsea exhibitor since 1986, whose track record runs from courtyard gardens to golf courses. Carries out overall designs, but has a special taste for herbaceous planting schemes.

Julie Toll
44 Sefton Road, Stevenage, Hertfordshire SG1 5RJ
☎ 01438 318494   📠 01438 747518
CONTACT   Julie Toll
WORKING AREA   Worldwide
ASSOCIATIONS   MSGD
SERVICES   Garden design
STARTED TRADING   1980
PROJECTS   Tecklington Wharf for St George Developments PLC; Buckinghamshire Golf Club; private town and country gardens.

Garden designer for commercial and private clients with a string of Gold Medals at Chelsea. Specialises in environmental designs.

June Gascoyne: Garden Designer
28 Lower South Wraxall, Bradford on Avon, Wiltshire
BA15 2RZ
☎ & 📠 01225 863362
CONTACT   June Gascoyne
WORKING AREA   200-mile radius of Bath
SERVICES   Garden design
STARTED TRADING   1994
PROJECTS   Large country gardens in Wiltshire and Gloucestershire; town gardens in Bath and Bristol

June Gascoyne has a Certificate in Garden Design from Pershore and offers to 'transform any expanse of land into your dream garden'.

Katherine Shock
369 Woodstock Road, Oxford, Oxfordshire OX2 8AA
☎ 01865 515584
CONTACT   Katherine Shock
WORKING AREA   50-mile radius of Oxford
ASSOCIATIONS   MSGD
SERVICES   Garden design
STARTED TRADING   1987
PROJECTS   Private gardens in Oxford and surrounding area

Garden designer, a member of the Oxford Design Associates.

Kaytie Fisher, Surrey
For full details see Nurseries section

Keepers Nursery, Kent
For full details see Nurseries section

Keir Watson Garden Design
35 Magdalen Road, St Leonards on Sea, East Sussex
TN37 6ET
☎ & 📠 01424 716958
CONTACT   Keir Watson
WORKING AREA   South-east England
SERVICES   Garden design; contractors; arboricultural services
STARTED TRADING   1989

Garden designer. Specialises in natural or habitat planting schemes. Works with contractor and can offer full design and build service.

Keith Banyard
Nettletree Farm, Horton Heath, Wimborne, Dorset
BH21 7JN
☎ 01202 828800   📠 01202 820128
CONTACT   Keith Banyard
WORKING AREA   Dorset, Hampshire, Wiltshire
ASSOCIATIONS   AAAC, BALI
SERVICES   Contractors; arboricultural services; water and riparian services
STARTED TRADING   1977

Keith Banyard is one of the largest arboricultural specialists in the south east. It offers a wide range of disciplines, including tree-surgery, tree-moving, interior landscapes, fencing and soil improving.

Keith Pullan Garden Design
1 Amotherby Close, Amotherby, Malton, North Yorkshire
YO17 0TG
☎ 01653 693885

CONTACT   Keith Pullan
WORKING AREA   North of England & north Midlands
ASSOCIATIONS   MSGD
SERVICES   Garden design
STARTED TRADING   1992
PROJECTS   Blackpool 6th Form college grounds; private gardens

Garden and landscape designer. Will help with preparation of tenders, appoint contractors and oversee.

Keith Rushforth
32 Park Lane, Fareham, Hampshire PO16 7JX
☎ & FAX 01329 284738

CONTACT   Keith Rushforth
WORKING AREA   Nationwide
ASSOCIATIONS   FAA, FICh Foresters, MIHort
SERVICES   Arboricultural services
STARTED TRADING   1984

Arboricultural consultant.

Ken Higginbotham Garden Landscaping
31 Elmfield, Chapel en le Frith, Stockport, Cheshire
SK12 6TZ
☎ & FAX 01298 813051

CONTACT   K R Higginbotham
WORKING AREA   Cheshire, Peak District, south Manchester
ASSOCIATIONS   BALI
SERVICES   Garden design; contractors; arboricultural services
STARTED TRADING   1979
PROJECTS   The Safeway Roundabout, Bakewell Road, Buxton

Specialise in the design and construction of private gardens, patios and driveways. Experienced in working with difficult sites. Also work with local authorities as landscapers and tree surgeons.

Kexby Design
12 College Lane, Apley Park, Wellington, Telford, Shropshire TF1 3DH
☎ 01952 249935   FAX 01952 641658

CONTACT   John Rickell
WORKING AREA   Nationwide, but mainly Midlands
ASSOCIATIONS   MIHort
SERVICES   Garden design; horticultural consultancy; landscape architecture
STARTED TRADING   1982
PROJECTS   Private design and advisory projects

Wisley-trained designer and horticultural consultant.

Keymer Landscapes, West Sussex
For full details see Nurseries section

Landcare
Birchwood, Kirkbridge Lane, Newhill, Huddersfield, West Yorkshire HD7 7LG
☎ 01484 686462   FAX 01484 688496

CONTACT   Matthew Corder
WORKING AREA   Midlands & northern England
ASSOCIATIONS   ALI, ILAM
SERVICES   Garden design; landscape architecture
STARTED TRADING   1988

Landscape architects.

Landscape Centre, Co. Antrim
For full details see Nurseries section

Landscape Design Studio
3 Hatton Mains Cottages, Dalmahoy, Kirknewton, Lothian
EH27 8EB
☎ 0131 333 1262

CONTACT   Lucy Eyers
WORKING AREA   Scotland & northern England
ASSOCIATIONS   BA, DipLA
SERVICES   Garden design; landscape architecture
STARTED TRADING   1991

Qualified landscape architect: the practice offers landscape architecture and garden design. Postal service available throughout the UK.

Landskip and Prospect
Talley, Llandeilo, Dyfed SA19 7YH
☎ 01558 685567   FAX 01558 685745

CONTACT   Dr Andrew Sclater
WORKING AREA   UK & Europe
ASSOCIATIONS   MIHort
SERVICES   Garden design; horticultural consultancy; landscape architecture; historical landscape survey and management plans
STARTED TRADING   1987

Specialists in garden and parkland improvement. With an associated office in Belgium, this is an international practice which includes aesthetic assessment, historical research and landscape management. They can also be contacted at 47 Norfolk Terrace, Cambridge CB1 2NG (Tel/Fax: 01223 461432).

LDC Ltd
The Courtyard Offices, Hatchlands, East Clandon, Surrey
GU4 7RT
☎ 01483 211616   FAX 01483 211548

CONTACT   Yvonne Owen
WORKING AREA   Southern England
ASSOCIATIONS   ALI, BALI
SERVICES   Garden design; contractors; landscape architecture
STARTED TRADING   1983
PROJECTS   Ruislip Lido; Hatchlands, Surrey; Chandler Close, Bath

Specialist design-and-build service which is led, unusually, by landscape architects.

LDP Consultants
Heath Villa, 14 Eaton Road, Tarporley, Cheshire CW6 0BP
☎ & ☎ 01829 733093

CONTACT   Michaela da Cunha
WORKING AREA   Gloucestershire, Herefordshire, South Wales
SERVICES   Garden design
STARTED TRADING   1991

Garden design and interior landscaping.

Lechlade Garden Centre, Gloucestershire
For full details see Nurseries section

Linda Fair – Garden Designer
29 Canons Close, Radlett, Hertfordshire WD7 7ER
☎ & ☎ 01923 853391

CONTACT   Linda Fair
WORKING AREA   North & west London, Hertfordshire
SERVICES   Garden design
STARTED TRADING   1986

Garden designer for mainly private clients.

Lingard + Styles Landscape
Walpole House, 35 Walpole Street, London SW3 4QS
☎ 0171 930 9233   ☎ 0171 930 9152

CONTACT   Peter Styles
WORKING AREA   UK, Ireland, Northern Europe
ASSOCIATIONS   FLI
SERVICES   Garden design; horticultural consultancy; landscape architecture
STARTED TRADING   1976
PROJECTS   Public and private gardens throughout UK

Landscape architects, planning and horticulture consultants. With a Kew-trained senior partner, this award-winning practice has a particular expertise in garden design. There is another office in Newtown, Powys (01686 27600).

Lisdoonan Herbs, Co. Down
For full details see Nurseries section

Longacre Nursery, Kent
For full details see Nurseries section

Longstock Park Nursery, Hampshire
For full details see Nurseries section

Lorne Landscapers, Strathclyde
For full details see Nurseries section

Lotus Landscapes
9 Beresford Close, Frimley Green, Camberley, Surrey GU16 6LB
☎ & ☎ 01252 838665

CONTACT   Christine Young
WORKING AREA   Berkshire, Hampshire, London, Surrey
ASSOCIATIONS   BALI

SERVICES   Garden design; horticultural consultancy; contractors; arboricultural services; water and riparian services
STARTED TRADING   1974
PROJECTS   Re-design of courtyards, Frimley Park Hospital

Garden design and construction.

Louis Vincent Architectural Garden Designer
2 Ford Cottage, Mamhead Road, Kenton, Exeter, Devon EX6 8LY
☎ 01626 890926

CONTACT   Louis Vincent or Anita de Visser
WORKING AREA   South-west England & The Netherlands
ASSOCIATIONS   MSGD
SERVICES   Garden design; horticultural consultancy
STARTED TRADING   1991
PROJECTS   150 private gardens

Can provide a full range of design and consultancy services, including fully illustrated plans and architecturally designed garden structures.

Lower Severalls Herb Nursery, Somerset
For full details see Nurseries section

Lucy M. Huntington
2 Church Cottages, Cothelstone, Taunton, Somerset TA4 3DS
☎ 01823 433812   ☎ 01823 433811

CONTACT   Francis Huntington
WORKING AREA   UK & USA
ASSOCIATIONS   BSc, DipLD, FSGD, MIHort
SERVICES   Garden design; horticultural consultancy
STARTED TRADING   1973

Experienced and well known garden designer. Services include consultation, design, planting plans, landscape schemes and project management.

Mallet Court Nursery, Somerset
For full details see Nurseries section

Manorbier Garden Centre, Dyfed
For full details see Nurseries section

Margaret Bareham
The Hill Cottage, Bausley, Crew Green, Shrewsbury, Shropshire SY5 9BP
☎ 01743 884320

CONTACT   M A Bareham
WORKING AREA   Shropshire, mid- & north Wales
SERVICES   Garden design; horticultural consultancy
STARTED TRADING   1991
PROJECTS   Moated Country House Hotel garden; 5 acre farmhouse garden development

Garden designer, trained at Pershore. Works with colleagues who include a Landscape Architect, Quantity Surveyor, designer/sculptor with construction experience.

Marianne Ford
Manor Farm House, Hulcott, Aylesbury, Buckinghamshire
HP22 5AX
☎ 01296 394364   FAX 01296 399007

CONTACT   Marianne Ford
WORKING AREA   Bedfordshire, Buckinghamshire, London,
Northamptonshire, Oxfordshire
ASSOCIATIONS   MSGD
SERVICES   Garden design
STARTED TRADING   1987

Garden designer specialising in gardens for nursing homes and
private clients. Services range from single consultation to
design and implementation.

Marina Adams Landscape Architects
3 Pembroke Studios, Pembroke Gardens, London W8 6HX
☎ 0171 602 5790   FAX 0171 602 4812

CONTACT   Marina Adams
WORKING AREA   UK & overseas
ASSOCIATIONS   ALI
SERVICES   Garden design; landscape architecture
STARTED TRADING   1980
PROJECTS   Archaelogical sites in Cyprus and Greece;
projects in Cambridge and Cumbria

Landscape architects with particular interests in the conservation of cultural landscapes and design of urban spaces.

Mark Collis Tree Service
Windy Gap Cottage, Mosses Wood Road, Leith Hill,
Dorking, Surrey RH5 6LX
☎ & FAX 01306 713317

CONTACT   Mark Collis
WORKING AREA   Surrey, Sussex, south London
ASSOCIATIONS   AAAC
SERVICES   Arboricultural services
STARTED TRADING   1986
PROJECTS   Tree maintenance for Royal Parks

Tree services including stump-removal and specialist planting
projects. Free quotations.

Mark Lutyens at Clifton Landscapes
5A Clifton Villas, London W9 2PH
☎ 0171 286 6622   FAX 0171 286 5655

CONTACT   Mark Lutyens
WORKING AREA   100-mile radius of Central London
ASSOCIATIONS   BALI, ALI
SERVICES   Garden design; horticultural consultancy;
contractors; arboricultural services; landscape architecture
STARTED TRADING   1940

Mark Lutyens joined Clifton Landscapes last year. There is a
full service for private and commercial clients, design,
construction, supply of plants (from Clifton Nurseries) and
maintenance for interior and exterior landscapes, terraces and
roof gardens.

Mark Ross Landscape Architects
Royal Arcade, Broad Street, Pershore, Hereford &
Worcester WR10 1AG
☎ 01386 561321   FAX 01386 561961

CONTACT   Garden Design Manager
WORKING AREA   England & Wales
ASSOCIATIONS   ALI, MIHort, FSCD
SERVICES   Garden design; horticultural consultancy; con-
tractors; water and riparian services; landscape architecture;
environmental assessment
STARTED TRADING   1990
PROJECTS   Work for Church of England; Wildfowl and
Wetland Trust; Environment Agency; private gardens

Landscape architects and environmental assessors for private
and commercial clients.

Mark Westcott Landscape Architects
77 Cowcross Street, London EC1M 6BP
☎ 0171 490 2984   FAX 0171 490 2989

CONTACT   Mark Westcott
WORKING AREA   Nationwide
ASSOCIATIONS   ALI, RIBA
SERVICES   Garden design; landscape architecture; architec-
ture
STARTED TRADING   1988
PROJECTS   Major new private garden in Sussex

Architects and landscape architects with additional experience of historic gardens work.

Martin Berkley Landscape Architects
40 Berkeley Street, Glasgow, Strathclyde G3 7DW
☎ 0141 204 1855   FAX 0141 204 1813

CONTACT   Martin Berkley
WORKING AREA   Scotland
ASSOCIATIONS   ALI, ARICS
SERVICES   Garden design; contractors; arboricultural
services; landscape architecture; land survey
STARTED TRADING   1980
PROJECTS   Great Western Road Retail Park; M77 road
planting

Landscape architects and surveyors for commercial and public
clients.

Mary Christodoulou
27 Caversham Avenue, Palmers Green, London N13 4LL
☎ 0181 882 3668

CONTACT   Mary Christodoulou
WORKING AREA   London & Hertfordshire
SERVICES   Garden design
STARTED TRADING   1993

Garden designer. Trained at Capel Manor and studied under
David Stevens.

Meadowcroft Fuchsias, Cambridgeshire
For full details see Nurseries section

Michael Jackson Garden Design
Ashfield House, Grange Lane, Ingham, Lincolnshire
LN1 2YD
☎ & ℻ 01522 730784
CONTACT   Michael Alwyn Jackson
WORKING AREA   East Midlands & Yorkshire
ASSOCIATIONS   MSGD
SERVICES   Garden design
STARTED TRADING   1975
PROJECTS   Landscape and planting schemes for English Golf
Union HQ and conference facility, Woodhall Spa

Trained at Pershore. Emphasises interesting plant associations.

Michael Littlewood Landscape Designer
Troutwells, Higher Hayne, Roadwater, Watchet, Somerset
TA23 0RN
☎ & ℻ 01984 641330
CONTACT   Michael Littlewood
WORKING AREA   UK & overseas
ASSOCIATIONS   FLI, FSGD
SERVICES   Garden design; horticultural consultancy;
contractors; arboricultural services; water and riparian
services; landscape architecture
PROJECTS   Millfield School, Street; Ladysmith School,
Exeter

Landscape architect since 1960 in UK and New Zealand.
Specialises in sustainable developments and permaculture
design, including urban forestry. Author of landscaping
reference books.

Mickfield Watergarden Centre, Suffolk
For full details see Nurseries section

Midland Tree Surgeons Ltd
Corner House Farm, Draycott-in-the-Clay, Ashbourne,
Derbyshire DE6 5BT
☎ 01283 820426   ℻ 01283 820086
CONTACT   R I Kennedy
WORKING AREA   Nationwide
ASSOCIATIONS   AAAC
SERVICES   Arboricultural services
STARTED TRADING   1960

Tree surgeons.

Mill Race Landscapes Ltd, Essex
For full details see Nurseries section

Milton Garden Plants, Dorset
For full details see Nurseries section

Monkton Elm Garden Centre, Somerset
For full details see Nurseries section

Muckross Garden Centre, Co. Kerry
For full details see Nurseries section

Nareys Garden Centre, Suffolk
For full details see Nurseries section

Neil Timm, Lincolnshire
For full details see Nurseries section

Nicholas Roeber Landscapes
19 Vernon Yard, London W11 2DX
☎ 0171 727 0176   ℻ 0171 221 1284
CONTACT   Nicholas Roeber
WORKING AREA   London & England
SERVICES   Garden design; horticultural consultancy;
contractors
STARTED TRADING   1987
PROJECTS   Italian courtyard, London; cloister garden and
grotto, London; woodland garden and temple glade, Kent

Garden design and construction by a landscaper with a degree
in environmental science. The team has experience in all
aspects of hard and soft landscaping.

Nigel Jeffries Landscapes
30 Yaverland Drive, Bagshot, Surrey GU19 5DX
☎ & ℻ 01276 476365
CONTACT   Nigel Jeffries
WORKING AREA   South-east England
ASSOCIATIONS   BALI
SERVICES   Garden design; contractors
STARTED TRADING   1983

Currently involved in many local authority and residential
projects.

Noël Kingsbury
18 Wellington Avenue, Montpellier, Bristol,
Gloucestershire BS6 5HP
☎ & ℻ 0117 9245602
CONTACT   Noël Kingsbury
WORKING AREA   Southern England, south-west Midlands,
south Wales
SERVICES   Garden design; horticultural consultancy
STARTED TRADING   1988
PROJECTS   Cowley Manor, Gloucestershire

Garden designer. Specialities include wildflower planting and
habitat creation, herbaceous plantings and conservatories.

North Devon Garden Centre, Devon
For full details see Nurseries section

North Wales Tree Service
Garmon View, School Hill, Trefriw, Gwynedd LL27 0NJ
☎ 01492 641009
CONTACT   J R Butters or K R Webber
WORKING AREA   North Wales & border counties
ASSOCIATIONS   AAAC
SERVICES   Arboricultural services
STARTED TRADING   1984

General tree works and inspections and reports. They sell
wood and wood chips and run arboricultural and forestry
training courses.

Notcutts Landscapes
Ipswich Road, Woodbridge, Suffolk IP12 4AF
☎ 01394 383344
WORKING AREA   See below
ASSOCIATIONS   BALI, FSGD, MIHort
SERVICES   Garden design; horticultural consultancy;
contractors
STARTED TRADING   1910

There are three Nottcutts Landscape Centres, including the
Woodbridge centre: between them they cover East Anglia,
the South-East and the West Midlands. All offer a full design
and construction service. The other centres are at: Stratford
Road, Shirley, Solihull, West Midlands B90 4EN (0121 733
6201); and Tonbridge Road, Pembury, Tunbridge Wells, Kent
TN2 4QN (01892 823843). They won their eleventh BALI
award last year.

Notcutts Landscapes, Cambridgeshire
For full details see Nurseries section

Notcutts Landscapes, Essex
For full details see Nurseries section

Notcutts Landscapes, Hertfordshire
For full details see Nurseries section

Notcutts Landscapes, Kent
For full details see Nurseries section

Notcutts Landscapes, London
For full details see Nurseries section

Notcutts Landscapes, Norfolk
For full details see Nurseries section

Notcutts Landscapes, Suffolk
For full details see Nurseries section

Notcutts Landscapes, Surrey
For full details see Nurseries section

Notcutts Landscapes, West Midlands
For full details see Nurseries section

O'Callaghan Associates
Valleyfield, 1a Stratford Road, Aigburth, Liverpool,
Merseyside L19 3RE
☎ 0151 494 1108/1525 [FAX] 0151 427 4541
CONTACT   D P O'Callaghan or M Lawson
WORKING AREA   UK, Republic of Ireland, Europe
ASSOCIATIONS   FAA
SERVICES   Arboricultural services; forestry; biological
sciences
STARTED TRADING   1982

Arboricultural consultancy practice which encompasses
surveys, planning, litigation, project management and
environmental impact studies.

Oak Cottage Herb Garden, Shropshire
For full details see Nurseries section

Oakwood
4 Queen Elizabeth's Walk, Wallington, Surrey SN6 8JF
☎ 01932 349233   [FAX] 0181 669 6056
CONTACT   N R Beardmore or A Gaynor
WORKING AREA   South-east England
ASSOCIATIONS   AAAC, Dip Hort (Kew)
SERVICES   Garden design; horticultural consultancy;
contractors; arboricultural services
STARTED TRADING   1987

Design, construction and consultancy work offered by the
unusual combination of a Kew graduate and a qualified
arboriculturist.

Orchard House Nursery, North Yorkshire
For full details see Nurseries section

Orchard Nurseries, Lincolnshire
For full details see Nurseries section

Orchardstown Landscapes, Co. Waterford
For full details see Nurseries section

Otter Nurseries Ltd, Devon
For full details see Nurseries section

Otters' Court Heathers, Somerset
For full details see Nurseries section

Oxford Garden Design Associates
The Old Rectory, Ducklington, Witney, Oxfordshire
OX8 7UX
☎ 01993 772722
CONTACT   Sally Craig
WORKING AREA   50-mile radius of Oxford
ASSOCIATIONS   MSGD
SERVICES   Garden design; contractors
STARTED TRADING   1994

Design and construction. The members of the group are Bill
Chase, Sally Craig, Brian and Julie Purcell-Smith, Katherine
Shock, Judith Walton and Ann Willmott. They will work
with any size and style of garden.

P H Kellett, Kent
For full details see Nurseries section

P A Searle
85 College Ride, Bagshot, Surrey GU18 5EP
☎ & [FAX] 01276 471586
CONTACT   Paul Searle
WORKING AREA   South-east England
ASSOCIATIONS   AAAC
SERVICES   Arboricultural services
STARTED TRADING   1980

Contractors to Rushmoor Borough Council.

P G Biddle

Willowmead, Ickleton Road, Wantage, Oxfordshire
OX12 9JA

☎ 01235 762478 ☐FAX☐ 01235 768034

CONTACT Dr P G Biddle
WORKING AREA Nationwide
ASSOCIATIONS FAA
SERVICES Arboricultural services
STARTED TRADING 1972

Arboricultural consultant specialising in root damage to buildings, and building near trees. Other insurance and legal work, including expert witness in accident cases. Dr Biddle is a past Chairman of the Arboricultural Association.

P J Chaffin Tree Surgery

16 The Paddock, Eastbourne, East Sussex BN22 9LJ

☎ & ☐FAX☐ 01323 504620

CONTACT Peter Chaffin
WORKING AREA South-east England
ASSOCIATIONS AAAC
SERVICES Arboricultural services
STARTED TRADING 1984

As well as tree services, Pete Chaffin acts as an instructor and assessor for chainsaw courses.

P W Milne Atkinson

Hemington House, Hemington, Derby, Derbyshire
DE74 2RB

☎ 01332 810295

CONTACT Mrs P. W. Milne Atkinson
WORKING AREA Midlands
ASSOCIATIONS FLI, AAA
SERVICES Garden design; landscape architecture
STARTED TRADING 1955
PROJECTS Business Park, design and maintenance; District General Hospital

Landscape architecture practice with expertise in hospital developments, business parks, sports centres and estates. They can arrange and supervise landscape maintenance contracts.

Pantiles Plant & Garden Centre, Surrey

For full details see Nurseries section

Pat Dickinson Garden Design

39 Oakfield Road, Selly Park, Birmingham, West Midlands
B29 7HH

☎ & ☐FAX☐ 0121 472 0383

CONTACT Pat Dickinson
WORKING AREA West Midlands, Warwickshire, Worcestershire
SERVICES Garden design
STARTED TRADING 1991
PROJECTS Private gardens in West Midlands

Garden designer. Trained at Pershore. Member of Focus Group of garden designers.

Pathfinder Gardening

The Island, Wraysbury, Berkshire TW19 5AS

☎ 01784 482677 ☐FAX☐ 01784 482511

CONTACT Mike Taylor
WORKING AREA London & south of England
ASSOCIATIONS BALI
SERVICES Garden design; contractors; water and riparian services
STARTED TRADING 1983

Landscaping contractors who have built several Gold Medal gardens at Chelsea. Their mini excavators can be hired.

Paul A Wallett

Simons, Station Road, Elsenham, Bishops Stortford,
Hertfordshire CM22 6LA

☎ 01279 813121

CONTACT Paul Wallett
WORKING AREA London & East Anglia
SERVICES Garden design

Garden designer for private gardens. Planting service available.

Paul Cooper

Ty Bryn, Old Radnor, Presteigne, Powys LD8 2RN

☎ 01544 230374

CONTACT Paul Cooper
WORKING AREA Nationwide
SERVICES Garden design
STARTED TRADING 1990

Garden designer with a modern approach and style. Lectures on garden design at Hereford College.

Paul Miles

23 Seckford Street, Woodbridge, Suffolk IP12 4LY

☎ 01394 383771 ☐FAX☐ 01394 380340

CONTACT Paul Miles
WORKING AREA International
ASSOCIATIONS Dip Hort, FMAA
SERVICES Garden design; horticultural consultancy
STARTED TRADING 1979
PROJECTS Gardens at Lyons Hall, Essex, and Copinger Hall, Suffolk: both open under the NGS

Wisley-trained, but also worked for Ingwersen, Nottcutts Landscape and the National Trust before going freelance. As well as design and consultancy, Paul Miles is an experienced photographer, writer and lecturer, and currently chairman of the Suffolk Gardens Trust. He can also be contacted at 43 Finlay Street, London SW6 6HE (Tel: 0171 371 7731. Fax: 0171 490 4417).

Paul Temple Associates

24 Waldegrave Park, Twickenham, London TW1 4TQ

☎ 0181 744 0100 ☐FAX☐ 0181 744 0104

CONTACT Paul Temple OBE
WORKING AREA UK & overseas
ASSOCIATIONS FIHort, FSGD
SERVICES Garden design; horticultural consultancy; interior landscapes
STARTED TRADING 1950

Experienced landscape designer and consultant. Specialities include Japanese gardens and interior landscapes and displays for businesses. For the latter they emphasise their horticultural knowledge and independence from contractors.

Pelham Landscapes
27 Sun Street, Lewes, East Sussex BN7 2QB
☎ 01273 472408
CONTACT   Sue Richards
WORKING AREA   Europe
SERVICES   Garden design
STARTED TRADING   1990
PROJECTS   Private gardens of all sizes

Trained at Merrist Wood and the Inchbald School. Services range from verbal consultancy, to full design service and supervision of contractors.

Penny Bennett Landscape Architects
8 High Peak, Blackstone Peak Old Road, Littleborough, Lancashire OL15 0LQ
☎ 01706 379378   FAX 01706 371103
CONTACT   Penny Bennett
WORKING AREA   Yorkshire, north-west England
ASSOCIATIONS   ALI
SERVICES   Garden design; landscape architecture
STARTED TRADING   1992
PROJECTS   Private garden, Saddleworth including borders, cascade and pool, courtyard and stone pergola

Landscape architects with experience of festival work, garden design and derelict land reclamation.

Perryhill Nurseries, East Sussex
For full details see Nurseries section

Petal Designs Ltd
76 Addison Road, London W14 8EB
☎ 0171 460 0737   FAX 0171 460 1162
CONTACT   Spindrift Al Swaidi
WORKING AREA   England, France, Italy, Jordan, USA
SERVICES   Garden design; horticultural consultancy; landscape architecture
STARTED TRADING   1989

Peter Barratt's Garden Centres, Co. Durham
For full details see Nurseries section

Peter Beales Roses, Norfolk
For full details see Nurseries section

Peter Hemsley
14 Stonethwaite, Woodthorpe, York, North Yorkshire YO2 2SY
☎ 01904 705296
CONTACT   Peter Hemsley
WORKING AREA   Northern England
ASSOCIATIONS   FAA, MIHort
SERVICES   Horticultural consultancy; lecturing
STARTED TRADING   1992

PROJECTS   Water garden, Harewood House, Yorkshire
Consultant for gardens and trees, lecturer.

Peter Rogers
Northdowns, Titsey Road, Limpsfield, Surrey RH8 0DF
☎ 01883 715818
CONTACT   Peter Rogers
WORKING AREA   Nationwide
ASSOCIATIONS   FRSA, FSGD, MIHort
SERVICES   Garden design; horticultural consultancy
STARTED TRADING   1973

Garden design services for private, commercial and public clients, including the refurbishment of private gardens.

Peter Wynn Arboricultural Consultant
Barclays Bank Chambers, Town Hall Street, Sowerby Bridge, West Yorkshire HX6 2DY
☎ 01422 834587   FAX 01422 831141
CONTACT   Peter Wynn
WORKING AREA   Lancashire, Lincolnshire, Midlands, North Wales, Yorkshire
ASSOCIATIONS   AAAC
SERVICES   Arboricultural services
STARTED TRADING   1976

Arboricultural consultant and expert witness. Vice President of the International Society of Arboriculture, 1993, and President 1995.

Philip Cave Associates
5 Dryden Street, London WC2E 9NW
☎ 0171 829 8340   FAX 0171 240 5600
CONTACT   Philip Cave
WORKING AREA   England & worldwide
ASSOCIATIONS   ALI, MIHort
SERVICES   Garden design; landscape architecture
STARTED TRADING   1980
PROJECTS   Atria in Guy's Phase 2 Hospital; roof gardens at the Lanesborough and One Knightsbridge; gardens in Hampstead

Landscape architect with special experience of historic and Japanese gardens. Projects have received several BALI awards in recent years.

Philip Swindells Associates
28 Albert Street, Harrogate, North Yorkshire HG1 1JT
☎ 01423 568081   FAX 01423 568080
CONTACT   Philip Swindells
WORKING AREA   UK & international
ASSOCIATIONS   MIHort
SERVICES   Horticultural consultancy; arboricultural services; educational, promotional and interpretive work for gardens open to the public
STARTED TRADING   1990
PROJECTS   Sharjah Botanical Gardens, United Arab Emirates

Horticultural polymath and international consultant. Advises on all aspects of conserving, managing and restoring historic gardens and amenity landscapes. Their work at Sharjah is the subject of a BBC TV documentary to be shown this year.

Pippa Whitmore
1 The Orchards, Hadfield Lane, Norton, Hereford &
Worcester WR5 2PY
☎ & 🗚 01905 820872
CONTACT Pippa Whitmore
WORKING AREA Gloucestershire, Hereford & Worcester,
South Midlands
SERVICES Garden design
STARTED TRADING 1993

Garden Designer. Trained at Pershore. Will also supply plants.

Plans for the Garden – Cheryl Bates Garden Design
3 Pellfield Court, Weston, Stafford, Staffordshire ST13 0JG
☎ 01889 271417
CONTACT Cheryl Bates
SERVICES Garden design
STARTED TRADING 1994

Garden designer with a degree in plant sciences. Services include designs and planting plans for private gardens.

Planscapes
P O Box 37, Stourport on Severn, Hereford & Worcester
DY13 9YT
☎ 01299 250805
CONTACT Fiona Browne
WORKING AREA Nationwide, but especially Midlands
ASSOCIATIONS MSGD
SERVICES Garden design; horticultural consultancy;
contractors
STARTED TRADING 1991

Garden design and construction for private clients.

Plantsmanship
20 Wellington Road, Hampton Hill, London TW12 1JT
☎ 0181 943 4471   🗚 0181 943 1236
CONTACT David Wright or Paula Perowne
WORKING AREA London & home counties
ASSOCIATIONS BALI, MSGD
SERVICES Garden design; contractors; water and riparian
services
STARTED TRADING 1987
PROJECTS Half-acre lake; numerous soft landscaping
projects, large and small

A full design-and-build service is available or they will work with other designers and specialists. Their gardens are planned for organic maintenance. Advice on irrigation and lighting can be given.

Plaxtol Nurseries, Kent
For full details see Nurseries section

PMA Plant Specialities, Somerset
For full details see Nurseries section

Pound Lane Nurseries, Hampshire
For full details see Nurseries section

Poyntzfield Herb Nursery, Highland
For full details see Nurseries section

Private Landscapes
33 Beechcroft Road, London SW17 7BX
☎ 0181 767 0179   🗚 0181 672 7080
CONTACT Janet Nott
WORKING AREA London & south-east England
SERVICES Garden design; contractors
STARTED TRADING 1992
PROJECTS Re-styling of Victorian Gothic conservation site,
North London; terrace garden, Chelsea; suburban country
garden

Formal training at Inchbald School of Garden Design after gardening and designing privately.

Professional Tree Services Ltd
Unit 12, Romsey Industrial Estate, Greatbridge Road,
Romsey, Hampshire SO51 0HR
☎ & 🗚 01794 513405
CONTACT Bill Kowalczyk
WORKING AREA Hampshire & East Wiltshire
ASSOCIATIONS AAAC, Dip Arb (RFS), FAA
SERVICES Contractors; arboricultural services
STARTED TRADING 1985

Full arboricultural service for trees and shrubs, including planting and design, surveys and consultancy work for private and public clients.

Provincial Tree Services Ltd
31 Bridge Street, Heywood, Lancashire OL10 1JF
☎ 01706 369355
CONTACT Mervyn Simpson
WORKING AREA Greater Manchester
ASSOCIATIONS AAAC
SERVICES Arboricultural services
STARTED TRADING 1979

Also based at Elizabeth Street Farm, Heywood, Lancashire.

Quartet Design
The Village School, Lillingstone Dayrell, Buckingham,
Buckinghamshire MK18 5AP
☎ 01280 860500   🗚 01280 860468
CONTACT David Newman
WORKING AREA UK & western Europe
ASSOCIATIONS Dip LA, MIHort, MLI
SERVICES Garden design; horticultural consultancy;
landscape architecture
STARTED TRADING 1986

Landscape architects offering full design and construction services.

Redesmere Garden Design
Mayfield, Giantswood Lane, Hulme Walfield, Congleton,
Cheshire CW12 2HH
☎ 01260 270611
CONTACT Bill Cartlidge
WORKING AREA UK, Europe, Pacific NW America

ASSOCIATIONS ARICS
SERVICES Garden design
STARTED TRADING 1994
PROJECTS 1-acre garden including Edwardian style sunken garden; garden for office building

Garden designer with full range of services.

Richard Key and Associates
40 Glenham Road, Thame, Oxfordshire OX9 3WD
☎ & [FAX] 01844 213051
CONTACT Richard Key
WORKING AREA South of England
ASSOCIATIONS MSGD
SERVICES Garden design
STARTED TRADING 1994
PROJECTS The Gallery Garden for The Prince's Youth Business Trust, Hampton Court 1996

Landscape and garden design for private and commercial clients, including equestrian areas.

Rivendell Nursery, North Yorkshire
For full details see Nurseries section

Robin Williams & Associates
Kennet House, 19 High Street, Hungerford, Berkshire RG17 0NL
☎ 01488 686150   [FAX] 01488 686124
CONTACT Robin Williams or Robin Templar Williams
WORKING AREA UK, Europe, USA, Japan, south-east Asia
ASSOCIATIONS FIHort, FSGD, MGSD, M.APLD (USA)
SERVICES Garden design; horticultural consultancy
STARTED TRADING 1977

Experienced garden design practice. Robin Williams is also co-director of the College of Garden Design, and an author and illustrator.

The Robinson Penn Partnership
4th Floor, Cathedral Buildings, Dean Street, Newcastle upon Tyne, Tyne & Wear NE1 1PG
☎ 0191 230 4339   [FAX] 0191 230 5509
CONTACT Dr Rachel Penn
WORKING AREA UK & overseas
ASSOCIATIONS ALI, IEA, IEEM
SERVICES Landscape architecture; environmental design and management
STARTED TRADING 1991

A partnership of a landscape architect and an environmental scientist with a multi-disciplinary supporting team. Their work has included large scale habitat creation, formal landscaping, golf courses, industrial parks and urban redevelopment.

Roots Garden Centre Ltd, Fife
For full details see Nurseries section

Rosemary Barry Landscape Design
25 Colne Park Road, White Colne, Colchester, Essex CO6 2PL
☎ 01787 223214   [FAX] 01787 224731
CONTACT Rosemary Barry

WORKING AREA East Anglia & London area
SERVICES Garden design; horticultural consultancy
STARTED TRADING 1993
PROJECTS Designs for new houses, wildlife pond, private garden re-design

Trained at Otley in garden design and construction with a degree in conservation. Designs and supervises construction for private and commercial clients. Also gives talks.

Rosemary Tebbett
Little Wyche, Upper Colwall, Malvern, Hereford & Worcester WR13 6PL
☎ 01684 563315
CONTACT Rosemary Tebbett
WORKING AREA Midlands
SERVICES Garden design; horticultural consultancy
STARTED TRADING 1993
PROJECTS Private gardens in Warwickshire, Worcestershire and Yorkshire

Garden designer. Trained at Pershore. Works with town and country gardens.

Ross Tree Services
The Old Pound, Llangarrow, Ross on Wye, Hereford & Worcester HR9 6PG
☎ 01989 770383   [FAX] 01989 770383
CONTACT J P Ross
WORKING AREA 30-mile radius
ASSOCIATIONS FAA, AAAC
SERVICES Arboricultural services
STARTED TRADING 1980

Full range of tree surgery and consultancy work, including stump-removal for local authority, commercial and private clients.

Rowden Gardens, Devon
For full details see Nurseries section

Roy Finch Tree Care Specialists
Welland Way, Gloucester Road, Welland, Malvern, Hereford & Worcester WR13 6LD
☎ 01684 310700   [FAX] 01684 310867
CONTACT Roy or Mark Finch
WORKING AREA 65-mile radius (contracting); nationwide (consultancy)
ASSOCIATIONS AAAC, FAA
SERVICES Arboricultural services
STARTED TRADING 1967
PROJECTS Work on properties of the Woodland Trust

Full range of arboricultural services and also consultancy work including safety, litigation and conservation matters.

Rupert Golby
South View, Cross Hill Road, Adderbury West, Banbury, Oxfordshire OX17 3EG
☎ 01295 810320
CONTACT Rupert Golby
WORKING AREA Central England
SERVICES Garden design; horticultural consultancy

STARTED TRADING 1986
Trained at Kew and Wisley. Working from the South Mid-lands he specialises in recreating the classic English country garden in less maintenance intensive forms.

Ruskins Arboricultural Group
St Mary's Lane, Upminster, Essex RA14 3HP
☎ 01768 641144   [FAX] 01768 641155
CONTACT   Robert Wilkins (Operations Manager)
WORKING AREA   UK & overseas
ASSOCIATIONS   BALI
SERVICES   Arboricultural services; tree moving; boxed specimen trees
STARTED TRADING 1986
Large arboricultural group including tree surgery, consultancy and management services. They supply specimen trees and have the biggest tree-moving machinery in the UK.

Ryans Nurseries, Co. Kerry
For full details see Nurseries section

S Warren-Brown
Steer Point House, Steer Point Road, Brixton, Devon PL8 2DQ
☎ 01752 880792/788424   [FAX] 01752 880792
CONTACT   S Warren-Brown
WORKING AREA   South Devon
ASSOCIATIONS   BALI, MSGD
SERVICES   Garden design; horticultural consultancy; contractors
STARTED TRADING 1987
PROJECTS   Decking project on 37% slope; roof garden with circular theme
Garden designer and consultant for private and commercial clients.

Sarah Massey
12 Park Drive, London NW11 7SH
☎ & [FAX] 0181 458 1510
CONTACT   Sarah Massey
WORKING AREA   UK & overseas
SERVICES   Garden design
STARTED TRADING 1991
PROJECTS   Formal garden for Georgian town house; Mediterranean style garden for modern building; landscaping for converted farmhouse, including meadows, orchard, excavation and adaptation of old mill workings
Landscape and garden design and consultancy with bases in London and Oxford.

Sarah Rutherford
Vine Cottage, Thame Road, Longwick, Princes Risborough, Buckinghamshire HP27 9TA
☎ & [FAX] 01844 342472
CONTACT   Sarah Rutherford
WORKING AREA   England
ASSOCIATIONS   MIHort
SERVICES   Horticultural consultancy; historic landscape consultancy

STARTED TRADING 1993
Kew-trained, with a degree in conservation studies. Horticultural consultant specialising in conservation of historic parks and gardens. Management plans include historical research and practical advice.

Sarah Rycroft Associates
634 Wilmslow Road, Didsbury, Greater Manchester M20 3QX
☎ & [FAX] 0161 445 6375
CONTACT   Sarah Rycroft
WORKING AREA   Nationwide
ASSOCIATIONS   ALI
SERVICES   Garden design; horticultural consultancy; arboricultural services; landscape architecture
STARTED TRADING 1987
PROJECTS   Restoration of Georgian walled garden, St Asaph; commercial development for Whitbread Bryant Country Homes; private gardens in north west England
Landscape architects and garden designers for public and private sector clients.

Scotsdale Nursery & Garden Centre, Cambridgeshire
For full details see Nurseries section

Scottlandscape
76 Bousley Rise, Ottershaw, Surrey KT16 0LB
☎ & [FAX] 01932 872667
CONTACT   Robert Scott
WORKING AREA   South-east England
ASSOCIATIONS   BALI
SERVICES   Garden design; contractors
STARTED TRADING 1965
PROJECTS   Maintenance for the Environment Agency at Cookham Lock and Penton Hook
Expanding family firm covering garden design, construction and maintenance. They won a BALI award for private garden construction in 1995.

Scotts Nurseries Ltd, Somerset
For full details see Nurseries section

Seaside Nursery and Garden Centre, Co. Galway
For full details see Nurseries section

Secret Garden Designs by Christina Oates
Fovant Hut, Fovant, Salisbury, Wiltshire SP3 5LN
☎ 01722 714756
CONTACT   Christina Oates
WORKING AREA   Dorset, Hampshire, Somerset, Wiltshire
SERVICES   Garden design; horticultural consultancy
STARTED TRADING 1990
Trained at the English Gardening School, and now teaches there. Garden design, including preparation of plans for DIY gardeners and consultancy visits.

Seymours Garden & Leisure Group
Pit House, By-Pass, Ewell, Surrey KT17 1PS
☎ 0181 393 0111   [FAX] 0181 393 0237
CONTACT James Seymour
WORKING AREA London, Surrey & adjoining areas
ASSOCIATIONS BALI, FSGD
SERVICES Garden design; contractors
STARTED TRADING 1918

James Seymour is a Wisley-trained horticulturist and garden designer, with gold medals at Chelsea and Hampton Court. The firm also acts as contractors. They are specialist suppliers of landscaping materials, and have two garden centres, one on the site; the other is Peters Plants in Stoke D'Abernon.

Simon Richards + Associates
17 St Peter's Road, Cirencester, Gloucestershire GL7 1RE
☎ & [FAX] 01285 650828
CONTACT Simon Richards
WORKING AREA Southern Britain
ASSOCIATIONS ALI, MIHort
SERVICES Garden design; water and riparian services; landscape architecture
STARTED TRADING 1984
PROJECTS Parish Wharf Leisure Centre, Portishead; new Waitrose car park at Witney

Award-winning landscape architecture practice which aims to combine imaginative hard detailing with low-maintenance planting schemes. Designs are structured to allow development in phases.

Simpsons Nursery and Landscaping, Norfolk
For full details see Nurseries section

Sol Jordens
Stocksbridge House, Coombe Bissett, Salisbury, Wiltshire SP5 4LZ
☎ 01722 77573
CONTACT Solbjorg Blytt-Jordens
WORKING AREA Nationwide
ASSOCIATIONS MSGD
SERVICES Garden design; garden consultancy
STARTED TRADING 1987
PROJECTS Many varied projects for gardens and estates at home and abroad

Trained at the College of Garden Design, and with John Brookes. Full range of garden design and consultancy services. Her philosophy is to create gardens which have interest, structure and imagination which, at the same time, harmonise with their surroundings.

Song of the Earth
218 West Malvern Road, West Malvern, Hereford & Worcester WR14 4BA
☎ & [FAX] 01684 892533
CONTACT Fiona Hopes
WORKING AREA Nationwide
ASSOCIATIONS FSGD, MIHort
SERVICES Garden design; horticultural consultancy
STARTED TRADING 1984

Trained at Pershore and Merrist Wood. Full design service. Specialises in ecological gardens. Fiona Hopes also writes and lectures.

Sophie Buchanan
16 Florence Road, Wimbledon, London SW19 8TJ
☎ & [FAX] 0181 241 8830
CONTACT Sophie Buchanan
WORKING AREA London & south-east England
ASSOCIATIONS MSGD
SERVICES Garden design
STARTED TRADING 1992

Garden designer for commercial and private clients. Co-author, with Robin Williams, of The Book of Garden Ideas produced in association with CAMAS Building Materials.

Southern Tree Surgeons
Crawley Down, West Sussex RH10 4HL
☎ 01342 712215   [FAX] 01342 717662
CONTACT M Coomber, Area Manager
WORKING AREA Nationwide
ASSOCIATIONS AAAC, BALI, FAA
SERVICES Garden design; arboricultural services
STARTED TRADING 1956
PROJECTS Tree survey at Hampton Court

Head office of a large firm of tree surgeons and consultants who work nationwide and in Europe. The firm has a royal warrant, and is the largest of its kind in Europe.

Southern Tree Surgeons
The Saddle Room, Capesthorne Hall, Macclesfield, Cheshire SK11 9JY
☎ 01625 890150   [FAX] 01625 890180
CONTACT A Mellor
WORKING AREA Midlands & northern England
ASSOCIATIONS AAAC
SERVICES Arboricultural services
STARTED TRADING 1952
PROJECTS Continuing work for Nottinghamshire County Council on the Major Oak, Sherwood Forest

Southern Tree Surgeons
52a Cowick Street, Exeter, Devon EX4 1AP
☎ 01392 214690
CONTACT David Williams
WORKING AREA South & south-west England

Southern Tree Surgeons
Hartleys Place, Church Lane, Wexham, Slough, Berkshire SL3 6LD
☎ 01753 551100   [FAX] 01753 553166
CONTACT Edward Butler
WORKING AREA Central, north & west London, home counties
ASSOCIATIONS AAAC
SERVICES Arboricultural services
STARTED TRADING 1950

Southern Tree Surgeons
Tring House, 77 High Street, Tring, Hertfordshire HP23 4AB
☎ 01442 828410/01753 551100 [FAX] 01753 553166

CONTACT   Lyndi Bell
WORKING AREA   Bedfordshire, Buckinghamshire, Hertfordshire
ASSOCIATIONS   AAAC
SERVICES   Arboricultural services
STARTED TRADING   1950

Southern Tree Surgeons
The Old Kennels, Cirencester Park, Tetbury Road, Cirencester, Gloucestershire GL7 1UR
☎ 01285 652421/654370 [FAX] 01285 885800

CONTACT   Brian Robinson
WORKING AREA   Gloucestershire, Oxfordshire, Wales
ASSOCIATIONS   AAAC, BALI, FAA
SERVICES   Arboricultural services

Southern Tree Surgeons
Gaywood, Mulhuddart, Co Dublin
☎ 00 353 1 821 3150   [FAX] 00 353 1 820 2589

CONTACT   A Worsnop
WORKING AREA   Ireland
SERVICES   Arboricultural services

Spinners, Hampshire
For full details see Nurseries section

St Ishmaels Nurseries, Dyfed
For full details see Nurseries section

Stella Caws Associates
Orchard House, Sedbury Park, Chepstow, Gwent NP6 7EY
☎ & [FAX] 01291 626645

CONTACT   Stella Caws
WORKING AREA   Anywhere
ASSOCIATIONS   ALI, MSGD
SERVICES   Garden design; landscape architecture
STARTED TRADING   1990

Undertakes public and private commissions, with a complete service available for projects of all sizes.

Stephen J White
8 Torwood Gardens, Bishopstoke, Hampshire SO50 8PD
☎ 01703 692773

CONTACT   Stephen J White
WORKING AREA   Southern England
ASSOCIATIONS   MSGD
SERVICES   Garden design; horticultural consultancy; lectures
STARTED TRADING   1976
PROJECTS   Restoration of Victorian Rectory garden; large garden for Cotswold Manor House

Kew-trained garden designer and consultant. He also gives lectures to horticultural societies.

Sue De Bock Rowles Garden Design
15 Ruden Way, Epsom Downs, Surrey KT17 3LL
☎ 01737 353898   [FAX] 01737 371887

CONTACT   Sue De Bock Rowles
WORKING AREA   London, Kent, Surrey & Sussex
SERVICES   Garden design
STARTED TRADING   1991

Trained at the College of Garden Design. Offers a comprehensive garden design service. Specialises in gardens for children.

Sue's Garden Designs, Suffolk
For full details see Nurseries section

Susan Buckley
124 Ashton Lane, Sale, Cheshire M33 5QJ
☎ & [FAX] 0161 905 2327

CONTACT   Susan Buckley
WORKING AREA   North-west England
ASSOCIATIONS   ALI
SERVICES   Garden design; landscape architecture
STARTED TRADING   1989
PROJECTS   Company headquarters; nature reserve; school grounds

Landscape architects with fifteen years' experience of private and public sector clients. Full professional service provided. Experienced in conservation of historic gardens, and establishing woodlands and semi-natural habitats.

Susanne Jahn Landscape Design
21 Chester Row, London SW1W 9JF
☎ & [FAX] 0171 730 7409

CONTACT   Susanne Jahn
WORKING AREA   UK & Europe
SERVICES   Garden design; horticultural consultancy; contractors
STARTED TRADING   1993

Garden and landscape designer.

Sutton, Griffin & Morgan
Albion House, Oxford Street, Newbury, Berkshire RG13 1JE
☎ 01635 521100   [FAX] 01635 44188

CONTACT   Roderick Griffin
WORKING AREA   UK & overseas
ASSOCIATIONS   FSGD, MIHort
SERVICES   Garden design; horticultural consultancy; chartered architects
STARTED TRADING   1910

Part of an architectural practice which also accepts garden design commissions. Recently designed for BBC *Front Gardens*. Their senior landscape designer is Roderick Griffin who worked as an assistant to Lanning Roper before spending ten years with Hilliers of Winchester.

Syon Courtyard, London
For full details see Nurseries section

Teamwork Landscaping
Myrtle Cottage, Knellers Lane, Totton, Southampton,
Hampshire SO40 7EB
☎ 01703 871919
CONTACT John or Linden Kuyser
WORKING AREA 30-mile radius
ASSOCIATIONS BALI
SERVICES Garden design; horticultural consultancy;
contractors
STARTED TRADING 1988

They specialise in design and construction and offer their
clients 'high quality, stylish gardens'.

The Botanic Nursery, Wiltshire
For full details see Nurseries section

The Romantic Garden Nursery, Norfolk
For full details see Nurseries section

Tim Brayford Landscapes
Hillside, Appleford Road, Godshill, Ventnor, Isle of Wight
PO38 3LE
☎ & FAX 01983 551412
CONTACT Tim Brayford
WORKING AREA Isle of Wight mainly
ASSOCIATIONS BALI
SERVICES Garden design; horticultural consultancy;
contractors
STARTED TRADING 1980

Design and construction, and redesign and maintenance undertaken. Gardens are tailored exactly to clients' requirements
including future levels of maintenance.

Tim Newbury Landscapes
The Shieling, Cow Common, Attleborough, Norfolk
NR17 1BD
☎ 01953 456954
CONTACT Tim or Kathy Newbury
WORKING AREA UK
ASSOCIATIONS BA, BPhil
SERVICES Garden design; contractors
STARTED TRADING 1986
PROJECTS Private gardens in London, Norfolk, Sussex

Landscape design and construction from a designer with
degrees in both architecture and landscape. Author of books
on garden design.

Tom La Dell, Kent
For full details see Nurseries section

Tony Benger Landscaping
Burrow Farm Gardens, Dalwood, Axminster, Devon
EX13 7ET
☎ & FAX 01404 831844
CONTACT Tony Benger
WORKING AREA Devon, Dorset, Somerset,
ASSOCIATIONS BALI
SERVICES Garden design; contractors

STARTED TRADING 1985
PROJECTS Prince of Wales School, Dorchester

Design, construction and maintenance service, winners of a
BALI award in 1995. The five-acre garden is open to the
public.

Town and Country Landscapes
46 Sanderstead Court Avenue, Sanderstead, South
Croydon, Surrey CR2 9AJ
☎ 0181 651 0341
CONTACT Nigel Oates
WORKING AREA South London
SERVICES Garden design; horticultural consultancy;
contractors
STARTED TRADING 1988
PROJECTS Butterfly garden for local authority; private
gardens

RHS certificate. Specialises in design and construction of low
maintenance gardens. Arboricultural work with small ornamental and fruit trees only.

Treemasters
53 Tadworth Street, Tadworth, Surrey KT20 5RG
☎ 01737 812389   FAX 01737 215546
CONTACT John Darter
WORKING AREA London & south-east England
ASSOCIATIONS AAAC
SERVICES Arboricultural services
STARTED TRADING 1986
PROJECTS Work at Royal Hospital, Chelsea

Arboricultural contractors.

Treeworld Services
1 Wendover Way, Tilehurst, Reading, Berkshire
RG30 4RU
☎ 0118 9561010   FAX 01734 419755
CONTACT Steven M Kelleher
WORKING AREA Southern England
ASSOCIATIONS FAA, AAAC, BALI
SERVICES Arboricultural services
STARTED TRADING 1986

Arboricultural services, including fencing and ground
maintenance.

Veronica Adams Garden Design
Lower Hopton Farm, Stoke Lacy, Bromyard, Hereford &
Worcester HR7 4HX
☎ 01885 490294
CONTACT Veronica Adams
WORKING AREA Nationwide
ASSOCIATIONS BALI
SERVICES Garden design
STARTED TRADING 1986
PROJECTS Spetchley Park

Trained at Inchbald School of Design, and in painting at Ruskin
School, Oxford. Specialises in gardens for English country
houses. Also paints botanical ceramics, porcelain and tiles.

Veronica Ross – Landscape Design
Burnroot Farmhouse, Dinnet, Aboyne, Grampian
AB34 5PN
☎ & 📠 01339 886690
CONTACT   Veronica Ross
WORKING AREA   North-east Scotland
ASSOCIATIONS   ALI
SERVICES   Garden design; landscape architecture
STARTED TRADING   1988
PROJECTS   Aberdeen Amusement Park; Drumoak Bowling
Green, Kincardineshire

Landscape designer with additional expertise in forest
landscape design and management.

Victor A Shanley
6 Eastry Avenue, Hayes, Bromley, Kent BR2 7PF
☎ 0181 462 1864   📠 0181 462 0988
CONTACT   Victor Shanley
WORKING AREA   London & south-east England
ASSOCIATIONS   FSGD
SERVICES   Garden design
STARTED TRADING   1990

Working for himself since 1990 (but 54 years gardening
behind him). Designs in varied styles, including roof gardens.
Victor Shanley is also a tutor at the English Gardening School.

W K W Tree Services
The Grange, Old Teversal, Nottinghamshire NG17 3JN
☎ 01623 512795   📠 01623 442329
CONTACT   William Kew-Winder
WORKING AREA   Derbyshire, Nottinghamshire, South York-
shire, adjoining parts of Leicestershire & Lincolnshire
ASSOCIATIONS   AAAC
SERVICES   Arboricultural services
STARTED TRADING   1980

Tree contracting and consultancy, including emergency
service. Supplies wood chips, bark and logs. Arboricultural
and chain-saw training. Consulting arboriculturist with
mortgage and insurance users group.

Waddesdon Plant Centre & Nursery, Buckinghamshire
For full details see Nurseries section

Water Meadow Design & Landscape, Hampshire
For full details see Nurseries section

Weaver Vale Garden Centre, Cheshire
For full details see Nurseries section

Webbs of Wychbold, Hereford & Worcester
For full details see Nurseries section

Wessex Tree Surgeons
1 William Road, Lymington, Hampshire SO41 9DZ
☎ 01590 675773   📠 01590 670429
CONTACT   G Snellgrove

WORKING AREA   Hampshire & adjoining counties
ASSOCIATIONS   AAAC
SERVICES   Arboricultural services
STARTED TRADING   1977

Tree surgery and consultancy work for commercial, public and
private clients, including planting.

West Kington Nurseries, Wiltshire
For full details see Nurseries section

Westside Forestry
Lower Madeley Farm, Harbours Hill, Belbroughton,
Stourbridge, West Midlands DY9 9XE
☎ 0121 457 9457   📠 0156 710293
CONTACT   B Kenward
WORKING AREA   West Midlands
ASSOCIATIONS   AAAC
SERVICES   Arboricultural services
STARTED TRADING   1976

Tree services and fencing. Supply wood chips and bark.

Whitehall Garden Centre, Wiltshire
For full details see Nurseries section

Wild Harmony
150 Weston Park, London N8 9PN
☎ 0181 341 1726
CONTACT   Lucy Chermaz
WORKING AREA   South-east & Midlands
SERVICES   Garden design
STARTED TRADING   1995

Recently established garden designer working with private
gardens.

Willerby Tree Surgeons Ltd
Albion Lane, Willerby, East Yorkshire HU10 6DT
☎ & 📠 01482 651185
CONTACT   C P Scaife
WORKING AREA   North Lincolnshire, North & East
Yorkshire
ASSOCIATIONS   AAAC
SERVICES   Arboricultural services
STARTED TRADING   1981

Tree surgery and tree consultancy, including surveys and
planting. They also hire out chippers and sell logs and mulch.

William Woodhouse
The Chapel, 29 High Street, West Wickham,
Cambridgeshire CB1 6RY
☎ 01223 290149   📠 01233 290049
CONTACT   William Woodhouse
WORKING AREA   East Anglia, London (larger projects
nationwide)
ASSOCIATIONS   ALI
SERVICES   Garden design; contractors; water and riparian
services; landscape architecture; building design in
environmentally sensitive areas and historic landscapes
STARTED TRADING   1985

PROJECTS Water gardens, Hertfordshire; rose garden and naturalised habitat garden, Suffolk

Landscape design, construction and small architectural projects. Aims to achieve harmony between buildings and surroundings.

Wilmslow Garden Centre, Cheshire
For full details see Nurseries section

Wolverhampton Tree Service
89 Common Road, Wombourn, Wolverhampton, Staffordshire WV5 0LW

☎ & 𝔽𝔸𝕏 01902 892652

CONTACT Bob Smith
WORKING AREA Shropshire, Staffordshire, West Midlands
ASSOCIATIONS AAAC
SERVICES Arboricultural services
STARTED TRADING 1985

Approved contractor for eight local authorities and British Rail.

Yes, Devon
For full details see Nurseries section

Yorkshire Garden World, North Yorkshire
For full details see Nurseries section

Zengarden
26 Falkland Road, Barnet, Hertfordshire EN5 4LG

☎ 0181 441 3415

CONTACT Andrew Moffat
WORKING AREA London, M25 & Europe
SERVICES Garden design; horticultural consultancy; contractors
STARTED TRADING 1994
PROJECTS Zen garden featured on BBC Radio 4

Garden designer who specialises in contemporary landscapes and Japanese designs. A full service is available including construction and maintenance, supply of furniture and sculpture.

18

Colleges & Horticultural Education

ENGLAND

BERKSHIRE

Berkshire College of Agriculture
Hall Place, Burchetts Green, Maidenhead, Berkshire
SL6 6QR
☎ 01628 824444　　📠 01628 824695
RANGE OF COURSES BTEC First Diploma & National Certificate in Horticulture (each one year). BTEC National Diploma in Horticulture (two years). Part-time courses include: RHS General Exam (one day a week for one year or one evening a week for two years); Introduction to Horticulture; RHS Diploma in Horticulture. The college also offers an extensive programme of short courses and garden workshops, possibly the best in UK.

Big county agricultural college, well-run and serious. Excellent modern brochure, very inspirational.

University of Reading
Dept of Horticulture, Plant Science Laboratories,
Whiteknights, Reading, Berkshire RG6 2AS
☎ 01734 318071　　📠 01734 750630
RANGE OF COURSES MSc/Diploma in Horticulture (one year full-time or three years part-time); BSc in Horticulture (with Studies in Europe and/or a sandwich year as extra options); BSc in Landscape Management (with Studies in Europe as an extra option). The Department of Horticulture also runs a two-year part-time Certificate course in Garden Design (4 pm – 9 pm over six ten-week terms). The University offers an exceptionally long and varied list of short courses, aimed partly at amateurs and partly at professionals in allied disciplines. Most run at least once a year, some more frequently. Among the titles are: Therapeutic Horticulture (three days); Honey Fungus (one day); Bracket Fungi (one day); Tree

Roots & Buildings (half a day); Plant Disease Diagnosis (half a day); Micropropagation (one day); Community & Landscape (ten half-days); Ecology in the Restoration & Maintenance of Historic Landscapes (three days); Pergolas & Arbours (one day); Gardens for Terraced Houses (one day); Planning a Drought-tolerant Garden (one day); Gardening for Disabled People; Plants of Southern Africa; Foliage Effects. The contact for these courses is Sue Simonds (01734 318294).

The leading university for horticulture – amenity, commercial, landscape and garden design. The gardens and learning resources are also among the best.

BUCKINGHAMSHIRE

Aylesbury College
Hampden Hall, Stoke Mandeville, Buckinghamshire
HP22 5TB
☎ 01296 434111　　📠 01296 614175
RANGE OF COURSES RHS General Examination in Horticulture (two years of evening classes or one year at one day a week). C & G Certificate in gardening (one morning a week for 10 weeks), with options in Trees & Shrubs, Propagation and Herbaceous Borders. C & G Certificate in Gardening (Garden Design): evening classes for 10 or 20 weeks. NVQ 1 & 2 Amenity Horticulture. NVQ 2 in Hard Landscaping or Nursery/Interior Landscape. Amateur: Gardening; Creative Flower-Arranging; Bee-Keeping.

CAMBRIDGESHIRE

Cambridgeshire College of Agriculture and Horticulture
Landbeach Road, Milton, Cambridge, Cambridgeshire
CB4 6DB
☎ 01223 860701　　📠 01223 860262

Nene Valley Adult Education

Prince William School, Herne Road, Oundle, Cambridgeshire PE8 4BS

☎ 01832 273550   🖷 01832 274942

RANGE OF COURSES RHS General Certificate in Horticulture (one evening a week for three terms).

CHESHIRE

Reaseheath College (Cheshire College of Agriculture)

Reaseheath, Nantwich, Cheshire CW5 6DF

☎ 01270 613211   🖷 01270 625665

RANGE OF COURSES National Certificate in Horticulture (one year, full-time). BTEC National Diploma in Landscape & Amenity Horticulture (two years).

Cheshire's main college for horticulture.

CORNWALL

Duchy College

Rosewarne, Camborne, Cornwall TR14 0AB

☎ 01209 710077   🖷 01209 612215

RANGE OF COURSES First Diploma in Horticulture. National Certificate in Horticulture, with options in Nursery Stock, Garden Centres, Amenity Horticulture and Commercial Crop Production (one year, full-time). National Diploma in Decorative Horticulture (two years, full-time).

Cornwall's College of the Countryside – small and specialist: they say that horticulture is a major concern.

CUMBRIA

Newton Rigg College

Cumbria College of Agriculture and Forestry, Newton Rigg, Penrith, Cumbria CA11 0AH

☎ 01768 863791   🖷 01768 867249

RANGE OF COURSES Foundation Course in Horticulture for people with learning difficulties (two years, full-time). BTEC First Diploma in Horticulture & landscaping (one year, full-time). BTEC National Diploma in Amenity Horticulture & Landscaping (two years, full-time). BTEC Higher National Diploma in Horticulture (Amenity Landscape Design & Management): two or three years, full-time. Part-time NVQ 2 & 3 in Amenity Horticulture.

Formerly known as the Cumbria College of Agriculture and Forestry, the college primarily serves the land-based industries and rural economy of Cumbria.

DERBYSHIRE

Broomfield College

Morley, Derby, Derbyshire DE7 6DN

☎ 01332 831345   🖷 01332 830298

RANGE OF COURSES BTEC First Diploma in Horticulture. BTEC course in Garden Design (one day a week for one year). NVQ 1 in Amenity Horticulture. NVQ 2 in Amenity Horti-

culture (with Nursery/Interior Landscapes or Hard Landscapes). NVQ 3 & 4 available on request. BTEC National Diploma in Horticulture (three-year sandwich course). C & G National Certificate in Horticulture. RHS General Examination in Horticulture. The college offers a range of day classes, evening classes and week-end courses principally for amateurs on such topics as: Hedge-laying; Dry-stone walling; Flowers for Christmas; Garden Landscape & Design; Organic gardens.

Broomfield is the Derbyshire College of Agriculture and Horticulture.

DEVON

Bicton School of Horticulture

East Budleigh, Budleigh Salterton, Devon EX9 7BY

☎ 01395 68353   🖷 01395 67502

St Loye's College

Topsham Road, Exeter, Devon EX2 6EP

☎ 01392 55428   🖷 01392 420889

RANGE OF COURSES Residential courses in Horticulture (Amenity & Commercial). They train people for employment, not for exams.

Established in 1937 to provide quality training for people with disabilities and long-term health problems.

DORSET

Kingston Maurward College

Kingston Maurward, Dorchester, Dorset DT2 8PY

☎ 01305 264738   🖷 01305 250059

RANGE OF COURSES Vocational Foundation Course in Horticulture (one year, including block release). NVQ Amenity & decorative Horticulture. NVQ 3 Garden Construction & Renovation. Garden Design course (35 weeks, one day a week). Conservation of Historic Gardens (30 weeks, one day a week – new). RHS General Certificate & Diploma in Horticulture. Sprayers & spraying (two days). Excellent series of courses for amateurs: Fruit & vegetables; Plant propagation; Gardening under glass; Organic gardening; Plant identification (new); Garden machinery.

A residential county-based horticultural college, 'Dorset's Centre of Excellence' has a particularly wide range of courses for amateurs.

CO. DURHAM

Finchale Training College

Co. Durham DH1 5RX

☎ 0191 386 2634   🖷 0191 386 4962

Finchale is a residential centre offering vocational training to adults who have become or were born disabled.

Houghall College

Houghall, Durham, Co. Durham DH1 3SG

☎ 0191 386 1351   🖷 0191 386 0419

RANGE OF COURSES BTEC First Diploma in Horticulture (one year, full-time). National Certificate in Horticulture (one year, full-time). BTEC National Diploma in Horticulture (two years, full-time). NVQ 1, 2, 3 & 4 in Amenity Horticulture (part-time). RHS Certificate & Diploma in Horticulture (part-time). C & G Gardening Certificate.

Houghall is the county college for Durham, with a long tradition of excellence.

ESSEX

Barking College of Technology
Dagenham Road, Romford, Essex RM7 0XU
☎ 01708 66841

RANGE OF COURSES One-year course in basic horticulture. C & G NVQ 1 & 2 in Amenity Horticulture.

Writtle College
Writtle, Chelmsford, Essex CM1 3RR
☎ 01243 420705   FAX 01243 420456

RANGE OF COURSES Part-time courses: NVQ 2, 3 & 4 Amenity Horticulture; College Diploma in Garden Design; NVQ 2 Commercial Horticulture; C & G Gardening. The courses that follow are full-time. RHS Diploma in Horticulture. BTEC Higher National Diploma in Horticulture (six options: Commercial Crop Production; Landscape & Amenity Management; Nursery; Retailing; Landscape Construction; Sports Turf Science & Management), all 2 years full-time or 3 years sandwich courses. BSc in Horticulture, Horticultural Business Management or Horticultural Crop production: all 3 years full-time or 4 years sandwich courses. BSc in Landscape Design or Landscape & Amenity Management (3 years full-time or 5 years sandwich). MSc in Crop Production in a Changing Environment or European Horticulture (with Den Bosch College, Netherlands), both one-year courses. New MSc in Landscape & Amenity management (two years, part-time). There is a wide-ranging choice of short courses run in association with the RHS (see main Calendar).

One of the top horticultural colleges, with a national reputation and a commitment to both amenity and commercial horticulture, as well as floristry and rural studies. Full programme of short courses in conjunction with the RHS. Many distinguished ex-alumni, including Peter Seabrook and the late Geoff Hamilton.

GLOUCESTERSHIRE

Cheltenham & Gloucester College of Higher Education
Francis Close Hall Campus, Swindon Road, Cheltenham, Gloucestershire GL50 4AZ
☎ 01242 532922   FAX 01242 532997

Hartpury College
Hartpury House, Gloucester, Gloucestershire GL19 3BE
☎ 01452 700283   FAX 01452 700629

RANGE OF COURSES First Diploma & National Certificate in Horticulture (both one year, full-time). National Diploma in Horticulture combined with a College diploma in Landscaping (two years, full-time). National Certificate in Garden Centre

Management (one year, full-time). National Diploma in Garden Centre Management (two years, full-time). NVQ 2 & 3 in Amenity Horticulture (part-time). NVQ 2 in Commercial Horticulture (part-time). C & G Certificate in gardening (part-time). RHS General Exam in Horticulture (part-time). Short courses in Garden Design and English Garden Follies.

The county college for Gloucestershire, with a long tradition of providing good training. They run an excellent series of residential Taster Courses to give potential students an insight into the main careers-based courses which the college offers.

National Star Centre
Ullenwood Manor, Cheltenham, Gloucestershire GL53 9QU
☎ 01242 527631   FAX 01242 222234

RANGE OF COURSES C & G Horticulture

This College specialises in serving students with physical disabilities and secondary handicaps.

HAMPSHIRE

Farnborough College of Technology
Boundary Road, Farnborough, Hampshire GU14 6SB
☎ 01252 391319   FAX 01252 549682

RANGE OF COURSES Part-time: RHS General Exam (two years, one evening a week).

Sparsholt College Hampshire
Sparsholt, Winchester, Hampshire SO21 2NF
☎ 01962 776441   FAX 01962 776587

RANGE OF COURSES BTEC First Diploma in Horticulture (one year, full-time). National Certificate in Horticulture (Interior Landscape Management or Garden Landscape Construction & Maintenance). BTEC National Diploma in Horticulture (Decorative Horticulture option only), three-year sandwich course.

Sparsholt runs amateur courses, too.

HEREFORD & WORCESTER

Holme Lacy College
Holme Lacy, Hereford & Worcester HR2 6LL
☎ 01432 870316   FAX 01432 870566

RANGE OF COURSES NVQ 2 Amenity Horticulture. GNVQ Intermediate Land & Environment with Horticulture.

Holme Lacy was formerly Herefordshire College of Agriculture.

Pershore College of Horticulture
Avonbank, Pershore, Hereford & Worcester WR10 3JP
☎ 01386 552443   FAX 01386 556528

RANGE OF COURSES Introductory courses: BTEC First Diploma in Horticulture. C & G National Certificate in Horticulture. Full-time Courses: BTEC National Diploma in Horticulture. BTEC Higher National Diploma in Horticulture (in association with Worcester College of Higher Education or University of Central England). BSc in Horticulture (in association with Worcester College of Higher Education). Part-time courses: Higher National Certificate in the Design

& Management of Gardens. NVQ 1, 2 & 3 in Amenity Horticulture. RHS General Exam in Horticulture. Amateur courses: Amateur Gardener's Evening Course (one evening a week for a year); Garden Design Week-end (RHS module); Garden Design (one-day specialist lectures).

The only specialist college of horticulture (no other subjects are taught), and a clear market-leader. It developed to provide education and training for everyone building a career in this industry. Pershore's contribution to every aspect of commercial and amenity horticulture over the last 35 years has been incalculable.

HERTFORDSHIRE

Oaklands College

Hatfield Road, St Albans, Hertfordshire AL4 0JA
☎ 01727 850651   FAX 01727 847987

RANGE OF COURSES BTEC First Diploma in Horticulture or Horticultural Mechanics (one year, full-time). National Certificate in Commercial Horticulture or Amenity Horticulture & Landscape Construction (one year). National Diploma in Amenity & Landscape Construction or Commercial Crop Production (two years, full-time). Higher National Diploma in Horticulture (two years, full-time). Part time courses include: RHS General Certificate & Diploma; NVQ 2 & 3 in Amenity Horticulture; NVQ 2 in Commercial Horticulture & Horticultural Mechanics; college course on machinery maintenance (one day a week for one year).

One of the leading national providers of commercial horticultural teaching, strongly geared to commercial horticulture. Its graduates have long enjoyed a good reputation for professionalism.

HUMBERSIDE

Bishop Burton College

Bishop Burton, Beverley, Humberside HU17 8QG
☎ 01964 550481   FAX 01964 551190

RANGE OF COURSES BTEC First Diploma in Horticulture. NVQ 2 & 3 Amenity Horticulture or Commercial Horticulture. BTEC National Diploma in Horticulture. BTEC Higher National Certificate in Garden Design or Plantsmanship. Year-long course in Creative gardening (principally for amateurs). RHS General Certificate in Horticulture. Garden visits, mainly for amateurs.

A go-ahead college, well supported by the local horticultural industry. The Head of the Horticultural Department, Douglas Stewart, is well-known on Radio Humberside. A student of the college won the IOH's Young Horticulturist of the Year Award in 1995.

KENT

Hadlow College

Hadlow, Tonbridge, Kent TN11 0AL
☎ 01732 850551   FAX 01732 851957

RANGE OF COURSES Vocational Foundation course (one year). BTEC First Diploma in Horticulture (one year).

Intermediate NVQ in Land & Environment Studies (one year). National Certificate in Horticulture: intensive glasshouse crop production, amenity horticulture or nursery stock production (one year); landscape & amenity (three years sandwich course). Advanced National Certificate in Commercial Fruit Production & Marketing (one year full-time). National Diploma in Horticulture or Landscape & Amenity, with a third-year option of fruit production, intensive glasshouse crop production or nursery stock production (three-year sandwich course). Professional Diploma in Nursery Stock Management (15 months). HND (awarded by University of Greenwich) in Horticulture, Garden Design or Landscape Management (three years). BSc (awarded by University of Greenwich) in Horticulture or Landscape Management (four years). BA in Garden Design (four years).

One of the few colleges offering specialist block release courses. There is a wide range of courses at Hadlow, also at Maidstone and Canterbury. The horticulture department covers 60ha and houses National Collections of hellebores and anemones. Many well-known ex-students, including Sue Phillips & Bruce McDonald.

University of Greenwich

School of Architecture and Landscape, Dartford Campus, Oakfield Lane, Dartford, Kent DA1 2SZ
☎ 0181 316 8000

RANGE OF COURSES BSc & HND in Commercial Horticulture, in association with Hadlow College (see above).

Wye College, University of London

Wye, Ashford, Kent TN25 5AH
☎ 01233 812401   FAX 01233 813320

RANGE OF COURSES BSc in Horticulture, Plant Sciences or Horticultural Business Management (all three years, full-time). MSc (one year) in Tropical & Subtropical Horticulture & Crop Science or Applied Plant Sciences.

The horticultural department of London University, and very highly regarded both academically and by business.

LANCASHIRE

Bolton College

Manchester Road, Bolton, Lancashire BL2 1ER
☎ 01204 31411   FAX 01204 380774

RANGE OF COURSES NVQ 1 & 2 in Horticulture.

The courses are taught in association with Myerscough College.

Myerscough College

Myerscough Hall, Bilsborrow, Preston, Lancashire PR3 0RY
☎ 01995 640611   FAX 01995 640842

RANGE OF COURSES Full-time: Foundation Certificate in Land-Based Studies (one or two years). NVQ 1 & 2, National Certificate in Horticulture & BTEC First Diploma in Horticulture (all one year). BTEC National Diploma (sandwich course) and Higher National Diploma in Horticulture (both three years). Part-time: Foundation Certificate in Horticulture (one year, day-release). RHS General Exam & Diploma (both

18 months, day-release). NVQ 2 in Horticulture & Commercial Horticulture (both two years, day-release).

A sound choice of courses from a college with a good reputation.

LEICESTERSHIRE

The University of Nottingham

Department of Agriculture and Horticulture, Sutton Nonington Campus, Loughborough, Leicestershire LE1 5RD
☎ 0115 951 6003   📠 0115 951 6032

RANGE OF COURSES BSc in Horticulture (three years, full-time); may be combined with European studies. BSc Horticulture & Technology (four years, full-time). BSc Plant & Crop Science (three years full-time); may be combined with European studies. Research MScs and PhDs also offered.

LINCOLNSHIRE

De Montfort University

School of Agriculture & Horticulture, Riseholme Hall, Lincoln, Lincolnshire LN2 2LG
☎ 01522 522252   📠 01522 545436

RANGE OF COURSES BTEC First Diploma in Horticulture. National Certificate in Horticulture (Conservation or Landscape Construction). National Diploma in Horticulture (Conservation Management or Landscape Practices). ANC in Garden Design. HND in Landscape Ecology (two years).

Only the HND in Landscape Ecology is taught at Riseholme: the other courses are run from Caythorpe Court.

LONDON

Capel Manor College

Bullsmoor Lane, Enfield, Middlesex EN1 4RQ
☎ 0181 366 4442   📠 01992 717544

RANGE OF COURSES BTEC First Diploma in Horticulture. National Certificate in Horticulture (Landscape Studies, Professional Gardening or Horticultural Practices and Groundsmanship). NVQ 1 & 2 in Amenity Horticulture. C & G Garden Design. Advanced National Certificate in Amenity Horticulture & Landscape Studies. BTEC National Diploma in Professional Gardening or Garden Landscape. BA in Garden Design (with Middlesex University). RHS General Exam & Diploma in Horticulture. National Certificate in Horticulture.

Some of the courses are available at Gunnersbury Park in West London and Upminster Court in East London. Capel Manor also offers a five-week course in Garden Design.

The English Gardening School

Chelsea Physic Garden, 66 Royal Hospital Road, London SW3 4HS
☎ 0171 352 4347   📠 0171 376 3936

RANGE OF COURSES One-year diploma course in Garden Design (two days a week). One-year certificate courses in Practical Horticulture, Botanical Illustration and Plants & Plantsmanship (all one day a week). Short courses (1 – 5 days)

on such subjects as: Garden Photography; Down-to-Earth Gardening; Planning & Planting; The Mixed Border; Gravel Gardens; Garden Lighting; Pruning Roses.

Inspirational course for (mainly) female and mature students. The venue cannot be bettered and the Principal, Rosemary Alexander, is a brilliant communicator. The English Garden School produces confident, stylish garden designers.

Inchbald School of Design

32 Eccleston Square, London SW1V 1PB
☎ 0171 630 9011   📠 0171 976 5979

RANGE OF COURSES One-year Diploma course in Garden Design. Two-year Higher Diploma course in History & Garden Design or Interior Design & Garden Design. Ten-week certificate courses in: Garden Design History; Garden & Landscape Design principles; Intermediate Garden Design; Advanced Garden Design. Short courses in Garden Design Drawing and Business Management for Garden Designers. Inchbald also offers garden design study weeks (e.g. Inspiration Gardens) and study tours.

An upmarket fee-paying school with the highest reputation for its tutors and graduates.

The Institute – Hampstead Garden Suburb

Central Square, London NW11 7BN
☎ 0181 455 9951   📠 0181 201 8063

RANGE OF COURSES RHS General Exam in Horticulture. Amateur courses: three all-day workshops on Saturdays and two five-week courses of one afternoon a week.

Kew School of Horticulture

Royal Botanic Gardens, Kew, Richmond, Surrey TW9 3AB
☎ 0181 332 5545

RANGE OF COURSES Full Time: Horticulture (3 years); Botanic Garden Management (2 months). PhD studentships are available. Kew also runs a four-week International Diploma Course in Botanic Garden Education, and eight-week International Diploma Courses in Botanic Garden Management, Plant Conservation Techniques and Herbarium Techniques.

The Kew Diploma is a three-year course at first degree level in amenity horticulture and horticultural administration. It is recognised as the premier qualification of its kind and vacancies are limited to sixteen a year. The list of 'Old Kewites' reads as a Who's Who of horticulture: Alan Titchmarsh, Anne Swithinbank and Matthew Biggs among broadcasters; Ursula Buchan of The Sunday Telegraph and Spectator; Ian Hodgson, Editor of The Garden; Tony Lord, Editor of The RHS Plant Finder; Graham Pattison of the NCCPG; Christopher Bailes, Curator at Rosemoor; and many others.

Lambeth College

Clapham Centre, 45 Clapham Common Southside, London SW4 9BL
☎ 0171 501 5048   📠 0171 501 5041

RANGE OF COURSES NVQ 1, 2 & 3 in Amenity Horticulture. C & G in Amenity Horticulture (Decorative). RHS General Certificate. C & G National Certificate in Horticulture.

Merton Adult College

Whatley Avenue, Wimbledon, London SW20 9NS
☎ 0181 543 9292   FAX 0181 544 1421

RANGE OF COURSES RHS General Exam. C & G Gardening.

A well-run and adventurous Adult Education college. In addition to the courses there are all-day courses on Saturdays on Garden Design & Container Gardening, and a Friday-evening lecture programme with such titles as 'The Problems with Pruning' and 'Successful Houseplants'.

MERSEYSIDE

Knowsley Community College, Landbased Industries

The Kennels, Knowsley Park, Prescot, Merseyside L34 4AQ
☎ 0151 549 1500

RANGE OF COURSES RHS General Exam. C & G Certificate in Gardening. NVQ 1 Amenity Horticulture. NVQ 2 Amenity Horticulture (options in Hard Landscaping, Arboriculture and Nursery/Interior Landscaping). NVQ 3 Amenity Horticulture (Constructing & Restoring Landscapes). All NVQ courses are full-time flexible, day-release or part-time. Short courses in Pesticides and Chainsaw Operation.

Southport College of Art and Technology

Mornington Road, Southport, Merseyside PR9 0TT
☎ 01704 500606   FAX 01704 546240

RANGE OF COURSES Amateur courses are offered, leading to the RHS General Horticulture exam.

NORFOLK

Easton College

Easton, Norwich, Norfolk NR9 5DX
☎ 01603 742105   FAX 01603 741438

RANGE OF COURSES BTEC First Diploma in Horticulture. NVQ 1 & 2 in Amenity Horticulture. NVQ 3 in Designing & Specifying Landscape Designs or Restoring Landscapes, plus options in Nursery Stock & Internal Landscaping or Hard Landscaping. RHS General Certificate & Diploma in Horticulture. C & G Garden Design. National Certificate in Horticulture, Amenity Horticulture, Landscape Construction or Arboriculture. National Diploma in Horticulture with options in Turf Culture, Amenity Horticulture, Landscape Construction or Arboriculture. Higher National Diploma in Landscape Construction and Amenity Management (in partnership with Writtle College). Horticultural Plantsman's course (one day a week for one year). Amateur Courses in such topics as: Building & Laying out your garden; Graphic Design for Garden Designers; Introduction to Garden design; Tree Climbing.

Norfolk's College of the Countryside, with a wide range of courses geared to commercial and business opportunities. They also offer an Apprenticeship Scheme and a Vocational Training Programme.

NORTHAMPTONSHIRE

Moulton College

West Street, Moulton, Northamptonshire NN3 1RR
☎ 01604 491131   FAX 01604 491127

RANGE OF COURSES BTEC First Diploma in Horticulture. National Certificate in Horticulture (one year, full-time; or two years, part time). RHS General Certificate & Diploma in Horticulture. NVQ 1 Amenity Horticulture. NVQ 2 Amenity Horticulture (Nursery or Landscape options). NVQ 3 Designing & Specifying Landscape Designs. Higher National Certificate in Landscape Management (two years, full-time). Short courses for allied professions (one to five days): Chainsaws; Basic Tree Climbing; Advanced Tree Climbing; Hanging Baskets; Laying Paths & Building Planters.

Moulton College used to be the county agricultural college for Northamptonshire.

NOTTINGHAMSHIRE

Brackenhurst College

Southwell, Nottinghamshire NG25 0QF
☎ 01636 817000   FAX 01636 815404

RANGE OF COURSES BTEC First Diploma in Horticulture. C & G National Certificate in Horticulture. BTEC National Diploma in Horticulture. RHS Diploma. BTEC Higher National Diploma in Landscape Design. BSc in Urban & Rural Open Space Management.

This associate college of the Nottingham Trent University offers a wide range of well-run courses, full-time and part-time, daytime and evening. Note the amateur courses in: Plant Photography; Culinary Horticulture; Victorian Garden; and Gardening skills workshop.

Portland College

Nottingham Road, Mansfield, Nottingham NG18 4TJ
☎ 01623 792141   FAX 01623 798798

RANGE OF COURSES NVQ 1 & 2 in Amenity Horticulture (Nursery & Interior Soft Landscape Maintenance option for NVQ 2).

The college is devoted to emphasising and developing the abilities of disabled people. Horticulture is a significant commitment.

OXFORDSHIRE

West Oxfordshire College

Warren Farm Centre, Horton-cum-Studley OX33 1BY
☎ 01865 351794   FAX 01865 358931

RANGE OF COURSES RHS General Certificate in Horticulture. BTEC First Diploma, NVQ 1 & 2, in Horticulture. NVQ 2 in Amenity Horticulture (Nursery Practice & Propagation). NVQ 2 in Landscape Design & Management. Garden Design Levels 1 & 2 (part time) for amateurs. Short courses by Mary Spiller (01865 351794) for amateurs at Waterperry in such topics as: Garden Design; Flower Garden; Garden Skills; Pruning Fruit; Growing under Glass; Understanding Plants.

SHROPSHIRE

Walford College of Agriculture
Baschurch, Shrewsbury, Shropshire SY4 2HL
☎ 01939 260461   📠 01939 261112
RANGE OF COURSES National Certificate in Horticulture

SOMERSET

Cannington College
Cannington, Bridgwater, Somerset TA5 2LS
☎ 01278 652226   📠 01278 652479
RANGE OF COURSES BTEC First Diploma in Horticulture (part-time or full-time). C & G National Certificate in Horticulture (1 year full-time). BTEC National Diploma in Horticulture (two-year full-time or three-year sandwich course). C & G Advanced National Certificate in Horticulture (full-time or part-time). BTEC Higher National Diploma in Horticulture (three-year sandwich course). Part time courses include: Garden Design (20 half-days); Plants in the Garden (20 half-days); NVQ 1 & 2 in Amenity or Commercial Horticulture; RHS General Exam; RHS Diploma in Horticulture; one-day course in Botanical Illustration.

Cannington is a large and well-run college, the leading centre for amenity horticulture in the south-west.

College of Garden Design
Cothelstone, Taunton, Somerset TA4 3DP
☎ 01823 433215   📠 01823 433812
RANGE OF COURSES Diploma Course in Garden Design (one day a week for 15 months). Two-week Garden Design Course in Atlanta, Georgia.

The College was established to provide professional training to people who wish to become garden designers. It runs just one course, at Pershore, which is designed for mature students. The tutors are Lucy Huntington, Robin Williams and his son Robin Templar Williams. The course has the approval of the Society of Garden Designers.

Horticultural Therapy
Goulds Ground, Vallis Way, Frome, Somerset BA11 3DW
☎ 01373 464782
RANGE OF COURSES Part Time: Therapeutic Horticulture (Diploma or Certificate). Short Courses: Horticultural Therapy.

One of the first colleges to develop a range of horticultural activities for therapeutic use, especially for the handicapped, ill, aged or disadvantaged.

Norton Radstock College
South Hill Park, Radstock, Bath, Somerset BA3 3RW
☎ 01761 433161   📠 01761 436173
RANGE OF COURSES NVQ 1, 2 & 3 in Amenity Horticulture. BTEC National Diploma in Horticulture.

A higher education college concentrating on NVQs. Many short courses. The Garden School for amateurs has free introductory evenings.

STAFFORDSHIRE

Stoke-on-Trent College
Burslem Campus, Moorland Road, Burslem, Staffordshire ST6 1JJ
☎ 01782 208208   📠 01782 828106

SUFFOLK

Otley College of Agriculture and Horticulture
Otley, Ipswich, Suffolk IP6 9EY
☎ 01473 785543   📠 01473 785353
RANGE OF COURSES BTEC First Diploma & National Diploma in Horticulture. BTEC Higher National Diploma in Amenity & Decorative Horticulture. C & G National Certificate in Horticulture, with wide range of options. C & G Advanced National Certificate in Amenity Horticulture. C & G NVQ 1, 2 & 3 in Amenity Horticulture & Commercial Horticulture (with full range of options). RHS General Certificate, Diploma & MSc in Horticulture.

'Suffolk's Countryside Centre' which offers a MHort in partnership with Writtle College. There is a wide range of courses for young and mature students. Otley also has a good Faculty of Landscape Design & Construction with a full range of courses, designed with the needs of industry in mind.

SURREY

Merrist Wood College
Worplesdon, Guildford, Surrey GU3 3PE
☎ 01483 232424   📠 01483 236518
RANGE OF COURSES RHS General Examination & Diploma in Horticulture. NVQ 1, 2 & 3 in Commercial Horticulture and Amenity Horticulture (options in Nursery (NVQ 1 & 2 only), Greenkeeping, Hard Landscape & Arboriculture). Two-week short course on Garden Design (full-time). Certificated course in Garden Design (one year, one day per week).

Merrist Wood is the Surrey college, and one of the leading centres for amenity horticulture. Both the staff and the pupils are among the most able nationally: they include many well-known gardening personalities. The college's brochure is particularly informative.

EAST SUSSEX

Brighton College of Technology
Pelham Street, Brighton, East Sussex BN1 4FA
☎ 01273 667788   📠 01273 667703
RANGE OF COURSES NVQ 1, 2 & 3 in Horticulture. C & G in Horticulture Skills, Garden Design or Garden History. RHS General Course. Plus a good range of courses for amateurs including Garden Plants from Seed, Herb gardening, Conservatory Gardening.

A large and well-equipped college. Most courses may be followed part-time or full-time.

WEST SUSSEX

Brinsbury College

North Heath, Pulborough, West Sussex RH20 1DL
☎ 01798 873832   📠 01798 873832

RANGE OF COURSES Full and Part Time: Landscape Studies (BTEC). Landscape Services (NC). Amenity Horticulture (NVQ 1, 2, 3 & 4). Commercial BTEC First Diploma in Horticulture (one year, full-time). C & G National Certificate in Landscape Services (one year, full time). BTEC National Diploma in Landscape Studies (three years, sandwich course). NVQ 1, 2 & 3 in Commercial Horticulture (Intensive Crop Production). NVQ 1 in Amenity Horticulture. NVQ 2 in Amenity Horticulture, plus options in Hard Landscape, Arboriculture or Nursery/Interior Landscaping. NVQ 3 in Restoring & Maintaining Landscapes. RHS General Certificate & Diploma in Horticulture. College Diploma in Garden Design. Fair range of short courses for amateurs.

The county agricultural college for West Sussex, offering a wide range of qualifications at most levels. Well organised.

WEST MIDLANDS

Bournville College of Further Education

Bristol Road South, Northfield, Birmingham, West Midlands B31 2AJ
☎ 0121 411 1414   📠 0121 411 2231

RANGE OF COURSES Amenity Horticulture (NVQ 1 & 2). RHS Certificate in Horticulture

Solihull College

Blossomfield Road, Solihull, West Midlands B91 1SB
☎ 0121 711 2111   📠 0121 711 2316

RANGE OF COURSES NVQ 1 & 2 in Amenity Horticulture. RHS General Certificate in Horticulture. Day courses in: House plant care; Creative gardening; Outdoor gardening. Some lectures for amateurs e.g. botanical illustration and flower embroidery.

South Birmingham College

Cole Bank Road, Hall Green, Birmingham, West Midlands B28 8ES
☎ 0121 694 5000   📠 0121 694 5997

Stourbridge College

Horticulture and Conservation Unit, Leasowes Park Nursery, Leasowes Lane, Stourbridge, West Midlands B62 8QF
☎ 0121 550 0007

RANGE OF COURSES NVQ 1, 2 & 3 in Amenity Horticulture (one or two years, part-time or day-release). RHS General Examination in Horticulture. C & G Gardening Certificate for Amateurs. Chainsaw training & assessment. Amateur courses in Practical Gardening and Garden Design for Beginners.

NORTH YORKSHIRE

Askham Bryan College

Askham Bryan, York, North Yorkshire YO2 3PR
☎ 01904 702121   📠 01904 702629

RANGE OF COURSES National Certificate in Horticulture. National Diploma in Amenity Horticulture. BTEC Higher National Diploma in Horticulture (three-year sandwich course).

A large agricultural and horticultural college. A new initiative is a one-year MSc course in Modern Approaches to Plant Health.

SOUTH YORKSHIRE

Barnsley College

Church Street, Barnsley, South Yorkshire S70 2AX
☎ 01226 730191   📠 01226 216529

RANGE OF COURSES NVQ 1 & 2 in Horticulture. C & G Gardening. RHS General Certificate.

Sheffield College

Parson Cross Centre, Remington Road, Sheffield S5 9PB
☎ 0114 260 2500   📠 0114 260 2501

RANGE OF COURSES NVQ 1 Foundation Course in Horticulture. NVQ 2 Horticulture. Course in Practical Horticulture for people with Learning Difficulties. Saturday morning Garden Club for amateurs.

WEST YORKSHIRE

Airedale & Wharfdale College

Calverley Lane, Horsforth, Leeds LS18 4RQ
☎ 0113 239 5800   📠 0113 239 5809

Calderdale College

Francis Street, Halifax, West Yorkshire HX1 3UZ
☎ 01422 357 357   📠 01422 399 320

RANGE OF COURSES RHS General Certificate in Horticulture. C & G Certificate in gardening. C & G NVQ 1 & 2 in Amenity Horticulture. C & G Phase 2 Decorative Horticulture.

Huddersfield Technical College

New North Road, Huddersfield, West Yorkshire HD1 5NN
☎ 01484 536521   📠 01484 511885

Shipley College

Exhibition Road, Saltaire, Shipley BD18 3JW
☎ 01274 757222   📠 01274 757201

RANGE OF COURSES BTEC First Diploma & National Diploma in Amenity Horticulture (both full-time). BTEC National Diploma in Environmental Horticulture with options in Interior Landscaping; Urban Landscaping; Countryside; Environmental Studies; Leisure & Sports. NVQs 1, 2 & 3 (all part-time) in Amenity Horticulture (NVQ 2 options in Hard Landscaping & Nursery; NVQ 3 options in Constructing & Restoring Landscapes and Designing and Specifying Landscapes). RHS Certificate in Horticulture and C & G Gardening in evening classes.

WILTSHIRE

Horticultural Correspondence College
Little Notton Farmhouse, 16 Notton, Lacock, Chippenham,
Wiltshire SN15 2NF
☎ 0800 378918   📠 01249 730326

RANGE OF COURSES RHS General Exam & Diploma in Horticulture. RHS MHort. Organic Gardening (approved by The Soil Association). Leisure Gardening. Garden Planting & Layout. Garden Landscape Construction. Interior Landscaping. NVQ 1 & 2 Amenity Horticulture. Garden Centre Course. An Introduction to Management. Herbs for Pleasure & Profit. Market Garden Course.

This college is one of the great success stories of recent years, largely due to the energy and skills of Oliver Menhinick and his staff (40+ tutors and course authors). Some of the courses are designed to help students to pass specific exams: others fill a market need for horticultural knowledge which is not satisfied by the exam structure. Students gained top places in the RHS General Exam in 1993 and 1995. TV-personality Nicholas Wray studied with the college for his MHort.

Lackham College
Lacock, Chippenham, Wiltshire SN15 2NY
☎ 01249 443111   📠 01249 444474

RANGE OF COURSES BTEC First Diploma in Horticulture (one year, full-time). C & G National Certificate in Horticulture (Professional Gardening, Organic Horticulture, Garden Centre Practice or Landscape Design & Construction: all one year full-time, or two/three years part-time). BTEC National Diploma in Horticulture (three year sandwich course). Advanced National Certificate in Horticulture (Professional Gardening: one year full-time or flexible part-time). NVQ 1 & 2 Amenity Horticulture (one day per week for a year). NVQ 3 Amenity Horticulture (part-time for two or three years). RHS General Certificate in Horticulture (one day per week for 2 years). RHS Diploma (60 days). College Certificate in Garden Planning & Design (one day per week for two years). College Certificate in Organic Horticulture (one day per week for 35 weeks).

One of the most go-ahead county colleges, with a substantial commitment to horticulture and floristry, and excellent demonstration gardens. It publishes a lively general prospectus and an extremely helpful faculty prospectus for horticulture.

WALES

CLWYD

Welsh College of Horticulture
Northop, Mold, Clwyd CH7 6AA
☎ 01352 840861   📠 01352 840731

RANGE OF COURSES National Certificate in Amenity Horticulture & Commercial Horticulture. Advanced National Certificate in Landscape Construction. BTEC National Diploma in: Landscape Technology; Commercial Crop Production; Protected Crop Production. Higher National Diploma in Landscape Science, in conjunction with Glamorgan University. Part-time day and evening classes are offered in: Garden Design; RHS General Exam; RHS Diploma; NVQ 2, 3 & 4 in Commercial & Amenity Horticulture.

The leading horticultural college in the Principality – very thorough, professional and go-ahead. The range of courses is geared to commercial needs. The short courses include the use of chainsaws and pesticides.

DYFED

Carmarthenshire College of Technology & Art
Alban Road, Llanelli, Dyfed SA15 1NG
☎ 01554 759165   📠 01554 758189

RANGE OF COURSES BTEC First Diploma in Horticulture. BTEC National Diploma in Horticulture. NVQ 1 & 2 in Commercial Horticulture (Intensive Crop Production) and Amenity Horticulture (Interior Landscaping/Propagation). NVQ 3 in Commercial Horticulture.

GWYNEDD

Coleg Menai
Bangor, Gwynedd LL57 2TP
☎ 01248 370125   📠 01248 370052

RANGE OF COURSES NVQ 2 in Amenity Horticulture. Garden Centre Studies (one year).

University College of Wales
School of Agricultural and Forest Sciences, Bangor,
Gwynedd LL57 2UW
☎ 01248 382439   📠 01248 354997

SOUTH GLAMORGAN

University of Wales Institute, Cardiff
Llandaff Centre, Western Avenue, Cardiff CF5 2YB
☎ 01222 551111

RANGE OF COURSES NVQ 2 in Amenity Horticulture. C & G Diploma in Amenity Horticulture. C & G Certificate in Gardening.

Formerly known as the Cardiff Institute of Higher Education.

WEST GLAMORGAN

Afan College
Margam, Port Talbot, West Glamorgan SA13 2AL
☎ 01639 883712   📠 01639 891288

RANGE OF COURSES NVQ 1 & 2 in Amenity Horticulture. NVQ 1 in Commercial Horticulture. The college also offers a number of amateur courses, including: Hanging Baskets; Propagation; Patio Containers; Shrub Care; Pond Construction & Maintenance.

SCOTLAND

DUMFRIES & GALLOWAY

The Barony College
Parkgate, Dumfries & Galloway DG1 3NE
☎ 01387 86251　　📠 01387 86395

FIFE

Elmwood College
Carslogie Road, Cupar, Fife KY15 4JB
☎ 01334 652781　　📠 01334 656795

RANGE OF COURSES Scotvec HND in Horticulture. Scotvec HNC in Amenity horticulture (full-time or part-time). Scotvec NC in Arboriculture or Amenity Horticulture.

Elmwood claims to offer the most comprehensive range of courses in horticulture of any Further Education College in Scotland.

GRAMPIAN

Aberdeen College
Clinterty Centre, Kinellar, Aberdeen, Grampian AB2 0TN
☎ 01224 640366　　📠 01224 790326

RANGE OF COURSES Part-time courses: Scotvec SVQ Horticulture Levels I – III. Scotvec National Certificate in Horticultural Engineering. Full-time: Scotvec SVQ Horticulture Level 3. Some amateur courses.

Aberdeen College incorporates the former Clinterty Agricultural College.

LOTHIAN

Oatridge Agricultural College
Ecclesmachan, Broxburn, West Lothian EH52 6NH
☎ 01506 854387　　📠 01506 853373

RANGE OF COURSES SVQ 2 & 3 in Amenity Horticulture (two to four years, day-release or block-release). National Certificate in Horticulture (one year, full-time). Higher National Certificate (one year full-time, or two years part-time). There is a wide choice of courses for amateurs at Suntrap. These include: Floral Art; Plants for Foliage Effect; Houseplants; Hanging Baskets; The Patio; Summer Colour; Pests and Diseases.

Royal Botanic Garden, Edinburgh
Inverleith Row, Edinburgh, Lothian EH3 5LR
☎ 0131 552 7171　　📠 0131 552 0382

RANGE OF COURSES RBG Edinburgh offers an interesting course, in association with the Scottish Agricultural College, in Horticulture with Plantsmanship, leading to a Higher National Diploma. Also available is an MSc or Postgraduate Diploma in the Biodiversity & Taxonomy of Plants.

STRATHCLYDE

Langside College
School of Horticulture, Woodburn House, 27 Buchanan Drive, Rutherglen, Strathclyde G73 3PF
☎ 0141 647 6300

Scottish Agricultural College
Auchincruive, Ayr, Strathclyde KA6 5HW
☎ 01292 525343　　📠 01292 520287

TAYSIDE

Angus College
Keptie Road, Arbroath, Tayside DD11 3EA
☎ 01241 432600　　📠 01241 876169

RANGE OF COURSES National Certificate & Higher National Certificate in Horticulture, one year, full-time. RHS General exam.

Go-ahead local authority college: 'small and friendly'. Amateurs can sometimes join day courses on a part-time basis.

NORTHERN IRELAND

CO. ANTRIM

Greenmount College of Agriculture & Horticulture
22 Greenmount Road, Antrim, Co Antrim BT41 4PU
☎ 01849 466666　　📠 01849 426606

RANGE OF COURSES Full-time & part-time courses in Amenity Horticulture & Nursery Stock production leading to NVQ 2. NVQ 3 in Amenity Horticulture Management. Also a full-time course for the National Certificate in Horticulture (Amenity) and a two-year sandwich course leading to a National Diploma in Amenity Horticulture. The college also offers several short courses e.g. mushroom production.

Greenmount is the only college with horticultural courses run by the Department of Agriculture for Northern Ireland.

CHANNEL ISLANDS

Highlands College
P O Box 1000, St Saviour, Jersey JE4 9QA
☎ 01534 608608　　📠 01534 608600

RANGE OF COURSES BTEC First Diploma in Horticulture. NVQ 1 & 2 in Amenity Horticulture and Commercial Horticulture. RHS General Certificate. Short courses in: Operating a Sprayer; Operating a Chain Saw; Pest Control.

EIRE

CO. CORK

Coláiste Stiofáin Naofa
Naofa, Traore Road, Cork, Co. Cork
☎ 00 353 21 961020   [FAX] 00 353 21 961320

RANGE OF COURSES   C & G National Certificate in Horticulture. NVC 2 in Horticulture. Courses are also available in Landscaping.

CO. DUBLIN

Teagasc College of Amenity Horticulture
National Botanic Gardens, Glasnevin, Co. Dublin
☎ 00 353 1 837 4388   [FAX] 00 353 1 837 7329

RANGE OF COURSES   Amenity Horticulture Diploma (three-year course).

The courses have the premier setting in the National Botanic Gardens at Glasnevin. Diploma students demonstrate a high level of achievement.

University College Dublin
Dept of Crop Science, Horticulture and Forestry, Belfield, Dublin, Co. Dublin
☎ 00 353 1 706 7752   [FAX] 00 353 1 706 1104

RANGE OF COURSES   Four-year degree courses in Landscape Horticulture and Commercial Horticulture. Taught Master's degree (MLA), two years. Research Master's degrees and doctorates in all disciplines within Horticulture.

CO. KILKENNY

Kildalton Agricultural and Horticultural College
Piltown, Co. Kilkenny
☎ 00 353 51 643105   [FAX] 00 353 51 643446

CO. LOUTH

An Grianan College of Horticulture
Termonfechin, Drogheda, Co. Louth
☎ 00 353 41 22158

CO. MEATH

Salesian College of Horticulture
Warrenstown, Drumree, Co. Meath
☎ 00 353 1 8259342   [FAX] 00 353 1 8259632

19

Courses for Amateurs: Learning More

All gardeners want to become better at gardening, to understand better, to learn more and to achieve more. Until comparatively recently there was really no provision for the fulfilment of this desire: you joined your local village gardening club and hoped that every so often there might be a really good lecture which you would learn something from. Now we are spoilt for choice, and the only problem is knowing how to go about finding something that will prove interesting, instructive and rewarding.

Start with your county horticultural colleges. Almost all will have a programme for amateurs, with courses and study days run by members of the teaching staff, alongside the vocational courses for young professionals. Kingston Maurward College in Dorset is typical: it has courses on *Botanical Illustration, The Conservation of Historic Gardens, Plant Propagation* and several other interesting and useful topics as well as a series of courses run on Saturday mornings on *Plant Identification* and *How to Raise Plants from Seeds and Cuttings*. Among the best are the courses at Capel Manor, Pershore College and Writtle College.

Many Further Education colleges also run recreational courses, seminars and lectures on aspects of gardening. Probus, in Cornwall, runs a good programme of events in conjunction with three local colleges. Among the many subjects offered are: *A History of Garden Design; Gardening in Dry Conditions; Seed Sowing; Plants for Flower Arranging; Orchids; Plant Hunting; Pruning*. The length of courses varies: some may be a single all-day course while others consist of a two-hour evening lecture once a week for six weeks.

It is worth investigating summer schools. They are usually attached to public schools and universities who wish to make the fullest use of their accommodation by renting it out during the summer holiday or long vacation. Such courses usually take place in the dog days of July and August, when there is little to do at home except to mow the grass and water the greenhouse. So, if you live near Eton, Millfield or St Mary's, it is worth ringing up to ask if you can be put in touch with the summer school organisers. We know, for example, that the summer school at Marlborough College in Wiltshire has a one-week course (half a day each day) on *The Painted Garden*, which traces the history of gardens through the paintings, drawings, prints and other illustrations.

Many of the leading nurseries and garden centres arrange courses, talks and practical demonstrations for their customers: some even become the centre for a thriving horticultural club. Whitehall Garden Centre in Wiltshire, for example, lays on a talk every Wednesday afternoon. Endsleigh Garden Centre in Devon offers a series of courses which meet once a week for several weeks: they include *Botanical Painting, Garden Design* and a course for the RHS Certificate in Horticulture. Other nurseries who run courses of which we have heard well include Hilliers Nurseries at Ampfield in Hampshire and Hollington Nurseries in Berkshire.

More garden owners are now beginning to run courses for people and use their garden as a teaching resource. These can be very rewarding. We have heard good reports of the courses run by Catriona Boyle at Penpergwm Lodge in Gwent and by Mary-Anne Robb at Cothay in Somerset.

Other sources for courses of which we know are: the Museum of Garden History, where Caroline Holmes is running a series of Day Courses with such titles as *The Georgian Garden* and *The Edwardian Garden*, and Clock House School of Garden Design, where John Brookes runs a four-week course on *Garden Design* (01243 542808).

The following organisations have a national profile and are experienced organisers of courses for amateurs:

Altamount Garden Trust
Altamount, Tullow, Co Carlow, Republic of Ireland
☎ 00 351 503 59128   [FAX] 00 351 503 59128

Altamount offers seven weekend courses, both residential and non-residential, from April to September. The themes are: A Gardening Course (with garden visits); A Painting Course (with Patricia Jorgensen); Flower Arranging (with Eve Kennedy).

Burford House Gardens
Burford House, Tenbury Wells, Hereford & Worcester WR15 8HQ
☎ 01584 810777   [FAX] 01584 810673

All-day garden courses on the fourth Friday of the month from April to September. They are designed around the monthly progress of Burford House Gardens throughout the season.

Cabbages & Kings
Wilderness Farm, Hadlow Down, East Sussex TN22 4HU
☎ 01825 830552

In recent years the Centre for Garden Design has run educational events from April to November. Garden walks and design surgeries draw on the experience of designer Ryl Nowell. Her day-courses explore such topics as the rôle of plants in garden design and problem gardens.

Cambridge Garden Courses
Dullingham House, Newmarket, Cambridgeshire CB8 9UP
☎ 01638 508186

A series of eight workshops, which can be attended individually, or as a course on consecutive Mondays. Gardeners are taught how to plan ahead, then offered practical sessions on such topics as: herbaceous perennials; pruning roses; seed collecting; lawn care; winter protection; planting bulbs; composts.

Courses at Englefield
Englefield Estate Office, Theale, Reading, Berkshire RG7 5DU
☎ 01734 302504   [FAX] 01734 323748

Englefield offers day-courses and evening lectures. The ones most likely to interest gardeners are: Alan Gear on Britain's Vanishing Vegetables (7.30 pm on 15 April); Jenny Jowett on Flowers in Water-colour (all day, 6 May); and Hew Prendergast on Plants for People (7.30 pm on 13 May).

English Gardening School
Chelsea Physic Garden, 66 Royal Hospital Road, London SW3 4HS
☎ 0171 352 4347   [FAX] 0171 376 3936

The English Gardening School at the Chelsea Physic Garden has short courses, seminars and demonstrations for amateurs on a wide choice of practical and creative topics. They may be all-day courses on such topics as Gravel Gardens & Ornamental Grasses or Foliage with Flowers, or longer courses such as the four-day course on Planting and Planning, personally run by the school's principal Rosemary Alexander and top garden-designer Anthony du Gard Pasley. They also offer a summer school on garden design for one week in July.

Gardeners' Breaks
Special Plants Nursery, Hill Farm Barn, Greenways Lane, Cold Ashton, Chippenham, Wiltshire SN14 8LA
☎ 01225 891868

Derry Watkins runs day-long courses in such topics as: Planting Up Containers; Taking Cuttings; Conservatory Gardening; Growing Plants for Sale. Most of the courses are in September, October & November.

Harlow Carr Botanical Gardens
Crag Lane, Harrogate, North Yorkshire HG3 1QB
☎ 01423 565418

The Northern Horticultural Society offers a wide range of courses and lectures, up to the level of the RHS General Examination in Horticulture. They are so numerous that we can only list a sample: Garden Design (14 consecutive Fridays); Plant Appreciation (10 consecutive Fridays); Plants & Gardens of Yorkshire (12 Tuesday evenings at fortnightly intervals); Botanical Painting (9 consecutive Mondays); Flower Photography (one day); Traditional Hedges and their Maintenance (one day); Soft Fruit Pruning (half day); Raising Plants from Seed (one day); Constructing Rock-gardens (one day); Garden Pests & Diseases (one day); Drystone Walling (one day).

Henry Doubleday Research Association
Ryton Organic Gardens, Ryton-on-Dunsmore, Coventry, Warwickshire CV8 3LG
☎ 01203 303517   [FAX] 01203 639229

HDRA runs day-long special events and workshops for people who wish to understand more about the organic approach to gardening. Titles include: Organic Garden Design; The Management of Small Woodlands; An Introduction to Permaculture; Compost-making.

Institute of Advanced Architectural Studies
The University of York, The King's Manor, York YO1 2EP
☎ 01904 433963

The IAAS is well-known in horticultural circles for the pioneering work of Dr Peter Goodbody on garden history. Every year, the Institute runs short courses (one to eight days) on such issues as Garden Maintenance, Public Parks, Management Plans and Garden Archaeology.

Kingcombe Centre
Toller Porcorum, Dorchester, Dorset DT2 0EQ
☎ 01300 320684

Residential courses include: Organic Gardening; Fungi. Some of the day courses may also be of interest.

Open College of the Arts
Houndhill, Worsborough, Barnsley, South Yorkshire
S70 6TU
☎ 01226 730495 [FAX] 01226 730838

The College offers courses in garden design, one for beginners and one for more advanced students. Both can be taken as correspondence courses or with face-to-face tuition.

Rodbaston School of Garden Design
Rodbaston College, The Lyme House, Castle Street, Eccleshall, Staffordshire ST21 6DF
☎ 01785 850240 [FAX] 01785 851665

Christopher Pickard tutors mature students to professional standards with the intention that they can then set up their own Garden Design practices. In addition to the Garden Design Course (full-time, one day a week for a year, or part-time, one evening a week for two years), he offers short courses on such topics as: Garden Design; Botanical Illustration; Flower Painting; Drawing for Garden Designers.

Royal Botanic Gardens, Kew
Education & Marketing department, Richmond, Surrey
TW9 3AB
☎ 0181 332 5626

Kew runs a week-long course called Aspects of Gardening which covers topics that are often considered too specialist for amateurs: water gardening and landscaping for example. Other all-week courses include: Flower Photography by Heather Angel, Botany for Beginners by Gail Bromley and Painting Flowers in Watercolour. Longer courses are available, including a two-week course on The Kew School of Botanical Illustration by Ann Farrer.

Royal Horticultural Society
Education Department, Wisley Garden, Woking, Surrey
GU23 6QB
☎ 01483 224234 [FAX] 01483 211750

The RHS has an extensive programme of educational events, courses, lectures and demonstrations. Some are listed in the Calendar section (q.v.). All such events receive good publicity in The Garden.

Summer Academy
Keynes College, The University, Canterbury, Kent
CT2 7NP

This company organises study holidays which usually last a week. Topics we particularly noticed in their 1997 brochure are: The Glory of the Garden (Sheffield, from 21 June); Houses & Gardens of Northumbria (Durham, from 5 July); The Gardens of Wessex (Southampton, from 5 July).

University of Oxford Public Education Programme
Botanic Garden, Rose Lane, Oxford OX1 4AX
☎ 01865 276920 [FAX] 01865 276920

Oxford Botanic Garden offers Study Days on such topics as Propagation, Taxonomy and Woodlands & Forests. The Winter Lecture series runs into April and includes Gardens of Ireland (13 March) and Back Gardens of Britain (24 April). There are garden tours around the Botanic garden in summer, and two short courses, one on Flowering Plant Families and the other on Botanical Illustration.

West Dean College
Chichester, West Sussex PO18 0QZ
☎ 01243 811301 [FAX] 01243 811343

West Dean College is set in one of the most beautiful and exciting gardens in the south of England. Its study days and residential courses (up to one week) cover the following topics: The Painted Garden; Reducing the Garden Workload; Country Garden Style; Pruning – Principles & Practice; Sculptural Pots for Plants; The Kitchen Garden for Beginners. Others are planned for later in the year.

20

Educational Grants and Grant-making Trusts

Many learned and educational bodies offer scholarships and bursaries for specific research projects. Scholars and students in need of funds are advised to make further enquiry: the Linnean Society and the Natural History Museum are among the institutions which may be able to assist. Students or would-be students in search of funding for university courses or research projects should look at *The Grants Register 1997*, published by Macmillan in 1996. It is wonderfully comprehensive: we cannot recommend it too highly. Also excellent, though not so directly useful for scholars in search of funding, is a Directory of Social Change Publication, *The Educational Grants Directory 1996/97* edited by John Smith and Kate Wallace. The following is a selection of opportunities which may be of interest to our readers.

Bedding Plants Foundation, Inc (US)

Harold Bettinger Memorial Scholarship

SUBJECTS Business and/or Marketing of Horticulture
NUMBER OFFERED One scholarship
FREQUENCY Annually
VALUE US$1,000
COUNTRY OF STUDY US or Canada
ELIGIBILITY Graduate or undergraduate, horticulture major with a business and/or marketing emphasis (or vice-versa), at an accredited college or university in US or Canada. Any nationality

CLOSING DATE 1 April
Application forms available on request

Bedding Plants Foundation, Inc (US)

John Carew Memorial Scholarship

SUBJECTS Horticulture: bedding or flowering pot plants
NUMBER OFFERED One scholarship
FREQUENCY Annually
VALUE US$1,500
COUNTRY OF STUDY US or Canada
ELIGIBILITY Graduates majoring in horticulture at an accredited college or university in US or Canada. Any nationality
CLOSING DATE 1 April

Application forms available on request. The Bedding Plants Foundation, Inc has two further scholarships which may be of interest: the Fran Johnson Scholarship for Non-Traditional Students and the James K Rathmell Jr Memorial Scholarship to Work/Study Abroad.

Dumbarton Oaks: Trustees for Harvard University

c/o The Assistant Director, Dumbarton Oaks, 1703 32nd Street NW, Washington DC 20007, US

Dumbarton Oaks Fellowships & Junior Fellowships

PURPOSE Support for study, research or doctoral theses
SUBJECTS Landscape architecture
NUMBER OFFERED 3 – 4
FREQUENCY Annually

VALUE   US$12,000 pa (Junior Fellowships). US$21,000 pa (Fellowships). Plus housing, expenses & travel allowances
TENABLE   For full time resident work at Dumbarton Oaks for up to 1 year. Not renewable
COUNTRY OF STUDY   US
ELIGIBILITY   Higher degree examinations for Junior Fellowship; PhD for Fellowship
CLOSING DATE   1 November

Some Summer Fellowships are available to scholars at any level to cover basic expenses for 6 – 9 weeks at Dumbarton Oaks

English-Speaking Union
Dartmouth House, 37 Charles Street, London W1X 8AB

Horticulture Scholarship
PURPOSE   Support for postgraduate study
SUBJECTS   Horticulture
NUMBER OFFERED   4
FREQUENCY   Annually
ELIGIBILITY   Candidates must have a horticultural qualification and be in the early stages of their career

Ask for an application form. The European Gardens Scholarship is a study tour of the UK by Europeans and a study tour of Europe by UK applicants. The Martin Mclaren Horticultural Scholarship/Garden Club of America Interchange Fellowship is one year spent in a UK/US university.

Friends of Israel Educational Trust
c/o John Levy, P O Box 7545, London NW2 2OX

Jerusalem Botanical Gardens Scholarship
PURPOSE   To provide the opportunity for botanists and horticulturists to work at the Jerusalem Botanical Gardens
SUBJECTS   Botany & horticulture
NUMBER OFFERED   Several
FREQUENCY   Annually
VALUE   Cost of return flight and accommodation
TENABLE   at the Jerusalem Botanical Gardens
COUNTRY OF STUDY   Israel
ELIGIBILITY   UK graduates in a relevant subject from recognised colleges and universities
CLOSING DATE   31 March

The Herb Society of America
9019 Kirtland Chardon Road, Mentor, OH 44060

Research Grant
PURPOSE   To further the knowledge & use of herbs
SUBJECTS   Research on herbal projects
NUMBER OFFERED   The grant may be split between two or more candidates
FREQUENCY   Annually
VALUE   Up to US$5,000
TENABLE   For up to one year
COUNTRY OF STUDY   Unrestricted
ELIGIBILITY   Persons with a programme of scientific, academic or artistic research into herbal plants
CLOSING DATE   31 January

Horticultural Research Institute (US)
c/o Ashby Ruden, Administrator, Suite 500, 1250 I Street NW, Washington, DC 20005

Various Grants
PURPOSE   The advancement of the nursery, greenhouse & landscape industry
SUBJECTS   Nursery industry, especially the production & use of woody landscape plants
NUMBER OFFERED   30+
FREQUENCY   Annually
VALUE   Variable: total budget US$25,000 (1996)
TENABLE   Federal or state universities, laboratories, institutes, arboreta or gardens. Sometimes renewable
COUNTRY OF STUDY   USA
ELIGIBILITY   Any research project which the Institute considers appropriate
CLOSING DATE   1 May

Horticultural Research International (UK)
c/o Personnel Officer, West Malling, Kent ME19 6BJ

Agricultural and Food Research Council Scholarships
PURPOSE   To assist a student with further studies & training
SUBJECTS   A wide range of horticultural sciences
NUMBER OFFERED   Variable
FREQUENCY   Variable
VALUE   £7,200 pa, plus fees
TENABLE   For three years at East Malling, Wye, Littlehampton or Wellesbourne
COUNTRY OF STUDY   UK
ELIGIBILITY   UK honours graduates
CLOSING DATE   28 February

Horticultural Research International (UK)
c/o Personnel Officer, West Malling, Kent ME19 6BJ

British Society for Horticultural Research Blackman Studentship
PURPOSE   To assist postgraduate study
SUBJECTS   Fields relating to horticulture
NUMBER OFFERED   One studentship
FREQUENCY   Periodically
VALUE   Maintenance allowance on government scale
TENABLE   3 years
COUNTRY OF STUDY   UK
ELIGIBILITY   British subjects with a first or upper second in a relevant subject from a British Commonwealth university

International Society of Arboriculture Research Trust
Box GG, Savoy, Illinois 61874, USA

Grants
PURPOSE   To encourage scientific or educational research on shade & landscape trees
SUBJECTS   Arboriculture

NUMBER OFFERED   Currently 10 grants
FREQUENCY   Annually
VALUE   US$5,000 (max)
TENABLE   1 year
COUNTRY OF STUDY   Any country
ELIGIBILITY   Very wide: any nationality, relevant academic disciplines
CLOSING DATE   1 November

The most favoured proposals are those which will 'help arborists earn their living by daily tree-care work'

Ministry of Agriculture, Fisheries & Food
c/o Mrs Barbara Keller, Nobel House, 17 Smith Square, London SW1P 3JR

Postgraduate Agricultural & Food Studentships
PURPOSE   To further the education of agricultural & food scientists
SUBJECTS   Many, including horticulture
NUMBER OFFERED   Up to 78 Studentships awarded to universities for research leading to a PhD or MSc courses
FREQUENCY   Annually
VALUE   Fees, plus £5,638 – £7,072 pa allowance
TENABLE   2 – 3 years at universities & approved colleges only
COUNTRY OF STUDY   UK
ELIGIBILITY   UK resident citizens of UK & Commonwealth, and some EC nationals
CLOSING DATE   31 July

Preference is given to applied research

The Royal Horticultural Society
c/o Joyce Stewart, 80 Vincent Square, London SW1P 2PE

Blaxall/Valentine Bursary
PURPOSE   To fund plant collections
SUBJECTS   Horticulture
NUMBER OFFERED   1 – 3 bursaries a year
FREQUENCY   Twice yearly
VALUE   Variable: the Society may require contributions from personal resources and/or others
ELIGIBILITY   Preference is given to UK & Commonwealth citizens aged 20 – 35
CLOSING DATE   30 June & 31 December

Report & accounts required on completion

The Royal Horticultural Society
c/o Joyce Stewart, 80 Vincent Square, London SW1P 2PE

The Expo '90 Osaka Travel Bursary
PURPOSE   To enable young people from UK & Japan to study in each other's country
SUBJECTS   Horticulture: mainly short courses & travel projects
NUMBER OFFERED   One bursary
FREQUENCY   Twice yearly

VALUE   Variable: the Society may require contributions from personal resources and/or others
COUNTRY OF STUDY   UK or Japan
ELIGIBILITY   British and Japanese citizens aged 20 – 35
CLOSING DATE   30 June, 31 December

Report & accounts required on completion

The Royal Horticultural Society
c/o Joyce Stewart, 80 Vincent Square, London SW1P 2PE

The Queen Elizabeth The Queen Mother Bursary
PURPOSE   To help young horticulturists finance specific projects
SUBJECTS   Horticulture: mainly short courses & travel projects
NUMBER OFFERED   1 – 3 bursaries a year
FREQUENCY   Twice yearly
VALUE   Variable: the Society may require contributions from personal resources and/or others
COUNTRY OF STUDY   No limitations
ELIGIBILITY   Preference is given to UK & Commonwealth citizens aged 20 – 35
CLOSING DATE   30 June, 31 December

Report & accounts required on completion

The Scottish Agricultural College
c/o The Secretary, Auchincruive, Ayr KA6 5HW

William John Thomson Scholarship
PURPOSE   To fund research training
SUBJECTS   Agriculture and horticulture
NUMBER OFFERED   One scholarship
FREQUENCY   Triennially
VALUE   Variable
TENABLE   At Auchincruive or its outstations, for three years
COUNTRY OF STUDY   UK
ELIGIBILITY   Any graduate in agricultural science working for a higher degree from Glasgow or Strathclyde university

Woman's National Farm & Garden Association, Inc (US)
c/o Mrs Elmer Braun (Chairwoman), 13 Davis Drive, Saginaw, MI 48602

Sarah Bradley Tyson Memorial Fellowship
PURPOSE   To assist with advanced study
SUBJECTS   Agriculture or horticulture
NUMBER OFFERED   One fellowship
FREQUENCY   Annually
VALUE   US$500
TENABLE   An educational institution of accepted standing
COUNTRY OF STUDY   US
ELIGIBILITY   Men and women, properly qualified, who have proved their ability by several years' experience
CLOSING DATE   15 April

Reports required at end of first semester and at completion

CHARITABLE TRUSTS

There are hundreds of private charitable trusts which award funds for horticultural projects. Most of the trusts mentioned in this chapter are listed in the 1996/97 edition of *The Directory of Grant-Making Trusts*, an invaluable reference book which readers are urged to consult in full.

All these trusts are known to have supported endeavours which can be classed as 'horticultural'. They may have done so only once, and have no plan to do so again: we cannot tell. If the principal concern of a trust is the welfare of people with disabilities, you can assume that its 'horticultural' interests are limited to projects which help such people.

Most trusts accept applications only from other registered charities, but some are prepared to make an exception to this general rule if an individual puts forward a particularly deserving or imaginative proposal. This list will be of particular interest to gardening clubs and conservation groups.

The Elsie Talbot Bridge Will Trust
C.C. No 279288
CORRESPONDENT Messrs Brown, Turner, Compton Carr & Co., 11 St. George's Place, Southport, Merseyside. PR9 0AL
TRUSTEES W. Ivers, B.G. Cox, D.T. Bushell, J. Kewle
OBJECTS General
FINANCES Income £23,405 Grants £ £16,740 Assets £276,063
YEAR 1988

The Countryside Trust
C.C. No 803496
CORRESPONDENT Mrs Lynne Garner (Secretary), The Countryside Trust, John Dower House, Crescent Place, Cheltenham, Gloucestershire GL50 3RA
TRUSTEES Sir John Johnson, M. Dower, J.L. Evans
OBJECTS To promote the conservation, preservation and restoration of the natural beauty of the countryside of England for public benefit
FINANCES Income £25,444 Grants £13,946 Assets £441,755
YEAR 1994

One-off payments towards a specific fund-raising event for community or voluntary bodies concerned with the care of the local countryside of England.

The Sarah d'Avigdor Goldsmid Charitable Trust
C.C. No 233083
CORRESPONDENT Mrs. R. C. Teacher, Hadlow Place, Golden Green, Tonbridge, Kent TN11 0BW.
TRUSTEES Lady d'Avigdor Goldsmid, Mrs. R. C. Teacher, A. J. M. Teacher.

OBJECTS General charitable purposes. Registered charities only: no applications by individuals. Unsuccessful applications not acknowledged.
FINANCES Income £28,000 Grants: £18,000 Assets: £400,000
YEAR 1994
Usually one-off grants.

The Dandelion Trust
C.C. No 328159
CORRESPONDENT Mrs J. Bowman, 41 The Limehouse Cut, 46 Morris Road, London E14 6NQ
TRUSTEES The Committee
OBJECTS General
FINANCES Income £95,812
YEAR 1992

The Elmgrant Trust
C.C. No 313398
CORRESPONDENT Mrs M.B. Nicholson (Secretary), Elmhirst Centre, Dartington Hall, Totnes, Devon TQ9 6EL
TRUSTEES Maurice Ash, Michael Young, Claire Ask Wheeler, Sophie Young, Marian Ash, David Young
OBJECTS General
FINANCES Income £130,523 Grants £99,908 Assets £2,161,163
YEAR 1994
Short-term and one-off grants for individuals and organisations.

J Paul Getty Jr General Charitable Trust
C.C. No 292360
CORRESPONDENT Bridget O'Brien Twohig (Administrator), 149 Harley Street, London W1N 2DH
TRUSTEES J. Paul Getty Jr. KBE, James Ramsden PC, Christopher Gibbs, Vanni Treves
OBJECTS General
FINANCES Income £1,382,449 Grants £1,242,065 Assets £33,870,568
YEAR 1993

The trustees meet four times a year. Applications from registered charities only are considered. Grants are made for capital or recurrent purposes, and sometimes for core funding and salaries. Garden restoration projects have received grants.

The Hamamelis Trust
C.C. No 280938
CORRESPONDENT The Secretary, c/o Penningtons, High-field, Brighton Road, Godalming, Surrey GU7 1NS.
TRUSTEES M. Fellingham, C.I. Slocock, Dr L. Martin, D. Stewart
OBJECTS General; specific projects for conservation of the countryside in the UK
FINANCES Income £90,500 Grants £73,350 Assets £1,500,000
YEAR 1993
UK charities only.

The Idlewild Trust

C.C. No   268124

CORRESPONDENT   Ms. Lyn Roberts, 54/56 Knatchbull Road, London SE5 9QY

TRUSTEES   Mrs P.B. Minet, Dr G. Beard, H.J. Parratt, Mrs F.L. Morrison-Jones, Mrs A.C. Grellier, Lady Goodison, M.H. Davenport

OBJECTS   Preservation for the benefit of the public of lands, buildings and other objects of beauty or historic interest of national importance

FINANCES   Income £173,468 Grants £130,613 Assets £1,669,344

YEAR   1993

Registered charities only.

The John Spedan Lewis Foundation

C.C. No   240473

CORRESPONDENT   N. Waldemar Brown, The Secretary, The John Spedan Lewis Foundation, 171 Victoria Street, London SW1E 5NN

TRUSTEES   S. Hampson, W.H. Melly, Miss D.N. Barrett, H.M.J. King, Miss C. Walton

OBJECTS   General charitable purposes, particularly those that reflect John Lewis's interest in education, the arts, the natural sciences (including horticulture) and the encouragement of disadvantaged talent.

FINANCES   Income: £60,316 Grants: £32,800 Assets: £667,524

YEAR   1994

Mostly straight donations which may be repeated. Preference is given to smaller, more imaginative appeals (but not normally to local branches, individual students or expeditions).

The Merlin Trust

C.C. No   803441

CORRESPONDENT   Valerie Finnis V.M.H. (Hon. Secretary), The Dower House, Boughton House, Kettering, Northamptonshire, NN14 1BJ

OBJECTS   To help young horticulturists to extend their knowledge

FINANCES   Not disclosed

Applicants should be UK citizens aged between 18 and 30, and show how their project would help their present work. All ideas are considered: travel, work experience, photography, seed collection, conservation work, travel to study plants: the trustees say that personal enthusiasm counts for more than qualifications.

The Paget Trust

C.C. No   327402

CORRESPONDENT   Joanna Herbert-Stepney, 41 Priory Gardens, London N6 5QU

TRUSTEES   Joanna Herbert-Stepney, Lesley Mary Rolling, Mrs Joy Pollard

OBJECTS   General

FINANCES   Income £87,323 Grants £68,000 £1,529,415

YEAR   1992

Organic horticulture been supported in the past.

The Royal Botanical and Horticultural Society of Manchester and the Northern Counties

C.C. No   226683

CORRESPONDENT   A. Pye MA FCA, P O Box 498, 12 Booth Street, Manchester M60 2ED

TRUSTEES   Official Custodian for charities

OBJECTS   Promotion of science and art in botany and horticulture by giving financial assistance to local gardens or other projects in the north west.

FINANCES   Income: £10,207 Grants: £7,321 Assets: £108,242

YEAR   1989

Mostly cash payments towards prize money or specific expenditure by horticultural societies, show organisers and gardens of horticultural interest

Stanley Smith Horticultural Trust

C.C. No   261925

CORRESPONDENT   Dr James Cullen, Cory Lodge, P O Box 365, Cambridge, CB2 1HR

TRUSTEES   C. D. Brickell, J. Dilger, J. L. Norton, Lady J. Renfrew, J. Simmons

OBJECTS   The support of amenity horticulture mainly, but not exclusively, in the United Kingdom

FINANCES   Income: £48,844 Grants: £49,992 Assets: £850,670

YEAR   1993

The Trustees welcome applications from individuals, organisations and institutions. They try to maintain a balance across the whole area of amenity horticulture and between small (up to £1,500) and larger grants at any time. The Trust has recently supported projects concerned with plant collecting, books on horticultural subjects, garden restoration, research on the production of new hybrids, and the maintenance of garden trainees. Grants are awarded twice a year, in April and October. Applications should be sent to the Director, who can also advise applicants as to how their applications should be presented.

21

Horticultural Libraries

Every keen gardener needs to consult reference books and sometimes to borrow them. Most people start their search for a particular book at their local library. Often the volume is not available at that particular branch, in which case the reader's search application form will be referred to other libraries within the same county, metropolitan area or region. Provided that records are readily accessible, and the software is up-to-date, most books are soon found. Those which are not available within the local area are passed to the Local Libraries Bureau, a federation of libraries which holds catalogues from each of its members. If this fails to locate a copy of the book, then the usual course is to refer the request to the British Library at Boston Spa to search through more and better catalogues until a source is found.

The Document Supply Centre of the British Library will also supply copies of articles free of charge to libraries which request them. It is a rule of this service that the copy must be read on the premises of the requesting library and lent, not given, to the reader. If the reader wishes to purchase it, the local library will sometimes give permission and levy a small charge.

Sometimes a reader needs to discover whether any books exist on a particular subject. The better libraries have extensive bibliographies and union lists of periodical publications. A good starting point is the British Library's catalogue: better still, the catalog of the Library of Congress.

Specialised collections like the Royal Horticultural Society's Lindley Library have extensive archives and large numbers of older books, especially those which were published before the Copyright Act 1911, came into effect. There are six legal deposit libraries which are entitled under the provisions of the Act to receive a free copy of any book published in the United Kingdom. They are: the British Library, The Bodleian Library at Oxford, the Cambridge University Library, the National Library of Scotland, the National Library of Wales and the library of Trinity College, Dublin. Their post-1911 collections of British gardening books are all complete.

Most of the libraries listed here offer such facilities as photocopying services, computer terminals, video viewers, and full microform and microfiche equipment, but not all are available at some of the smaller, more specialised libraries.

Much of the information in this chapter comes from Guide to Libraries & Information Units, 1995/96, edited by Peter Dale and published the British Library Board, which gives further details of the services offered by each and by hundreds of other libraries throughout Britain and Ireland.

Libraries in England: London

The British Library
2 Sheraton Street, London W1V 4BH
☎ 0171 636 1544
OPEN Reading Room, weekdays 9.30 am – 5.30 pm (9 pm on Tuesday – Thursday), Saturday 9.30 am – 1 pm.

The British Library is the UK's national library, at the centre of the library and information network. It was established in 1973 to consolidate the library departments of the British Museum, the National Central Library, the National Lending Library for Science and Technology, the British National Bibliography Ltd, and, in 1974, the Office for Scientific and Technical Information. Its services are based on the largest collections in the UK: over 18 million volumes at 18 buildings in London and the Document Supply Centre in West Yorkshire.

Most books and articles relating to horticulture, apart from more recent issues of popular magazines, can be read at the Humanities and Social Sciences reading rooms at the British Museum. A British Library Reader's Pass is needed: information about eligibility is available from the Reader Admissions Office. Some gardening books, especially those which deal with practical or scientific topics, are stored at the

Aldwych and Holborn reading rooms of the Science Reference and Information Service which open to the general public without charge or formality, but the great majority of material is at the British Museum.

The British Library is in the process of moving to purpose built accommodation at St Pancras, London NW1 but the planned opening has been delayed several times but may take place this year.

The British Library, Document Supply Centre

Boston Spa, Wetherby, West Yorkshire LS23 7BQ
☎ 01937 546000

The British Library offers two important services from the Document Supply Centre. The first is, in effect, a book-finding service for readers who apply through their local public or college libraries. The other is a rapid loan and photocopy service. The Document Supply Centre subscribes to 55,000 current journals in addition to acquiring monographs, conference proceedings and scientific reports. Some 88% of the 3,750,000 requests received each year are satisfied from stock.

Library and Archives, Royal Botanic Gardens

Kew, Richmond, Surrey TW9 3AE
☎ 0181 332 5414 [FAX] 0181 332 5278

OPEN Monday–Thursday, 9 am – 5.30 pm (5 pm on Fridays).

Books are available to **bona fide** researchers by written appointment only. The library's collection includes: plant taxonomy, distribution and conservation, horticulture, economic botany, plant anatomy, genetics, biochemistry and tropical botany. The library has 170,000 volumes (120,000 monographs), 140,000 pamphlets, 1,800 current periodicals and 3,200 no longer current. The archive collection has 250,000 modern and recent items, including the papers of Sir Joseph Banks, Sir William Hooker, Sir Joseph Hooker and George Bentham.

Ministry of Agriculture, Fisheries and Food Library

3 Whitehall Place, London SW1A 3HH
☎ 0171 270 8420/8421 [FAX] 0171 270 8419

OPEN Monday – Friday, 9.30 am – 5 pm, by prior appointment giving at least 24 hours notice.

The library has 160,000 volumes and subscribes to 2,000 current periodicals. It also publishes a library guide, reading lists and subject bibliographies. We have found it a valuable source, especially for foreign periodicals.

Linnean Society of London Library

Burlington House, Piccadilly, London W1V 0LQ
☎ 0171 434 4479 [FAX] 0171 287 9364

OPEN Monday – Friday, 10 am – 5 pm, by appointment.

The library's collection includes: natural history, taxonomy, botany, the history of science, the history of biology, evolutionary theory and some horticultural studies. Its special collections incorporate the Insch Tea Library, the Balfour Bequest Bird Library and the library of Carolus Linnaeus. It has over

100,000 volumes, nearly 1000 current periodicals and a good collection of pamphlets, photographs and other illustrations.

Chelsea Physic Garden

66 Royal Hospital Road, London SW3 4HS
☎ 0171 352 5654

OPEN Monday – Friday, 8 am – 3 pm by appointment.

The library concentrates on British and foreign pharmacological, herbal and medicinal studies, and its special collections include historic herbals dating back to 1472, small historic herbaria (e.g. Moore's Clematis), and a general reference collection on medicinal plants.

Consumers' Association Library

2 Marylebone Road, London NW1 4DX
☎ 0171 486 5544 [FAX] 0171 935 1606

OPEN Monday – Friday, 10 am – 6 pm. Admission is at the discretion of the Chief Librarian.

Principally concerned with consumer protection, the library has a good collection of gardening sources which are used by the staff of *Gardening Which?*. The library has 3,000 volumes and subscribes to 850 current periodicals.

Architectural Association Library

34-36 Bedford Square, London WC1B 3ES
☎ 0171 436 8740

OPEN Monday – Friday, 10 am – 6.30 pm (6 pm on Mondays & Wednesdays) in termtime: 10 am – 5 pm in holidays.

The library has 25,000 volumes and 80,000 slides on architecture & allied subjects including gardens and landscsapes.

Commonwealth Development Corporation

1 Bessborough Gardens, London SW1V 2JQ
☎ 0171 828 4488 [FAX] 0171 828 6505

OPEN 9.30 am – 5.30 pm.

The Corporation's library has a useful collection of books and periodicals on tropical agriculture & forestry.

Farming Information Centre

22 Long Acre, London WV2E 9LY
☎ 0171 331 7293 [FAX] 0171 331 7382

OPEN 10.30 am – 16.30 pm (12 noon on Friday).

A service provided by the National Farmers' Union. 5,000 books, 15,000 pamphlets and 2,000 photographs on agriculture and horticulture.

The Natural History Museum

Library Services, Cromwell Road, London SW7 5BD
☎ 0171 938 9191 [FAX] 0171 938 9290

OPEN Monday – Saturday, 10 am – 6 pm. Reader's ticket required.

A large collection of books, focused on life and earth sciences: natural history, botany, entomology, palaeontology, mineralogy, geology, anthropology, zoology and horticulture. Also a good collection of drawings, manuscripts, archives, catalogues and papers. There are 800,000 volumes and 10,000 current periodicals.

The Royal Horticultural Society, Lindley Library

80 Vincent Square, London SW1P 2PE

☎ 0171 821 3050

OPEN   Monday – Friday, 9.30 am – 5.30 pm. Members of the public are entitled to use the library at any time during these hours.

The library has nearly 50,000 books and the largest collection of nursery catalogues in the UK. It subscribes to a wide range of British and foreign periodicals. It also has an unrivalled collection of horticultural papers and foreign works. Some volumes can be borrowed by members of the Society.

Libraries in England: Outside London

Bodleian Library

Broad Street, Oxford OX1 3BG

☎ 01865 277000   FAX 01865 277182

OPEN   Term time: Monday – Friday, 9 am – 8 pm, Saturday, 9 am – 1 pm. During vacations: Monday – Friday, 9 am – 7 pm, Saturday, 9 am – 1 pm. The library is open to non-University readers on payment for a Reader's Ticket (from £2 for two-day ticket, to £10 for one year).

The Bodleian is a copyright library, so the horticultural collection is very comprehensive, although there are comparatively few older works. The Bodleian has a total of 5.5 million volumes and subscribes to 54,800 current periodicals.

Cambridge University Library

West Road, Cambridge CB3 9DR

☎ 01223 333000   FAX 01223 333160

OPEN   Monday to Friday 9 am – 7.15 pm (10 pm during Easter Term), Saturday 9 am – 1 pm; closed for some Bank Holidays and for one week in September. Open to non-members of the University: enquiries in writing to the admissions officer.

The library is a copyright library, with a comprehensive collection of 20th century books on gardening. There are 4 million volumes and nearly 60,000 current periodicals, but these include all subjects.

Writtle Agricultural College Library

Writtle College, Chelmsford, Essex CM1 3RR

☎ 01245 420705   FAX 01245 420456

OPEN   Term time: Monday – Thursday, 8.45 am – 8.30 pm, Friday, 8.45 am – 5 pm, Saturday, 9 am – 12 pm. During vacations: Monday – Thursday, 8.45 am – 5.15 pm, Friday, 8.45 am – 4.45 pm. This is a membership library: apply to the chief librarian for details.

The collection includes agriculture, horticulture and other land-based subjects, with related science and management, and there are many historical books relating to agriculture and horticulture. The library has 37,000 volumes and subscribes to 375 current periodicals.

University of Reading Library

P O Box 223, Whiteknights, Reading, Berkshire RG6 2AE

☎ 01734 318770   FAX 01734 312335

OPEN   Term time: Monday – Thursday, 9 am – 10.15 pm, Friday, 9 am – 7 pm, Saturday, 9 am – 12.30 pm, Sunday, 2 pm – 6 pm. During vacations: Monday – Friday, 9 am – 5 pm.

There is a good natural sciences and agriculture collection as well as horticulture. There are 800,000 volumes and 4,000 current periodicals but these statistics cover all the university's facilities. Nevertheless, Reading has one of the best university collections of horticultural books in the country.

Pershore College of Horticulture Library

Pershore, Worcestershire WR10 3JP

☎ 01386 552443   FAX 01386 556528

OPEN   Monday – Thursday, 9 am – 8 pm, Friday, 9 am – 5 pm by appointment.

The horticultural collection covers science, landscaping, management, arboriculture and beekeeping, as well as amenity and commercial horticulture. There are 10,000 volumes, 130 current periodicals and 2,500 pamphlets.

University of Bristol Library

Tyndall Avenue, Bristol BS8 1TJ

☎ 0117 930 3030   FAX 0117 925 5334

OPEN   Term time: Monday – Thursday, 8.45 am – 11 pm, Friday and Saturday, 8.45 am – 6 pm, Sunday, 2 pm – 8 pm. Christmas vacation: Monday – Thursday, 8.45 am – 7 pm, Friday, 8.45 am – 4.45 pm. Summer vacation: Monday – Friday, 8.45 am – 4.45 pm, Saturday, 8.45 am – 1 pm. Applications to use the library should be made in writing to the University Librarian.

The library has some rare botany books but, more importantly, houses the book collection of the Garden History Society. There is a total of 940,000 volumes and 6,500 current periodicals, but these figures include all university faculties.

Horticulture Research International

Wellesbourne Library, Wellesbourne, Warwick CV35 9EF

☎ 01789 470382   FAX 01789 470552

OPEN   Monday – Friday, 9am – 5 pm (4.30 pm on Fridays) by appointment.

Topics covered include horticulture, plant breeding, entomology, plant pathology, seed technology, genetics, vegetable production, soil science, pesticide science and plant physiology. Wellesbourne has 14,000 volumes and subscribes to 500 current periodicals. There is also a small collection of rare 18th and 19th century gardening books and an archive collection of modern books – 'modern' means post 1789.

CAB International

Library Services Centre, Silwood Park, Ascot, Berkshire SL5 7TA

☎ 01344 872747   FAX 01344 872901

OPEN   Monday to Friday 10 am – 5.30 pm: External users must make an appointment in advance.

The main library of the former Commonwealth Agricultural Bureau has 50,000 volumes and a vast collection of journals (2000 current journals), the back-up to its authoritative series of scientific *Abstracts*.

Countryside Commission
John Dower House, Crescent Place, Cheltenham, Gloucestershire GL50 3RA

☎ 01242 521381   📠 01242 584270

OPEN   By prior appointment: 9.30 am – 12.30 pm and 2 pm – 4 pm.

The Commission's library has about 16,000 books: topics covered include landscape planning and countryside recreation.

Forestry Commission Library
Alice Holt Lodge, Wrecclesham, Farnham, Surrey GU10 4LH

☎ 01420 22255   📠 01420 23653

OPEN   9 am – 4.30 pm: open to anyone with a bona fide interest in forestry.

The library has about 10,000 books and 1,000 periodicals, most of them foreign, on all topics related to trees and arboriculture.

Libraries in Scotland

National Library of Scotland
George IV Bridge, Edinburgh EH1 1EW

☎ 0131 226 4531

OPEN   Reading room, weekdays, 9.30 am – 8.30 pm (Wednesday 10 am – 8.30 pm), Saturday 9.30 am – 1 pm. Scottish Science Library, weekdays 9.30 am – 5 pm (Wednesday 10 am – 8.30 pm).

The Library became the National Library of Scotland by Act of Parliament in 1925. Its collection of printed books and MSS is very large and it has an unrivalled collection of Scottish material. The Reading Room is open to readers for research which cannot conveniently be pursued elsewhere. Admission is by ticket issued to an approved applicant.

The Library, Royal Botanic Garden Edinburgh
Inverleith Row, Edinburgh EH3 5LR

☎ 0131 552 7171   📠 0131 552 0382

OPEN   Monday – Friday, 9.30 am – 4.30 pm (4 pm on Fridays).

Collection includes: systematic botany, amenity horticulture and landscape architecture: there are 180,000 volumes, 25,000 pamphlets, and the library subscribes to over 1,700 current periodicals.

Scottish Crop Research Institute
Invergowrie, Dundee DD2 5DA

☎ 01382 562731   📠 01382 562426

OPEN   9 am – 5 pm: prior appointment with the librarian required.

16,000 books relating to crop research, but especially good for works on potatos and raspberries.

Libraries in Wales

Welsh College of Horticulture
Coleg Garddwriaeth Cymru
Northop, Mold, Clwyd CH7 6AA

☎ 01352 86861   📠 01352 86731

OPEN   Term time: Monday – Friday, 9 am – 8.30 pm: times variable during the vacation. Reference only: no borrowing.

Subjects include horticulture, floristry, interior landscape, landscape, amenity horticulture, garden centres, retail horticulture, commercial horticulture and greenkeeping. The library has 4,000 volumes and subscribes to 50 current periodicals.

The National Library of Wales
Llyfrgell Genedlaethol Cymru
Aberystwyth Dyfed SY23 3BU

☎ 01970 623816   📠 01970 615709)

OPEN   Monday to Friday 9.30 am – 6 pm (5 pm on Saturdays). Membership open to any person over 18 years of age.

A legal deposit ('copyright') library with a large modern collection on horticultural topics. 3.5 million volumes on all subjects. The library has a good collection of bibliographies on Welsh topics, including aspects of horticulture and garden history.

Library in Northern Ireland

Greenmount College of Agriculture & Horticulture
22 Greenmount Road, Antrim BT41 4PU

☎ 01849 462114

OPEN   9 am – 5 pm daily, and some evenings during termtime.

The Department of Agriculture keeps its horticultural collection of about 8,000 books here: the bulk of the collection, some 52,000 books on every aspect of agriculture, fisheries and food is in the Department's main library at Dundonald House, Upper Newtownards Road, Belfast BT4 3SB (Tel: 01232 524401).

Library in the Republic of Ireland

Trinity College Library
College Street, Dublin 2

☎ 00 353 1 772941   📠 00 353 1 719003

OPEN   Monday – Friday 9.30 am – 10 pm (5 pm during vacations, 1 pm on Saturdays). Members of the public may use the library to consult material not available elsewhere.

A deposit library for both Ireland and Britain. There are 3 million volumes and the library subscribes to 12,000 current periodicals.

22

Specialist Bookshops

New gardening books appear each year in unrelenting numbers. Some are excellent, most more run-of-the-mill. Branches of nationwide chains such as Waterstones and Dillons, Foyles, and the university booksellers, including Heffers and Blackwells, all carry an impressive selection of new books and usually offer mail order or account facilities. Ordinary secondhand bookshops can prove fruitful hunting grounds for reasonably priced gardening books but much of their stock is out-of-date and best forgotten. The specialists are your most reliable source for older and more recent classics, floras and affordable but worthwhile titles from overlooked authors. They will also have highly illustrated and collectable books: since these appeal also to non-gardeners, you must expect to pay accordingly. The Provincial Booksellers Fairs Association (PBFA) (01763 249212) organises regular sales around the country. This year we have included some overseas booksellers in our selection.

Anna Buxton Books

Redcroft, 23 Murrayfield Road, Edinburgh, Lothian EH12 6EP
☎ 0131 337 1747   [FAX] 0131 337 8174

CONTACT   Mrs Anna Buxton
SPECIALITY   New books; secondhand and antiquarian books; botany; general gardening; horticulture; illustrated books or prints; trees and forestry; Scottish gardening; plant hunters; garden history
CATALOGUE   On request. Christmas supplement
MAIL ORDER   Yes

An attractively produced and readable list, which includes general titles, collectable works and some new books. All books are described, and appear alphabetically by author.

Arnold Books

11 New Regent Street, Christchurch, New Zealand
☎ 00 64 3 365 7188   [FAX] 00 64 3 365 2630

CONTACT   John Palmer
SPECIALITY   Botany; horticulture; natural history

The leading bookshop in New Zealand for second-hand gardening books. Readers should also ask for their Economic Botany list, for that is where books on fruit, vegetables and herbs are listed.

Besleys Books

4 Blyburgate, Beccles, Suffolk NR34 9TA
☎ 01502 715762

CONTACT   P. Besley
OPEN   9.30 am – 5 pm. Closed Wednesdays and Sundays and sometimes for lunch. After hours contact 01502 675649
SPECIALITY   Secondhand and antiquarian books; botany; flower arranging; general gardening; horticulture; illustrated books or prints; natural history; trees and forestry
CATALOGUE   On request. 1 a year
MAIL ORDER   Yes
SHOWS   PBFA

An annotated sectional list: bibliographic details rather than descriptions. A wide selection from general gardening titles to specialist and illustrated books.

Bookmark, Books of the World

P O Box 728, Nowra, NSW 2541, Australia
☎ 00 61 44 217360   [FAX] 00 61 44 235195
SPECIALITY   New books; botany; horticulture
CATALOGUE   Free
MAIL ORDER   Yes

This bookshop is a good source of English-language titles from non-UK publishers. Their list of Australian publications is particularly comprehensive.

Brooks Books

P O Box 21473, 1343 New Hampshire Drive, Concord, CA 94521, USA
☎ 00 1 510 672 4566   [FAX] 00 1 510 672 3338

CONTACT   Philip Nesty
SPECIALITY   Botany; horticulture
MAIL ORDER   Yes

Probably the biggest second-hand bookshop in the world that specialises in botany and ornamental horticulture, with the emphasis on plants rather than design or history. Their general list is an excellent source of English-language books from every country. In addition, they publish regular lists devoted to Cacti & Succulents and Trees & Shrubs.

BSBI Publications; F & M Perring

Green Acre, Wood Lane, Oundle, Peterborough, Northamptonshire PE8 5TP

☎ 01832 273388   📠 01832 274568

CONTACT   Mrs Margaret Perring
OPEN   By appointment only
SPECIALITY   New books; botany; natural history; county floras and check lists
CATALOGUE   On request. Regular supplements
MAIL ORDER   Yes

Official agents for the Botanical Society of the British Isles. In addition to the society's publications, they stock local, British and overseas floras and other botanical, conservation and reference titles.

Capability's Books, Inc

2359 Highway 46, Deer Park, Wisconsin 54007, USA

☎ 00 1 715 269 5346

CONTACT   Paulette Rickard
SPECIALITY   New and secondhand books
CATALOGUE   Free
MAIL ORDER   Yes

This excellent American bookshop lists about 60% of all horticultural titles now in print and a large number that are no longer available. It is also worth remembering that what is out-of-print in the UK may still be available in the USA. The list is especially helpful: it gives longish descriptions of each title.

Cape Seed & Book Suppliers

P O Box 23709, Claremont 7735, Cape Town, South Africa

☎ 00 27 21 61 2005   📠 00 27 21 683 3379

SPECIALITY   Botany; horticulture; natural history
MAIL ORDER   Yes

This company specialises in books about South African botany, horticulture and natural history. Its list is impressively comprehensive and should be the first point of reference for anyone who wants information about their country.

Carol Barnett, Books

3562 NE Liberty St., Portland, OR 97211-7258, USA

☎ 00 1 503 282 7036

SPECIALITY   Horticulture; natural history

Carol Barnett produces regular catalogues on Botany and Gardening. She is an excellent source for second-hand books on every aspect of American gardening.

Cassell plc

Stanley House, 3 Fleets Lane, Poole, Dorset BH15 3AJ

☎ 01202 665432   📠 01202 666219

CONTACT   Customer Services
OPEN   8.30 am – 5 pm, Monday – Friday
SPECIALITY   New books; botany; flower arranging; general gardening
CATALOGUE   On request
MAIL ORDER   Ring Customer Services

Gardening titles direct from the publisher. This extensive list includes titles from Ward Lock, Blandford and the RHS Wisley Handbooks.

Chantrey Books

24 Cobnar Road, Sheffield, South Yorkshire S8 8QB

☎ 0114 2748958

CONTACT   Clare Brightman
OPEN   By appointment only
SPECIALITY   Secondhand and antiquarian books; botany; general gardening; horticulture; illustrated books or prints; natural history; rural life
CATALOGUE   On request. 3 a year
MAIL ORDER   Yes
SHOWS   Malvern Spring; Harrogate (Spring); Harrogate (Autumn); PBFA

A pleasing general list, divided into subheadings. Some interesting older books too, as well as natural history and rural titles.

Chris Hollingshead (Books)

17 Bonser Road, Strawberry Hill, Twickenham, London TW1 4RQ

☎ 0181 892 8798

CONTACT   Chris Hollingshead
SPECIALITY   Botany; flower arranging; horticulture
MAIL ORDER   Yes

A new bookseller, specialising in second-hand, out-of-print and scarce horticultural and botanical books. His first lists have contained some very interesting titles.

Fa. C. Esveld

Rijneveld 72, 2771 XS Boskoop, The Netherlands

☎ 00 31 1727-13289   📠 00 31 1727-15714

SPECIALITY   New books
MAIL ORDER   Yes

This bookshop is situated in the garden centre attached to one of Europe's biggest nurseries. It stocks new books in several languages.

Garden Books

11 Blenheim Crescent, London W11 2EE

☎ 0171 792 0777   📠 0171 792 1991

CONTACT   Valerie Scriven
OPEN   9 am – 6 pm, Monday to Saturday
SPECIALITY   New and secondhand books; horticulture
MAIL ORDER   Books sent worldwide

New bookshop in Notting Hill which stocks mostly new gardening titles. The range is balanced and focused, and they are happy to order and post anything that is not in stock. A visit is recommended (specialist cookery and travel bookshops are nearby).

Herbaceous Books

15 Westville Avenue, Ilkley, West Yorkshire LS29 9AH

☎ 01943 602422

CONTACT   Yvonne Luke
SPECIALITY   Secondhand and antiquarian books
CATALOGUE   Free

MAIL ORDER   Yes

Despite its name, this firm offers a wide range of titles, not just confined to hardy plants. The books tend to be good practical guides and inexpensive classics, rather than antiquarian.

Honingklip Book Sales
402 CPOA, 231 Main Road, Rondebosch, 7700 Cape Town, South Africa
☎ 00 27 21 689 1940   📠 00 27 21 689 1945

CONTACT   W.J. & Mrs E. R. Middelmann
SPECIALITY   Secondhand and antiquarian books; botany; horticulture; flora & gardens of Southern Africa
CATALOGUE   Free
MAIL ORDER   Yes

Honingklip is an excellent source of botanical and horticultural books about every aspect of South African plants, gardens and wild flowers. The list has prices in US$, but cheques in sterling are accepted.

Ingrid Sophie Hörsch
Garten- und Pflanzenbücher International, Hagenwiesenstr. 3, D-73006 Uhingen, Germany
☎ 00 49 7163 4196   📠 00 49 7163 4789

CONTACT   Ingrid Sophie Hörsch
OPEN   2 pm – 10 pm daily
SPECIALITY   New and secondhand books
CATALOGUE   Free
MAIL ORDER   Yes

This well-established dealer issues two lists a year (new & old) and special lists for Roses, Rhododendron & Camellias, Trees & Shrubs and Climbers, among others. About half the titles are in German and half in English, from USA, South Africa, Australia, New Zealand and Canada, as well as the UK. Mrs Hörsch speaks excellent English and her husband is secretary of the German group of the International Clematis Society.

Ivelet Books Ltd
18 Fairlawn Drive, Redhill, Surrey RH1 6JP
☎ 01737 764520   📠 01737 760140

CONTACT   Mr D. J. and Mrs E. A. Ahern
SPECIALITY   Secondhand and antiquarian books; general gardening; horticulture; illustrated books or prints; natural history; landscape and architecture; garden history
CATALOGUE   On request. 3 or 4 a year
MAIL ORDER   Yes
SHOWS   RHS Westminster; PBFA

A good range for gardeners and collectors: the list is strongest on twentieth-century classics such as Jekyll and Bowles, and is also a source for standard and historical works. They also specialise in Landscape and Architecture.

John Henly
Brooklands, Walderton, Chichester, West Sussex PO18 9EE
☎ 01705 631426   📠 01705 631544

CONTACT   John Henly
OPEN   By appointment only

SPECIALITY   Secondhand and antiquarian books; botany; general gardening; horticulture; natural history; trees and forestry; geology; palaeontology
CATALOGUE   On request. 4 a year
MAIL ORDER   Yes
SHOWS   PBFA

The catalogues are helpfully sub-divided into subjects. Individual entries have full bibliographic notes, but descriptions are kept to a minimum. Good for standard works, especially from the mid-twentieth century.

Kew Shop
Mail Order Section, Royal Botanic Gardens, Kew, Richmond, Surrey TW9 3AB
☎ 0181 332 5653

OPEN   9 am – 5 pm for telephone orders; Victoria Gate Shop normally open 9.30 am – 5.30 pm (summer and Christmas period) or until last garden admissions
SPECIALITY   New books; botany; flower arranging; horticulture; natural history; trees and forestry
CATALOGUE   Books & gifts; scientific
MAIL ORDER   Yes

An excellent choice of current horticultural and botanical books, including numerous scientific publications. A large section is devoted to children's books and attractive gift items. Entrance is normally through the garden, but you can get in directly if you give advance notice. The closing time changes with the season (information on 0181 940 1171).

Landsman's Bookshop Ltd
Buckenhill, Bromyard, Hereford & Worcester HR7 4PH
☎ 01885 483420   📠 01885 483420

CONTACT   K. J. Stewart
OPEN   9 am – 4.30 pm, Monday – Friday, Saturdays by appointment
SPECIALITY   New books; remaindered books; secondhand and antiquarian books; botany; flower arranging; general gardening; horticulture; natural history; trees and forestry
CATALOGUE   £1.25
MAIL ORDER   Yes
SHOWS   Malvern Spring; Harrogate (Spring); Southport

From their substantial catalogue Landsman's aims to supply all gardening books which are in print. Mainly mail-order and through agricultural and horticultural shows. They also have remaindered and second-hand material (of interest to horticultural students). Agriculture is stocked in similar depth, and they publish a few titles of their own.

Lloyds of Kew
9 Mortlake Terrace, Kew, Richmond, Surrey TW9 3DT
☎ 0181 940 2512   📠 01932 571416

CONTACT   Lloyds of Kew
OPEN   10 am – 4 pm, Monday – Friday; 10 am – 5 pm, Saturdays. Closed Wednesdays and Sundays
SPECIALITY   Secondhand and antiquarian books; botany; flower arranging; general gardening; horticulture; illustrated books or prints; trees and forestry
CATALOGUE   On request
SHOWS   Chelsea

Specialists for secondhand and antiquarian gardening books. Tucked away just off Kew Green, the shop also carries a general secondhand stock. They operate a free finding service (without obligation).

Mary Bland
Augop, Evenjobb, Presteigne, Powys LD8 2PA
☎ 01547 560218

CONTACT   Mary Bland
OPEN   By appointment only
SPECIALITY   Secondhand and antiquarian books; botany; flower arranging; general gardening; horticulture; illustrated books or prints; trees and forestry
CATALOGUE   On request. About 3 a year
MAIL ORDER   Yes
SHOWS   RHS Westminster; Malvern Spring; Chelsea

Good general and collectors' stock, with many interesting and reasonably priced titles across the whole range of gardening books. The list is divided into sections, with bibliographic details and some descriptions. Prints available at shows. Will search for titles.

Mike Park
351 Sutton Common Road, Sutton, Surrey SM3 9HZ
☎ 0181 641 7796

CONTACT   Mike Park or Ian Smith
OPEN   Sales mainly mail order and shows; viewing occasionally possible by appointment
SPECIALITY   Remaindered books; secondhand and antiquarian books; botany; flower arranging; general gardening; horticulture; illustrated books or prints; natural history; trees and forestry; foreign floras
CATALOGUE   1 or 2 a year
MAIL ORDER   Yes
SHOWS   RHS Westminster; Malvern Spring; Chelsea; Hampton Court; PBFA

Mike Park is a familiar exhibitor at RHS shows in Vincent Square; good for recent titles and standard or reference works.

Peter M Daly
Thompson Antiques, 20a Jewry Street, Winchester, Hampshire SO23 8RZ
☎ 01962 867732

CONTACT   Peter M. Daly
OPEN   10 am – 4.30 pm, Wednesdays and Fridays; 10 am – 1 pm, 2 pm – 5 pm, Saturdays. Other times by appointment
SPECIALITY   Remaindered books; secondhand and antiquarian books; botany; flower arranging; horticulture; illustrated books or prints; natural history; landscape gardening
CATALOGUE   No
MAIL ORDER   No
SHOWS   PBFA

RHS Enterprises Ltd
RHS Garden, Wisley, Woking, Surrey GU23 6QB
☎ 01483 211113   ☎ 01483 211003

CONTACT   B. M. C. Ambrose

OPEN   10 am – 5.30 pm, Monday – Saturday, closes at 6.30 pm in summer; 11.30 am – 5.30pm Sundays, March – December, 10 am – 4pm, January, February
SPECIALITY   New books; botany; flower arranging; general gardening; horticulture; illustrated books or prints; natural history; trees and forestry; plant monographs; floras; academic
CATALOGUE   On request. 2 a year
MAIL ORDER   Yes (01483 211320)
SHOWS   RHS Westminster; Malvern Spring; Harrogate (Spring); Chelsea; BBC GW Live; Hampton Court; Harrogate (Autumn)

The range of gardening and botanical books on sale at Wisley is among the best in the country. Twice-yearly catalogues detail an extensive part of the stock, and allow for mail-order purchase. New books only, including many from overseas. The shop also sells gift items.

Search Press Books by Post
Wellwood, North Farm Road, Tunbridge Wells, Kent TN2 3DR
☎ 01892 510850   📠 01892 515903

CONTACT   Barbara Duck and Mary Ellingham
SPECIALITY   New books; horticulture; organic; crafts
CATALOGUE   On request
MAIL ORDER   Yes

Mail order service from this craft and organic gardening publisher. Orders are post-free over £20.

St Ann's Books
Rectory House, 26 Priory Road, Great Malvern, Hereford & Worcester WR14 3DR
☎ 01684 562818   📠 01684 566491

CONTACT   Chris Johnson
SPECIALITY   Secondhand and antiquarian books; botany; horticulture; natural history
CATALOGUE   Two a year
MAIL ORDER   Yes

This well-established dealer in second-hand books on ornithology published an excellent catalogue of antiquarian and second-hand books on botany and gardening last year. Many are of interest to collectors, but it is also a good source for not-so-collectable books that are just hard to find nowadays.

Summerfield Books
Summerfield House, High Street, Brough, Kirkby Stephen, Cumbria CA17 4BX
☎ 017683 41577   📠 017683 41577

CONTACT   Jon and Sue Atkins
OPEN   By appointment
SPECIALITY   New books; remaindered books; secondhand and antiquarian books; botany; horticulture; illustrated books or prints; natural history; trees and forestry; country and foreign floras; cryptogams
CATALOGUE   On request. 4 a year
MAIL ORDER   Yes

A substantial list with an individual style. Very good for local and foreign floras (old and new), botany, plant hunting, cryptogams and forestry titles. Some interesting general titles also:

everything from collectors' rarities to £2 bargains. Free finding service.

W C Cousens
The Leat, Lyme Road, Axminster, Devon EX13 5BL
☎ 01297 32921

CONTACT W. C. Cousens
OPEN By appointment only
SPECIALITY Secondhand and antiquarian books; flower arranging; general gardening; horticulture; trees and forestry
CATALOGUE SAE; four a year
SHOWS PBFA

Book-search facility available.

Wells & Winter
Mere House Barn, Mereworth, Maidstone, Kent ME18 5NB
☎ 01622 813627

CONTACT Sir John Wells
OPEN Sell from shows only
SPECIALITY New books; remaindered books; secondhand and antiquarian books; general gardening; horticulture; trees and forestry
MAIL ORDER No
SHOWS RHS Westminster; Malvern Spring; Chelsea; Hampton Court; Courson

New and second-hand books: available at shows only. The stand also sells botanical cards, labels and other garden products.

Whitestone Gardens Ltd
Sutton, Thirsk, North Yorkshire YO7 2PZ
☎ 01845 597467   FAX 01845 597035
SPECIALITY Secondhand and antiquarian books; horticulture

This excellent nursery for cactus and succulents also has the best list of second-hand and out-of-print books on the subject in the UK. It includes German, American and South African works.

Wyseby House Books
Kingsclere Old Bookshop, 2a George Street, Kingsclere, Newbury, Berkshire RG20 5NQ
☎ 01635 297995   FAX 01635 297995

CONTACT Dr Tim Oldham
OPEN 10 am – 5 pm, Tuesday – Saturday
SPECIALITY Secondhand and antiquarian books; botany; general gardening; horticulture; natural history; trees and forestry; garden history; architecture
CATALOGUE On request. Monthly
MAIL ORDER Yes
SHOWS PBFA

The horticultural titles run from affordable classics from the last 150 years to more recent works. Of interest to both gardeners and specialists. Other areas include zoology and the history of science.

23

Books,
Periodicals &
Videos

New Books 1996

500 More Fuchsias, Miep Nijhuis (Batsford, 1996) £15.99.

A Flower for Every Day, Nigel Colborn (Quadrille Publishing, 1996) £19.99.

Alan Mitchell's Trees of Britain, Alan Mitchell (Collins, 1996) £14.99.

Alien Grasses of the British Isles, T. B. Ryves, E. J. Clement & M. C. Foster (Botanical Society of the British Isles, 1996) £10.50.

The price includes postage and packing.

Antiques from the Garden, Alistair Morris (Garden Art Press, 1996) £25.00.

This is a fascinating survey of old garden buildings, ornaments and tools: compulsory reading for anyone with a collecting instinct or who wishes to create a garden in appropriate style for an old house.

Arcadian Thames, Mavis Batey, Henrietta Buttery, David Lambert & Kim Wilkie (Barn Elms Publishing, 1996) £16.50.

Conservation, wildlife, landscape and history are combined in this book which is both guide and loving record. Royalties go to the Garden History Society.

Begonias, The Complete Guide, Eric Catterall (The Crowood Press, 1996) £10.99.

The Cattleyas and Their Relatives, Volume IV: The Bahamian and Caribbean Species, Carl L. Withner (Timber Press, 1996) £31.50.

Charleston Kedding: History of Kitchen Gardening, Susan Campbell (Ebury, 1996) £30.00.

Clematis, The Complete Guide, Ruth Gooch (The Crowood Press, 1996) £14.99.

The Complete Guide to Gardening with Containers, Susan Berry & Steve Bradley (Collins & Brown, 1996) £16.99.

Conifers: The Illustrated Encyclopedia, D. M. van Gelderen & J. R. P. van Hoey Smith (Timber Press, 1996) £90.00.

Two volume illustrated set.

Conservatory and Indoor Plants: Volume I, Roger Philips & Martyn Rix (Macmillan, 1996) £19.99.

Contemporary Botanical Artists: The Shirley Sherwood Collection, Shirley Sherwood (Weidenfeld, 1996) £40.00.

Creating a Garden, Mary Keen (Conran Octopus, 1996) £25.00.

Mary Keen has one of the best brains among gardening writers and her use of the English language is second to none. All the more pity, therefore, that her talents have too often been put at the service of packagers and popularisers. So it is a treat to have a book which she has written slowly over several years and into which she has poured her creative and analytical skills. No doubt Conran Octopus thought that Mary Keen's experiences of making and re-making a garden round her Cotswold Old Vicarage would be interesting and helpful to everyone who buys a house and takes over someone else's garden. But what they have got is not just an account of *what* she did, but an explanation of *how* she does things and *why*. She emphasises how important it is to consider the whole site, its relation to the house and the countryside beyond. Likewise, time and again, she puts her observations into the wider context so that the experiences she describes gain a universal application. She discusses momentum: how you should move around a garden and see its features to their best advantage. She tells you how to learn: she taught herself how to use colour in the garden by experimenting with short-lived annuals. She admits her mistakes: when 'Tai Haku' has to be replaced, she explains why a double-flowered gean looks more natural and appropriate. Each paragraph stands up to detailed analysis. Everyone who makes a garden should read the preface and learn it by heart. The more carefully you ponder her every word, the more the whole thing hangs together. Andrew Lawson's photographs are an added bonus: so are the montages which show the provenance of Mary Keen's ideas. Definitely the best gardening book of the year.

Cultivation of Bulbs, Brian Mathew (Batsford, 1996) £25.00.

The Cutting Garden, Sarah Raven (Frances Lincoln, 1996).

The Daily Telegraph Gardener's Guide to Britain, Patrick Taylor (Pavilion, 1996) £12.99.

Quite simply, the best guide to visiting British gardens : crisp, opinionated, accurate and stylishly written.

Dramatic Effects with Architectural Plants, Noël Kingsbury (Mitchell Beazley, 1996) £16.99.

This is a picture book in the best sense. Kingsbury tackles a fashionable but under-described approach to gardening, while the publishers combine original visual design with exquisite photography. The text reinforces a style which leaps off the page: the centrality of form, whether it arises from foliage, stems or flowers. It is an alternative to the hard landscaping approach and does not suffer from a tendency to ignore structure when plants are made the key element of the garden. Other attractions include the suitability of the style to both small and large gardens, and the growing numbers of specialist nurseries which major on architectural plants. If we have a slight reservation, it is the sheer quality of the photographs: the frosted eryngiums or static onion seedheads are instantly appealing but as photographs, frozen in time and season, seem too fragile, too transitory to build a design around.

The English Garden Abroad, Charles Quest-Ritson (Viking, 1996) £16.00, pbk.

Family Gardens, Bunny Guinness (David & Charles, 1996) £20.00.

Bunny Guinness has written a book dedicated to the idea that gardens can be fun for every member of the family. She subscribes to the view that it is perfectly possible to have a pretty garden which satisfies the keenest gardener (be they parent or grandparent) and is, at the same time, by thoughtful design and planting, both fun and safe for children. She has a refreshing approach to gardening with water: do not rule it out, but make it safe. All is eminently practical, unfussy and lively. The projects she describes in detail range from a simple sandpit to ambitious plans for a tree-house. Her gardens are all places to be lived in and used, not just looked at and admired. The book would make a marvellous present for a family moving house.

Fantastic Trees, Edwin A. Menninger (Timber Press, 1996) £22.50.

Favourite Roses, Peter Harkness (Ward Lock, 1996) £12.99, pbk.

The First-Time Gardener, Pattie Barron (Conran Octopus, 1996) £14.99.

Flora Britannica, Richard Mabey (Sinclair-Stevenson, 1996) £30.00.

The Flowers of William Morris, Derek Baker (Barn Elms Publishing, 1996) £16.50.

The gardens made by William Morris and the flowers he grew in them are the main focus of this book, but it also studies how Morris used flowers in his designs.

Fuchsias: Step by Step to Growing Success, George Bartlett (The Crowood Press, 1996) £8.99.

This is a revised edition in the Crowood Gardening Guides series. As always, they are practical and easy to follow.

Fuchsias: A Colour Guide, George Bartlett (The Crowood Press, 1996) £19.99.

The book describes over 2000 species and cultivars. It is arranged in alphabetical order with more than 700 colour photographs.

Garden Antiques, Alistair Morris (Garden Art Press, 1996) £25.00.

Garden Doctors, Dan Pearson & Steve Bradley (Boxtree, 1996) £18.99.

The Garden Pack: Everything You Need to Plan Your Own Garden, Sue Phillips & Charles Ensor (Weidenfeld, 1996) £19.99.

3-dimensional garden planning kit.

Garden Trees, The Royal Horticultural Society Plant Guides, (Dorling Kindersley, 1996) £14.99.

The Gardener's Book of Colour, Andrew Lawson (Frances Lincoln, 1996) £25.00.

Such is the reputation of Andrew Lawson the reader would expect to find nothing less than a beautifully presented volume full of marvellous photographs. *The Gardener's Book of Colour* has these in abundance, but is much more than just a pretty book to leave lying around. Lawson starts by giving his understanding of colour, tone, hue and distribution. He shows the importance of shape and outline by juxtaposing colour and black and white photographs. He goes on to deal at length with single colour plantings. Attached to each colour section is a descriptive list of possible plants, grouped by season and hue. Sections on colour harmonies and colour contrasts follow, this time without plant lists. The groupings chosen show his eye for effect: they include both obvious and thought-provoking combinations. There is a good range of plant material imaginatively used. Density and shape are not ignored. Some of the main plantings featured are detailed in outline plans. It would have been more instructive if both the season and the gardens (a number of which are open to the public) had been identified in the captions, instead of an acknowledgement at the back of the book. That apart, there is much to inspire all gardeners, new or experienced.

The Gardener's Guide to Growing Hostas, Diana Grenfell (David & Charles, 1996) £16.99.

The Gardener's Weed Book: Earth Safe Controls, Barbara Pleasant (Batsford, 1996) £11.99.

Gardening Britain, Stefan Buczacki (BBC Books, 1996) £14.99.

Gardening for Pleasure, Ursula Buchan (Conran Octopus, 1996) £20.00.

Gardening Hints & Tips, Pippa Greenwood (Dorling Kindersley, 1996) £12.99.

Gardening with Bulbs, Patrick Taylor (Pavilion, 1996) £9.99.

Gardening with Old Roses, John Scarman (HarperCollins, 1996) £16.99.

Out of the stable of rose nurseries Roses du Temps Passé (and now Cottage Garden Roses) this book is written by John Scarman and illustrated by his wife, Teresa. The sections which deal with the use of old roses in design and planting are interesting and recommended to less experienced gardeners who will find much valuable advice. Better still is the treatment of pruning and training, a thoughtful and stimulating master-class even for experienced rose growers. Less good is the descriptive rose directory which is marred by some inaccuracies and an odd bias among an otherwise solid selection. We question whether the choice of more than a dozen of Scarman's own roses, none introduced before 1995, can be justified among only 160 cultivars out of a possible 2000.

Gardens of the National Trust, Stephen Lacey (The National Trust) £29.99.

Gertrude Jekyll and the Arts and Crafts Garden, Gertrude Jekyll and Lawrence Weaver (Garden Art Press, 1996) £25.00.

A new presentation of *Gardens for Small Country Houses* with colour illustrations.

Gertrude Jekyll at Munstead Wood, Judith B. Tankard & Martin A. Wood (Sutton Publishing Limited, 1996) £18.99.

This study of Gertrude Jekyll at her home for forty years draws on her scrapbooks, notebooks and photographs.

Gertrude Jekyll: Essays on the life of a working amateur, Michael Tooley & Primrose Arnander (Michaelmas Books, 1996) £20.00.

Gladiolus in Tropical Africa, Peter Goldblatt (Timber Press, 1996) £29.99.

Glorious Gardens of Cornwall, Sue Pring (Editor) (Cornwall Gardens Trust, 1996) £11.95.

Good Gardens Guide 1997, Peter King (Ebury, 1996) £14.99.

Great English Gardens, Andrew Lawson & Jane Taylor (Weidenfeld, 1996) £25.00.

This book is picture-led, and rightly so. Andrew Lawson is the most accomplished photographer of gardens and gardening and the publishers have given him full licence to develop a book around his pictures. Those pictures are - predictably - ravishing. Lawson has the unique ability to see and to portray gardens so that we see something new even in the best-known. Jane Taylor has therefore had an unenviable job, composing a narrative that complements Lawson's photographs but can stand alone as a series of essays. In fact we end up with two

books in one: Andrew Lawson's brilliant photographs and Jane Taylor's exploration of such themes as rose gardens, the landscape movement, water in the garden and herbaceous borders. It is a pity that what should have been a duet sounds like two soloists.

Green Thumb Wisdom: Garden Myths Revealed, Doc & Kathy Abraham (Batsford, 1996) £10.99.

Greenhouse Gardening: Step by Step to Growing Success, Jonathan Edwards (The Crowood Press, 1996) £8.99, pbk Crowood Gardening Guides.

Redesigned and revised series.

The Harmonious Garden, Catherine Ziegler (Timber Press, 1996) £32.50.

Harvesting the Edge, G. F. Dutton (Menard Press, 1966) £8.99.

Herb Gardening: Step by Step to Growing Success, Jessica Houdret (The Crowood Press, 1996) £8.99, pbk.

Practical manual with easy to follow instructions.

A History of the Orchid, Merle A. Reinikka (Timber Press, 1996) £22.50.

Updated and expanded reprint of a book initially published in 1972.

Hugh Johnson's Gardening Companion, Hugh Johnson (Mitchell Beazley, 1996) £25.00.

This revised edition of Hugh Johnson's modern classic is almost as good as the first. Johnson's text is actually better, for he has improved it without losing any of the freshness and awe which made the original such an attractive overview of English gardening. But the attempt to update its design and presentation is a disappointment. The photographs are fewer and occupy much less of the page. Instead of providing a parallel message from which the reader can learn, they have become entirely subservient to the text. We now have one book, and a very good book too, where once we had two for the price of one. This has the effect of moving the readership upmarket. The book becomes a meditation for accomplished and experienced gardeners, instead of a call to conversion which attracts novices to the pleasures of gardening. The very freshness of the first edition flowed from Johnson's own recent conversion and enabled him to speak directly to the beginner. But it depended for its effect upon the design and illustrations, and those have now been lost: no amount of redesigning can turn a Ford motorcar into a Mercedes. It is still a book to give your mother-in-law for Christmas, but not for her to give to you.

Il Cercapiante, Filippo Cerrina Feroni & Tiziana Volta (Giorgio Mondadori, 1996).

This is the first Italian Plantfinder ever to be published: cost Lit 25,000. Its scope is truly remarkable and it opens the doors to the riches of Italian nurseries. We had no idea that there are so many quality producers, or that they stock such a wide range of interesting plants. Interest in English-style gardening is growing in Italy so we hope it will soon go into a second edition.

In search of Lost Roses, Thomas Christopher (Bloomsbury, 1996) £10.99.

Jane Austen and the English Landscape, Mavis Batey (Barn Elms Publishing, 1996) £19.99.

Leaf, Bark and Berry, Ethne Clark (David & Charles, 1996) £20.00.

Malcolm Hillier's Herb Garden, Malcolm Hillier (Dorling Kindersley, 1996) £14.99.

Miniature Roses: Their Care and Cultivation, Sean McCann (Cassell, 1996) £12.99.

The New Kitchen Garden, Anna Pavord (Dorling Kindersley, 1996) £16.99.

A highly attractive treatment of a popular subject. Proclaiming the integration of vegetables and ornamental plants, this book is very much in the *potager* style of kitchen gardening. The earthier fundamentals are here too, but relegated to the far end of the book, though in the Dorling Kindersley house style even the photographs of pathogens look appealing. This might suggest that design takes precedence over practical information, but that would be unfair. The text is clearly structured and always informative, and is enlivened by stray asides that greatly add to the book's charm. Among the added attractions are well-chosen recipes and pointers towards particularly ornamental forms of commonly-grown vegetables.

The New Perennial Garden, Noël Kingsbury (Frances Lincoln, 1996) £20.00.

Anyone in seach of a definitive account of the new 'German' style of planting will be disappointed by this book. It is all style and no substance. The photographs bear little relation to the text and seem to have been culled from scores of different sources. Kingsbury takes his inspiration from such gardens as Westpark in Munich, but appears not to have visited the best examples of modern German planting at Grugapark, Essen and Westfalenpark, Dortmund. Nor does he explore to the full the many years of detailed research which has been done by the horticultural institutes at Weihenstephan and Hermannshof in Weinheim. In order to establish permanent communities one needs to know how the different component taxa will perform in cultivation. It is not good enough to cover a large area with a mixture of plants that takes your fancy and then leave it to develop at its own pace: sooner or later one species will dominate and the rest will die. The best things about this book are Kingsbury's enthusiasm for the subject and the detailed illustrated guide he gives to planting a German style garden in England. But much greater understanding of the subject is needed before this new form of planting can expect to be successful in England and that means much more research than is evidenced by this book.

New Rose Expert, D. G. Hessayon (Expert Books, 1996) £5.99, pbk.

Paradise Transformed: the Private Garden for the Twenty-first Century, Gordon Taylor & Guy Cooper (Monacelli Press, 1996) £35.00.

Pelargoniums, Diana Miller (Batsford, 1996) £25.00.

Pelargoniums: Growing and Identifying the Species, Diana Miller (Batsford, 1996) £25.00.

The Penguin Book of Garden Writing, David Wheeler (Editor) (Viking, 1996) £20.00.

Anthologies depend entirely on the personality and taste of the compiler. David Wheeler has an acknowledged interest in stylish garden writing. That explains why he has been such a successful editor of *Hortus* these last ten years: indeed, some entries are culled from its pages. Wheeler's selection is wide-ranging in style, content and date, from Bacon and Evelyn onwards. Some prose is flowery and of purple hue. Other selections, such as that from H. E. Bates, are down-to-earth and brisk. So, if you enjoy both anthologies and gardening - and not everyone does - buy it and keep it for dipping into on non-gardening days.

Perennials: The Royal Horticultural Society Plant Guides, Rodney Leed, Linden Hawthorne and others (Dorling Kindersley, 1996) £14.99.

This is a portable, colour, reference guide to perennials. 1000 plants are arranged by size, flowering season, and then by colour: all are illustrated. The format should be familiar to users of other RHS/Dorling Kindersley books: the photographs are clear, the text is concise and authoritative. A number of tender species and indoor plants are included. This is initially slightly disconcerting but, once you get used to the it, adds a welcome, less insular dimension to our ideas of what a perennial should be. You can browse through the guide for inspiration, or use the index to go to cultivars, but we tested it on a difficult proposition: white flowers for a dry shady border. The guide proved easy to use and, from the best results that were offered, one we had already considered (*Geranium phaeum* 'Album') while the other (*Anemone* × *hybrida* 'Honorine Joubert') was a useful suggestion. A quicker route would have been through the 'Planters' guide to perennials', part of a sound collection of introductory material, although puzzlingly not all the plants listed here appear in the index under the same names.

Perfect Plants for Your Garden, Roger Phillips & Martyn Rix (Macmillan, 1996) £12.99.

The companion volume to the CD Rom Perfect Plants.

The Planting Planner, Graham Rice (Macmillan, 1996) £9.99.

Plants for the Future, Jerome Malitz (1996) £25.00.

Plants that Merit Attention, Volume II: Shrubs, Janet Meakin Poor & Nancy Peterson Brewster (Editors) (Timber Press, 1996) £45.00.

Pomona's Harvest: An Illustrated Chronicle of Antiquarian Fruit Literature, H. Frederic Janson (Timber Press, 1996) £37.50.

PPP Index, Anne & Walter Erhardt (Verlag Eugen Ulmer, 1996).

Garden historians will look back on this second edition of the German plant finder and see it as the first step towards establishing German dominance over the whole European market in national plant finders. The new title PPP stands for *Pflanzen, Plantes, Plants* and the editors have included many more nurseries from neighbouring countries and from the UK than in the first edition. The lesson to be learned from

PPP, which is of course written in all three languages, is that there are many good plants and nurseries across the Channel which can only benefit our gardens once we are prepared to find out what they offer. And every copy comes with a free CD, complete and unencrypted, so that you can run search programmes as well as browsing through the book. Nevertheless, we suggest that you wait for the next edition, due out later this year: it will be so comprehensive that it may begin to overshadow the English plant finder.

The Pruning Handbook, Steve Bradley (The Crowood Press, 1996) £12.99.

The Rhododendron Story, Cynthis Postan (Editor) (Royal Horticultural Society, 1996) £15.00.

The Royal Horticultural Society celebrated fifty years of Rhododendron Yearbooks with this wonderful survey of the history of rhododendrons in cultivation. There are over 216 pages, broken up into 16 essays by different authors, each contributing to the spirit of enlightenment which imbues the whole endeavour. There is Alan Leslie on taxonomy, Mary Forrest on Hooker's rhododendrons, George Argent on the vireyas, Peter Cox on collectors, Lionel de Rothschild on nineteenth-century British hybridising, Brent Elliott on the place of rhododendrons in British gardens, and so on. The book is well illustrated with period photographs and the enlightened editors have included comprehensive bibliographies where possible. At the end is an even longer list of national rhododendron societies than we publish elsewhere in *The Gardener's Yearbook. The Rhododendron Story* is a classic work that should find a place on every gardener's bookshelf.

Rock Gardens of North America, (Timber Press, 1996) £37.50.

An anthology from the Bulletin of the North American Rock Garden Society.

The Rose and The Clematis (As Good Companions), Dr John Howells (Antique Collectors' Club, 1996) £19.95.

The Chairman of the British Clematis Society describes the best ways of growing climbing roses and clematis together.

Roses: The Royal Horticultural Society Plant Guides, (Dorling Kindersley, 1996) £14.99.

The Rothschild Gardens, Miriam Rothschild, Kate Garton & Lionel de Rothschild (Gaia Books, 1996) £25.00.

The Rothschilds certainly had a passion for gardening. It was part of a bigger obsession with collecting: every branch of this family seems to have collected houses, gardens and works of art for the sheer joy of possessing them. But this is a curate's egg of a book. Parts of it are excellent. Those parts are Andrew Lawson's incisive photographs; the old family photographs which bring the Rothschilds and their estates to life; and the lucid and instructive essay by Lionel de Rothschild which tells the story of his grandfather (also called Lionel de Rothschild), Exbury and all those rhododendrons. But the rest is indifferent, which is a shame, because the story needs telling. The truth is that Miriam Rothschild is not the right the person to tell it. Her contribution is an undisciplined mixture of personal anecdote and uncritical praise for her relations. Her text contains too many errors to render it authoritative. And she does not

use her analytical skills to draw out the common themes. The book would have been better written by a social historian.

The Royal Horticultural Society A – Z Encyclopaedia of Garden Plants, Christopher Brickell (Editor) (Dorling Kindersley, 1996) £55.00.

Most readers will be familiar with the phenomenal success of Chris Brickell's *RHS Gardener's Encyclopaedia of Gardens Plants and Flowers* from the same publisher. Although superficially similar in format, this A – Z is an even more substantial enterprise, with nearly twice as many entries. Of the 15,000 plants described, nearly 6,000 are accompanied by photographs. Who is it for? It is clearly a reference book – even in the two-volume version you could scarcely describe it as portable. The photographs are an improvement on its predecessor's: their definition is clearer – as it must be if you want to use them for identification purposes. Its smaller sister was arranged by season and size, with an unillustrated reference dictionary at the end. This never seemed quite right: the book was large enough in scope to be a reference work but the organisation made it hard to use it as one. Full marks then to the A – Z which integrates the illustrations with the plant directory. The text is clear, concise and to the point: propagation, cultivation and pest notes all strike the right balance of informativeness. The most serious gardener will still cling to Macmillan's four-volume *New RHS Dictionary of Gardening,* but we would wholeheartedly recommend this authoritative and attractive encyclopaedia as the core reference book for others. It is not cheap, but it is easily worth three or four of the plethora of low-content, highly-illustrated gardening books that might otherwise fill the shelves.

Scottish Plants for Scottish Gardens, Jill, Duchess of Hamilton (HMSO for RBG Edinburgh, 1996) £12.95, pbk.

Scottish Wild Plants: Their History, Ecology and Conservation, Phil Lusby & Jenny Wright (HMSO for RBG Edinburgh, 1996) £12.95, pbk.

Shrubs and Climbers: The Royal Horticultural Society Plant Guides, (Dorling Kindersley, 1996) £14.99.

The Siberian Iris, Currier McEwen (Timber Press, 1996) £29.99.

Success with Clematis, Walter Hörsch (Merehurst, 1996) £3.99.

A useful introduction to clematis. The first section is called 'All about Clematis' and tells the reader how to cultivate and propagate the genus. The middle section 'Garden Design' shows the versatility of clematis as a garden plant. The final section is a well-chosen list of popular species and cultivars: these include a number of recently introduced hybrids from central and eastern Europe. All in all, an excellent publication. We would like to see the author working on a more substantial account of this genus in cultivation.

Summer Garden Glory, Adrian Bloom (HarperCollins, 1996) £16.99.

A shortish but colourful book, not unlike the British summer you might think, though Bloom stretches the season generously to make a pair with his earlier *Winter Garden Glory.* The best of it is a commentary on the features and possibilities of a summer garden photographed at stages throughout the season at Foggy Bottom. Bloom's writing is clear and enlightening and the excellent photography, also by the author, helps to make his case. There is also a briefer section applying the principles to smaller gardens. The book ends with an extensive and well-done plant directory. This style of planting is not universally admired, but I warmed to Bloom's advocacy of gardens where the structure is provided by the plants rather than imposed by hard landscaping. Foggy Bottom itself, if you have not been, is well worth a visit too.

Taylor's Guide to Fruits and Berries, Roger Holmes (Ed.) (Houghton Mifflin, 1996) £12.99.

Treatise on the Carnation and Other Flowers, Thomas Hogg (Picton Publ., 1996) £35.00.

A complete facsimile of Thomas Hogg's classic opus, first published in 1839.

The Ultimate Container Garden, David Joyce (Frances Lincoln, 1996) £20.00.

The Ultimate Planting Guide, Noël Kingsbury (Ward Lock, 1996) £20.00.

The Ultimate Water Garden Book, Jean-Claude Arnoux (Batsford, 1996) £25.00.

Vandas and Ascocendas and Their Combinations with Other Genera, David L. Grove (Timber Press, 1996) £32.50.

Visions of Arcadia, May Woods (Aurum Press, 1996) £25.00.

May Woods has an interesting theme for her trot through three hundred years of garden history. It is the idea of Arcadia, a land of harmony where man can live an ideal life of perfect satisfaction in a tranquil landscape. Her charming introduction explains how garden-makers were fired by their vision of this heaven on earth. She is on safe ground when she talks about Arcadia in the gardens of the early Renaissance and later, when she finds it in both the Rococo and the landscape styles. However, the book itself has very little to do with Arcadia: it is a history of gardens in Western Europe from about 1460 to 1760. May Woods offers us a competent account, but the publishers may find it hard to inspire an English readership with widespread enthusiasm for the subject. The author is more interested in history than plants and in form than colour: most English book-buyers are not. The period plans and drawings are well chosen and come out well. The modern colour photographs are abysmal. It seems a pity that such an able historian should be so badly let down in this respect.

Visions of Roses, Peter Beales with photographs by Vivian Russell (Little, Brown, 1996) £25.00.

Visions of Roses promised much to rose-lovers. An armchair tour of beautiful rose gardens in Britain, France, Italy and the United States in the company of a knowledgeable rose grower and a photographer with a sure artistic eye should have been a special treat. It is still a treat, but not so special. Vivian Russell's photographs are a delight but, since Peter Beales visited the gardens separately, sometimes even when the roses were not in flower, the text and the photographs lack a unifying spontaneity. Moreover, Vivian Russell is an inpired

photographer: Peter Beales is a pedestrian writer. Some of the gardens are open regularly to the public, others once or twice a year or only by appointment, or even not at all. This is perhaps a mistake. Only if you feel that a glimpse, in word and pictures, is better than nothing will you be satisfied by this vision.

Water Features in Small Gardens, Francesca Greenoak (Conran Octopus, 1996) £10.99.

Water Gardening, Water Lilies and Lotuses, Perry D. Slocum & Peter Robinson with Frances Perry (Timber Press, 1996) £45.00.

Weather in the Garden, Jane Taylor (John Murray, 1996) £20.00.

Westonbirt Arboretum, Jessica Houdret (The Crowood Press, 1996) pbk, Crowood Gardening Guide.

The Winter Garden, Eluned Price (Salamander Books, 1996) £20.00.

Yew & Non-Yew, James Bartholomew (Century, 1996) £9.99.

This is an irreverent (but amusing and accurate) guide to the social niceties of gardening. It also tells you about the best bedding (if that's what you fancy), the smartest nurseries and the best names to drop with a resounding clang. Some readers may be surprised to learn that *Cortaderia selloana* 'Rosea' is listed in *The RHS Plant Finder*.

New Books 1997

Bloom, Anne Swithinbank, Bill Chudziak & Joanna Redmond (Collins & Brown, 1997) £20.00.

The book to accompany the Channel 4 series.

Bulbs of the Holy Land, Ori Fragman & Avi Shmida (Batsford, 1997) £30.00.

Bulbs: The Royal Horticultural Society Plant Guides, (Dorling Kindersley, 1997) £14.99.

Bulbs (which includes Dahlias in this treatment) joins this attractive and functional series. 500 plants are included, all illustrated. The main presentation is by size, season and colour as usual. Display panels of selected featured genera open up vistas of greater detail and comparison than the format would otherwise allow.

The Conran Octopus Garden Book, Ursula Buchan & David Stevens (Conran Octopus, 1997) £19.99.

Creative Containers, Paul Williams (Conran Octopus, 1997) £12.99.

Creative Vegetable Gardening, Joy Larkcom (Mitchell Beazley, 1997) £19.99.

Cyclamen, Christopher Grey-Wilson (Batsford, 1997) £25.00.

The Defined Garden, Paul Bangay (Viking, 1997) £25.00.

The Australian landscaper writes about his work.

Edith Wharton's Italian Gardens, Vivian Russell (Frances Lincoln, 1997).

The English Formal Garden, Günther Mader and Leila Neubert-Mader (Aurum Press, 1997) £30.00.

Originally published in Germany in 1992, this study examines the evolution of modern gardens and, in particular, of the best-known style: Hidcote, Sissinghurst and the whole caboodle.

Garden Plants Made Easy, Jane Fearnley-Whittingstall (Weidenfeld, 1997) £19.99.

Gardener Cook, Christopher Lloyd (Frances Lincoln, 1997).

Christopher Lloyd, one of Britain's most famous gardeners and garden writers, is an equally accomplished cook. His advice and recipes should be well worth having.

The Gardener's Guide to Pests and Diseases, Roland Fox (Batsford, 1997) £17.99.

The Gardener's Perpetual Almanac, Martin Hoyles (Thames & Hudson, 1997) £9.95.

Gardening with Antique Plants, David Stuart (Conran Octopus, 1997) £25.00.

Gardening with Climbers, Christopher Grey-Wilson & Victoria Matthews (HarperCollins, 1997) £16.99.

Gardening without a Garden, Gay Search (Dorling Kindersley, 1997).

Good Enough to Eat: Growing and Cooking Edible Flowers, Jekka McVicar (Kyle Cathie, 1997) £14.99.

Great Plants for Small Gardens, Nigel Colborn (Conran Octopus, 1997) £17.99.

Growing Bulbs: The Complete Practical Guide, Brian Mathew (Batsford, 1997) £25.00.

How to Win at Patios and Small Gardens, Richard Jackson & Carolyn Hutchinson (HarperCollins, 1997) £9.99.

Matthew Bigg's Complete Book of Vegetables, Matthew Biggs (Kyle Cathie, 1997) £19.99.

Medieval Flowers, Miranda Innes & Clay Perry (Kyle Cathie, 1997) £18.99.

Orchid Species Culture: Dendrobium, Margaret L. Baker & Charles O. Baker (Timber Press, 1997).

Orchids for the Collector, Jack Kramer (Garden Art Press, 1997) £25.00.

Ornamental Herb Garden, Catherine Mason (Conran Octopus, 1997) £12.99.

Penelope Hobhouse's Garden Designs, Penelope Hobhouse (Frances Lincoln, 1997).

The Perfect Country Garden, Sunniva Harte (Conran Octopus, 1997) £20.00.

Planting Companions, Jill Billington (Ryland Peters & Small, 1997) £20.00.

Jill Billington is a well-known garden designer. Her book on plant associations gives ideas for plants which look good together in a variety of garden settings.

Plants from Test Tubes, Lydiane Kyte & John Kleyn (Timber Press, 1997) £22.50.

This is the third edition, revised and updated, of the guide to micropropagation. Said to be written for the lay reader as well

as the scientist, the book includes instructions, here called recipes, for propagating at home and in a laboratory.

Pocket Garden Herbs, Lesley Bremness (Dorling Kindersley, 1997) £5.99.

Pocket Medicinal Herbs, Penelope Ody (Dorling Kindersley, 1997) £5.99.

PPP Index, Anne & Walter Erhardt (Verlag Eugen Ulmer, 1997).

The latest edition of *PPP* will have a truly European coverage, including all the best nurseries in Britain. The French and Dutch plant finders have already agreed to co-operate with the Germans, and the Italians are also collaborating. Spain and Portugal too have opened up their nurseries to the inquisitive and systematic Germans, who are infinitely curious about their European partners and do not suffer from the English delusion that foreigners can teach them nothing about plants. Written in English as well as in German and French, *PPP* will be an essential reference book for every keen gardener from Uppsala to Palermo and from Lisbon to Cracow.

Rock Plants: The Royal Horticultural Society Plant Guides, (Dorling Kindersley, 1997) £14.99.

Edited by a team which includes Christopher Grey-Wilson and Linden Hawthorne, this addition to the RHS Plant Guides maintains the strengths of the series, with clear photographs and an exemplary if rather spare text.

Roof Gardens, Balconies & Terraces, David Stevens (Mitchell Beazley, 1997) £19.99.

The Royal Horticultural Society: Pests & Diseases, Pippa Greenwood & Andrew Halstead (Dorling Kindersley, 1997) £16.99.

The Royal Horticultural Society: Water Gardening, Peter Robinson (Dorling Kindersley, 1997) £25.00.

The Self-Sustaining Garden, Peter Thompson (Batsford, 1997) £20.00.

The Sensuous Garden, Montague Don (Conran Octopus, 1997) £20.00.

The Smaller Perennials, Jack Elliott (Batsford, 1997) £20.00.

The Summer Garden, Jill Billington (Ward Lock, 1997) £16.99.

Topiary and the Art of Shaping Plants, Kathryn Bradley-Hole (Frances Lincoln, 1997).

The Tropical Garden, William Warren (Thames & Hudson, 1997) £32.00.

The Ward Lock Gardening Encyclopedia, Anita Pereire (Ward Lock, 1997) £16.99, pbk.

Videos

Brilliant Gardens, £12.95.

A Celebration Of Old Roses, Peter Beales (Vivian Russell Inc Ltd) £12.99, (01787 77307).

Chelsea '96, Alan Titchmarsh (Royal Horticultural Society) £12.99, (01483 211320).

The Complete Guide, (Oscroft's Dahlias) £15.00, (01564 782450) Price includes packing and postage.

Container Growing, (Royal Horticultural Society) £12.99, (01483 211320).

Dahlias of Today, (Oscroft's Dahlias) £15.00, (01564 782450) Price includes packing and postage.

The Diary of the Dahlia, (Oscroft's Dahlias) £12.00, (01564 782450) Price includes packing and postage.

Garden Heritage, Roy Lancaster, Geoff Hamilton and John Kelly £13.99.

Gardening under Lights, (GroWell Hydroponics and Plant Lighting Ltd) £15.00, (01675 443950).

Gardens of England and Wales, (Seer TV) £12.99, (01222 751159).

Gardens of England and Wales: Gardeners' Views, (Seer TV) £12.99, (01222 751159).

Gardens of England and Wales: The Tour Continues, (Seer TV) £12.99, (01222 751159).

Gardens of South Africa, Alan Titchmarsh (Royal Horticultural Society) £12.99.

Growing Leeks with the Experts, (National Pot Leek Society) £21.00, (0191 5494274), price includes packing and postage.

Guide to African Violets, Tony Clements and Anne Swithinbank £12.99.

Guide to Clematis, Steven Bradley £12.99.

Guide to Dried Flowers, Malcolm Hillier £12.99.

Guide to Fuchsias, David Clark, Helen Biddlecombe and Harry Smith (Periwinkle Productions) £12.99, (01489 885645).

Guide to Hanging Baskets, Harry Smith and Helen Biddlecombe (Periwinkle Productions) £12.99, (01489 885645).

Guide to Pelargoniums, Anne Swithinbank, Harry Smith and David Clark (Periwinkle Productions) £12.99, (01489 8856445).

Guide to Roses, Harry Smith, Steve Bradley & Ken Grapes £12.99.

Herbs, Jekka McVicar (Royal Horticultural Society) £12.99.

Hydroponic Gardening, (GroWell Hydroponics and Plant Lighting Ltd) £12.50, (01675 443950).

Making a Small Garden, (Royal Horticultural Society) £12.99, (01483 211320).

The Masters Choice, (Oscroft's Dahlias) £15.00, (01564 782450) Price includes packing and postage.

My Garden, Beth Chatto £14.99.

My World of Dahlias, (Oscroft's Dahlias) £12.00, (01564 782450) Price includes packing and postage.

Rosemoor - A Garden in the Making, (Royal Horticultural Society) £12.99.

Secret Gardens, Alan Titchmarsh £12.95.

The Small Greenhouse and Conservatory, (Royal Horticultural Society) £12.99, (01483 211320).

Soft Fruit Growing, (Royal Horticultural Society) £12.99, (01483 211320).

Super Gardening, Alan Titchmarsh (Virgin Video Library) £10.99.

Top Fruit Growing, (Royal Horticultural Society) £12.99, (01483 211320).

Training a Standard Fuchsia Vol 1, Pam Hutchinson £19.99.

Treasure Gardens, Alan Titchmarsh £12.95.

Treasure of the Trust, Robert Hardy £13.95.

Vegetable Growing, (Royal Horticultural Society) £12.99, (01483 211320).

Water Gardening, (Royal Horticultural Society) £12.99.

Wisley through the Seasons: Autumn, (Royal Horticultural Society) £12.99, (01483 211320).

Wisley through the Seasons: Spring, (Royal Horticultural Society) £12.99, (01483 211320).

Wisley through the Seasons: Summer, (Royal Horticultural Society) £12.99, (01483 211320).

Wisley through the Seasons: Winter, (Royal Horticultural Society) £12.99, (01483 211320).

Winter Garden Glory, Adrian Bloom (1995) £14.99.

24

Latest Scientific Research

A vast corpus of horticultural research is undertaken by universities, institutes, nurserymen and enthusiasts worldwide and many of the results are published in obscure journals. Several organisations compile abstracts of these publications, so that students and researchers can know what is happening in their particular fields. By far the best is *Horticultural Abstracts*, published by C A B International Information Services, Wallingford, Oxfordshire, OX10 8DE. (Tel: 01491 832111; Fax: 01491 833508) and most of the papers which we summarise here have appeared, or will appear, each year in its pages alongside more than 10,000 other horticultural abstracts. The amateur has something useful to learn from every one. Readers with wider interests should consult *Plant Breeding Abstracts*, also published by C A B International Information Services.

Regeneration, growth and flowering of cut rose cultivars as affected by propagation material and method. N Bredmose & J Hansen. *Scientia Horticulturae* (1995) pp.103-111.

This experiment explodes two long-cherished beliefs of rose growers. Rosarians have for at least 100 years supposed that the source of the budwood they use for propagating roses has an effect upon the growth of the subsequent plants. After all, many horticulturally desirable plants are deliberately propagated from juvenile parts of the parent. Rose growers say that it is unwise to use blind shoots (i.e. shoots which do not end with a flower) for budwood, because the resulting plants will be less floriferous: there can be no other explanation, they reason, for the deterioration they perceive in modern rose stocks – they

have been propagated to death. Rosarians also maintain that budded roses are more vigorous and more floriferous than own-root plants. This experiment in Denmark investigates the two myths, by comparing the floriferousness of plants grown from blind side-shoots with those coming from flowering shoots and by comparing own-root plants with budded ones. The experiments were exhaustive, and showed some variations between the two cultivars they used, 'Frisco' and 'Gabriella'. However the general conclusions were quite clear: blind shoots actually produced more flowers than flowering shoots and more flowers were produced by plants grown on their own roots than by the budded ones. Budding is a 19th-century practice which evolved at a time when plants could not be patented and when a hybridist had to use every piece of his plant to bulk it up for maximum sales in the first year or so. We think it is about time that rose growers abandoned it and gave us roses growing on their own roots again. And the perceived deterioration in roses' vigour is easily explained: it is due to the presence of viruses which were introduced by the rootstocks.

Bodenpflegeverfahren mit reduziertem Herbizideindatz im Apfelbau. (The effect of reducing the use of herbicides in apple farming). *Obst- und Weinbau*, 1996, p.67.

The disadvantages of an all-organic approach to growing fruit can be seen in this short abstract in the journal of the Swiss research station at Wädenswil. It compares the effect of four different ways of managing rows of apples, grown in rows on dwarfing rootstocks. The four regimes were [1] mulching with organic matter [2] leaving the rows green [3] hoeing [4] using a regular succession of herbicides (simazine, diuron, terbacil and glyphosate). Two measurements were taken: fruit yield and soil fertility. The most adverse effect on fertility resulted from leaving the rows green: the catch crop of grass and weeds deprived the soil of more than half its nitrogen. The best yields came from using herbicides, some 60% greater than was achieved when the rows were left green and when the plants were mulched with bark. In practice, Swiss fruit-growers use a lot of organic manure as a mulch-cum-fertiliser, as well keeping the rows clean with a programme of herbicides, and this combination brings the greatest increase in both yields and fertility. But 'green' gardeners will no doubt echo the Danish prime minister's comment that 'everyone knows small apples taste better'.

The Effect of Root Pruning on Growth, Fruiting & Apple Quality of 'Empire' and 'Spartan' apple trees. *Journal of Fruit & Ornamental Plant Research* (1995) pp.153-164. Polish Research Institute of Pomology & Floriculture, Skierniewice.

More about apples. Root pruning has long been practised as a means of increasing the flowering or fruiting of ornamental and economic plants: think of the Parable of the Vineyard. The received wisdom is that, since the plant fears for its instant demise, it produces a swan-song crop of enormous volume. But then it survives and grows well again – until its roots are pruned again. This Polish experiment put the theory to the test in an orchard of twelve-year-old 'Spartan' and 'Empire' apples, grown on M26 rootstocks. All were root-pruned using a shape blade drawn by a tractor, some at a distance of 0.75m from the trees and others at 1.35m, at different times of the year and with different frequencies. What would be the effect? In fact, the pruning had no effect at all on the number of fruits set. Nor did it increase their size: the fruits were actually smaller. One surprising result was that the apples were also better coloured and firmer after root pruning: this may be caused by ingesting less nitrogen. But as for the theory that root-pruning would actually increase the size of the crop, the experiments showed that in fact the very opposite occurred.

Vine performance, fruit composition, and wine sensory attributes of Gewürztraminer in response to vineyard location and canopy manipulation. A G Reynold, D Wardle & M Dever. *American Journal of Enology & Viticulture* (1996) 47 (1) pp.77-92.

The great value of the Gewürztraminer grape to vineyard owners is the distinctive taste, smell and aroma of the wine it makes. This test set out to prove (very North American this) that these benefits were the result of proper cultivation, and did not depend upon such accidents as the siting of the vineyard. Provided they could give the vines the growing conditions they required, a wine-maker could produce wine which was every bit as good as anything produced in Alsace or Germany. The experiments were carried out in British Columbia, in three different locations. They centred on the effect of hard pruning, thinning and the removal of leaves to open up the canopy. The results seem show that hard pruning and removing the spare leaves reduces the total weight of grapes but do indeed increase the quality of the wine. These wines were more intensely fruity, more strongly muscat-flavoured, and had greater body and a more pronounced aftertaste. However, one of the three sites produced consistently better wines whatever treatment its vines received: so, whatever the benefits of good cultivation, there is still hope for the traditional Gewürztraminer growers of Alsace and the Palatinate.

Palmito sustainability and economics in Brazil's Atlantic coastal forest. T Orlande, J Laarman & J Mortimer, *Forest Ecology & Management* (1996) pp.257-265.

Not all scientific abstracts rely for their conclusions upon scientific method. This is a review of the economics of the illegal trade in edible palm-hearts. Wild plants of *Euterpe edulis* are killed by low-income workers who cut out their growing-point and sell them to middle-men who deliver them in turn to wholesalers and processors. Unfortunately, *Euterpe edulis* is an endangered species whose numbers are declining rapidly. The researchers sought to establish whether better returns could be offered to all parties by a controlled system of palm-heart farming. The main problem they encountered was that the police were so lax in enforcing the law against wild-cropping that no-one really knew how much the trade was worth i.e. production, prices, costs and margins which every member of the clandestine trade could expect. The researchers' solution was to make certain assumptions which showed, to their own satisfaction, that the managed cropping of palm-hearts would bring bigger rewards for everyone than the uncontrolled destruction of wild populations. However, there were two factors which made a considerable difference to the figures: profit margins and the value of money. Both these evils undermined the real value of the rewards and made the controlled cultivation of palm-hearts difficult to sustain. In fact, the high profit margins which the middlemen expect is itself a result of inflation. This report brought home to us the sheer economic complexity of all those attempts to turn peasant foragers into cultivators. It is not as easy as one might suppose, and the success stories (for example among the bulb-collectors of southern Turkey) are all the more remarkable when understood against this background.

Identification of genetic diversity among *Loropetalum chinense* var. *rubrum* introductions. *Journal of Environmental Horticulture* (1996) pp. 38-41.

This is really quite a simple story about genetic mapping. *Loropetalum chinense* is a very pretty shrub for subtropical climates: it produces its white flowers almost continuously on an evergreen bush. The white flower is not particularly striking because the eye does not distinguish it well from the greyish leaves. However, several new pink-flowered forms have recently been introduced, which show up very well and make very desirable plants for large landscaping schemes like motorway plantings. Some of the pink forms are patented in the US but others are not. The trouble is that they all look alike. This experiment used random examination of the DNA of every pink form in commerce and discovered that they all belong to one of four cultivars, quite distinct in their genetic make-up though obviously not to the human eye. The researchers were able to establish with some certainty just which forms were patented so that everyone knew whether or not they had to pay a royalty. But it brought home to us that genetic screening will in future be an essential tool in the protection of breeding rights and is likely to feature prominently in disputes about the rights of patent-owners. And in due course it will throw new light on many contentious fields like the myths surrounding the ancestry of our modern roses.

Cold Hardiness of evergreen azaleas is increased by water stress imposed at three dates. T Anisko & O M Lindstrom. *Journal of American Society for Horticultural Science* (1996) pp. 296-300 and **Seasonal changes in the cold hardiness of Rhododendron 'Catawbiense Boursault' grown under continuous and periodic water stress.** T Anisko & O M Lindstrom. *Journal of American Society for Horticultural Science* (1996) pp. 301-306.

It has long been believed that many plants are hardier in dry soils than waterlogged ones. These experiments put the belief to scientific test. Plants of three azaleas (*Rhododendron* 'Coral Bell', 'Hinodegiri' and 'Red Ruffle') were deprived of water in late summer and early autumn, to measure whether this had an effect on their ability to survive cold temperatures. In fact, all three showed that they could survive temperatures of up to 4°C lower when they were dry at the roots. The picture was not quite so simple, however, for Rhododendron 'Catawbiense Boursault', one of the hardier evergreen hybrids, but still not hardy enough for the coldest zones of North America. Its hardiness was examined under both

continuous and periodic water stress i.e. dry at the roots for a long time, or only intermittently. The surprise result was that it depended on the degree and duration of the dryness, but was not directly proportionate to them. Mild dehydration made no difference to the plants' hardiness during the first winter, but increased it during the second winter. On the other hand, severely dehydrated plants were hardier in the first winter, but not in subsequent winters. The reasons for this contradictory result are not yet clear. However, it is clear that dehydration has a marked effect on hardiness. Gardeners need to understand this better. We all know that you can grow tender plants if you place them in a suitably sheltered position like the lee of a wall or close to the roots of a tree. What we have to realise is that it is the dryness that makes them hardier, not the supposed warmth of the wall or the wind-protection of the tree-canopy.

Seed hydration memory in Sonoran desert cacti and its ecological implication. *American Journal of Botany* (1996) pp. 624-632.

All seeds are subject to fluctuations in humidity, both in nature and when we acquire them for our gardens. The purpose of this study was to discover how ungerminated seeds cope with these fluctuations and what the effect is upon the seeds' survival. Experiments were done with seed of *Stenocereus thurberi* and two other cacti. They were subjected to periods of hydration (when they were able to soak up water) and dehydration (when they lost it). What effect did this regime have upon the eventual germination and establishment of the seedlings? The main finding was that the process of hydration and dehydration was important to breaking the seeds' dormancy. Only when they had been subjected to several days of damp were they able to germinate. But the surprise discovery was that germination came in response to the total time spent in damp conditions i.e. the seeds had a 'memory' and would eventually germinate when they had spent enough time being wetted, even if this wetting took place irregularly over several months. This ensures that some cactus seeds germinate whenever there is an appreciable rainfall. Their subsequent performance depends upon the weather that follows: if it is too hot and dry the newly-germinated plants will die. But the plants' inbuilt memory spreads the risks and increases the chances of survival. The moral for ordinary gardeners is this: we must appreciate that every seed has an inbuilt requirement for the right conditions for germination. If that means, in an English climate, waiting several years before you see the first cotyledons, then there may be ways in which you can experiment with speeding up the process.

Aufgang von Gurkensaatgut. (The Germination of cucumber seeds). *Gemüse* (1995) pp.634-635.

More about germination. This short article explores what elements a cucumber seed needs to germinate: is it heat, moisture or light? This is an important question for temperate climates where most gourds have to be started off under glass so that they have an optimum chance of cropping: gherkins are very popular in Germany. The results showed that light plays no part in the germination of seeds: they come up perfectly well when buried 2 cms deep in their compost. Most gardeners could have told them that. But temperature is actually more important for germination than moisture content. Obviously, the seeds will not germinate if the soil is too dry, but the results are much better at temperatures around 30°C than at 20°C. In fact 30°C is the optimum temperature, in conjunction with a comparatively high moisture content of 60–80%: cucumbers germinate within six days. The trouble is that they are very sensitive to a fall in temperature, which is usually associated with growing them on or planting them out under much cooler temperatures. On the other hand, the rate of germination at 20°C is a meagre 20%. There is no solution to the problem in a climate as moderate at the UK's.

25

Holidays

The following list includes a number of specialised garden and botanical tour operators. In addition to the companies below, some general tour operators will organise holidays which include a significant number of interesting gardens in their itinerary. Several of the horticultural societies arrange their own trips for their members. The Alpine Garden Society will be running tours for people who wish to visit mountains and see the flowers. Their destinations in 1997 include: Switzerland (Pontresina & Arosa), Turkey (Adana & Antioch), China (north-west Yunnan, twice) and Russia (the Altai mountains). The Royal Horticultural Society (01394 691201) is organising four tours in the UK (Devon & Cornwall, Scotland, 'Great Gardens', 'Rose Gardens') as well as to Ireland (Dublin area), USA (Californian gardens), China (botanising in western Sichuan), Italy (gardens of Rome & Tuscany), Germany ('Great Gardens'), South Africa (botanising) and Madeira. The Friends of Kew have a particularly interesting list of destinations this year: Cameroon, Sichuan, Pantanal, the Amazon basin and Java, as well as the Italian lakes, southern Ireland, southern England, Northumberland and the Welsh marches. Members of the International Dendrology Society have access to many otherwise closed gardens through the IDS tours to Costa Rica, Madeira, east Scotland, Austria, Finland and Thailand: members only, though. And Scotland's Garden Scheme is running a six-day tour of the gardens of northern Scotland at the end of June.

Accompanied Cape Tours

Hill House, Much Marcle, Ledbury, Hereford & Worcester HR8 2NX
☎ 01531 660210   FAX 01531 660494

CONTACT   Virginia Carlton
1997 TOURS   South Africa: Natal Coast, Eastern Transvaal & the Cape
FOUNDED   1991

Specialises in private gardens, historic houses and wine estates. Small groups of 6 – 12 allow for a flexible programme which can be altered to suit individual interests. A chance to meet and talk with South Africans is an important feature of the trips.

ACE Study Tours

Babraham, Cambridge CB2 4AP
☎ 01223 835055   FAX 01223 837394

1997 TOURS   French Riviera, the Campagna, Italian lakes, Polish national parks, Tuscany, Norfolk
FOUNDED   1958
MEMBER   ATOL, ABTOT

ACE stands for Association for Cultural Exchange and is an educational charity, specialising in study tours and courses. The venues, facilities and leaders are all high quality.

Boxwood Tours: Quality Garden Holidays

56 Spring Road, Abingdon, Oxfordshire OX14 1AN
☎ 01235 532791   FAX 01235 532791

CONTACT   Sue Macdonald
1997 TOURS   California, Tuscany & Rome, Jersey, Flanders, Northumberland, L'île de France, Andalucia
FOUNDED   1990
MEMBER   Client trust account operated

Boxwood offer visits to private and better-known gardens and good hotels. Distinguished leaders accompany each tour: both partners are themselves Kew-trained.

Brightwater Holidays

Eden Park House, Cupar, Fife KY15 4HS
☎ 01334 657155   FAX 01334 657144

1997 TOURS   Tresco, Crete, Dutch bulbfields, Ireland, Cornwall, the Highlands & Islands, the Borders, Normandy, Scotland's west coast, Ayrshire, Somerset, Yorkshire, the Lake District, Rome & Ninfa, the French Riviera
MEMBER   ABTOT, ATOL

Brightwater runs tours for the National Trust for Scotland, *The Scotsman* and *The Daily Telegraph*, among others. Some are based round specific flower shows: Chelsea, Hampton Court, Harrogate (spring), Southport, Courson & Scotland's new National Gardening Show.

Carolanka

Rowden House, Brentnor, Tavistock, Devon PL19 0NG
☎ 01822 810230   FAX 01822 810230

CONTACT   Mrs Carol Cameron
1997 TOURS   Sri Lanka
FOUNDED   1991

Guided tours including visits to all the major botanic gardens and institutes on the island of Ceylon. Personalised itineraries can be arranged to concentrate on gardens and villa rentals.

Cox & Kings Travel
Fourth Floor, Gordon House, 10 Greencoat Place, London SW1P 1PH
☎ 0171 873 5000   📠 0171 630 6038

1997 TOURS   Rhodes, southern Cyprus, Crete, south-west Turkey, Romania, Slovenia, Wengen, French Pyrenees, Colorado's Rockies, High Pyrenees, Obergurgl, Corfu, Andalucia, southern Morocco, Dominica, Costa Rica, Malaysia
FOUNDED   1758
MEMBER   ABTA; ATOL; IATA

Specialised botany and wild flower tours with top tour leaders, including Mary Briggs. Destinations this year include many of the classic botanical areas of Europe.

David Sayers Travel
10 Barley Mow Passage, London W4 4PH
☎ 0181 995 3642   📠 0181 742 1066

CONTACT   Andrew Brock Travel
1997 TOURS   Equador, Cyprus, Andalucia, Prague
FOUNDED   1982
MEMBER   ABTA; AITO; ATOL

Specialist botanical tours, operated by Andrew Brock Travel. Kew-trained horticulturist David Sayers accompanies most of the tours. The Prague tour is based on gardens: the others are for wild flowers.

Fine Art Travel Ltd
15 Savile Row, London W1X 1AE
☎ 0171 437 8553   📠 0171 437 1733

CONTACT   Charles FitzRoy or Jane Rae
1997 TOURS   Florence & Rome
FOUNDED   1984

There are no tours specifically for gardeners, but this top-end of the market firm has the entrée to many fine gardens. High points of this year's itineraries include Robin Lane-Fox's trip to Rome which visits the romantic gardens of Ninfa.

Gardeners' Delight Holidays
Garden House, 45 Church Road, Saxilby, Lincoln LN1 2HH
☎ 01522 703773

1997 TOURS   Devon & Cornwall, Sussex, Perthshire, Cotswolds, Cambridge, Lancashire, the Marches, Dorset, Gloucestershire, Thames Valley, Derbyshire, Durham, Germany, the Loire
MEMBER   ABTOT

The UK tours tend to be long weekends or Monday to Friday, often with lectures and talks in the evening from well-known gardening personalities. The Loire is a week and Germany 10 days: all go to excellent gardens, public and private.

Motts Leisure Ltd
4 Buckingham Street, Aylesbury, Buckinghamshire HP20 2LD
☎ 01296 336666   📠 01296 336667

1997 TOURS   Cornish gardens, Wicklow gardens, Paris parks, Dutch bulbfields
MEMBER   BCH

Inexpensive coach tours, including a growing number to visit gardens at home and abroad.

Naturetrek
Chautara, Bighton, Alresford, Hampshire SO24 9RB
☎ 01962 733051   📠 01962 733368

CONTACT   David Mills
1997 TOURS   Wengen, the Dolomites, Cyprus, Andalucia, South Africa, Nepal, Sikkim, Bhutan
FOUNDED   1986
MEMBER   AITO; ATOL

Specialist treks for wildlife enthusiasts with some exciting venues. These trips are primarily for botanists. Treks are graded for difficulty. For the adventurous.

Page & Moy
136–140 London Road, Leicester LE2 1EN
☎ 0116 254 2000

1997 TOURS   Tuscany, Crete, the Cape, Ireland
MEMBER   ATOL, IATA, ABTA

Page & Moy are official tour operators to the National Trust. Destinations for the Trust include: Ireland; Holland; Gardens of the French Riviera; and several 4-5 day tours in different parts of England. They offer tours for lovers of art and architecture as well as great gardens. All are accompanied by two leaders.

Peregrine Holidays
41 South Parade, Summertown, Oxford OX2 7JP
☎ 01865 511642   📠 01865 512583

1997 TOURS   Andalucia, Corfu, the Peleponnese
MEMBER   ABTA, ATOL

Mainly wildlife tours, but they also offer botany-cum-wildlife tours in the above three locations.

Saga Holidays Ltd
The Saga Building, Middelburg Square, Folkestone, Kent CT20 1AZ
☎ 0800 300 500

1997 TOURS   Guernsey, Jersey, Hampshire, Cornwall, West Country, Sussex, Essex, East Anglia, Shropshire, Wales, Peak District, Cumbria, Northumbria, Scotland, County Dublin, Dorset, Devon, the Marches, North Yorkshire, Paris, Madeira, Portugal, Majorca
MEMBER   ATOL

Saga have a special Garden Holidays brochure for the young-at-heart over-50s. It offers a very wide choice of UK destinations, particularly in the West Country, and leisurely tours abroad. Roy Cheek and Kate Garton are among their tour leaders.

Specialtours
81a Elizabeth Street, London SW1W 9PG
☎ 0171 730 2297

1997 TOURS   Picos de Europa
MEMBER   ATOL, ABTOT

Specialtours runs tours for the National Art Collections Fund, mainly to see good architecture, but this trip to the Picos is specifically to see and paint wild flowers. Specialtours also run many made-to-measure garden tours: this year, for example, they are running six trips to UK & Europe for the American Horticultural Society and two for the Horticultural Magazine (Boston).

Travelscene Ltd
11–15 St Ann's Road, Harrow, Middlesex HA1 1AS
☎ 0181 427 8800   [FAX] 0181 861 3674

1997 TOURS   Dutch bulbfields
MEMBER   ABTA, AITO, ATOL
Moderately priced short breaks to see the Dutch bulbfields.

Trossachs Garden Tours
Orchardlea House, Callander, Perthshire FK17 8BG
☎ 01877 330798   [FAX] 01877 330543

CONTACT   Mrs Hilary Gunkel
1997 TOURS   East Anglia, Dumfries, Edinburgh, Pitlochry, Fife, Clydeside, Montrose, Callander
FOUNDED   1989

Attractively packaged weekend and midweek visits for small groups to private and public Scottish gardens. This year they travel to East Anglia for a week of plant-buying from famous nurseries.

Victoria Travel
30 Hewell Road, Barnt Green, Birmingham B45 8NE
☎ 0121 445 5656   [FAX] 0121 445 6177

1997 TOURS   Italian lakes, Madeira, the Caribbean, Germany, Madeira, Paris, the Loire, Namaqualand, Ireland, Chile, New Zealand

Victoria Travel organises holidays for BBC Gardeners' World Magazine. They have an impressive list of tour guides, including Roy Lancaster, Nigel Colborn and Pippa Greenwood.

Voyages Jules Verne
Travel Promotions Ltd, 21 Dorset Square, London NW1 6QG
☎ 0171 616 1000   [FAX] 0171 723 8629

1997 TOURS   The Cape, Madeira
MEMBER   ABTA, ATOL
Most of Voyages Jules Verne's tours are not specifically for garden-lovers, but the trips to these two destinations have a distinct horticultural interest.

Hotels with Good Gardens
Some of the houses attached to historic landscapes have become hotels. In several cases the gardens themselves have been well maintained or even improved by the new owners. Sometimes the gardens remain in good condition but in different ownership: the house is sold separately as a hotel. Many people find the idea of staying in a hotel with a beautiful garden particularly attractive. Here is a selection of hotels with gardens which are good enough to mention

in their own right. Their size and services vary considerably, from simple B & B to 5-Star ratings.

The Beeches Hotel & Plantation Garden
4–6 Earlham Road, Norwich NR2 3DB
☎ 01603 621167   [FAX] 01603 620151

Famous Victorian garden in the Italian style (with Gothic details), lost within the 3 acres of grounds until uncovered in the 1980s. It is being restored by a registered charity, the Plantation Preservation Trust.

Cannizaro House
West Side, Wimbledon Common, London SW19 4UF
☎ 0181 879 14641   [FAX] 0181 879 7339

An elegant Georgian house right on the edge of Cannizaro Park: see Gardens chapter.

Cliveden House Hotel
Taplow, Maidenhead, Berkshire SL6 0JF
☎ 01628 668561   [FAX] 01628 661837

One of the greatest gardens in the Thames Valley: see Gardens chapter.

Congham Hall Hotel
Lynn Road, Grimston, King's Lynn, Norfolk PE32 1AH
☎ 01485 600250   [FAX] 01485 601191

40 acres of parkland and a good kitchen garden: best for its herb garden, with over 300 varieties, many available for purchase.

Five Arrows Hotel
High Street, Waddesdon, Buckinghamshire HP18 0JE
☎ 01296 651727   [FAX] 01296 658596

On the edge of the Waddesdon estate, with access not only to the gardens (see Gardens chapter), but also to the Rothschild cellars.

Gliffaes Country House Hotel
Crickhowell, Powys NP8 1RH
☎ 01874 730371   [FAX] 01874 730463

29 acres of grounds; wonderful rhododendrons, maples and conifers dating from the 19th century.

Gravetye Manor
Vowels Lane, East Grinstead, West Sussex RH19 4LJ

This wonderful hotel has a seriously important garden – William Robinson's own. It has been imaginatively restored and replanted by Peter Herbert and is immaculately maintained: see Gardens chapter.

Greywalls
Muirfield, Gullane, Lothian EH31 2EG
☎ 01620 842144   [FAX] 01620 842241

Designed by Lutyens, planted by Jekyll: beautifully maintained and restored. Roses everywhere, and innumerable architectural jokes.

Hanbury Manor Hotel
Ware, Hertfordshire SG12 0SD
☎ 01921 487722   📠 01920 487692

Extensive parkland and immaculately maintained gardens: the walled garden is extremely pretty, but there are a secret garden, rose garden, woodland walk and arboretum too.

Hawkstone Park Hotel
Weston-under-Redcastle, Shrewsbury, Shropshire SY4 5UY
☎ 01939 20061   📠 01939 200311

Hawkstone is a historic Grade I park, laid out in the 18th century by Sir Rowland Hill and covering 100 acres of rugged cliffs and exotic follies. Chief among them are the Swiss Bridge and the Grotto but they are tacked together by sinuous paths and precipitous walks. The monkey puzzles and rhododendrons are a Victorian bonus.

Hope End Hotel
Ledbury, Hereford & Worcester HR8 1JQ
☎ 01531 633613   📠 01531 636366

Late Georgian landscape garden, laid out by John Loudon for Elizabeth Barrett Browning's father in 1809. Temple, grotto, wooded walks, carp pool and shady seats. Splendid walled garden, all organic.

Lainston House Hotel & Restaurant
Sparsholt, Winchester, Hampshire SO21 2LT
☎ 01962 863588   📠 01962 776672

63 acres of parkland surround this very handsome William & Mary house with a spectacular lime avenue, but the modern flower gardens by the house are a model of mixed planting: small trees, shrubs, roses and herbaceous plants all mixed.

Le Manoir aux Quat' Saisons
Church Road, Great Milton, Oxford OX44 7PD
☎ 01844 278881   📠 01844 278847

World famous restaurant: 19 rooms. Beautiful flower gardens in the English romantic style and impressive kitchen gardens.

Leeming House Hotel
Watermillock, Ullswater, Penrith, Cumbria CA11 0JJ
☎ 017684 86622   📠 017684 86443

Leeming House has 20 splendid acres of Victorian park and garden above the lake: there are mature conifers and magnificent billowing clumps of rhododendrons.

Little Thakenham Hotel
Merrywood Lane, Storrington, West Sussex RH20 3HE
☎ 01903 744416   📠 01903 745022

Lutyens house, with a period garden; paved walks and courtyards, a rose pergola and magnificent flowering trees and shrubs.

Long Cross Hotel
Trelights, Port Isaac, Cornwall PL29 3TF
☎ 01208 880243

Dramatic gardens, substantially remade in the late Victorian style, with many tender plants. Being so close to the sea, the plants were chosen for their resistance to sea spray - Monterey pine and glossy evergreens in particular.

The Lygon Arms
Broadway, Hereford & Worcester WR12 7DU
☎ 01386 852255   📠 01386 858611

Beautiful walled garden of roses and fruit trees: magnificent summer bedding.

Meudon Hotel
Mawnan Smith, Falmouth, Cornwall TR11 5HT
☎ 01326 250541   📠 01326 250543

8 acres of lushly planted valley running down to its own private beach on the Helford estuary: tree ferns, bananas, cordylines, drimys, camellias and vast clumps of *Gunnera*. Members of the German rose society who stayed there on their 1995 tour and said it was the best garden in Cornwall!

Middlethorpe Hall
Bishopthorpe Road, York YO2 1QB
☎ 01904 641241   📠 01904 620176

Handsome modern gardens in the formal style, to complement the William & Mary house: splendid old cedar.

Rhinefield House Hotel
Rhinefield, Brockenhurst, Hampshire SO42 7QB
☎ 01590 622922   📠 01590 622800

Grand Italian garden (actually late Victorian), well restored recently: magnificent conifers.

Riber Hall Hotel
Matlock, Derbyshire DE4 5JU
☎ 01629 582795   📠 01629 580475

Very pretty rock garden, herbaceous borders and mixed plantings near the hotel; splendid bluebell walks in the woods.

South Lodge Hotel
Lower Beeding, Horsham, West Sussex RH13 6PS
☎ 01403 891711   📠 01403 891766

90 acres of grounds surround this wisteria-clad mansion, including a fine collection of mature rhododendrons, conifers, ponds and a rock garden.

Ston Easton Park
Ston Easton, Somerset BA3 4DF
☎ 01761 241631   📠 01761 241377

Humphry Repton landscape, carefully restored by the hotel owners: see Gardens chapter.

Summer Lodge Hotel
Evershot, Dorchester, Dorset DT2 0JR
☎ 01935 83424   📠 01935 83005

Thomas Hardy, as a young architectural draughtsman, designed the drawing-room. Penny Hobhouse has been replanting the luscious mixed borders.

Thornbury Castle Hotel
Thornbury, Bristol, Avon BS12 1HH
☎ 01454 281182   📠 01454 416188

High Victorian formal garden within the castellated enceinte.

Tylney Hall Hotel

Rotherwick, Hook, Hampshire RG27 9AZ
☎ 01256 764881   FAX 01256 768141

67 acres of late Victorian exotica: avenues of wellingtonias, Italian garden, lakes and massive rhododendrons. Gertrude Jekyll designed the rock garden.

Willapark Manor Hotel

Bossiney, Tintagel, Cornwall PL34 0BA
☎ 01840 770782

14 acres on a magnificent headland. The owner is a keen gardener: he inherited good rhododendrons and spring flowers, and is extending the display.

Woolley Grange Hotel

Woolley Green, Bradford-on-Avon, Wiltshire BA15 1TX
☎ 01225 864705   FAX 01225 864059

Cotswold manorhouse with a small Italianate garden (c.1900), pretty lily pool and bright rose garden, though it would all benefit from a higher standard of maintainance. Best, perhaps, in February, when aconites flood the grass beneath old conker trees.

Ynyshir Hall

Eglwysfach, Machynlleth, Powys SY20 8TA
☎ 01654 781209   FAX 01654 781366

The drive runs past giant wellingtonias: 14 acres of Victorian woodland gardens with splendid old rhododendrons and azaleas.

In addition, we recommend the following hotels which are listed in the Gardens chapter: Ardnamona, Co Donegal; Loch Melfort Hotel, Arduaine, Strathclyde; Gidleigh Park, Devon; Kildrummy Castle, Grampian; Owlpen Manor, Gloucestershire; West Park Lodge, Beale Arboretum, Hertfordshire. If a garden is not separately listed in the Gardens section of The Gardener's Yearbook, you should first ask whether it is ever open to non-patrons. The owners' attitudes to visitors who are not guests of the hotel differ greatly. Cliveden and Waddesdon are examples of hotels whose associated gardens may freely be visited most of the year. Others are open infrequently: the Beale Arboretum, attached to West Park Lodge Hotel, is an instance. And some owners are concerned to emphasise that their gardens are never open to the public, but reserved entirely for the pleasure of visitors to the hotel or restaurant: at Gravetye Manor and Gidleigh Park, for example, the delights of the garden may only be known to guests of the business.

Other Accommodation

Several organisations offer Bed & Breakfast accommodation to keen gardeners. The Hardy Plant Society publishes a list of about 120 members who have a B & B business: please send a SAE to Mrs Pam Adams, Little Orchard, Great Comberton, Pershore, Hereford & Worcester, WR10 3DP. Among the owners of important gardens who are listed by the Hardy Plant Society are: Jane Sterndale-Bennett of White Windows, Hampshire; Alan Bloom of Bressingham Hall, Norfolk; and Mr & Mrs J. McCutchan of Bates Green Farm, East Sussex. The list also includes several members in Europe and overseas. We also strongly recommend a pamphlet called Bed and Breakfast for Garden Lovers: please send a SAE to Mrs S. Colquhoun, Handywater Farm, Sibford Gower, Banbury, Oxfordshire OX15 5AE which lists garden owners all over the country who do B & B. The guide also identifies those which are mentioned in the Yellow Book or Good Gardens Guide, so that would-be visitors can do their holiday homework before deciding where to stay. The Wolsey Lodges Guide, 17 Chapel Street, Bildeston, Suffolk, IP7 7EP (Tel 01449 741297) is a marketing organisation for upmarket B & B in private houses throughout Britain. Several of the properties listed in the Gardens section of The Gardener's Yearbook appear in its pages, including Docton Mill in Devon. We also recommend the Irish equivalent, an excellent booklet called The Hidden Ireland which is available for £1 from Bord Fáilte (The Irish Tourist Board) and from the Northern Irish Tourist Board, as well as from The Secretary, The Hidden Ireland, P O Box 4414, Dublin 4 (Tel 00 353 1 6681423; Fax 00 353 1 6686578). The 40 or so houses, manors, lodges and demesnes tend to be grander than their British equivalents, and there is a sprinkling of English and Irish titles among the owners. Some properties, such as Ardnamona in Co Donegal, have gardens that qualify for an entry in the Gardens chapter of The Gardener's Yearbook.

Working holidays are becoming increasingly popular, especially the chance to follow semi-educational courses attached to environmental conservation. The National Trust alone offers about 400 week-long and weekend projects every year and has about 3,000 holiday makers. Organisations offering working holidays include: National Trust Working Holidays (Tel: 01285 651818); the National Trust for Scotland (0131 226 5922); and the British Trust for Conservation Volunteers, Natural Break Department (Tel: 01491 839766). The 1996 BTCV brochure of working holidays included reclamation at the Lost Gardens of Heligan in Cornwall and restoring a Japanese garden in Cornwall.

The National Trust for Scotland offers holiday lets in a number of its properties. It also has upmarket apartments on the top floor of Culzean Castle, which it runs as a private hotel.

We recommend The National Trust 1997 Holiday Cottage Brochure, available in return for a donation of £1: please telephone 01225 791133. The lets may be cottages on the estate, converted lodges, water towers, estate buildings or stables, or even a flat in part of the house itself. Prices vary from about £150 pw to £350 pw, but the top properties in high season will cost as much as £1,000 pw, which is actually a measure of just how good the best ones really are. Last year there were two at Cliveden in Buckinghamshire; ten at Cotehele in Cornwall; three at Glendurgan in Cornwall; four at Trelissick in Cornwall; three at Acorn Bank in Cumbria; one at Castle Drogo in Devon; two at Coleton Fishacre in Devon; two at Mottistone Manor in the Isle of Wight; two at Felbrigg Hall in Norfolk; three at Nymans in West Sussex; one at Beningbrough in North Yorkshire; three at Studley Royal in North Yorkshire; one at Bodnant in Clwyd; one at Colby Woodland Garden in Dyfed; one at Powis Castle in Powys; one at Rowallane in Co Down; one at Florence Court in Co Fermanagh.

Although it is not a National Trust property, readers may also like to know that the Gothick orangery at Frampton Court in Gloucestershire has been converted into a holiday self-catering home. It is right at the heart of the famous gardens, at the head of the Dutch Canal, and is available for short or long lets. Write for a copy of the illustrated brochure.

When You Go Away

Whether you're soaking up sun and sangria in Spain during the winter months or just cruising the Norfolk Broads for a long weekend, how will the garden manage without you? The answer depends on how well it manages when you are there. Work out how much time you spend tending your plot each week and you'll have a pretty good idea what sort of arrangements, if any, will be needed in your absence. After all, if a grudging hour or so at the weekend is par for the course, then it probably won't even notice you're not there. If, on the other hand, hour upon hour, week in, week out, go to grooming the garden to perfection, then either you'll need someone else to keep up the standard till you return, or else you should think about going away at a quieter season horticulturally.

Should you fall somewhere in between, then there is a choice of steps you can take to keep the upper hand. So, given that most people go away in summer, the main problem is protecting your plants from British heat and drought. It helps if you can remove pots and hanging baskets to a place of shade and shelter while you are away. Plants in pots fare even better if you plunge them in the ground and water the earth around them well.

Consider introducing any or all of the following: mulches on the borders, and especially around newly planted trees and shrubs, to reduce the amount of water lost through evaporation; shade netting; capillary matting or plunge beds for pots, inside and out; a time controlled watering system. This last need not be as expensive as it sounds. Use seepage hoses and/or an electronic clock which switches on after dusk when watering is most effective. And remember that no system is suitable for long periods.

After water, the main problem is growth. Puritanical journalists will advise you to cut the heads of flowers which have not yet faded, or perhaps not even opened, before you leave. Necessary or not, the grass won't cut itself and produce will not pick itself, so you'll have to get a friend or neighbour to fight this battle by proxy. Don't expect them to spare as much time as you would: their little will make all the difference.

For bigger gardens and more intensive cultivation, you will probably need to rely on expert help. Greenhouse gardening is a high-risk activity. Precious specimens are best entrusted to the safe custody of an experienced gardening friend to look after in his or her own greenhouse. If this is impossible, you must find a knowledgeable person to water and ventilate your greenhouse as frequently as you do yourself. Remember that the usual fault of inexperienced caretakers is to overwater everything. Leave long and detailed instructions in writing, run through them point by point, and give a practical demonstration of your requirements. If you don't have a gardener already, consider arranging for contract gardeners to fill in for you. You will have to set out their duties precisely, and expect to pay from £10 an hour for their time. Alternatively, you can ask one of the specialist agencies to find you a residential houseminder.

Houseminders carry out the basic domestic and garden duties that you would normally perform yourself. These usually involve caring for pets, answering the telephone, and providing the security of a presence in the house, as well as watering the tomatoes and mowing the lawn. Large gardens or greenhouses which demand hours of commitment may require a higher fee. Most agencies are happy to make special arrangements to accommodate your particular needs. The terms they offer differ enormously, not so much in price, but more in the smaller details. Agencies include:

Animal Aunts
45 Fairview Road, Headley Down, Hampshire, GU35 8HQ
☎ 01428 712611   ⊠ 01428 717190

Founded in 1987. Mainly for people with pets and other animals, particularly those with special requirements.

Country Cousins

10a Market Square, Horsham, West Sussex RH12 1EX

☎ 01403 210415

Founded more than 30 years ago, they specialise in the care of the elderly, but individual carers may be willing to undertake some light garden duties while you are away.

Holiday Homewatch

Nursery Cottage, Penybont, Llandrindrod Wells, Powys, LD1 5SP

☎ 01597 851840

Founded in 1988. Supply supervisors who specialise in assignments where there are horses and farm livestock as well as domestic pets to look after.

Home & Pet Care

Greenrigg Farm, Caldbeck, Wigton, Cumbria, CA7 8AH

☎ 016974 78515

Founded in 1988. Primarily a House Sitting company, and particularly for people with pets, but they are also quite happy to maintain gardens.

Homesitters Ltd

Buckland Wharf, Buckland, Aylesbury, Buckinghamshire, HP22 5LQ

☎ 01296 630730

Founded in 1980. Perhaps the largest agency, Homesitters are particularly conscious of the problems of garden owners who wish to go on holiday. 'When you take a spring break, they will nurture the seedlings and ventilate the greenhouse; while you relax on your summer holiday, they will mow the lawn regularly and water the hanging baskets'.

Housewatch Ltd

Little London, Berden, Bishops Stortford, Hertfordshire, CM23 1BE

☎ 01279 777412   FAX 01279 777049

Housewatchers will care for your animals and undertake basic domestic and garden duties.

Universal Aunts

P O Box 304, London SW4 0NN

☎ 0171 738 8937   FAX 0171 622 1914

Founded in 1921 and celebrating its 75th birthday this year. This famous name attaches to a registered employment agency which supplies Property Caretakers and gardeners on a temporary basis. They are experienced in all types of domestic need, particularly those which involve looking after people.

26

Charities

Many people wish to support a horticultural charity but do not know how to do so or which to choose. There are two main welfare charities specifically concerned with gardeners and their families: the Royal Gardeners' Orphan Fund and the Gardeners' Royal Benevolent Society (see below for details of their aims and achievements). Many other horticultural organisations enjoy charitable status – most clubs and societies for instance, as well as educational institutes. An ever-increasing number of gardens are registering as charities, from Achamore on the Isle of Gigha to Trebah in Cornwall.

Donations are always welcome and account for a substantial part of the income of every charity, but the benefit can be enhanced if people are willing to structure their giving in a tax-efficient way rather than leaving it to impulse. Gifts to charity can be exempted from Income Tax, Capital Gains Tax and Inheritance Tax. Take Income Tax, for example. If you put a £10 note in a collecting box, you are giving away money on which you have paid tax and there is no way in which the charity can have the benefit of that tax. But if you use a covenant, gift aid or payroll scheme, the charity can reclaim the basic rate tax which you have already paid so that, with basic rate at 23%, the £10 is worth £12.99.

A covenant is an undertaking to pay a fixed sum for four or more years. It has to follow the prescribed form and be signed as a deed for the charity to recover the basic rate tax which the giver is deemed to have deducted from the gift. A suitable form is shown in the next column.

Gift Aid is the most efficient way for UK residents to make a one-off cash gift to a charity. The donation should be for more than £250 and you have to sign a form when making the gift so that the charity can reclaim the tax which you have already paid. There is an advantage to the giver as well as the charity if you are a higher-rate tax-payer: the charity reclaims tax at the basic rate but the difference (17%) between higher and basic tax rates is reclaimed by the giver. Gift Aid has proved very beneficial to charities.

Payroll giving has been widely introduced and many employees use it to ensure that a small part of their income

I [Jane Smith] of [13 Acacia Avenue, Newtown, Barsetshire], hereby undertake to pay to [name of charity] for a period of 4 years from the date hereof or during my lifetime, whichever is the shorter, on the [1st] day of [April] in each year such sum as will after the deduction of income tax at the basic rate for the time being in force amount to the sum of £[100] such sum to be paid out of my general fund of taxed income.

Dated this [21st] day of [March] [1997]

Signed as a Deed by [Signed] Jane Smith
the said Jane Smith in
the presence of:

[Signature, name, address
& description of
witness]

[Date]

goes to charity in the form of a regular donation. The charity can claim back the basic tax which has been deducted from your salary by your employer, at no cost to you. The best way to find out more about payroll giving is to speak to your employer.

Legacies in people's wills can make an enormous difference to the fortunes of a charity. The Anthony Pettit bequest funded the acquisition and maintenance of the Alpine Garden Society's new headquarters at Pershore. The gift of Netherbyres has quite transformed the ability of the Gardeners' Royal Benevolent Society to care for elderly retired gardeners and their spouses in Scotland. We recommend you to seek professional advice when making a legacy. The consequences of getting it wrong can be worse than having no will at all. Equally, it is important not to leave making a will until it is too late. By instructing a solicitor to write your will, you can be sure that your wishes are expressed correctly, so that your executors can put them into effect. Most charities can put you in touch with a suitable person to undertake the legal drafting.

Finally, it is worth remembering that the best source of advice on every aspect of giving to charity is the Charities Aid Foundation, 48 Pembury Road, Tonbridge, Kent TN9 2JD. (Tel 01732 771333; Fax 01732 350570). The Charities Aid Foundation is itself a charity. It exists to enable individuals and organisations to improve the quality and value of their donations to charity. 'For more than 150,000 private individuals' they claim, 'the Charities Aid Foundation is simply the best way to give.

The Royal Gardeners' Orphan Fund. 48 St Alban's Road, Codicote, Hertfordshire ST4 8UT (Tel: 01438 820783. Secretary: Mrs Kate Wallis). Founded in 1887 to help the orphans of gardeners 'by giving them regular allowances and grants for special purposes'. Since 1985 the Fund has also offered assistance to needy children, not necessarily orphans, whose parents are employed full-time in horticulture. The Fund's counselling service advises on such problems as may arise when a family which has been living in tied accommodation has to move elsewhere on the death of the bread-winner, sometimes to a different area and far from friends and familiar surroundings. The Fund is supported by many institutions including The National Gardens Scheme, Scotland's Gardens Scheme, The Worshipful Company of Gardeners, The Royal Horticultural Society and many horticultural and flower clubs around the country. The total value of grants made to some 62 beneficiaries in 1995 was £49,237.

The Gardeners' Royal Benevolent Society, Bridge House, 139 Kingston Road, Leatherhead, Surrey, KT22 7NT (Tel 01372 373962; Fax 01372 362575. Patron: H M Queen Elizabeth The Queen Mother. President: H R H Princess Alice, Duchess of Gloucester. Chief Executive: C R C Bunce). The Society was founded in 1839 by a group of horticultural growers who were appalled by the fate of men, gardeners all their lives, who became too old to work and had to face starvation or the workhouse. The aim of the Society remains, as it always has been, to help gardeners suffering from ill health and to provide pensions in their old age. Income in 1995 included £107,091 from donations, £480,297 from investment income, £707,808 from rents and £107,252 from deposits.

The Gardeners' Royal Benevolent Society has been very active in recent years in expanding its· activities. Today there are over five hundred pensioners, fifty of whom are resident in the Society's country home, Red Oaks, Henfield, Sussex. Red Oaks was purpose built in 1971 and the Society has now obtained planning permission to rebuild it to take account of the requirements of modern nursing. There are also twenty one sheltered housing flats in the grounds of Red Oaks. The Society also owns a group of seven bungalows at Barton in Cambridgeshire which are used to accommodate retired gardening couples, some of whom have had to vacate tied cottages on retirement. To meet cases of particular difficulty the Society has a Good Samaritan fund from which grants are made for such specific purposes as fuel, house repairs and special food in cases of illness.

The Society's Scottish home, Netherbyres at Eyemouth near Berwick-on-Tweed, was given to the Society under the terms of the will of Lt. Col. Simon Furness in 1991 and has grounds of 40 acres. All fifteen places at Netherbyres have now been filled. In 1991 the Society also opened a small development of sheltered housing bungalows at Kings Stanley in Gloucestershire. In 1994 the Society was left York Gate at Adel in West Yorkshire: the garden is a masterpiece of good modern design and planting and was created by the late Robin Spencer and his parents in the 1970s and 1980s. The society will continue to open it to the public.

The National Gardens Scheme Charitable Trust, Hatchlands Park, East Clandon, Guildford, Surrey GU4 7RT (Tel: 01483 211535. Administrator and Director: Lt. Col. Tim Marsh). Despite its high profile, the National Gardens Scheme was not originally intended as a horticultural charity: when founded in 1927, its purpose was to help elderly district nurses. Best known for its National Gardens Scheme, over 90% of its income comes from the 3,500 or so gardens which are open to the public, and from the sale of its Yellow Book. In 1995 the total received was rather less than in the previous year but nevertheless it enabled the scheme to pay out £1,303,202 to charities. By far the biggest beneficiaries were the Cancer Relief Macmillan Fund (£738,500) and the Gardens Fund of the National Trust (£250,000), but donations were also made to county nursing associations (£29,460), the Queen's Nursing Institute (£68,000), the Nurses' Welfare Service (£46,500), the Gardeners' Royal Benevolent Society (£28,500) and the Royal Gardeners' Orphan Fund (£28,500). The balance of £113,742 was shared among other charities nominated by garden owners who are able to specify that up to 25% of their takings should be directed to such organisations as CAFOD and St John's Ambulance.

Scotland's Gardens Scheme, 31 Castle Terrace, Edinburgh EH1 2EL (Tel: 0131 229 1870. General Organiser: R S St. Clair-Ford). Over 300 gardens throughout Scotland open for this charity which is closely modelled on the English National Gardens Scheme. Owners are encouraged to open their gardens to the public and the proceeds are then distributed among various charities. In 1995 the total income raised from garden openings exceeded £280,000, a higher return per garden than the English scheme, and £182,036 was paid out. £46,445 was donated to the Queen's Nursing Institute, Scotland; £50,408 to the Gardens Fund of the National Trust for Scotland; £2,200 to the Gardeners' Royal Benevolent Society; and £2,200 to the Royal Gardeners' Orphan Fund. Owners are able to donate up to 40% to a charity of their choice and, as a result, £80,783 was made available to help and support 142 different charities.

The Worshipful Company of Gardeners has a Charities Fund which makes grants to deserving projects, such as horticultural therapy schemes and garden designs for special schools. Details are available from the Master.

27

Royal Warrants

Any tradesman who, for a minimum of five years, has been supplying one or more of the Royal Households who award warrants may apply for the grant of a Royal Warrant. Further details are available from: The Secretary, The Royal Warrant Holders' Association, 7 Buckingham Gate, London SW1E 6JY. (Telephone: 0171 828 2268. Fax: 0171 834 5912). Here is a list of the warrants currently granted to tradesmen in the horticultural sector.

Royal Warrants Of Appointment To Her Majesty Queen Elizabeth II

Department Of Her Majesty's Privy Purse

List of Tradesmen in the Department of Her Majesty's Privy Purse permitted to style themselves 'By Appointment to Her Majesty The Queen' or 'By Appointment to Her Majesty Queen Elizabeth II' and entitling them to display the Royal Arms.

Abbey Rose Gardens	Rose Growers & Nurserymen	Burnham
Aberdeen Landscapes &		
Specialist Tree Service	Tree Surgeons	Inverurie
Angus Chain Saw Services	Horticultural Engineers	Lawton, by Arbroath
Atco Ltd	Manufacturers of Motor Mowers	Stowmarket
Bartlett Tree Expert Co Ltd		
(Southern Tree Surgeons)	Tree Surgeons	Crawley
Bartram Mowers Ltd	Suppliers of Horticultural Equipment	Norwich
Blooms of Bressingham Ltd	Suppliers of Hardy Nursery Stock	Diss
Carters Tested Seeds Ltd	Seedsmen	Torquay
Cocker, James & Son	Suppliers of Roses	Aberdeen
Darby Nursery Stock Ltd	Suppliers of Ornamental Shrubs & Trees	Thetford
Delamore, R Ltd	Suppliers of Chrysanthemum Stock	Wisbech
Dobbie & Co Ltd	Seedsmen & Nurserymen	Lasswade
Paul Double Nurseries Ltd	Tree Nurserymen	Ipswich
FARGRO Ltd	Horticultural Sundriesmen	Littlehampton
Findlay Clark (Aberdeen)	Seedsmen & Nurserymen	Aberdeen
Greens Nurseries Ltd	Supplier of Soft Fruit Plants	Dereham
Hillier Nurseries Ltd	Nurserymen & Seedsmen	Ampfield
ICI Fertilisers	Manufacturers of Fertilisers	Cleveland
Ken Leech Trees	Fruit Tree Nurserymen	Bulmer Tye, Sudbury
Levington Horticulture Ltd	Manufacturers of Horticultural Products	Ipswich
Netlon Ltd	Manufacturers of Plastic Mesh	Blackburn

Ransomes Sims & Jefferies Ltd	Manufacturers of Horticultural Machinery	Ipswich
Ben Reid & Co Ltd	Nurserymen & Seedsmen	Aberdeen
Frank Row	Suppliers of Chrysanthemum Stock	Wellington, Somerset
Peter J Smith	Suppliers of Horticultural Plants	Ashington
Suttons Seeds Ltd	Seedsmen	Torquay
O A Taylor & Sons Bulbs Ltd	Bulb Growers	Holbeach
Vitax Ltd	Manufacturers of Fertilisers & Insecticides	Leicester
Willmot Pertwee Ltd	Suppliers of Horticultural Chemicals	Colchester
William Wood & Sons Ltd	Garden Contractors & Horticultural Builders	Taplow

Royal Warrants Of Appointment To Her Majesty Queen Elizabeth The Queen Mother

List of Tradesmen who hold Warrants of Appointment to Queen Elizabeth The Queen Mother from the Lord Chamberlain to Her Majesty, permitted to style themselves 'By Appointment' to Her Majesty, with authority to display Her Majesty's Arms.

Carters Tested Seeds Ltd	Seedsmen	Torquay
Dettlyn Ltd (Egham Mower Service)	Suppliers of Horticultural Machinery	Winchfield, Hampshire
Findlay Clark (Aberdeen)	Seedsmen & Nurserymen	Aberdeen
Hillier Nurseries Ltd	Nurserymen & Seedsmen	Winchester
Suttons Seeds Ltd	Seedsmen	Torquay
O A Taylor & Sons Bulbs Ltd	Bulb Growers	Holbeach
William Wood & Sons Ltd	Garden Contractors & Horticultural Builders	Taplow

Royal Warrants Of Appointment To His Royal Highness The Prince Of Wales

List of Tradesmen who hold Warrants of Appointment to The Prince of Wales, permitted to style themselves 'By Appointment to His Royal Highness', and entitling them to display The Prince of Wales Badge of Three Feathers.

Blom, Walter & Son Ltd	Supplier of Flower Bulbs	Milton Earnest
Five Trees Partnership	Supplier of Gardening Materials	Tetbury
John Miller (Corsham) Ltd	Suppliers of Garden Machinery	Chippenham

28

Gardens

This section recommends gardens in Great Britain and Ireland. Our aim is to supply sufficient detail to enable readers to decide whether and when to plan a visit. The list is not exhaustive. It offers a selection of the different types of garden which are open to the public: ancient and modern, large and small, public and private. The editors welcome suggestions for additions, deletions or alterations to entries.

Gardens are listed by county or region (for Scotland), and then alphabetically by name. The order is England, Wales, Scotland, Northern Ireland and Eire. The book's introduction explains why we continue to use the 1974 boundaries, with the exception of Avon, Cleveland and Humberside. This section also serves as a reference source for the rest of the book, where gardens are referred to only by their name, followed by their county, as in Marwood Hill, Devon, and Rowallane, Co. Down. All the counties of Sussex and Yorkshire appear under 'S' and 'Y' respectively.

The number of gardens open to the public continues to grow. We list about 20 new gardens this year, as well as deleting a few whose owners, like Mr & Mrs Michael Smith of Broadlands, Dorset, have decided to close. Martin Lane Fox has sold Hazelby House, Hampshire, and the trustees of Jenkyn Place, Hampshire, have seen fit to sell the garden together with the house, which was in separate ownership. It is much to be regretted that these two modern gardens, perhaps the finest in the south of England, should no longer be open to visitors. In a very few instances gardens have been omitted from this edition of *The Gardener's Yearbook* because the owners have ignored our requests for up-to-date information.

Some garden owners died during the course of last year, among them Lord Luke of Odell Castle, Bedfordshire, and Lt Col Campbell-Preston of Ardchattan, Strathclyde, though fortunately his daughter Sarah Troughton, already well-known as a horticulturist, is continuing to open the garden. Other gardens should be seen before their owners pass away. When you read that a garden has been made by the present owner over the last forty years, you may assume that both are now mature and will not last for ever.

Our source for practical information about directions, opening times, admission charges, parking, loos, disabled facilities, shops and refreshments has been the owners or their staff, backed up by our own enquiries where appropriate. The accuracy of these details is not guaranteed, but is believed to be correct at the time of going to press. In order to assist readers who are hoping to arrange a group visit by special appointment, we have taken the unusual step of listing the telephone and fax numbers to which enquiries should be directed. In many cases this is the private telephone line of the owners: readers are strongly urged to respect their privacy. If telephone and fax numbers have been omitted, this is because the owners prefer to receive such requests by letter. A pre-booked group can often make a visit at a time when the garden is not open to individual visitors. Most gardens offer special rates and, if details are not given, it may be worth asking whether a reduction is available and what minimum number is acceptable. Not all gardens offer reductions for parties: popular gardens which already suffer from wear and tear may not welcome extra visitors. Special rates for families are sometimes available, especially at larger gardens attached to stately homes, where the garden is only one of many entertainments offered to the visitor. There are endless permutations on the numbers of adults and/or children which constitute a 'family' and the age at which a child becomes an adult and has to pay the full entry price. Season tickets are sometimes available, and good value for people who live near a large garden or stately home. National Trust members are usually admitted free to Trust properties. Readers are strongly recommended to join the National Trust in any event: its portfolio of blue chip gardens is so comprehensive that no garden tour is complete without a visit to one or more of its properties.

We generally give prices and times for visiting the garden only. If the house is open at the same time, a supplement may be payable. Entrance fees vary, and some owners have told us that they may increase fees in the middle of the season. Some have a high season for a month or so – like Leonardslee in May. Others have a special day of the week or open days for charity when the entrance fee is higher. A few owners had not yet fixed their 1997 times or admission charges and, with their agreement, we have therefore indicated that the times or prices quoted are for 1996. All entrance fees are, in any event, liable to be changed: visitors would do well to take more money than they think they will need. Many gardens have honesty boxes, and it is also important to take lots of change, so that you are not forced to choose between paying too much or too little.

Remember that most gardens have a last admission time. Typically it will be thirty or forty-five minutes before they close, but it can be much longer. The last admission to Stowe is one hour before it closes, while Stratfield Saye actually closes its gates to visitors at 4 pm, two hours before they are required to leave. The guide indicates whether parking is available: this may be at the garden itself or on a public road very close to it. Parking may be at some distance from the house. At Saltram it is 500 yards away, and this is by no means exceptional. You can however expect better parking facilities at a popular property which offers a wide range of entertainments than at a small plantsman's garden in a country lane. In the case of refreshments, however, we have referred only to what is offered within the garden itself, and not to restaurants, tea-rooms and public houses nearby.

We have not specified the nature of the special facilities offered to the disabled, but in most cases it includes loos and ramps which are suitable for the wheelchairbound. It is best to enquire in advance of a visit if particular items of special equipment are required. The National Trust is especially good at adapting its properties to accommodate the needs of disabled visitors and publishes an excellent free 56-page booklet called *Information for Visitors with Disabilities*, which details the many special facilities available at its properties. It is available from the National Trust's head office in London.

It is often a condition of admission that no photograph taken within a garden may be sold or used for public reproduction without the consent of the property owner. Visitors should also remember that almost all gardens accept dogs only if they are kept on leads. Some restrict dogs to particular areas of a property, like the car park, or the woods and parkland rather than the garden proper. Private owners are generally better disposed towards dogs than corporate owners like the National Trust or English Heritage.

Information about outsize trees is taken from a fascinating publication *Champion Trees in the British Isles* by Alan F Mitchell, Victoria E Schilling and John E J White (4th Edition 1994, HMSO £5). There are two ways of measuring trees: height and girth. Sometimes the tallest specimen will also have the thickest trunk – but not always. Both the tallest and the biggest can claim to be the champion tree, and we have made this distinction when noting record breakers in gardens. Tree measurements can never be fully up to date: some records have not been verified since the great gales of 1987 and 1990. Nevertheless *Champion Trees in the British Isles* clearly indicates where the best collections of trees are: there are, for example, 101 record-breaking trees at Westonbirt Arboretum in Gloucestershire and 51 at the Sir Harold Hillier Gardens & Arboretum in Hampshire. Birr Castle has the leading collection in Ireland with 51 tree records, while in Scotland the largest number is at the Royal Botanic Garden in Edinburgh, which has 45. The dominance of conifers in western and central Scotland may also be noted. Further information about champion trees is available from the *Tree Register of the British Isles*, c/o Mrs Victoria Schilling, 2 Church Cottages, Westmeston, Hassocks, West Sussex, BN6 8RJ.

We have noted those NCCPG National Collections which are held at the gardens we list. Not all genera are the subject of a National Collection: there are still some horticulturally important groups of plants which have not yet been seriously collected and studied under the auspices of the NCCPG. Other genera have been split into a number of different collections. This is particularly necessary in the case of such a large genus as *Rhododendron* or those, like *Euphorbia*, which require a great variety of growing conditions. Moreover, the NCCPG has wisely introduced a system of duplicate collections so that plants are grown in two or more gardens. The need to maintain duplicate collections and split large genera explains why certain names occur several times in our list of National Collections. The 1997 edition of *The National Plant Collections Directory* has now been published and lists about 550 National Plant Collections: copies are available from bookshops or directly from the NCCPG, The Pines, Wisley Garden, Woking, Surrey GU23 6QB (£4 including UK postage).

A word about our choice of gardens is appropriate. We aim to be comprehensive but realistic. All major gardens which are open regularly are listed as a matter of course. These include many gardens of the National Trust and the National Trust for Scotland as well as botanic and public gardens and those attached to stately homes. But many gardens do not open to visitors regularly: the National Gardens Scheme includes over three thousand. We have found space for a selection of these gardens which open only once a year or by appointment. Some guides would omit them on the grounds that it is not worthwhile to give publicity to gardens which so few people can visit. We take the view that, if a good garden is seldom open, it is all the more important to know when the opportunity to see it will arise. And there are bound to be inconsistencies. We have, for example, omitted several excellent gardens where entry is free – Howth Castle Rhododendron Gardens in Co. Dublin and the Botanic Gardens Park in Belfast are two that spring immediately to mind – while we have included others such as the Royal Botanic Garden at Edinburgh and Chiswick House in London.

The starting point for garden visiting must be the 'Yellow Book' which the National Gardens Scheme publishes annually in February under the full title *Gardens of England & Wales Open to the Public*. The Yellow Book is a best seller. Its sales immediately after publication exceed 5,000 copies per week, three times the rate of its nearest rival among best-selling paperback reference books. It is wonderfully comprehensive and totally undiscriminating. The owners write their own garden entries, with the result that a really good garden may come across as self-deprecatingly boring, while an exciting description can often lead to disappointment. Beware of self-publicists: you can usually spot the hype. The Yellow Book lists nearly 3,500 gardens and is the single most important guide to visiting gardens in England and Wales, and the least expensive. Copies of *Gardens of England & Wales Open to the Public in 1997* are available from bookshops at the price of £3.50, or for £4.25 (including UK postage) directly from the National Gardens Scheme, Hatchlands Park, East Clandon, Guildford, Surrey GU4 7RT.

Scotland has its own Yellow Book called *The Gardens of Scotland*. This is available from bookshops at the price of £2.50 or for £3.25 directly from Scotland's Gardens Scheme, 31 Castle Terrace, Edinburgh EH1 2EL. It lists over 300 gardens throughout Scotland but, like the Yellow Book, does not always mention that some gardens are open at other times, not for the benefit of the Scheme. Indeed, some open for the Scheme only one day a year, and for their own funds for the other 364 days. However, the 1997 edition of *The Gardens of Scotland* remains essential reading for anyone who wishes to visit Scottish gardens, and is far too seldom seen south of the border. We also recommend *The Good Scottish Gardens Guide* by Joyce and Maurice Lindsay (Chambers, 1995: £9.99) which satisfies an unmet need by treating 72 of the larger Scottish gardens in considerable detail and describing their history as well as their present design and plantings and their current facilities for visitors.

The leading guide to the whole of the British Isles is *The Good Gardens Guide 1997* by Peter King (Vermilion, £14.99). Its quality is inevitably somewhat uneven because the entries are written by many different hands and the standard of their judgements varies. It can also be criticised for not revising and improving its garden descriptions often enough. Nevertheless it accounts for many good gardens in more detail than any other book and, above all, it sorts out and evaluates many of the private gardens in the Yellow Book. *The Good Gardens Guide 1997* itself lists over one thousand gardens, some across the Channel within a day's journey of the Tunnel. It saves so much time and money – not to mention good humour – which would otherwise be lost driving many miles to a disappointing garden, that *The Good Gardens Guide 1997* must be worth every penny of its price.

The best of the garden guides is *The Daily Telegraph Gardener's Guide to Britain 1997* by Patrick Taylor (Pavilion, £12.99) which is beautifully laid out and elegantly written. It describes rather too few gardens and nurseries, and their geographic spread is sometimes too thin to make it really useful. However, it is updated annually and receives a thorough biennial revision which keeps it fresh. It is also based on personal visits, and therefore utterly reliable, in a way that *The Good Gardens Guide* is not. Patrick Taylor has a happy talent for tracking down new and interesting gardens which other writers have overlooked, and his judgements cannot be faulted – accurate, observant and intelligent.

The Good Gardens Guide and *The Daily Telegraph Good Gardener's Guide to Britain* are especially valuable because they list a substantial number of public parks where entry is free and unrestricted. These may not be gardens in the popular sense, but they are often of great interest to garden visitors. Both books include good nurseries: Patrick Taylor in particular recognises that visiting new nurseries is just as enjoyable and important to a keen gardener as seeing other people's gardens.

The most scholarly guide currently in print is *The Blue Guide to Gardens of England* (£14.99). Its scope is limited to about 300 gardens, all in England, but they are described in great detail and often illustrated with drawings and plans of layouts.

Johansens publish an A4 format paperback guide *Historic Houses, Castles & Gardens in Great Britain and Ireland*. The 1997 edition costs £7.99 and lists about 1,000 historic properties in the United Kingdom and Ireland, including many of the grander gardens in this section. This large, well-illustrated handbook is a most useful source of information for planning a trip, although the garden descriptions tend to be short and bland. Since garden-visiting is increasingly treated as a function of the leisure industry, readers may also like to know of *Days Out in Britain & Ireland 1997*, to be published in March by the Automobile Association and available at a cost of £6.99 from bookshops or for £7.69 directly from offices of the AA. It claims to be Britain's most comprehensive guide to heritage and leisure attractions.

The National Trust Gardens Handbook describes fully about 130 gardens. Most are attached to historic houses. Some are little known, and deservedly so: we have included only those which readers will find worth visiting. As a handbook, however, it is excellent, and it details the altitude and terrain of a garden, as well as how many gardeners are employed there. It also lists such special features as NCCPG collections and garden architecture, suggests the best time to visit a garden and, most usefully, tells you when to avoid it. Although it is limited to National Trust properties and its scope does not extend to Scotland or Eire, *The National Trust Gardens Handbook* is a model guide to gardens: a snip at £4.50.

English Heritage publishes a *Guide to English Heritage Properties 1997*, which is issued to all members. Although many of its properties are ancient monuments, notably castles and abbeys, English Heritage does own a number of good gardens, including Belsay Hall and Audley End. In Scotland, some historic gardens are maintained by Historic Scotland: they include such important examples as Edzell Castle. There are no gardens of importance maintained by CADW, the Welsh Historic Monuments Commission, although it is actively involved in assessing the conservation needs of historic landscapes within the principality. The Ulster Gardens Scheme raises funds every year for work in National Trust Gardens which would not otherwise be possible. It is run by the Northern Ireland region of the National Trust at Rowallane House, Saintfield, Ballynahinch, Co. Down, BT24 7LH (Tel: 01238 510721; Fax: 01238 511242). Last year it listed about twelve gardens, mainly in Down, Armagh and Derry, and each opened only once. All are smallish private gardens made by the present owners: the Ulster Gardens Scheme eschews the big gardens of the stately homes and the National Trust itself. The Ulster Gardens Scheme also issues a second list of some 25 gardens which are open only for group visits by appointment.

Local promotions abound. Visitors to the west coast of Scotland should ask for the magnificent colour guide to eighteen gardens published as *Glorious Gardens of*

Argyll and Bute and available free from Tourist Information Centres throughout Scotland. In the south-west, the Cornwall Garden Society holds sway and visitors should seek out the *Gardens of Cornwall Open Guide*, published by the Cornwall Garden Society and the Cornish Tourist Board with support from the National Trust. The guide is a model of helpfulness: it offers comprehensive information on 67 gardens, all the dates associated with the Cornwall Festival of Spring Gardens, and a really useful map – no road is too small.

Tourist boards are an invaluable source of local information. We have found the *Tourist Information Centres Map & Directory*, published by the British Tourist Authority (£1.20, or £1.80 to include p&p) is particularly useful. It lists all the tourist offices in Britain, shows their positions on a map, and gives their telephone numbers. Local staff are well informed about their area: one telephone call is enough to answer almost any question about opening hours and prices. The Scottish Tourist Board publishes an excellent *Visitors' Guide to Scotland's Gardens*, with details of about 150 top Scottish gardens. There are no photographs, but the garden descriptions are substantial. About twenty gardens are illustrated in a slimline brochure called *Visit Scotland's Best*, printed by the National Trust for Scotland. The Scottish Highlands and Islands Board also issues an attractive coloured booklet *Great Gardens of the Scottish Highlands and Islands*: it describes 32 gardens, mainly in Inverness, Ross and Argyll, but gives only the minimum of practical information about facilities and opening times.

The Northern Ireland Tourist Board has published a handsome brochure called *An Information Guide to Gardens and Historic Demesnes* which is handsomely illustrated and describes some 26 parks and gardens in considerable detail. It is available free from tourist offices in Northern Ireland, directly from NITB, 59 North Street, Belfast BT1 1NB, or from their offices in Glasgow and Dublin. The Irish Tourist Board (PO Box 273, Dublin 8) publishes a handsomely illustrated 24-page guide to *Gardens of Ireland*. In addition to 37 of the best gardens in Eire, it lists 16 Country House Hotels. The guide is invaluable, and whets the armchair visitor's appetite. Readers should also know of The County Wicklow Gardens Festival, the best in Ireland, which runs from 16 May to 22 June. The festival brochure gives details of about 40 gardens which are open either continuously or at some time during those five weeks and lists places of every quality for visitors to stay. Copies are available from Wicklow County Tourism, St Manntan's House, Kilmantin Hill,

Wicklow. Tel: 00 353 0 404 66058; Fax: 00 353 0 404 66057.

ENGLAND

BEDFORDSHIRE

Luton Hoo
The Mansion House, Luton Hoo, Luton LU1 3TQ
☎ 01582 22955　　📠 01582 34437
OWNER　Trustees of Luton Hoo Foundation
LOCATION　Signposted from Jct 10 of M1
OPEN　12 noon – 5 pm; Friday – Sunday and Bank Holiday Mondays; 24 March to 12 October
ADMISSION　Garden only: Adults £2.50; Senior Citizens & Students £2.25; Children £1
FACILITIES　Parking; loos; access for the disabled; gift shop; restaurant; picnic area
FEATURES　Landscape designed by Capability Brown; lake; rock garden; fine trees; largest *Acer platanoides* in the British Isles
ENGLISH HERITAGE GRADE　II*

A wonderfully nostalgic, once-great garden that has clearly seen better days, but where one can still capture a whisper of the authentic Edwardian opulence it once enjoyed. The house is stately – sort of neo-classical – and almost overwhelms the grand Italianate formal gardens. Beyond is an ornamental park where cherries are underplanted with drifts of daffodils. A broad valley runs down to a rhododendron wood, which conceals a huge sheer-sided, rock-garden with vast overgrown Japanese maples. And all around, running down to two long sinuous lakes, is a spacious Capability Brown landscape.

The Swiss Garden
Old Warden, Biggleswade SG18 9ER
☎ 01234 228330　　📠 01234 228921
OWNER　Bedforshire County Council
LOCATION　1½ miles west of Biggleswade
OPEN　1.30 pm – 6 pm (but 10 am – 6 pm on Sundays & Bank Holidays); daily except Tuesdays; 1 March to 30 September. 11 am – 3 pm; Sundays & New Year's Day; 1 January to 28 February and 1 to 31 October (all 1996 dates: ring to check 1997)
ADMISSION　Adults £2.25; Concessions & Children £1.25; Family £5
FACILITIES　Parking; loos; facilities for the disabled; plants for sale; publications and souvenirs shop; restaurant at neighbouring Shuttleworth collection
FEATURES　Interesting for children; picturesque landscape; rhododendrons; Pulhamite grotto; fernery; Swiss cottage; much restoration & replanting (1997)
ENGLISH HERITAGE GRADE　II*
FRIENDS　Details available at the entrance

A rustic, gothic landscape garden, largely developed by the Shuttleworth family in the 19th century. Winding paths and sinuous waterways; little cast-iron, ornamental bridges; picturesque huts and quaint kiosks; soaring ironwork arches; gullies and ferneries; vast conifers and cheerful rhododendrons; an

early grotto-glasshouse (note the small panes of glass) planted as a fernery. In short – great fun to visit, but the garden is a long walk from the carpark, so you need patience and a stout pair of legs.

Toddington Manor
Toddington LU5 6HJ
☎ 01525 872576　　📠 01525 874555
OWNER　Sir Neville & Lady Bowman-Shaw
LOCATION　Signposted from village
OPEN　11 am – 5 pm; Wednesday – Sunday; 1 May to 28 September
ADMISSION　Adults £3.50; Senior Citizens £2.50; Children £1.50; Family £9
FACILITIES　Parking; dogs permitted; loos; facilities for the disabled; plants for sale; gift shop; home-made teas & light refreshments
FEATURES　Herbaceous borders; fine conifers; herbs; old roses; woodland garden; interesting for children; vintage tractors; largest *Tilia tomentosa* 'Petiolaris' in the British Isles

A newish garden, made by the owners in less than 20 years, around some magnificent old trees. It has some excellent features, notably a lime avenue which leads into a cherry walk, but some consider it over-designed and under-planted – an agreeable garden that could do with more variety. However, we have never seen such a wonderfully high standard of maintenance in any garden.

Woburn Abbey
Woburn MK43 0TP
☎ 01525 290666　　📠 01525 290271
OWNER　The Marquess of Tavistock
LOCATION　1½ miles from Woburn on A4012
OPEN　10.45 am – 3.45 pm; daily; 24 March to 2 November. Private gardens open for NGS: 11 am – 5 pm; 20 April & 24-26 May. Maze open: 26 May & 18 August.
ADMISSION　Park: £5 per car: NGS extra
FACILITIES　Parking; loos; facilities for the disabled; plants for sale; two shops; lunches & teas
FEATURES　Landscape designed by Capability Brown; fine conifers; lake; landscape designed by Humphry Repton; interesting for children; deer park; tallest *Zelkova sinica* (17m.) in the British Isles
ENGLISH HERITAGE GRADE　I

Not a gardeners' garden, though the park has many rare trees: the best way to see the famous redwood avenue is from the cable car. The private gardens are simple and formal, mainly 19th-century and Italianate, but they include the hornbeam maze which has a Chinese pavilion in the centre.

Wrest Park
Silsoe MK45 4HS
☎ 01525 860152 (weekends)
OWNER　English Heritage
LOCATION　¾ mile east of Silsoe
OPEN　10 am – 6 pm; Saturdays, Sundays & Bank Holiday Mondays; 1 April to 30 September
ADMISSION　Adults £2.50; Concessions £1.90; Children £1.30 (1996 prices)

FACILITIES Parking; dogs permitted; loos; gift shop; light refreshments

FEATURES Landscape designed by Capability Brown; follies and garden buildings; lake; garden sculpture; grand parterres; long vistas; largest pink chestnut *Aesculus × carnea* in the British Isles

ENGLISH HERITAGE GRADE I

The 'English Versailles', dominated by a graceful long canal which runs down to the classical domed pavilion built by Thomas Archer in 1710. Capability Brown came here later, but worked around the earlier design. The house came later still, in the 1830s. A garden of grandeur.

BERKSHIRE

Englefield House

Englefield, Theale, Reading RG7 5EN
☎ 01734 302221   [FAX] 01734 302226

OWNER Sir William & Lady Benyon

LOCATION On A340, 1 mile from M4 Jct 12

OPEN 10 am – dusk; Mondays (plus Tuesdays – Thursdays from 1 April to 31 July); all year. And for NGS

ADMISSION Adults £2; Children Free

FACILITIES Parking; access for the disabled; plants for sale; refreshments on NGS days

FEATURES Herbaceous borders; daffodils; rhododendrons and azaleas; old roses; woodland garden; deer park

ENGLISH HERITAGE GRADE II

A splendid woodland garden with underplantings of maples, viburnums, magnolias and many good shrubs. The Elizabethan house has a formal garden in front of it: wonderful colour borders along its walls.

Folly Farm

Sulhamstead, Reading RG7 4DF
☎ 01734 303098

LOCATION 1 mile from A4, brown gates on right-hand side in Sulhampstead

OPEN 2 pm – 6 pm; 13 April, 26 May, 22 June. Private bookings on written application (midweek only)

ADMISSION £1.50 on open days, otherwise £2.50, for charity

FACILITIES Parking; loos; home-made teas

FEATURES Planted by Gertrude Jekyll; modern roses; old roses; good topiary; lavender; lilies; paeonies; iris; lupins; delphiniums

ENGLISH HERITAGE GRADE II*

One of the most enchanting gardens to come from the partnership between Sir Edwin Lutyens and Gertrude Jekyll, the structure of Folly Farm is intact. The most famous incidents are the canal garden, running up to a double-gabled wing of the house, and the sunken rose garden, where a cruciform bed of lavender rises from a tank of waterlilies. The plantings have been adapted to modern conditions and to the owners' taste for floribunda roses. Folly Farm is particularly lovely in spring when drifts of anemones flower under cherries and crabs.

Foxgrove Farm

Skinners Green, Enborne, Newbury RG14 6RE
☎ 01635 40554

OWNER Miss Audrey Vockins

LOCATION On edge of village

OPEN 2 pm – 6 pm; 22 February, and for NGS (see Yellow Book)

ADMISSION Adults £1.50; Children Free

FACILITIES Parking; loos; plants for sale; tea & cakes

FEATURES Herbaceous borders; gravel or scree garden; snowdrops; primulas; spring and autumn bulbs; new shade bed (1996)

A plantsman's garden, linked to Louise Vockins' nursery next door. Bulbs, alpines and herbaceous plants are Audrey Vockins' great interest. The hellebores, crocus and snowdrops give a great display in March; colchicums are the main reason to visit in October. There are good shrubs, roses and handsome small trees too.

The Harris Garden

Plant Sciences Laboratory, University of Reading, Whiteknights, Reading RG6 2AS
☎ 01734 318071   [FAX] 01734 750630

OWNER University of Reading

LOCATION On A327, 1 mile south-east of Reading

OPEN 2 pm – 6 pm; 27 April, 1 June, 27 July & 28 September

ADMISSION Adults £1.50; Children Free

FACILITIES Parking; loos; facilities for the disabled; plants for sale; teas (not 1 June)

FEATURES Good collection of trees; herbaceous borders; ecological interest; glasshouses and conservatories to visit; herbs; lake; plantsman's garden; rock garden; old roses; subtropical plants; particularly interesting in winter; Mediterranean shrubs; hardy annuals; heathers; primula dell

NCCPG NATIONAL COLLECTIONS *Iris*

FRIENDS The Friends of the Harris garden has an active programme of events and gives members free access to the garden. Ring Dr David Collett (01734 318024) in Department of Applied Statistics

This is the new botanic garden attached to Reading University, which is the leading centre for teaching economic and amenity horticulture. Started in 1988, there is already much to see and to learn. Visit it now, in the early years, and return as it matures.

Old Rectory Cottage

Tidmarsh, Pangbourne RG8 8ER
☎ 01734 843241

OWNER Mr & Mrs A W A Baker

LOCATION Small lane off A340 on right 200 yards north of Tidmarsh village

OPEN For NGS: see Yellow Book. And by appointment

ADMISSION £2

FACILITIES Parking; loos; plants for sale

FEATURES Good collection of trees; herbaceous borders; ecological interest; gravel or scree garden; herbs; lake; plantsman's garden; climbing roses; old roses; woodland garden; particularly good in July-August; cyclamen; colchicums;

hardy geraniums; snowdrops; plants collected in the wild; small lake; collection of birds; wonderful lilies

This is the marvellous garden of a great plantsman who has collected in all four corners of the world – the introducer of such staples as *Geranium palustre* and *Symphytum caucasicum*. The garden is a treasure house of unusual species, forms and home-made hybrids. Snowdrops, crocus, cyclamen, hellebores and winter stem colours justify a visit in February. Lilies are a special interest in early July – Bill Baker breeds them in thousands.

The Old Rectory, Burghfield
Burghfield RG3 3TH
☎ 01734 833200

OWNER   R Merton
LOCATION   Right at Hatch Gate Inn and first entrance on right
OPEN   11 am – 4 pm; second & last Wednesday in month; February to October
ADMISSION   Adults £2; Children Free
FACILITIES   Parking; loos; facilities for the disabled; plants for sale; teas
FEATURES   Herbaceous borders; plantsman's garden; pond; rock garden; snowdrops; stone troughs; exotic displays in tubs; hellebores; lilies

Highly acclaimed garden, whose *tour de force* is a double herbaceous border where plants build up their impact through repetition, backed by yew hedges which get taller towards the end, to cheat the perspective. It leads to a pool framed by dense plantings of strong foliage – ferns, hostas, maples.

Wyld Court Rainforest
Hampstead Norreys, Thatcham, Newbury RG18 0TN
☎ 01635 202221   📠 01635 202440

OWNER   The World Land Trust
LOCATION   Signed from Jct 13 on M4
OPEN   10 am – 5.30 pm (4.30 pm November – February); daily; all year
ADMISSION   Adults £3.50; OAPs £3; Children £2
FACILITIES   Parking; loos; facilities for the disabled; plants for sale; gift shop; refreshments
FEATURES   Glasshouses and conservatories to visit; plantsman's garden; interesting for children

Three large glasshouses, set to create three different rainforest climates. Each has a thickly planted collection of exotic plants of every kind, many of them endangered or vulnerable to extinction. Wonderful in winter, when the tropical orchids flower, and particularly rewarding in summer when *Victoria amazonica* fills one of the pools. But fascinating whatever the season or the weather outside.

BUCKINGHAMSHIRE

Ascott House & Gardens
Wing, Leighton Buzzard LU7 0PS
☎ 01296 688242   📠 01296 681904

OWNER   The National Trust
LOCATION   ½ mile east of Wing

OPEN   Garden only: 2 pm – 6 pm; Tuesday – Sunday; 28 March to 4 May and 2 to 30 September. Plus Wednesdays & last Sundays in month; 5 May to 31 August. House closed for refurbishment throughout year
ADMISSION   Garden only: £4 Adults; £2 Children
FACILITIES   Parking; loos; access for the disabled
FEATURES   Herbaceous borders; fine conifers; lake; garden sculpture; good topiary; woodland garden; spring bulbs; Dutch garden; tallest *Cedrus atlantica* 'Aurea' in the British Isles
ENGLISH HERITAGE GRADE   II*

Opulent late-Victorian extravaganza. Tremendous set piece fountains by Story, grand terraces, magnificent trees and a giant sundial of box and golden yew. Almost too good to be true.

Blossoms
Cobblers Hill, Great Missenden
☎ 01494 863140

OWNER   Dr & Mrs Frank Hytten
LOCATION   At Cobblers Hill
OPEN   By appointment only
ADMISSION   £1.50 for NGS
FACILITIES   Parking; loos; access for the disabled; plants for sale
FEATURES   Herbaceous borders; lake; plantsman's garden; rock garden; woodland garden

A large modern plantsman's garden: five acres of very varied habitats from beechwoods to lakes and from screes to cutting borders.

Chenies Manor
Chenies, Rickmansworth WD3 6ER
☎ 01494 762888

OWNER   Mrs A MacLeod Matthews
LOCATION   Centre of Chenies village
OPEN   2 pm – 5 pm; Wednesdays, Thursdays & Bank Holidays; April to October
ADMISSION   Garden only, £2.25; House & garden, £4.50
FACILITIES   Parking; loos; access for the disabled; plants for sale; tea, coffee, home-made cakes
FEATURES   Fruit of special interest; herbs; good topiary; physic garden; award-winning maze
ENGLISH HERITAGE GRADE   II*

Three acres of tightly designed gardens full of variety. A Tudor bulb garden, modelled on Hampton Court; a Physic garden for herbs; Edwardian skittle alley; grass labyrinth; beautiful old lawns, yew hedges and walls alive with clever modern colour-conscious planting. Ethereally English.

Cliveden
Taplow, Maidenhead SL6 0JA
☎ 01628 605069   📠 01628 669461

OWNER   The National Trust
LOCATION   2 miles north of Taplow, M4 Jct 7
OPEN   11 am – 6 pm; daily; 1 March to 2 November. 11 am – 4 pm; daily; 3 November to 31 December
ADMISSION   Adults (Grounds) £4.50; (House) £1; Children half price

FACILITIES Parking; dogs permitted; loos; access for the disabled; National Trust shop, Wednesday – Sunday; light refreshments and meals, Wednesday – Sunday

FEATURES Herbaceous borders; fruit of special interest; modern roses; garden sculpture; snowdrops; woodland garden; plantings by Graham Thomas; particularly interesting in winter; good autumn colour; tallest *Juglans cinerea* (24m.) in the British Isles; distinguished head gardener (Philip Cotton)

ENGLISH HERITAGE GRADE I

NCCPG NATIONAL COLLECTIONS *Catalpa*

A vast landscape garden, just stuffed with whatever money could buy: balustrading from the Villa Borghese in Rome, the dramatic 'Fountain of Love' and a huge parterre below the house, now dully planted by the National Trust. The best bits are the Arcadian ilex wood, quite magical, and newly restored rose garden, originally made by Geoffrey Jellicoe in 1932.

Great Barfield

Bradenham, High Wycombe HP14 4HP
☎ 01494 563741

OWNER Richard Nutt

LOCATION Turn into village from A4010 at Red Lion and first right – ½ a mile

OPEN 2 pm – 5 pm, 23 February. 2 pm – 6 pm, 6 April. 2 pm – 6 pm, 6 July. 2 pm – 5 pm, 15 September. And by appointment.

ADMISSION Adults £1.50; Children (under 16) Free

FACILITIES Parking; access for the disabled; plants for sale; home-made teas

FEATURES Herbaceous borders; plantsman's garden; old roses; snowdrops; woodland garden; particularly interesting in winter; wonderful hellebores in February; lilies (notably martagons) naturalising; colchicums; good autumn colour & fruits

NCCPG NATIONAL COLLECTIONS *Iris unguicularis*; *Leucojum*; *Ranunculus ficaria*

One of the best modern plantsman's gardens in southern England, not least because it is beautifully designed, labelled and maintained. Whatever the season, Great Barfield amazes the visitor by the number and variety of plants in flower and their thoughtful placing.

Hughenden Manor

High Wycombe HP14 4LA
☎ 01494 532580

OWNER The National Trust

LOCATION 1½ miles north of High Wycombe

OPEN 1 pm – 5 pm; Saturdays & Sundays in March; Wednesday – Sunday plus Bank Holiday Mondays from 2 April to 31 October

ADMISSION House & garden £3.80; Garden only £1

FACILITIES Parking; loos; facilities for the disabled; National Trust shop; refreshments

FEATURES Herbaceous borders; 61 old apple varieties; rolling parkland; formal Victorian parterres with bright bedding out as in Disraeli's day

ENGLISH HERITAGE GRADE II

Not a great garden, but interesting for its association with Disraeli. The garden was made by his wife c.1860 and is a classic formal design of its period. Recently restored, using photographs taken in 1881, the parterre is once again planted with Victorian bedding.

The Manor House, Bledlow

Bledlow, Princes Risborough HP27 9PB

OWNER Lord & Lady Carrington

LOCATION Off B4009

OPEN 2 pm – 6 pm; for NGS. And by appointment

ADMISSION £3

FACILITIES Parking; access for the disabled; plants for sale

FEATURES Herbaceous borders; fruit of special interest; lake; modern roses; old roses; garden sculpture

One of the best gardens of our times: beautifully planted and well maintained. The kitchen garden is particularly impressive, with a gazebo in the middle. Fun collection of modern sculptures. Lord Carrington was the star of Rosemary Verey's series *The English Country Garden* on BBC2 last year.

Stowe Landscape Gardens

Stowe, Buckingham MK18 5EH
☎ 01280 822850   📠 01280 822437

OWNER The National Trust

LOCATION 3 miles north-west of Buckingham

OPEN 10 am – 5 pm or dusk (last admissions 4 pm); daily; 1 to 5 January; 24 March to 2 November, but closed on Tuesdays, Thursdays & Saturdays from 15 April to 5 July and from 10 September to 2 November

ADMISSION Adults £4.20; Family ticket £10.50; Groups by prior arrangement. Music & fireworks 18-20 July

FACILITIES Parking; dogs permitted; loos; facilities for the disabled; plants for sale at weekends; light meals 11 am – 5 pm

FEATURES Landscape designed by Capability Brown; worked on by Kent; particularly interesting in winter; Temple of Concord & Victory restored and re-opened (1996); tallest *Fraxinus angustifolia* 'Lentiscifolia' (24m.) and largest × *Crataemespilus grandiflora* (9m.) in the British Isles

ENGLISH HERITAGE GRADE I

Mega landscape, considered by some the most important in the history of gardens. The National Trust acquired control from the boys' public school six years ago, and the restoration will take many years. Go if you have not been already, and go again if you have. Stowe is not obvious: stomp round slowly, and contemplate the history and symbolism of each feature. Read the National Trust's excellent guide and then go round again, this year, next year, every year, and commune with the *genius loci*.

Turn End

Townside, Haddenham, Aylesbury HP17 8BG
☎ 01844 291383

OWNER Mr & Mrs Peter Aldington

LOCATION Turn at Rising Sun in Haddenham, then 300 yds on left. Park in street

OPEN 10 am – 4 pm; Wednesdays in June. 2 pm – 6 pm, 30 March, 5 May & 14 September for NGS. Groups by appointment

ADMISSION   Adult £1.50; Children 50p; guided groups £2.50
FACILITIES   Loos; plants for sale; refreshments on NGS days
FEATURES   Plantsman's garden; rock garden; old roses; ferns; grasses; brilliant design

Only one acre, but never was space so used to create an illusion of size. A brilliant series of enclosed gardens, sunken or raised, sunny or shady, each different and yet harmonious, contrasts with lawns, borders and glades. Much featured in the glossies, and deservedly.

Waddesdon Manor

Aylesbury HP18 0JH
☎ 01296 651226   [FAX] 01296 651142

OWNER   The National Trust
LOCATION   A41 Bicester & Aylesbury; 20 miles from Oxford
OPEN   10 am – 5 pm; Wednesday – Sunday & Bank Holiday Mondays; 1 March to 21 December
ADMISSION   Grounds only: Adults £3; Children (5 – 17) £1.50; under 5 Free
FACILITIES   Parking; loos; facilities for the disabled; plants for sale; gift & wine shop; tea-room
FEATURES   Herbaceous borders; daffodils; lake; particularly interesting in winter
ENGLISH HERITAGE GRADE   II*

A grand park, splendid formal gardens, a rococo aviary and extravagant bedding are the first fruits of restoring the grounds of this amazing Rothschild palace. An exciting addition to the National Trust's portfolio of historic gardens.

West Wycombe Park

West Wycombe HP14 3AJ
☎ 01494 488675

OWNER   The National Trust
LOCATION   West end of West Wycombe on A40
OPEN   2 pm – 6 pm; Sunday – Thursday; 1 June to 31 August. Also, Gardens only, Sundays, Wednesdays & Bank Holidays from 30 March to 31 May
ADMISSION   Adults £2.50
FACILITIES   Parking; loos; facilities for the disabled
FEATURES   Follies and garden buildings; lake; garden sculpture
ENGLISH HERITAGE GRADE   I

Early landscape park, with a lake in the shape of a swan. Classical temples and follies, plus three modern eye-catchers designed by Quinlan Terry.

The Wheatsheaf

Weedon HP22 4NS
☎ 01296 641581

OWNER   Mrs W Witzmann
LOCATION   2 miles north of Aylesbury
OPEN   By appointment; all year
ADMISSION   £1
FACILITIES   Parking; plants for sale; wide range of meals & refreshments
FEATURES   Plantsman's garden; fine old walnut tree

Neat and busy garden made by the present owners of the Inn since 1985 on 3½ acres of open field and woodland. There is an emphasis upon winter colour from evergreens and heathers, but a profusion of flowers in spring and summer too.

CAMBRIDGESHIRE

Abbots Ripton Hall

Abbots Ripton
☎ 014873 555   [FAX] 014873 545

OWNER   Lord De Ramsey
LOCATION   Off B1090
OPEN   2 pm – 6 pm; five days (details to be announced), May to August
ADMISSION   Adults £2; Children (under 16) £1
FACILITIES   Parking; loos; access for the disabled; plants for sale; teas
FEATURES   Irises; grey border; Chinese bridge; trellis work; tallest *Pyrus pyraster* (12m.) in the British Isles; new rose garden planted by Peter Beales
ENGLISH HERITAGE GRADE   II

Humphrey Waterfield, Lanning Roper and Jim Russell all worked here, and few garden owners have had as many gardening friends as Lord & Lady De Ramsey, who made and remade this garden over more than 50 years. The result is a garden of stylish individuality – as witness the gothic trellis work and the bobbles of yellow philadelphus – but also of great unity: pure enchantment.

Anglesey Abbey

Lode CB5 9EJ
☎ 01223 811200

OWNER   The National Trust
LOCATION   Off B1102
OPEN   11 am – 5.30 pm (last entry 4.30 pm); Wednesday – Sunday, plus Bank Holiday Mondays; 22 March to 2 November. Plus Mondays & Tuesdays from 7 July to 7 September. Closed Good Friday
ADMISSION   Adults: £3.20; Groups (12+) £2.50 (not Sundays or Bank Holiday Mondays). Evening walks with head gardener (phone for dates & details)
FACILITIES   Parking; loos; facilities for the disabled; plants for sale; National Trust shop; licensed restaurant & picnic area
FEATURES   Herbaceous borders; garden sculpture; snowdrops; landscaping on the grandest scale; long avenues of trees; dahlias; cyclamen; good autumn colour
ENGLISH HERITAGE GRADE   II*

Sixty years old, no more, but the grounds at Anglesey already deserve to be famous, for they are the grandest made in England this century. Majestic avenues and 35 acres of grass are the stuff of it: visit Anglesey when the horse chestnuts out and tulips glow in the meadows. Large formal gardens, carved out of the flat site by yew hedges, house the first Lord Fairhaven's collection of homoerotic sculpture. Then there are smaller gardens, said to be more intimate, where thousands of dahlias and hyacinths hit the eye: glorious or vainglorious, Anglesey has no match.

Cambridge University Botanic Garden

Cory Lodge, Bateman Street, Cambridge CB2 1JF

☎ 01223 336265   FAX 01223 336278

OWNER   University of Cambridge

LOCATION   Entrance on Bateman Street, 1 mile to the south of the City Centre

OPEN   10 am – 4 pm in winter, (5 pm in spring & autumn, 6 pm in summer); daily, except Christmas Day & Boxing Day

ADMISSION   Adults £1.50; Senior Citizens & Children £1

FACILITIES   Loos; facilities for the disabled; light refreshments

FEATURES   Good collection of trees; herbaceous borders; ecological interest; glasshouses and conservatories to visit; lake; particularly good in July-August; particularly interesting in winter; important rock garden; species roses; tallest *Broussonetia papyrifera* (15m.) in the British Isles (and 22 other record trees)

ENGLISH HERITAGE GRADE   II*

NCCPG NATIONAL COLLECTIONS   *Alchemilla; Bergenia; Fritillaria; Geranium; Lonicera; Ribes; Ruscus; Saxifraga; Tulipa*

FRIENDS   A very active association – contact the Friends Administrator 01223 336271

One of the best botanic gardens in the world for the way it matches amenity and public recreation to education, research, conservation, ecology, systematic taxonomy and horticultural excellence. The two rock gardens, one limestone and the other sandstone, are particularly successful and alone worth a long journey. For all-round interest, Cambridge B G runs close to Kew, Wisley and Edinburgh.

Clare College Fellows' Garden

Clare College, Cambridge CB2 1TL

☎ 01223 333222   FAX 01223 333219

OWNER   The Master & Fellows

LOCATION   Enter from Clare Old Court, Trinity Lane or Queens Road

OPEN   11 am – 4.30 pm; daily; April to September

ADMISSION   £1.50

Clare has the best herbaceous borders in Cambridge, splendid in July and August.

Crossing House Garden

Meldreth Road, Shepreth, Royston SG8 6PS

☎ 01763 261071

OWNER   Mr & Mrs D G Fuller

LOCATION   8 miles south of Cambridge off A10

OPEN   Dawn – dusk; daily; all year

ADMISSION   Donation to NGS

FACILITIES   Parking; dogs permitted; access for the disabled

FEATURES   Plantsman's garden

One of the wonders of modern gardening, the Crossing House celebrates the achievements of its makers over the last 30 years, on an unpropitious site right beside the main line to Cambridge. It contains over 5000 varieties of plant, densely planted in the cottage style. Peat beds, screes, arches, topiary, pools and raised beds are some of the features which add variety to the most intensely and intensively planted small garden in England. And every few minutes a London express whizzes past.

Docwra's Manor

Shepreth, Royston SG8 6PS

☎ 01763 260235/261557

OWNER   Mrs John Raven

LOCATION   Off A10 to Shepreth

OPEN   10 am – 4 pm; Wednesdays and Fridays; all year; 2 pm – 4 pm, first Sunday of April to October. And by appointment. See also Yellow Book

ADMISSION   £2 (£3 for special openings)

FACILITIES   Parking; loos; access for the disabled; plants for sale; teas for NGS openings

FEATURES   Herbaceous borders; plantsman's garden; modern roses; old roses; Mediterranean plants

Very much a plantsman's garden, whose lush profusion defies the dry, cold site. Docwra's Manor is a series of small gardens – walled, wild, paved and so on – each brimming with rarities. Unstructured and informal, and yet the garden *works*. Do read John Raven's charming and erudite *The Botanist's Garden*, now in print again.

Elton Hall

Peterborough PE8 6SH

☎ 01832 280468   FAX 01832 280584

OWNER   Mr & Mrs William Proby

LOCATION   A605, 8 miles west of Peterborough

OPEN   2 pm – 5 pm; Wednesdays; June. Also Thursdays & Sundays in July & August, plus 25 & 26 May and 24 & 25 August. 2 pm – 6 pm on 29 June for Rose 2000 Appeal

ADMISSION   House & garden: Adults £4; Children £2. Garden only: Adults £2; Children £1

FACILITIES   Parking; loos; plants for sale; tea-room

FEATURES   Good collection of trees; herbaceous borders; old roses; handsome hedges; good colour plantings; new gothic orangery (1996)

ENGLISH HERITAGE GRADE   II*

The house is a castellated monstrosity, but the Victorian gardens have been energetically restored in recent years and make Elton highly visitable. The knot garden and the collection of old roses are the high spots, best in June.

Hardwicke House

High Ditch Road, Fen Ditton, Cambridge CB5 8TF

☎ 01223 292246

OWNER   John Drake

LOCATION   ¾ mile from village crossroad

OPEN   For NGS, & by appointment

ADMISSION   £1.50

FACILITIES   Plants for sale

FEATURES   Herbaceous borders; plantsman's garden; bulbs

NCCPG NATIONAL COLLECTIONS   *Aquilegia*

Essentially a plantsman's garden with an emphasis on herbaceous plants, roses and bulbs. The owner has a particular interest in Asia Minor, as witness an area devoted to Turkish bulbs.

Padlock Croft

West Wratting CB1 5LS

☎ 01223 290383

OWNER   Peter & Susan Lewis

LOCATION   2½ miles off B1307 (was A604) between Linton & Horseath

OPEN   10 am – 6 pm; Wednesday – Saturday plus Bank Holiday Mondays; April to 15 October or by appointment

ADMISSION   Donation

FACILITIES   Parking; access for the disabled; plants for sale

FEATURES   Plantsman's garden; rock garden; new shade garden (1994)

NCCPG NATIONAL COLLECTIONS Adenophora; Campanula; Platycodon; Symphyandra

One acre of plantsmanship, 'interesting' rather than 'exquisite' say the owners. But they do themselves an injustice, because this is a fascinating garden. Plants are crammed in, growing where they will do best. Not only are there four National Collections, but a nursery as well, specialising in Campanulaceae. Visit from mid-June onwards, when the campanulas are a knock-out.

Peckover House

North Brink, Wisbech PE13 1JR

☎ & ☏ 01945 583463

OWNER   National Trust

LOCATION   Signposted from Wisbech

OPEN   House & Garden: Saturdays, Sundays & Wednesdays. Garden: Saturdays & Tuesdays; 6 April to 27 October

ADMISSION   House & garden: Adult £3; Children £1.50. Garden only: Adult £2; Children £1

FACILITIES   Parking; loos; facilities for the disabled; plants for sale

FEATURES   Victorian shrubberies; orangery; fernery; Malmaison carnations; new centenary border (1996); tallest Acer negundo (18m.) in the British Isles

ENGLISH HERITAGE GRADE   II

Charming example of a not-too-grand Victorian garden, complete with monkey puzzle, fernery and spotted laurel shrubberies. One of the orange trees in the conservatory is 200 years old.

Wimpole Hall

Arrington, Royston SG8 0BW

☎ 01223 207257   ☏ 01223 207838

OWNER   The National Trust

LOCATION   On A603, south-west of Cambridge

OPEN   1 pm – 5 pm; Tuesday – Thursday, Saturdays & Sundays; 25 March to 5 November. Bank Holiday Sundays & Mondays 11 am – 5 pm

ADMISSION   House & garden: £5. Garden: £2. Park: Free

FACILITIES   Parking; loos; facilities for the disabled; National Trust shop; restaurant & tea-room

FEATURES   Landscape designed by Capability Brown; daffodils; landscape designed by Humphry Repton; old roses; woodland garden; interesting for children; Chinese bridge; current holder of Sandford Award

ENGLISH HERITAGE GRADE   I

NCCPG NATIONAL COLLECTIONS Juglans

A classical 18th-century landscape where Bridgeman, Brown and Repton have all left their mark. The grand Victorian parterres have been restored and are brightly planted with traditional bedding-out.

CHESHIRE

Adlington Hall

Macclesfield SK10 4LF

☎ 01625 829206   ☏ 01625 828756

OWNER   Mrs C J C Legh

LOCATION   5 miles north of Macclesfield off A523

OPEN   By prior appointment only

ADMISSION   House & gardens: Adults £4; Children £1.50; groups (25+) £3.50

FACILITIES   Parking; dogs permitted; loos; access for the disabled; gift shop and home produce; tea-room, home made cakes, scones

FEATURES   Follies and garden buildings; woodland garden

ENGLISH HERITAGE GRADE   II*

An old avenue of lime trees, planted in 1688 to celebrate the accession of William and Mary, leads to a woodland 'wilderness' with follies. These include a Shell Cottage, a Temple to Diana, a Chinese bridge and a Hermitage. The new owners are restoring these buildings, and have plans for further developments. A new maze and rose garden were opened last year.

Arley Hall & Gardens

Great Budworth, Northwich CW9 6NA

☎ 01565 777353   ☏ 01565 777465

OWNER   Viscount Ashbrook

LOCATION   5 miles west of Knutsford

OPEN   12 noon – 5 pm; Tuesday – Sunday; 28 March to 28 September

ADMISSION   Adults £3.30; OAPs £2.90; Children (5-16) £1.70

FACILITIES   Parking; dogs permitted; loos; access for the disabled; plants for sale; shop; lunches & light refreshments

FEATURES   Herbaceous borders; old roses; good topiary; woodland garden; HHA/Christie's Garden of the Year in 1987; grove garden expanded (1995)

ENGLISH HERITAGE GRADE   II*

FRIENDS   New Friends of Arley Hall & Gardens. Talks, events and voluntary projects. Details from The Membership Secretary, 54 High Street, Great Budworth, Cheshire. CW9 6HF

Arley has pleached limes, red Primula florindae, clipped ilex cylinders (30 feet high) and pretty old roses. But its claim to fame is the double herbaceous border, backed and buttressed by yew hedges, one of the oldest and still one of the best in England.

Bridgemere Garden World

Bridgemere, Nantwich CW5 7QB

☎ 01270 521100   ☏ 01270 520215

OWNER   J Ravenscroft

LOCATION   On A51 south of Nantwich

OPEN 10 am – 8 pm (5 pm in winter); daily; all year except 25 & 26 December
ADMISSION Adults £1.50; Children & OAPs £1
FACILITIES Parking; loos; access for the disabled; plants for sale; several shops, as well as the famous garden centre; refreshments
FEATURES Herbaceous borders; fruit of special interest; glasshouses and conservatories to visit; herbs; lake; plantsman's garden; rock garden; modern roses; old roses; woodland garden; young garden; particularly good in July-August

More than twenty immaculate show gardens in different styles and the television set of Gardeners' Diary are just some of Bridgemere's innumerable attractions: definitely worth a visit, whatever the season.

Capesthorne Hall
Siddington, Macclesfield SK11 9JY
☎ 01625 861221   FAX 01625 861619

OWNER W A Bromley-Davenport
LOCATION A34, 3 miles south of Alderley Edge
OPEN 12 noon – 6 pm; Wednesdays, Sundays & Bank Holidays; 1 March to 31 October
ADMISSION Adults £4; Children £1.50; OAPs £3.50
FACILITIES Parking; loos; facilities for the disabled; small gift shop; tea-rooms
FEATURES Good collection of trees; lake; woodland garden; historic park

Classic English landscape, with some pretty modern planting by Vernon Russell-Smith by the lakes, a 19th-century arboretum and formal gardens.

Cholmondeley Castle Gardens
Malpas SY14 8AH
☎ 01829 720383   FAX 01829 720519

OWNER The Marchioness of Cholmondeley
LOCATION Off A49 Tarporley-Whitchurch road
OPEN 12 noon – 5.30 pm; Sundays & Bank Holiday Mondays. Plus 12 noon – 5 pm on Wednesdays & Thursdays. 28 March to 28 September
ADMISSION Adults £2.50; Senior Citizens £2; Children 75p
FACILITIES Parking; dogs permitted; loos; facilities for the disabled; plants for sale; gift shop; tea-room, light lunches, home-made teas
FEATURES Good collection of trees; herbaceous borders; follies and garden buildings; lake; rock garden; woodland garden; Japanese cherry walk; rhododendrons
ENGLISH HERITAGE GRADE II

Handsome early 19th-century castle in rolling parkland, redeveloped since 1960s with horticultural advice from Jim Russell. The new plantings have been well integrated into the classical landscape. The exquisite temple garden, curling the whole way around a small lake, is breathtakingly beautiful. Highly recommended.

Dorfold Hall
Nantwich CW5 8LD
☎ 01270 625245   FAX 01270 628723

OWNER R C Roundell

LOCATION 1 mile west of Nantwich on A534
OPEN 2 pm – 5 pm; Tuesdays & Bank Holiday Mondays; 1 April to 31 October. See also Yellow Book
ADMISSION House & gardens: Adults £3; Children £1.50
FACILITIES Parking; dogs permitted
FEATURES Bluebells; rhododendrons and azaleas; woodland garden
ENGLISH HERITAGE GRADE II

William Nesfield designed the formal approach but the main reason for visiting the gardens is the new woodland garden of rhododendrons and other shrubs, leading down to a stream where *Primula pulverulenta* has naturalised in its thousands. Do not miss the incredible hulk of an ancient Spanish chestnut in the stable yard.

Granada Arboretum
Jodrell Bank, Macclesfield SK11 9DL
☎ 01477 571339   FAX 01477 571695

OWNER Manchester University
LOCATION On A535 between Holmes Chapel and Chelford
OPEN 10.30 am – 5.30 pm; daily; 15 March to 26 October. 11 am – 4.30 pm; Saturdays & Sundays; 1 November to 14 March
ADMISSION Grounds, Science Centre & Planetarium: Adults £3.80; Senior Citizens £2.70; Children £2
FACILITIES Parking; loos; access for the disabled; shop; self-service cafeteria
FEATURES Good collection of trees; Heather Society's *Calluna* collection
NCCPG NATIONAL COLLECTIONS *Malus*; *Sorbus*

Originally known as the Jodrell Bank Arboretum and founded by Sir Bernard Lovell in 1971, this arboretum specialises in alders, birches, crab apples, pine and *Sorbus*. Long straight drives lead spaciously into the distance, by way of large collections of heaths (*Erica* and heathers (*Calluna*). The plantings are young and vigorous, the groupings imaginative. A huge radio telescope dominates the site: an awesome presence.

Hare Hill Garden
Garden Lodge, Over Alderley, Macclesfield SK10 4QB
☎ 01625 828981

OWNER The National Trust
LOCATION Between Alderley Edge and Prestbury
OPEN 10 am – 5.30 pm; Wednesdays, Thursdays, Saturday, Sundays & Bank Holiday Mondays (but daily from 12 May to 2 June); 29 March to 29 October
ADMISSION Adults: £2.50; Children £1.25
FACILITIES Parking; loos
FEATURES Herbaceous borders; plantsman's garden; rock garden; woodland garden

Basically, a woodland garden, thickly planted with trees and underplanted with rhododendrons, azaleas and shrubs by Jim Russell in the 1960s. In the middle is a walled garden which has been developed as a flower garden with a pergola, arbour and tender plants against the walls. Planting continues: much *Rhododendron ponticum* has been cleared recently and replaced by new cultivars. Best in May but there are still some rhododendrons to flower with the roses in July.

Little Moreton Hall

Congleton CW12 4SD
☎ 01260 272018

OWNER The National Trust
LOCATION 4 miles south of Congleton on A34
OPEN 12 noon - 5.30 pm; Wednesday - Sunday; 22 March to 2 November. Plus 11 am - 5.30 pm on Bank Holiday Mondays and 12 noon - 4 pm on Saturdays & Sundays from 8 November to 21 December
ADMISSION Adults: £3.80; Children £1.90
FACILITIES Parking; loos; access for the disabled; plants for sale; restaurant - lunches, coffee, teas
FEATURES Herbaceous borders; fruit of special interest; herbs; plantings by Graham Thomas
ENGLISH HERITAGE GRADE I

Little Moreton Hall is the handsomest timber-framed house in England. When the National Trust asked Graham Thomas to design and plant a suitable period garden, he specified box-edged parterres with yew topiary and gravel infilling - and very fine they are too. In the kitchen garden, a speciality has been made of old varieties of fruit and vegetables. Peaceful, charming and orderly.

Lyme Park

Disley SK12 2NX
☎ 01663 762023   FAX 01663 765035

OWNER The National Trust
LOCATION 6½ miles south-east of Stockport on A6, just west of Disley
OPEN 11 am - 5 pm; daily; 29 March to 31 October. 12 noon - 4 pm; Saturdays & Sundays; 1 November to 21 December
ADMISSION Garden only: Adults £2; Children £1; Car £3.30
FACILITIES Parking; loos; facilities for the disabled; shop; light refreshments from Easter to October
FEATURES Herbaceous borders; follies and garden buildings; lake; old roses; spring bulbs; bedding out; newly restored Edwardian rose garden (1996); orangery by Wyatt; 'Dutch' garden
ENGLISH HERITAGE GRADE II*
NCCPG NATIONAL COLLECTIONS Vicary Gibbs plants

There is much of horticultural interest at Lyme, as well as the razzmatazz of a country park: traditional bedding out, two enormous camellias in the conservatory, and a Jekyll-type herbaceous border by Graham Thomas whose colours run from orange to deepest purple. Best of all is the sunken Dutch garden whose looping box and ivy parterres contain the most extravagant bedding displays. The National Trust has now assumed full control of the garden and begun to restore the structure. Lyme Park featured as Pemberley in the BBC's *Pride & Prejudice*.

Ness Botanic Gardens

Neston L64 4AY
☎ 0151 353 0123   FAX 0151 353 1004

OWNER University of Liverpool
LOCATION Signed off A540, Chester to Hoylake

OPEN 9.30 am - 4 pm; daily; 1 November to 28 February. 9.30 am - dusk; daily; 1 March - 31 October
ADMISSION Adults £3.60; Senior Citizens & Students £2.60. (1996 prices). RHS members Free
FACILITIES Parking; loos; facilities for the disabled; plants for sale; gift shop; two restaurants
FEATURES Good collection of trees; fine conifers; glass-houses and conservatories to visit; lake; rock garden; old roses; tallest *Alnus cremastogyne* (3.3m.) in the British Isles
ENGLISH HERITAGE GRADE II
FRIENDS Membership of the 7,500-strong Friends of Ness Gardens gives lectures, a newsletter, and a seed list (max 10 pkts). Contact Dr Joanna Sharples

Ness was started by A.K. Bulley, who sponsored George Forrest the plant collector, and it was here that many Chinese plants were first grown in Europe - notably candelabra primulas. It retains the sense of being a private garden not a botanic one. The borders and shrubberies teem with interesting plants: rhododendrons, *Sorbus*, lilies, willows, roses, heathers and conifers - including a magnificent *Sequoia sempervirens* 'Adpressa'. The rock garden is particularly well planted, and the mild climate and acid soil allow a wide variety of different plants to flourish. Ness is one of those gardens where you tend to spend much longer than you intended.

Norton Priory Museum & Gardens

Tudor Road, Runcorn WA7 1SX
☎ 01928 569895

OWNER Norton Priory Museum Trust (Cheshire County Council)
LOCATION Well signposted locally
OPEN 12 noon - 5 pm (but 6 pm at weekends & Bank Holidays); weekdays; 1 March - 31 October
ADMISSION Adults £2.90; Senior Citizens £1.60
FACILITIES Parking; loos; facilities for the disabled; plants for sale; garden produce shop; refreshments at museum site
FEATURES Herbaceous borders; fruit of special interest; herbs; rock garden; modern roses; old roses; collection of *Cydonia* varieties; current holder of Sandford Award; old pear orchard recently restored (1994)

A new layout in the old walled garden, modelled on 18th-century precedents and intended to instruct and please modern visitors. A cottage garden border, medicinal herb garden and orchard rub shoulders with colour borders, children's gardens and a scented garden. Beyond are 16 acres of woodland garden with Georgian summerhouses and glades by the stream.

Penn

Macclesfield Road, Alderley Edge SK9 7BT
☎ 01625 583334

OWNER R W Baldwin
LOCATION ¾ mile east of Alderley village on B5087
OPEN 2 pm - 5 pm; 4, 5, 25 & 26 May
ADMISSION Adults £2; Senior Citizens £1.50; Children 50p
FACILITIES Loos; plants for sale; light refreshments
FEATURES Camellias; rhododendrons and azaleas; woodland garden; magnolias; embothriums

Penn is famous for its rhododendrons, thickly planted in the woods above the house, and the wide views across the lawns to the valley. But the range of good plants is very wide, and the collections of magnolias and camellias also comprehensive.

Peover Hall

Over Peover, Knutsford
☎ 01565 722656

OWNER   R Brooks Ltd
LOCATION   3 miles south of Knutsford
OPEN   2 pm – 4.30 pm; Mondays & Thursdays (but not Bank Holidays); 1 May to 30 September
ADMISSION   Garden only on Thursdays: Adults £2; Children £1. House & garden: Adults £3; Children £1.50
FACILITIES   Parking; loos; access for the disabled; refreshments on Mondays only
FEATURES   Herbs; old roses; good topiary; walled garden; landscaped park; rhododendrons
ENGLISH HERITAGE GRADE   II

First a classic 18th-century parkland, then an Edwardian overlay of formal gardens – yew hedges and brick paths. Now Peover has modern plantings too – borders in colour combinations, a herb garden, and a rhododendron dell in the woods.

Reaseheath College

Nantwich CW5 6DF
☎ 01270 625131   [FAX] 01270 625665

OWNER   Rease Heath College
LOCATION   1 mile north of Nantwich on A51
OPEN   1.30 pm – 5 pm; Wednesdays; 24 May to 2 August. Plus College Open Days 12.30 pm – 5.30 pm on 18 & 19 May
ADMISSION   Donation
FACILITIES   Parking; loos
FEATURES   Good collection of trees; herbaceous borders; lake; rhododendrons and azaleas; rock garden; modern roses; woodland garden; heather garden; candelabra primulas

Formal gardens, island beds, a woodland garden and a lake with water lilies: there is much to enjoy and learn from here.

Rode Hall

Church Lane, Scholar Green, Stoke on Trent ST7 3QP
☎ 01270 882961   [FAX] 01270 882962

OWNER   Sir Richard Baker Wilbraham
LOCATION   5 miles south-west of Congleton between A34 and A50
OPEN   2 pm – 5 pm; Tuesday-Thursday & Bank Holidays; 31 March to 30 September
ADMISSION   Garden only: £2
FACILITIES   Parking; dogs permitted; loos; plants for sale; garden produce
FEATURES   Fine conifers; follies and garden buildings; fruit of special interest; old roses; good topiary; woodland garden; ice house; rhododendrons; grotto
ENGLISH HERITAGE GRADE   II

Landscaped by Repton c.1790 and given a formal garden by Nesfield in 1860, the main horticultural interest comes from the massed banks of azaleas and rhododendrons in the late Victorian 'Wild Garden'.

Stapeley Water Gardens Ltd

London Road, Stapeley, Nantwich CW5 7LH
☎ 01270 623868   [FAX] 01270 624919

OWNER   Stapeley Water Garden Ltd
LOCATION   A51, 1 mile south of Nantwich
OPEN   10 am – 5.30 pm (5 pm in winter); daily; all year except 25 December
ADMISSION   Palms Tropical Oasis: Adults £3.35; Senior Citizens £2.50; Children £1.65
FACILITIES   Parking; loos; facilities for the disabled; cafeteria & terrace restaurant
FEATURES   Glasshouses and conservatories to visit; interesting for children; particularly interesting in winter; collection of hardy water lilies; Victoria amazonica, the giant water lily
NCCPG NATIONAL COLLECTIONS   Nymphaea

Part entertainment, part nursery and part display garden, the Palms Tropical Oasis is worth a visit in its own right. A long rectangular pool in the Moorish style is flanked by tall palms, strelitzias and other showy tropical flowers. Visit in winter.

Tatton Park

Knutsford
☎ 01565 750780   [FAX] 01565 650179

OWNER   The National Trust (managed by Cheshire County Council)
LOCATION   Off M6 Jct 19 and M56 Jct 7 – well signposted
OPEN   10.30 am – 6 pm (but 4 pm from 24 October to 31 March); Tuesday – Sunday, plus Bank Holiday Mondays; all year
ADMISSION   Adults £2.50; Children £1.50; Family £7.50
FACILITIES   Parking; loos; facilities for the disabled; plants for sale; shop; hot meals & snacks (summer only)
FEATURES   Good collection of trees; herbaceous borders; landscape designed by Capability Brown; follies and garden buildings; lake; landscape designed by Humphry Repton; rhododendrons & azaleas in May; biggest Quercus × schochiana in the British Isles; work starting (1996) on restoring kitchen garden; current holder of Sandford Award; Europa Nostra award for restored orangery & fernery
ENGLISH HERITAGE GRADE   II*
NCCPG NATIONAL COLLECTIONS   Adiantum; Inula

Humphry Repton laid out the parkland. Joseph Paxton designed both the formal Italian garden and the exquisite fernery, claimed as the finest in the United Kingdom. Later came a Japanese garden and Shinto temple, such follies as the African hut, and the mass plantings of rhododendrons and azaleas. Tatton Park is wonderfully well organised for visitors, and gets better every year. Be prepared for a long and absorbing visit.

Tirley Garth Trust

Utkinton, Tarporley CW6 0LZ
☎ 01829 732301   [FAX] 01829 732265

OWNER   The Tirley Garth Trust
LOCATION   2½ miles north of Tarporley, just north of Utkinton on road to Kelsall
OPEN   2 pm – 6 pm; 11, 18, 25 & 26 May, 1 June
ADMISSION   Adults £2.50; Children 50p

FACILITIES Parking; dogs permitted; loos; facilities for the disabled; plants for sale; home baking, home-made ices
FEATURES Herbaceous borders; rhododendrons and azaleas; rock garden; modern roses; woodland garden
ENGLISH HERITAGE GRADE II
FRIENDS Friends of Tirley Garth: details available from the gardens

Famous example of Thomas Mawson's work: wonderful terraces, paths, retaining walks and garden buildings. Good rhododendrons and azaleas in the woodland below.

CORNWALL

Antony House
Torpoint PL11 2QA
☎ & ℻ 01752 812364

OWNER The National Trust
LOCATION 5 miles west of Plymouth, 2 miles north-west of Torpoint
OPEN 1.30 pm – 5.30 pm; Tuesday – Thursday & Bank Holidays; April to October; also Sundays from June to August
ADMISSION Adults £3.80; Children £1.80
FACILITIES Parking; loos; access for the disabled; tea-room
FEATURES Herbaceous borders; landscape designed by Capability Brown; fine conifers; lake; landscape designed by Humphry Repton; magnolias; yew hedges; William Pye water sculpture (1996); tallest Japanese loquat *Eriobotrya japonica* (8m.) in the British Isles (and two other tree records)
ENGLISH HERITAGE GRADE II
NCCPG NATIONAL COLLECTIONS *Hemerocallis*

A classic 18th-century landscape, influenced by Humphry Repton, in a superb position above the Tamar estuary. Yew hedges nearer the house enclose modern plantings while the kitchen garden houses the vast National Collection of *Hemerocallis* or day lilies – some 575 cultivars!

Antony Woodland Garden
Antony House, Torpoint PL11 2QA
☎ & ℻ 01752 812364

OWNER The Carew Pole Garden Trust
LOCATION 5 miles west of Plymouth, 2 miles north-west of Torpoint
OPEN 11 am – 5.30 pm; daily; March to October
ADMISSION Adults £2; Accompanied Children Free
FACILITIES Parking; loos; tea-room
FEATURES Fine conifers; lake; plantsman's garden; woodland garden; camellias; magnolias; rhododendrons & azaleas

This is the 'Cornish' part of the grounds at Antony, still controlled by the Carew Pole family rather than the National Trust. They have planted it with the best modern forms of rhododendrons, azaleas, magnolias, camellias and other trees.

Bosvigo
Bosvigo Lane, Truro TR1 3NH
☎ & ℻ 01872 275774

OWNER Wendy & Michael Perry
LOCATION ¾ mile from Truro centre. Turn off A390 at Highertown near Sainsbury roundabout then 500 yds down

OPEN 11 am – 6 pm; Wednesday – Saturday; 1 March to 30 September. Plus 1 June for Cornwall Macmillan Fund, 29 June for NGS & 20 July for South-west Children's Hospice
ADMISSION Adults £2; Children 50p
FACILITIES Parking; loos; plants for sale
FEATURES Herbaceous borders; plantsman's garden; woodland garden; young garden; unusual perennials; Victorian conservatory; colour borders

Not a typical Cornish garden, the emphasis at Bosvigo is upon herbaceous plants, chosen for all their qualities and planted in fine colour combinations. Many are rare: some for sale.

Burncoose Gardens
Gwennap, Redruth TR16 6BJ
☎ 01209 861112   ℻ 01209 860011

OWNER F J Williams CBE
LOCATION On A393 between Lanner and Ponsanooth
OPEN 9 am – 5 pm (open 11 am on Sundays); Monday to Saturday; all year
ADMISSION Adults £2; Children Free
FACILITIES Parking; dogs permitted; loos; access for the disabled; important nursery adjacent; teas & light refreshments
FEATURES Bluebells; camellias; plantsman's garden; rhododendrons and azaleas; woodland garden; magnolias; rare trees & shrubs

Thirty acres of traditional Cornish woodland garden, planted with ancient rhododendrons and handsome trees, but re-invigorated by extensive shrub planting since 1981 – the result of a partnership between the Williams family and Cornwall's leading nurseryman.

Caerhays Castle Gardens
Gorran, St Austell PL26 6LY
☎ 01872 501310   ℻ 01872 501870

OWNER F J Williams
LOCATION Between Mevagissey & Portloe
OPEN 11 am – 4 pm; Monday – Friday; 17 March to 2 May. Charity openings: 30 March, 20 April, 5 May
ADMISSION Adults £3; Children (under 14) £1.50
FACILITIES Parking; dogs permitted; loos; plants for sale; tea-rooms & beach shop/café in car park
FEATURES Good collection of trees; fine conifers; plantsman's garden; woodland garden; camellias; magnolias; rhododendrons; tallest specimen of *Emmenopterys henryi* (17m.) in the British Isles, and 37 further record-breaking trees (including eight *Acer* species)
ENGLISH HERITAGE GRADE II*

The Williams family subscribed to many of the great plant collecting expeditions and the fruits of their labours flourish at Caerhays. Wilson and Forrest are represented by thousands of trees and shrubs, and one of the joys of Caerhays is to stumble upon magnificent old specimens deep in its 100 acres of woodland. There are splendid collections of *Nothofagus* and *Lithocarpus* as well as the three genera for which Caerhays is famous – magnolias, camellias and rhododendrons. The original × *williamsii* camellias still flourish, including 'J.C. Williams', 'Mary Christian' and 'St. Ewe'. There is much to discover at Caerhays: allow plenty of time.

Carclew Gardens

Perran-ar-Worthal, Truro TR3 7PB

☎ 01872 864070

OWNER Mrs Robert Chope

LOCATION A39 east at Perran-ar-Worthal, 1 mile to garden

OPEN 2 pm – 5.30 pm; 13, 20, 27 April, 3, 12, 18 & 25 May

ADMISSION Adults £2; Children 50p; Groups by appointment

FACILITIES Parking; loos; home-made teas

FEATURES Lake; modern roses; garden sculpture; woodland garden; rhododendrons; tallest *Pseudolarix amabilis* (23m.) in the British Isles

ENGLISH HERITAGE GRADE II

The gardens first opened to the public in 1927 and have continued to do so for charity every year since then. Vast hummocks of old rhododendrons, some grown from Sir Joseph Hooker's Himalayan collections nearly 150 years ago. Good trees, including a large gingko and a *Quercus* × *hispanica* which looks different from 'Lucombeana'. Mrs Chope has been busy with replanting and restoring: the waterfall is now fully restored.

Carwinion

Mawnan Smith, Falmouth TR11 5JA

☎ 01326 250258

OWNER Anthony Rogers

LOCATION From Mawnan Smith, turn left at Red Lion, 500 yds up hill on right

OPEN 10 am – 5.30 pm; daily or by appointment; all year

ADMISSION £2

FACILITIES Parking; dogs permitted; loos; plants for sale

FEATURES Fine conifers; lake; subtropical plants; woodland garden; 100 species of bamboo; gunnera; bluebells; new Fern Garden in the old quarry (1995)

10 acres of Cornish jungle, exotically thick with rhododendrons, camellias, Drimys and the largest collection of bamboos in the south-west.

Chyverton

Zelah, Truro TR4 9HD

☎ 01872 540324

OWNER Nigel Holman

LOCATION 1 mile south-west of Zelah on A30

OPEN By appointment; March to June

ADMISSION Adults £3.50; Children (under 16) Free; Groups (20+) £3

FACILITIES Parking; dogs permitted; loos

FEATURES Fine conifers; lake; plantsman's garden; woodland garden; magnolias, including four record-breakers; nothofagus; extensive new planting (1995)

ENGLISH HERITAGE GRADE II

The garden of a distinguished plantsman who is also a landscaper with plants. Magnolias are a special interest: several Chyverton seedlings now bear cultivar names. Many other established plants have also been grown from seed: rhododendron hybrids from Brodick, for instance, and *Eucalyptus nicholii* from a wild collection. But there is much more to interest the plantsman. A large *Berberidopsis corallina* and

a lanky red-stemmed hedge of *Luma apiculata* below the house are both outstanding. And the planting continues.

Cotehele

St Dominick, Saltash PL12 6TA

☎ 01579 351346   FAX 01579 351222

OWNER The National Trust

LOCATION 14 miles from Plymouth via Saltash

OPEN 11 am – 5.30 pm (dusk if earlier); daily; all year

ADMISSION 28 March – 2 November £2.80; rest of year, £1 donation

FACILITIES Parking; loos; facilities for the disabled; plants for sale; National Trust gift shop; restaurant for meals and drinks

FEATURES Good collection of trees; daffodils; lake; modern roses; good topiary; woodland garden; palms; ferns; pretty dovecote; largest *Davidia involucrata* in the British Isles

ENGLISH HERITAGE GRADE II

Broad Victorian terraces below the house support many tender climbers such as *Jasminum mesnyi* while the beds beneath have wallflowers and roses. Down the wooded valley are camellias, rhododendrons and shade-loving plants which thrive in an ancient woodland, kept damp by a small stream. Much gentle restoration and renewal in recent years.

Glendurgan Gardens

Helford River, Mawnan Smith, Falmouth TR11 5TR

☎ 01326 250906

OWNER The National Trust

LOCATION 1 mile west of Mawnan Smith, west to Trebah

OPEN 10 am – 5.30 pm (last admissions 4.30 pm); Tuesday – Saturday, plus Bank Holidays except Good Friday; 1 March to 31 October

ADMISSION £3

FACILITIES Parking; loos; plants for sale; small shop; teas & light lunches

FEATURES Fine conifers; lake; subtropical plants; woodland garden; laurel maze; wild flowers; huge tulip tree; tallest *Eucryphia lucida* (13m.) in the British Isles; new path opened for National Trust Centenary (1995); new Bhutanese valley planting (1996)

ENGLISH HERITAGE GRADE II

A steep, sub-tropical valley garden on the Helford River with a good collection of old rhododendrons and camellias. Glendurgan also boasts an extraordinary 1830s maze of clipped cherry laurel, which the National Trust has recently restored. A lovely garden, almost best when just viewed from the top – but the temptation to wander down and into it is irresistible!

Headland

Polruan-by-Fowey PL23 1PW

☎ 01726 870243

OWNER Jean & John Hill

LOCATION Find Polruan: go to the bottom of Fore Street, along West Street, left up Battery Lane to end

OPEN 2 pm – 6 pm; Thursdays; June to September

ADMISSION Adults £1; Children 50p

FACILITIES Cream teas in garden

A cliff garden with the sea on three sides and its own sandy beach, Headland is a lesson in what will tolerate salt-laden winds: aloes, eucalyptus, acacias, foxgloves, columbines and junipers. Only 1¼ acres, but it seems much larger.

The Lost Gardens of Heligan
Pentewan, St Austell PL26 6EN
☎ 01726 844157/843566 🖷 01726 843023

OWNER   Heligan Gardens Ltd
LOCATION   St Austell to Mevagissey Road, following brown tourist signs
OPEN   10 am – 6 pm; daily; all year
ADMISSION   Adults £3.40; Senior Citizens £2.90; Children £2
FACILITIES   Parking; dogs permitted; loos; facilities for the disabled; plants for sale; tea-room with sandwiches, salads, etc.
FEATURES   Follies and garden buildings; rhododendrons and azaleas; rock garden; subtropical plants; woodland garden; beautiful ferny gully
ENGLISH HERITAGE GRADE   II
FRIENDS   Friends subscription £15.00 includes newsletters

Heligan – the accent is on the i – calls itself 'The Lost Gardens of Heligan' and has been spectacularly rescued from a jungle of neglect. To date the restoration team has uncovered the Italian garden, the Crystal Grotto, the wishing well, the Bee Boles, a Melon Garden, the Sundial Garden and other authentic features. The enthusiasm of the restorers is infectious and their achievements are already substantial. They are also brilliant at getting financial support and publicity, even if the reality does not always match the hype.

Ken Caro
Bicton, Liskeard PL14 5RF
☎ 01579 362446

OWNER   Mr & Mrs K R Willcock
LOCATION   Signed from A390, midway between Callington & Liskeard
OPEN   2 pm – 6 pm; Sunday – Wednesday; 14 April to 26 June; plus Tuesdays & Wednesdays in July & August
ADMISSION   £2
FACILITIES   Parking; loos; plants for sale
FEATURES   Herbaceous borders; fine conifers; oriental features; plantsman's garden; aviary and waterfowl; lots of new plantings (1995)

Started in 1970 as two acres of intensely planted formal gardens in different styles, and extended in 1993 by taking in a further 2 acres. Very much a plantsman's garden with good herbaceous plants and shrubs, not at all a typical Cornish garden. The owners are flower arrangers: look for architectural plants and original combinations.

Lamorran House
Upper Castle Road, St Mawes TR2 5BZ
☎ 01326 270800   🖷 01326 270801

OWNER   Mr & Mrs Robert Dudley-Cooke
LOCATION   ½ a mile from village centre
OPEN   Wednesdays & Fridays; 1 April to 1 October. Plus 27 April, 11 May & 1 June for charity. And by appointment
ADMISSION   Adults £2.50; Children Free
FACILITIES   Parking; loos; plants for sale

FEATURES   Good collection of trees; herbaceous borders; follies and garden buildings; lake; oriental features; plantsman's garden; subtropical plants; young garden

Made since 1980 on a steep site above the sea and tightly designed in the Italian style, but also full of unusual plants. An English Mediterranean garden in Cornwall, say the owners, a mainland Tresco. One of their latest ventures is a bank planted with cacti and succulents. Definitely a garden to watch.

Lanhydrock
Bodmin PL30 5AD
☎ 01208 73320   🖷 01298 74084

OWNER   The National Trust
LOCATION   2½ miles south-east of Bodmin
OPEN   11 am – 5.30 pm (5 pm in October); daily (but house closed on Mondays); 1 March to 2 November
ADMISSION   House & garden £6. Garden only £3. Children half price
FACILITIES   Parking; loos; plants for sale; National Trust shop; restaurant & bar, cream teas
FEATURES   Herbaceous borders; good topiary; woodland garden; Victorian parterres; spring bulbs
ENGLISH HERITAGE GRADE   II*
NCCPG NATIONAL COLLECTIONS   Crocosmia

A grand mansion, mainly 19th-century with one of the best formal gardens in Cornwall – clipped yews, box parterres and bedding out, as well as large herbaceous borders which contain the National Collection of crocosmias. The woodlands behind are impressive for their size and colourful rhododendrons in spring. But it is the magnolias which impress the visitor most: 140 different species and cultivars.

Lanterns
Restronguet, Mylor Bridge TR11 5ST
☎ 01326 372007

OWNER   Mrs Irene Chapman
LOCATION   Follow signs to Restronguet from Mylor Bridge: on right just before the waterfront
OPEN   11 am – dusk; daily; all year
ADMISSION   Collection box
FACILITIES   Parking; dogs permitted; plants for sale
FEATURES   Plantsman's garden

Plantsman's garden with a wide range of subjects that flourish in the mild climate but tolerate salt-bearing winds.

Mount Edgcumbe Gardens
Cremyll, Torpoint PL10 1HZ
☎ 01752 822236   🖷 01752 822199

OWNER   Cornwall County Council & Plymouth City Council
LOCATION   At the end of the B3247 in south-east Cornwall, or by ferry from Plymouth
OPEN   Formal gardens & park: dawn to dusk; all year. House & Earl's Garden: 11 am – 5 pm; Wednesday – Sunday; 3 April to 31 October
ADMISSION   House & Earl's Garden: Adults £3.50. Formal gardens & park: Free

FACILITIES Parking; dogs permitted; loos; facilities for the disabled; gift and book shops; camellias for sale; orangery restaurant in formal gardens
FEATURES Good collection of trees; herbaceous borders; daffodils; follies and garden buildings; glasshouses and conservatories to visit; lake; subtropical plants; summer bedding; deer park; formal gardens; fern dell; genuine Victorian rose garden; tallest cork oak *Quercus suber* (26m.) in the British Isles
ENGLISH HERITAGE GRADE I
NCCPG NATIONAL COLLECTIONS *Camellia*
FRIENDS Contact Mrs. C. Gaskell Brown (01752 822236)

A long, stately grass drive runs down from the house to Plymouth Sound, through oak woods interplanted with large ornamental trees. Here is the National Collection of Camellias, meticulously labelled, which will eventually include all 32,000 known varieties. The formal gardens are right down on the waterside, protected by a clipped ilex hedge 30 feet high. There are no less than ten acres of gardens here, including an Italian garden (c.1790), a French garden (early Victorian), an American garden, a modern New Zealand garden complete with geyser, Milton's Temple, an orangery, a conservatory and the fern dell. Allow plenty of time to do justice to these majestic pleasure gardens.

Pencarrow
Washaway, Bodmin PL30 3AG
☎ 01208 841369

OWNER The Trustees of the Molesworth-St Aubyn Family
LOCATION 4 miles north-west of Bodmin – signed off the A389 at Washaway
OPEN 1.30 pm – 5 pm; Sunday – Thursday; Easter to 15 October. Open at 11 am on Bank Holiday Mondays & from 1 June to 10 September
ADMISSION House & Garden: Adults £4; Children £2. Garden only: Adults £2; Children Free
FACILITIES Parking; dogs permitted; loos; facilities for the disabled; plants for sale; craft centre; light lunches, cream teas
FEATURES Fine conifers; rock garden; old roses; Italian garden; rhododendrons; camellias
ENGLISH HERITAGE GRADE II

A long drive through rhododendrons and vast conifers leads to the pretty Anglo-Palladian house. Below is an Italian garden, laid out in the 1830s, and next to it a great granite rock garden where boulders from Bodmin Moor lie strewn among the trees and shrubs. Pencarrow is famous for its conifers: an ancestor planted one of every known variety in the mid 19th century and the survivors are so venerable that the great Alan Mitchell wrote a guide to them. Recent plantings have concentrated upon planting rhododendrons (over 700 of the best modern varieties) and adding new conifers to the old. It is good to see the fortunes of such a distinguished garden revived.

Penjerrick
Budock, Falmouth TR11 5ED
☎ 01872 870105

OWNER Mrs Rachel Morin
LOCATION 3 miles south-west of Falmouth, entrance at junction of lanes opposite Penmorvah Manor Hotel

OPEN 1.30 pm – 4.30 pm; Wednesdays, Fridays & Sundays; 1 March to 30 September
ADMISSION Adults £1; Children 50p
FACILITIES Parking; dogs permitted
FEATURES Lake; woodland garden; rhododendrons; camellias; tree ferns
ENGLISH HERITAGE GRADE II

Famous for the Barclayi and Penjerrick hybrid rhododendrons and now a mature woodland garden recovering well from a period of neglect: very Cornish. Last year the lower pond in the valley was reclaimed and restored.

Pine Lodge Gardens
Cuddra, St Austell PL25 3RQ
☎ 01726 73500

OWNER Mr & Mrs Raymond Clemo
LOCATION East of St Austell between Holmbush and Tregrehan
OPEN 1 pm – 5 pm; 25 May, 29 June & 27 July for charity. Groups (20+) by appointment at any time of year
ADMISSION Adults £2.50; Children £1. Guided groups £3
FACILITIES Parking; loos; access for the disabled; plants for sale; cream teas on charity days
FEATURES Good collection of trees; herbaceous borders; fine conifers; fruit of special interest; lake; plantsman's garden; garden sculpture; woodland garden; bog gardens; new lake & four-acre pinetum (1994/95); new maze (1996); new fernery (1996); Japanese garden (1997)
NCCPG NATIONAL COLLECTIONS *Grevillea*

A modern garden, rather different from the typical Cornish garden. There are rhododendrons and azaleas, of course, but they are planted and underplanted with other shrubs and herbaceous plants to create lasting colour effects. The pace of the garden's development is very exciting.

St Michael's Mount
Marazion TR17 0HT
☎ 01736 710507   FAX 01736 711544

OWNER Lord St Levan & The National Trust
LOCATION 1 mile south of Marazion
OPEN 10.30 am – 5.30 pm; Monday – Friday; 1 April to 31 May (plus most weekends during summer)
ADMISSION £2
FACILITIES Loos; plants for sale; refreshments
FEATURES Herbaceous borders; ecological interest; rock garden; subtropical plants; woodland garden; wild narcissus; naturalised kniphofias and agapanthus
ENGLISH HERITAGE GRADE II

A triumph of man's ingenuity in the face of Atlantic gales, salt spray and bare rock with sand for a garden soil. Careful experiment over the generations has enabled the owners to plant a remarkable garden of plants which resist the elements: *Luma apiculata*, rugosa roses, correas, nerines, Hottentot figs and naturalised agapanthus. On the north side, a sparse wood of sycamores and pines gives protection to camellias, azaleas and hydrangeas. Nigel Nicolson calls it 'the largest and loveliest rock-garden in England'. There is nothing rare about the plants: the wonder is that they grow at all.

Trebah Garden Trust
Mawnan Smith, Falmouth TR11 5JZ
☎ 01326 250448 📠 01326 250781

OWNER The Trebah Garden Trust
LOCATION 4 miles south-west of Falmouth, signposted from Hillhead roundabout on A39 approach to Falmouth
OPEN 10.30 am – 5 pm (last admission); daily; all year
ADMISSION Adults £3; Senior Citizens £2.80; Children (5 – 15 yrs) & disabled visitors £1; Children (under 5) Free. RHS members Free
FACILITIES Parking; dogs permitted; loos; access for the disabled; excellent nursery; coffee shop & picnic area
FEATURES Good collection of trees; herbaceous borders; fine conifers; lake; plantsman's garden; subtropical plants; woodland garden; interesting for children; particularly interesting in winter; Tarzan camp and Tarzan trails for children; access to private beach; massed hydrangeas; water garden restored (1995) with 5,000+ arum lilies and candelabra primulas; extensive new plantings of palms & succulents at the top of the water garden; tallest hardy palm *Trachycarpus fortunei* (15m.) in the British Isles and three other tree records; new Tasmanian tree fern glade (1994)
ENGLISH HERITAGE GRADE II
FRIENDS The Trebah Trust is a registered charity which aims to preserve the gardens for posterity: details from 01326 250448

Glorious Trebah! This lost garden has been vigorously restored and improved since the Hibberts bought it in 1980. The view from the top is magical – a secret valley which runs right down to the Helford estuary. Vast trees, natural and exotic, line the steep sides, while the central point is held by a group of elegant tall palms. Trebah is popular with children, whose curiosity is aroused by trails, quizzes and educational games. But it is a garden for all people and for all seasons – open every day of the year.

Tregrehan
Par PL24 2SJ
☎ 01726 812438 📠 01726 814389

OWNER T C Hudson
LOCATION 1 mile west of St Blazey on A390
OPEN 10.30 am – 5 pm; daily except Easter Sunday; mid-March to June
ADMISSION Adults £2.50; Children Free
FACILITIES Parking; loos; access for the disabled; plants for sale; teas
FEATURES Woodland garden; camellias; pinetum; walled garden; sunken garden
ENGLISH HERITAGE GRADE II*

An old Cornish garden whose 20 acres include a fine range of Victorian conservatories, tall conifers and lanky rhododendrons. But Tregrehan is best known for the camellias bred there by the late Gillian Carlyon, especially 'Jennifer Carlyon' which won her the Cory Cup from the RHS.

Trehane
Probus, Truro TR2 4JG
☎ 01872 520270

OWNER David & Simon Trehane
LOCATION Signposted from A39 by Tresillian Bridge
OPEN 2 pm – 5 pm; 23 March; 6 & 20 April; 4 & 18 May; 1, 15 & 29 June; 20 July; 3 & 17 August
ADMISSION Adults £1.50; Children Free
FACILITIES Parking; dogs permitted; loos; plants for sale; refreshments
FEATURES Herbaceous borders; fine conifers; plantsman's garden; woodland garden; bluebells

You would expect camellias from anyone called Trehane, and their eponymous garden has a fine collection. There is, however, no limit to their interests and there are many other good things here, especially magnolias, crocosmias, geraniums and other herbaceous plants.

Trelissick Garden
Feock, Truro TR3 6QL
☎ 01872 862090 📠 01872 865808

OWNER The National Trust
LOCATION Take B3289 off main Truro – Falmouth Road
OPEN 10.30 am – 5.30 pm, Monday – Saturday; 12.30 pm – 5.30 pm, Sunday; 1 March to 2 November; March & October closes at 5 pm
ADMISSION Adult £4; Children £2
FACILITIES Parking; loos; facilities for the disabled; gift and plant shop; refreshments
FEATURES Fine conifers; plantsman's garden; garden sculpture; woodland garden; particularly good in July-August; aromatic plant garden; fig garden; hydrangeas; new thatched summerhouse (1995); tallest tree fern *Dicksonia antarctica* (6m.) in the British Isles
ENGLISH HERITAGE GRADE II

Once famous for its fig garden, still maintained by the National Trust, Trelissick is particularly colourful in August and September when the hydrangeas are in full flower. There are over 100 varieties, some in a special walk. But venerable conifers and tender plants are also features: *Rosa bracteata* and *Yucca whipplei* are among the many good things to admire in summer, not to mention daffodils, rhododendrons and camellias in spring.

Trengwainton Gardens
Madron, Penzance TR20 8RZ
☎ 01736 63148 📠 01736 68142

OWNER Lt Col E T Bolitho & The National Trust
LOCATION 2 miles north-west of Penzance, ½ a mile west of Heamoor
OPEN 10.30 am – 5.30 pm (5 pm in March & October); Wednesday – Saturday & Bank Holidays; 1 March to 31 October
ADMISSION Adults £3; Children £1.50
FACILITIES Parking; dogs permitted; loos; facilities for the disabled; plants for sale; new National Trust shop; coffee, snacks, teas

FEATURES Lake; old roses; subtropical plants; woodland garden; lilies; acacias; *Myosotidium hortensia*; tree ferns; tallest *Xanthoceras sorbifolium* (7m.) in the British Isles (and two record trees)

ENGLISH HERITAGE GRADE II

Trengwainton has the best collection of tender plants on the Cornish mainland, all thanks to the Bolitho family who started planting seriously only in 1925. Much came from original seed from such collectors as Kingdon Ward: some rhododendrons flowered here for the first time in the British Isles, among them *RR. macabeanum, elliottii* and *taggianum*. The plants in many Cornish gardens are past their best. Not so at Trengwainton, where so many are in their prime. It is a garden to wander through slowly, giving yourself as much time as you need to enjoy its riches.

Trerice

Newquay TR8 4PG
☎ 01637 875404   📠 01637 879300

OWNER The National Trust
LOCATION 3 miles south-east of Newquay – turn right off A3058 at Kestle Mill
OPEN 11 am – 5.30 pm (5 pm in October); daily except Tuesdays & Saturdays (but open every day from 28 July to 7 September); 1 April to 31 October
ADMISSION House £3.80; Garden Free
FACILITIES Parking; loos; access for the disabled; plants for sale; National Trust shop; restaurant & tea-room
FEATURES Oriental features; modern roses; colour borders; good collection of apple trees; new summerhouse in orchard (1997)

A perfect West Country manor house with pretty Dutch gables, Trerice is unusual among Cornish gardens. It is small and comparatively formal: the design and herbaceous plantings are its best points. It is not surrounded by swirling rhododendron woodland. There is a perfect harmony between the Jacobean architecture and the gardens. Somewhat anomalously, it boasts the largest collection of mid-Victorian to current-day lawn mowers in the country. They are both interesting and fun.

Tresco Abbey

Isles of Scilly TR24 0QQ
☎ 01720 422849   📠 01720 422807

OWNER Robert Dorrien Smith
LOCATION Direct helicopter flight from Penzance
OPEN 10 am – 4 pm; daily; all year
ADMISSION Adults £5; Children (under 14) Free
FACILITIES Dogs permitted; loos; facilities for the disabled; plants for sale; shop; light refreshments
FEATURES Fine conifers; follies and garden buildings; plantsman's garden; subtropical plants; interesting for children; particularly good in July-August; particularly interesting in winter; cacti; succulents; South African, Australian and New Zealand plants; tallest *Luma apiculata* (20m.), *Metrosideros excelsa* (20m.) and *Cordyline australis* (15m.) in the British Isles

ENGLISH HERITAGE GRADE I

NCCPG NATIONAL COLLECTIONS *Acacia*

Tresco has recovered brilliantly from the Arctic weather of January 1987 and the hurricane of January 1990. Kew donated hundreds of plants and English Heritage helped to plant new shelter belts. The amazing profusion of exotica is intact. The helicopter service makes access easier than ever, but it does distract you while actually visiting the garden.

Trewithen

Grampound Road, Truro TR2 4DD
☎ 01726 883647   📠 01726 882301

OWNER A M J Galsworthy
LOCATION A390 between Probus and Grampound
OPEN 10 am – 4.30 pm; Monday – Saturday (& Sundays in April & May); 1 March to 30 September
ADMISSION Adults £2.80; Children £1.50; Groups (12+) £2.50. RHS members Free
FACILITIES Parking; dogs permitted; loos; facilities for the disabled; plants for sale; garden shop; tea-room with light refreshments
FEATURES Good collection of trees; herbaceous borders; camellias; plantsman's garden; rhododendrons and azaleas; woodland garden; magnolias; quarry garden; cyclamen; tallest *Magnolia campbellii* ssp. *mollicomata* (19m.) in the British Isles and sixteen more record-breaking tree species

ENGLISH HERITAGE GRADE II*

Trewithen's setting is magnificent. Instead of the steep terraces of most Cornish gardens, there is a spacious flat lawn that stretches 200 yards into the distance, with gentle banks of rhododendrons, magnolias and rare shrubs on all sides. It sets the tone for the garden's grandeur, which was entirely the work of George Johnstone in the first half of this century. Johnstone was a great plantsman. He subscribed to plant hunting expeditions, such as those of Frank Kingdon Ward. Note how he used laurel hedges to divide up the woodland and give structure to the garden. He also had an eye for placing plants to advantage. As a breeder, he gave us *Rhododendron* 'Alison Johnstone', *Ceanothus* 'Trewithen Blue' and *Camellia saluensis* 'Trewithen White'. The Michelin Guide gives Trewithen its top award of three stars – *vaut le voyage!*

Wetherham

St. Tudy, Bodmin PL30 3NJ
☎ & 📠 01208 851492

OWNER Mr & Mrs Richard Amor
LOCATION 1 mile south of St Tudy, signed from the road to St Mabyn
OPEN 10.30 am – 5 pm (or dusk if earlier); daily; all year except 23–25 December
ADMISSION Adults £2.50; Children £1.50
FACILITIES Parking; dogs permitted; loos; facilities for the disabled; plants for sale; new gift shop opening this year; tea-room by mill pond
FEATURES Follies and garden buildings; lake; old roses; good topiary; parterres

A forgotten garden, undergoing extensive restoration and set to rival Heligan. Some of the features so far uncovered are: a hexagonal walled rose garden; a shell grotto; a canal; knot gardens; dovecote. The planting is intended to emphasise its Carolean origins.

CUMBRIA

Acorn Bank Garden

Acorn Bank, Temple Sowerby, Penrith CA10 1SP
☎ 017683 61281   [FAX] 017683 61893

OWNER   The National Trust
LOCATION   North of Temple Sowerby, 6 miles east of Penrith on A66
OPEN   10 am – 5.30 pm; daily; 24 March to 2 November
ADMISSION   Adults £2.10; Children £1
FACILITIES   Parking; loos; facilities for the disabled; plants for sale; National Trust shop; light refreshments
FEATURES   Herbaceous borders; fruit of special interest; herbs; old roses; woodland garden; spring bulbs; woodland walk past Mill

Acorn Bank boasts the largest collection (250 varieties) of culinary and medicinal plants in north, but it is almost better visited in spring when thousands and thousands of daffodils fill the woodland slopes, and the fruit trees flower in the old walled garden. Best of all is the huge quince tree, a wondrous sight in flower or fruit.

Brantwood

Coniston LA21 8AD
☎ 015394 41396

OWNER   The Education Trust
LOCATION   East side of Coniston Water, 2½ miles from Coniston, 4 miles from Hawkshead
OPEN   11 am – 5.30 pm; daily; mid-March to mid-November. 11 am – 4 pm; Wednesday – Sunday; mid-November to mid-March
ADMISSION   House & garden: £3.25. Garden only: £1
FACILITIES   Parking; dogs permitted; loos; plants for sale; bookshop & craft gallery; meals, light refreshments & drinks all day
FEATURES   Lake; rhododendrons and azaleas; woodland garden; daffodils; bluebells
FRIENDS   Friends of Brantwood, very active, ring 015394 41396 for details

20 acres of woodland garden, laid out by John Ruskin from 1871 onwards and restored with a grant from the European Community. Working with natural materials, Ruskin accentuated the natural character of the site with woodland plantings and rhododendrons. Open plantings at the front of the house frame wonderful views across Coniston Water.

Dalemain

Penrith CA11 0HB
☎ 017684 86450   [FAX] 017684 86223

OWNER   Robert Hasell-McCosh
LOCATION   M6 (Jct 40), A66 (West 1m), A592
OPEN   11.15 am – 5.00 pm; Sunday – Thursday; 23 March to 5 October
ADMISSION   House & garden: £5. Gardens only: £3

FACILITIES   Parking; loos; facilities for the disabled; gift shop; small plant centre; morning coffee, light lunches, afternoon teas
FEATURES   Herbs; old roses; woodland garden; interesting for children; *Meconopsis*; old flower and fruit varieties; adventure playground; biggest *Abies cephalonica* in the British Isles
ENGLISH HERITAGE GRADE   II*
FRIENDS   Details from Dalemain Estate Office

This historic garden has a 16th-century terrace, and 17th-century parterre, and a kitchen garden with fruit trees planted 250 years ago. All have been beautifully restored and replanted with period flowers. Charming and not at all self-conscious.

Graythwaite Hall

Ulverston, Hawkshead LA12 8BA
☎ 015395 31248   [FAX] 015395 30060

OWNER   Graythwaite Estate Trustees
LOCATION   Between Newby Bridge and Hawkshead
OPEN   10 am – 6 pm; daily; 1 April to 30 June
ADMISSION   Adults £2; Children Free
FACILITIES   Parking; dogs permitted; loos
FEATURES   Good collection of trees; rock garden; modern roses; old roses; good topiary

Thomas Mawson on home ground and at his best. Formal gardens by the house drop down to sweeping lawns; beyond the stream is a woodland with rhododendrons and azaleas.

Holehird Gardens

Lakeland Horticultural Society, Patterdale Road, Windermere LA23 1NP
☎ 01539 446008

OWNER   Lakeland Horticultural Society
LOCATION   1 mile north of Windermere town, off A592
OPEN   Dawn – dusk; daily; all year
ADMISSION   Donation (min. £1)
FACILITIES   Parking; loos
FEATURES   Glasshouses and conservatories to visit; herbs; lake; rock garden; woodland garden; heathers; roses; hostas; ferns; Victorian garden; walled garden; excellent new herbaceous border (1995)
NCCPG NATIONAL COLLECTIONS *Astilbe*; *Hydrangea*; *Polystichum*
FRIENDS   The Lakeland Horticultural Society is a registered charity: details from the Secretary

A demonstration and trial garden, maintained almost entirely by local volunteers to promote appropriate horticultural practices for the Lake District. Particularly good to see what flourishes in a cool damp climate: alpines, azaleas, heathers, ferns and much, much more.

Holker Hall

Cark-in-Cartmel, Grange-over-Sands LA11 7PL
☎ 015395 58328   [FAX] 015395 58776

OWNER   Lord Cavendish of Furness
LOCATION   Jct 36 off M6, follow brown and white tourist signs
OPEN   10 am – 6 pm (last admission 4.30 pm); Sunday – Friday; 1 April to 30 October

ADMISSION Adults £3.15; Children £1.80 (under 6 Free). (1996 prices)

FACILITIES Parking; loos; facilities for the disabled; plants for sale; shop; clocktower cafeteria (licensed)

FEATURES Modern roses; old roses; woodland garden; rhododendrons; formal gardens; fine limestone cascade & fountain; new beech walk (1996); HHA/Christie's Garden of the Year in 1991; tallest *Ilex latifolia* (15m.) in the British Isles (and two other tree records)

ENGLISH HERITAGE GRADE II*

NCCPG NATIONAL COLLECTIONS *Styracaceae*

19th-century formal gardens below the house with scrumptious herbaceous borders. The woodland has rhododendrons and splendid trees: Joseph Paxton supplied a monkey puzzle and Lord George Cavendish the cedars grown from the seeds he brought back from the Holy Land.

Hutton-in-the-Forest
Skelton, Penrith CA11 9TH
☎ 017684 84449   [FAX] 017684 84571

OWNER Lord Inglewood

LOCATION 3 miles from Jct 41 of M6 on B5305

OPEN House: 1 pm – 4 pm; 30–31 March, then Thursdays, Fridays, Sundays, Bank Holiday Mondays & August Wednesdays from May to September. Gardens: 11 am – 5 pm; all year except Saturdays

ADMISSION House & gardens: Adults £3.50; Children (7 – 16) £1.50. Gardens only: Adults £2; Children Free

FACILITIES Parking; dogs permitted; loos; refreshments when house open

FEATURES Herbaceous borders; good topiary; woodland garden; rhododendrons; herbaceous borders in the walled garden

ENGLISH HERITAGE GRADE II

Handsomely sited house with high Victorian terraces and grand views across the valley. Romantic parkland and good modern plantings. A garden to watch.

Levens Hall
Kendal LA8 0PD
☎ 015395 60321   [FAX] 015395 60669

OWNER C H Bagot

LOCATION 5 miles south of Kendal on A6

OPEN 11 am – 5 pm; Sunday – Thursday; 30 March to 30 September

ADMISSION House & garden: Adults £4.80; Children £2.50. Garden only: Adults £3; Children £1.80 (1996 prices)

FACILITIES Parking; loos; access for the disabled; gift shop and plant centre; light lunches & teas

FEATURES Good topiary; interesting for children; spring & summer bedding; new fountain garden; HHA/Christie's Garden of the Year in 1994

ENGLISH HERITAGE GRADE I

Levens means topiary: huge overgrown chunks of box and yew left over from a simple formal parterre laid out in 1694 and supplemented by golden yews in the 19th century. The arbours and high yew hedges, some of them crenellated, are spangled with *Tropaeolum speciosum* and the parterres

planted annually with 15,000 plants, which makes Levens one of the best places to study the expensive art of bedding out. Well maintained.

Lingholm
Keswick CA12 5UA
☎ 01768 772003   [FAX] 01768 775213

OWNER The Viscount Rochdale

LOCATION 2 miles west of Keswick, signed from A66

OPEN 10 am – 5 pm; daily; 28 March to 31 October

ADMISSION Adults £2.80; Children Free; Groups (20+) £2.40

FACILITIES Parking; loos; facilities for the disabled; plants for sale; tea-room from 11 am, for morning coffee, light lunches, teas

FEATURES Fine conifers; old roses; rhododendrons; azaleas; daffodils

Set on the hillside above Derwentwater, the main feature of Lingholm is its rhododendron and azalea woodland. The trees include fine conifers yet the overall impression is of naturalness and peace.

Muncaster Castle
Ravenglass CA18 1RQ
☎ 01229 717614   [FAX] 01229 717010

OWNER Mrs P R Gordon-Duff-Pennington

LOCATION A595 1 mile east of Ravenglass on west coast of Cumbria

OPEN Grounds: 11 am – 5 pm; daily; all year; Castle: 1 pm – 4 pm; Sunday – Friday; 16 March to 2 November

ADMISSION Gardens: Adults £3.40; Children £1.90; Family (2+2) £9 (1996 prices)

FACILITIES Parking; dogs permitted; loos; facilities for the disabled; plants for sale; two gift shops; snacks & full meals

FEATURES Fine conifers; woodland garden; rhododendrons; camellias; maples; tallest *Nothofagus obliqua* (31m.) in the British Isles; lots of new plantings

ENGLISH HERITAGE GRADE II*

Visit Muncaster in May, when the rhododendrons are at their peak. Many are grown from the original seed introduced by such plant hunters as Forrest and Kingdon Ward in the 1920s and 1930s. Muncaster also has a developing collection of hardy hybrid rhododendrons. The castle was revamped 150 years ago: its steep slopes and the lakeland hills behind create an intensely romantic landscape.

Rydal Mount
Ambleside LA22 9LU
☎ 015394 33002   [FAX] 015394 31738

OWNER Rydal Mount Trust (Wordsworth Family)

LOCATION 1½ miles north of Ambleside on A591, turn up Rydal Hill

OPEN 9.30 am – 5 pm, 1 March to 31 October; 10 am – 4 pm, 1 November to 28 February

ADMISSION Adults £3; Children £1; OAPs, Groups (10+) & Students £2.50. Garden only: £1.50

FACILITIES Parking; dogs permitted; loos

FEATURES Lake; trees; rhododendrons; newly-found terrace (Dora Wordsworth's?) undergoing restoration (1996)

ENGLISH HERITAGE GRADE   II

Kept very much as it was in the poet's day, the garden at Rydal Mount is a memorial to William Wordsworth. He believed that a garden should be informal in its design, harmonise with the country and keep its views open.

Sizergh Castle

Kendal LA8 8AE

☎ 015396 60070

OWNER   The National Trust

LOCATION   3½ miles south of Kendal

OPEN   12.30 pm – 5.30 pm; Thursday – Sunday; 1 April to 31 October

ADMISSION   Castle & garden: £3.80. Garden only: £2

FACILITIES   Parking; loos; facilities for the disabled; plants for sale; tea-room from 1.30 pm

FEATURES   Herbaceous borders; wildflower meadow; tender plants

ENGLISH HERITAGE GRADE   II*

NCCPG NATIONAL COLLECTIONS *Asplenium scolopendrium*; *Cystopteris*; *Dryopteris*; *Osmunda*

One of the best National Trust gardens, with lots of interest from wild daffodils and alpines in April to hydrangeas and a hot half-hardy border in September – *Beschorneria yuccoides*, *Buddleia colvilei*. Best of all is the 1920s rock garden, made of local limestone, whose dwarf conifers and Japanese maples have grown to a great size.

DERBYSHIRE

Calke Abbey

Ticknall DE7 1LE

☎ 01332 863822

OWNER   The National Trust

LOCATION   10 miles south of Derby in village of Ticknall

OPEN   11 am – 5 pm; Saturday – Wednesday; 29 March to 2 November

ADMISSION   £2.20

FACILITIES   Parking; loos; facilities for the disabled; National Trust gift shop; restaurant

FEATURES   Herbaceous borders; fruit and vegetables of special interest; dahlias; good Victorian-style bedding; deer park; horse-chestnut trees; local varieties of apples & soft fruit; newly restored orangery with glass dome (1996); vinery fully restored (1997)

ENGLISH HERITAGE GRADE   II*

The 'sleeping beauty' house is not really matched by its garden, but when funds are available it will be replanted in the early 19th-century style, with period ornamental and fruit varieties, a physic garden and an orangery. The drive runs along a magnificent avenue of ancient limes. In the walled garden is the only surviving Auricula Theatre, originally built to display the perfection of these beautiful 'florist's' plants.

Chatsworth

Bakewell DE45 1PP

☎ 01246 582204   [FAX] 01246 583536

OWNER   Chatsworth House Trust

LOCATION   8 miles north of Matlock off B6012

OPEN   11 am – 5 pm; daily; 19 March to 2 November

ADMISSION   Adults £3.50; Senior Citizens £3; Children £1.75; Family ticket £9

FACILITIES   Parking; dogs permitted; loos; facilities for the disabled; plants for sale in Potting Shed Shop, in Orangery; self-service restaurant, licensed

FEATURES   Good collection of trees; landscape designed by Capability Brown; lake; rhododendrons and azaleas; rock garden; modern roses; garden sculpture; good topiary; woodland garden; interesting for children; pinetum; maze; tulip tree avenue; adventure playground; tallest *Pinus strobus* (42m.) in the British Isles

ENGLISH HERITAGE GRADE   I

FRIENDS   Season ticket available, ring 01264 582204

Everyone knows of Chatsworth: 105 acres of Capability Brown, a 'conservative wall' to keep the heat and ripen fruit trees, Paxton's rockeries (huge boulders surrounded by conifers), a serpentine hedge with yews of different hues, enormous *Camellia reticulata* 'Captain Rawes' with trunks 80 cms thick, and of course the famous long cascade. But there is so much more: well run and fun for all the family. New maze and kitchen garden opened in 1994.

Dam Farm House

Ednaston, Ashbourne DE6 3BA

☎ 01335 360291

OWNER   Mrs Jean Player

LOCATION   Turn off A52 to Bradley, opposite Ednaston Lane end

OPEN   1.30 pm – 4 pm; 25 May; 8 & 22 June; 13 July & 10 August. And by appointment 1 April to 31 October

ADMISSION   Adults £2; Children Free

FACILITIES   Parking; loos; access for the disabled; plants for sale; for NGS Sundays

FEATURES   Good collection of trees; old roses; scree garden

Mrs Player (born a Loder) has made this outstanding garden on a greenfield site since 1980. The design is firm, and the planting exuberant. Rare plants abound, but it is their treatment which makes the garden such an exciting place to visit and learn from: their planting, training and cultivation are a model for our times.

Darley House

Darley Dale, Matlock DE4 3BP

☎ 01629 733341

OWNER   Mr & Mrs G H Briscoe

LOCATION   On A6, 2 miles north of Matlock

OPEN   For NGS, and by appointment

ADMISSION   Adults £1.50; Children Free

FACILITIES   Parking; loos; access for the disabled; plants for sale; picture gallery; light refreshments

FEATURES   Herbaceous borders; plantsman's garden

Basically a modern, plantsman's garden, just over an acre, but planted with good colour sense and commendable restraint. Interesting too because it belonged to Sir Joseph Paxton in the 1840s and his layout still gives the whole garden its structure. Restoration continues.

Elvaston Castle County Park

Borrowash Road, Elvaston DE72 3EP

☎ 01332 571342   [FAX] 01332 758751

OWNER   Derbyshire County Council

LOCATION   5 miles south-east of Derby. Signed from A6 and A52

OPEN   Dawn – dusk (Old English Garden, 9 am – 5 pm); daily; all year

ADMISSION   Gardens free. Car park 60p midweek, £1.20 weekends, coaches £6

FACILITIES   Parking; dogs permitted; loos; facilities for the disabled; two gift shops; restaurant open all year 10 am – 4.30 pm

FEATURES   Herbaceous borders; lake; old roses; good topiary; particularly interesting in winter

ENGLISH HERITAGE GRADE   II*

A historic garden, once famous for its topiary, and saved from oblivion by Derby County Council 25 years ago. The parterres have been replaced and the walled garden replanted with roses and herbaceous plants, and renamed the Old English Garden.

Haddon Hall

Bakewell DE45 1LA

☎ 01629 812855   [FAX] 01629 814379

OWNER   The Duke of Rutland

LOCATION   1½ miles south of Bakewell on A6

OPEN   11 am – 5.45 pm; daily except Sundays in August; 27 March to 30 September

ADMISSION   House & Garden: Adults £4.75; Senior Citizens £3.90; Children £2.95; Groups (20+) £3.75. Parking 50p

FACILITIES   Parking; loos; coffee, lunch, afternoon teas

FEATURES   Herbaceous borders; good topiary; roses of every kind; clematis; delphiniums; Christie's/HHA Garden of the Year in 1994

ENGLISH HERITAGE GRADE   I

Terraced neo-Tudor gardens to complement a castellated Elizabethan prodigy house. Fine balustrading and old yews, spring bulbs and herbaceous borders but, above all, roses, roses, roses.

Hardwick Hall

Doe Lea, Chesterfield S44 5QJ

☎ 01246 852353   [FAX] 01246 854200

OWNER   The National Trust

LOCATION   Signposted from M1 Jct 29

OPEN   Gardens: 12 noon – 5.30 pm; daily; 1 April – 31 October. Hall: 12.30 pm – 4.30 pm; Wednesdays, Thursdays, Saturdays, Sundays

ADMISSION   Hall & garden: Adults £5.50; Children £2. Garden only: Adults £2.50; Children £1

FACILITIES   Parking; loos; facilities for the disabled; plants for sale; weekend plant sales only; refreshments Wed/Thurs/Sat/Sun when Hall is open

FEATURES   Herbaceous borders; herbs; old roses; daffodils; fine hedges; mulberry walk; hollies; herb garden newly re-planted (1995)

ENGLISH HERITAGE GRADE   I

NCCPG NATIONAL COLLECTIONS Scabiosa caucasica

The formal gardens are extensive: avenues of hornbeam and yew and a newly restored 'Elizabethan' (actually 1970s) herb

garden (lavender and eglantine) in the kitchen garden. Hardwick has wonderful old fruit trees, mulberries, old roses and modern borders in the Jekyll style. In the park are fine cedars and Hungarian oaks. This is one of the best National Trust gardens, and getting still better.

Kedleston Hall

Derby DE22 5JH

☎ 01332 842191   [FAX] 01332 841972

OWNER   The National Trust

LOCATION   5 miles north-west of Derby

OPEN   11 am – 6 pm; Saturday – Wednesday; 29 March to 2 November. Plus 5 June for NGS.

ADMISSION   Adults £4.50; Children £2.20. Park & garden only £2

FACILITIES   Parking; loos; access for the disabled; National Trust shop; lunches & teas, licensed

FEATURES   Lake; rhododendrons and azaleas; modern roses; handsome Adam orangery

ENGLISH HERITAGE GRADE   I

The landscaped park runs down to a long lake: impressive and important. The pleasure gardens are neither, but quite jolly in a National Trust sort of way.

Lea Gardens

Lea, Matlock DE4 5GH

☎ 01629 534380   [FAX] 01629 534260

OWNER   Mr & Mrs J Tye

LOCATION   3 miles south-east of Matlock

OPEN   10 am – 7 pm; daily; 20 March to 6 July

ADMISSION   Adults £2.50; Children 50p; Season ticket £3.50. Wheelchair-bound free

FACILITIES   Parking; dogs permitted; loos; plants for sale; light lunches & teas

FEATURES   Rhododendrons and azaleas

This is the garden of a rhododendron lover: over 650 varieties as well as kalmias, magnolias, maples and dwarf conifers. Best in May, when it is frankly spectacular.

Melbourne Hall

Melbourne DY3 1EN

☎ 01332 862502   [FAX] 01322 862263

OWNER   Lord Ralph Kerr

LOCATION   8 miles south of Derby

OPEN   2 pm – 6 pm; Wednesdays, Saturdays, Sundays & Bank Holiday Mondays; 1 April to 30 September

ADMISSION   Adults £3; OAPs £2

FACILITIES   Parking; loos; access for the disabled; shop; refreshments

FEATURES   Herbaceous borders; lake; garden sculpture; turf terracing; grand avenues; new Visitors' Centre

ENGLISH HERITAGE GRADE   I

Near-perfect example of an early 18th-century garden, influenced by Le Nôtre. Statues, gravel, bassins, lumpy old hedges and the famous yew tunnel.

Renishaw Hall
Renishaw, Sheffield S31 9WB
☎ 01246 432042/0777 860755
OWNER   Sir Reresby Sitwell
LOCATION   2½ miles from M1 Jct 30
OPEN   10.30 am – 4.30 pm; Friday – Sunday, plus Bank Holiday Mondays; 5 April to 15 September
ADMISSION   Adults £3; Senior Citizens £2; Children £1
FACILITIES   Parking; dogs permitted; loos; access for the disabled; plants for sale; small tea-rooms
FEATURES   Herbaceous borders; fine conifers; lake; modern roses; old roses; woodland garden; daffodils; Italian garden
ENGLISH HERITAGE GRADE   II*

Lots of horticultural interest, including a good collection of shrub roses, but best for the formal Italian garden laid out by Sir George Sitwell c.1900, and at last appreciated as a meticulous and scholarly creation.

DEVON

Arlington Court
Arlington, Barnstaple EX31 4LP
☎ 01271 850296   FAX 01271 850625
OWNER   The National Trust
LOCATION   8 miles north of Barnstaple on A39
OPEN   11 am – 5.30 pm; Sunday – Friday; 28 March to 2 November
ADMISSION   House & Gardens: Adult £4.90; Children £2.40. Gardens only: Adults £2.60; Children £1.30
FACILITIES   Parking; dogs permitted; loos; facilities for the disabled; National Trust shop; restaurant & tea-rooms
FEATURES   Fine conifers; huge old rhododendrons; Victorian walled garden restored & reopened (1995)
ENGLISH HERITAGE GRADE   II

Mature parkland on a dead flat site in front of a fine Georgian house. Pretty Victorian formal garden and conservatory. Peacocks.

Bicton Park Gardens
East Budleigh, Budleigh Salterton EX9 7DP
☎ 01395 568465   FAX 01395 568889
OWNER   Mr & Mrs Stevens
LOCATION   On A376 north of Budleigh Salterton
OPEN   10 am – 6 pm (or dusk if earlier); daily; all year
ADMISSION   Adults £4.95
FACILITIES   Parking; dogs permitted; loos; facilities for the disabled; plants for sale; shop; self-service restaurant; licensed bar
FEATURES   Good collection of trees; herbaceous borders; fine conifers; glasshouses and conservatories to visit; lake; oriental features; plantsman's garden; modern roses; old roses; woodland garden; interesting for children; play area; miniature railway; tallest monkey puzzle *Araucaria araucana* (30m.) in the British Isles (and nine further record-breaking trees)
ENGLISH HERITAGE GRADE   I

60 acres and well maintained. Italian garden; important trees; oriental garden; American garden; collection of dwarf conifers; more than 2000 heathers; an avenue of monkey puzzles; a

hermitage; and the finest pre-Paxton palm house built 1815-20 from thousands of tiny panes of glass. Allow lots of time.

Buckland Abbey
Yelverton PL20 6EY
☎ 01822 853607   FAX 01822 855448
OWNER   The National Trust
LOCATION   Signposted from A386 at Yelverton
OPEN   10.30 am – 5.30 pm; Friday-Wednesday; April to October. 2 pm – 5 pm; Saturdays & Sundays; November to March
ADMISSION   Adults £2.10; Children £1 (1996 prices)
FACILITIES   Parking; loos; facilities for the disabled; refreshments
FEATURES   Herbs; new thyme garden (1996)

Originally a Cistercian Abbey, then the house of Sir Francis Drake, the main interest for garden lovers is the charming herb garden along the side of the Great Barn.

Burrow Farm Gardens
Dalwood, Axminster EX13 7ET
☎ 01404 831285   FAX 01404 831844
OWNER   Mr & Mrs J Benger
LOCATION   Turn north off A35 at Taunton Cross: ½ a mile
OPEN   2 pm – 7 pm; daily; 1 April to 30 September
ADMISSION   Adults £2; Children 50p
FACILITIES   Parking; dogs permitted; loos; plants for sale; cream teas on Wednesdays, Sundays & Bank Holidays
FEATURES   Plantsman's garden; rhododendrons and azaleas; primulas

Five acres of plantsmanship, with long views over the rolling hills. A formal pergola walk is planted with shrubs and climbing roses, while the woodland garden is underplanted with azaleas and interesting herbaceous plants.

Castle Drogo
Drewsteignton EX6 6PB
☎ 01647 433306   FAX 01647 433186
OWNER   The National Trust
LOCATION   Drewsteignton village: signs from A30 & A382
OPEN   10.30 am – 5.30 pm; daily; 26 March to 2 November
ADMISSION   Adults £2.30; Children £1.10
FACILITIES   Parking; loos; facilities for the disabled; plants for sale; National Trust shop; self-service tea-room, waitress-service restaurant
FEATURES   Herbaceous borders; planted by Gertrude Jekyll; designed by Lutyens; rock garden; modern roses; old roses; woodland garden; interesting for children; tallest *Acer capillipes* (16m.) in the British Isles
ENGLISH HERITAGE GRADE   II*

Major 1920s garden high on the edge of Dartmoor. Handsome yew hedges; formal design; rich and spacious herbaceous borders, contrasting with the austere castle on its windy bluff. Weather-beaten, lichen-heavy *Prunus* and acers on the slopes below. All on a vast scale.

Coleton Fishacre Garden

Coleton, Kingswear, Dartmouth TQ6 0EQ
☎ & FAX 01803 752466

OWNER The National Trust
LOCATION 3 miles from Kingswear off Lower-Ferry Road
OPEN 10.30 am – 5.30 pm; Wednesday – Friday, Sundays
& Bank Holidays; 26 March to 2 November (plus Sundays in
March 2 pm – 5 pm)
ADMISSION Adults £3.30; Children £1.60; Pre-booked
Groups £2.60
FACILITIES Parking; loos; facilities for the disabled; plants
for sale; tea-hut, snacks & ice creams
FEATURES Herbaceous borders; plantsman's garden; sub-
tropical plants; woodland garden; rhododendrons; rare trees;
tallest *Catalpa bungei* in the British Isles (and two other
record trees); interesting new plantings in the 'Holiwell' area
ENGLISH HERITAGE GRADE II

Twenty acres of rhododendron and camellia woodland crash-
ing down a secret valley to the sea. Almost frost-free, the range
and size of Southern Hemisphere trees and shrubs is astound-
ing. Rare bulbs in the warm terraces around the Lutyensesque
house.

Dartington Hall

Dartington, Totnes TQ9 6EL
☎ & FAX 01803 862367

OWNER Dartington Hall Trust
LOCATION 2 miles north-west of Totnes
OPEN Dawn to dusk; daily; all year. Groups by prior ap-
pointment only.
ADMISSION Donation (£2 suggested)
FACILITIES Parking; loos; access for the disabled; plants for
sale
FEATURES Garden sculpture; good topiary; woodland gar-
den; magnolias; rhododendrons; camellias; tilt-yard
ENGLISH HERITAGE GRADE II*

Grand mid-20th century garden with some famous associations. Beatrix Farrand designed the terraces, including the
so-called tilt-yard, and Percy Cane built the long staircase and
spring plantings on either side. Henry Moore deposited a
reclining woman. Some consider the garden grandiose and
cold: we think it is magnificent, and wholly appropriate to the
scale of house and landscape.

Docton Mill

Lymebridge, Hartland, Bideford EX39 6EA
☎ & FAX 01237 441369

OWNER Mr & Mrs M G Bourcier
LOCATION Take road from Hartland to Stoke and follow
signposts towards Elmscott
OPEN 10 am – 5 pm; daily; 1 March to 31 October
ADMISSION Adults £2.50; Children under 14, 50p
FACILITIES Parking; dogs permitted; loos; plants for sale;
light refreshments & cream teas
FEATURES Fruit of special interest; lake; woodland garden;
apple orchards

The main attraction is a working water mill, but the garden is
developing quickly and the new owners have already made
further improvements. Worth watching.

Escot

Ottery St Mary, Exeter EX11 1LU
☎ 01404 822188   FAX 01404 822903

OWNER John-Michael Kennaway
LOCATION Signposted from A30 at Fairmile
OPEN 10 am – 6 pm (5 pm from October to Easter); daily;
all year
ADMISSION Adults £2.60; OAPs & Children £2.20; under
fives Free
FACILITIES Parking; dogs permitted; loos; access for the disabled; water-plants for sale; home-cooked lunches & cream
teas
FEATURES Bluebells; fine conifers; rhododendrons and azaleas; snowdrops

An up-and-coming low-budget old/new garden, responding
well to vigorous replanting. The house is an elegant Regency
sugarlump, with distant views to East Hill (Capability Brown
advised on the prospect), but the woodlands around the house
are full of good Victorian rhododendrons and the walled
garden sports a basic collection of old and English roses.

Exeter University Gardens

Exeter EX4 4PX
☎ 01392 263059   FAX 01392 264547

OWNER The University of Exeter
LOCATION 3 miles north of City Centre, all around Univer-
sity
OPEN Dawn – dusk; daily; all year
ADMISSION Free
FACILITIES Parking; dogs permitted
FEATURES Fine conifers; rhododendrons and azaleas; tender
plants; heathers; summer bedding
NCCPG NATIONAL COLLECTIONS *Azara*

One of the best University campuses, the gardens are educational, attractive & important. Based on the 19th-century
Veitch collections of exotic trees, the plantings were supplemented by Chinese species collected 80 years ago by E H
Wilson.

The Garden House

Buckland Monachorum, Yelverton PL20 7LQ
☎ 01822 854769

OWNER Fortescue Garden Trust
LOCATION Signed off A386 on Plymouth side of Yelverton
OPEN 10.30 am – 5 pm; daily; 1 March to 30 October
ADMISSION Adults £3; Senior Citizens £2.50; Children £1;
RHS members Free.
FACILITIES Parking; loos; plants for sale; tea-room open in
season with light lunches
FEATURES Herbaceous borders; gravel or scree garden;
plantsman's garden; alpine bank; flowering cherries; wisterias;
new 4-acre extension with *Acer* glade, spring garden, quarry
garden, wildflower meadow and rhododendron walk

A plantsman's garden, made by the late Lionel Fortescue, who
insisted on planting only the best forms of plants. The setting

is awesome: a ruined abbey on the edge of Dartmoor, with stupendous views. Much of the effect is achieved through rigorous cultivation. Plants are well fed and firmly controlled: they flourish on the treatment. Exciting new developments on a huge scale.

Gidleigh Park Hotel
Chagford TQ13 8HH
☎ 01647 432367   [FAX] 01647 432574

OWNER   Paul Henderson
LOCATION   15 miles west of Exeter. Turn off in Chagford: do not go to Gidleigh
OPEN   Guests of the hotel & restaurant only
ADMISSION   Free to hotel & restaurant clients
FACILITIES   Parking; loos; delicious food in Hotel
FEATURES   Lake; woodland garden

45 acres of woodland on the edge of Dartmoor with a 1920s garden round the Tudorised house. Nothing very rare or special, but the position is stupendous and the sense of space, even grandeur, is enhanced by immaculate maintenance. Innumerable awards for the hotel & restaurant over the last 11 years.

Gnome Reserve & Wild Flower Garden
The Pixie Kiln, West Putford, Bradworthy EX22 7XE
☎ 01409 241435

OWNER   The Atkin Family
LOCATION   Between Bideford & Holsworthy, signed from A39, A386 & A388
OPEN   10 am – 6 pm; daily; 21 March to 31 October
ADMISSION   Adults £1.75; Recycled Teenagers (OAPs) £1.50; Children £1.25
FACILITIES   Parking; dogs permitted; loos; large shop selling gnomes; drinks & ice-creams
FEATURES   Gnomes & more gnomes

There are four reasons to visit this remarkable conservation centre: first, the two-acre gnome reserve in a beech wood with a stream; second the two-acre pixies' wildflower meadow, with 250 labelled species; third, the kiln where pottery gnomes & pixies are born; fourth, the museum of rare early gnomes.

Hill House Garden
Landscove, Ashburton, Newton Abbot TQ13 7LY
☎ & [FAX] 01803 762273

OWNER   R & V A Hubbard
LOCATION   Off A384, follow signs for Landscove
OPEN   11 am – 5 pm; daily; all year
ADMISSION   Free
FACILITIES   Parking; dogs permitted; loos; facilities for the disabled; plants for sale; garden shop; Mother Hubbard's Tea-Room (home made cakes)
FEATURES   Fine conifers; glasshouses and conservatories to visit; particularly interesting in winter; daffodils; garden temple; cyclamen and snowdrops; new picnic area; two new herbaceous borders each 150ft long (1997)

Victorian Old Vicarage made famous by Edward Hyams' *An Englishman's Garden*. Now the centre of an ambitious young nursery.

Killerton
Broadclyst, Exeter EX5 3LE
☎ 01392 881345

OWNER   The National Trust
LOCATION   West side of B3181, Exeter to Cullompton Road
OPEN   10.30 am – 5.30 pm (dusk in winter); daily; all year
ADMISSION   £3.10 (£1 from 1 November to 28 February)
FACILITIES   Parking; loos; facilities for the disabled; National Trust shop; small well-run plant centre; waitress-service restaurant and self-service tea-room
FEATURES   Good collection of trees; daffodils; rhododendrons and azaleas; rock garden; snowdrops; woodland garden; particularly interesting in winter; tallest Ostrya carpinifolia (22m.) in the British Isles (and eight further record trees); magnolias; drifts of Crocus tommasinianus; new wild flower areas (1995)
ENGLISH HERITAGE GRADE   II*

A historic giant among gardens, whose long connections with Veitch's Nursery have bequeathed a great tree collection. Innumerable record-breaking specimens, many from collectors' seed, but one's sense of awe is spoilt by droning traffic on the M5 below.

Knightshayes Garden
Tiverton EX16 7RG
☎ 01884 254665   [FAX] 01884 253264

OWNER   The National Trust
LOCATION   Off A396 Tiverton – Bampton Road
OPEN   10.30 am – 5.30 pm; daily; 1 April to 31 October
ADMISSION   Adults £3.25
FACILITIES   Parking; loos; access for the disabled; plants for sale; National Trust shop; licensed restaurant 10.30 am – 17.30 pm daily; coffee, lunch & teas
FEATURES   Herbaceous borders; good topiary; woodland garden; plantings by Graham Thomas; cyclamen; bulbs; peat beds; centenary planting of 100 trees along visitors' entrance; tallest *Quercus cerris* (40m.) in the British Isles
ENGLISH HERITAGE GRADE   II*
FRIENDS   National Trust Culm & Eve Valleys Centre

Brilliant herbaceous plantings and stunning formal gardens, but Knightshayes is above all a garden in a wood, delightful at all seasons and notable for its rare plants and high standard of maintenance. Good new designs and plantings by the adventurous head gardener.

Marwood Hill Gardens
Barnstaple EX31 4EB
☎ 01271 42528

OWNER   Dr J A Smart
LOCATION   Signed from A361 Barnstaple & Braunton Road
OPEN   Dawn to dusk; daily; all year except Christmas Day
ADMISSION   Adults £2
FACILITIES   Parking; dogs permitted; loos; plants for sale; teas, April – September, Sundays & Bank Holidays only

FEATURES Alpines; good collection of trees; bog garden; herbaceous borders; camellias; daffodils; glasshouses and conservatories to visit; gravel or scree garden; lake; plantsman's garden; rhododendrons and azaleas; climbing roses; old roses; particularly good in July-August; particularly interesting in winter; birches; *Eucalyptus*; camellias; hebes; plants, more plants & yet more plants.

NCCPG NATIONAL COLLECTIONS *Astilbe*; *Iris ensata*; *Tulbaghia*

A remarkable plantsman's garden, conceived on a grand scale and fast maturing, though it is still expanding along the long sheltered valley which gives such rewarding growth. Exciting for its scale, variety, and the energy of its owner. There is no better place in the south west to learn about plants of every kind.

Overbecks

Sharpitor, Salcombe TQ8 8LW

☎ 01548 843238

OWNER The National Trust

LOCATION 2 miles south of Salcombe

OPEN 10 am – 8 pm (or dusk, if earlier); daily; all year

ADMISSION Garden only: Adults £2.30; Children £1.10

FACILITIES Parking; National Trust shop; tea-room for light refreshments

FEATURES Bluebells; subtropical plants; palms; mimosas; cyclamen; *Magnolia campbellii*

ENGLISH HERITAGE GRADE II

A small, intensely planted, almost jungly garden, perched above the Salcombe estuary. The formal terraces (rather 1930s) are stuffed with interesting tender plants: *Musa basjoo*, phormiums, agapanthus, self-sown *Echium pininana* and every kind of South African daisy, all held together in a framework of hundreds of *Trachycarpus* palms.

Paignton Zoo & Botanical Gardens

Totnes Road, Paignton TQ4 7EU

☎ 01803 557479　　FAX 01803 523457

OWNER Whitley Wildlife Conservation Trust

LOCATION On A385 Totnes Road, 1 mile from Paignton

OPEN 10 am – 6 pm (5 pm in winter); daily; all year

ADMISSION Adults £6.50; Senior Citizens £5; Children £4

FACILITIES Parking; loos; access for the disabled; shops; large self-service restaurant

FEATURES Herbaceous borders; fine conifers; rock garden; interesting for children; glasshouses with tropical plants

NCCPG NATIONAL COLLECTIONS *Buddleja*; *Sorbaria*

Once a private garden devoted to blue-flowered & blue-leaved plants, now an inspiring combination of zoo, botanic collection, public park and holiday entertainment. Plans to increase the commitment to conservation have begun with six new habitats.

Powderham Castle

Exeter EX6 8JQ

☎ 01626 890243　　FAX 01626 890729

OWNER Lord & Lady Courtenay

LOCATION Off A379 Dawlish to Exeter Road at Kenton

OPEN 10 am – 5.30 pm; daily; 23 March to 27 October

ADMISSION Adults £4.50; Senior Citizens £4.35; Children £2.95. Charges include guided tour of Castle

FACILITIES Parking; dogs permitted; loos; access for the disabled; plants for sale; licensed restaurant

FEATURES Landscape designed by Capability Brown; modern roses; newly re-opened woodland garden (1995)

ENGLISH HERITAGE GRADE II

Not a major garden, but the 18th-century landscaped park is serenely English and there is a cheerful modern rose garden all along the front of the house.

RHS Garden, Rosemoor

Great Torrington EX38 8PH

☎ 01805 624067　　FAX 01805 624717

OWNER The Royal Horticultural Society

LOCATION 1 mile south of Torrington on B3220

OPEN 10 am – 6 pm (but 5 pm October to March); daily except Christmas Day; all year

ADMISSION Adults £3.20; Children £1; Groups (10+) £2.75. RHS members Free

FACILITIES Parking; loos; facilities for the disabled; plants for sale; good range of book & gifts; licensed restaurant

FEATURES Lake; plantsman's garden; modern roses; old roses; woodland garden; interesting for children; young garden; particularly interesting in winter; stream and bog garden; foliage garden; colour theme gardens; fruit and vegetable gardens; herb garden; cottage garden; tallest *Eucalyptus glaucescens* (21m.) in the British Isles (and seven further record trees)

NCCPG NATIONAL COLLECTIONS *Ilex*; *Cornus*

Rosemoor was created by Lady Anne Berry, who generously donated it to the RHS, with 32 acres of pastureland, in 1989. The RHS has made the new Rosemoor its West Country flagship through a wide-ranging development programme. The results are already impressive: good design, good plantings, an exceptionally high standard of maintenance, and the best-grown roses in England. But the people are the garden's making – friendly and helpful staff with a warm welcome for children, which makes a visit to Rosemoor so different from many grand gardens.

Saltram

Plympton, Plymouth PL7 3UH

☎ 01752 335546　　FAX 01752 336474

OWNER The National Trust

LOCATION 2 miles west of Plympton

OPEN 11 am – 4 pm on Saturdays & Sundays from 2 to 23 March. Then 10.30 am – 5.30 pm; Sunday – Thursday; 28 March to 30 October

ADMISSION Adults £2.40; Children £1.20

FACILITIES Parking; loos; facilities for the disabled; National Trust shop in stable block; licensed restaurant 12 noon – 5.30 pm. Also light refreshments

FEATURES Camellias; rhododendrons and azaleas; parkland; handsome orangery; lime avenue; tallest *Acer palmatum* 'Osakazuki' (13m.) in the British Isles

ENGLISH HERITAGE GRADE II*

20 acres of beautiful parkland, whose huge and ancient trees are underplanted with camellias and rhododendrons. Best in spring when the daffodils flower in hosts.

Tapeley Park

Instow EX39 4NT
☎ 01271 42371

OWNER   N D C I Ltd

LOCATION   Off A39 between Barnstaple & Bideford

OPEN   10 am – 6 pm; daily, except Saturdays; Good Friday to 30 September

ADMISSION   Adults £2.50; Senior Citizens £2; Children £1.50; Season ticket £10

FACILITIES   Parking; dogs permitted; loos; facilities for the disabled; plants for sale; gift shop; licensed lunches & cream teas

FEATURES   Follies and garden buildings; fruit of special interest; glasshouses and conservatories to visit; lake; woodland garden; interesting for children; newly re-designed rockery; British Jousting Centre

ENGLISH HERITAGE GRADE   II*

FRIENDS   Friends of Tapeley set up in 1995

Fine Italianate formal garden laid out on several levels c.1900 and planted with tender plants (*Sophora tetraptera* and *Myrtus communis* 'Tarentina'). Beyond are palm trees and a rhododendron woodland: worth exploring. All parts are undergoing restoration and replanting with advice from Mary Keen and Carol Klein. A garden to watch.

Wylmington Hayes Gardens

Wilmington, Honiton EX14 9JZ
☎ 01404 831751   FAX 01404 831826

OWNER   Mr & Mrs P Saunders

LOCATION   Signposted off A30: turn north off A35 in Wilmington

OPEN   2 pm – 5 pm; Sundays & Bank Holidays; 1 May to 30 June

ADMISSION   Adults £3; Children £1; Wheelchair occupants £1

FACILITIES   Parking; loos; facilities for the disabled; plants for sale; gift stand; home-made refreshments & cream teas

FEATURES   Good collection of trees; lake; good topiary; woodland garden

An Edwardian house in the Tudor style, with a formal Italian garden and ornamental woodland planted with rhododendrons, azaleas, camellias, acers and magnolias.

DORSET

Abbotsbury Sub-Tropical Gardens

Abbotsbury, Weymouth DT3 4LA
☎ 01305 871387   FAX 01305 871902

OWNER   Ilchester Estates

LOCATION   B3157, on coast, in village

OPEN   10 am – 5 pm (3 pm from November to March); daily; all year

ADMISSION   Adults £4.20; OAPs £3.80; Children £1.50; Family (2+2) £10

FACILITIES   Parking; dogs permitted; loos; access for the disabled; plants for sale; shop; refreshments

FEATURES   Good collection of trees; bluebells; camellias; plantsman's garden; rhododendrons and azaleas; modern roses; subtropical plants; woodland garden; particularly interesting in winter; magnolias; candelabra primulas; rare trees; freestanding loquat *Eriobotrya japonica*; tallest English oak *Quercus robur* (40m.) in the British Isles; five other record trees

ENGLISH HERITAGE GRADE   I

NCCPG NATIONAL COLLECTIONS *Hebe* (large leaved); *Hoheria*

A woodland garden of splendid specimens and trees of great rarity which has enjoyed a spectacular renaissance in recent years. Palms, eucalyptus, pittosporum & camellias all grow lushly in the sheltered valley and romantic walled garden. A stylish Visitors' Centre and excellent nursery make for added value.

Athelhampton House & Gardens

Dorchester DT2 7LG
☎ 01305 848363   FAX 01305 848135

OWNER   Patrick Cooke

LOCATION   1 mile east of Puddletown on A35

OPEN   11 am – 5 pm; Sunday – Friday; 23 March to 26 October

ADMISSION   House & garden: £4.50. Garden only: £2.80

FACILITIES   Parking; loos; access for the disabled; plants for sale; shop; refreshments

FEATURES   Lake; good topiary; gazebos; beautiful walls and hedges; two *Metasequoia glyptostroboides* from the original seed; Queen Victoria Walk restored (1994) with advice from Penelope Hobhouse

ENGLISH HERITAGE GRADE   I

Inigo Thomas designed this about 100 years ago as the perfect garden for the perfect manor house. Sharply cut pyramids of yew, a long canal with water lilies, and rambling roses in early summer.

Chiffchaffs

Chaffeymoor, Bourton, Gillingham SP8 5BY
☎ 01747 840841

OWNER   Mr & Mrs K R Potts

LOCATION   At Wincanton end of Bourton, off A303

OPEN   2 pm – 5.30 pm; Wednesdays & Thursdays, plus first & third Sundays of the month & Bank Holiday weekends; April to September

ADMISSION   £2

FACILITIES   Parking; plants for sale; for groups, by appointment

FEATURES   Plantsman's garden; woodland garden; spring bulbs; dwarf rhododendrons

A pretty cottage, with an excellent small nursery attached, and just off the A303. Only fifteen years old, the garden has a flowing design, exploits a great variety of habitats and burgeons with good plants. A bluebell-lined path leads to the woodland garden, which boasts a splendid collection of rhododendrons, drifts of daffodils and candelabra primulas, and yet more carpets of bluebells.

Compton Acres Gardens

Canford Cliffs Road, Poole BH13 7ES

☎ 01202 700778   [FAX] 01202 707537

OWNER   L Green
LOCATION   Well signposted locally
OPEN   10.30 am – 6.30 pm; daily; March to October
ADMISSION   Adults £4.50; Senior Citizens £3.50
FACILITIES   Parking; loos; access for the disabled; plants for sale; several shops; tea-rooms & light lunches
FEATURES   Fine conifers; follies and garden buildings; oriental features; rock garden; modern roses; garden sculpture; subtropical plants; woodland garden
ENGLISH HERITAGE GRADE   II*

Very touristy, very Bournemouth, and very 1920s. Compton Acres offers ten totally unconnected but highly entertaining gardens, all in different styles but joined by tarmac paths. Best are the Italian garden, the palm court, the white azaleas in the watery glen which runs down to the harbour, and the stupendous Japanese garden. There is opulence, vulgarity, overcrowding and blatant commercialism, but the standards are among the highest in any garden: no visitor could fail to be cheered up by the bravura of it all.

Cranborne Manor

Cranborne, Wimborne BH21 5PP

☎ 01725 517248   [FAX] 01725 517862

OWNER   Viscount Cranborne
LOCATION   10 miles north of Wimborne on B3078
OPEN   9 am – 5 pm; Wednesdays; 1 March to 30 September
ADMISSION   Adults £3; Senior Citizens & Students £2.50; Children (under 16) 50p
FACILITIES   Parking; loos; garden centre
FEATURES   Herbaceous borders; old roses; good topiary; Jacobean mount
ENGLISH HERITAGE GRADE   II*

The garden at Cranborne is modern, but employs Elizabethan elements. The mixed borders in the charming courtyard are good. However, the garden has gone back in recent years and some of the plantings are looking threadbare.

Dean's Court

Wimborne BH21 1EE

☎ 01202 888478

OWNER   Sir Michael & Lady Hanham
LOCATION   2 mins walk from central Wimborne
OPEN   2 pm – 6 pm; 30 March, 5 October and first & last Sundays in April, May, and July to September. Plus 10 am – 6 pm Bank Holiday Mondays
ADMISSION   Adults £1.50; Children 70p
FACILITIES   Parking; loos; plants for sale; organic herb plants and vegetables; whole-food refreshments, June – September
FEATURES   Herbs; lake; plantsman's garden; rock garden; old roses; monastery fishpond; good trees; all organic; tallest Catalpa bignonioides (19m.) in the British Isles

A very wholesome garden: everything, including 150 different herb varieties, is grown without artificial fertilisers, pesticides or herbicides.

Edmondsham House

Edmondsham, Wimborne BH21 5RE

☎ 01725 517207

OWNER   Mrs Julia E Smith
LOCATION   Off B3081 between Cranborne & Verwood
OPEN   2 pm – 5 pm; Wednesdays, Sundays & Bank Holiday Mondays; 1 April to 31 October
ADMISSION   Adults £1; Children 50p
FACILITIES   Parking; loos; access for the disabled; plants for sale; refreshments on Wednesdays in April & October
FEATURES   Herbaceous borders; fruit of special interest; herbs; old roses; grass cockpit

The walled garden is maintained organically, with borders round the sides. It is intensively cultivated and brims with interesting vegetables. Fine trees in the park.

Forde Abbey

Chard TA20 4LU

☎ 01460 220231   [FAX] 01460 220296

OWNER   The Trustees of the G D Roper settlement
LOCATION   4 miles south of Chard
OPEN   10 am – 4.30 pm; daily; all year
ADMISSION   Adults £3.50; Senior Citizens £3.25 (1996 prices). RHS members Free
FACILITIES   Parking; dogs permitted; loos; facilities for the disabled; plants for sale; shop; cafeteria
FEATURES   Good collection of trees; bog garden; herbaceous borders; lake; rock garden planted by Jack Drake; HHA/ Christie's Garden of the Year in 1993; tallest Cornus controversa (16m.) in UK
ENGLISH HERITAGE GRADE   II*

A garden of great variety around the rambling house, part Jacobean, part Gothick. The planting is modern, and includes rhododendrons, azaleas, acers, magnolias, irises, Meconopsis and candelabra primulas. But there are also mature Victorian conifers (Sequoia sempervirens, Calocedrus decurrens), lakes, ponds, streams, cascades, bogs and such oddities as the Beech House.

Ivy Cottage

Aller Lane, Ansty, Dorchester DT2 7PX

☎ 01258 880053

OWNER   Anne & Alan Stevens
LOCATION   Midway between Blandford & Dorchester
OPEN   10 am – 5 pm; Thursdays; 1 April to 31 October. See also Yellow Book for NGS dates
ADMISSION   Adults £2; Children (under 13) Free. Parties by appointment only
FACILITIES   Parking; plants for sale
FEATURES   Herbaceous borders; plantsman's garden

1½ acres of cottage garden made by the present owners over the last 30 years and crammed with interesting things, particularly herbaceous plants and bulbs. Springs and streams, combined with greensand soil, multiply the possibilities – drifts of marsh marigolds and candelabra primulas.

Kingston Lacy
Wimborne Minster BH21 4EA
☎ 01202 883402

OWNER The National Trust
LOCATION 1½ miles from Wimborne on B3082 to Blandford
OPEN 11.30 am – 6 pm; Saturday – Wednesday; 1 April to 31 October
ADMISSION £2.20 Adults; £1.10 Children
FACILITIES Parking; loos; access for the disabled; plants for sale; lunches & teas
FEATURES Fine conifers; garden sculpture; snowdrops; Victorian fernery; Dutch parterre; huge cedars of Lebanon planted by visiting royalty; current holder of Sandford Award
ENGLISH HERITAGE GRADE II
NCCPG NATIONAL COLLECTIONS Anemone nemorosa; Convallaria

250 acres of classic 18th-century parkland, still undergoing restoration by the National Trust, with a cedar avenue, Egyptian obelisk and laurel walk dating from Victorian times.

Kingston Maurward Gardens
Kingston Maurwood College, Dorchester DT2 8PY
☎ 01305 264738   FAX 01305 250059

OWNER Kingston Maurward College
LOCATION 1 mile east of Dorchester from A35: signposted
OPEN 10 am – 5 pm; daily; 28 March to 31 October
ADMISSION Adults £3; Children £1.50
FACILITIES Parking; loos; facilities for the disabled; plants for sale; cakes & drinks
FEATURES Herbaceous borders; daffodils; modern roses; old roses; good topiary; cyclamen; autumn crocus
ENGLISH HERITAGE GRADE II*

Kingston Maurward belonged to the Hanbury family who owned La Mortola on the Riviera, and laid out the formal garden here in the Italian style (c.1920). It is being restored in the country house style with herbaceous borders and old fashioned roses, but the old kitchen garden is a splendid modern teaching garden with innumerable demonstrations of what can be grown in Dorset. Highly instructive.

Knoll Gardens
Stapehill Road, Wimborne BH21 7ND
☎ 01202 873931   FAX 01202 870842

OWNER John & Jane Flude, & Neil Lucas
LOCATION Signposted from B3073 at Hampreston
OPEN 10 am – 5.30 pm; daily except Mondays & Tuesdays from 1 to 31 March, then daily from 1 April to 31 October. 10 am – 4 pm; Wednesday – Saturday; 1 November to 24 December
ADMISSION Adults £3.25; OAPs £2.90; Children £1.70. Group rates available
FACILITIES Parking; loos; access for the disabled; plants for sale; good shop; restaurant & refreshments
FEATURES Herbaceous borders; fine conifers; rhododendrons and azaleas; rock garden; Eucalyptus
NCCPG NATIONAL COLLECTIONS Ceanothus, Phygelius

Around the massive new rock garden of Purbeck stone are the relics of a higgledy-piggledy plantsman's collection. Visit it now, before it becomes altogether too touristy and loses its charm.

Mapperton Gardens
Beaminster DT8 3NR
☎ 01308 862645   FAX 01308 863348

OWNER The Earl & Countess of Sandwich
LOCATION 2 miles south-east of Beaminster
OPEN 2 pm – 6 pm; daily; 1 March to 31 October
ADMISSION Adults £3; Children (5–18) £1.50 (under 5, Free); Wheelchair-bound Free
FACILITIES Parking; loos; plants for sale; small shop selling terracotta pots; soft drinks
FEATURES Good collection of trees; good topiary
ENGLISH HERITAGE GRADE II*

An old/new garden, steeply terraced down a hidden combe, and dominated by tensions between a theatrical orangery at the top and two long lily pools at the bottom. Great fun. Part of the new film of 'Emma' was filmed here.

Minterne
Minterne Magna, Dorchester DT 7AU
☎ 01300 341370   FAX 01300 341747

OWNER Lord Digby
LOCATION On A352, 2 miles north of Cerne Abbas
OPEN 10 am – 7 pm; daily; 28 March to 10 November
ADMISSION Adults £3; Children Free
FACILITIES Parking; dogs permitted; loos
FEATURES Rhododendrons and azaleas; subtropical plants; woodland garden; cherries; cyclamen; Lathraea clandestina; tallest Chamaecyparis pisifera 'Filifera' (25m.) in the United Kingdom
ENGLISH HERITAGE GRADE II

A woodland garden, best in spring, and well integrated into the park around the hideous Edwardian house. The oldest rhododendrons came from Hooker's collection, but the remarkable late Lord Digby also supported Farrer, Forrest, Rock and Kingdon Ward, which makes Minterne one of the best Himalayan collections. The walk down a greensand valley to the woodland stream is ravishing, but parts are somewhat weedy and run down.

Parnham House
Beaminster DT8 3NA
☎ 01308 862204   FAX 01308 863494

OWNER Mr & Mrs J Makepeace
LOCATION On A3066 north of Bridport
OPEN 10 am – 5 pm; Sundays, Wednesdays & Bank Holidays; 3 April to 30 October; & groups by appointment
ADMISSION House & garden: Adults £4; Children (over 10) £2
FACILITIES Parking; dogs permitted; loos; facilities for the disabled; woodware & contemporary crafts; tea, coffee, hot & cold lunches
FEATURES Lake; old roses; good topiary; new Courtyard garden (1995); herbaceous borders extended (1995)
ENGLISH HERITAGE GRADE II*

A handsome Jacobean mansion, approached through a courtyard, with formal terraces running down to lakes and bluebell woods. The gardens have been restored and imaginatively replanted with mixed borders and, above all, roses. But Parnham offers much more beside: iris borders, a meadow of fritillaries, an Italian garden, topiary, gazebos, rhododendrons and splendid modern sculptures including a larger-than-life Morecambe and Wise.

Red House Museum & Gardens

Quay Road, Christchurch BH23 2NF

☎ 01202 482860   FAX 01202 481924

OWNER   Hampshire County Council

LOCATION   Brown signs from High Street

OPEN   10 am – 5 pm; Tuesday – Saturday & Bank Holiday Mondays; all year. Plus 2 pm – 5 pm on Sundays

ADMISSION   Adults £1; OAPs & Children 60p

FACILITIES   Loos; access for the disabled; Museum shop; coffee shop

FEATURES   Herbs; old roses; garden sculpture

This half-acre oasis in Christchurch's conservation area concentrates on plants of historic interest and contemporary sculpture. Worth knowing.

Stapehill Abbey

Stapehill, Wimborne BH21 2EB

☎ 01202 861686

OWNER   Stapehill Enterprises Ltd

LOCATION   Signed from A31

OPEN   10 am – 5 pm; daily; 1 April to 31 October. Plus 10 am – 4 pm; Wednesday–Sunday; 1 February to 31 March & 1 November to 24 December

ADMISSION   Adults £4.50; OAPs £4; Children £3

FACILITIES   Parking; loos; facilities for the disabled; plants for sale; licensed coffee-shop

FRIENDS   Friends of Stapehill started: ring for details

Once a convent, Stapehill is now a craft centre and claims to offer a fun-filled day for all the family. The gardens are modern, made-to-measure and lively: within the walled garden are an orchid house, rose garden and herbaceous borders. But you can wander off into woods where the hand of commercialism has yet to strike: here among the rhododendrons you will find the quiet and contentment that the nuns knew.

Sticky Wicket

Buckland Newton, Dorchester DT2 7BY

☎ 01300 345476

OWNER   Peter & Pam Lewis

LOCATION   11 miles from Dorchester & Sherborne

OPEN   10.30 am – 8 pm; Thursdays; 12 June to 25 September

ADMISSION   Adults £2; Children £1

FACILITIES   Parking; loos; access for the disabled; plants for sale; tea, coffee & home-made cakes

FEATURES   Ecological interest; plantsman's garden; young garden; made since 1987; good colour associations; new white garden (1995); new hay-meadow (1996)

An original garden, worth watching. The owners are both designers and conservationists, and their devotion to ecology guides their garden-making. A scented garden, a white garden and a colour wheel are secondary to the need to attract birds, insects and other wild life. The garden is still expanding – worth seeing now in its youth, and returning in later years –

especially since the owners may decide to take a few years off from opening.

CO. DURHAM

Barningham Park

Richmond DL11 7DW

☎ 01833 621202   FAX 01833 621298

OWNER   Sir Anthony Milbank Bt

LOCATION   10 miles north-west of Scotch Corner off A66

OPEN   2 pm – 6 pm; 1 & 8 June, 14 September

ADMISSION   Adults £2, Children 50p

FACILITIES   Parking; dogs permitted; loos; plants for sale; home-made teas

FEATURES   Herbaceous borders; lake; rock garden; terraced gardens; rhododendrons

Terraced early 18th-century landscape, leading up to the old bowling green and down to the skating pond. Reworked by keen horticultural Milbanks in the 1920s. Unknown and perhaps underrated, if Barningham were in the Home Counties everyone would rave about it.

The Bowes Museum Garden & Park

Barnard Castle DL12 8NP

☎ 01833 690606   FAX 01833 637163

OWNER   Durham County Council

LOCATION   ½ mile west of Barnard Castle town

OPEN   Museum: 10 am – 4 pm, Monday – Saturday; 2 pm – 4 pm, Sundays; November to February. 10 am – 5 pm, Monday – Saturday; 2 pm – 5 pm, Sundays; March, April & October. 10 am – 5.30 pm, Monday – Saturday; 2 pm – 5 pm, Sundays, May to September. Closed 25 & 26 December & 1 January. Garden always open

ADMISSION   Adults £3; Senior Citizens & Children £2 (under review). Garden Free

FACILITIES   Parking; dogs permitted; loos; facilities for the disabled; shop; museum café

FEATURES   Good collection of trees; old roses; parterre; large monkey puzzle

ENGLISH HERITAGE GRADE   II

FRIENDS   Friends of Museum & Park, ring 01833 690606 for details

Rather run down and municipal, but the formal gardens are good and fine trees pepper the park, especially conifers.

Houghall College Gardens

Durham DH1 3SG

☎ 0191 386 1351   FAX 0191 386 0419

OWNER   Durham College of Agriculture & Horticulture

LOCATION   Follow A177 from A1 to Durham

OPEN   12.30 pm – 4.30 pm; daily; all year

ADMISSION   Free

FACILITIES   Parking; loos; facilities for the disabled; plants for sale; shop; tea-room (closed in winter)

FEATURES   Alpines; good collection of trees; bog garden; herbaceous borders; glasshouses and conservatories to visit; rock garden; modern roses; heathers; hardy fuchsias; seasonal bedding; fuchsias; excellent young pinetum

NCCPG NATIONAL COLLECTIONS *Sorbus; Meconopsis*
FRIENDS   Houghall Horticultural Society linked to the college

A well-run teaching garden attached to the County horticultural college. Many trials are conducted here, for example on the hardiness of fuchsias: 'if it grows at Houghall it will grow anywhere'. The arboretum has more than 500 different trees.

University of Durham Botanic Garden
Hollingside Lane, Durham DH1 3TN
☎ 0191 374 7971   📠 0191 374 7478

OWNER   University of Durham
LOCATION   In the south of the City of Durham
OPEN   10 am – 5 pm; daily; 1 March to 31 October. 1 pm – 4 pm; daily; 1 November to 29 February
ADMISSION   Free (but under review)
FACILITIES   Parking; loos; facilities for the disabled; plants for sale; tea, coffee, cold drinks & snacks
FEATURES   Good collection of trees; old roses; primulas; *Meconopsis*; autumn colour; new alpine garden and Mediterranean glasshouse (1996); sculpture by Ian Hamilton Findlay
FRIENDS   300 members and a full programme – details from the curator

Moved to its present site in 1970, this garden impresses with its youthful energy. The new 'American arboretum' was planted to copy natural associations 13 years ago. A woodland garden dates from 1988, a wetland one from 1989, and 1992 saw the opening of the 'Prince Bishop's Garden' with statues transferred from the Gateshead garden festival.

Westholme Hall
Winston, Darlington DL2 3QL
☎ 01325 730442   📠 01325 730946

OWNER   Mrs J H McBain
LOCATION   On B6274 north towards Staindrop
OPEN   2 pm – 6 pm; by appointment
ADMISSION   Adults £2; Children 50p
FACILITIES   Parking; dogs permitted; loos; access for the disabled; plants for sale; tea-rooms
FEATURES   Lake; old roses; rhododendrons

Five acres of late-Victorian gardens, recently restored and revived, around a smashing Jacobean house. Designed and planted for all seasons: there are parts for spring (bulbs and azaleas), summer (roses and lilacs) and autumn (herbaceous borders). All is maintained by the owners' own hard work and enthusiasm. Worth a long detour to see.

ESSEX

Audley End
Saffron Walden
☎ 01799 522842/520052   📠 01799 522131

OWNER   English Heritage
LOCATION   On B1383, 1 mile west of Saffron Walden
OPEN   Garden: 10 am – 6 pm; Wednesday – Sunday, plus Bank Holiday Mondays; 1 April to 30 September
ADMISSION   Gardens: Adults £3.30; Senior Citizens £2.50; Children £1.70 (1996). RHS members free after 22 March

FACILITIES   Parking; dogs permitted; loos; access for the disabled; plants for sale; shop; restaurant & picnic site
FEATURES   Landscape designed by Capability Brown; follies and garden buildings; bedding out; parterre; magnificent plane trees
ENGLISH HERITAGE GRADE   I

Capability Brown landscaped the park (rather too many Canada geese) but the recent excitement at Audley End has been the rejuvenation of the formal garden behind the house. This dates from the 1830s and has 170 geometric flower beds crisply cut from the turf and planted with simple perennials for late summer effect. Work continues.

The Beth Chatto Gardens
Elmstead Market, Colchester CO7 7DB
☎ 01206 822007   📠 01206 825933

OWNER   Beth Chatto
LOCATION   7 miles east of Colchester
OPEN   9 am – 5 pm; Monday – Saturday; March to October; 9 am – 4 pm; Monday – Friday; November to February. Closed on Bank Holidays
ADMISSION   £2.50
FACILITIES   Parking; loos; big nursery adjacent to the garden; drinks machine
FEATURES   Herbaceous borders; gravel or scree garden; lake; colour contrasts

Superb modern planting, particularly good for herbaceous plants, chosen for foliage as much as flower: all made by Beth Chatto since 1960. There are two types of planting here and it is the contrast between them which makes the garden. First there are the parts on dry gravelly soil, where Mediterranean plants flourish; second, there are the water- and bog-gardens made on clay. But gardens are only one of Beth Chatto's gifts: her writings and nearby nursery have made her famous.

Olivers
Olivers Lane, Colchester CO2 0HJ
☎ 01206 330575   📠 01206 330336

OWNER   Mr & Mrs David Edwards
LOCATION   3 miles south-west of Colchester between B1022 & B1026
OPEN   For NGS. And by appointment
ADMISSION   Adults £2; Children Free
FACILITIES   Parking; loos; facilities for the disabled; plants for sale; refreshments for pre-booked parties
FEATURES   Herbaceous borders; fruit of special interest; lake; modern roses; old roses; bluebells; rhododendrons

Quite a modern garden, started in 1960 around two small lakes, with an eye-catching walk to one side leading down to a statue of Bacchus. Good plants and planting everywhere, from the parterres by the house to the woodland where roses and rhododendrons flourish. This is the garden of enthusiastic and energetic owners: an inspiration.

Park Farm
Chatham Hall Lane, Great Waltham, Chelmsford CM3 1BZ
☎ 01245 360871

OWNER   J Cowley & D Bracey
LOCATION   On B1008 north from Chelmsford

OPEN 4, 5, 11, 18, 25 & 26 May; 1, 2, 8, 9, 15, 16, 22, 23, 29 & 30 June; 6, 7, 13 & 14 July
ADMISSION Adults £1.20; Children 50p
FACILITIES Loos; access for the disabled; plants for sale; teas & home-made cakes
FEATURES Herbaceous borders; plantsman's garden; old roses

A young garden, still developing, with good colour combinations and a willingness to experiment. Rooms are enclosed by hedges of box and yew for solidity in winter and there is also a winter garden of hellebores, snowdrops and aconites. Add in a Chinese garden, a garden of the Giants (outsize plants), a hot garden, an arid garden and a Russian garden, and you have the measure of Park Farm's variety. Nevertheless, it is all pulled together by sheer good design: Jill Cowley was the star of the 1995 BBC series on Italian Gardens.

RHS Garden, Hyde Hall
Royal Horticultural Society Garden, Rettendon, Chelmsford CM3 8ET
☎ 01245 400256   [FAX] 01245 401363

OWNER Royal Horticultural Society
LOCATION 6 miles south-east of Chelmsford, signposted from A130
OPEN 11 am - 6 pm (5 pm in September & October); Wednesday - Sunday and Bank Holidays; 26 March to 26 October
ADMISSION Adults £3; Children (6 - 16) 70p; Groups (10+) £2.50
FACILITIES Parking; loos; access for the disabled; plants for sale; licensed restaurant serving hot & cold lunches, afternoon teas, tea/coffee
FEATURES Herbaceous borders; glasshouses and conservatories to visit; plantsman's garden; woodland garden; particularly interesting in winter; bearded irises; magnolias; South African bulbs; paeonies; spring bulbs; ponds; heathers; roses of every kind
NCCPG NATIONAL COLLECTIONS Malus; Viburnum

Acquired by the RHS in 1992, this outstanding modern garden (started in 1955) was developed from a greenfield site. The scale of the planting is outstanding for a private garden. Works begins this year on further expansion and improvement.

Saling Hall
Great Saling, Braintree CM7 5DT
OWNER Mr & Mrs Hugh Johnson
LOCATION 2 miles north of the Saling Oak on A120
OPEN 2 pm - 5 pm; Wednesdays; May, June & July. Groups by appointment on weekdays
ADMISSION £2 for NGS
FACILITIES Parking; loos; access for the disabled
FEATURES Good collection of trees; herbaceous borders; lake; oriental features; plantsman's garden
ENGLISH HERITAGE GRADE II

A thinking man's garden, Saling also provokes thought in its visitors. The plantsmanship is impressive, particularly the choice and placing of trees and shrubs. Few modern gardens are conceived on such a scale, or mix classical and Japanese elements so smoothly. The moods, and the lessons, are endless.

Volpaia
54 Woodlands Road, Hockley SS5 4PY
☎ 01702 203761

OWNER Mr & Mrs Derek Fox
LOCATION 3 miles north-east of Rayleigh
OPEN 2.30 pm - 6 pm; Thursdays & Sundays; 13 April to 22 June, or by appointment
ADMISSION Adults £1; Children 30p
FACILITIES Plants for sale; Bullwood Nursery attached; tea & biscuits
FEATURES Plantsman's garden; woodland garden; rhododendron species; liliaceous plants; woodlanders

This is the woodland garden of a keen plantsman who has now turned his hobby to a nursery. Rhododendrons, camellias and magnolias are the main shrubs, underplanted with erythroniums and woodland herbaceous plants, plus candelabra primulas in the boggy bits.

GLOUCESTERSHIRE

Abbotswood
Stow-on-the-Wold, Cheltenham GL54 1LE
☎ 01451 830173

OWNER Robin Scully
LOCATION 1 mile west of Stow-on-the-Wold
OPEN For NGS: see Yellow Book
ADMISSION Adults £2; Children Free
FACILITIES Parking; dogs permitted; loos; teas
FEATURES Good collection of trees; herbaceous borders; fine conifers; planted by Gertrude Jekyll; lake; plantsman's garden; rock garden; modern roses; old roses; good topiary; woodland garden; magnolias; heather garden
ENGLISH HERITAGE GRADE II*

One of the most interesting gardens in the Cotswolds. Handsome formal gardens in front of the house: very Lutyens, very photogenic. A magnificent rock garden with a stream (artificially pumped, but you would never know) which meanders through alpine meadows, bogs and moraines, past dwarf azaleas, primulas, lysichitons, heaths and heathers until it disappears again. There is also a small arboretum, rather overgrown, but with some unusual forms, fascinating to browse around.

Badminton
Chipping Sodbury GL9 1DB
☎ 01454 218202

OWNER The Duke of Beaufort
LOCATION 5 miles east of Chipping Sodbury
OPEN 2 pm - 6 pm; 22 June
ADMISSION Adults £1.50; Senior Citizens £1; Children (under 10) Free
FACILITIES Parking; dogs permitted; loos; access for the disabled; plants for sale; tea, lemonade, cakes & scones
FEATURES Herbaceous borders; glasshouses and conservatories to visit; old roses; subtropical plants
ENGLISH HERITAGE GRADE I

The late Duchess planted a series of small formal gardens to the side of the house, which do not interfere with the grand 18th-century vistas across three counties. These modern gardens run into each other like the rooms of the house and are each different in character.

Barnsley House

Barnsley, Cirencester GL7 5EE

☎ & FAX 01285 740281

OWNER   Charles Verey

LOCATION   On B4425 in Barnsley village

OPEN   10 am – 6 pm; Mondays, Wednesdays, Thursdays & Saturdays; all year

ADMISSION   Adults £3; Senior Citizens £21; Children Free. Season ticket £6. December & January free. Parties by appointment

FACILITIES   Parking; loos; access for the disabled; plants for sale

FEATURES   Herbaceous borders; follies and garden buildings; fruit of special interest; herbs; plantsman's garden; old roses; ornamental *potager*; Simon Verity's sculpture

A compact, modern garden, much copying and much copied. Barnsley is interesting at all seasons, but best when the little laburnum walk and the purple alliums underneath are in flower together.

Batsford Arboretum

The Estate Office, Moreton-in-Marsh GL56 9QF

☎ 01608 650722   FAX 01608 650290

OWNER   The Batsford Foundation (a Registered Charity)

LOCATION   Off A44 between Moreton-in-Marsh & Burton-on-the-Hill

OPEN   10 am – 5 pm; daily; 1 March to 5 November

ADMISSION   Adults £3; Senior Citizens & Children (5 – 16) £2.50

FACILITIES   Parking; dogs permitted; loos; facilities for the disabled; plants for sale; shop; light meals & refreshments

FEATURES   Good collection of trees; fine conifers; oriental features; bluebells; maple glade; tallest *Betula platyphylla* (19m.) in the British Isles (and 12 other tree records)

ENGLISH HERITAGE GRADE   I

Batsford has an openness which makes its hillside a joy to wander through, passing from one dendrological marvel to the next. Begun in the 1880s, the Arboretum also has several oriental curiosities brought from Japan by Lord Redesdale – a large bronze Buddha and an oriental rest-house for instance. Lord Dulverton has renewed the plantings over the last 30 years: both the collection and the amenities are improving all the time.

Berkeley Castle

Berkeley GL13 9BQ

☎ 01453 810332

OWNER   R J G Berkeley

LOCATION   Off A38

OPEN   2 pm – 5 pm, Tuesday – Sunday; 28 – 30 March, April & May. 11 am – 5 pm, Tuesday – Saturday; also 2 pm – 5 pm, Sundays; May to September. Closed on Mondays in June & September. 2 pm – 4.30 pm; Sundays; October. 11 am – 5 pm; Bank Holiday Mondays

ADMISSION   Garden only: Adults £1.70; Children 85p

FACILITIES   Parking; loos; plants for sale; shop at Castle Farm; light lunches & afternoon tea

FEATURES   Herbaceous borders; fine conifers; plantsman's garden; old roses

ENGLISH HERITAGE GRADE   II*

The grim battlements of Berkeley Castle are host to an extensive collection of tender plants. On three terraces are *Cestrum*, *Cistus* and *Rosa banksiae* among hundreds of plant varieties introduced by the owner's grandfather, a nephew of Ellen Willmott. An Elizabethan-style bowling green and a water-lily pond fit well into the overall scheme.

Bourton House

Bourton-on-the-Hill, Moreton-in-Marsh GL56 9AE

☎ 01386 700121   FAX 01386 701081

OWNER   Mr & Mrs Richard Paice

LOCATION   On A44, 1½ miles west of Moreton-in-Marsh

OPEN   12 noon – 5 pm; Thursdays & Fridays; 29 May to 27 September, plus 25 & 26 May, 24 & 25 August

ADMISSION   £2.50

FACILITIES   Parking; loos; plants for sale; self-service tea & coffee

FEATURES   Herbaceous borders; gravel or scree garden; modern roses; old roses; good topiary

ENGLISH HERITAGE GRADE   II

First laid out by Lanning Roper in the 1960s, but consistently improved by the present owners, the garden at Bourton House is both fashionable and a delight. A knot garden, a small *potager*, a raised pond, the topiary walk, white-painted trellis work, a croquet lawn, exuberant climbing roses and borders bulging with good colour schemes – purple-leaved prunus with yellow roses, for instance.

Cowley Manor

Cowley, Cheltenham GL53 9NL

☎ 01242 870540   FAX 01242 870225

LOCATION   In village

OPEN   10 am – 6 pm; Tuesday – Thursday, Saturdays, Sundays & Bank Holidays; 1 May – 31 October

ADMISSION   Adults £2.50; OAPs & Children £1.50

FACILITIES   Parking; loos; plants for sale; by arrangement

FEATURES   Herbaceous borders; young garden

A new garden which seeks to pioneer the modern principles of planting worked out in Germany. It uses broad masses of naturalistic plantings in ecological mixes which enable a balance to be maintained between cultivated and wild plants. It is bold, striking, effective and labour-saving: but decide on its value for yourself.

Dyrham Park

Chippenham SN14 8ER

☎ 0117 937 2501

OWNER   The National Trust

LOCATION   On A46, 8 miles north of Bath

OPEN   11 am – 5.30 pm; Friday – Tuesday; 22 March to 2 November

ADMISSION   House & garden £5.20; Park & garden £2.60; Park £1.60

FACILITIES Parking; loos; access for the disabled; plants for sale; tea-room

FEATURES Herbaceous borders; deer park; handsome conservatory

ENGLISH HERITAGE GRADE II*

Fascinating for garden historians, who can study the Kip plan and trace the lines of the 17th-century formal garden which Humphry Repton turned into classic English parkland. But not a Mecca for the dedicated plantsman.

The Ernest Wilson Memorial Garden

High Street, Chipping Campden GL55 6AF

☎ 01386 840764

OWNER Chipping Campden Town Council

LOCATION North end of Main Street

OPEN Dawn to dusk; daily; all year

ADMISSION Donation

FACILITIES Dogs permitted; access for the disabled

FEATURES Herbaceous borders; trees & shrubs

A collection of plants all introduced by Ernest H. Wilson, the greatest of European plant hunters in China: Chipping Campden was his birthplace. *Acer griseum*, *Clematis montana rubens* and the pocket-handkerchief tree *Davidia involucrata* are among his best-known introductions: all are represented here.

Essex House

Badminton, Chipping Sodbury GL9 1DD

☎ 01454 218288

OWNER James Lees-Milne

LOCATION Far end of Badminton High Street, on village green, facing Estate Office

OPEN By appointment only, preferably groups

ADMISSION £2 for Macmillan nurses appeal

FACILITIES Parking; dogs permitted

FEATURES Old roses; good topiary; pretty parterres; unusual plants; weeping pears

A small garden made by the distinguished garden writer Alvilde Lees-Milne. The formal design uses box edging, topiary, silver foliage and soft colours to create a sense of space and quiet enchantment.

Frampton Court

Frampton-on-Severn GL2 7EU

☎ 01452 740698

OWNER Mrs Peter Clifford

LOCATION Signed to Frampton-on-Severn from M5

OPEN By appointment all year; also for NGS, NADFAS & Red Cross

ADMISSION House & Garden £4; Garden £1

FACILITIES Parking; dogs permitted; loos

FEATURES Follies and garden buildings; lake

ENGLISH HERITAGE GRADE I

Beautiful and mysterious garden, little changed since 1750. The Dutch water garden – a long rectangular pool – reflects the orangery of Strawberry Hill Gothic design. But do also ask to see the collection of botanical watercolours known as the Frampton Flora.

Goldney Hall

Lower Clifton Hill, Clifton, Bristol BS8 1BH

☎ 0117 926 5698   FAX 0117 929 3414

OWNER The University of Bristol

LOCATION Top of Constitution Hill

OPEN 2 pm – 6 pm; 27 April & 11 May

ADMISSION Adults £1.50; Senior Citizens, Students & Children 80p (1996 prices)

FACILITIES Loos; cream teas in the Orangery

FEATURES Herbaceous borders; follies and garden buildings; glasshouses and conservatories to visit; interesting for children; holm oak hedge; many varieties of fruit; the *Chronicles of Narnia* were filmed in the grotto

ENGLISH HERITAGE GRADE II*

A Bristol merchant's extravagance, nearly 300 years ago. Ten acres in the middle of the City, with an elegant orangery, a gothic folly tower and the gorgeous Goldney Grotto, which sparkles with crystalline rocks among the shells and follies.

Hidcote Manor Garden

Hidcote Bartrim, Chipping Campden GL55 6LR

☎ 01386 438333

OWNER The National Trust

LOCATION Signposted from B4632, Stratford/Broadway Road

OPEN 11 am – 7 pm (6 pm in October); daily except Tuesday & Friday; 1 April to 31 October. Open Tuesdays in June

ADMISSION Adults £5.30; Children £2.60; Family £13.20 (2 adults & up to 4 children). RHS members Free

FACILITIES Parking; loos; facilities for the disabled; plants for sale; National Trust shop; licensed restaurant, coffee & lunches 11 am – 2 pm; teas 2.15 pm – 5 pm

FEATURES Herbaceous borders; follies and garden buildings; plantsman's garden; rock garden; modern roses; old roses; good topiary; woodland garden; plantings by Graham Thomas; tallest pink acacia *Robinia* × *ambigua* 'Decaisneana' (19m.) in the British Isles

ENGLISH HERITAGE GRADE I

NCCPG NATIONAL COLLECTIONS *Paeonia*

Probably the most influential 20th-century garden in the world – certainly the most important and most copied. Essential visiting for all garden owners.

Hodges Barn

Shipton Moyne, Tetbury GL8 8PR

☎ 01666 880202   FAX 01367 880373

OWNER Mrs Charles Hornby

LOCATION 3 miles south of Tetbury on Malmesbury Road from Shipton Moyne

OPEN 2 pm – 5 pm; Mondays, Tuesdays & Fridays; 1 April to 15 August. Plus 2 pm – 5 pm; 4 May & 6 July

ADMISSION £2.50

FACILITIES Parking; dogs permitted; loos; teas by arrangement

FEATURES Herbaceous borders; plantsman's garden; climbing roses; old roses; good topiary; woodland garden; daffodils; bluebells; cyclamen

A big garden – six acres – and all intensively planted. Terraces, courtyards and gardens enclosed by stone walls or yew hedges are planted to give year-round colour. One has *rugosa* roses underplanted with hellebores, forget-me-nots and early bulbs for winter. Shrub roses and climbers are another Hornby passion. The woodland garden is almost an arboretum of ornamental trees – birches, maples, whitebeams and magnolias – underplanted with daffodils and primroses. Hodges Barn is a garden of great energy and loveliness.

Hunts Court
North Nibley, Dursley GL11 6DZ
☎ 01453 547440

OWNER   T K & M M Marshall
LOCATION   Signposted in centre of village
OPEN   9 am – 5 pm; Tuesday – Saturday & Bank Holiday Mondays in spring; all year, except August. Also for NGS
ADMISSION   Adults £1.50; Children Free
FACILITIES   Parking; loos; access for the disabled; first-rate nursery attached; refreshments on NGS days
FEATURES   Plantsman's garden; climbing roses; modern roses; old roses

The best collection of old roses in the west of England, and still expanding. Keith and Margaret Marshall say they have 'the collector's touch of madness': the result is charming, peaceful and educational.

Kiftsgate Court
Chipping Campden GL55 6LW
☎ & FAX 01386 438777

OWNER   Mr & Mrs J Chambers
LOCATION   3 miles from Chipping Campden opposite Hidcote Manor
OPEN   2 pm – 6 pm; Wednesdays, Thursdays, Sundays & Bank Holiday Mondays; April, May, August & September; plus 12 noon – 6 pm on Wednesdays, Thursdays, Saturdays & Sundays in June & July
ADMISSION   Adults £3.50
FACILITIES   Parking; loos; plants for sale; tea-room in the house
FEATURES   Herbaceous borders; plantsman's garden; woodland garden; roses of every kind; colour plantings
ENGLISH HERITAGE GRADE   II*

Famous for its roses, especially the eponymous *Rosa filipes*, Kiftsgate is all about plants and the use of colour. The best example is the yellow border, where gold and orange are set off by occasional blues and purples. After some dull years, everything about Kiftsgate has revived again: new thinking, new plantings and new enthusiasm have restored its excellence.

Lydney Park Gardens
Lydney Park GL15 6BU
☎ 01594 842844   FAX 01594 842027

OWNER   Viscount Bledisloe
LOCATION   Off A48 between Lydney & Aylburton
OPEN   11 am – 6 pm; Sundays, Wednesdays & Bank Holidays; 30 March to 8 June
ADMISSION   £2.20, but £1.20 on Wednesdays
FACILITIES   Parking; dogs permitted; plants for sale; some souvenirs for sale; light teas

FEATURES   Fine conifers; woodland garden; deer park; rhododendrons, azaleas & camellias

A remarkable collection of rhododendrons planted over the last 45 years is the backbone to this extensive woodland garden. And not just rhododendrons, but azaleas and camellias too, all carefully planted to create distinct effects from March to June. The numbers are still growing, and include plants grown from collected seed and hybrids from distinguished breeders, many as yet unnamed, while others have yet to flower. Lydney is now recognised as one of the best rhododendron gardens in England.

Miserden Park
Miserden, Stroud GL6 7JA
☎ 01285 821303   FAX 01285 821530

OWNER   Major M T N H Wills
LOCATION   Signed from A417, or turn off B4070 between Stroud & Birdlip
OPEN   9.30 am – 4.30 pm; Tuesdays, Wednesdays & Thursdays; 1 April to 25 September. Plus 6 April & 29 June for NGS
ADMISSION   Adults £2.50
FACILITIES   Parking; dogs permitted; loos; access for the disabled; plants for sale
FEATURES   Herbaceous borders; fine conifers; planted by Gertrude Jekyll; good topiary; fritillaries; martagon lilies; roses, old & new; domed yew hedges; cyclamen; cedar walk replaced by new avenue (1994/95); new border (1997)
ENGLISH HERITAGE GRADE   II*

The Jacobean Cotswold house has wide views across the Golden Valley, while the open spacious gardens lie to the side. Most were laid out in the 1920's – a charming rose garden, the long yew walk and expansive herbaceous borders, but there is also an older arboretum and an Edwardian shrubbery. Very peaceful.

Owlpen Manor
Uley, Dursley GL11 5BZ
☎ 01453 860261   FAX 01453 860819

OWNER   Nicholas Mander
LOCATION   Off B4066 near Uley
OPEN   2 pm – 5 pm; Tuesday – Sunday & Bank Holiday Mondays; 1 April to 31 October
ADMISSION   House & Garden: Adults £3.50; Children £2. Garden only: Adults £2; Children £1
FACILITIES   Parking; loos; plants for sale; guidebooks & postcards for sale; licensed restaurant (noon – 5 pm)
FEATURES   Lake; old roses; good topiary; standard gooseberries
ENGLISH HERITAGE GRADE   II

Dreamy Cotswold manor house whose loveliness depends upon its site, but there is a small terraced garden with box parterres and overgrown topiary yews and plantings of roses and herbs, most of them added since 1980 by the present owners. The aim is to suggest an earlier garden 're-ordered conservatively' in about 1700. Owlpen is not worth a special journey, but the restaurant, the setting and the house all add up to a good place for an outing.

Painswick Rococo Garden

Painswick, Stroud GL6 6TH

☎ 01452 813204

OWNER   Painswick Rococo Garden Trust

LOCATION   Outside Painswick on B4073

OPEN   11 am – 5 pm; Wednesday – Sunday; 8 January to 30 November. Daily in July & August

ADMISSION   Adults £2.90; Senior Citizens £2.60; Children £1.50

FACILITIES   Parking; dogs permitted; loos; plants for sale; gift shop; licensed restaurant, coffee, teas & light snacks

FEATURES   Follies and garden buildings; garden sculpture; woodland garden; snowdrop wood; new herbaceous plantings in front of the gothic exedra (1995)

ENGLISH HERITAGE GRADE   II*

FRIENDS   The Painswick Rococo Gardens Trust was established in 1988 to preserve the gardens in perpetuity. Details from Lord Dickinson

Only ten years of restoration work lie behind the unique rococo garden at Painswick which has re-emerged from back-to-nature woodland. A white Venetian Gothic exedra, a Doric seat, the plunge pool, an octagonal pigeon house, a Gothic gazebo called the Eagle House, a bowling green, the fish pond and a Gothic alcove have all been reconstructed in their original positions thanks to the efforts of Lord Dickinson and the Painswick Rococo Gardens Trust. A remarkable garden and brilliant theatrical achievement.

The Priory

Kemerton GL20 7JN

☎ 01386 725258

OWNER   The Hon Mrs Healing

LOCATION   In Kemerton village

OPEN   2 pm – 6 pm; Thursdays; 29 May to 25 September Plus 25 May, 22 June, 13 July, 3 & 24 August, 7 September

ADMISSION   £1.50 in June, then £2

FACILITIES   Parking; dogs permitted; loos; access for the disabled; plants for sale; refreshments on open Sundays

FEATURES   Herbaceous borders; gravel or scree garden; plantsman's garden; old roses; particularly good in July-August

The Priory is a late-summer comet, brilliant in August & September when annuals & tender plants supplement the perennial colour planting. The late Peter Healing spent 50 years perfecting his colour gradings. The results are worth a long journey to see and to study: the crimson border is the best there has ever been.

Rodmarton Manor

Rodmarton, Cirencester GL7 6PF

☎ 01285 841253

OWNER   Simon Biddulph

LOCATION   Off A433 between Cirencester & Tetbury

OPEN   2 pm – 5 pm; Saturdays; 17 May to 30 August

ADMISSION   £2.50

FACILITIES   Parking; loos; access for the disabled

FEATURES   Herbaceous borders; fine conifers; plantsman's garden; modern roses; old roses; good topiary; woodland garden; much renovation and replanting (1995 & 1996)

ENGLISH HERITAGE GRADE   II*

A splendid arts & crafts garden, with a strong design and exuberant planting. Simon Biddulph says there are 18 different areas within the garden, from the trough garden for alpine plants to the famous double herbaceous borders, now entirely renovated, which lead to a Cotswold summerhouse. Highly original – contemporary, but made without any contact, with Hidcote. Very photogenic.

Sezincote

Moreton-in-Marsh GL56 9AW

OWNER   Mr & Mrs D Peake

LOCATION   On A44 to Evesham, 1½ miles out of Moreton-in-Marsh

OPEN   2 pm – 6 pm (or dusk, if earlier); Thursdays, Fridays & Bank Holiday Mondays; 1 January to 30 November

ADMISSION   Adults £3; Children £1

FACILITIES   Parking; loos

FEATURES   Good collection of trees; follies and garden buildings; lake; oriental features; landscape designed by Humphry Repton; garden sculpture; subtropical plants; woodland garden; plantings by Graham Thomas; tallest maidenhair tree *Ginkgo biloba* (26m.) in the British Isles (and 5 other record trees)

ENGLISH HERITAGE GRADE   I

The house was the model for Brighton Pavilion, and seems inseparable from the cruciform Moghul garden that sets off its Indian façade so well: yet this brilliant formal garden was designed as recently as 1965. On the other side are sumptuous borders planted by Graham Thomas and a luscious water garden of candelabra primulas and astilbes around the Temple to Surya, the Snake Bridge and Brahmin bulls. Humphry Repton had a hand in the original landscape, but the modern gardens are far more satisfying.

Snowshill Manor

Broadway WR12 7JU

☎ & ◻FAX◻ 01386 852410

OWNER   The National Trust

LOCATION   In Snowshill village

OPEN   12 noon – 5 pm; daily except Tuesday; 24 March to 31 October, except Good Friday

ADMISSION   House & Grounds (timed ticket system): £5.40. Gardens only: £2

FACILITIES   Parking; loos; National Trust shop; refreshments

FEATURES   Herbaceous borders; follies and garden buildings; old roses

ENGLISH HERITAGE GRADE   II

Praised for its changes of levels and collection of curious artefacts – an armillary sphere and a gilt figure of St George and the Dragon, for instance. Snowshill is as curious as its maker, Charles Wade, and the spooky bric-a-brac which fills his house, but many visitors find it 'charming' or 'interesting'. Perhaps its finest ornament is the head gardener, a splendid fellow who persuaded his employers to let him run Snowshill as a completely organic garden, the National Trust's first.

Stancombe Park

Dursley GL11 6AU
☎ 01453 542815

OWNER   Mrs Basil Barlow
LOCATION   Off the B4060 between Dursley & Wotton-under-Edge
OPEN   Groups by appointment
ADMISSION   Adults £2.50; Children (under 10) 50p
FACILITIES   Parking; loos; access for the disabled; plants for sale
FEATURES   Good collection of trees; herbaceous borders; daffodils; follies and garden buildings; lake; plantsman's garden; modern roses; old roses; temple in folly garden restored (1995); new red border (1996); landscaping around the temple re-worked (1997)
ENGLISH HERITAGE GRADE   I

Stancombe has everything: a handsome house above a wooded valley, a flower garden of wondrous prettiness, and a gothic horror of an historic Folly Garden at the valley bottom. Start at the top. Peter Coates, Lanning Roper and Nadia Jennett all worked on the rose gardens and mixed borders by the house: there is more to learn about good modern design and planting here than any garden in Gloucestershire. Then wander down the valley where the path narrows and the incline steepens to a ferny tunnel, and start the circuit of the follies, best described as an open-air ghost train journey without the ghosts. Highly recommended.

Stanway House

Stanway, Cheltenham GL54 5PQ
☎ 01386 584469   FAX 01386 584688

OWNER   Lord Neidpath
LOCATION   On B4077
OPEN   2 pm – 5 pm; Tuesdays & Thursdays; June to September. And by appointment
ADMISSION   Adults £3.50; Senior Citizens £3; Children £1
FACILITIES   Parking; dogs permitted; loos; access for the disabled
FEATURES   Fine conifers; follies and garden buildings; woodland garden
ENGLISH HERITAGE GRADE   I

Huge terraces behind the house lead up to a pyramid folly. This was the apex of a vast cascade which ran down to a long still tank, now a grassy plateau halfway up the hillside. Little remains, though there are plans for restoration. Rather poignant.

Stowell Park

Northleach GL54 3LE
☎ 01285 720308   FAX 01285 720360

OWNER   Lord Vestey
LOCATION   A429 between Cirencester & Northleach
OPEN   2 pm – 5 pm; 18 May & 29 June
ADMISSION   £2
FACILITIES   Parking; loos; plants for sale on 18 May only; teas
FEATURES   Herbaceous borders; climbing roses
ENGLISH HERITAGE GRADE   II

A historic landscape in a magnificent position, with a pleasure garden and walled garden, stylishly replanted with advice from Rosemary Verey of nearby Barnsley.

Sudeley Castle & Gardens

Winchcombe GL54 5JD
☎ 01242 602308   FAX 01242 602959

OWNER   Lady Ashcombe
LOCATION   8 miles north-east of Cheltenham B4632
OPEN   10.30 am – 5.30 pm (4.30 pm in March); daily; 1 March to 31 October
ADMISSION   Adults £4; Senior Citizens £3.20; Children £1.80 (1996 rates)
FACILITIES   Parking; loos; plants for sale; good shop, rather upmarket; restaurant & tea-rooms
FEATURES   Herbaceous borders; fine conifers; follies and garden buildings; herbs; modern roses; old roses; good topiary; ruins of banqueting hall, now a pretty garden; new 'Tudor Knot' garden (1996); adventure playground
ENGLISH HERITAGE GRADE   II*

Sudeley tries hard and ought to be a good garden: Jane Fearnley-Whittingstall did the roses and Rosemary Verey planted some borders. There are fine old trees, magnificent Victorian topiary (mounds of green and gold yew) and a raised walk around the pleasure gardens that may be Elizabethan in origin. But it lacks intimacy, and some find the commercialism rather distasteful.

University of Bristol Botanic Garden

Bracken Hill, North Road, Leigh Woods, Bristol BS8 3PF
☎ & FAX 0117 973 3682

OWNER   University of Bristol
LOCATION   Take M5 Jct 19 towards Clifton, left into North Road before suspension bridge
OPEN   9 am – 5 pm; Monday – Friday; all year
ADMISSION   None (only on NGS days)
FACILITIES   Parking; loos
FEATURES   Good collection of trees; ecological interest; glasshouses and conservatories to visit; gravel or scree garden; plantsman's garden; rock garden; cistus; hebes; sempervivums; paeonies; aeoniums; salvias
FRIENDS   Good programme and privileges (e.g. seed list). Details from Membership Secretary c/o address above

An educational and accessible garden that bridges the gap between botany and horticulture. Because of the climatic conditions in its unusual position above the Avon gorge, it has a particularly fine collection of South African and New Zealand plants. And of course there is the rare endemic *Sorbus bristoliensis*.

Westbury Court

Westbury-on-Severn GL14 1PD
☎ 01452 760461

OWNER   The National Trust
LOCATION   9 miles south-west of Gloucester on A48
OPEN   11 am – 6 pm, Wednesday – Sunday & Bank Holiday Mondays; 29 March to 31 October. And by appointment
ADMISSION   Adults £2.50; Children £1.25 (1996)

FACILITIES   Parking; loos; facilities for the disabled; picnic area

FEATURES   Herbaceous borders; fruit of special interest; herbs; old roses; garden sculpture; good topiary; biggest holm oak *Quercus ilex* in the British Isles; new restoration of pool & fountain as shown by Kip in 1712

ENGLISH HERITAGE GRADE   II*

Restored over the last 20 years to become the best example of a 17th-century Dutch garden in England. A pretty pavilion, tall and slender, looks down along a long tank of water. On the walls are old apple and pear varieties. Parterres, fine modern topiary and a T-shaped tank with a statue of Neptune in the middle make up the rest of the garden, with an opulent rose garden (old varieties only) underplanted with pinks, tulips and herbs. Immaculately maintained.

Westonbirt Arboretum

Westonbirt, Tetbury GL8 8QS

☎ 01666 880220   [FAX] 01666 880559

OWNER   Forestry Commission

LOCATION   3 miles south of Tetbury on A433

OPEN   10 am – 8 pm (or dusk if earlier); daily; all year. Visitor centre open 10 am – 5 pm; daily; March to December

ADMISSION   Adults £3.20; Senior Citizens £2.20; Children £1. RHS members free after 22 March

FACILITIES   Parking; dogs permitted; loos; facilities for the disabled; plants for sale; gift shop; cafeteria

FEATURES   101 species of record breaking trees, including 25 maples (*Acer* spp.) and 21 *Sorbus*

ENGLISH HERITAGE GRADE   I

NCCPG NATIONAL COLLECTIONS *Acer*; *Salix*

The finest and largest arboretum in the British Isles: 500 acres, 17 miles of paths, 4,000 species, 18,000 trees. The maple glade is famous, and so are the bluebells in the part known as Silk Wood. Brilliantly managed by the Forestry Commission, whose Visitor Centre is a marvel of helpfulness. Brightest perhaps in spring and autumn, but the best place we know for a long winter walk.

GREATER MANCHESTER

Dunham Massey

Altrincham WA14 4SJ

☎ 0161 941 1025   [FAX] 0161 946 9291

OWNER   The National Trust

LOCATION   3 miles south-west of Altrincham off A56, well signposted (Dunham Massey Hall and Park)

OPEN   11 am – 5.30 pm; daily; 22 March to 2 November

ADMISSION   Gardens only: Adults £2.50; Children £1

FACILITIES   Parking; loos; facilities for the disabled; plants for sale; garden shop; large restaurant

FEATURES   Herbaceous borders; follies and garden buildings; lake; good topiary; interesting for children; hydrangeas; skimmias; Edwardian parterre; current holder of Sandford Award

ENGLISH HERITAGE GRADE   II*

Dunham Massey's 250 acres include an ancient deer park, a mediaeval moat made into a lake in the 18th century, an Elizabethan mount, an 18th-century orangery and some early landscape avenues. All remain as features of the grounds, but the National Trust has decided to major on its even more interesting Victorian relics – evergreen shrubberies, ferns and colourful bedding out schemes. Even that does not preclude the Trust from planting the most modern forms, such as the hybrids of *Rhododendron yakushimanum* and latest *occidentale* hybrid azaleas. The result is a potent cross-section of historical and modern styles with a solid core of Victorian excellence, while the standard of maintenance is perhaps the highest in any National Trust garden.

Fletcher Moss Botanical Gardens

Mill Gate Lane, Didsbury M20 8SD

☎ 0161 434 1877

OWNER   Manchester City Council

OPEN   8 am – dusk, Monday – Friday; 9 am – dusk, Weekend & Bank Holidays; all year

ADMISSION   Free

FACILITIES   Parking; dogs permitted; loos; facilities for the disabled; plants for sale; cafeteria

FEATURES   Fine conifers; lake; rock garden; bulbs; heathers; rhododendrons; orchid house; new tropical pool (1996)

A model municipal botanic garden, beautifully maintained but free to the public. There are good collections of small conifers, maples and aquatics. Excellent autumn colour: almost as good in spring.

HAMPSHIRE

Bramdean House

Bramdean, Alresford SO24 0JU

☎ 01962 771214   [FAX] 01962 771095

OWNER   Mr & Mrs H Wakefield

LOCATION   On A272 between Winchester & Petersfield

OPEN   2 pm – 5 pm; 30 & 31 March, 20 April, 18 May, 22 June, 20 July, 17 August, and by appointment

ADMISSION   Adults £2; Children Free

FACILITIES   Parking; loos; refreshments

FEATURES   Herbaceous borders; daffodils; fruit of special interest; climbing roses; old roses; good topiary; handsome cedars; paeonies; winter aconites; flowering cherries

ENGLISH HERITAGE GRADE   II

Beautifully designed by the late Mrs Feilden and immaculately maintained by her daughter, the gardens at Bramdean are much admired, and rightly so. Two wide herbaceous borders lead up from the terrace behind the house, against a backdrop of mature beeches and cedars. At the end of the central axis, steps lead to a walled kitchen garden whose central bed is planted with 'Catillac' pears, perennials and annuals. The vista runs yet further, through an orchard to a gazebo some 300 yards from the house. The views in both directions are stunning.

Brandy Mount House

East Street, Alresford SO24 9EG

☎ 01962 732189

OWNER   Mr & Mrs Michael Baron

LOCATION   Left into East Street from Broad Street, 50 yds first right

OPEN   11 am – 4 pm; 5, 8 & 9 February. 2 pm – 5 pm; 16 March, 27 April, 11 May, 22 June, and by appointment
ADMISSION   £1.50
FACILITIES   Dogs permitted; access for the disabled; plants for sale; extensive plant sales area; refreshments in summer
FEATURES   Herbaceous borders; gravel or scree garden; plantsman's garden; rock garden; snowdrops; young garden; paeony species; cardamines; collected plants; woodland plants; auriculas; stone troughs
NCCPG NATIONAL COLLECTIONS   Daphne; Galanthus

Essentially a plantsman's garden, but a plantsman who is also a distinguished plant collector and exhibitor of alpine plants. The garden is fascinating, immaculately maintained, and linked to a thriving small nursery which has propagated Galanthus by twin-scaling.

Broadlands
Romsey
☎ 01794 517888   [FAX] 01794 518884

OWNER   Lord & Lady Romsey
LOCATION   On Romsey by-pass by town centre roundabout
OPEN   12 noon – 4 pm; daily; 14 June to 7 September
ADMISSION   Adults £5; Senior Citizens £4.25; Children (12 – 16) £3.50
FACILITIES   Parking; loos; facilities for the disabled; plants for sale; gift shop; tea-rooms & picnic area by river
FEATURES   Herbaceous borders; landscape designed by Capability Brown; lake; woodland garden; tallest swamp cypress Taxodium distichum (36m.) in the British Isles
ENGLISH HERITAGE GRADE   II*

Classic Capability Brown landscape, handsome old trees and an open park which runs slowly down to a lake and the River Test.

Exbury Gardens
Exbury, Southampton SO4 1AZ
☎ 01703 891203   [FAX] 01703 243380

OWNER   Edmund de Rothschild
LOCATION   3 miles south of Beaulieu
OPEN   10 am – 5.30 pm (or dusk if earlier); daily; 1 March to 2 November
ADMISSION   Too complicated to detail: from £4.80 for Adults in high season, to £1.70 for Children in low season
FACILITIES   Parking; dogs permitted; loos; facilities for the disabled; plants for sale; gift shop; artist's studio; hot & cold lunches, cream teas
FEATURES   Herbaceous borders; lake; landscape designed by Humphry Repton; rock garden; old roses; woodland garden; candelabra primulas; rare trees; much new planting (1994/95); tallest shagbark hickory Carya ovata (21m.)in the British Isles (and five other tree records)
ENGLISH HERITAGE GRADE   II*

Rhododendrons, rhododendrons, rhododendrons: over one million of them in 200 acres of natural woodland. More than 40 have won awards from the Royal Horticultural Society. But there are magnolias, camellias and rare trees too, many grown from the original seed introduced by famous plant collectors. A place of wonder in May.

Fairfield House
Hambledon, Waterlooville PO7 4RY
☎ 01705 632431

OWNER   Mrs Peter Wake
LOCATION   East Street, Hambledon
OPEN   6 April, 11 May, 23 June, and by appointment
ADMISSION   Adults £2
FACILITIES   Parking; dogs permitted; loos; access for the disabled; plants for sale; teas on open day
FEATURES   Herbaceous borders; fine conifers; plantsman's garden; modern roses; old roses; beautifully grown roses; new meadow garden for wildflowers and butterflies (1995)

Fairfield is one of the best private rose gardens in England. Old roses and climbers were the late Peter Wake's main interest and he grew them unusually well. The shrubs are trained up a cat's cradle of string drawn between five wooden posts. The results make you gasp – 'Charles de Mills' ten feet high.

Furzey Gardens
Minstead, Lyndhurst SO4 7GL
☎ 01703 812464   [FAX] 01703 812297

OWNER   Furzey Gardens Charitable Trust
LOCATION   Off A31 or A337 to Minstead
OPEN   10 am – 5 pm (earlier in winter); daily except 25 & 26 December
ADMISSION   March – October: Adults £3; Senior Citizens £2.50; Children £1.50; Family £7. November – February: Adults £1.50; Senior Citizens £1; Children 50p; Family £3.50
FACILITIES   Parking; loos; plants for sale; small shop
FEATURES   Bluebells; bog garden; camellias; fine conifers; rhododendrons and azaleas; interesting for children; naturalised dieramas; heathers; spring bulbs
FRIENDS   No friends organisation but the gardens are owned by a charitable trust

Furzey demonstrates how woodland garden effects can be created in quite small areas. Parts are a maze of narrow curving paths running between hedges of Kurume azaleas, unforgettable in April – May, but the late summer flowering of eucryphias runs them close and the autumn colour of Nyssas, Parrotias and Enkianthus are worth a visit in October.

Highclere Castle
Highclere, Newbury RG15 9RN
☎ 01635 253210   [FAX] 01635 810193

OWNER   The Earl of Carnarvon
LOCATION   South of Newbury off A34
OPEN   11 am – 5 pm; Tuesday – Sunday & Bank Holiday Mondays; 4 May to 28 September
ADMISSION   Gardens only: Adults £3; Children £1.50
FACILITIES   Parking; loos; facilities for the disabled; plants for sale; shop; good restaurant
FEATURES   Herbaceous borders; landscape designed by Capability Brown; follies and garden buildings; rhododendrons and azaleas; particularly good in July-August; good collection of cedars; long avenues
ENGLISH HERITAGE GRADE   I
NCCPG NATIONAL COLLECTIONS   Rhododendron

A major historic garden – when Capability Brown landscaped it in the 1770s he left intact the avenues and follies of the early 18th century, but the park is dominated now by hundreds of huge cedars. Salvin's imposing house has 365 windows. Jim Russell advised on the planting in the walled garden, though the 'Secret Garden' is not among his best.

Hinton Ampner House

Bramdean, Alresford SO24 0LA

☎ & 📠 01962 771305

OWNER   The National Trust
LOCATION   On A272 1 mile west of Bramdean
OPEN   1.30 pm – 5 pm; Tuesdays, Wednesdays, Saturdays, Sundays & Bank Holiday Mondays; 16 & 23 March, then 29 March to 30 September
ADMISSION   Adults £2.80; Children £1.40
FACILITIES   Parking; loos; facilities for the disabled; teas & home-made cakes
FEATURES   Garden sculpture; good topiary; daffodils; yew trees
ENGLISH HERITAGE GRADE   II

The gardens at Hinton Ampner were laid out by the scholarly Ralph Dutton in the middle of this century with great regard to line, landscape and historical propriety. Statues, buildings, axes and views have been restored with exquisite judgement to lead you subtly along the exact route that Dutton intended. Good plantings, too.

Houghton Lodge Garden & Hydroponicum

Houghton, Stockbridge SO20 6LQ

☎ 01264 810502/810177   📠 01794 388072

OWNER   Martin Busk
LOCATION   Off A30 at Stockbridge
OPEN   2 pm – 5 pm; Mondays, Tuesdays, Thursdays & Fridays. 10 am – 5 pm; Saturdays, Sundays & Bank Holidays. 1 March to 30 September
ADMISSION   £2.50. Groups at special rates
FACILITIES   Parking; dogs permitted; loos; facilities for the disabled; plants for sale
FEATURES   Follies and garden buildings; glasshouses and conservatories to visit; lake; good topiary; daffodils; cyclamen; new herb garden (1996)
ENGLISH HERITAGE GRADE   II*

A lovely Gothic *cottage ornée* on a ledge above the River Test, with long spacious views down the river and across the watermeadows. Houghton also boasts the first hydroponic greenhouse open to the public, where plants are grown in nutrient-rich solutions instead of soil.

Longstock Water Gardens

Longstock, Stockbridge SO20 6EH

☎ 01264 810894   📠 01264 810439

OWNER   John Lewis Partnership
LOCATION   1½ miles north-east of Longstock Village
OPEN   2 pm – 5 pm; 1st & 3rd Sunday in the month; 1 April to 30 September
ADMISSION   Adults £2; Children 50p. (1996)

FACILITIES   Parking; loos; facilities for the disabled; plants for sale
FEATURES   Herbaceous borders; ecological interest; lake; plantsman's garden; woodland garden; interesting for children

Quite the most extraordinary and beautiful water garden in England, a little Venice where dozens of islands and all-but-islands are linked by small bridges and intensely planted with water-loving plants. Drifts of astilbes, primulas, kingcups, hemerocallis, musks, water irises and lilies. The ground is so soft that the islands seem to float, and a remarkable accumulation of peat has allowed such calcifuge plants as *Meconopsis betonicifolia* and *Cardiocrinum giganteum* to flourish in this chalky valley.

Longthatch

Lippen Lane, Warnford, Southampton SO32 3LE

☎ 01730 829285

OWNER   Peter & Vera Short
LOCATION   1 mile south of West Meon on A32, turn right by George & Falcon, & right again. 400m on right
OPEN   10 am – 5 pm; Wednesdays; 5 March to 27 August. And 2 pm – 5 pm; 9, 16 & 23 March; 20 April; 25 & 26 May; 22 June; 13 July; 31 August for NGS. Groups at other times by appointment
ADMISSION   £1.50
FACILITIES   Parking; loos; access for the disabled; plants for sale; tea & coffee; cake on NGS days
FEATURES   Alpines; plantsman's garden; new woodland area; damp-loving plants
NCCPG NATIONAL COLLECTIONS   *Helleborus*

Two acres of plantsmanship, best in spring when the garden is busy with hellebores, pulmonarias, primulas and bog plants.

The Loyalty Garden

Basing House Ruins, Redbridge Lane, Basing, Basingstoke RG24 7HB

☎ 01256 467294   📠 01256 26283

OWNER   Hampshire County Council
LOCATION   Signposted from M3 Jct 6
OPEN   2 pm – 6 pm; Wednesday – Sunday & Bank Holiday Mondays; 28 March to 28 September
ADMISSION   Adults £1.80; Senior Citizens & Children £1
FACILITIES   Parking; dogs permitted; loos; access for the disabled; tea-room open some Sundays
FEATURES   Herbs; parterres

A charming modern garden in the ruins of Old Basing castle: parterres of sage, santolina and box, and the motto of the Paulet family *Aymez Loyautei*, from which it takes its name.

The Manor House, Upton Grey

Upton Grey, Basingstoke RG25 2RD

☎ 01256 862827   📠 01256 861035

OWNER   Mrs John Wallinger
LOCATION   In Upton Grey village
OPEN   By appointment only: 10 am – 4 pm; weekdays; May to July
ADMISSION   £3.50, to include guidebook
FACILITIES   Loos; plants for sale; refreshments for groups

FEATURES Herbaceous borders; planted by Gertrude Jekyll; lake; climbing roses; old roses

ENGLISH HERITAGE GRADE II

Ros Wallinger has restored this Jekyll garden since 1984 using the original planting plans (now at Berkeley University, California). She has gone to great pains to recreate it exactly in all its Edwardian loveliness. Some of the roses were extinct here until re-introduced from private gardens in France and Italy after years of searching. The rich herbaceous borders drift from cool blues, white and pinks at either end to hot reds, oranges and yellows in the middle. There is no better place to study Gertrude Jekyll's plantings, but what makes it so special is that it is a 'young' garden again.

Mottisfont Abbey

Romsey SO51 0LJ

☎ 01794 340757　　FAX 01794 341492

OWNER The National Trust

LOCATION 4 miles north-west of Romsey

OPEN 12 noon – 6 pm (8.30 pm in June); Saturday – Wednesday (plus Thursday & Friday in June); 23 March to 29 October

ADMISSION £4 (but £5 in rose season)

FACILITIES Parking; loos; facilities for the disabled; plants for sale; good shop selling books and National Trust smellies; light refreshments

FEATURES Herbaceous borders; plantsman's garden; climbing roses; old roses; plantings by Graham Thomas; guided walks and 'rose clinics' in season; tallest *Paulownia tomentosa* (13m.) in the British Isles

ENGLISH HERITAGE GRADE II

NCCPG NATIONAL COLLECTIONS *Platanus; Rosa*

The park and gardens near the house are stately: Russell Page, Geoffrey Jellicoe and Norah Lindsay all worked here. But it is the old rose collection in the walled garden which has made Mottisfont's name. It is Graham Thomas's best known work, a collection of all the roses he has discovered, assembled, preserved and made popular through his writings. They are surrounded by brilliant herbaceous plantings: purple 'Zigeunerknabe' with yellow *Digitalis grandiflora*, for instance. Surely the best rose garden in Britain.

Petersfield Physic Garden

c/o 32 College Street, Petersfield GU31 4AF

☎ 01730 268583

OWNER Hampshire Gardens Trust

LOCATION Behind 16 The High Street

OPEN 9 am – 5 pm; daily except Christmas Day

ADMISSION Free

FACILITIES Facilities for the disabled; new Visitor Centre

FEATURES Herbs

A small town garden, surrounded by walls and planted with the fruit trees, roses, herbs and other plants that were known in the 17th century. An initiative of that most energetic and successful organisation, the Hampshire Gardens Trust.

Sir Harold Hillier Gardens & Arboretum

Jermyns Lane, Ampfield, Romsey SO51 0QA

☎ 01794 368787　　FAX 01794 368027

OWNER Hampshire County Council

LOCATION Signposted from A31 & A3057

OPEN 10.30 am – 6 pm (5 pm, or dusk if earlier, from November to March); every day except Bank & Public Holidays over Christmas

ADMISSION April to October: Adults £4; Senior Citizens £3.50; Children £1. November to March: Adults £3; Senior Citizens £2.50; Children £1. RHS members Free

FACILITIES Parking; loos; facilities for the disabled; plants for sale; light refreshments from Easter to end of October, & most weekends

FEATURES Good collection of trees; herbaceous borders; fine conifers; plantsman's garden; old roses; interesting for children; particularly good in July-August; particularly interesting in winter; 1993 winner of Sandford Award; fifty-one record trees, including eleven *Sorbus*

NCCPG NATIONAL COLLECTIONS *Carpinus; Cornus; Corylus; Cotoneaster; Hamamelis; Ligustrum; Lithocarpus; Photinia; Pinus; Quercus; 'Hillier'* plants

FRIENDS Details of the Friends scheme are available from the Curator: benefits include trips to other gardens, coffee mornings and a quarterly newsletter

Quite the most important modern arboretum in UK, for the number of its taxa – over 11,000 in 160 acres and totalling 40,000 plants. Every part of the garden is an education and a pleasure whatever the season or weather. Exemplary labelling and helpful guidebooks available. Hilliers' nursery shares a car park with the arboretum. Guided walks are given on the first Sunday in each month, and on Wednesdays from May to October.

Spinners

Boldre, Lymington SO4 5QE

☎ 01590 673347

OWNER Diana & Peter Chappell

LOCATION Signed off A337 between Brockenhurst & Lymington

OPEN 10 am – 5 pm; Tuesday – Saturday; all year. Other days by appointment

ADMISSION £1.50 from 14 April to 14 September; free at other times

FACILITIES Parking; loos; plants for sale

FEATURES Good collection of trees; herbaceous borders; fine conifers; gravel or scree garden; lake; plantsman's garden; woodland garden; rhododendrons; woodland plants; rarities and novelties; new peat beds & bog garden; biggest *Eucalyptus perriniana* in the British Isles

Only two acres, but what a garden! Spinners is a plantsman's paradise, where the enthusiast can spend many happy hours browsing at any time of the year. Everything is well labelled and Peter Chappell's nursery sells an extraordinary range of good plants: you always come away with a bootful of novelties.

Stratfield Saye House

Stratfield Saye, Basingstoke RG7 2BT

☎ 01256 882882   📠 01256 882345

OWNER   The Duke of Wellington

LOCATION   1 mile west of A33 between Reading and Basingstoke

OPEN   11.30 am – 6 pm (last admissions 4 pm); daily, except Friday; 1 June to 31 August. Plus Saturdays, Sundays & Bank Holiday Mondays in May & September

ADMISSION   House & garden: £5

FACILITIES   Parking; dogs permitted; loos; facilities for the disabled; plants for sale; gift shop; light refreshments

FEATURES   Herbaceous borders; fine conifers; lake; modern roses; camellia house in walled garden; American garden; tallest Hungarian oak *Quercus frainetto* (33m.) in the British Isles

ENGLISH HERITAGE GRADE   II

Not a great garden, but there are some fine incidents: a huge kitchen garden, a large and cheerful rose garden, rhododendrons in the park, and magnificent trees, including wellingtonias, named after the Iron Duke.

Tudor House Garden

Tudor House, Bugle Street, Southampton SO14 2AD

☎ 01703 635904   📠 01703 339601

OWNER   Southampton City Council

LOCATION   Bugle Street is just off the High Street in the old city

OPEN   10 am – 5 pm, Tuesday – Friday; 10 am – 4 pm, Saturdays; 2 pm – 5 pm, Sundays. All year (but house may be closed for restoration. Please telephone for information)

ADMISSION   Free

FACILITIES   Loos; facilities for the disabled

FEATURES   Herbs; good topiary; interesting for children

Sylvia Landsberg's unique reconstruction of a Tudor garden with knot garden, fountain, secret garden and contemporary plantings of herbs and flowering plants all crammed into a tiny area. Some call it a pastiche, others a living dictionary of Tudor garden language.

West Green House

Hartley Wintney, Basingstoke RG27 8JB

☎ 01252 844611

OWNER   The National Trust

LOCATION   In West Green village

OPEN   10.30 am – 3.30 pm; Wednesdays; 20 May to 31 July

ADMISSION   £3 (no reductions for National Trust members)

FACILITIES   Parking

FEATURES   Follies and garden buildings; woodland garden; parterres, exuberant plantings

West Green is open this year for the first time for five years. The new tenant, a dynamic Australian, has reclaimed, restored, remade and replanted the ingenious and amusing garden that Lord McAlpine made in the 1970s and 1980s. Formality, variety, invention and sheer beauty are here in abundance. Visit it, if you can, and see one of the greatest modern gardens come to life again.

White Windows

Longparish, Andover SP11 6PB

☎ & 📠 01264 720222

OWNER   Mr & Mrs B Sterndale-Bennett

LOCATION   In village centre

OPEN   2 pm – 6 pm; by appointment from March to September on Wednesdays. And for NGS

ADMISSION   £1.50

FACILITIES   Loos; access for the disabled; plants for sale

FEATURES   Herbaceous borders; plantsman's garden; old roses; young garden; euphorbias

NCCPG NATIONAL COLLECTIONS   *Helleborus*

One of the best small modern plantsman's gardens on chalk, remarkable for the way Jane Sterndale-Bennett arranges her material. Layer upon layer, White Windows bulges with good plants. Leaves and stems are as important as flowers, especially in the combinations and contrasts of colour – gold and yellow, blue and silver, and crimsons, pinks and purples. Much use is made of evergreens and variegated plants. Perhaps the most luxuriant chalk garden in Hampshire and all made since 1979.

HEREFORD & WORCESTER

Abbey Dore Court Garden

Abbey Dore, Hereford HR2 0AD

☎ 01981 240419   📠 01981 240279

OWNER   Mrs Charis Ward

LOCATION   3 miles west of A465, midway between Hereford – Abergavenny

OPEN   11 am – 6 pm; daily except Wednesdays; 1 March to 19 October. Other times by appointment to see hellebores

ADMISSION   Adults £2; Children 50p

FACILITIES   Parking; loos; facilities for the disabled; county gift gallery, teddy bears loft, good nursery; licensed restaurant, coffee, lunch & tea; all food home-made

FEATURES   Herbaceous borders; plantsman's garden; rock garden; handsome wellingtonias; ferns; hellebores; much new planting in 1996-97

Plantsman's garden on a damp cold site, with fine borders leading down to the ferny river walk. Mrs Ward says it has 'stopped getting any bigger', but the garden grows, changes and improves with every visit: very exciting.

Arrow Cottage

Weobley HR4 8RN

☎ 01544 318468   📠 01544 318468

OWNER   Jane & Lance Hattatt

LOCATION   1 mile from Weobley: off Wormsley road, signposted Ledgemoor & second right, first house on left

OPEN   2 pm – 5 pm; Wednesday – Friday & Sundays; 1 April to 31 July and 1 to 30 September

ADMISSION   Adults £2. Unsuitable for children

FACILITIES   Parking; loos; plants for sale; refreshments

FEATURES   Herbaceous borders; plantsman's garden; old roses; stream; new Gothic Garden (1995); new formal 50m rill (1996)

Young and expanding garden, or series of gardens, in the modern style. Garden rooms create the space for different styles, but all are maintained to the highest standard. Much plantsmanship and artistry.

Berrington Hall

Leominster HR6 0DW

☎ 01568 615721   FAX 01568 613263

OWNER   The National Trust

LOCATION   On A49, 3 miles north of Leominster

OPEN   12.30 pm – 6 pm (5 pm in October); Friday – Sunday in April & October; Wednesday – Sunday in May, June & September; daily in July & August. Plus 26–27 & 29–31 March & Easter Monday

ADMISSION   £1.70

FACILITIES   Parking; loos; facilities for the disabled; National Trust shop; licensed restaurant for lunch & teas

FEATURES   Landscape designed by Capability Brown; fruit of special interest

ENGLISH HERITAGE GRADE   II*

This majestic park is classic Capability Brown. The National Trust has laid out a one-mile parkland walk which takes in the best vantage points and shows you how the landscape would have looked when young. In the old walled garden, a comprehensive collection of Hereford Pomona is supplemented by old pear varieties, quinces and medlars.

Bryan's Ground

Stapleton, Presteigne LD8 2LP

☎ 01544 260001   FAX 01544 260015

OWNER   David Wheeler & Simon Dorrell

LOCATION   On minor road between Stapleton and Kinsham

OPEN   2 pm – 5 pm; Fridays & Sundays; 4 April to 22 September. Groups at any time by appointment

ADMISSION   Adults £1.50; Children 50p

FACILITIES   Parking; loos; access for the disabled; plants for sale; tea-rooms

FEATURES   Young garden; good modern design

A young garden: incredibly, the owners moved here as recently as November 1993. They have made wonderfully good use of the inherited structure (yew hedges and mature trees around the Surrey stockbroker house) and filled it with good plants. Full of original ideas – Frances Lincoln has commissioned a book about its making – Bryan's Ground is destined to become an influential and fashionable garden.

Burford House Gardens

Treasures of Tenbury, Tenbury Wells WR15 8HQ

☎ 01584 810777   FAX 01584 810673

OWNER   Treasures of Tenbury

LOCATION   A456 between Tenbury Wells and Ludlow

OPEN   10 am – 5 pm (dusk in winter); daily; all year

ADMISSION   Adults £2.50; Children £1; Groups (10+) £2 (by prior arrangement)

FACILITIES   Parking; loos; facilities for the disabled; tea-rooms (light lunches, afternoon teas), beverages

FEATURES   Herbaceous borders; fine conifers; plantsman's garden; climbing roses; old roses; *Rosa* 'Treasure Trove' NCCPG NATIONAL COLLECTIONS *Clematis*

Glamorous 4-acre modern garden to complement a stylish Georgian house. The fluid design is enhanced by interesting plants, imaginatively used and comprehensively labelled. There are good roses and herbaceous borders, and a magnificent series of water gardens, but Burford means *Clematis* – 200 varieties – cleverly trained, grown and displayed among shrubs. The new owners have plans to restore the balance within the garden which was slightly lost towards the end of John Treasure's time.

Dinmore Manor

Hereford HR4 8EE

☎ 01432 830322   FAX 01432 830503

OWNER   Dinmore Manor Estate Ltd

LOCATION   6 miles north of Hereford on A49

OPEN   10 am – 5.30 pm; daily; all year

ADMISSION   Adults £2.50; Children under 14 free

FACILITIES   Parking; loos; access for the disabled; plants for sale; plant centre; refreshments by arrangement

FEATURES   Pond; rock garden; old roses; 1200-year old yew

The 1920s rock garden is cheerfully planted with dwarf conifers and Japanese maples. The 1200-year old yew is an impressive sight.

Eastgrove Cottage Garden & Nursery

Sankyns Green, Shrawley, Little Witley, Worcester WR6 6LQ

☎ 01299 896389

OWNER   Malcolm & Carol Skinner

LOCATION   On road between Great Witley & Shrawley

OPEN   2 pm – 5 pm; Thursday – Monday; 27 March to 31 July. Also Thursday – Saturday; 4 September to 18 October. Also 14 & 28 September, 12 October

ADMISSION   Adults £2

FACILITIES   Parking; loos; access for the disabled; attached to good small nursery

FEATURES   Herbaceous borders; herbs; plantsman's garden; old roses

A tiny cottage garden attached to a cottage garden nursery. The scale itself is small, but crammed in are herbs, dwarf conifers, a bog garden, a 'secret garden' and such elements of modern plantsmanship as clever combinations of colour and form.

Eastnor Castle

Eastnor, Ledbury HR8 1RL

☎ 01531 633160   FAX 01531 631776

OWNER   Mr James & The Hon Mrs Hervey-Bathurst

LOCATION   2 miles east of Ledbury

OPEN   11 am – 4.30 pm; Sundays & Bank Holiday Mondays; 30 March to 5 October. Also daily except Saturdays in July & August

ADMISSION   Adults £2; Children £1

FACILITIES   Parking; dogs permitted; loos; access for the disabled; plants for sale; souvenirs and gift shop

FEATURES   Good collection of trees; fine conifers; lake; spring bulbs; tallest deodar *Cedrus deodara* (38m.) in the British Isles, plus eleven more record trees

ENGLISH HERITAGE GRADE   II*

Eastnor is all about trees. The arboretum planted by Lord Somers 150 years ago is now mature, and full of champion specimens. Many are rare. The conifers are particularly fine in early spring and complement the shaggy neo-Norman castle.

Hergest Croft Gardens

Kington HR5 3EG
☎ 01544 230160   [FAX] 01544 230160
OWNER   W L Banks
LOCATION   Signposted from A44
OPEN   1.30 pm – 6.30 pm; daily; 28 March to 26 October
ADMISSION   Adults £2.50; Children (under 15) Free; Groups (20+) £2
FACILITIES   Parking; dogs permitted; loos; plants for sale; home-made teas
FEATURES   Good collection of trees; herbaceous borders; fruit of special interest; old roses; rhododendrons; new autumn borders made to commemorate the garden's centenary in 1996; tallest *Cercidiphyllum japonicum* (25m.), *Toona sinensis* (27m.) and *Corylus colurna* (27m.) in the British Isles, among seventeen record trees
ENGLISH HERITAGE GRADE   II*
NCCPG NATIONAL COLLECTIONS *Acer; Betula; Zelkova*

Wonderful woodland garden and arboretum around a whopping Edwardian house. There is no end to the garden's marvels: huge conifers, magnificent birches, scores of interesting oaks, many acres of billowing rhododendrons. Plus good herbaceous borders, alpine collections, autumn gentians and kitchen garden, all on a scale that most of us have forgotten.

How Caple Court Gardens

How Caple, Hereford HR1 4SX
☎ 01989 740626   [FAX] 01989 740611
OWNER   Mr & Mrs Peter Lee
LOCATION   Signposted on B4224 & A449 junction
OPEN   9.30 am – 5.00 pm; Monday – Saturday; all year. Plus 10 am – 5 pm; Sundays; May to October
ADMISSION   Adults £2.50; Children £1.25
FACILITIES   Parking; dogs permitted; loos; facilities for the disabled; clothes shop; nursery; ice-cream & soft drinks
FEATURES   Fine conifers; old roses; garden sculpture; good topiary; woodland garden; Italian terraces
FRIENDS   New Friends Association: ask for details

Spectacular formal gardens laid out at the turn of the century (some Italianate, others more Arts & Crafts), and now undergoing restoration. Pergolas, loggias, dramatic terraces and *giardini segreti* with stunning views across a lushly wooded valley. How Caple is a garden of national importance, unjustly ignored by English Heritage and little known even locally.

Lakeside

Gaines Road, Whitbourne, Worcester WR6 5RD
OWNER   Chris Philip & Denys Gueroult
LOCATION   9 miles west of Worcester off A44 at county boundary sign
OPEN   2 pm – 6 pm; 13 April, 29 June
ADMISSION   Adults £2; Children Free
FACILITIES   Parking; loos; plants for sale; teas
FEATURES   Herbaceous borders; lake; plantsman's garden; climbing roses; old roses; woodland garden; young garden; ferns; hollies; heathers

Six acres of dramatic planting by the editor of *The Plant Finder*. Tender plants flourish against the old kitchen garden walls. Daffodils bred by Michael Jefferson Brown run down to the lake, where clean-limbed alders stretch gothically heavenwards. Throughout the garden are good plants, used well: Lakeside is an inspiration to new gardeners, and a place from which all can learn.

The Manor House, Birlingham

Birlingham, Pershore WR10 3AF
☎ & [FAX] 01386 750005
OWNER   Mr & Mrs David Williams-Thomas
LOCATION   In village
OPEN   11 am – 5.30 pm; 5, 9, 26 & Wednesdays in May; Wednesdays & Thursdays from 1 June to 17 July; Thursdays in September. Plus 2 pm – 5 pm on 25 May & 11 am – 5 pm for Rare Plants Fair on 29 June
ADMISSION   Adults £1.50; Children Free
FACILITIES   Parking; loos; access for the disabled; plants for sale; teas
FEATURES   Herbaceous borders; plantsman's garden; walled garden

The walled garden of this beautiful house has been laid out and planted in the best old/new style. Rare plants are used in unusual combinations to bring out contrasts and harmonies of form and colour.

Overbury Court

Overbury, Tewkesbury GL20 7NP
☎ 01386 725312   [FAX] 01386 725528
OWNER   Mr & Mrs Bruce Bossom
LOCATION   5 miles north-east of Tewkesbury
OPEN   For NGS, and groups by appointment
ADMISSION   Adults £1.50
FACILITIES   Parking; dogs permitted; access for the disabled; plants for sale
FEATURES   Good topiary; landscaped park; daffodils
ENGLISH HERITAGE GRADE   II*

A peaceful and expansive garden laid out around the large, handsome, Georgian house, with a view of the parish church worked in. Geoffrey Jellicoe, Aubrey Waterfield and Russell Page all worked on the design and planting and the result is a garden of exceptional harmony.

Queen's Wood Arboretum & Country Park

Dinmore Hill, Leominster HR6 0PY
☎ 01568 797052   [FAX] 01568 879305
OWNER   Hereford & Worcester County Council
LOCATION   Midway between Leominster & Hereford on A49
OPEN   9 am – dusk; daily; all year
ADMISSION   Free, but 50p for parking
FACILITIES   Parking; dogs permitted; loos; facilities for the disabled; gift shop; light meals from 9 am – 5 pm
FEATURES   Bluebells; fine conifers; woodland garden; interesting for children; wood anemones

A vigorous young arboretum, planted over the last 40 years with public amenity in mind. Wonderful for walking, whatever the season, and well run in a friendly, efficient manner so that visitors get the most from it.

Spetchley Park

Worcester WR5 1RS
☎ 01905 345224

OWNER   R J Berkeley Esq
LOCATION   2 miles east of Worcester on A422
OPEN   11 am – 5 pm; Tuesday – Friday & Bank Holiday Mondays, (plus 2 pm – 5 pm on Sundays); 1 April to 30 September
ADMISSION   Adults £2.70; Children £1.30
FACILITIES   Parking; loos; access for the disabled; teas & refreshments
FEATURES   Good collection of trees; herbaceous borders; daffodils; lake; plantsman's garden; rhododendrons and azaleas; modern roses; old roses; particularly good in July-August; deer park; good new plantings in the kitchen garden; naturalised lilies
ENGLISH HERITAGE GRADE   II*

In a classic English landscaped park, three generations of Berkeleys have created one of the best plantsman's gardens in the Midlands. Ellen Willmott was the owner's great aunt and many of the most exciting trees and shrubs date from her time. The planting continues: this garden offers something to everyone.

Stone House Cottage Garden

Stone, Kidderminster DY10 4BG
☎ & [FAX] 01562 69902

OWNER   Mr & Mrs James Arbuthnott
LOCATION   In village, 2 miles from Kidderminster on A448
OPEN   10 am – 5.30 pm; Wednesday – Saturday; 1 March to 18 October. And by appointment
ADMISSION   Adults £2
FACILITIES   Parking; loos; access for the disabled; excellent nursery attached
FEATURES   Alpines; herbaceous borders; herbs; plantsman's garden; climbing roses; old roses; young garden; particularly good in July-August; unusual climbing plants

The garden of a famous nursery, which it matches for the range of beautiful and unusual plants it offers. Exquisite plantings, and an eccentric collection of follies built as towers in the garden walls. Bliss.

Whitfield

Allensmore HR2 9BA
☎ 01981 570202

OWNER   G M Clive
LOCATION   8 miles south-west of Hereford on A465
OPEN   2 pm – 6 pm; 8 June or parties by appointment
ADMISSION   Adults £2; Children £1
FACILITIES   Parking; dogs permitted; access for the disabled
FEATURES   Good collection of trees; fine conifers; good topiary; huge grove of redwoods; tallest dwarf alder Alnus nitida and durmast oak Quercus petraea in the British Isles
ENGLISH HERITAGE GRADE   II

Whitfield has magnificent trees, planted by the Clives over the last 200 years. Zelkova serrata, a weeping oak, and a ginkgo planted in 1778 are some of the highlights, but there is nothing to beat the grove of twenty or so Sequoia sempervirens now pushing 150ft in height.

HERTFORDSHIRE

The Beale Arboretum

West Lodge Park, Cockfosters Road, Hadley Wood, Barnet EN4 0PY
☎ 0181 441 5159 x 304   [FAX] 0181 449 9916

OWNER   Edward Beale CBE
LOCATION   A111 halfway between M25 Jct 24 and Cockfosters station
OPEN   2 pm – 5 pm; Wednesdays; 1 April to 31 October. Plus: 2 pm – 5.30 pm, 18 May; 12 noon – 4 pm, 19 October
ADMISSION   £1.50, but £2 for NGS
FACILITIES   Parking; dogs permitted; loos; facilities for the disabled; refreshments
FEATURES   Good collection of trees; fine conifers; woodland garden; 300-year-old specimen of Arbutus unedo; new head gardener (1995)
NCCPG NATIONAL COLLECTIONS   Carpinus

10 acres of young arboretum, begun 25 years ago and shortly to double in size. Among the older specimens – Victorian cedars and redwoods – is a fine collection of trees planted with a view to the overall effect and underplanted with rhododendrons. Little known as yet, but undoubtedly to be reckoned among the great late 20th-century gardens.

Benington Lordship

Benington, Stevenage SG2 7BS
☎ 01438 869668   [FAX] 01438 869622

OWNER   C H A Bott
LOCATION   Off A602 Stevenage to Hertford, in Benington village
OPEN   12 noon – 5 pm; Wednesdays; April to September. 2 pm – 5 pm; Sundays; April to August plus 19 October. Telephone for details of snowdrop openings
ADMISSION   Adults £2.50; Season ticket £7
FACILITIES   Parking; loos; plants for sale
FEATURES   Herbaceous borders; rock garden; modern roses; old roses; snowdrops; heather garden; cowslip bank; lots of new plantings (1995); new wildlife pond (1996)
ENGLISH HERITAGE GRADE   II

A sort-of-Georgian house with a mock Norman gateway and the ruins of a real Norman castle in the grounds. The extensive gardens have been revived and replanted in recent years without destroying the older features: a Pulhamite folly, an Edwardian rock garden, a magnificent double herbaceous border, and a sense of spacious parkland.

The Gardens of the Rose

Chiswell Green, St Albans AL2 3NR
☎ 01727 850461   [FAX] 01727 850360

OWNER   The Royal National Rose Society

LOCATION 1 mile from junction of M1 & M25; 2 miles south of St Albans

OPEN 9 am – 5 pm (10 am – 6 pm on Sundays & Bank Holidays); daily; 14 June to 12 October

ADMISSION Adults £4; Groups £3.50; Disabled £3; Members & Children Free

FACILITIES Parking; dogs permitted; loos; facilities for the disabled; plants for sale; shop with rose books & souvenirs; licensed cafeteria

FEATURES Plantings by Graham Thomas; particularly good in July-August; roses, roses, roses

The most comprehensive rose garden in Britain, with a 1960s design which emphasises modern roses but also has excellent collections of old roses (in a garden designed by Graham Stuart Thomas), shrub roses, climbers, ramblers, miniatures, ground cover and wild species of rose. 30,000 rose bushes and 1,750 varieties, plus a further 600 unnamed novelties in the trial grounds. Ambitious plans to expand to 60 acres began with the opening of the 'Peace' garden in 1995: more new features are promised for this year.

Hatfield House

Hatfield AL9 5NQ

☎ 01707 262823   FAX 01707 275719

OWNER The Marquess of Salisbury

LOCATION Off A1(M) Jct 4

OPEN 25 March to 12 October. West gardens: 11 am – 6 pm; daily except Good Friday. East gardens: 2 pm – 5 pm, Mondays except Bank Holidays

ADMISSION Park & garden: Adults £3; Senior Citizens £2.80; Children £2.30

FACILITIES Parking; loos; facilities for the disabled; plants for sale; souvenirs and gift shop; licensed restaurant, coffee shop, snacks & hot lunches

FEATURES Herbaceous borders; herbs; good topiary; knot gardens; physic garden; organic kitchen garden

ENGLISH HERITAGE GRADE I

Interesting old/new gardens to suit a historic stately home. An 1890s parterre, very pretty, is the main feature. The new knot garden has plants dating from the 17th century (Lady Salisbury is a stalwart of the Tradescant Trust), but there are *allées*, *rondpoints*, more knots and parterres: the complete design vocabulary for how-to-Tudorise your garden.

Hill House

Stanstead Abbots, Ware SG12 8BX

☎ 01920 870013

OWNER Mr & Mrs Ronald Pilkington

LOCATION Next to the Parish Church in Capell Lane

OPEN 2 pm – 5 pm; 11 May, 8 & 15 June

ADMISSION Adults £2; Children 50p

FACILITIES Parking; loos; facilities for the disabled; plants for sale; art exhibition in June; home-made teas

FEATURES Herbaceous borders; glasshouses and conservatories to visit; lake; woodland garden

Outstanding plantings in the old kitchen garden include colour borders of purple and gold, weeping pears, and vegetables all

as neat as imaginable. Pretty woodland garden and lush growth around the small lake.

Knebworth House

Knebworth, Stevenage SG3 6PY

☎ 01438 812661   FAX 01438 811908

OWNER Lord Cobbold

LOCATION Off A1(M) Jct 7

OPEN 11 am – 5.30 pm; daily; 22 March to 7 April and 24 May to 2 September; plus weekends and Bank Holidays 12 April to 18 May and weekends only 6 September to 28 September

ADMISSION Adults £4.50; Children & Senior Citizens £4 (1996 prices)

FACILITIES Parking; loos; licensed cafeteria

FEATURES Herbaceous borders; planted by Gertrude Jekyll; designed by Lutyens; modern roses; sunken lawn; gold garden; wilderness; newly replanted Victorian maze (1994)

ENGLISH HERITAGE GRADE II*

FRIENDS Knebworth House Education and Preservation Trust – details from the Secretary c/o Knebworth House

Most of the garden was laid out by Lutyens, who married a daughter of the house. It has been well restored over the last 15 years with Jekyll plantings where appropriate. Inventive and harmonious, few gardens make such good use of space and perspective.

St Paul's Walden Bury

Whitwell, Hitchin SG4 8BP

☎ 01438 871218   FAX 01438 871229

OWNER St Paul's Walden Bury Estate Co

LOCATION B651 5 miles south of Hitchin

OPEN 2 pm – 7 pm; 20 April, 11 May, 1 & 22 June. And for groups by arrangement

ADMISSION Adults £2

FACILITIES Parking; dogs permitted; loos; facilities for the disabled; plants for sale; teas & home-made cakes

FEATURES Follies and garden buildings; garden sculpture; woodland garden; formal French landscape

ENGLISH HERITAGE GRADE I

Highly important as a unique example of the French 18th-century style – three hedged *allées* lead off into the woodland towards temples, statues and pools. The present owner's father (the Queen Mother's brother) was a past President of the RHS, and was able to blend rhododendrons, azaleas, maples and magnolias (plus much more besides) into parts of the woodland. A garden that appeals to historian, plantsman and artist equally.

ISLE OF WIGHT

Barton Manor Gardens & Vineyards

Whippingham, East Cowes PO32 6LB

☎ 01983 292835   FAX 01983 293923

OWNER R Stigwood

LOCATION Next to Osborne House on East Cowes Road (A3021)

OPEN 10 am – 5 pm; daily; 2 April to 29 August

ADMISSION   Adults £3.75; Senior Citizens & parties £3.20; Children Free (1 per adult)

FACILITIES   Parking; loos; plants for sale; gift shop with Barton Manor wines; cafeteria

FEATURES   Herbaceous borders; lake; modern roses; woodland garden; rhododendrons; royal connections; new tree carving of Dionysius (1994)

NCCPG NATIONAL COLLECTIONS *Kniphofia*

Laid out by Prince Albert, Barton was for many years part of the Osborne estate. He planted some of the best trees, including the cork plantation near the house. Now Barton is run as a commercial vineyard and the gardens are being expanded both for private enjoyment and as a commercial resource.

Mottistone Manor

Newport

☎ 01983 740012

OWNER   The National Trust

LOCATION   On B3399 west of Brighstone

OPEN   2 pm – 5 pm; Wednesdays and Bank Holiday Mondays; 27 March to 2 October

ADMISSION   £1.80

FACILITIES   Parking; dogs permitted; loos

FEATURES   Herbaceous borders; fine conifers; fruit of special interest; modern roses; bluebells; irises

A cleverly designed modern garden on a difficult site – steep and narrow. Much has been terraced and enclosed to allow a rose garden and good herbaceous borders. Most of the rest is given to a wide variety of fruit trees, trained to make avenues and underplanted with vegetables or spring bulbs. A model for this type of planting, and made long before the current fashion for ornamental *potagers*.

North Court

Shorwell PO30 3JG

☎ & FAX 01983 740415

OWNER   Mr & Mrs John Harrison

LOCATION   4 miles south-west of Newport, off B3323

OPEN   2.30 pm – 5 pm; dates to be announced; May, June & September. Groups at any time by appointment

ADMISSION   £1.60

FACILITIES   Parking; dogs permitted; loos; access for the disabled; plants for sale; refreshments

FEATURES   Herbaceous borders; fruit of special interest; planted by Gertrude Jekyll; lake; plantsman's garden; modern roses; old roses; subtropical plants; woodland garden; large plane trees; B & B for garden-lovers

The Harrison family which owns North Court inherited fine grounds with some magnificent trees and a clear stream at the bottom. John Harrison has extensively replanted it with a plantsman's enthusiasm and a special interest in tender exotica. Definitely a garden to watch in future.

Nunwell House

Brading, Ryde PO36 0JQ

☎ 01983 407240

OWNER   Colonel & Mrs J A Aylmer

LOCATION   Signed off A3055, 1 mile to the west of Brading

OPEN   1 pm – 5 pm; Monday–Wednesday; 29 June – 30 July & 18 August – 17 September

ADMISSION   House & garden: Adults £4; Senior Citizens £3; Children (under 12) £1. Gardens only: £2.50

FACILITIES   Parking; loos; plants for sale on 29 June

FEATURES   Good collection of trees; herbs; plantsman's garden; modern roses; garden sculpture; obelisks

ENGLISH HERITAGE GRADE   II

A pretty garden, largely replanted by Vernon Russell-Smith about 30 years ago: he also planted a small arboretum. The present owners have added some highly attractive garden ornaments and are restoring the fabric and the plantings after some years of neglect. Work continues: this year they have begun restoring the walled garden.

Ventnor Botanic Garden

Undercliff Drive, Ventnor PO38 1UL

☎ 01983 855397   FAX 01983 856154

OWNER   Isle of Wight Council

LOCATION   1½ miles west of Ventnor on A3055

OPEN   Dawn – dusk; daily; all year

ADMISSION   Garden: Free. Show House: 50p. Parking charges

FACILITIES   Parking; dogs permitted; loos; facilities for the disabled; plants for sale; new nursery specialising in rare plants from the garden; cafeteria & bar with snacks, tea/coffee, lunches

FEATURES   Herbaceous borders; plantsman's garden; subtropical plants; interesting for children; particularly interesting in winter; palms; olives; bananas; medicinal herbs from all over the world; tallest *Peumus boldus* in UK; largest collection of New Zealand plants in UK

NCCPG NATIONAL COLLECTIONS *Pseudopanax*

FRIENDS   Friends of Garden (Tel: 01983 855397), seed list distributions

Originally an offshoot of Hilliers Nursery, the Ventnor Botanic Garden is devoted to exotic plants. Many – perhaps most – are from the southern hemisphere but flourish in the unique microclimate of the 'Undercliff': widdringtonias from Zimbabwe and Tasmanian olearias, for instance. Almost destroyed by the gales of 1987 and 1990, the collection is rapidly forming again. The young head gardener has a wonderful eye for planting.

KENT

Bedgebury National Pinetum

Goudhurst, Cranbrook TN17 2SL

☎ 01580 211044   FAX 01580 212423

OWNER   Forestry Commission

LOCATION   1 mile east of A21 at Flimwell on B2079

OPEN   10 am to dusk; daily; all year

ADMISSION   Adults £2; Senior Citizens £1.50; Children £1.20

FACILITIES   Parking; dogs permitted; loos; plants for sale; cold drinks

FEATURES   Fine conifers; lake; particularly interesting in winter; rhododendrons; fungi; new Japanese glade planted 1996; eighteen record tree species, including two broadleaves

ENGLISH HERITAGE GRADE II*

NCCPG NATIONAL COLLECTIONS *Chamaecyparis lawsoniana* cvs.; *Juniperus*; *Taxus*

FRIENDS Details from the Curator

Take any of the trails through this magnificent woodland garden, or go to the excellent Visitors' Centre to see the cone collection, and the new exhibit which tells the story of the Great Storm of 1987. It is difficult to realise that all the plantings are less than 70 years old.

Belmont Park

Belmont, Throwley, Faversham ME13 0HH

☎ 01795 890202

OWNER The Harris (Belmont) Charity

LOCATION Signposted from A251 at Badlesmere

OPEN 2 pm – 5 pm; Saturdays, Sundays & Bank Holiday Mondays; Easter Sunday to September

ADMISSION Garden: Adults £2.75; Children £1

FACILITIES Parking; dogs permitted; loos; facilities for the disabled; plants for sale; teas

FEATURES Rock garden; shell grotto; rhododendrons; pets' cemetery; pinetum

ENGLISH HERITAGE GRADE II

Quiet parkland surrounds this handsome Samuel Wyatt house, while the pleasure gardens are so obviously for the pleasure of the owners, not for display, that they add considerably to the sense of domesticity. There is nothing spectacular or vulgar about Belmont.

Brogdale

Brogdale Road, Faversham ME13 8XZ

☎ 01795 535286   FAX 01795 531710

OWNER Brogdale Horticultural Trust

LOCATION 1 mile south-west of Faversham

OPEN 9.30 am – 5 pm; daily; Easter to Christmas. 10 am – 4 pm; daily; Christmas to Easter

ADMISSION RHS members Free

FACILITIES Parking; loos; access for the disabled; plants for sale; Excellent shop with rare fruit varieties for sale in season; light lunches & teas

FEATURES Fruit of special interest; interesting for children

NCCPG NATIONAL COLLECTIONS *Corylus*;   *Fragaria*; *Malus*; *Prunus* (cherry & plum; *Pyrus*; *Ribes*; *Vitis*

Brogdale describes itself as 'a living museum' and claims to have the largest collection of fruit cultivars in the world: more than 2,300 apples, 400 pears and 360 plums. There are demonstrations, exhibitions, workshops and events throughout the year. Over 400 different apples were shown (and available for tasting) at last year's Apple Day show. Fruit from the collections is sold, and scion wood supplied.

Chartwell

Westerham TN16 1PS

☎ 01732 866368   FAX 01732 868193

OWNER The National Trust

LOCATION A25 to Westerham then signposted from B2026

OPEN 11 am – 5.30 pm, Wednesday – Friday; 11 am – 5.30 pm, Saturdays, Sundays & Bank Holiday Mondays; April to October

ADMISSION Gardens only: Adults £2.50; Children £1.25

FACILITIES Parking; dogs permitted; loos; facilities for the disabled; National Trust shop; new Visitor Reception building (1996); restaurant

FEATURES Lake; modern roses

ENGLISH HERITAGE GRADE II*

The spacious and extensive gardens are well laid out and planted in a slightly old-fashioned style. One of the rose gardens has the variety 'Winston Churchill' but every part has a deep sense of history and all is maintained to a very high standard.

Crittenden House

Crittenden Road, Matfield, Tonbridge TN12 7EN

OWNER B P Tompsett

LOCATION 2 miles north of Pembury

OPEN 2 pm – 6 pm; 5 & 25 May

ADMISSION Adults £2; Children 25p

FACILITIES Parking; loos

FEATURES Herbaceous borders; lake; plantsman's garden; modern roses; old roses; *Malus* 'Crittenden'

Plantsman's garden built up by the owner over the last 40 years and still intensifying. Island beds surrounded by grass give an informal structure and there are three ponds, each planted differently. Fascinating plants everywhere – many given by famous gardeners and collectors, some collected by Ben Tompsett himself.

Emmetts Garden

Ide Hill, Sevenoaks TN14 6AY

☎ 01732 750367/750429

OWNER The National Trust

LOCATION Between Sundridge and Ide Hill off B2042

OPEN 11 am – 5 pm (last ticket 4 pm); Wednesdays, Saturdays, Sundays & Bank Holiday Mondays; 1 January to 2 November

ADMISSION Adults £3; Children £1.50; Family £7.50; Pre-booked groups £2

FACILITIES Parking; dogs permitted; loos; tea-room 2 pm – 5 pm (may close in bad weather)

FEATURES Rock garden; Italianate rose garden; rare trees and shrubs; autumn colour

ENGLISH HERITAGE GRADE II

A stiff walk up from the carpark brings you to this windswept hilltop garden, laid out in Edwardian times and maintained on a slim budget. The formal Italianate rose garden is pretty in July, but better still is the informal woodland garden laid out with trees and shrubs in the William Robinson style. Best in bluebell time.

Godington Park

Ashford TN23 3BW

☎ 01233 620773/612669   FAX 01223 612667

OWNER The Godington House Preservation Trust

LOCATION Godington Lane, Potters Corner A20

OPEN 2 pm – 5 pm or by appointment; Sundays & Bank Holidays; 1 June to 30 September. Also Easter Saturday to Monday

ADMISSION £1

FACILITIES Parking; loos
FEATURES Lake; garden sculpture; good topiary; formal Italianate garden; waterlilies
ENGLISH HERITAGE GRADE I

Godington is perhaps the prettiest house in Kent, a Jacobean mansion reworked in the 1920s by Sir Reginald Blomfield, who made the charming Italian garden (statues, loggia, summer-house). Add in the 18th-century park, the late 19th-century plantings and the woodland garden which the present owners have been making, and you have a garden of great charm and authenticity.

Goodnestone Park
Wingham, Canterbury CT3 1PL
☎ 01304 840107

OWNER Lord & Lady FitzWalter
LOCATION Follow brown tourist signs from B2046
OPEN 11 am – 5 pm; Mondays, Wednesday–Friday; 24 March to 24 October. 12 noon – 6 pm; Sundays; 31 March to 20 October
ADMISSION Adults £2.50; Senior Citizens £2.20; Children (under 12) 20p; Disabled in wheelchairs £1; Group (20+) £2.20; Guided Group £3
FACILITIES Parking; loos; facilities for the disabled; plants for sale; teas
FEATURES Herbaceous borders; old roses; snowdrops; good topiary; woodland garden; cedar walk; rhododendrons
ENGLISH HERITAGE GRADE II*

A handsome Palladian house associated with Jane Austen (her brother married a daughter of the house). Fine parkland, a formal garden in front of the house, a 1930s woodland garden (maples, camellias, azaleas) undergoing modern expansion, and good mixed plantings in the old kitchen garden.

Great Comp
St Mary's Platt, Borough Green, Sevenoaks TN15 8QS
☎ 01732 886154

OWNER Great Comp Charitable Trust
LOCATION 2 miles east of Borough Green B2016 off A20
OPEN 11 am – 6 pm; daily; 1 March to 31 October
ADMISSION Adults £3; Children £1
FACILITIES Parking; loos; facilities for the disabled; plants for sale; gifts, plants and souvenirs; refreshments at weekends & Bank Holidays
FEATURES Herbaceous borders; follies and garden buildings; lake; plantsman's garden; garden sculpture; woodland garden; ground cover; dwarf conifers; new walled garden (1994)
FRIENDS Great Comp Society, mainly to support the annual music festival in July and September

Great Comp is a controversial garden. Everyone admires the energy of its founder Roderick Cameron, and Clay Jones called it the best garden he had ever seen. Others consider the reliance on heathers, dwarf conifers and ground cover to be tedious, the modern follies hideous, and the meandering design plain boring. But go with an open mind and you will find much to admire.

Groombridge Place Gardens
Groombridge, Tunbridge Wells TN3 9QG
☎ 01892 863999   [FAX] 01892 863996

OWNER Andrew de Candole
LOCATION On B2110, 4 miles south-west of Tunbridge Wells
OPEN 10 am – 6 pm; daily; 28 March to 26 October
ADMISSION Adults £5; OAPs £4.50; Children £3.50
FACILITIES Parking; loos; facilities for the disabled; plants for sale; gift shops; light lunches and teas

Hever Castle
Edenbridge TN8 7NG
☎ 01732 865224   [FAX] 01732 866796

OWNER Broadland Properties Ltd
LOCATION 3 miles south-east of Edenbridge, signposted from M25 Jct 6
OPEN 11 am – 5 pm; daily; 1 March to 30 November
ADMISSION Adults £4.40; Senior Citizens £3.90; Children (5-16) £2.60; Family £11.40 (1996 prices)
FACILITIES Parking; dogs permitted; loos; facilities for the disabled; plants for sale; plant centre; shop; two restaurants
FEATURES Bluebells; follies and garden buildings; lake; rhododendrons and azaleas; old roses; good topiary; woodland garden; particularly good in July-August; new Tudor herb garden (1995); Christie's/HHA Garden of the Year in 1995; new 120-yds herbaceous border opening in June; new water-maze opening in July
ENGLISH HERITAGE GRADE I

One of the most important Edwardian gardens in England. The pretty moated castle sits in a park of oaks and firs (under-planted with rhododendrons) with a yew maze and formal neo-Tudor garden to one side. The best part is a spectacular Italian garden where a long pergola (cool dripping fountains all along) leads past a series of exquisite Italian gardens, stuffed with sculptures, urns, sarcophagi and other loot brought by William Waldorf Astor from Rome; it finally bursts onto a theatrical terrace and a 35-acre lake, hand-dug by 800 workmen.

Hole Park
Rolvenden, Cranbrook TN17 4JB
☎ 01580 241251   [FAX] 01580 241882

OWNER David Barham
LOCATION Off B2086 between Rolvenden & Cranbrook
OPEN 2 pm – 6 pm; 13, 20, 23 April; 4, 11, 21, 25 May; 25 June; 23 July; 12, 19 October
ADMISSION Adults £2.50; Children 50p
FACILITIES Parking; loos; access for the disabled
FEATURES Good design and good plants

A great garden, and little known. The drive runs under an avenue of horse chestnuts through classical parkland. The pleasure garden is Edwardian in origin, but revived and re-planted by the present owner. Solid hedges and clipped speci-mens of yew are everywhere: backing the excellent herbaceous borders, around the waterlily pond and framing a croquet lawn with standard wisterias. The flowery woodlands have palm trees in the dell, while the lake is surrounded by purple rhododendrons and orange azaleas. Bluebells, daffodils and wonderful views are added delights.

Ightham Moat

The National Trust, Ivy Hatch, Sevenoaks TN15 0NT

☎ 01732 810378   📠 01732 811029

OWNER   The National Trust
LOCATION   Signed from A25 in Ightham village
OPEN   11.30 am – 5.30 pm (opens 10.30 am on Sundays & Bank Holiday Mondays); daily except Tuesdays & Saturdays; 31 March to 1 November
ADMISSION   Adults £4; Children £2 (1996 prices)
FACILITIES   Parking; loos; facilities for the disabled; National Trust shop; light refreshments
FEATURES   Lake; woodland garden
ENGLISH HERITAGE GRADE   II

A moated Mediaeval manor in a wooded Kentish valley, with borders of pinks, old roses and lilies. Nothing very special, but dreamily English.

Ladham House

Goudhurst TN17 1DB

☎ 01580 211203

OWNER   Mr & Mrs Alastair Jessell
LOCATION   Left at Chequers Inn on Cranbrook road, then right to Curtisdem Green
OPEN   11 am – 5.30 pm; 4 & 26 May. And by appointment
ADMISSION   Adults £2 (£3 for private visits); Children (under 12) 50p
FACILITIES   Parking; dogs permitted; loos; teas
FEATURES   Good collection of trees; herbaceous borders; woodland garden; magnolias

Laid out by a botanist Master of the Rolls in the mid-19th century, and enthusiastically restored and updated by the present owner. Many new plantings (the rock garden was replanted last year) and some fine specimens, especially a deep red form of *Magnolia campbellii* which has been named 'Betty Jessell'.

Leeds Castle

Maidstone ME17 1PL

☎ 01622 765400   📠 01622 735616

OWNER   Leeds Castle Foundation
LOCATION   Jct 8 off the M20
OPEN   10 am – 5 pm, 1 March to 31 October (but closed on 28 June & 5 July); 10 am – 3 pm, 1 November to 28 February (but closed on 8 November & 25 December)
ADMISSION   Park & gardens: Adults £6.50; Senior Citizens & Students £5; Children £4; Disabled Adults £3; Disabled Children £1.80
FACILITIES   Parking; loos; facilities for the disabled; plants for sale; shop in Castle Greenhouse; refreshments in the 17th-century tithe barn
FEATURES   Herbaceous borders; herbs; lake; designed by Page; old roses; woodland garden; interesting for children; tallest *Acer cappadocicum* 'Aureum' (23m.) in the British Isles; new maze disappears into an underground grotto!
ENGLISH HERITAGE GRADE   II*
NCCPG NATIONAL COLLECTIONS *Monarda*; *Nepeta*

More a romantic castle than a garden, best seen across the lake, Leeds is run by a high profile charitable trust with a big advertising budget. The results are admirable, though the 'Culpeper Garden' is not one of Russell Page's best plantings.

Long Barn

Long Barn Road, Weald, Sevenoaks TN14 6NH

OWNER   Mr & Mrs Brandon Gough
LOCATION   3 miles south of Sevenoaks; end of village
OPEN   2 pm – 5 pm; 22 June, 20 July
ADMISSION   Adults £2; Senior Citizens £1; Children 50p
FACILITIES   Parking; loos
FEATURES   Herbs; old roses; rhododendron glade; pergola; parterres; secret garden; white garden
ENGLISH HERITAGE GRADE   II*

Chiefly of interest for its association with Harold Nicolson and Vita Sackville-West, and well restored to their period by the present owners. The strong designs and exuberant plantings of Sissinghurst are all here in their infancy.

Northbourne Court

Northbourne, Deal CT14 0LW

☎ 01304 611281   📠 01304 614512

OWNER   The Hon Charles James
LOCATION   Just beyond the village centre
OPEN   2 pm – 5 pm; Sundays; 1 June to 31 August
ADMISSION   Adults £3; Children & Senior Citizens £2.50
FACILITIES   Parking; occasional teas
FEATURES   Herbaceous borders; glasshouses and conservatories to visit; good topiary; Elizabethan walls and terraces
ENGLISH HERITAGE GRADE   II*

A series of smallish flower gardens, each intensely planted with cottagey perennials and, for the most part, arranged by the artist Aubrey Waterfield. Wonderful combinations of colours and shades.

Penshurst Place

Penshurst, Tonbridge TN11 8DG

☎ 01892 870307   📠 01892 879866

OWNER   Viscount De L'Isle
LOCATION   Follow brown tourist signs from Tonbridge
OPEN   11 am – 6 pm, Saturday & Sunday, March & October; All week, 28 March to 30 September
ADMISSION   House & gardens: Adults £5.50; Senior Citizens £5.10; Children £3; Family £14.50. Gardens only: Adult £4; Senior Citizens £3.50; Children £2.75; Guided tours for groups (20+) £6.50. Garden season ticket £20
FACILITIES   Parking; loos; access for the disabled; dried flowers for sale; self-service restaurant
FEATURES   Herbaceous borders; daffodils; lake; designed by Roper; climbing roses; modern roses; formal Italian garden; spring bulbs; new plant centre (1995)
ENGLISH HERITAGE GRADE   I

A garden with substantial genuine Tudor remains, but well restored and developed in recent years. A vast Italianate parterre dominates the immediate pleasure garden: it is planted with scarlet polyantha roses – another is planted as a Union Jack. There are borders by Lanning Roper and John Codrington, a 100-yard bed of paeonies, a new lake, and a brand new garden for the blind, straight off the peg at the Chelsea Flower Show in 1994.

Riverhill House Gardens

Sevenoaks TN15 0RR

☎ 01732 458802

OWNER The Rogers Family

LOCATION 2 miles south of Sevenoaks on A225

OPEN 12 noon – 6 pm; Sunday & Bank Holiday weekends; 29 March to 30 June. Plus 24 May to 1 June daily

ADMISSION Garden only: Adults £2.50; Children 50p

FACILITIES Parking; loos; small gift shop; home-made teas

FEATURES Bluebells; fine conifers; rhododendrons and azaleas; tallest *Magnolia* × *soulangeana* (13m.) in the British Isles

ENGLISH HERITAGE GRADE II

Riverhill is a handsome Queen Anne house with grand views on a stately hillside, surrounded by billowing rhododendrons.

Scotney Castle Garden

Lamberhurst, Tunbridge Wells TN3 8JN

☎ 01892 891081   📠 01892 890110

OWNER The National Trust

LOCATION On A21, south of Lamberhurst

OPEN 11 am – 6 pm (but 2 pm – 6 pm on Saturdays & Sundays); Wednesday – Sunday; 29 March to 2 November. Plus 12 noon – 6 pm on Bank Holiday Sundays & Mondays

ADMISSION Adults £3.60; Children £1.80

FACILITIES Parking; loos; access for the disabled; shop

FEATURES Lake; plantsman's garden; designed by Roper; woodland garden; rhododendrons; azaleas; water lilies; wisteria; good autumn colour; ruins of 14th-century Castle; new stream garden (1995)

ENGLISH HERITAGE GRADE I

Moated and abandoned castle surrounded by rhododendrons and azaleas: very romantic and very photogenic. Among the ruins are a herb garden and cottage garden, surprisingly appropriate and effective. Lanning Roper had a hand in it.

Sissinghurst Castle Garden

Sissinghurst, Cranbrook TN17 2AB

☎ 01580 715330   📠 01580 713911

OWNER The National Trust

LOCATION 1 mile east of Sissinghurst village, ½ mile off A262. Cross-country footpath from village

OPEN 1 pm – 6.30 pm; Tuesday – Friday; 28 March to 15 October. Plus 10 am – 5.30 pm; Saturdays, Sundays & Good Friday

ADMISSION Adults £6

FACILITIES Parking; loos; facilities for the disabled; plants for sale; National Trust gift shop; self-service restaurant

FEATURES Herbaceous borders; herbs; plantsman's garden; old roses; too many visitors have eroded the fabric of this famous and wonderful garden

ENGLISH HERITAGE GRADE I

Too well known to need description, Sissinghurst is part of every English gardener's education and a source of wonder and inspiration to which to return time and again. There is a 'timed ticket' system to restrict visitors to 400 at a time, which may mean waiting. Best visited out of season, in April, September or October.

Squerryes Court

Westerham TN16 1SJ

☎ 01959 562345   📠 01959 565949

OWNER J & A Warde

LOCATION ½ mile from A25, signposted from Westerham

OPEN 12 noon – 5.30 pm; Wednesdays, Saturdays, Sundays & Bank Holiday Mondays; 1 April to 30 September

ADMISSION Garden only: Adults £2.20; OAPs £2; Children £1

FACILITIES Parking; dogs permitted; loos; small shop in house; homemade teas

FEATURES Lake; old roses; good topiary; formal design; gazebo; ice-house; dovecote; Wolfe cenotaph

ENGLISH HERITAGE GRADE II

The gardens have been excellently restored with advice from Tom Wright since 1987, using a plan of the original garden made in 1731. Formal beds (box & santolina) lead to Edwardian borders, beautifully planted, and the 18th-century park beyond.

Stoneacre

Otham, Maidstone ME15 8RS

☎ 01622 862871   📠 01622 862157

OWNER The National Trust

LOCATION 1 mile south of A20; north end of Otham village

OPEN 2 pm – 5 pm; Wednesdays & Saturdays; 1 April to 31 October

ADMISSION Adults £2.20; Children £1.10

FACILITIES Parking

FEATURES Spring bulbs, autumn colour, strong design

Stoneacre is particularly interesting because the tenant since 1989 has been Rosemary Alexander, Principal of the English Gardening School at the Chelsea Physic Garden. This is where she works out her ideas and shows her students how the principles of design and planting look 'on the ground'. It is one of the most exciting new gardens we know, and in perfect harmony with the Tudorised house.

LANCASHIRE

Bank House

Borwick, Carnforth LA6 1JR

☎ 01524 732768

OWNER Mr & Mrs R G McBurnie

LOCATION 2 miles north-east of Carnforth off A6

OPEN 2 pm – 6 pm; Sunday; 6 July

ADMISSION Adults £1.50; Children Free

FACILITIES Plants for sale; tea & coffee

FEATURES Plantsman's garden; collection of carnivorous plants

A successful private garden made over the last 30 years by the present owners. It manages to shoe-horn such features as a woodland garden, gravel garden, old-fashioned rose collection and a mini-arboretum into two acres. But it works.

Hoghton Tower
Hoghton, Preston PR5 0SH
☎ 01254 852986   [FAX] 01254 852109
OWNER Sir Bernard de Hoghton Bt
LOCATION A675 midway between Preston & Blackburn
OPEN 1 pm – 5 pm; Sundays; Easter to 31 October. Also
11 am – 4 pm; Tuesday – Thursday; July & August
ADMISSION Adults £1; Children (under 5) Free
FACILITIES Parking; loos; gift shop; tea-room
FEATURES Herbaceous borders; rhododendrons & azaleas
ENGLISH HERITAGE GRADE II

A series of spacious courtyards and walled gardens surround
this fierce castellated house. Not a great garden, but the setting
is impressive and there are fine spring walks in the rhododendron woods below.

Leighton Hall
Carnforth LA5 9ST
☎ 01524 734474   [FAX] 01524 720357
OWNER R G Reynolds
LOCATION Signed from A6 junction with M6
OPEN 2 pm – 5 pm; daily except Saturday & Monday; 1 May
to 30 September
ADMISSION Adults £3.50; Children £2.30; Senior Citizens
& groups £2.95
FACILITIES Parking; loos; access for the disabled; plants for
sale; gift shop; tea-rooms
FEATURES Herbaceous borders; fruit of special interest;
herbs; old roses; 'caterpillar' path maze; first prize, Britain in
Bloom 1993 (north-west region)

The handsome semi-castellated house is set in lush parkland
with the moors as a backdrop, but the garden is in the old
walled garden, where rose borders, herbs and the gravel maze
bring a touch of fancy to the whole.

Rufford Old Hall
Rufford, Ormskirk
☎ & [FAX] 01704 821254
OWNER The National Trust
LOCATION 7 miles north of Ormskirk on A59
OPEN 12 noon – 6 pm; Saturday – Wednesday; 29 March
to 2 November
ADMISSION Garden only: Adults £1.70; Children 85p
FACILITIES Parking; dogs permitted; loos; access for the dis-
abled; National Trust shop; lunches & teas (no lunches on
Sundays)
FEATURES Herbaceous borders; rhododendrons and azaleas;
old roses

One of the National Trust's most successful re-creations, the
gardens are laid out in the Regency style around a remarkable
15th-century timber-framed house.

LEICESTERSHIRE

Belvoir Castle
Belvoir, Grantham
☎ 01476 870262   [FAX] 01476 870443
OWNER The Duke of Rutland

LOCATION 6 miles west of Grantham
OPEN 11 am – 5 pm; Tuesday – Thursday, Saturdays, Sundays
& Bank Holiday Mondays; 28 March to 30 September. Also
Sundays in October
ADMISSION Castle & gardens: Adults £4.50; Senior Citizens
£3.50; Children £3; Family £13
FACILITIES Parking; loos; gift shop; refreshments: lunches
and teas; picnic site
FEATURES Modern roses; woodland garden; tallest bird
cherry *Prunus avium* (28m.) and yew tree *Taxus baccata*
(29m.) in the British Isles
ENGLISH HERITAGE GRADE II

Formal gardens on the Victorian terraces beneath the castle.
The Spring Garden, a pretty woodland garden, has recently
been restored to its early 19th-century form and is open by
appointment to groups at any time of the year.

Burrough House
Burrough on the Hill, Melton Mowbray LE14 2JQ
☎ 01664 454226   [FAX] 01664 454854
OWNER Mrs Barbara Keene
LOCATION 6 miles west of Oakham
OPEN 1 pm – 6 pm; 4, 5, 11, 25 & 26 May, 8 June, 13 July,
24 & 25 August
ADMISSION £2
FACILITIES Parking; loos; plants for sale; home-made refresh-
ments
FEATURES Lake; rock garden; modern roses; woodland gar-
den; rhododendrons; new white summer garden (1995)

A 1920s garden revived and improved by the present owner.
A parterre, moon gate, Italian garden, rose garden, paeony
border, croquet lawn, woodland walk and secret garden are a
measure of what pleasure the garden is designed to offer.

Long Close
60 Main Street, Woodhouse Eaves, Loughborough
LE12 8RZ
☎ 01509 890616 (daytime)
OWNER Mrs George Johnson
LOCATION 4 miles south of Loughborough
OPEN 9.30 am – 1 pm and 2 pm – 5.30 pm; Monday –
Saturday; 1 April to 15 July. Also for NGS. Parties by appoint-
ment
ADMISSION Adults £2; Children 20p. Tickets from Pene
Crafts Gift Shop, opposite
FACILITIES Parking; dogs permitted; loos; access for the dis-
abled; plants for sale; teas on NGS days
FEATURES Fine conifers; old roses; woodland garden; rhodo-
dendrons; azaleas; heathers

A plantsman's garden, begun by the present owner 45 years
ago, and now magnificently mature. Five acres, crammed into
a long narrow site that spreads out at the end into woodland,
underplanted with massed rhododendrons and azaleas.

The University of Leicester Botanic Garden

Beaumont Hall, Stoughton Drive, Oadby LE2 2NA

☎ 0116 271 7725

OWNER   The University of Leicester

LOCATION   3 miles south of Leicester on A6 London Road opposite Racecourse: badly signposted

OPEN   10 am – 4 pm (3.30 pm Friday); Monday – Friday; all year except Bank Holidays

ADMISSION   Free

FACILITIES   Parking; loos; plants for sale

FEATURES   Fine conifers; glasshouses and conservatories to visit; rhododendrons and azaleas; rock garden; modern roses; old roses; cacti; succulents; heathers; fuchsias; tallest red maytree *Crataegus laevigata* 'Paul's Scarlet' (12m.) in the British Isles

NCCPG NATIONAL COLLECTIONS *Aubrieta*; *Chamaecyparis lawsoniana*; *Fuchsia*; *Hesperis*; *Skimmia*

FRIENDS   Membership offers newsletters, special access, plant exchanges, monthly meetings and guide. Application forms from: The Curator, Botany Dept., Leicester University, Leicester LE1 7RH

16 acres, and one of the best modern botanic gardens, with a wide variety of plants from historic trees to a 1980s ecological meadow. A pretty Edwardian pergola draped with roses, a well-planted rock-garden and a splendid display of hardy fuchsias from the National Collection all add to its interest.

Wartnaby Gardens

Wartnaby, Melton Mowbray LE14 3HY

☎ 01664 822549   📠 01664 822296

OWNER   Lady King

LOCATION   3 miles north of Melton Mowbray on A606. Left at A6 Kettley then 1 mile

OPEN   2 pm – 6 pm; 16 June, 21 July, and by appointment (preferably week-days)

ADMISSION   £2

FACILITIES   Parking; dogs permitted; loos; access for the disabled; plants for sale; refreshments available

FEATURES   Good collection of trees; fruit of special interest; glasshouses and conservatories to visit; old roses; colour borders

A model modern garden, where rare plants are displayed in an endless variety of situations and habitats. Roses feature significantly, with good herbaceous underplanting and satisfying colour schemes. Still expanding.

Whatton House

Long Whatton, Loughborough LE12 5BG

☎ 01509 842302   📠 01509 842268

OWNER   Lord Crawshaw

LOCATION   Jct 24, Kegworth A6 towards Hathern

OPEN   2 pm – 6 pm; Sundays & Bank Holiday Mondays; Easter to 30 August. And for NGS

ADMISSION   Adults £2; Senior Citizens & Children £1 (1996 prices)

FACILITIES   Parking; dogs permitted; loos; facilities for the disabled; plants for sale; refreshments

FEATURES   Good collection of trees; herbaceous borders; follies and garden buildings; fruit of special interest; rock garden; modern roses; old roses; climbing plants; bark temple; canyon garden; Chinese garden

ENGLISH HERITAGE GRADE   II

15 acres attached to a garden centre. Most of the features date from c.1900 but there has been much replanting in recent years. The Chinese garden sports some extraordinary mythological figures. There is also a mysterious 'bogey hole'. Great fun to visit.

LINCOLNSHIRE

Belton House

Grantham NG32 2LS

☎ 01476 566116   📠 01476 579071

OWNER   The National Trust

LOCATION   3 miles north-east of Grantham on the A607

OPEN   11 am – 5.30 pm; Wednesday – Sunday; 29 March to 2 November

ADMISSION   Adults £4.80; Children £2.40

FACILITIES   Parking; loos; facilities for the disabled; gift shop; lunches, teas, licensed restaurant

FEATURES   Herbaceous borders; follies and garden buildings; lake; snowdrops; good topiary; woodland garden; interesting for children; daffodils; biggest sugar maple *Acer saccharum* in the British Isles

ENGLISH HERITAGE GRADE   I

Grandeur and amenity go hand in hand at Belton. There are 1000 acres of wooded deer park, a Wyattville orangery, a Dutch garden and an Italian garden with statues and parterres. But the adventure playground and other facilities make it popular with all ages.

Doddington Hall

Doddington, Lincoln LN6 4RU

☎ 01522 694308   📠 01522 682584

OWNER   Anthony Jarvis

LOCATION   Signposted off the A46 Lincoln bypass

OPEN   Garden only: 2 pm – 6 pm; Sundays; 1 March to 30 April. House & garden: Wednesdays, Sundays & Bank Holiday Mondays; 1 May to 30 September

ADMISSION   House & Garden: Adults £3.80; Children £1.90. Garden only: £1.90; Children 95p

FACILITIES   Parking; loos; facilities for the disabled; licensed restaurant

FEATURES   Herbaceous borders; lake; old roses; turf maze; new wild garden and bog garden (1994); new topiary in courtyard (1995)

ENGLISH HERITAGE GRADE   II*

A ravishing Elizabethan house around which successive generations have made a successful Tudor-style garden. Simple and open at the front, Edwardian knots and parterres in the walled garden (thickly and richly planted), and then a modern herb garden and pleached hornbeams. Wonderfully harmonious.

Grimsthorpe Castle Trust Ltd

The Estate Office, Grimsthorpe Castle, Bourne PE10 0NB
☎ 01778 591205　　📠 01778 591259

OWNER　Grimsthorpe & Drummond Castle Trust Ltd
LOCATION　On A151 4 miles north-west of Bourne
OPEN　11 am – 6 pm; Thursdays, Sundays & Bank Holidays; 30 March to 28 September. Plus daily in August except Friday & Saturday
ADMISSION　Adults £3; Concessions £2
FACILITIES　Parking; loos; access for the disabled; tea-rooms (licensed)
FEATURES　Good collection of trees; landscape designed by Capability Brown; lake; modern roses; good topiary
ENGLISH HERITAGE GRADE　I

First Capability Brown, then a late Victorian Italian garden, still maintained with summer bedding. The most interesting feature is a formal vegetable garden, made in the 1960s before the craze for *potagers*, right below the Italian garden. Well designed and well maintained, but is it not too close to the house?

Gunby Hall

Gunby, Spilsby PE23 5SS
☎ 01909 486411

OWNER　The National Trust
LOCATION　2½ miles north-west of Burgh-le-Marsh
OPEN　2 pm – 6 pm; Wednesdays (plus Thursdays for garden only); 1 April to 30 September
ADMISSION　House & garden: Adults £3.50, Children £1.50. Garden only: Adults £2.50, Children £1
FACILITIES　Parking; dogs permitted; loos; access for the disabled; plants for sale
FEATURES　Herbaceous borders; fruit of special interest; herbs; old roses; Ghost Walk pond & border restored (1995); orchard gallery re-opened (1996)
ENGLISH HERITAGE GRADE　II

Ignore the parkland and make for the two walled gardens. Here is all the action: rich herbaceous borders, an arched apple walk, shrub roses, herbs and vegetables.

Riseholme Hall

Lincolnshire College of Agriculture & Horticulture, Riseholme LN2 2LG
☎ 01522 522252　　📠 01522 545436

OWNER　De Montfort University, Lincoln
LOCATION　2 miles north of Lincoln on A15
OPEN　Daylight hours; daily; all year. Special Open Day: 10.30 am – 4 pm; 11 May
FACILITIES　Parking; dogs permitted; loos; access for the disabled; refreshments for groups by arrangement
FEATURES　Good collection of trees; herbaceous borders; ecological interest; fruit of special interest; glasshouses and conservatories to visit; lake; rock garden; modern roses; old roses; woodland garden; heather garden; tender plants
ENGLISH HERITAGE GRADE　II

The old house has an 18th-century landscape – park, lake and broad trees. The Bishop's Walk is Edwardian: tender plants flourish between the yew hedge and brick wall. However the main garden is strictly educational, with demonstrations of roses, herbaceous plants, fruit and vegetables, alpine plants and annuals, all beautifully maintained and meticulously labelled.

Springfields Show Gardens

Spalding PE12 6ET
☎ 01775 724843　　📠 01775 711209

OWNER　Springfields Horticultural Society Ltd
LOCATION　1 mile from Spalding, off new bypass
OPEN　10 am – 6 pm; daily; 22 March to 11 May
ADMISSION　Adults £3; Senior Citizens £2.70; Children (accompanied) Free
FACILITIES　Parking; loos; facilities for the disabled; plants for sale; gift shop; restaurant and café
FEATURES　Lake; modern roses; woodland garden; millions of bulbs
FRIENDS　Associate Membership available: £10

Originally a cor blimey display garden for the Lincolnshire bulb trade, Springfields now offers fun and colour all through the season, with roses providing the midsummer display and bold bedding taking over until the autumn frosts. An eyeful of a garden, splendidly maintained.

LONDON

26 Thompson Road

London SE22 9JR
☎ & 📠 0181 693 4832

OWNER　Anthony Noel
LOCATION　Dulwich
OPEN　2.30 pm – 6 pm; 21 September
ADMISSION　Adults £2; OAPs £1
FEATURES　Good design

Anthony Noel's last garden in Fulham was much praised. This will be the first opening of his new garden: small, elegant and modern.

Cannizaro Park

West Side Common, Wimbledon, London SW19
☎ 0181 946 7349

OWNER　London Borough of Merton
LOCATION　West side of Wimbledon Common
OPEN　8 am – sunset, Monday – Friday; 9 am – sunset, Saturday Sunday & Bank Holidays; all year
ADMISSION　Free
FACILITIES　Parking; loos; some refreshments at summer weekends
FEATURES　Herbaceous borders; fine conifers; modern roses; woodland garden; azaleas; magnolias; summer bedding; tallest *Sassafras albidum* (17m.) in the British Isles
ENGLISH HERITAGE GRADE　II*

Famous for its azaleas, planted about 40 years ago and almost too much of a good thing when in full flower. Little known, even to Londoners, Cannizaro deserves recognition as one of the best Surrey-type woodland gardens in the country.

Capel Manor

Bullsmoor Lane, Enfield EN1 4RQ
☎ 0181 366 4442

OWNER   Capel Manor Corporation
LOCATION   A10 by Jct 25 of M25
OPEN   10 am – 5.30 pm (or dusk if sooner); daily; all year
ADMISSION   £3 Adults; £2 Senior Citizens; £1.50 Children
FACILITIES   Parking; dogs permitted; loos; facilities for the disabled; small shop; refreshments
FEATURES   Alpines; good collection of trees; herbaceous borders; daffodils; ecological interest; fruit and vegetables of special interest; glasshouses and conservatories to visit; herbs; lake; oriental features; plantsman's garden; good topiary; interesting for children; roses of every kind
NCCPG NATIONAL COLLECTIONS Achillea; Sarcococca

High profile demonstration garden attached to a horticultural college. Brilliant for new ideas, especially for small gardens: there is a walled garden, herb garden, knot garden, disabled garden, shade garden, an Italianate holly maze, a pergola, alpine beds and some historical recreations. Perhaps the best garden attached to a further education college.

Chelsea Physic Garden

66 Royal Hospital Road, London SW3 4HS
☎ 0171 352 5646   [FAX] 0171 376 3910

OWNER   Chelsea Physic Garden Company
LOCATION   Please look at your London A to Z
OPEN   2 pm – 5 pm, Wednesdays; 2 pm – 6 pm, Sundays; 6 April to 26 October. Plus 12 noon – 5 pm, 19 to 23 May & 2 to 6 June
ADMISSION   Adults £3.50; Students, Children & Unemployed £1.80
FACILITIES   Loos; facilities for the disabled; plants for sale; light refreshments
FEATURES   Herbaceous borders; glasshouses and conservatories to visit; herbs; 18th-century rock garden; new borders of herbs for perfume industry; largest Koelreuteria paniculata in England; new 'Garden of World Medicine' (1995)
ENGLISH HERITAGE GRADE   I
NCCPG NATIONAL COLLECTIONS Cistus
FRIENDS   Friends have unrestricted rights of entry in office hours: worth considering if you live nearby

This oasis of peace between Royal Hospital Road and the Chelsea Embankment started life in 1673 as a pharmacological collection, and has kept its original design, but it also has the oldest rock garden in Europe, the largest olive tree in Britain, a vast number of rare and interesting plants, and probably the last known specimen of the 1920s white Hybrid Tea rose 'Marcia Stanhope'.

Chiswick House

Burlington Lane, Chiswick, London W4 2RP
☎ 0181 742 1225

OWNER   English Heritage
LOCATION   South-west London on A4 and A316
OPEN   8 am – dusk; daily; all year
ADMISSION   Free

FACILITIES   Parking; dogs permitted; loos; access for the disabled; refreshments
FEATURES   Camellias; follies and garden buildings; glasshouses and conservatories to visit; worked on by Kent; parterres; summer bedding; luxuriant evergreens
ENGLISH HERITAGE GRADE   I

Laid out by Bridgeman and Kent for Lord Burlington, Chiswick is the best baroque garden in Britain, and the exquisite house is pure Palladian. A Duke of Devonshire added an Italian renaissance garden early in the 19th century, and a Camellia House with slate benches and huge bushes, mainly of old japonica varieties. Forget the dogs and the joggers – almost all free-entry gardens have a municipal heart – but explore the pattes d'oie, allées and ilex groves of the main garden on a hot July morning and you might be doing a Grand Tour of Italy 250 years ago.

Fenton House

Hampstead Grove, London NW3 6RT
☎ 0171 435 3471

OWNER   The National Trust
LOCATION   Entrances in Hampstead Grove near Hampstead Underground station
OPEN   2 pm – 5 pm; Saturdays & Sundays; March. 11 am – 5.30 pm; Saturdays, Sundays & Bank Holiday Mondays; and 2 pm – 5.30 pm; Wednesday – Friday; April to 31 October
ADMISSION   Adults £3.60; Children £1.75
FACILITIES   Loos
FEATURES   Herbaceous borders; herbs; old roses; restored Edwardian garden; new autumn border on north terrace (1995)

A country garden in Hampstead. Neat, terraced gardens near the house, rather more informal at the bottom. Not outstandingly flowerful, but the hedges are good and plants are firmly trained: definitely worth knowing.

Ham House

Richmond TW10 7RS
☎ 0181 940 1950

OWNER   The National Trust
LOCATION   On River Thames, signed from A307
OPEN   10.30 am – 6 pm, or dusk, if earlier; daily except Fridays, Christmas & New Year; all year
ADMISSION   Gardens: free
FACILITIES   Parking; loos; facilities for the disabled; National Trust shop; restaurant open when house open
FEATURES   Fruit of special interest; herbs; climbing roses; modern roses; parterres; holm oak avenue
ENGLISH HERITAGE GRADE   II*
FRIENDS   A new appeal will be launched this spring to raise funds for further period ornaments and embellishments for the garden

A modern re-creation of the 17th-century original. The best bit is a grand series of hornbeam enclosures with white summerhouses and seats. Less successful is a stodgy parterre of lavender, santolina and box. Acres of crunchy gravel: the National Trust at its most sanitised.

Hampton Court Palace

KT8 9AU

☎ 0181 781 9500

OWNER   Historic Royal Palaces Agency

LOCATION   North side of Kingston bridge over the Thames on A308 Jct with A309

OPEN   Park: dawn – dusk; daily; all year. King's Privy Garden: 9.30 am – 5.30 pm (1 April to mid October) & 9.30 am – 4 pm (mid October to 31 March)

ADMISSION   Parking £1.75. Privy Garden: Adults £1.70; Children £1

FACILITIES   Parking; dogs permitted; loos; access for the disabled; shop

FEATURES   Herbaceous borders; fruit of special interest; herbs; lake; modern roses; old roses; good topiary; interesting for children; particularly good in July-August; famous maze; laburnum walk; knot gardens

ENGLISH HERITAGE GRADE   I

66 acres of famous garden and 600 acres of deer park. Here are some highlights: Charles II's Long Canal with radiating lime avenues to imitate the *pattes d'oie* at Versailles; the broad walk, now a herbaceous border 100 yards long; bowling alleys, tilt yards, the great maze and the Great Vine (actually 'Black Hamburgh'), the newly restored King's Privy Garden, the priory garden, knot garden and all those bulbs in spring.

Isabella Plantation

Richmond Park, Richmond

☎ 0181 948 3209   ℻ 0181 332 2730

OWNER   The Royal Parks Agency

LOCATION   Richmond Park

OPEN   Dawn – dusk; daily; all year

ADMISSION   Free

FACILITIES   Parking; dogs permitted; access for the disabled

FEATURES   Good collection of trees; fine conifers; lake; rhododendrons and azaleas; woodland garden; primulas

NCCPG NATIONAL COLLECTIONS   *Rhododendron* (Kurume azaleas)

FRIENDS   Friends of Richmond Park. Secretary, Howard Stafford, 0181 789 4601

42 acres of rhododendrons and azaleas under a deciduous canopy in Richmond Park. Best in May when the candelabra primulas flower and the hostas are in new leaf. Little known.

Kenwood

Hampstead Lane, London NW3 7JR

OWNER   English Heritage

LOCATION   North side of Hampstead Heath

OPEN   8 am to dusk (8.30 pm if sooner); daily; all year

ADMISSION   Free (to Park)

FACILITIES   Dogs permitted; loos; access for the disabled; refreshments during the daytime

FEATURES   Good collection of trees; herbaceous borders; lake; garden sculpture; woodland garden

ENGLISH HERITAGE GRADE   II*

These 100 acres of superb 18th century parkland around two glittering lakes were recently half-restored to Repton's original designs. Compromises were however made with the modern demands of public recreation. Despite the stalemate, Kenwood remains a haven of calm from London's busyness.

The Museum of Garden History

Lambeth Palace Road, London SE1 7LB

☎ 0171 261 1891   ℻ 0171 401 8869

OWNER   The Tradescant Trust

LOCATION   Between Lambeth Bridge and Lambeth Palace

OPEN   10.30 am – 4 pm (5 pm on Sundays); Sunday – Friday; early March to early December

ADMISSION   Donation

FACILITIES   Dogs permitted; loos; access for the disabled; plants for sale; books, cards and gifts; light refreshments

FEATURES   Herbs

FRIENDS   Friends of the Tradescant Trust : ask for details

The garden is small, and secondary to the Museum's collections, but designed as a 17th-century knot garden and planted with plants associated with the Tradescants. A garden for contemplation.

Myddelton House Gardens

Bulls Cross, Enfield EN2 9HG

☎ 01992 717711   ℻ 01992 651406

OWNER   Lee Valley Regional Park Authority

LOCATION   Off A10 onto Bullsmoor Lane: signposted at Bulls Cross. Or train to Turkey Street Station

OPEN   10 am – 3.30 pm; weekdays except Bank Holidays; all year. Plus last Sundays February to October

ADMISSION   Adults £1.50; Concessions 75p

FACILITIES   Parking; loos; access for the disabled

FEATURES   Good collection of trees; herbaceous borders; daffodils; plantsman's garden; pond; climbing roses; old roses; snowdrops; particularly interesting in winter

ENGLISH HERITAGE GRADE   II

NCCPG NATIONAL COLLECTIONS   *Iris*

FRIENDS   E A Bowles of Myddelton House Society c/o The Secretary, 102 Myddelton Avenue, Enfield EN1 4AG

Holy ground for plantsmen with a sense of history, E A Bowles' garden was abandoned for 30 years. Lee Valley Regional Park Authority has slowly started to restore it. The irises and roses are still impressive. In autumn, the colchicums and cyclamen match the carpets of crocuses and snowdrops of spring.

Osterley Park

Isleworth TW7 4RB

☎ 0181 560 5421

OWNER   The National Trust

LOCATION   5 miles west of central London on A4

OPEN   9 am – 7.30 pm (or dusk, if earlier); daily; all year

FACILITIES   Parking; dogs permitted; loos; facilities for the disabled; new National Trust shop; tea-room

FEATURES   Fruit of special interest; herbs; lake; woodland garden; particularly interesting in winter; fine rare oaks; autumn colour; tallest variegated chestnut *Castanea sativa* 'Albomarginata' (16m.) in the British Isles

ENGLISH HERITAGE GRADE   II*

Classical 18th-century landscape. Fine temple and semi-circular conservatory by Robert Adam. Good trees – cedars and oaks.

Royal Botanic Gardens, Kew

Kew, Richmond TW9 3AB

☎ 0181 940 1171

OWNER   Trustees of the Royal Botanic Gardens
LOCATION   Kew Green, south of Kew bridge, or Underground Station
OPEN   9.30 am – 6 pm (7 pm at weekends) or 30 minutes before dusk, if earlier; daily; all year except Christmas & New Year's Day. Glasshouses close at 5.30 pm
ADMISSION   Adults £4.50; Senior Citizens & Students £3; Children £2.50 (under 5 free)
FACILITIES   Parking; loos; facilities for the disabled; gift & book shop; orangery & pavilion restaurants & bakery
FEATURES   Alpines; good collection of trees; herbaceous borders; fine conifers; ecological interest; follies and garden buildings; fruit of special interest; glasshouses and conservatories to visit; gravel or scree garden; herbs; lake; oriental features; plantsman's garden; rock garden; climbing roses; modern roses; old roses; garden sculpture; snowdrops; subtropical plants; woodland garden; interesting for children; particularly interesting in winter; heather gardens; 138 record trees – more than any other garden in the British Isles – including 38 different oaks (*Quercus sp.*)
ENGLISH HERITAGE GRADE   I
FRIENDS   Friends of Kew: very active and good value – write or telephone for details

Kew has such superstar status that it needs no description. Go in lilac time, if you wish, but go too in winter when there is much to see both in and out of the glasshouses. Visit the newly restored Palm House, as well as the new Princess of Wales Conservatory (worth a whole afternoon) and do not miss the alpine house. In summer there are very good bedding-out schemes, but the garden is plagued by Canada geese, which foul the grass, and aircraft noise.

Syon Park

Brentford TW8 8JF

☎ 0181 560 0881   [FAX] 0181 568 0936

OWNER   The Duke of Northumberland
LOCATION   Between Brentford and Isleworth, north bank of Thames
OPEN   10 am – 6 pm, or sunset if earlier; daily except 25 & 26 December; all year
ADMISSION   Adults £2.50; Children £2; Family (2+2) £5
FACILITIES   Parking; loos; access for the disabled; plants for sale; garden centre; shops, restaurants, all the fun of the fair
FEATURES   Good collection of trees; herbaceous borders; landscape designed by Capability Brown; fine conifers; follies and garden buildings; glasshouses and conservatories to visit; woodland garden; interesting for children; cacti; ferns; exhibition of gardening for the disabled; rose garden restored and replanted – opens in April; tallest *Catalpa ovata* (22m.) in the British Isles (and fourteen further record trees); tropical butterfly house
ENGLISH HERITAGE GRADE   I

Syon is a mixture of 18th-century landscape, 19th-century horticultural seriousness, 20th-century plantsmanship and 21st-century theme park. Splendid conservatories with good collections, worth visiting in winter.

Walpole House

Chiswick Mall, London W4 2PS

OWNER   Mr & Mrs Jeremy Benson
LOCATION   Parallel to A4 between Hammersmith flyover & Hogarth roundabout
OPEN   2 pm – 6 pm, 11 May
ADMISSION   Adults £1.50
FACILITIES   Plants for sale
FEATURES   Herbaceous borders; plantsman's garden; woodland garden
ENGLISH HERITAGE GRADE   II

A large town garden, designed and planted in the Hidcote style and made to seem much larger than its ⅔ acre. Big trees, a large lily-pond and densely planted herbaceous borders all contribute to the sense of *rus in urbe*.

MERSEYSIDE

Croxteth Hall & Country Park

Croxteth Hall Lane, Liverpool L12 0HB

☎ 0151 228 5311   [FAX] 0151 228 2817

OWNER   City of Liverpool
LOCATION   Muirhead Avenue East
OPEN   11 am – 5 pm; daily; 28 March to 30 September
ADMISSION   Walled garden: Adults £1; OAPs & Children 60p. Grounds free
FACILITIES   Parking; loos; facilities for the disabled; plants for sale; cafeteria
FEATURES   Herbaceous borders; fruit of special interest; glasshouses and conservatories to visit; herbs; interesting for children; current holder of Sandford Award
ENGLISH HERITAGE GRADE   II
NCCPG NATIONAL COLLECTIONS   *Fuchsia*
FRIENDS   Friends of Croxteth Hall & Country Park: details from Mr E E Jackson

Very much a public amenity, Croxteth Hall majors on fruit, vegetables and herbs – showing in its walled garden what visitors can try at home. Good greenhouses. Heart-warming.

NORFOLK

Blickling Hall & Garden

Blickling, Norwich NR11 6NF

☎ 01263 733084   [FAX] 01263 734924

OWNER   The National Trust
LOCATION   1 mile west of Aylsham on B1354
OPEN   11 am – 5 pm; daily except Monday & Thursday, but open every day in July & August; 23 March to 3 November
ADMISSION   Adults £3.20; Children £1.60
FACILITIES   Parking; loos; facilities for the disabled; plants for sale; National Trust shop; light snacks, lunches & teas

FEATURES Herbaceous borders; landscape designed by Capability Brown; lake; old roses; woodland garden; particularly good in July-August; herbaceous borders at peak July/August
ENGLISH HERITAGE GRADE II*

The garden with everything. Jacobean mansion, handsomely symmetrical; early landscape (Doric Temple, c.1735); smashing conservatory by Samuel Wyatt; mid-19th century parterre by Nesfield (topiary pillars); and 1930s herbaceous colour plantings by Nancy Lindsey (her masterpiece). Fabulous bluebells in the woods.

Bressingham Gardens & Steam Museum

Bressingham, Diss IP22 2AB
☎ 0137988 386

OWNER Alan Bloom
LOCATION On A1066, 3 miles west of Diss
OPEN 10 am – 5.30 pm; daily; 1 April to 31 October
ADMISSION Gardens & Steam Museum: Adults £3.80
FACILITIES Parking; loos; access for the disabled; plants for sale; refreshments in adjacent plant centre
FEATURES Bog garden; herbaceous borders; fine conifers; plantsman's garden; particularly good in July-August
FRIENDS Monthly lectures April – October

There is no better place to learn about herbaceous plants – what they look like, how they grow and how to place them. The Dell is a complex of island beds, which act as a trial ground for the herbaceous and alpine plants for which Alan Bloom is famous. Foggy Bottom contains Adrian Bloom's collection of conifers and exemplifies his ideas for planting them. Herbaceous interplantings are replacing the heathers: the results are fascinating.

East Ruston Old Vicarage

East Ruston, Norwich NR12 9HN
☎ 01603 632350   [FAX] 01603 664217

OWNER Graham Robeson & Alan Gray
LOCATION 3 miles north of Stalham on Stalham-Happisburgh road. Ignore 3 signposts to East Ruston
OPEN 2 pm – 5 pm; Wednesdays & Sundays; 4 May to 29 October
ADMISSION Adults £3; Children £1
FACILITIES Parking; loos; facilities for the disabled; plants for sale; tea-room
FEATURES Young garden; architectural plants; 'tropical' borders

This is a modern garden on a grand scale: 12 acres of firm design and extravagant plantings. Being close to the sea, the garden supports many plants that are usually too tender for East Anglia. The names of two of the garden rooms tell it all: the Tropical Border and the Mediterranean Garden.

Elsing Hall

Elsing, Dereham NR20 3DX
☎ & [FAX] 01362 637224

OWNER Mr & Mrs D H Cargill
LOCATION B1110 to North Tuddenham, then follow signs

OPEN 2 pm – 6 pm; Sundays; 1 June to 30 September; and by appointment
ADMISSION £3
FACILITIES Parking; dogs permitted; loos; plants for sale
FEATURES Good collection of trees; fruit of special interest; lake; old roses; kitchen garden; formal garden now mature; enlarged collection of old roses (1996)

A garden of great charm, whose owners have planted many good trees, roses and a formal garden to enhance the mediaeval house and its romantic moat. An avenue of ginkgos, a collection of willows and a small arboretum of trees chosen for their coloured bark are some of the most recent additions. And the garden expands.

Fairhaven Gardens Trust

South Walsham, Norwich NR13 6EA
☎ & [FAX] 01603 270449

OWNER Fairhaven Garden Trust
LOCATION 9 miles north-east of Norwich on the B1140
OPEN 11 am – 5.30 pm (Saturdays 2 pm – 5.30 pm); Tuesday – Sunday, plus Bank Holidays; 28 March to 1 October
ADMISSION Adults £3; Senior Citizens £2.70; Children £1
FACILITIES Parking; dogs permitted; loos; access for the disabled; small shop; new visitors' centre; new plant sales area; tea-room
FEATURES Bluebells; lake; woodland garden; rhododendrons; lilies; candelabra primulas

Basically an enormous plantsman's garden (200 acres) round one of the Norfolk broads. Rhododendrons and azaleas under a canopy of oak and alder, plus extensive plantings of candelabra primulas, lysichitons, astilbes, and other bog plants in and around the water. Splendid autumn colour.

Felbrigg Hall

Roughton, Norwich NR11 8PR
☎ 01263 837444   [FAX] 01263 838297

OWNER The National Trust
LOCATION Entrance off B1436, signed from A148 & A140
OPEN 11 am – 5.30 pm; Saturday – Wednesday; 28 March to 2 November
ADMISSION Adults £2; Children £1; Family (2+2) £4
FACILITIES Parking; loos; facilities for the disabled; plants for sale; National Trust shop; restaurant & tea-room
FEATURES Herbaceous borders; fruit of special interest
ENGLISH HERITAGE GRADE II*
NCCPG NATIONAL COLLECTIONS Colchicum

The best bit of Felbrigg is the walled kitchen garden, oriented on a large brick dovecote flanked by Victorian vineries. Fruit trees are trained against the walls (figs, pears, plums) and the garden laid to neatly grown vegetables with herbaceous borders along the box-edged gravel paths. Felbrigg's colchicums were the star of last year's RHS Great Autumn Show.

Holkham Hall

Holkham, Wells-next-the-Sea NR23 1AB
☎ 01328 710227   [FAX] 01328 711707

OWNER The Earl of Leicester
LOCATION Off A149, 2 miles west of Wells

OPEN 11.30 am – 5.30 pm; 30 & 31 March; 4 & 5 May. Then 1.30 pm – 5 pm; Sunday – Thursday; 25 May to 30 September. Park open daily
ADMISSION House: Adults £4; Children £2. Park free
FACILITIES Parking; dogs permitted; loos; access for the disabled; gift shop; garden centre; refreshments
FEATURES Landscape designed by Capability Brown; lake; garden sculpture
ENGLISH HERITAGE GRADE I

A big landscape garden, worked on by Kent, Brown and Repton. Mighty impressive. In the nearby garden centre (see Nurseries section) is a walled garden with several demonstration gardens – herbs, roses, perennials etc.

Mannington Gardens
Mannington Hall, Norwich NR11 7BB
☎ 01263 584175   FAX 01263 761214

OWNER Lord Walpole
LOCATION Signposted from B1149 at Saxthorpe
OPEN 12 noon – 5 pm; Sundays; May – September. And 11 am – 5 pm; Wednesday – Friday; June – August
ADMISSION Adult £3; Concessions £2.50; Children Free
FACILITIES Parking; loos; facilities for the disabled; roses for sale; light refreshments, teas
FEATURES Climbing roses; old roses
ENGLISH HERITAGE GRADE II

Mannington has a moated house, two lakes, a scented garden and handsome herbaceous borders, but the best part is the Heritage Rose Garden, made in association with Peter Beales, where thousands of old fashioned roses are displayed to illustrate the History of the Rose.

Oxburgh Hall
Oxborough, King's Lynn PE33 9PS
☎ 01366 328258

OWNER The National Trust
LOCATION 7 miles south-west of Swaffham on Stoke Ferry road
OPEN 11 am – 5.30 pm; Saturday – Wednesday; 29 March to 2 November
ADMISSION Adults £2.20; Children £1.10
FACILITIES Parking; loos; facilities for the disabled; gift shop; light lunches & tea
FEATURES Herbaceous borders; modern roses; French-style parterre; trained fruit trees
ENGLISH HERITAGE GRADE II

The baroque 19th-century parterre has been replanted by the National Trust with such herbs as rue and santolina making permanent companions for annuals and bedding plants. Good fruit trees in the walled garden: medlars, quinces, and mulberries. Not a great garden, but a good one.

Raveningham Hall
Raveningham, Norwich NR14 6NS
☎ 01508 548222   FAX 01508 548958

OWNER Sir Nicholas Bacon Bt
LOCATION Signed off A146 at Hales
OPEN 1 pm – 4 pm on Wednesdays; 2 pm – 5 pm on Sundays & Bank Holiday Mondays; 1 May to 31 July

ADMISSION Adults £2; Children Free
FACILITIES Parking; dogs permitted; loos; access for the disabled; plants for sale; refreshments on Sundays & Bank Holiday Mondays only
FEATURES Good collection of trees; herbaceous borders; modern roses
ENGLISH HERITAGE GRADE II

Raveningham is set in a splendid 18th-century park, but it is the modern plantings which are the main attraction now. Rare plants, beautifully arranged, are used in the long herbaceous border, and there is a young arboretum too. Raveningham also offers a splendid range of plants by mail order: enquiries to the Estate Office.

Sandringham House
Sandringham, King's Lynn PE35 6EN
☎ 01553 772675   FAX 01485 541571

OWNER H M The Queen
LOCATION Signed from A148
OPEN 10.30 am – 5 pm; Easter to October; (except 28 July to 7 August)
ADMISSION Adults £3; Senior Citizens £2.50; Children £1.50 (1996)
FACILITIES Parking; loos; facilities for the disabled; plants for sale; gift shop; restaurant & tea-rooms
FEATURES Herbaceous borders; lake; rhododendrons; azaleas; maples; hydrangeas
ENGLISH HERITAGE GRADE II*

The best of the royal gardens. The woodland and lakes are rich with ornamental plantings, and the splendid herbaceous borders were designed by Geoffrey Jellicoe, but it is the scale of it all that most impresses, and the grandeur too.

Sheringham Park
Gardener's Cottage, Sheringham Park, Sheringham NR26 8TB
☎ 01263 823778

OWNER The National Trust
LOCATION Jct of A148 & B1157
OPEN Dawn – dusk; daily; all year
ADMISSION Cars £2.50; Coaches £7.50
FACILITIES Parking; dogs permitted; loos; facilities for the disabled; refreshments
FEATURES Landscape designed by Capability Brown; fine conifers; lake; landscape designed by Humphry Repton; woodland garden; rhododendrons
ENGLISH HERITAGE GRADE II*

One of the best Repton landscapes outstanding, but fleshed out with a great early 20th-century collection of rhododendrons and glorified by a classical temple, designed by Repton but not eventually built until 1975. Currently undergoing substantial restoration as the rhododendron woods are cleaned up and replanted: interesting to study.

Wyke House
Mill Road, Bergh Apton, Norwich NR15 1BQ
☎ 01508 480322

OWNER Mr & Mrs R W Boardman

LOCATION Off A146 at Hellington Corner, 300 yds down Mill Road
OPEN 11 am – 6 pm; for NGS see Yellow Book
ADMISSION £1.50
FACILITIES Parking; dogs permitted; plants for sale; refreshments on open Sundays
FEATURES Plantsman's garden; grass garden (1995)

Up-and-coming plantsman's garden in 3½ acres of old orchard, with an array of plants – eucalyptus, salvias and bamboos – that is unusual in this part of the country.

NORTHAMPTONSHIRE

Althorp House
Althorp, Northampton NN7 4HQ
☎ 01604 770107   [FAX] 01604 770042

OWNER Earl Spencer
LOCATION Signposted from M1, Jct 16
OPEN 1 pm – 5 pm; 1-31 August
ADMISSION Adults £2
FACILITIES Parking; dogs permitted; loos; facilities for the disabled; plants for sale; gift shop; tea-room
FEATURES Fine conifers; formal gardens; biggest *Abies bracteata* (38m.) in the British Isles
ENGLISH HERITAGE GRADE I

Interesting more for its ex-royal associations than as a great garden, which it is not. But the 19th-century formal gardens are impressive and the traditional parkland deeply pastoral.

Boughton House
Kettering NN14 1BJ
☎ 01536 515731   [FAX] 01536 417255

OWNER The Duke & Duchess of Buccleuch & The Living Landscape Trust
LOCATION A43, three miles north of Kettering
OPEN 1 pm – 5 pm; Saturday – Thursday; 1 May to 15 September. Plus Fridays in August
ADMISSION Adults £1.50; OAPs & Children £1
FACILITIES Parking; dogs permitted; loos; facilities for the disabled; plants for sale; shop
FEATURES Herbaceous borders; modern roses; interesting for children; current holder of Sandford Award; adventure playground
ENGLISH HERITAGE GRADE I

A seriously important landscaped park dating from the early 18th century. Rides, avenues, *allées*, pools, canals and prospects.

Canons Ashby House
Daventry NN11 3SD
☎ 01327 860044   [FAX] 01327 860168

OWNER The National Trust
LOCATION Signposted from A5 & A422
OPEN 1 pm – 5 pm; Saturday – Wednesday; 21 March to 2 November. House and garden may close at end of September for rebuilding: ring to check
ADMISSION Adults £3.50; Children £1.70; Family £8.70

FACILITIES Parking; loos; facilities for the disabled; light lunches & teas
FEATURES Herbaceous borders; fruit of special interest; good topiary
ENGLISH HERITAGE GRADE II*

A rare survivor among gardens. The Drydens, who owned it, never really took to the landscape movement. The early 18th-century layout is intact and has been carefully restored by the National Trust. The terraces below the house (*very* pretty) are planted with clipped Portugal laurel and period fruit trees. A place to contemplate old Tory values.

Castle Ashby Gardens
Castle Ashby, Northampton NN7 1LQ
☎ 01604 696696   [FAX] 01604 696516

OWNER Marquess of Northampton
LOCATION Off A428 between Northampton and Bedford
OPEN 10 am – dusk; daily; all year
ADMISSION Adults £2.50; Senior Citizens & Children £1; Family £6
FACILITIES Parking; dogs permitted; facilities for the disabled; plants for sale; gift shops; refreshments
FEATURES Good collection of trees; landscape designed by Capability Brown; glasshouses and conservatories to visit; lake; good topiary; particularly interesting in winter
ENGLISH HERITAGE GRADE I

Much thought and money has been spent on restoring the gardens recently. The Italian formal gardens were among the first to be renewed, and the arboretum has been restocked. There are a stylish orangery and greenhouses by Sir Matthew Digby Wyatt but perhaps the best thing about Castle Ashby is the park – 200 acres of it, designed by Capability Brown.

Coton Manor
Guilsborough, Northampton NN6 8RQ
☎ 01604 740219   [FAX] 01604 740838

OWNER Ian Pasley-Tyler
LOCATION Signposted from A50 and A428
OPEN 12 noon – 5.30 pm; Wednesday – Sunday & Bank Holiday Mondays; Easter to 30 September
ADMISSION Adults £3; Senior Citizens £2.40; Children £1
FACILITIES Parking; loos; access for the disabled; plants for sale; home produce & gifts; tea-room
FEATURES Herbaceous borders; gravel or scree garden; lake; modern roses; woodland garden; bluebells; waterfowl; fifty different hebes; lots of pots; new herb garden (1994); new wild flower meadow (1995); new Mediterranean bank

A nicely designed and thoughtfully planted garden – rarities and common plants chosen for effect – made by three generations over 70 years. The standard of maintenance is excellent, and the presence of a few ornamental birds adds quite another dimension to a visit.

Cottesbrooke Hall
Northampton NN6 8PF
☎ 01604 505808   [FAX] 01604 505619

OWNER Captain & Mrs John Macdonald-Buchanan
LOCATION 10 miles north of Northampton

OPEN 2 pm – 5.30 pm; Wednesday-Friday & Bank Holiday Mondays & Sundays in September; Easter to 30 September. House closed on Wednesdays & Fridays

ADMISSION House & Garden £4. Garden only: Adults £2.50; Children £1.25. Groups by appointment

FACILITIES Parking; loos; plants for sale; tea/coffee & cold drinks

FEATURES Herbaceous borders; old roses; garden sculpture

ENGLISH HERITAGE GRADE II

The garden with everything: a two-mile drive, majestic parkland, a classical bridge, a fabulously pretty house, an 18th-century park, lakes, waterfalls, bluebell woods, rhododendrons, acres of daffodils, 27 varieties of snowdrop, half-a-dozen garden rooms, Scheemaker's statues from Stowe, an armillary garden, pergolas, *allées*, 300-year old cedars, new developments every year, immaculate maintenance, an enlightened owner, a brilliant head gardener, plants a-plenty, and the signatures of Geoffrey Jellicoe and Sylvia Crowe among the designers who have helped to develop it. If only more people knew of it...

Holdenby House Gardens

Holdenby, Northampton NN6 8DJ

☎ 01604 770074   ☏ 01604 770962

OWNER Mr & Mrs James Lowther

LOCATION 6 miles north-west of Northampton, off A50 or A428

OPEN 2 pm – 6 pm; Sunday – Friday; 30 March to 30 September

ADMISSION Adults £3.75; Senior Citizens £2.25; Children £2

FACILITIES Parking; dogs permitted; loos; facilities for the disabled; plants for sale; souvenirs and crafts for sale; tea-room in original Victorian kitchen

FEATURES Herbaceous borders; herbs; old roses; interesting for children; Elizabethan-style garden; fragrant and silver borders; current holder of Sandford Award

ENGLISH HERITAGE GRADE II*

Pretty modern gardens designed and planted by the present owners with help from Rosemary Verey. The Elizabethan-style garden uses only plants available in 1580.

The Old Rectory, Sudborough

Sudborough NN14 3BX

☎ 01832 733247   ☏ 01832 733832

OWNER Mr & Mrs A P Huntington

LOCATION In village centre, by church, off A6116

OPEN By appointment

ADMISSION Adults £2.50; Children Free

FACILITIES Loos; plants for sale; refreshments by arrangement

FEATURES Herbaceous borders; fruit of special interest; herbs; modern roses; old roses; handsome new *potager*

Neat new garden, three acres in size, around a handsome Georgian rectory. Good snowdrops and hellebores; unusual vegetables. The garden is thickly and thoughtfully planted so that every season is rich in interest.

Rockingham Castle

Market Harborough LE16 8TH

☎ 01586 770240   ☏ 01586 771692

OWNER Cdr L M M Saunders Watson

LOCATION 2 miles north of Corby on A6003

OPEN 1 pm – 5 pm; Sundays, Thursdays, Bank Holiday Mondays & following Tuesdays (plus all Tuesdays in August); Easter Sunday to 30 September

ADMISSION Adults £2.50

FACILITIES Parking; dogs permitted; loos; access for the disabled; tea-room

FEATURES Good collection of trees; herbaceous borders; old roses; current holder of Sandford Award

ENGLISH HERITAGE GRADE II*

12 acres around the historic castle. The formal circular rose garden on the site of the old keep is surrounded by a billowing 400 year old yew hedge. The wild garden in a ravine was replanted 20 years ago as a mini-arboretum: very effective.

Sulgrave Manor

Sulgrave, Banbury OX17 2SD

☎ & ☏ 01295 760205

OWNER Sulgrave Manor Board

LOCATION 7 miles from Banbury

OPEN 10.30 am – 1 pm (but mornings by appointment only on weekdays except in August) & 2 pm – 5.30 pm (4.30 pm in March, November & December); daily except Wednesdays (but weekends only in March, November & December); 1 March to 24 December, plus 27 to 31 December

ADMISSION Adults £3.50; Children £1.75

FACILITIES Parking; dogs permitted; loos; access for the disabled; plants for sale; tea-room

FEATURES Herbaceous borders; fruit of special interest; herbs; modern roses; good topiary

ENGLISH HERITAGE GRADE II

Famous (and highly visitable) for two reasons: first, its association with George Washington; second, its formal design, unchanged since it was laid out by Sir Reginald Blomfield in 1921.

NORTHUMBERLAND

Belsay Hall

Belsay, Newcastle-upon-Tyne NE20 0DX

☎ 01661 881636   ☏ 01661 881043

OWNER English Heritage

LOCATION At Belsay on A696 Ponteland to Jedburgh road

OPEN 10 am – 6 pm (4 pm from 1 October to 31 March); daily except 1 January & 24 – 26 December

ADMISSION Adults £3.50; Concessions £2.60; Children £1.80. RHS members free after 22 March

FACILITIES Parking; dogs permitted; loos; facilities for the disabled; plants for sale; gift shop; refreshments in summer and at weekends

FEATURES Fine conifers; rhododendrons and azaleas; snowdrops; particularly interesting in winter; extraordinary quarry garden; tallest Portuguese laurel *Prunus lusitanica* (14m.) in the British Isles

ENGLISH HERITAGE GRADE I
NCCPG NATIONAL COLLECTIONS *Iris*

Wildly romantic Victorian gardens, including several acres of disused quarry with *Trachycarpus* palms, a sequence of gloomy chasms, splendid woodfuls of hardy hybrid rhododendrons, intensive modern herbaceous plantings, brooding conifers and the ruins of Belsay Castle. Superbly maintained.

Bide-a-Wee Cottage
Stanton, Netherwitton, Morpeth NE65 8PR
☎ 01670772 262

OWNER N M Robson
LOCATION 7 miles north-west of Morpeth
OPEN 1.30 pm – 5 pm; Saturdays; 4 May to 31 August
ADMISSION £1.75
FACILITIES Parking; new small nursery selling plants from garden
FEATURES Gravel or scree garden; lake; plantsman's garden; rock garden

Mark Robson's youth has turned this newish garden into something of a cult. But deservedly so, for both design and plantings are brilliant. And the situation is extraordinary: the entire garden is hidden in a disused quarry on the edge of a 500 ft. ridge.

Chillingham Castle
Chillingham NE66 5NJ
☎ 01668 215359   FAX 01668 215463

OWNER Sir Humphry Wakefield Bt
LOCATION Off A1 between Alnwick and Berwick
OPEN 12 noon – 5 pm; daily except Tuesday; 1 May to 1 October. Plus Tuesdays from July to September. Plus Easter Holiday
ADMISSION Adults £3.75; Senior Citizens £3; Children Free
FACILITIES Parking; loos; museum, antique and curio shop; tea-room
FEATURES Herbaceous borders; fine conifers; lake; modern roses; old roses; good topiary; woodland garden; Italian; daffodils; bluebells; vast yew trees and magnificent redwoods
ENGLISH HERITAGE GRADE II

Chillingham has made great efforts to smarten up for visitors. The results are very encouraging: a 19th-century Italianate garden by Wyattville, a modern herbaceous border in the old walled garden and splendid hardy hybrid rhododendrons in the woodland walks which surround the lake. Chillingham itself is a formidable mediaeval castle with amazing views down long 18th-century rides.

Cragside
Rothbury, Morpeth NE65 7PX
☎ 01669 621267

OWNER The National Trust
LOCATION 15 miles north-west of Morpeth off A697 & B6341
OPEN 10.30 am – 6.30 pm; Tuesday – Sunday; 1 April to 30 October
ADMISSION Adults £3.80; Children £1.90
FACILITIES Parking; loos; plants for sale; National Trust shop; refreshments

FEATURES Fine conifers; fruit of special interest; lake; rock garden; old roses; interesting for children; massive rock garden, rather dimly planted with heathers; Armstrong's hydro-electric system fascinates adults and children alike; Italianate terrace replanted (1995); tallest *Abies nordmanniana* (50m.), *Cupressus nootkatensis* (33m.) and *Picea glauca* (28m.) in the British Isles
ENGLISH HERITAGE GRADE II*

Two gardens. The newly-acquired Italianate formal garden has splendid carpet bedding, ferneries and a fruit house with rotating pots. Even more impressive are the rhododendron woods – hundreds and hundreds of acres of 19th-century hybrids, plus trusty R.R. *ponticum* and *luteum*, breathtaking in late May.

Herterton House Gardens & Nursery
Hartington, Cambo NE61 4BN
☎ 01670 774278

OWNER Mr & Mrs Frank Lawley
LOCATION 2 miles north of Cambo (B6342)
OPEN 1.30 pm – 5.30 pm; daily except Tuesdays & Thursdays; 1 April to 30 September. And for NGS
ADMISSION £1.80
FACILITIES Parking; loos; plants for sale
FEATURES Herbaceous borders; herbs; plantsman's garden; knot garden

A plantsman's garden attached to a small nursery. The knot garden is famous, and much photographed, full of herbs and pharmacological plants. More impressive still are the herbaceous plantings, all weaving through each other in beautiful colour-co-ordinated schemes. More new gardens are planned.

Hexham Herbs
Chesters Walled Garden, Chollerford, Hexham NE46 4BQ
☎ 01434 681483

OWNER Mrs S White
LOCATION 6 miles north of Hexham, off B6318 near Chollerford
OPEN 10 am – 5 pm; daily; March to October. Telephone for winter opening times
ADMISSION Adults £1.20; Children (under 10) free
FACILITIES Parking; access for the disabled; nursery attached
FEATURES Herbs; old roses; woodland garden; 'Roman' garden; new formal pool garden (1994); new potager (1995)
NCCPG NATIONAL COLLECTIONS *Origanum; Thymus*

An energetic and successful small modern nursery garden, strategically placed near the fort at Chesters. The herb collection is remarkable (over 900 varieties) and the design within a brick walled garden is charming. Dye plants, a Mediterranean garden, an astilbe bed and a knot garden are just some of the features.

Howick Hall Gardens
Alnwick NE66 3LB
☎ & FAX 01665 577285

OWNER Howick Trustees Ltd
LOCATION Off B1399 between Longhoughton and Howick
OPEN 1 pm – 6 pm; daily; 1 April to 31 October

ADMISSION   Adults £2; Senior Citizens & Children £1 (1996)

FACILITIES   Parking; loos

FEATURES   Fine conifers; lake; plantsman's garden; rhododendrons and azaleas; old roses; spring bulbs; eucryphias; biggest stone pine *Pinus pinea* in the British Isles

ENGLISH HERITAGE GRADE   II

Rather an un-Northumbrian garden, because its closeness to the sea makes possible the cultivation of such tender plants as *Carpenteria* and *Ceanothus*. Formal terraces below the house, well planted, but the great joy of the garden at Howick is a small woodland which has acid soil. This was planted in the 1930s with a fine collection of rhododendrons and camellias: other plants are still added. The result looks more west coast than east.

Kirkley Hall Gardens

Ponteland NE20 0AQ

☎ 01661 860808   FAX 01661 860047

OWNER   Kirkley Hall College

LOCATION   Signposted in Ponteland

OPEN   10 am – 4 pm; daily; 31 March – 31 December

ADMISSION   Adults £1.50; Senior Citizens & Children 70p

FACILITIES   Parking; loos; access for the disabled; new garden centre under development; light refreshments

FEATURES   Herbaceous borders; fine conifers; fruit and vegetables of special interest; glasshouses and conservatories to visit; plantsman's garden; pond; woodland garden

NCCPG NATIONAL COLLECTIONS   *Fagus; Hedera; Salix*

FRIENDS   Friends of Kirkley Hall

The three-acre walled garden is one of the best in the north of England to learn how to garden. The emphasis is on plants – their selection, cultivation and enjoyment. Along the front of the house is handsome traditional bedding-out: a rising star among gardens.

Seaton Delaval Hall

Seaton Sluice, Whitley Bay NE26 4QR

☎ 0191 237 3040

OWNER   Lord Hastings

LOCATION   ½mile from coast between Whitley Bay & Blyth

OPEN   2 pm – 6 pm; 3, 4, 5, 24, 25 & 26 May; Wednesdays & Sundays in June; Wednesdays, Thursdays, Sundays & Bank Holiday Mondays in July & August

ADMISSION   Adults £3; Children £1

FACILITIES   Parking; loos; tea-rooms

FEATURES   Laburnum tunnel

ENGLISH HERITAGE GRADE   II*

The garden is modern: one of Jim Russell's earliest works, it dates from 1948. Parterres and topiary of yew and box are used to enclose old-fashioned roses, handsome ornaments and a fountain: a fair match for the sumptuous house – Vanburgh's masterpiece.

Wallington

Cambo, Morpeth NE61 4AR

☎ 01670 774283

OWNER   The National Trust

LOCATION   6 miles north-west of Belsay (A696)

OPEN   10.30 am – 7 pm (4 pm or dusk, if earlier, from 1 November to 31 March); daily; all year

ADMISSION   Adults £2.80; Children £1.40 (prices may go up early in year)

FACILITIES   Parking; dogs permitted; loos; access for the disabled; restaurant

FEATURES   Herbaceous borders; daffodils; glasshouses and conservatories to visit; lake; rhododendrons and azaleas; climbing roses; old roses; woodland garden; plantings by Graham Thomas; particularly interesting in winter; new cut-flower border (1996); tallest *Sorbus discolor* (7m.) in the British Isles

ENGLISH HERITAGE GRADE   II*

NCCPG NATIONAL COLLECTIONS   *Sambucus*

There are three reasons to visit Wallington. First, because Capability Brown was born in nearby Kirkharle. Second, to gawp at the ancient tree-like specimen of *Fuchsia* 'Rose of Castille' in the conservatory. Third, to admire the modern mixed borders (*very* Graham Thomas) in the long, irregular, walled garden, in a sheltered valley far from the house. Worth the journey for any of them, but prepare for a longish walk to the walled garden.

NOTTINGHAMSHIRE

Clumber Park

The Estate Office, Worksop S80 3AZ

☎ 01909 476592   FAX 01909 500721

OWNER   The National Trust

LOCATION   Off A614 Nottingham Road, 4 miles south of Worksop

OPEN   Park: dawn to dusk; every day; all year. Walled garden, vineries and garden tool museum: Saturdays, Sundays & Bank Holidays; 1 April to 30 September

ADMISSION   Park: free. Garden: Adults 70p, Children 30p. Car parking £2.50

FACILITIES   Parking; dogs permitted; loos; facilities for the disabled; plants for sale; National Trust shop; restaurant

FEATURES   Landscape designed by Capability Brown; lake; woodland garden; autumn colour; vineries; old rhubarb cultivars; superb trees; tallest *Ilex aquifolium* 'Laurifolia' (20m.) in the British Isles

ENGLISH HERITAGE GRADE   I

3,800 acres of thickly wooded parkland with a Gothic chapel, classical bridge, temples, an avenue of cedars, a heroic double avenue of limes and masses of rhododendrons. Good conservatories and a garden tools exhibition in the old walled garden. The scale is enormous: very impressive.

Felley Priory

Underwood NG16 5FL

☎ 01773 810230

OWNER   The Hon Mrs Chaworth-Musters

LOCATION   ½ mile west of M1 on A608

OPEN   9 am – 12.30 pm; Tuesdays, Wednesdays & Fridays; all year. Plus 9 am – 4 pm; 2nd & 4th Wednesday of every month; February to October. 11 am–4 pm; 13 April & 29 June for NGS. Plants fairs 12 noon – 4 pm; 1 June & 5 October

month; February to October. 11 am – 4 pm; 13 April & 29 June for NGS. Plants fairs 12 noon – 4 pm; 1 June & 5 October
ADMISSION £1.50
FACILITIES Parking; loos; access for the disabled; nursery attached; tea-room
FEATURES Herbaceous borders; modern roses; knot gardens, two pergolas and new rose garden, orchard of daffodils, new pleached hedge of *Crataegus tanacetifolia*; rare shrubs; new mediaeval garden of roses & pinks (1995)

Charming, modern, plantsman's garden, stylishly designed and planted, and attached to a small but promising nursery. Handsome yew hedges, only 15 years old, with curvy tops and bobbles. There is a profusion of roses in high summer, with some varieties imported direct from French nurseries, while the red sandstone walls give shelter to an astonishing range of tender plants. And it gets better all the time.

Hodsock Priory
Blyth, Worksop S81 0TY
☎ 01909 591204   [FAX] 01909 591578
OWNER Sir Andrew & Lady Buchanan
LOCATION Signed off the B6045 Blyth – Worksop
OPEN 1 pm – 5 pm; Tuesday – Thursday, plus second Sundays in April & May; 1 April to 31 August Also 10 am – 4 pm; daily; February/March (telephone for exact dates) for snowdrops
ADMISSION Adults £2.50; Children Free
FACILITIES Parking; loos; facilities for the disabled; tea-room
FEATURES Herbaceous borders; lake; old roses; lilies; gardening courses

Richly planted modern garden on an ancient moated site. Excellent rose gardens and mixed borders, plus some fine old trees. The snowdrops and aconites in February are spectacular.

Holme Pierrepoint Hall
Holme Pierrepoint NG12 2LD
☎ & [FAX] 0115 933 2371
OWNER Robin Brackenbury
LOCATION 3 miles east of Trent Bridge
OPEN 2 pm – 6 pm; Sundays in June; Thursday & Sundays in July; Tuesdays, Thursdays, Fridays, Sundays & Bank Holiday Monday in August
ADMISSION House & Gardens £3; Gardens £1.50
FACILITIES Parking; dogs permitted; loos; access for the disabled; plants for sale; teas in the long gallery
FEATURES Old roses; young garden; formal gardens
ENGLISH HERITAGE GRADE II

The main attraction of this garden is a large courtyard garden, designed in 1875, whose box parterre is filled with modern plantings. But there are fine recent additions too: an old rose collection, splendid herbaceous borders and interesting fruit trees.

Newstead Abbey
Newstead Abbey Park NG15 8GE
☎ 01623 793557   [FAX] 01623 797136
OWNER Nottingham City Council
LOCATION 4 miles south of Mansfield on A60
OPEN 10 am – 8 pm (5 pm in winter); daily; all year

ADMISSION Adults £1.70; Children £1; Concessions £1 (1996 prices)
FACILITIES Parking; dogs permitted; loos; facilities for the disabled; plants for sale; restaurant & refreshments
FEATURES Herbs; lake; oriental features; rock garden; modern roses; old roses
ENGLISH HERITAGE GRADE I

Chiefly of interest for being the debt-ridden estate Lord Byron inherited and had to sell, but Newstead has a good modern garden. Best are the Japanese garden and substantial rockery. The Council has restored and replanted it all extensively as a public amenity: lots of cheerful roses and summer bedding.

OXFORDSHIRE

Blenheim Palace
Woodstock, Oxford OX20 1PX
☎ 01993 811091   [FAX] 01993 813527
OWNER The Duke of Marlborough
LOCATION 8 miles north of Oxford
OPEN 10.30 am – 5.30 pm; daily; 16 March to 31 October
ADMISSION Palace & gardens: Adults £7.50; OAPs & Children £5.30
FACILITIES Parking; loos; access for the disabled; plants for sale; good shops; one restaurant & two self-service cafés
FEATURES Landscape designed by Capability Brown; follies and garden buildings; lake; garden sculpture; interesting for children; formal gardens; new maze; current holder of Sandford Award
ENGLISH HERITAGE GRADE I

The grandest of grand gardens. Vanburgh, Bridgeman, Hawksmoor and Wise worked here. The huge (2,000 acre) park was laid out by Capability Brown, and Achille Duchêne restored the formal baroque gardens in the 1920s; most impressive too are the 8 acres of walled kitchen garden.

Brook Cottage
Well Lane, Alkerton, Banbury OX15 6NL
☎ 01295 670303/670590
OWNER Mr & Mrs D M Hodges
LOCATION 6 miles west of Banbury, ½ mile off A422
OPEN 9 am – 6 pm; Monday – Friday; 1 April to 31 October
ADMISSION Adults £2; Senior Citizens £1.50; Children Free
FACILITIES Parking; dogs permitted; loos; plants for sale; DIY tea and coffee; groups by arrangement
FEATURES Herbaceous borders; plantsman's garden; rock garden; old roses; 40 different clematis

First-rate modern garden made by the present owners since 1964 on 4 acres of open pasture. Good plants and good plantings but, above all, a good sense of colour and form. Beautiful flowering trees in spring, opulent roses in summer and fine autumn colour.

Broughton Castle
Banbury OX15 5EB
☎ 01295 262624
OWNER Lord Saye
LOCATION 2½ miles west of Banbury on the B4035

OPEN   2 pm – 5 pm; Wednesdays & Sundays; 18 May to 14 September. Plus Thursdays in July & August and Bank Holiday Sundays and Bank Holiday Mondays (including Easter)
ADMISSION   Castle & Gardens: Adults £3.70; Senior Citizens & Students £3.20; Children £2
FACILITIES   Parking; dogs permitted; loos; facilities for the disabled; plants for sale; tea-room
FEATURES   Herbaceous borders; planted by Gertrude Jekyll; designed by Roper; climbing roses; old roses
ENGLISH HERITAGE GRADE   II*

Mainly designed and planted by Lanning Roper 25 years ago, with a blue-yellow-white border contrasting with a pink-and-silver one. The neat knot garden with roses and lavender is best seen from the house: it was designed by Lady Algernon Gordon-Lennox in the 1890s.

Buscot Park

Faringdon SN7 8BU
☎ 01367 240786   [FAX] 01367 241794
OWNER   The National Trust
LOCATION   On A417 west of Faringdon
OPEN   House & garden: 2 pm – 6 pm; Wednesday – Friday, plus 2nd & 4th Saturday/Sunday each month. garden only: 2 pm – 6 pm; Mondays & Tuesdays. April to September
ADMISSION   Adults: £4 House & Garden; £3 Garden only
FACILITIES   Parking; loos; plants for sale; light refreshments
FEATURES   Herbaceous borders; follies and garden buildings; fruit of special interest; old roses; good topiary; tallest *Pinus nigra* var. *cebennensis* (32m.) in the British Isles
ENGLISH HERITAGE GRADE   II*

One of the most exciting gardens of this century, planned by Harold Peto as a water garden (long canals & bridges), with a *patte d'oie* groundplan. Peter Coats planted lush herbaceous borders in the 1970s and Tim Rees did a good conversion job in the walled garden ten years later: climbing vegetables as climbing plants and gooseberries grown as standards are among his quirkier features.

Clock House

Coleshill, Swindon SN6 7PT
☎ 01793 762476   [FAX] 01793 861615
OWNER   Denny Wickham
LOCATION   On B4019 between Highworth & Faringdon
OPEN   2 pm – 6 pm; Thursdays; May to September. Plus 18 May, 15 June, 14 September, 5 October for NGS. And by appointment
ADMISSION   £1.50
FACILITIES   Parking; loos; plants for sale; teas & cakes
FEATURES   Herbaceous borders; herbs; old roses

A garden of charm and vigour, whose borders burgeon with good growth, unusual juxtapositions and original colour schemes. An inspiration.

Greenways

40 Osler Road, Headington, Oxford OX3 9BJ
☎ 01865 67680 (after dark)
OWNER   Mr & Mrs N H N Coote
LOCATION   Osler Road is off London Road, within Ring road

OPEN   See Yellow Book
ADMISSION   £2.50
FACILITIES   Plants for sale; teas on NGS days
FEATURES   Herbaceous borders; plantsman's garden; sub-tropical plants; particularly good in July-August

Quite new, and totally different. The Cootes have emphasised the Provençal looks of the house by planting a rich Mediterranean garden – glittering evergreens, terracotta pots, old oil jars, gravel, parterres – with an exuberance of tender plants including olives, daturas, yuccas, oleanders, acanthus and *Albizia julibrissin*. Quite the most exciting young garden we know, and intensively maintained to the highest standard.

Greystone Cottage

Colmore Lane, Kingwood Common, Henley-on-Thames RG9 5NA
☎ 01491 628559   [FAX] 01491 628839
OWNER   Mr & Mrs William Roxburgh
LOCATION   Between B481 & Stoke Row road
OPEN   2 pm – 6 pm; 9 March, 11 May, 15 June & by appointment March to September
ADMISSION   Adults £2; Children Free
FACILITIES   Parking; access for the disabled; small nursery; home-made teas
FEATURES   Fine conifers; rock garden; old roses; woodland garden; snowdrops; hellebores; narcissus; fritillaries; enlarged pool and gravel garden (1996); another new pool (1997)

One hectare of perfect plantsmanship, this garden is full of unusual plants in innumerable mini-habitats. It is an inspiration at its March opening, and there are drifts of *Fritillaria meleagris* in April and meadow flowers in June, but every part is highly rewarding at all seasons.

Kelmscott Manor

Kelmscott, Lechlade GL7 3HJ
☎ 01367 252486   [FAX] 01367 253754
OWNER   The Society of Antiquaries of London
LOCATION   Signposted from B4449
OPEN   11 am – 1 pm and 2 pm – 5 pm on Wednesdays; 2 pm – 5 pm on the 3rd Saturday of the month; April to September. Groups by appointment on Thursdays & Fridays
ADMISSION   Adults £6; Children £3
FACILITIES   Parking; loos; access for the disabled; gift shop; lunches & teas

William Morris's garden is being remodelled and restored. Worth a visit if you are interested in the Arts & Crafts movement: the price of a ticket includes a tour of the house.

Lime Close

35 Henley's Lane, Drayton, Abingdon OX14 4HU
☎ & [FAX] 01235 531231
OWNER   Marie-Christine de Laubarède
LOCATION   Off main road through Drayton
OPEN   2 pm – 6 pm; 20 April & 22 June
ADMISSION   Adults £2; Children Free
FACILITIES   Parking; dogs permitted; loos; access for the disabled; plants for sale from Green Farm Plants; cream teas
FEATURES   Herbaceous borders; herbs

This modern garden has been much praised, and deservedly, for its wide range of plants and the way in which they are grouped. As well as the rare plants, it can boast a recently-planted shade border, a pond, an ornamental kitchen garden, a herb garden designed by Rosemary Verey and a wonderful selection of scree beds, gravel beds, raised beds and troughs. And all within 3 acres.

Manor House, Stanton Harcourt

Stanton Harcourt, Witney OX8 1RJ
☎ 01865 881928

OWNER   The Hon Mrs Gascoigne
LOCATION   In village
OPEN   2 pm – 6 pm; 30,31 March; 10, 13, 24, 27 April; 4, 5, 15, 18, 25, 26 May; 5, 8, 19, 22 June; 5, 8, 17, 20, 31 July; 3, 14, 17, 24, 25 August; 11, 14, 25, 28 September
ADMISSION   House & Garden: Adults £4; OAPs & Children £2. Garden only: Adults £2.50; OAPs & Children £1.50
FACILITIES   Parking; loos; access for the disabled; plants for sale; teas
FEATURES   Herbaceous borders; daffodils; climbing roses; modern roses

Wonderful late mediaeval manorhouse, surrounded by Edwardian gardens in the Elizabethan style. Parts are romantically overgrown. Others have been spruced up in contemporary taste with David Austin roses and espaliered fruit trees.

Mount Skippet

Ramsden, Witney OX7 3AP
☎ 01993 868253

OWNER   Dr M A T Rogers
LOCATION   Take B4022 4 miles north from Witney, turn right to Finstock and immediately right again
OPEN   By appointment
ADMISSION   £1 for NGS
FACILITIES   Parking; loos; access for the disabled; plants for sale
FEATURES   Herbaceous borders; gravel or scree garden; plantsman's garden; rock garden; alpine troughs; alpine house

An alpine plantsman's collection, brimful with rarities in pots, troughs, screes, and raised beds. The owner considers that his garden maintenance is not as good as it used to be, but visitors disagree and find infinite interest in this beautifully sited two-acre treasure house for good plants. And not just alpines, but trees, shrubs, bulbs and herbaceous plants too.

Nuneham Courtenay Arboretum

Nuneham Courtenay
☎ 01865 276920

OWNER   University of Oxford
LOCATION   6 miles south of Oxford on the Henley Road
OPEN   10 am – 5 pm; daily; 1 May to 31 October. 10 am – 4.30 pm; Monday-Friday; 1 November to 30 April. Closed 22 December to 4 January and 28 to 31 March
ADMISSION   Donation
FACILITIES   Parking
FEATURES   Good collection of trees; fine conifers; woodland garden
NCCPG NATIONAL COLLECTIONS Bamboos

50-acre arboretum developed since 1950 around a nucleus of American conifers planted c.1840. Experimental plantations and conservation areas rub along with cushioned rhododendrons, a bluebell wood and an *Acer* glade to match Weston-birt.

The Old Rectory, Farnborough

Farnborough, Wantage OX12 8NX
☎ 01488 638298

OWNER   Mr & Mrs Michael Todhunter
LOCATION   In village
OPEN   See Yellow Book. And by written appointment
ADMISSION   Adults £1.50; Private parties £3 each
FACILITIES   Parking; loos; access for the disabled; plants for sale; refreshments
FEATURES   Herbaceous borders; climbing roses; old roses

Excellent modern garden, made by the owners on a high, cold, windy site over the last 25 years. Lots of hedges and thick planting were the keys to survival, but the effect now is of shelter and luxuriance. Splendid double herbaceous border and clever colour plantings.

Oxford Botanic Garden

High Street, Oxford OX1 4AX
☎ & 🖷 01865 276920

OWNER   University of Oxford
LOCATION   East end of High Street next to river
OPEN   9 am – 5 pm (4.30 pm from October to March); daily; all year except Good Friday & Christmas Day
ADMISSION   Donation box, but £1.50 in summer
FACILITIES   Facilities for the disabled
FEATURES   Fine conifers; glasshouses and conservatories to visit; herbs; rock garden; old roses; garden sculpture; interesting for children; systematic beds; huge service tree; tallest *Diospyros virginiana* (18m.) in UK and five other record trees
ENGLISH HERITAGE GRADE   I
NCCPG NATIONAL COLLECTIONS *Euphorbia*
FRIENDS   Friends of Oxford Botanic Garden: details from the Secretary, c/o Oxford University Botanic Garden etc.. Seed list, lectures, use of library, plant sales

A beautifully laid out, well-labelled, progressive, yet classical, botanic garden, founded in 1621. Everything you would expect, from ferns to carnivorous plants, but also a grace and calm that is far from the bustle outside.

Rousham House

Steeple Aston, Bicester OX6 3QX
☎ & 🖷 01869 347110

OWNER   C Cottrell-Dormer
LOCATION   A4260 then off the B4030
OPEN   10 am – 4.30 pm; daily; all year
ADMISSION   Adults £3. No Children under 15
FACILITIES   Parking; loos; access for the disabled
FEATURES   Worked on by Kent; lake; early 18th-century landscape
ENGLISH HERITAGE GRADE   I

Rousham is the most perfect surviving example of William Kent's landscaping: *Kentissimo*, according to Horace

Walpole. The main axis brings you to Scheemakers's statue of a lion devouring a horse, high above the infant River Cherwell. Follow the circuit correctly: the serpentine landscape lies away to the side. Here are Venus' Vale, the Cold Bath and Townsend's Building, from which a lime walk will lead you to the Praeneste. Rousham is an Arcadian experience. The pretty herbaceous border in the walled garden and the modern rose garden by the dovecote seem almost an irrelevance.

Stansfield

49 High Street, Stanford-in-the-Vale SN7 8NQ
☎ 01367 710340

OWNER Mr & Mrs D Keeble
LOCATION Off A417 opposite Vale garage
OPEN 10 am – 4 pm; Tuesdays; 2 April to 24 September. And by appointment
ADMISSION Adults £1; Children Free
FACILITIES Plants for sale; refreshments
FEATURES Herbaceous borders; gravel or scree garden; plantsman's garden

A modern plantsman's garden, and a model of what enthusiastic collecting can produce in a few years. Over 2,000 different plants in just over one acre, with troughs, screes, open borders and endless micro-habitats. Fascinating.

Stonor Park

Henley-on-Thames RG9 6HF
☎ & FAX 01491 638587

OWNER Lord Camoys
LOCATION 5 miles north of Henley-on-Thames
OPEN 2 pm – 5.30 pm; Sundays & Bank Holiday Mondays from April to September; Wednesdays from May to September; Thursdays in July & August; Saturdays in August
ADMISSION £2
FACILITIES Parking; loos; access for the disabled; tea-room
FEATURES Daffodils; rock garden; old roses
ENGLISH HERITAGE GRADE I

Stonor fills a hillside and can all be seen from the road below: classical parkland, the Elizabethan house, lawns, terraces, a walled garden, and finally the wood at the top. Nothing appears to have changed for 200 years: the effect is miraculous.

Waterperry Gardens

Wheatley, Oxford OX33 1JZ
☎ 01844 339226   FAX 01844 339883

OWNER School of Economic Science
LOCATION Near Jct 8 on M40, well signed locally
OPEN 10 am – 5.30 pm (6 pm on Saturdays & Sundays); daily; March to October. 10 am – 5 pm; daily; November to March
ADMISSION April to October: Adults £2.40; Senior Citizens £1.90; Children £1.10. November to March: all £1
FACILITIES Parking; dogs permitted; loos; access for the disabled; plants for sale; home produce, stoneware, books; tea-shop; wine licence
FEATURES Herbaceous borders; fine conifers; fruit of special interest; glasshouses and conservatories to visit; herbs; rock garden; modern roses
NCCPG NATIONAL COLLECTIONS Saxifraga

Essentially a teaching garden with a commercial nursery grafted on, Waterperry has a slightly uncoordinated feel to it. But the herbaceous borders and alpine collections are worth the journey.

Westwell Manor

Burford OX18 4JT
FAX 0171 371 2178

OWNER Mr & Mrs T H Gibson
LOCATION 2 miles from A40, west of Burford roundabout
OPEN 2 pm – 6.30 pm; 6 July
ADMISSION £2
FACILITIES Loos; plants for sale
FEATURES Herbaceous borders; fruit of special interest; old roses; good topiary; pergola planted with green & white climbers (1994); new water rills and cistern (1995)

Busy Cotswold garden with several distinct 'rooms' and well-used converted outbuildings. Roses in profusion, bulbs for spring and climbers draping the walls and hedges.

SHROPSHIRE

Attingham Hall

The National Trust, Attingham Park, Shrewsbury SY4 4TP
☎ 01743 709203   FAX 01743 709352

OWNER The National Trust
LOCATION 5 miles south-east of Shrewsbury on B4380
OPEN 8 am – 8 pm (5 pm from November to March); daily; all year
ADMISSION Adults £1.50; Children 75p
FACILITIES Parking; dogs permitted; loos; facilities for the disabled; National Trust shop; light lunches & teas
FEATURES Daffodils; landscape designed by Humphry Repton; rhododendrons and azaleas; newly restored orangery
ENGLISH HERITAGE GRADE II*

No garden to speak of, but the classical late 18th-century parkland round the vast Georgian house is a joy to walk around at any time of the year.

Benthall Hall

Broseley TF12 5RX
☎ & FAX 01952 882159

OWNER The National Trust
LOCATION 1 mile north-west of Broseley (B4375)
OPEN 1.30 pm – 5.30 pm; Sundays, Wednesdays & Bank Holiday Mondays; April to September
ADMISSION House & Garden: Adults £2
FACILITIES Parking; loos; facilities for the disabled
FEATURES Herbaceous borders; herbs; old roses; garden sculpture; plantings by Graham Thomas

Smallish, but well restored with a Graham Thomas rose garden. Home of the 19th-century botanist George Maw. His Mediterranean collection is still the backbone of the garden – crocus naturalised everywhere.

Erway Farm House

Pentre Coed, Ellesmere SY12 9ED
☎ 01691 690479

OWNER A A & B N Palmer

LOCATION Signposted from B5068 & B5069
OPEN 2 pm – 6 pm (1 pm – 5 pm in February); last Sunday of month; February to September. Plus Easter Saturday – Monday and groups by appointment all year
ADMISSION Adults £1.50; Children Free
FACILITIES Parking; loos; plants for sale
FEATURES Oriental features; plantsman's garden; old roses; snowdrops; hellebores; *Lathraea clandestina*; tulips; cyclamen

A cottage garden full of rare plants, inspired by Margery Fish. Layers of different plants from tiny bulbs to tall trees. Visit early for the snowdrops and *Helleborus orientalis* forms.

Hodnet Hall Gardens
Hodnet, Market Drayton TF9 3NN
☎ 01630 685202   [FAX] 01630 685853

OWNER A E H Heber-Percy
LOCATION Near junction of A53 & A442
OPEN 2 pm – 5 pm; Tuesday – Saturday; 12 noon – 5.30 pm Sundays & Bank Holiday Mondays; 28 March to 30 September
ADMISSION Adults £2.80; Senior Citizens £2.30; Children £1
FACILITIES Parking; dogs permitted; loos; facilities for the disabled; plants for sale; gift shop; 17th-century tea-rooms
FEATURES Herbaceous borders; lake; old roses; woodland garden; camellias; primulas; rhododendrons; HHA/Christie's Garden of the Year in 1985
ENGLISH HERITAGE GRADE II

A large garden, still expanding, and well maintained. Best known for the lakes and ponds planted with primulas and aquatics, but the rhododendrons alone demand a visit. Good in late summer too, with hydrangeas and astilbes. One of the greatest 20th-century gardens.

Lower Hall
Worfield, Bridgnorth WV15 5LH
☎ 01746 716607   [FAX] 01746 716325

OWNER C F Dumbell
LOCATION In centre of village of Worfield
OPEN 22 June for NGS; 29 June for local flower show. And by appointment
ADMISSION £2
FACILITIES Dogs permitted; loos; tea & coffee
FEATURES Herbaceous borders; lake; plantsman's garden; modern roses; old roses; garden sculpture

Lanning Roper helped to get this splendid garden going 30 years ago. It bestrides the River Worfe and every part has a distinct character. Lush streamside plantings, infinite colour schemes, and a woodland area at the bottom. Formal designs, straight brick paths, a pergola and more colour themes in the old walled garden. One of the best modern gardens and neatly kept.

Preen Manor
Church Preen, Church Stretton SY6 7LQ
☎ 01694 771207

OWNER Philip Trevor-Jones

LOCATION Signposted from B4371 Much Wenlock/Church Stretton
OPEN For NGS: 29 May; 12 & 26 June; 10 & 24 July; 5 October. And by appointment
ADMISSION Adults £2; Children 50p
FACILITIES Parking; loos; plants for sale; home-made teas
FEATURES Fruit of special interest; gravel or scree garden; lake; woodland garden; fern garden

A new garden for an old site, with some original ideas. A chess garden, a collection of plants in handsome old pots, a fern garden and that symbol of the 1990s – a gravel garden. And it gets better every year.

Ruthall Manor
Ditton Priors, Bridgnorth WV16 6TN
☎ 0174 634 608

OWNER Mr & Mrs G T Clarke
LOCATION Take Weston road from church then 2nd left
OPEN 2 pm – 6 pm; for NGS & by appointment
ADMISSION Adults £1.50; Children Free
FACILITIES Parking; loos; access for the disabled
FEATURES Plantsman's garden

One acre plantsman's garden, some 800ft up, made over 20 years. Good trees, rare shrubs and lots of ground cover. Pretty pool with aquatics and marginals. Very satisfying.

The Shrewsbury Quest
193 Abbey Foregate, Shrewsbury SY2 6AH
☎ 01743 243324   [FAX] 01743 244342

OWNER Beringar Ltd
LOCATION Signposted, on south side of city
OPEN 10 am – 5 pm (4 pm from November to March); daily; all year
ADMISSION Adults £3.95; Concessions £3.20; Children £2.50
FACILITIES Parking; loos; facilities for the disabled; plants for sale; light lunches, teas & refreshments
FEATURES Herbs; mediaeval plants

This interactive experience of mediaeval life includes a herb garden and a simple monks' garden of ancient plants. Particularly interesting for children.

Swallow Hayes
Rectory Road, Albrighton, Wolverhampton WV7 3EP
☎ 01902 372624

OWNER Mrs P Edwards
LOCATION M54, Jct 3, then A41 towards Wolverhampton & first right after garden centre
OPEN 11 am – 4 pm; 19 January. 2 pm – 6 pm; 1 June. And groups by appointment
ADMISSION Adults £1.50; Children 10p
FACILITIES Parking; dogs permitted; loos; access for the disabled; plants for sale; teas on open days
FEATURES Herbaceous borders; fine conifers; fruit of special interest; gravel or scree garden; herbs; rock garden; new grotto (1996)

25 years of plantsmanship and 3000 plants have made Swallow Hayes a model modern garden, where ground cover helps to

minimise labour and maximise enjoyment. The owners have crazes which add enormously to the visitor's pleasure: the current one is geraniums – over 100 different varieties 'on trial'.

SOMERSET

The American Museum

Claverton Manor, Bath BA2 7BD

☎ 01225 460503   [FAX] 01225 480726

OWNER   Trustees of the American Museum in Britain

LOCATION   Off A36 south of Bath

OPEN   1 pm – 6 pm, Tuesday – Friday; 12 noon – 6 pm, Saturdays, Sundays & Bank Holiday Mondays; 22 March to 2 November

ADMISSION   Adults £2; Children £1 (1996). Private tours by prior arrangement

FACILITIES   Parking; dogs permitted; loos; access for the disabled; plants for sale; book shop, herb shop and country store; light lunches at weekends; tea, coffee and American cookies

FEATURES   Good collection of trees; herbaceous borders; fruit of special interest; herbs; designed by Roper; old roses; good topiary

ENGLISH HERITAGE GRADE   II

FRIENDS   Apply to Membership Secretary (01225 460503)

15 immaculate acres devoted to elements of American gardening, including a Colonial herb garden ('Colonial' = pre-1778), old roses (best in June) and a pastiche of Mount Vernon. But some say it is *all* a pastiche, a chunk of American folksiness slightly incongruous in the Avon Valley.

Ammerdown Park

Kilmersdown, Radstock, Bath BA3 5SH

☎ 01761 437382

OWNER   Lord Hylton

LOCATION   West of Terry Hill crossroads: A362/A366

OPEN   11 am – 5 pm; Bank Holiday Mondays; Easter Monday to August

ADMISSION   Adults £3; Children Free

FACILITIES   Parking; dogs permitted; access for the disabled; refreshments

FEATURES   Planted by Gertrude Jekyll; designed by Lutyens

ENGLISH HERITAGE GRADE   II*

Ammerdown's lay-out is Lutyens at his most ingenious. The lie of the land precludes right angles, but long straight views cover up the irregularities. Some nice plants, particularly trees, but the design is everything and there are some interesting new plantings.

Barrington Court

Barrington, Ilminster TA19 0NQ

☎ 01460 241480

OWNER   The National Trust

LOCATION   In Barrington village

OPEN   11.30 am – 5.30 pm; Saturday – Thursday; 1 April to 30 September

ADMISSION   Adults £4

FACILITIES   Parking; loos; access for the disabled; plants for sale; tea-room & licensed restaurant

FEATURES   Good collection of trees; fruit of special interest; planted by Gertrude Jekyll; old roses; particularly good in July-August; rose & iris garden restored to original Jekyll plans (1995)

ENGLISH HERITAGE GRADE   II*

There is still an Edwardian opulence about Barrington. Massive plantings of irises, lilies and rich dark dahlias. And good design detail too: the patterns of the brick paving are a study in themselves.

Bath Botanic Gardens

Royal Victoria Park, Bath

☎ 01225 448433   [FAX] 01225 480072

OWNER   Bath City Council

LOCATION   West of city centre by Upper Bristol Road

OPEN   9 am – dusk; daily; all year except Christmas Day

ADMISSION   Free

FACILITIES   Parking; dogs permitted; facilities for the disabled

FEATURES   Good collection of trees; rock garden; autumn colour; fine bedding displays; good *Scilla* collection; tallest tree of heaven *Ailanthus altissima* (31m.) and tallest hornbeam *Carpinus betulus* (27m.) in England (and eleven other record trees)

FRIENDS   Very active – 330 members – telephone 01225 448433 for details. Quarterly newsletter; lectures and tours all through the year

9 acres of trees, shrubs, borders, limestone-loving plants and scented walks. Essentially a 'closed' collection and now run as a public amenity. Standards are high, maintenance is good, and the seasonal highlights of bulbs and bedding are among the best. Some splendid old trees recall the garden's origin as a private garden.

Cannington College Heritage Garden

Cannington, Bridgwater TA5 2LS

☎ 01278 652226   [FAX] 01278 652479

OWNER   Cannington College

LOCATION   3 miles west of Bridgwater on A39

OPEN   2 pm – 5 pm; daily; 1 April to 31 October

ADMISSION   Adults £1.50; Senior Citizens & Children 75p (1996 prices)

FACILITIES   Parking; loos; plants for sale; student canteen open to visitors

FEATURES   Alpines; herbaceous borders; fine conifers; fruit of special interest; glasshouses and conservatories to visit; plantsman's garden; subtropical plants; roses of all sorts

NCCPG NATIONAL COLLECTIONS   *Abutilon*; *Argyranthemum*; *Osteospermum*; *Wisteria*

Cannington has long been the leading West Country college for ornamental horticulture. The collections in its teaching gardens are very extensive and beautifully displayed.

Cothay Manor

Greenham, Wellington TA21 0JR

☎ 01823 672283   [FAX] 01823 672345

OWNER   Mr & Mrs Alastair Robb

LOCATION   1 mile west of Thorne St Margaret

OPEN Thursdays & first Sundays in month; May to September
ADMISSION £2
FACILITIES Parking; loos; access for the disabled; plants for sale; cream teas
FEATURES 1920s design; 1990s plants
ENGLISH HERITAGE GRADE II*

An exciting old/new garden on either side of the River Tone: 8 acres of formal 1920s design (chunky yew hedges) completely replanted, room by room, colour by colour, since the present owners came here in 1993. Cothay makes a model study of how a garden can be rejuvenated.

Crowe Hall
Widcombe Hill, Bath BA2 6AR
☎ 01225 310322

OWNER John Barratt
LOCATION Off A36 up Widcombe Hill
OPEN 2 pm – 6 pm; 23 March, 20 April, 11 & 25 May, 15 June, 13 July, & by appointment
ADMISSION Adults £1.50; Children 50p
FACILITIES Parking; dogs permitted; loos; teas
FEATURES Follies and garden buildings; rock garden; old roses; Victorian greenhouse (built 1852, restored 1995); Hercules garden re-opened (1996)
ENGLISH HERITAGE GRADE II

One of the most extraordinary gardens we know. It looks straight out at the Capability Brown landscape at Prior Park, and 'borrows' it. Below the house is an Italianate terrace, which leads to a ferny rock garden (real rocky outcrops here) and down into a modern garden in the woodland. Recent developments include a 'Sauce' garden, in memory of Lady Barratt, a former owner, and a 'Roman' garden.

Dunster Castle
Minehead TA24 6SL
☎ 01643 821314

OWNER The National Trust
LOCATION 3 miles south-east of Minehead on A39
OPEN 11 am – 4 pm (6 pm from April to September); daily; 1 February to 12 December
ADMISSION Adults £2.70; Children £1.30; Family £6.50
FACILITIES Parking; loos; facilities for the disabled; National Trust shop; tea-rooms at Dunster Mill
FEATURES Lake; subtropical plants; woodland garden; particularly interesting in winter; *Arbutus* grove; tallest *Taxodium ascendens* (23m.) in the British Isles
ENGLISH HERITAGE GRADE I
NCCPG NATIONAL COLLECTIONS *Arbutus*

A Victorian woodland on a steep slope, terraced in places and planted with tender exotica – mimosa, *Beschorneria* and a 150-year-old lemon tree in an unheated conservatory.

East Lambrook Manor Garden
East Lambrook, South Petherton TA13 5HL
☎ 01460 240328   FAX 01460 242344

OWNER Mr & Mrs Andrew Norton
LOCATION Signed from A303 at South Petherton

OPEN 10 am – 5 pm; Monday – Saturday; 1 March to 31 October
ADMISSION Adults £2.50; Children & Students 50p; Groups by arrangement £2
FACILITIES Parking; loos; book, picture gallery & gift shop; coffee & biscuits
FEATURES Herbaceous borders; plantsman's garden; cottage garden plants; geraniums; 'ditch garden'
ENGLISH HERITAGE GRADE I
NCCPG NATIONAL COLLECTIONS *Geranium*

The archetypal super-cottage garden, made by Margery Fish, the popular and influential writer, and ambitiously restored by the present owners. Ground cover, narrow paths and, above all, plants, plants, plants.

Gaulden Manor
Tolland, Lydeard St Lawrence TA4 3PN
☎ & FAX 01984 667213

OWNER James Starkie
LOCATION 1 mile east of Tolland church, off B3224
OPEN 2 pm – 5.30 pm; Sundays, Thursdays & Bank Holidays; 4 May to 7 September. And groups by appointment at other times
ADMISSION £1.75
FACILITIES Parking; loos; access for the disabled; plants for sale; book & gift shop; teas on Sundays & Bank Holidays
FEATURES Herbaceous borders; herbs; lake; modern roses; old roses; woodland garden; scent gardens; secret garden

A modern garden, and well planted. Small garden rooms, each devoted to a different theme (roses, herbs etc.), and a good stream garden made beneath the monks' pond, its sides planted with candelabra primulas, ferns and gunnera.

Greencombe Gardens
Porlock TA24 8NU

OWNER Greencombe Garden Trust
LOCATION ½ mile west of Porlock on left of road to Porlock Weir
OPEN 2 pm – 6 pm; Saturday – Tuesday; 1 April to 31 July, and 5 October to 5 November
ADMISSION Adults £3; Children (under 16) 50p
FACILITIES Parking; loos; access for the disabled; plants for sale; teas for large groups
FEATURES Herbaceous borders; ecological interest; plantsman's garden; woodland garden
NCCPG NATIONAL COLLECTIONS *Erythronium*; *Gaultheria*; *Polystichum*; *Vaccinium*

Rather a cult garden, an organic showpiece, best for its woodland walks where stately gentleness dominates. Interesting plants galore.

Hadspen Garden
Castle Cary BA7 7NG
☎ & FAX 01749 813707

OWNER N & S Pope
LOCATION 2 miles east of Castle Cary on A371
OPEN 9 am – 6 pm; Thursday – Sunday & Bank Holiday Mondays; 6 March to 28 September
ADMISSION Adults £2.50; Children 50p

FACILITIES Parking; loos; facilities for the disabled; nursery; light lunches & teas

FEATURES Herbaceous borders; gravel or scree garden; lake; plantsman's garden; old roses; Eric Smith's *Hosta* collection NCCPG NATIONAL COLLECTIONS *Rodgersia*

Little remains of Penelope Hobhouse's first garden: the Popes have remade and improved it in the modern idiom, using a wide range of rare plants to create exquisite decorative effects. Rather a cult garden now, and deservedly.

Hestercombe House

Somerset County Council, Cheddon Fitzpaine, Taunton TA2 8LQ

☎ 01823 413923 FAX 01823 413030

OWNER Somerset County Council Fire Brigade
LOCATION 4 miles north of Taunton
OPEN 9 am – 6 pm (5 pm in winter); daily; all year
ADMISSION Adults £3; Children (12-16) £1
FACILITIES Parking; dogs permitted; loos; refreshments
FEATURES Herbaceous borders; planted by Gertrude Jekyll
ENGLISH HERITAGE GRADE I

Famously restored garden with lots of Lutyens' hallmarks: iris-choked rills, pergolas, relieved staircases and pools where reflections twinkle on recessed apses. Gertrude Jekyll's planting is bold and simple, which adds to the vigour. Very photogenic.

Lytes Cary Manor

Charlton Mackrell, Somerton TA11 7HU

☎ & FAX 01458 223297

OWNER The National Trust
LOCATION Near A303 junction with A372 & A37
OPEN 2 pm – 6 pm; Mondays, Wednesdays & Saturdays; April to October
ADMISSION Adults £3.70
FACILITIES Parking; loos; access for the disabled; plants for sale
FEATURES Herbaceous borders; garden sculpture; good topiary; plantings by Graham Thomas; large mixed border replanted to Graham Thomas's original design (1996)
ENGLISH HERITAGE GRADE II

Neo-Elizabethan garden to go with the prettiest of manor houses. Yew hedges, hornbeam walks, alleys and lawns. Medlars, quinces and a simple Elizabethan flower border.

The Manor House, Walton-in-Gordano

Walton-in-Gordano, Clevedon, Bristol BS21 7AN

☎ 01275 872067

OWNER Simon & Philippa Wills
LOCATION North side of B3124 on Clevedon side of Walton-in-Gordano
OPEN For NGS
ADMISSION See Yellow Book
FACILITIES Parking; loos; access for the disabled; plants for sale
FEATURES Alpines; herbaceous borders; fine conifers; fruit of special interest; gravel or scree garden; herbs; lake; plantsman's garden; pond; rock garden; climbing roses; modern roses; old roses; woodland garden; particularly good in July-August

A really interesting plantsman's garden on a substantial scale, offering something for every taste, from autumn-flowering bulbs to rare conifers. The range of the Wills' interests is breath-taking and there is always much for the visitor to learn and enjoy, whatever the season. Beautifully maintained, too.

Milton Lodge

Old Bristol Road, Wells BA5 3AQ

☎ 01749 672168

OWNER D C Tudway Quilter
LOCATION Old Bristol road off of A39
OPEN 2 pm – 6 pm; Sunday – Friday; Easter to 31 October
ADMISSION Adults £2; Children (under 14) free
FACILITIES Parking; loos; plants for sale; teas on Sundays (May to August)
FEATURES Good collection of trees; herbaceous borders; modern roses; tallest *Populus alba* (20m.) in the British Isles
ENGLISH HERITAGE GRADE II

Impressive Edwardian garden, terraced down against a backdrop of Wells Cathedral. Yew hedges, good modern plantings and an 8-acre arboretum in a combe, replanted in recent years. Excellently maintained and constantly improving.

Montacute House

Montacute, Yeovil TA15 6XP

☎ 01935 823289

OWNER The National Trust
LOCATION In Montacute village
OPEN 11.30 am – 5.30 pm (dusk if earlier); daily except Tuesday; all year
ADMISSION Adults £2.70; Children £1.20
FACILITIES Parking; loos; facilities for the disabled; plants for sale; light lunches & teas, licensed restaurant
FEATURES Herbaceous borders; lake; old roses; exquisite gazebos
ENGLISH HERITAGE GRADE I

The garden is subsidiary to the amazing Elizabethan mansion, apart from a border started by Vita Sackville-West, worked over by Phyllis Reiss and finished by Graham Thomas. But it cannot be beaten for its sense of English renaissance grandeur.

Prior Park

Bath

☎ 01225 833422

OWNER The National Trust
LOCATION 1½ miles south of Bath city centre
OPEN 12 noon – 5.30 pm; Wednesday – Monday; daily except 1 January and 25 & 26 December
ADMISSION Adults £3.80; Children £1.90
FACILITIES Facilities for the disabled
ENGLISH HERITAGE GRADE I

This great Palladian park is at last open to the public. There is a snag, however: the Trust can offer no onsite parking. Badgerline runs buses (Nos. 2 & 4) from the bus station or Dorchester Place, every 10 minutes.

Sherborne Garden

Pear Tree House, Litton BA3 4PP

☎ 01761 241220

OWNER Mr & Mrs John Southwell

LOCATION On B3114, ½ a mile west of Litton village

OPEN 11 am – 6 pm; Mondays & Sundays; 1 June to 29 September. Other times by appointment. Parties by arrangement

ADMISSION Adults £1.50; Children Free

FACILITIES Parking; dogs permitted; loos; access for the disabled; plants for sale; tea/coffee

FEATURES Fine conifers; ecological interest; gravel or scree garden; herbs; lake; plantsman's garden; rock garden; modern roses; old roses; woodland garden; collection of hollies (180 varieties) and hardy ferns (250 varieties)

Plantsman's garden, started in a modest way in 1964 on ¾ acre but now extending to nearly 4 acres. Thickly planted, and wild at the edges. The owners are particularly interested in trees and plant them closely in groups for comparison: hence the holly wood, the larch wood and the salicetum (*Salix* = willow). But there is much more than trees and it is a garden to dawdle in and learn from.

Ston Easton Park

Ston Easton, Bath BA3 4DF

☎ 01761 241631 FAX 01761 241377

OWNER Peter L Smedley

LOCATION Intersection of A37 and A39

OPEN By appointment, unless visiting restaurant

ADMISSION Free

FACILITIES Parking; access for the disabled; plants for sale; Ston Easton Park is a hotel: all meals available to non-residents

FEATURES Fine conifers; fruit of special interest; lake; ice-house; new colour-graded foliage border for cutting (100+ yds)

ENGLISH HERITAGE GRADE II

A country house hotel, voted Hotel of the Year in 1992, with a Humphry Repton landscape. His 'red book' still exists. A sham castle and ruined grotto are two of the features he built, but there are fine trees, spacious lawns and the highest standard of maintenance to enjoy too.

Tintinhull House

Tintinhull, Yeovil BA22 8PZ

☎ 01935 822545

OWNER The National Trust

LOCATION In Tintinhull village

OPEN 12 noon – 6 pm; Wednesdays – Sunday; April to September

ADMISSION Adults £3.50; Children £1.60

FACILITIES Parking; loos; refreshments

FEATURES Herbaceous borders; old roses; good topiary; particularly good in July-August; colour borders

ENGLISH HERITAGE GRADE II

A series of formal garden rooms, beautifully designed to maximise a small site (only 1½ acres) and planted with rarities in exquisite colour combinations. No labels: they would spoil the dream.

Wayford Manor

Crewkerne TA18 8QG

☎ 01460 73253

OWNER Mr & Mrs R L Goffe

LOCATION 3 miles south-west of Crewkerne off A30 or B3165

OPEN 2 pm – 6 pm; 13 April, 4 & 18 May, 1 June, for NGS, or parties by appointment

ADMISSION Adults £2; Children 50p

FACILITIES Parking; dogs permitted; loos; plants for sale; teas

FEATURES Herbaceous borders; rhododendrons; spring bulbs; maples; tallest *Photinia davidiana* (13m.) in the British Isles

ENGLISH HERITAGE GRADE II

One of the best gardens designed by Harold Peto: terraces and courtyards, pools and arbours, balustrades and staircases, Tuscan and Byzantine. Parts are now rather dominated by overgrown shrubs, but the whole garden is presently being restored by the enthusiastic and knowledgeable owners.

STAFFORDSHIRE

Alton Towers

Alton, Stoke-on-Trent ST10 4DB

☎ 0990 204060 FAX 01538 704099

OWNER Tussauds Group

LOCATION Signposted for miles around

OPEN 9 am – 6/7 pm depending on season; daily; March to November

ADMISSION Adults £17.50; Children £13.50; Senior Citizens £5.75 (1996 prices)

FACILITIES Parking; loos; facilities for the disabled; many restaurants

FEATURES Herbaceous borders; fine conifers; follies and garden buildings; lake; oriental features; rock garden; modern roses; woodland garden; interesting for children; particularly good in July-August

ENGLISH HERITAGE GRADE I

300 acres of dotty and exuberant display, best seen from the cable-car. Ignore the theme park: the gardens are by and large detached from the razzmatazz. Splendid Victorian conifers and gaudy bedding, magnificently done. A Swiss Cottage, Roman bridge, Chinese pagoda, flag tower, and corkscrew fountain. Excellent entertainment but not for contemplative souls. Best in term time.

Biddulph Grange Garden

Biddulph, Stoke-on-Trent ST8 7SD

☎ 01782 517999

OWNER The National Trust

LOCATION ½ mile north of Biddulph, 3½ miles south-east of Congleton

OPEN 12 noon – 6 pm, Wednesday – Friday (closed Good Friday); 11 am – 6 pm; Saturdays, Sundays & Bank Holiday Mondays; 29 March to 2 November. Also 12 noon – 4 pm; Saturdays & Sundays; 8 November to 21 December

ADMISSION Adults £4 (£2 in November & December); Children £2; Family £10

FACILITIES   Parking; loos; plants for sale; gift shop; tea-room
FEATURES   Fine conifers; follies and garden buildings;
oriental features; interesting for children; wellingtonia avenue
replanted (1996)
ENGLISH HERITAGE GRADE   I

A fantastic folly garden, very Victorian, energetically restored
by the National Trust. Yew hedges cut to make an Egyptian
temple; a statue of a sacred cow; a Scottish glen; a four-acre
Chinese garden complete with Great Wall of China and
look-out tower; a dahlia walk; a bowling green, quoits ground
and 'stumpery'. Work continues.

The Dorothy Clive Garden
Willoughbridge, Market Drayton TF9 4EU
☎ 01630 647237

OWNER   Willoughbridge Garden Trust
LOCATION   A51, midway between Nantwich and Stone
OPEN   10 am – 5.30 pm; daily; 29 March to 31 October
ADMISSION   Adults £2.70; OAPs & Groups (20+) £2.30;
Children £1
FACILITIES   Parking; dogs permitted; loos; facilities for the
disabled; tea-room with beverages & home-baked food
FEATURES   Herbaceous borders; camellias; fine conifers; rock
garden; woodland garden; rhododendrons; azaleas; heather;
cyclamen

Meticulously maintained and still expanding, this 40-year-old
garden seems ageless. Made on an unpromising site, a cold
windy hilltop, it is best perhaps in May, when the woodland
quarry is brilliant with rhododendrons. But the scree and rock
garden (reflected in the lake) are hard to beat at any season.
Highly recommended.

Moseley Old Hall
The National Trust, Moseley Old Hall Lane, Fordhouses
WV10 7HY
☎ & FAX 01902 782808

OWNER   The National Trust
LOCATION   South of M54 between A449 & A460
OPEN   1.30 pm – 4 pm; 23 February. 1.30 pm – 5.30 pm;
Saturdays & Sundays (& 1 April & Tuesdays in July &
August); 11 am – 5 pm Bank Holiday Mondays; 1 April to
31 October
ADMISSION   Adults £3.30; Children £1.65; Family £8.25
FACILITIES   Parking; dogs permitted; loos; access for the dis-
abled; plants for sale; gift shop; tea-room
FEATURES   Herbs; snowdrops; good topiary; current holder
of Sandford Award

Modern reconstruction of a 17th-century town garden. Neat
box parterres, a nut walk and an arched pergola hung with
clematis. Plantings all of a period. Quietly inspirational.

Shugborough Hall
c/o The Estate Office, Milford, Stafford ST17 0XB
☎ 01889 881388   FAX 01889 881323

OWNER   The National Trust
LOCATION   Signed from Jct 13 M6
OPEN   11 am – 5 pm; daily; 23 March to 30 September, plus
Sundays in October. And parties by appointment
ADMISSION   Vehicles £1.50; Coaches free

FACILITIES   Parking; dogs permitted; loos; facilities for the
disabled; garden centre; lunches, snacks, tea & evening dinners
FEATURES   Herbaceous borders; follies and garden buildings;
lake; oriental features; old roses; woodland garden; plantings
by Graham Thomas; interesting for children; new herbaceous
border (1994); much tree planting in the park (1994/95);
current holder of Sandford Award
ENGLISH HERITAGE GRADE   I

Classical and neo-classical landscape with Chinese additions
and a handsome Nesfield terrace dominated by dumplings of
clipped golden yew. 50 oaks in the new arboretum. Rose
garden restored by Graham Thomas. All very popular with the
locals.

Trentham Park Gardens
Trentham, Stone Road, Stoke-on-Trent ST4 8AX
☎ 01782 657341

OWNER   Trentham Leisure Ltd
LOCATION   Signposted from M6
ENGLISH HERITAGE GRADE   II*

This grandest of grand Victorian gardens, set among a Capability Brown park, was reported to be up for sale as we went
to press. We hope it will continue to be open to the public:
the tourist office in Stoke will have the latest details – 01782
284600.

Weston Park
Weston-under-Lizard, Shifnal TF11 8LE
☎ 01952 850 207   FAX 01952 850 430

OWNER   The Weston Park Foundation
LOCATION   Off the A5 to Telford
OPEN   11 am – 7 pm (last admissions 5 pm); 29 March –
1 April; 3–5, 11, 12, 13, 17, 18, 24–31 May; 1, 7, 8, 14, 15 June;
16 June – 27 July (daily except Mondays, Fridays & 19 July);
28 July – 15 August; 18 – 31 August; 6, 7, 13, 14, & 20 &
21 September
ADMISSION   Garden only: Adults £3.50; Concessions £2.50;
Children £2
FACILITIES   Parking; dogs permitted; loos; facilities for the
disabled; gift shop; tea-rooms
FEATURES   Good collection of trees; landscape designed by
Capability Brown; woodland garden; landscaped park; rhodo-
dendrons; good new (1994) shrub plantings around the
Church Pool
ENGLISH HERITAGE GRADE   II*

18th-century landscape with 19th-century Italianate parterre,
a temple of Diana and an handsome orangery by Paine. But
best for its trees, some of them record-breakers, and the
collection of *Nothofagus* planted by the late Lord Bradford.

SUFFOLK

Euston Hall
Euston, Thetford IP24 2QP
☎ 01842 766366   FAX 01842 766764

OWNER   The Duke of Grafton
LOCATION   On A1088 3 miles south of Thetford

OPEN 2.30 pm – 5 pm; Thursdays; 5 June to 25 September, plus 29 June & 7 September

ADMISSION Gardens only: £1. House & garden: Adults £3; Senior Citizens £2; Parties (12+) £2; Children 50p

FACILITIES Parking; loos; access for the disabled; craft shop; home-made teas

FEATURES Landscape designed by Capability Brown; lake; old roses; William Kent temple and summerhouse

ENGLISH HERITAGE GRADE II*

Classic 18th-century parkland on a sweeping site, formal terraces by the house and a pretty modern garden with shrub roses. Not spectacular, but satisfying.

Haughley Park
Stowmarket IP14 3JY
☎ 01359 240205   FAX 01359 240546

OWNER R J Williams

LOCATION Signed from A14

OPEN 3 pm – 5.30 pm; Tuesdays; May to September plus first two Sundays in May

ADMISSION Adults £2; Children £1

FACILITIES Parking; dogs permitted; loos; facilities for the disabled

FEATURES Bluebells; herbaceous borders; rhododendrons and azaleas; woodland garden; lily-of-the-valley; 1,000-year-old oak

Parkland round a Jacobean mansion with competent modern flower gardens and fine trees (*Davidia involucrata*). The walled garden is undergoing conversion to a flower garden. But the acres of lily-of-the-valley in the woodland garden are worth the journey no matter how far.

Helmingham Hall
Stowmarket IP14 6EF
☎ 01473 890363   FAX 01473 890776

OWNER Lord Tollemache

LOCATION 9 miles north of Ipswich on B1077

OPEN 2 pm – 6 pm; Sundays; 27 April to 7 September; plus individuals & groups on Wednesdays by prior arrangement

ADMISSION Adults £3; Senior Citizens £2.50; Children £1.50

FACILITIES Parking; dogs permitted; loos; access for the disabled; plants for sale; shop; tea-rooms

FEATURES Herbaceous borders; old roses; deer park; moat; fine walled garden

ENGLISH HERITAGE GRADE I

Most of the garden is modern, but cleverly done with old flowers and knot gardens to suit the Elizabethan house. Wonderful modern planting in the walled garden: billowing, chunky shrub roses and triumphant herbaceous borders.

Ickworth
National Trust Office, Horringer, Bury St Edmunds
IP29 5QE
☎ & FAX 01284 735270

OWNER The National Trust

LOCATION 3 miles south-west of Bury St Edmunds

OPEN 10 am – 5 pm (4 pm in winter); daily except Good Friday; all year

ADMISSION Adults £2; Children 50p

FACILITIES Parking; dogs permitted; loos; facilities for the disabled; National Trust shop; large licensed restaurant, self-service

FEATURES Landscape designed by Capability Brown; autumn colour; Italian garden; Victorian 'stumpery'; tallest *Quercus pubescens* (29m.) in the British Isles

ENGLISH HERITAGE GRADE II*

NCCPG NATIONAL COLLECTIONS *Buxus*

An extraordinary garden for an extraordinary house: the main borders follow the curves of the house. There are also an Italian garden in front of the house, and long vistas in the park, but the old kitchen garden is bare.

Shrubland Hall
Coddenham, Ipswich IP6 9QP
☎ 01473 830221   FAX 01473 832202

OWNER Lord de Saumarez

LOCATION Between Claydon and Coddenham: come by A14 or A140

OPEN 12 noon – 5.30 pm; Sundays; 30 March to 7 September. And some Mondays

ADMISSION Adults £2.50; Senior Citizens & Children £1

FACILITIES Parking; loos; tea-tent

FEATURES Herbaceous borders; follies and garden buildings; lake; modern roses; woodland garden; box maze; Swiss Chalet

ENGLISH HERITAGE GRADE I

A grand Victorian garden designed by Charles Barry and famous for its spectacular Italianate staircase which connects the terrace around the house with the formal gardens below. William Robinson later helped with the planting, both around the formal garden and in the park and woodland gardens beyond. Much restoration and recovery has been completed in recent years: Shrubland is getting better and better.

Somerleyton Hall & Gardens
Somerleyton, Lowestoft NR32 5QQ
☎ 01502 730224   FAX 01502 732143

OWNER Lord & Lady Somerleyton

LOCATION 4 miles north-west of Lowestoft on B1074

OPEN 12.30 pm – 5.30 pm; Thursdays, Sundays & Bank Holiday Mondays, plus Tuesdays & Wednesdays in July & August; Easter Sunday to last Sunday in September

ADMISSION Adults £4.20; Senior Citizens £3.80; Children £1.95; Family (2+2) £11.70. Special rates for groups

FACILITIES Parking; loos; facilities for the disabled; souvenir gift shop; light lunches & teas

FEATURES Glasshouses and conservatories to visit; modern roses; maze; miniature railway; new summerhouse (1996)

ENGLISH HERITAGE GRADE II*

A grand formal garden around the monstrous Victorian house. Nesfield laid out the terraces, and Paxton built the curving greenhouses which have just been re-roofed. Good 19th-century maze (not too difficult) and masses of cheerful bedding and roses.

Wyken Hall

Stanton, Bury St Edmunds IP31 2DW

☎ 01359 250287   📠 01359 252256

OWNER   Sir Kenneth & Lady Carlisle

LOCATION   Stanton, 9 miles north-east from Bury St Edmunds; brown signs from A143 at Ixworth to Wyken Vineyard

OPEN   10 am – 6 pm; Thursdays, Sundays & Bank Holiday Mondays; 1 February to 24 December

ADMISSION   Adults £2; Senior Citizens £1.50; Children Free

FACILITIES   Parking; dogs permitted; loos; facilities for the disabled; plants for sale; country store shop; lunches & teas

FEATURES   Herbaceous borders; fine conifers; fruit of special interest; herbs; plantsman's garden; modern roses; old roses; woodland garden; award-winning seven-acre vineyard

The garden is ingeniously designed: a series of old-style gardens to complement the Elizabethan house. These include a knot garden, herb garden, traditional English kitchen garden, wildflower meadows, nuttery and a copper beech maze. All are in scale with the house and the farmland around. Stylish and well maintained, this is one of the best modern private gardens in the country.

SURREY

Brook Lodge Farm Cottage

Blackbrook, Dorking RH5 4DT

OWNER   Mrs Basil Kingham

LOCATION   Signed from A24 past Plough Inn in Blackbrook

OPEN   2 pm – 5 pm; 21 May, 15 & 18 June, 20 & 23 July, 17, 20 & 31 August

ADMISSION   Adults £2; Children Free

FACILITIES   Parking; loos; access for the disabled; plants for sale; home-made teas

FEATURES   Herbaceous borders; fine conifers; plantsman's garden; old roses; woodland garden

Planted by the present owner 45 years ago, this garden has matured into a fine plantsman's garden with much variety: shrub roses, a rockery, a woodland walk, herbaceous borders and two cottage gardens.

Chilworth Manor

Chilworth, Guildford

☎ 01483 561414

OWNER   Lady Heald

LOCATION   In middle of village, up Blacksmiths Lane

OPEN   2 pm – 6 pm; 5 & 6 April, 3 & 4 May, 14 & 15 June, 12 & 13 July, 9 & 10 August, or by appointment

ADMISSION   £1.50

FACILITIES   Parking; dogs permitted; loos; teas & cakes

FEATURES   Herbaceous borders; woodland garden; rhododendrons; interesting new shrub plantings; flower arrangements in the house; tallest *Ilex aquifolium* 'Bacciflava' (10.5m.) and largest *Ilex aquifolium* 'Pendula' in the British Isles

A remarkable garden, tiered up seven distinct levels, the top three being c.1700 and walled around (beautiful brickwork). Good climbers and shrubs against the walls, and a bog garden

in the woods at the bottom. The main herbaceous border has just been replanted by a Dutch designer.

Clandon Park

West Clandon, Guildford GU4 7RQ

☎ 01483 222482

OWNER   The National Trust

LOCATION   Off the A247 at West Clandon

OPEN   Noon – 5.30 pm (4 pm on Saturday); Saturday – Wednesday & Good Friday; 30 March to 30 October

ADMISSION   Adults £4; Children (under 17) £2

FACILITIES   Parking; loos; access for the disabled; garden centre; restaurant

FEATURES   Landscape designed by Capability Brown; daffodils; parterres; grotto; Dutch garden; Maori summerhouse

ENGLISH HERITAGE GRADE   II

Capability Brown's magnificent mature beeches are now underplanted with gloomy Victorian shrubberies and slabs of comfrey, bergenias and *Geranium macrorrhizum* – the apotheosis of National Trust ground cover. There is a modern pastiche of a Dutch garden in front of the house – competent, rather than inspired – but the daffodils in spring are breathtaking.

Claremont Gardens

Portsmouth Road, Esher KT10 9JG

☎ 01372 469421

OWNER   The National Trust

LOCATION   On southern edge of town (A307)

OPEN   10 am – 6 pm, but 5 pm from November to March and 7 pm on Saturdays, Sundays & Bank Holiday Mondays from April to October (sunset, if earlier); all year (1994 times & dates)

ADMISSION   Adults £3

FACILITIES   Parking; loos; access for the disabled; shop; restaurant

FEATURES   Landscape designed by Capability Brown; follies and garden buildings; worked on by Kent; lake; plantings by Graham Thomas; tallest service tree *Sorbus domestica* (23m.) in the British Isles, and two further record trees

ENGLISH HERITAGE GRADE   I

A vast historic landscape worked over by Vanburgh, Bridgeman, Kent and Capability Brown. The stunning turf amphitheatre is best seen flanked by spreading cedars from across the dark lake. Very popular locally, and apt to get crowded at summer weekends.

Hatchlands

East Clandon, Guildford GU4 7RQ

☎ 01483 222482   📠 01483 223479

OWNER   The National Trust

LOCATION   Off A246 Guildford to Leatherhead

OPEN   2 pm – 6 pm; Tuesday – Thursday, Sundays & Bank Holiday Mondays; 1 April to 2 November. Also Fridays in August

ADMISSION   Adults £4; Children (under 17) £2

FACILITIES   Parking; loos; facilities for the disabled; National Trust shop; restaurant

FEATURES Landscape designed by Capability Brown; planted by Gertrude Jekyll; landscape designed by Humphry Repton; woodland garden

Apart from the Jekyll garden (roses, lupins, box and columbines) Clandon is an 18th-century landscape with parkland. But the garden buildings are charming and the National Trust has started to restore and replant it.

Munstead Wood
Heath Lane, Busbridge, Godalming GU7 1UN
☎ 01483 417867   [FAX] 01483 425041
OWNER   Sir Robert & Lady Clark
LOCATION   1 mile south of Godalming on B2130: turn along Heath Lane. Parking in field 300 yds along on left
OPEN   2 pm – 6 pm; 25 May, 20 July & 28 September
ADMISSION   Adults £2; OAPs £1; Children Free
FACILITIES   Parking; dogs permitted; loos; access for the disabled; plants for sale; cream teas
FEATURES   Herbaceous borders; planted by Gertrude Jekyll; rock garden; old roses; woodland garden
ENGLISH HERITAGE GRADE   I

Gertrude Jekyll's own garden was nearly lost before the Clarks bought it. Helped by an inspired head gardener, they have successfully restored much to its original state. The roses and colour plantings are inspirational. Work continues, and the lawns still end where the birches begin, to make Munstead 'a garden in a wood'.

Painshill Park
Portsmouth Road, Cobham KT11 1JE
☎ 01932 868113/864674   [FAX] 01932 868001
OWNER   Painshill Park Trust
LOCATION   Signposted from M25 Jct 10
OPEN   10.30 am – 6 pm (last tickets 4.30 pm); Tuesday – Sunday & Bank Holiday Mondays; 1 April to 31 October
ADMISSION   Adults £3.50; Senior Citizens & Students £3; Children (under 16) £1; Groups £2.80
FACILITIES   Parking; loos; facilities for the disabled; plants for sale; souvenirs, books, cards, etc.; light refreshments
FEATURES   Lake; 'American' garden; grotto; Turkish tent; tallest Juniperus virginiana (26m.) in the British Isles
ENGLISH HERITAGE GRADE   I

Charles Hamilton went bust making this extravagant Gothic landscape in the 1770s. It has been industriously restored over the last ten years and now looks as new and stagey as ever. A £848,000 grant from the Heritage Lottery Fund means that the park will open fully this year for the first time.

Pinewood House
Heath House Road, Worplesdon Hill, Woking GU22 0QU
☎ 01483 473241
OWNER   Mr & Mrs J Van Zwanenberg
LOCATION   Turning off A322, opposite Brookwood cemetery wall
OPEN   Parties (up to 35) by appointment, 1 March to 31 October
ADMISSION   Adults £2
FACILITIES   Parking; loos; access for the disabled; home-made teas if pre-booked

FEATURES   Good collection of trees; fine conifers; lake; young garden; wild garden; walled garden; rhododendrons

5 acres of old garden, to go with a new house. Lovely woodland, lakes and underplantings with rhododendrons.

Polesden Lacey
Great Bookham, Dorking RH5 6BD
☎ 01372 458203   [FAX] 01372 452023
OWNER   The National Trust
LOCATION   Off A246 between Leatherhead & Guildford
OPEN   11 am – 6 pm; daily; all year
ADMISSION   Adults £3
FACILITIES   Parking; dogs permitted; loos; facilities for the disabled; plants for sale; large National Trust shop; self-service restaurant & tea-rooms
FEATURES   Herbaceous borders; climbing roses; modern roses; old roses; snowdrops; plantings by Graham Thomas; new landscape walks (1996)
ENGLISH HERITAGE GRADE   II*

Best for the long terraced walk, laid out by Sheridan, and the return through an Edwardian-style rose garden whose pergolas drip with ramblers.

Ramster
Chiddingfold GU8 4SN
☎ 01428 644422   [FAX] 01428 658345
OWNER   Mr & Mrs Paul Gunn
LOCATION   1½ miles south of Chiddingfold on A283
OPEN   11 am – 5.30 pm; daily; 19 April to 20 July. Parties by appointment at other times
ADMISSION   Adults £2.50; Children Free. Season ticket £7.50
FACILITIES   Parking; dogs permitted; loos; access for the disabled; plants for sale; home-made teas
FEATURES   Good collection of trees; fine conifers; lake; rhododendrons; camellias; azaleas; bluebells; largest Euonymus europaeus (6m.) in the British Isles

20 acres of Surrey woodland underplanted with camellias, rhododendrons and all manner of rare shrubs by Mrs Gunn's grandmother 70 years ago. She was the second Lord Aberconway's sister and many of her plants came from Bodnant: some of the rhododendrons and azaleas are her hybrids.

RHS Garden, Wisley
Woking GU23 6QB
☎ 01483 224234   [FAX] 01483 211750
OWNER   The Royal Horticultural Society
LOCATION   Near M25 Jct 3
OPEN   10 am – 7 pm or dusk if earlier (4.30 pm November to January); daily; all year except Christmas Day. Sundays reserved for RHS members only
ADMISSION   Adults £5; Children £1.75. Discounts for groups (pre-booked 21 days) – contact Sally Hallum
FACILITIES   Parking; loos; facilities for the disabled; plants for sale; marvellous bookshop and souvenir shop; restaurant & cafeteria
FEATURES   Good collection of trees; herbaceous borders; fine conifers; fruit of special interest; glasshouses and conservatories to visit; gravel or scree garden; lake; plantsman's garden;

rock garden; modern roses; old roses; snowdrops; subtropical plants; woodland garden; particularly good in July-August; particularly interesting in winter; heather garden; herb garden; horticultural trials; vegetable gardens; tallest *Ostrya virginiana* (15.5m.) in the British Isles, and 19 further record trees ENGLISH HERITAGE GRADE II*

NCCPG NATIONAL COLLECTIONS *Bruckenthalia*; *Calluna vulgaris*; *Crocus*; *Daboecia*; *Epimedium*; *Erica*; *Galanthus*; *Rheum*

Too well known to need description, Wisley is a garden to visit and revisit in search of new knowledge and inspiration. You can spend a a week there and still find corners you never knew existed.

The Savill Garden

c/o Crown Estate Office, Great Park, Windsor SL4 2HT
☎ 01753 860222   [FAX] 01753 859617

OWNER   Crown Property
LOCATION   At Englefield Green, 3 miles west of Egham off the A30 & 5 miles from Windsor
OPEN   10 am – 6 pm (4 pm from November to February); daily except 25 & 26 December
ADMISSION   Adults £3.50; Senior Citizens £3; Children under 16 Free; Groups (20+) £3
FACILITIES   Parking; plants for sale; gift and book shop; lavatories; licensed restaurant & picnic area
FEATURES   Good collection of trees; camellias; gravel or scree garden; lake; plantsman's garden; modern roses; woodland garden; particularly good in July-August; particularly interesting in winter; Kurume azaleas; mahonias; magnolias; magnificent late summer borders; tallest silver birch *Betula pendula* (30m.) in the British Isles (& 13 other record trees); vast new glasshouse (1995), rather too intrusive in this sylvan setting
ENGLISH HERITAGE GRADE I
NCCPG NATIONAL COLLECTIONS *Ilex*; *Magnolia*; *Mahonia*; *Pernettya*; *Pieris*; *Rhododendron*; Ferns; Dwarf Conifers
FRIENDS   Active Friends Organisation: details from John Bond, Keeper of the Gardens

Quite simply the finest woodland garden in England, crammed with rhododendrons, magnolias, azaleas, maples, mahonias and hydrangeas and underplanted with drifts of meconopsis, primulas and wild narcissus. The primulas come in monospecific masses, from the earliest *PP. rosea & denticulata* through to *P. florindae* in July and August. But the late summer herbaceous borders are also an inspiration and the gravel garden is one of the oldest and largest.

Vale End

Albury, Guildford
☎ & [FAX] 01483 202296

OWNER   Mr & Mrs John Foulsham
LOCATION   500 yards west of Albury on A248
OPEN   10 am – 5 pm; 22 June & 27 July
ADMISSION   Adults £1.50; Children Free
FACILITIES   Parking; dogs permitted; loos; plants for sale; refreshments

FEATURES   Herbaceous borders; plantsman's garden; old roses; new decorative kitchen and herb garden (1995)

A modern plantsman's garden, the best we know on Bagshot sand, where a love of plants has not been allowed to obscure either the design or the landscape beyond.

The Valley Gardens

c/o Crown Estate Office, Great Park, Windsor SL4 2HT
☎ 01753 860222

OWNER   Crown Property
LOCATION   At Englefield Green, 5 miles from Windsor, off A30; follow signs for Savill Garden
OPEN   8 am – 7 pm, or sunset if earlier; daily; all year
ADMISSION   Car & occupants £3 (use 10p, 50p & £1 coins only)
FACILITIES   Parking; dogs permitted; toilets; refreshments at the Savill Garden
FEATURES   Good collection of trees; lake; plantsman's garden; rhododendrons and azaleas; woodland garden; magnolias; heathers; hydrangeas
NCCPG NATIONAL COLLECTIONS *Ilex*; *Magnolia*; *Mahonia*; *Pernettya*; *Pieris*; *Rhododendron*; Dwarf conifers

A bigger and better Savill Gardens: all is planted on a royal scale in a wilder woodland setting. Best known is the Punch Bowl, where massed ranks of Kurume azaleas fill a natural combe with amazingly garish mixtures. Other parts are underplanted with hostas, ferns, bergenias and candelabra primulas. There is also a fine pinetum and a good collection of hydrangeas. But the gardens extend to 300 acres: not to be undertaken by the frail or faint-hearted.

Vann

Hambledon, nr Godalming GU8 4EF
☎ 01428 68 3413   [FAX] 017267 9344

OWNER   Mr & Mrs Martin Caroe
LOCATION   2 miles from Chiddingfold. Signs from A283 at Hambledon on NGS days
OPEN   10 am – 6 pm; daily; 18 to 23 April, 1 to 6 May, & 24 May to 4 June. Also 2 pm – 7 pm on 30 April. And by appointment 1 April to 31 August
ADMISSION   Adults £2.50; Children 50p. Pre-booked groups welcome
FACILITIES   Parking; loos; teas by arrangement
FEATURES   Bluebells; herbaceous borders; planted by Gertrude Jekyll; lake; woodland garden; wood anemones; newly replanted double border (1994); alterations to lawn bed (1996)
ENGLISH HERITAGE GRADE II

High-profile Jekyll garden, well restored and meticulously maintained by the present Caroes, the third generation to live here. Start at the back of the house and move along the Arts & Crafts pergola which leads straight to the lake. This is the heart of the garden, from which five or six distinct gardens lead from one to the next and melt into the Surrey woods: among them, a yew walk, a water garden, a woodland cherry walk, a hazel coppice and a woodland garden under vast oaks. The plantings are dense and thoughtful.

Winkworth Arboretum

Hascombe Road, Godalming GU8 4AD

☎ 01483 208477

OWNER   The National Trust

LOCATION   2 miles south-east of Godalming, off B2130

OPEN   All year; dawn – dusk. Groups *must* pre-book in writing

ADMISSION   Adults £2.50; Children (5 – 16) £1

FACILITIES   Parking; dogs permitted; loos; shop; tea-room

FEATURES   Good collection of trees; lake; woodland garden; plantings by Graham Thomas; bluebells; wood anemones; autumn colour; tallest *Acer davidii* (19m.) in the British Isles, and 5 further record trees

NCCPG NATIONAL COLLECTIONS   *Sorbus* (Aria & Micromeles groups)

Beautiful arboretum, planted with particularly decorative species (maples, *Sorbus*, magnolias and *Hamamelis*) in large groups for maximum effect. Good in May when the azaleas are underscored by bluebells: better still for autumn colour in October.

EAST SUSSEX

Bateman's

Burwash, Etchingham TN19 7DS

☎ 01435 882302

OWNER   The National Trust

LOCATION   Signposted at west end of village

OPEN   11 am – 5.30 pm; Saturday – Wednesday; 1 April to 31 October

ADMISSION   Adults £4.50; Children £2.25; Family £11

FACILITIES   Parking; loos; access for the disabled; National Trust shop; restaurant & café

FEATURES   Herbaceous borders; herbs; old roses; interesting for children; arcade planted with pears and clematis; water mill

ENGLISH HERITAGE GRADE   II

10 acres on the banks of the River Dudwell, where Rudyard Kipling lived from 1902 until his death in 1936. Fun for children, because there is a working flour mill, but not spectacular for the knowledgeable gardener, except for the *Campsis grandiflora* on the house.

Bates Green Farm

Arlington, Polegate BN26 6SH

☎ & FAX 01323 482039

OWNER   Mr & Mrs J R McCutchan

LOCATION   3 miles south-west of Hailsham

OPEN   10.30 am – 6 pm; Thursdays; 1 April to 31 October. Also for NGS and by appointment

ADMISSION   £2

FACILITIES   Parking; loos; access for the disabled; plants for sale; refreshments by arrangement

FEATURES   Herbaceous borders; lake; rock garden; woodland garden; colour borders; bluebells

Made by the present owners over the last 20 years. Several different areas: a large rock garden (renovated last winter), a shady garden, and wonderful mixed borders planted for year-round colour associations. The owners seek perfection, but wonder if they will ever achieve it.

Brickwall House & Gardens

Frewen College, Northiam TN31 6NL

☎ 01797 223329   FAX 0179 742567

OWNER   Frewen Educational Trust

LOCATION   Off B2088

OPEN   2 pm – 5 pm; Saturdays & Bank Holiday Mondays; 5 April to 30 September

ADMISSION   £2.50

FACILITIES   Parking; dogs permitted; loos; access for the disabled; postcards and guide books but no shop; by arrangement for groups

FEATURES   Good collection of trees; herbaceous borders; herbs; good topiary; young garden; extensively redesigned since 1980

ENGLISH HERITAGE GRADE   II*

Designed as a Stuart garden, to match the house, Brickwall has borders planted exclusively with old fashioned plants and a chess garden where green and yellow yew shapes are grown in squares of black or white chips. Very neatly maintained.

Clinton Lodge

Fletching, Uckfield TN22 3ST

☎ 01825 722952

OWNER   Mr & Mrs M R Collum

LOCATION   In main village street

OPEN   2 pm – 6 pm; 15, 16, 18, 25 June, 2 July

ADMISSION   £2.50

FACILITIES   Parking; loos; access for the disabled; home-made teas

FEATURES   Herbaceous borders; herbs; old roses; yew hedges; lime walks; *potager*; knot gardens

A rising star among new gardens, designed round a handsome 17th-century house. 6 acres of formal gardens of different periods, starting with a 'mediaeval' *potager* and an Elizabethan herb garden. The most successful parts are the pre-Raphaelite walk of lilies and pale roses, and the Victorian herbaceous borders in soft pastel shades.

Cobblers

Mount Pleasant, Jarvis Brook, Crowborough TN6 2ND

☎ 01892 655969

OWNER   Mr & Mrs Martin Furniss

LOCATION   Turn off B2100 into Tollwood Road: ¼ mile on right

OPEN   2.30 pm – 5.30 pm; 26 May, 22 June, 13 July, and 3 & 25 August; plus 5.50 pm – 8 pm 11 June

ADMISSION   Adults £3.50; Children £1: home-made teas included

FACILITIES   Parking; loos; access for the disabled; plants for sale; home-made teas

FEATURES   Herbaceous borders; plantsman's garden; modern roses

Tightly planned and beautifully planted garden made by an architect who is also a plantsman. There is a great variety of habitats and plants (bog, alpine, hot-coloured, shade-loving etc.) within a design which opens out its perspectives slowly.

Great Dixter

Dixter Road, Northiam TN31 6PH
☎ 01797 252878   [FAX] 01797 252879

OWNER   Christopher Lloyd

LOCATION   Off A28 at Northiam Post Office

OPEN   2 pm – 5 pm; daily except Monday; 28 March to 15 October, plus Bank Holiday Mondays

ADMISSION   Adults £3; Children 25p

FACILITIES   Parking; loos; plants for sale; gift shop

FEATURES   Herbaceous borders; herbs; plantsman's garden; modern roses; old roses; subtropical plants; good topiary; particularly good in July-August; meadow garden; colour schemes

ENGLISH HERITAGE GRADE   I

Several well-defined enclosures surround the Lutyens house but they change constantly as Christopher Lloyd rethinks, reworks and replants. Dixter is a living lesson in the choice and use of plants, a garden to revisit frequently.

Michelham Priory

Upper Dicker, Hailsham BN27 3QS
☎ 01323 844224   [FAX] 01323 844030

OWNER   The Sussex Archaeological Society

LOCATION   Signposted from A22 and A27

OPEN   Open daily; 15 March to 31 October. 11 am – 4 pm, March & October; 11 am – 5 pm, April-July & September; 10.30 am – 5.30 pm August. Closed Mondays & Tuesdays, except Bank Holidays & in August

ADMISSION   Adults £4; Senior Citizens £3.20; Children £2; Family £10 (2+2)

FACILITIES   Parking; loos; facilities for the disabled; plants for sale; restaurant & tea-room

FEATURES   Herbaceous borders; fine conifers; herbs; modern roses; old roses

The old Augustinian priory has an Elizabethan barn, blacksmith shop, rope museum and moat. The Physic Garden is planted with medieval herbs.

Paradise Park

Avis Road, Newhaven BN9 0DH
☎ 01273 616001   [FAX] 01273 616005

OWNER   Jonathan Tate

LOCATION   Signposted from A26 & A259

OPEN   10 am – 5 pm; daily; all year

FACILITIES   Parking; loos; facilities for the disabled; plant centre; large coffee-shop

FEATURES   Glasshouses and conservatories to visit

Part of a leisure complex attached to a garden centre, the most interesting features are a tropical house and a cactus house, each landscaped with handsome species chosen for display. A haven in winter.

Pashley Manor Garden

Ticehurst, Wadhurst TN5 7NE
☎ 01580 200692   [FAX] 01580 200102

OWNER   James A Sellick

LOCATION   On B2099 between A21 and Ticehurst

OPEN   11 am – 5 pm; Tuesday – Thursday, Saturday & Bank Holiday Mondays; 12 April to 27 September

ADMISSION   Adults £3.50; Senior Citizens £3

FACILITIES   Parking; loos; plants for sale; fresh produce for sale; lunches & teas

FEATURES   Fine conifers; lake; climbing roses; old roses; Victorian shrubberies; hydrangeas; irises; new 'Elizabethan' garden; new golden garden (1993) maturing well

A new/old garden, made or remade in the Victorian style over the last ten years with advice from Tony Pasley. The results are gentle shapes, spacious expanses, harmonious colours and solid plantings. It gets better every year.

Sheffield Park Garden

Uckfield TN22 3QX
☎ 01825 790231

OWNER   The National Trust

LOCATION   Between East Grinstead & Lewes on A275

OPEN   11 am – 4 pm (6 pm or dusk if earlier from 1 April to 9 November); Tuesday – Sunday & Bank Holiday Mondays (but Saturdays & Sundays only in March, and Wednesday – Sunday only from 12 November to 21 December); 1 March to 6 November and 9 November to 17 December

ADMISSION   Adults £4; Children £2; pre-booked weekday parties £3 (15+). RHS members Free

FACILITIES   Parking; loos; facilities for the disabled; National Trust shop; refreshments nearby

FEATURES   Good collection of trees; landscape designed by Capability Brown; fine conifers; lake; landscape designed by Humphry Repton; woodland garden; plantings by Graham Thomas; daffodils; bluebells; kalmias; autumn crocuses; rhododendrons; tallest *Nyssa sylvatica* (21m.) in the British Isles, plus two other record trees

ENGLISH HERITAGE GRADE   I

NCCPG NATIONAL COLLECTIONS   Rhododendron (Ghent azaleas)

Little remains of Capability Brown and Repton except the lakes which now reflect the plantings of exotic trees – landscaping on the grandest of scales. Wonderful leaf colours whatever the season, plus gentians in autumn.

Standen

East Grinstead RH19 4NE
☎ 01342 323029   [FAX] 01342 316424

OWNER   The National Trust

LOCATION   2 miles south of East Grinstead, signposted from B2110

OPEN   12.30 pm – 6 pm; Wednesday – Sunday & Bank Holiday Mondays; 26 March to 2 November. 1 pm – 4 pm; Friday – Sunday; 7 November to 21 December

ADMISSION   Adults £3; Children £1.50

FACILITIES   Parking; loos; plants for sale; National Trust shop; light lunches & afternoon teas

FEATURES   Herbaceous borders; fine conifers; rock garden; old roses; rhododendrons; azaleas; woodland shrubs

Small Edwardian garden with magnificent views across the valley. A series of enclosed gardens around the house gives way to woodland slopes and an old quarry furnished with ferns.

WEST SUSSEX

Berri Court
Yapton, Arundel BN18 0ED
☎ 01243 551663
OWNER Mr & Mrs John M Turner
LOCATION Yapton, 5 miles south-west of Arundel, centre of village next to Black Dog pub
OPEN For NGS: see Yellow Book
ADMISSION Adults £1.50; Children Free
FACILITIES Parking; dogs permitted; loos; facilities for the disabled; plants for sale
FEATURES Herbaceous borders; rhododendrons and azaleas; old roses; eucalyptus; hydrangeas; lily ponds

A plantsman's garden with a compact design, some 3 acres in extent.

Borde Hill Garden
Haywards Heath RH16 1XP
☎ 01444 450326   FAX 01444 440427
OWNER Borde Hill Garden Ltd
LOCATION 1½ miles north of Haywards Heath
OPEN 10 am – 6 pm; daily
ADMISSION Adults £2.50; Children £1
FACILITIES Parking; dogs permitted; loos; facilities for the disabled; plants for sale; small gift shop; tea-rooms, restaurant & pub
FEATURES Good collection of trees; lake; plantsman's garden; woodland garden; interesting for children; rhododendrons; azaleas; magnolias; plants from original seed; new rose-garden by Robin Williams (1996); 48 different record trees, one of the largest collections in the British Isles
ENGLISH HERITAGE GRADE II*

This important woodland garden has a significant collection of rhododendron species grown from such introducers as Forrest and Kingdon Ward. It has recently been revamped for the recreation market and is all the better for the new capital. There are good new borders, a lake, and all sorts of facilities like an adventure playground and a smart restaurant: very cockle-warming to see Borde Hill on the up again.

Coates Manor
Fittleworth, Pulborough RH20 1ES
☎ 0179 8865356
OWNER Mrs S M Thorp
LOCATION ½ mile off B2138, signposted Coates
OPEN 11 am – 6 pm; 19 & 20 October for autumn colour, and by appointment at other times
ADMISSION Adults £1.50; Children Free
FACILITIES Parking; loos; access for the disabled; refreshments on open days
FEATURES Herbaceous borders; colour planting; foliage plants

A small, neatly designed and intensely planted garden which crams a lifetime's learning into its plantings. Long-term colour

effects are its outstanding quality: leaves, berries, trunks, stems, form, shadow and texture are all individually exploited to the maximum. A model of its kind and beautifully maintained.

Cooke's House
West Burton, Pulborough RH20 1HD
☎ 0179 831353
OWNER Miss J B Courtauld
LOCATION Turn off A29 by White Horse at foot of Bury Hill
OPEN 2 pm – 6 pm; 6 to 8 & 13 to 15 April & by appointment
ADMISSION Adults £1; Children under 14 free
FACILITIES Parking; loos; access for the disabled; tea & biscuits
FEATURES Herbaceous borders; old roses; good topiary
ENGLISH HERITAGE GRADE II

A neat and well maintained garden, pretty in spring when the primulas and bulbs are out. Even better at midsummer when the roses and herbaceous plants crammed into small enclosures create a sense of great richness and harmony.

Cowdray Park
Midhurst GU29 0AQ
☎ 01730 812423   FAX 01730 815608
OWNER The Viscount Cowdray
LOCATION South of A272, 1 mile east of Midhurst
OPEN 2 pm – 6 pm; 25 May
ADMISSION £2
FACILITIES Parking; loos; refreshments
FEATURES 300-year-old Lebanon cedar; wellingtonia avenue; rhododendrons; tallest *Abies concolor* f. *violacea* (28m.) and *Chamaecyparis pisifera* (29m.) in the United Kingdom
ENGLISH HERITAGE GRADE II*

Seldom open, but worth a long journey to see the extraordinarily overwrought house and its contemporary (100 years old) collection of trees, particularly conifers. Some are now record-breakers, and the sweeps of rhododendrons and azaleas, especially the hardy hybrids down The Dell, are on the grand scale too. Pretty awesome.

Denmans
Fontwell, Arundel BN18 0SU
☎ 01243 542808   FAX 01243 544064
LOCATION Off A29 or A27, near Fontwell racecourse
OPEN 9 am – 5 pm; daily; 1 March to 31 October. Or by appointment
ADMISSION Adults £2.50; Senior Citizens £2.25; Children (over 5) £1.50; groups (15+) £1.95
FACILITIES Parking; loos; access for the disabled; shop; garden centre; lunches & teas
FEATURES Herbaceous borders; gravel or scree garden; herbs; lake; old roses; spring bulbs

This small modern garden is a showpiece for John Brookes' ideas and commitment to easy care. He uses foliage, gravel mulches, contrasts of form, coloured stems, winter bark and plants as elements of design. Garden decoration *in excelsis*.

Gravetye Manor Hotel

East Grinstead RH19 4LJ
☎ 01342 810567   [FAX] 01342 810080
OWNER   Peter Herbert
LOCATION   4 miles south-west of East Grinstead
OPEN   Hotel guests only; all year
FACILITIES   Parking
FEATURES   Good collection of trees; herbaceous borders; plantsman's garden; old roses; good topiary; woodland garden; alpine meadow; gazebo
ENGLISH HERITAGE GRADE   II*

William Robinson's own garden, very influential 80 years ago, and scrupulously maintained by Peter Herbert as it was in its prime. Gravetye is still a garden to learn from: there is much to admire and copy.

The High Beeches

Handcross RH17 6HQ
☎ 01444 400589
OWNER   High Beeches Gardens Conservation Trust
LOCATION   South of B2110, 1 mile east of M23 at Handcross
OPEN   1 pm – 5 pm; daily, except Wednesdays; 29 March to 30 June and 1 September to 31 October. Plus Mondays & Tuesdays in July & August
ADMISSION   Adults £3. Coaches by appointment
FACILITIES   Parking; loos; drinks & ice-creams
FEATURES   Good collection of trees; fine conifers; ecological interest; plantsman's garden; woodland garden; rhododendrons; tallest *Stuartia monodelpha* (11m.) in the British Isles
ENGLISH HERITAGE GRADE   II*
NCCPG NATIONAL COLLECTIONS *Stewartia*
FRIENDS   High Beeches Gardens Conservation Trust is an active organisation with many events of interest to gardeners: details from the Curator

One of the best of the famous Sussex gardens, a valley of ponds and woodland glades, with splendid rhododendrons, azaleas, magnolias and camellias, but wonderful spring and autumn colours too, and a policy of letting good plants naturalise – wild orchids, willow gentians and *Primula helodoxa*. A great credit to the Boscawens who have devoted 25 years to its maintenance and improvement.

Highdown

Littlehampton Road, Goring-by-Sea BN12 6NY
☎ 01903 239999 ext 2539 [FAX] 01903 821384
OWNER   Worthing Borough Council
LOCATION   Signposted from A259
OPEN   10 am – 6 pm (4.30 pm October & November, 4 pm December & January, 4.30 pm February & March); daily (but not weekends from October to March); all year. Closes at 8 pm at weekends and on Bank Holiday Mondays from April to September
ADMISSION   Free – donations welcome
FACILITIES   Parking; loos; refreshments in high season
FEATURES   Good collection of trees; herbaceous borders; fine conifers; plantsman's garden; rock garden; old roses; woodland garden; tallest specimen of *Carpinus turczaninowii* in the United Kingdom, a handsome tree

ENGLISH HERITAGE GRADE   II*

A very important garden. Its maker, Sir Frederick Stern, was determined to try anything that might grow on chalk. 80 years on, the results are some handsome trees, vigorous roses, and long-forgotten paeony hybrids. Best of all are the naturalised hellebores, tulips and anemones. Alas, Stern made a mistake in leaving it to Worthing Borough Council.

Leonardslee Gardens

Lower Beeding, Horsham RH13 6PP
☎ 01403 891212   [FAX] 01403 891305
OWNER   R R Loder
LOCATION   4 miles south-west of Handcross at Jct of A279 & A281
OPEN   10 am – 6 pm; daily; 1 April to 31 October
ADMISSION   Adults £3.50 (£4.50 in May); Children £2
FACILITIES   Parking; loos; plants for sale; gift shop; licensed restaurant & café
FEATURES   Bluebells; fine conifers; glasshouses and conservatories to visit; lake; oriental features; plantsman's garden; rhododendrons and azaleas; rock garden; woodland garden; new alpine house; wallabies; summer wild flower walk; new Millennium plantings (90 oak species in 1995; 120 maple species in 1996); tallest fossil tree *Metasequoia glyptostroboides* (28m.) and *Magnolia campbellii* (27m.) in the British Isles, and 5 further champion trees
ENGLISH HERITAGE GRADE   I

A spectacular collection of rhododendrons and azaleas is the essence of Leonardslee, and the way they are planted in drifts of one colour. But there are magnolias, camellias and innumerable rare plants, as well as a formidable bonsai collection. The 80 acres open to the public are laced with lakes, dells and groves; they have just been extended to 240 acres. Ravishing in May.

Nymans Garden

Handcross, Haywards Heath RH17 6EB
☎ 01444 400321   [FAX] 01444 400253
OWNER   The National Trust
LOCATION   Handcross, off the main road
OPEN   11 am – 6 pm; Wednesday – Sunday, plus Bank Holiday Mondays; 1 March to 2 November
ADMISSION   Adults £4.50; Children £2.25. RHS members free
FACILITIES   Parking; loos; facilities for the disabled; plants for sale; shop; teas
FEATURES   Good collection of trees; herbaceous borders; fine conifers; plantsman's garden; rock garden; modern roses; old roses; good topiary; woodland garden; house open this year for first time; eight different record-breaking trees
ENGLISH HERITAGE GRADE   II*

The sumptuous mansion in the West Country style has been gutted by fire, but the garden is intact, with opulent yellow-and-blue herbaceous borders in the walled garden, a pioneering collection of old roses, a stupendous wisteria pergola and vast collections of magnolias and camellias. Yet some say Nymans is overrated...

Parham

Parham House, Pulborough RH20 4HS

☎ 01903 742021   FAX 01903 746557

OWNER   Parham Park Trust

LOCATION   On A283 midway between Pulborough and Storrington

OPEN   1 pm – 6 pm; Wednesdays, Thursdays, Sundays & Bank Holiday Mondays; 30 March to 30 October

ADMISSION   Gardens only: Adults £3; Children 50p (1996 prices)

FACILITIES   Parking; dogs permitted; loos; plants for sale; shop; self-service teas

FEATURES   Herbaceous borders; fruit of special interest; lake; plantsman's garden; old roses; new maze; HHA/Christie's Garden of the Year in 1990

ENGLISH HERITAGE GRADE   I

An ethereal English garden for the loveliest of Elizabethan manor houses. In the park are a landscaped lake and a cricket ground. The fun for garden-lovers is in the old walled garden: lush borders, colour plantings in yellow, blue and mauve, old and new fruit trees, and all maintained to the highest standard.

Petworth House

Petworth GU28 0AE

☎ 01798 342207

OWNER   The National Trust

LOCATION   At Petworth, well signed

OPEN   House: 1 pm – 5.30 pm; Saturday – Wednesday & Bank Holidays; 1 April to 31 October. Park: 8 am – 9 pm, or dusk if sooner; daily; all year

ADMISSION   House: Adults £4.50; Children £2; Groups (15+) £4. Park: free

FACILITIES   Parking; dogs permitted; loos; facilities for the disabled; shop; restaurant; tea-rooms

FEATURES   Herbaceous borders; landscape designed by Capability Brown; lake; woodland garden; deer park; one million daffodils; nine record-holding trees all felled by the Great Gale of 1987

ENGLISH HERITAGE GRADE   I

One of the best Capability Brown landscapes in England sweeps up to the windows of the house itself. The National Trust has decided to add modern attractions: herbaceous borders and acres of azaleas in a new woodland garden. Both park and garden have enjoyed a renaissance since the Great Gale.

Stonehurst

Ardingly RH17 6TN

☎ 01444 892052

OWNER   D R Strauss

LOCATION   1 mile north of Ardingly on B2028

OPEN   11 am – 5 pm; 20 April, 5 & 26 May

ADMISSION   Adults £2.50; Children £1

FACILITIES   Parking; dogs permitted; loos; plants for sale; orchids, rhododendrons & camellias for sale; teas

FEATURES   Herbaceous borders; follies and garden buildings; lake; rock garden; camellias; magnolias; azaleas; SSSI

ENGLISH HERITAGE GRADE   II

Stonehurst is in a rock-lined secret valley, where springs issue to form a series of small lakes, and rare liverworts have special scientific interest. The Strausses have made it known as a garden for rhododendrons, camellias and rare trees and shrubs which regularly win prizes at RHS shows in London. Well maintained.

Telegraph House

North Marden, nr Chichester PO18 9JX

☎ 01730 825206

OWNER   Mr & Mrs Gault

LOCATION   Entrance on B2141, 2 miles south of Harting

OPEN   6 pm – 6 pm, 21 & 22 June, 12 & 13 July. And 1 May to 30 August by appointment

ADMISSION   Adults £1.50; Children 75p

FACILITIES   Parking; dogs permitted; loos; access for the disabled; plants for sale; refreshments at open weekends

FEATURES   Herbaceous borders; old roses; woodland garden; 1 mile avenue of copper beeches

The house is c.1900 and French in style, but the garden has been made by the present owners over the last 20 years. Yew hedges enclose a series of terraces and intimate gardens: roses, shrubs and herbaceous plantings. Nearby are 150 acres of natural woodland, much of it ancient yew.

Wakehurst Place

Ardingly, Haywards Heath RH17 6TN

☎ 01444 894066   FAX 01444 894069

OWNER   R B G, Kew

LOCATION   On B2028 between Turner's Hill & Ardingly

OPEN   10 am – 7 pm (6 pm in March & October, 5 pm in February & 4 pm from November to January); daily except Christmas Day & New Year's Day; all year

ADMISSION   Adults £4.50 (1996)

FACILITIES   Parking; loos; facilities for the disabled; bookshop & gift-shop; light refreshments & new restaurant

FEATURES   Alpines; good collection of trees; bluebells; bog garden; camellias; daffodils; ecological interest; gravel or scree garden; lake; plantsman's garden; rhododendrons and azaleas; climbing roses; old roses; woodland garden; particularly interesting in winter; Asian heath garden; pinetum; cardiocrinums; good autumn colour; tallest *Ostrya japonica* (15m.) in the British Isles, plus 25 further tree records

ENGLISH HERITAGE GRADE   II*

NCCPG NATIONAL COLLECTIONS *Betula*; *Hypericum*; *Nothofagus*; *Skimmia*

FRIENDS   Part of the Friends of Kew organisation

Allow plenty of time for Wakehurst: it is very big, and there is much to see. Near the house are the winter garden, two ponds, the new Asian heath garden and the southern hemisphere garden. No garden combines so perfectly the function of a major botanic institute with the sense of being a private garden still.

West Dean Gardens

West Dean, Chichester PO18 0Q2

☎ 01243 811301 or 818210   FAX 01243 811342

OWNER   The Edward James Foundation

LOCATION   6 miles north of Chichester on A286

OPEN   11 am – 5 pm; daily; 1 March to 26 October
ADMISSION   Adults £3.50; Senior Citizens £3; Children
£1.50; Groups (20+) £3; Family ticket £9
FACILITIES   Parking; loos; facilities for the disabled; plants for
sale; licensed restaurant
FEATURES   Glasshouses and conservatories to visit; old roses;
museum of old lawn mowers; tallest *Cupressus goveniana*
(22m.) and *Ailanthus vilmoriniana* (26m.) in UK; amazing
kitchen garden; new Visitors' Centre (1995)
ENGLISH HERITAGE GRADE   II*
NCCPG NATIONAL COLLECTIONS *Aesculus; Liriodendron*

Laid out in the 1890s and 1900s, West Dean has now been
extensively restored: Harold Peto's 100-metre pergola has
been replanted with roses; much of the damage to the arboretum caused by the 1987 storm has been made good; and the
great range of glasshouses in the walled garden has been
repaired – the garden itself planted as a working kitchen
garden. We know of no private garden with so many beautifully grown fruit and vegetables.

Yew Tree Cottage
Crawley Down, Turners Hill RH10 4EY
☎ 01342 714633

OWNER   Mrs K Hudson
LOCATION   Opposite Grange Farm on B2028
OPEN   By appointment
ADMISSION   £1
FACILITIES   Parking; dogs permitted; plants for sale; refreshments for small parties
FEATURES   Herbaceous borders; fruit of special interest; old
roses; cottage garden style; colour borders; new gravel beds in
the German style (1996)

This miraculous small garden (⅓ acre) has been designed,
planted and maintained by the nonagenarian owner over many
years and won infinite plaudits for its display of plants in the
Jekyll manner. There is no better example of the cottage garden
style.

TYNE & WEAR

Bede's World Herb Garden
Bede's World, Church Bank, Jarrow NE32 3DY
☎ 0191 489 2196   [FAX] 0191 428 2361

OWNER   Jarrow 700 AD Ltd
LOCATION   Signposted from A185
OPEN   Dawn to dusk; daily; all year
ADMISSION   Garden only: free
FACILITIES   Parking; loos; facilities for the disabled; shop for
herbal products; lunches & light refreshments
FEATURES   Herbs; interesting for children
FRIENDS   Friends of Bede's World

A herb garden based on 9th-century descriptions: a small part
of an ambitious enterprise which seeks to impart a feeling for
the Anglo-Saxon world. In front of the new museum are four
raised beds planted as a late mediaeval formal garden.

WARWICKSHIRE

Arbury Hall
Nuneaton CV10 7PT
☎ 01203 382804   [FAX] 01203 641147

OWNER   Viscount Daventry
LOCATION   3 miles south-east of Nuneaton off the B4102
OPEN   2 pm – 5.30 pm; Sundays & Bank Holiday Mondays;
Easter Sunday to 29 September. Plus Wednesdays from May
to July
ADMISSION   Adults £2.50; Children £1.50
FACILITIES   Parking; dogs permitted; loos; access for the disabled; gift & crafts shop; tea-rooms
FEATURES   Bluebells; daffodils; follies and garden buildings;
lake; rhododendrons and azaleas; modern roses; woodland
garden; wisteria
ENGLISH HERITAGE GRADE   II*

Good trees (especially purple beeches), handsome parkland,
lakes and ponds – Arbury has good bones for a garden. Then
there are bluebell woods, pollarded limes, a large rose garden,
a walled garden and a huge wisteria. Nothing is outstanding in
itself, but the ensemble is an oasis of peace on the edge of
industrial Daventry and worth the journey from far away.

Charlecote Park
Wellesbourne, Warwick CV35 9ER
☎ 01789 470277   [FAX] 01789 470544

OWNER   The National Trust
LOCATION   Signed from A429
OPEN   11 am – 6 pm; Friday – Tuesday; 29 March to 31 October
ADMISSION   £4.60; Children (5-16) £2.30
FACILITIES   Parking; loos; facilities for the disabled; National
Trust shop; restaurant
FEATURES   Landscape designed by Capability Brown; fine
conifers; glasshouses and conservatories to visit; lake; good
topiary; deer park; orangery; newly restored 1890s box parterres with bright bedding plants (1996)
ENGLISH HERITAGE GRADE   II*

Fine cedars and a Capability Brown park are the main claims
to Charlecote's fame, but the young William Shakespeare is
reputed to have poached deer from the park, so the National
Trust has planted a border with plants mentioned in his works.

Coughton Court
Alcester B49 5JA
☎ 01789 400777   [FAX] 01789 765544

OWNER   Mrs Clare Throckmorton
LOCATION   2 miles north of Alcester on A435
OPEN   11 am – 5.30 pm; Saturdays & Sundays (plus Monday
– Wednesday from May to September); 15 March to 19
October. Plus 31 March, 1 & 2 April, and Fridays from 25 July
to 29 August
ADMISSION   Adults £3.50; Children £1.75
FACILITIES   Parking; loos; access for the disabled; gift shop &
plant centre; restaurant/café

The garden is new, and designed by Christina Birch, the
owner's daughter. An Elizabethan-style knot garden fills the
courtyard, and extensive new plantings beyond lead the eye

out to the distant landscape. There is a new rose labyrinth and a herb garden, as well as an orchard planted with local varieties of fruit. The new bog garden will open later this year.

Farnborough Hall

Banbury OX17 1DU
☎ 01295 690002

OWNER   The National Trust
LOCATION   Off A423, 6 miles north of Banbury
OPEN   2 pm – 6 pm; Wednesdays & Saturdays; 1 April to 30 September. Also 4 & 5 May
ADMISSION   Grounds £1.50; Terrace Walk £1 (Thursdays & Fridays only)
FACILITIES   Parking; dogs permitted; loos; access for the disabled
FEATURES   Follies and garden buildings; lake; old roses; good topiary; woodland garden; newly restored cascade (1994), now functioning
ENGLISH HERITAGE GRADE   I

Sanderson Millar's masterpiece – grand vistas, classical temples and a dominating obelisk. Plus a long curving terraced walk to the adjoining estate of Mollington. No flowers, but space and peace.

The Mill Garden, Warwick

55 Mill Street, Warwick CV34 4HB
☎ 01926 492877

OWNER   Arthur Measures
LOCATION   Off A425, beside castle gate
OPEN   9 am – dusk; daily; Easter to mid-October
ADMISSION   Adults £1; Children Free. Groups by appointment
FACILITIES   Access for the disabled; plants for sale
FEATURES   Plantsman's garden; water plants

No garden has such an idyllic setting, on the banks of the Avon at the foot of Warwick castle: the views in all directions are superb. The garden is planted in the cottage style and seems much larger than its one acre: it burgeons with plants, and the use of annuals to supplement the varied permanent planting enables it to have colour and form, contrasts and harmonies, at every season.

Packwood House

Packwood Lane, Lapworth, Solihull B94 6AT
☎ 01564 782024   01564 782014

OWNER   The National Trust
LOCATION   2 miles east of Hockley Heath: signposted from A3400
OPEN   1.30 pm – 6 pm; Wednesday – Sunday; April to September. Plus: 12.30 pm – 4.30 pm; Wednesday – Sunday; October
ADMISSION   Garden only: Adults £2; Children £1
FACILITIES   Parking; loos; access for the disabled; National Trust shop; refreshments available at peak times
FEATURES   Good topiary
ENGLISH HERITAGE GRADE   I

Long famous for its topiary, but Packwood also has good herbaceous borders which make a visit in July or August particularly rewarding.

Ryton Organic Gardens

Henry Doubleday Research Association,
Ryton-on-Dunsmore, Coventry CV8 3LG
☎ 01203 303517   01203 639229

OWNER   The Henry Doubleday Research Association (HDRA)
LOCATION   5 miles south-east of Coventry off A45
OPEN   10 am – 5.30 pm; daily; all year
ADMISSION   Adults £2.50; Senior Citizens £1.75; Children £1.25 (1996 prices). RHS members Free
FACILITIES   Parking; loos; facilities for the disabled; plants for sale; shop with gardening products, books, food, wine & gifts; organic whole-food restaurant
FEATURES   Ecological interest; fruit and vegetables of special interest; glasshouses and conservatories to visit; herbs; rock garden; modern roses; old roses; woodland garden; interesting for children
FRIENDS   Join the HDRA – details above

Ryton is the UK centre for organic gardening where experiments are made in using only natural fertilisers and trying to operate without pesticides. It is very well laid out, with dozens of different small gardens, all highly instructive. The staff's commitment is also impressive. You may not be convinced by what you see, but it will make you think. The excellent restaurant and substantial shop will add considerably to your enjoyment.

Sherbourne Park

Sherbourne, Warwick CV35 8AP
☎ 01926 624506

OWNER   Robin Smith-Ryland
LOCATION   A429 between M40 and Barford
OPEN   By appointment: 01926 624506 ask for Sonia Farey
ADMISSION   Adults £3; Senior Citizens & Children (12 – 16) £2; Children under 12 free
FACILITIES   Parking; dogs permitted; loos; access for the disabled; refreshments by arrangement
FEATURES   Herbaceous borders; lake; plantsman's garden; old roses; lilies; frescoed garden pavilion (1994)

A splendid post-war garden planned and planted to produce a series of smallish enclosed gardens around the house, each distinct and beautifully planted. The shelter of walls and hedges allows such tender genera as *Olearia* and *Carpenteria* to survive, and sometimes to flourish.

Upton House

Banbury OX15 6HT
☎ 01295 670266

OWNER   The National Trust
LOCATION   A422, 7 miles north-west of Banbury
OPEN   2 pm – 6 pm; Saturday – Wednesday; 29 March to 2 November
ADMISSION   Adults £2.40; Children £1.20
FACILITIES   Parking; loos; facilities for the disabled; plants for sale; National Trust shop; tea-room
FEATURES   Herbaceous borders; fruit of special interest
ENGLISH HERITAGE GRADE   II*
NCCPG NATIONAL COLLECTIONS   Aster

High on a ridge near the site of the battle of Edgehill, Upton is terraced right down to the pool at the bottom. The centrepiece is a kitchen garden, reached by flights of Italianate stairs. There are also modern formal gardens, one with standard *Hibiscus* 'Bluebird' underplanted with eryngiums, another a rose garden. Further down are a bog garden, a cherry garden and grand herbaceous borders to lead you back to the house. Fascinating, and not at all what you expect when you first see the house.

Warwick Castle

Warwick CV34 4QU
☎ 01926 495421   ℻ 01926 401692

OWNER   Tussauds Group
LOCATION   In town centre
OPEN   10 am – 6 pm (5 pm in winter); daily; all year except 25 December
ADMISSION   Adults £8.75; Senior Citizens £6.25; Children £5.25 (prices will be reviewed in March)
FACILITIES   Loos; shop; refreshments
FEATURES   Fine conifers; rhododendrons and azaleas; old roses; good topiary; Capability Brown landscape; handsome conservatory
ENGLISH HERITAGE GRADE   I

A classic 18th-century landscape, looking good after recent restoration, to which have been added a late 19th-century formal garden, a Backhouse rock garden, and a 1980s Victorian rose garden, pretty but not very profound.

WEST MIDLANDS

Birmingham Botanical Gardens & Glasshouses

Westbourne Road, Edgbaston, Birmingham B15 3TR
☎ 0121 454 1860   ℻ 0121 454 7835

OWNER   Birmingham Botanical & Horticultural Society
LOCATION   Follow brown tourist signs in Edgbaston
OPEN   9 am (Sunday 10 am) – 7 pm, or dusk if earlier; daily; all year
ADMISSION   Adults £3.80 (Summer Sunday & Bank Holiday £4.20); Concessions £1.20. Party rates available
FACILITIES   Parking; loos; facilities for the disabled; plants for sale; gift shop; restaurant & light refreshments
FEATURES   Herbaceous borders; fine conifers; fruit of special interest; glasshouses and conservatories to visit; plantsman's garden; rock garden; modern roses; old roses; interesting for children; new lawn aviary & rose garden (1996); children's gardens; adventure playground; three new 'historic' gardens – Roman, Mediaeval & Tudor
ENGLISH HERITAGE GRADE   II*
NCCPG NATIONAL COLLECTIONS   *Verbascum*
FRIENDS   Membership details available from Reception

Part botanic garden, part public park, wholly delightful, the Birmingham Botanical Gardens can boast a historic lay-out (John Loudon), rare trees and shrubs, gardens for rhododendrons, roses, herbs and alpines, and four glasshouses (tropical, palm house, orangery and cacti house) as well as a good

restaurant, brilliant standards of maintenance and a brass band playing on Sunday afternoons in summer. A garden to *enjoy*.

Castle Bromwich Hall

Chester Road, Castle Bromwich B36 9BT
☎ 0121 749 4100   ℻ 0121 749 4100

OWNER   Castle Bromwich Hall Gardens Trust
LOCATION   5 miles from city centre just off A47
OPEN   1.30 pm – 4.30 pm; Monday – Thursday. 2 pm – 6 pm; Saturdays, Sundays & Bank Holiday Mondays; Easter to September
ADMISSION   Adults £2; Concessions £1.50; Children 50p
FACILITIES   Parking; dogs permitted; loos; facilities for the disabled; plants for sale; gift shop; refreshments
FEATURES   Interesting for children; green walks; fruit garden; maze; wilderness; historic garden undergoing restoration
ENGLISH HERITAGE GRADE   II*
FRIENDS   Friends of the Gardens organisation

Garden archaeology at work. Castle Bromwich is being restored as it was in 1700 by a privately funded trust. Quietly awe-inspiring, and the tiny orangery, little more than a summerhouse, is very covetable.

Wightwick Manor

Wightwick, Wolverhampton WV6 8EE
☎ 01902 761108   ℻ 01902 764663

OWNER   The National Trust
LOCATION   3 miles west of Wolverhampton on A454
OPEN   11 am – 6 pm; Wednesdays, Thursdays & Saturdays; 1 March to 31 December
ADMISSION   Adults £2.20; Children £1.10
FACILITIES   Parking; dogs permitted; loos; access for the disabled; coffee & soft drinks
FEATURES   Herbaceous borders; rock garden; climbing roses; old roses; good topiary; current holder of Sandford Award; newly restored peach house (1994); new pergola in rose garden (1994); new 'bridge' garden by Mathematical Bridge (1995)

High Victorian camp, designed by Thomas Mawson and planted by Alfred Parsons. Topiary, a rose arbour, avenues of Irish yews and a Poets' Corner where all the plants were taken as cuttings from the gardens of literary men – Keats, Tennyson and Dickens among them.

WILTSHIRE

Avebury Manor

Avebury, Marlborough
☎ 01672 539203

OWNER   The National Trust
LOCATION   In the village, well signposted
OPEN   11 am – 5 pm; daily except Mondays & Thursdays; 28 March to 2 November
ADMISSION   Adults £2.20; Children £1.40
FACILITIES   Parking; access for the disabled; shop just outside the garden; refreshments in village
FEATURES   Herbaceous borders; rock garden; old roses; good topiary; double lavender walk

A recent owner did much to revive and restore this great Edwardian garden. We hope that the National Trust will continue the good work.

Bolehyde Manor

Allington, Chippenham
☎ 01249 652105   [FAX] 01249 659296

OWNER   Earl & Countess Cairns
LOCATION   2 miles west of Chippenham
OPEN   2.30 pm – 6 pm; 23 June, and by appointment
ADMISSION   £1.50
FACILITIES   Parking; dogs permitted; loos; access for the disabled; plants for sale
FEATURES   Herbaceous borders; fruit of special interest; plantsman's garden; old roses; climbing roses; half-hardy plants

Charming series of enclosed gardens around old stone-built house. Brilliantly developed by the owners with help from Melanie Chambers.

Bowood House

Calne SN11 0LZ
☎ 01249 812102   [FAX] 01249 821757

OWNER   The Earl of Shelburne
LOCATION   Off A4 in Derry Hill village between Calne and Chippenham
OPEN   11 am – 6 pm; daily; 22 March to 2 November
ADMISSION   Adults £5; Senior Citizens £4.20; Children £2.80
FACILITIES   Parking; loos; facilities for the disabled; plants for sale; gift shop; buffet lunches & afternoon teas in licensed restaurant
FEATURES   Landscape designed by Capability Brown; fine conifers; follies and garden buildings; lake; landscape designed by Humphry Repton; good topiary; woodland garden; interesting for children; bluebells; immodest sculpture; adventure playground; tallest *Thuya occidentalis* 'Wareana' in the United Kingdom
ENGLISH HERITAGE GRADE   I

Beautifully maintained and welcoming, Bowood has something from every period of English garden history. Capability Brown made the lake and Charles Hamilton the famous cascade. There are an important 19th-century pinetum laid out on pre-Linnaean principles, handsome Italianate formal gardens, and modern rhododendron drives in a bluebell wood. Be sure to miss the reclining nude above the formal gardens.

Broadleas

Devizes
☎ 01380 722035

OWNER   Broadleas Gardens Charitable Trust
LOCATION   1 mile south of Devizes
OPEN   2 pm – 6 pm; Wednesdays, Thursdays & Sundays; 1 April to 31 October
ADMISSION   Adults £2.50; Children £1
FACILITIES   Parking; dogs permitted; loos; access for the disabled; plants for sale; teas on summer Sundays
FEATURES   Good collection of trees; herbaceous borders; plantsman's garden; modern roses; old roses; woodland garden
ENGLISH HERITAGE GRADE   II

Broadleas has a rose garden, grey border, a rock garden and a 'secret' garden hidden behind a hedge of *Prunus* × *blireana*, all near the Regency house. But the main attraction is the Dell, a greensand combe that stretches down to the valley below, its sides just stuffed with good things – rare trees, vast magnolias, sheets of *Primula whitei* and cyclamen.

Bryher

Yard Lane, Bromham, Chippenham SN15 2DT
☎ 01380 850455

OWNER   Richard & Shirley Packham
LOCATION   Turn right, off A342, 4 miles north of Devizes
OPEN   11 am – 5 pm; Wednesdays; 29 May to 18 June. And for the NGS
ADMISSION   £1
FACILITIES   Parking; access for the disabled; plants for sale
FEATURES   Alpines; herbaceous borders; plantsman's garden; foliage effects

Inspirational young garden where discriminating plantsmanship is combined with a fine eye for harmonies and contrasts of colour, form and texture. Few gardens make such effective use of foliage.

Conock Manor

Devizes SN10 3QQ

OWNER   Mr & Mrs Bonar Sykes
LOCATION   5 miles south-east of Devizes off A342
OPEN   2 pm – 6 pm; 18 May
ADMISSION   Adults £1.50; Children (under 16) free
FACILITIES   Parking; access for the disabled; plants for sale; tea & home-made biscuits
FEATURES   *Cottages ornées*; fine trees and mixed borders; good *Sorbus* and *Eucalyptus*; new brickwork paving based on Persian patterns (1996)
ENGLISH HERITAGE GRADE   II

Beautiful parkland surrounds this covetable Georgian house. Behind the copper-domed stables an elegant shrub walk meanders past *Sorbus*, maples and magnolias.

Corsham Court

Corsham SN13 0BZ
☎ 01249 701610/701611   [FAX] 01249 444556

OWNER   Trustees of the Methuen Estate
LOCATION   Signposted from A4 Bath to Chippenham
OPEN   11 am – 5.30 pm; Tuesday – Sunday; 1 April to 31 October. Plus 2 pm – 4.30 pm; Saturdays & Sundays; 1 – 30 November & 1 January – 31 March
ADMISSION   Adults £2; Senior Citizens £1.50; Children £1
FACILITIES   Parking; dogs permitted; loos; access for the disabled; plants for sale
FEATURES   Good collection of trees; designed by Capability Brown and Humphrey Repton; amazing oriental plane *Platanus orientalis* whose sweeping limbs have rooted over a huge area
ENGLISH HERITAGE GRADE   II*

Major 18th-century landscape garden, with pretty 1820s flower garden and ambitious modern arboretum: strongly recommended.

The Courts
Holt, Trowbridge BA14 6RR
☎ 01225 782340

OWNER   The National Trust
LOCATION   In the middle of Holt village
OPEN   2 pm – 5 pm; Sunday – Friday; 28 March to 31 October
ADMISSION   Adults £2.80; Children £1.40
FACILITIES   Parking; access for the disabled
FEATURES   Good collection of trees; herbaceous borders; lake; plantsman's garden; good topiary; lower pond area replanted (1996); 180,000 scilla bulbs planted 1995/96
ENGLISH HERITAGE GRADE   II

1920s masterpiece in the Hidcote style. Rich colour plantings in a series of garden rooms. Excellent plants, beautifully used: well maintained.

Heale House
Middle Woodford, Salisbury SP4 6NT
☎ 01722 782504

OWNER   Guy Rasch
LOCATION   Signposted off the western Woodford valley road, and from A345 & A360
OPEN   10 am – 5 pm; daily; all year
ADMISSION   Adults £2.75; Groups (20+) £2.50
FACILITIES   Parking; dogs permitted; loos; access for the disabled; large plant centre; garden & gift shop
FEATURES   Herbaceous borders; fruit of special interest; lake; oriental features; old roses; snowdrops; Christie's/HHA Garden of the Year in 1984
ENGLISH HERITAGE GRADE   II*

A Peto garden round the prettiest house in Wiltshire. Formal walks, ponds, lawns and balustrading. Rich colours and clever planting. Japanese garden around genuine tea-house. Pure enchantment.

Hillbarn House
Great Bedwyn, Marlborough SN8 3NU

OWNER   Alistair J Buchanan
LOCATION   In High Street, opposite garage
OPEN   For NGS: see Yellow Book
ADMISSION   £2 Adults; 50p Children
FACILITIES   Loos; tea & biscuits

Lanning Roper's masterpiece makes brilliant use of a small steep site by dividing space to create an illusion of size. Well maintained.

Home Covert
Roundway, Devizes SN10 2JA
☎ 01380 723407

OWNER   Mr & Mrs John Phillips
LOCATION   1 mile north of Devizes in Roundway Village
OPEN   2 pm – 6 pm; 11 May, 20 July for NGS; parties by appointment
ADMISSION   £2
FACILITIES   Access for the disabled; plants for sale; teas
FEATURES   Lake; plantsman's garden; woodland garden; extensive new woodland plantings (1995/96)

One of the finest plantsman's gardens in southern England; 'a botanical madhouse' say the owners. Rare trees (Cercis racemosa) and shrubs (Heptacodium jasminoides): Lathraea clandestina and swathes of candelabra primulas in the bog garden.

Iford Manor
Bradford-on-Avon BA15 2BA
☎ 01225 863146

OWNER   Mrs E Cartwright-Hignett
LOCATION   7 miles south-east of Bath, signed from A36 and Bradford-on-Avon
OPEN   2 pm – 5 pm; Sundays & Easter Monday; April & October. Plus Tuesday – Thursday, Saturdays, Sundays & Bank Holiday Mondays from May to September
ADMISSION   Adults £2.20; Senior Citizens & Children (over 10) £1.60
FACILITIES   Parking; dogs permitted; loos; teas on Bank Holidays and some weekends
FEATURES   Follies and garden buildings; garden sculpture; Italian cypresses and handsome Phillyrea; martagon lilies; cyclamen
ENGLISH HERITAGE GRADE   I
NCCPG NATIONAL COLLECTIONS Acanthus

Harold Peto's own Italianate garden on a steep wooded hillside, meticulously restored and maintained. Romanesque cloister, octagonal cloister and much architectural bric-à-brac. Wonderfully photogenic.

Lackham Country Attractions
Lacock, Chippenham
☎ 01249 443111   FAX 01249 444474

OWNER   Lackham College
LOCATION   3 miles south of Chippenham on A350
OPEN   11 am – 5 pm; daily; Easter to 31 October
ADMISSION   Adults £3; OAPs £2; Children £1
FACILITIES   Parking; dogs permitted; loos; access for the disabled; plants for sale; souvenirs for sale; refreshments
FEATURES   Alpines; good collection of trees; bluebells; herbaceous borders; daffodils; fruit and vegetables of special interest; glasshouses and conservatories to visit; herbs; plantsman's garden; interesting for children; particularly good in July-August; roses of every kind; adventure playground; farm museum
NCCPG NATIONAL COLLECTIONS Populus
FRIENDS   Friends of Lackham Charitable Trust. Also Lackham Garden Club. Details on 01249 443111

Among the best of county college gardens, Lackham is a living monument to the knowledge and initiative of Oliver and Ann Menhinnick. A major extension was opened last year but the heart of Lackham is the walled garden, beautifully laid out to educate and delight, with a magnificent glasshouse collection of orchids, tropical fruits and bulbs.

Longleat House
Warminster BA12 7NW
☎ 01985 844400   FAX 01985 844885

OWNER   The Marquess of Bath
LOCATION   Off A362 Warminster to Frome road

OPEN Daylight hours; daily; all year except 25 December
ADMISSION Grounds & gardens: Adults £2; Senior Citizens £1.50; Children 50p
FACILITIES Parking; dogs permitted; loos; access for the disabled; shops; cafeterias & restaurants
FEATURES Good collection of trees; herbaceous borders; landscape designed by Capability Brown; lake; rhododendrons and azaleas; climbing roses; modern roses; old roses; good topiary; woodland garden; interesting for children; particularly good in July-August; Safari Park; orangery; world's largest maze; new Maze of Love with saucily-named roses; newly planted Sun Maze & Lunar Labyrinth
ENGLISH HERITAGE GRADE I

Forget the lions and the loins, Longleat has a classic 18th-century landscape by Capability Brown, a home park of 600 acres best seen from Heaven's Gate and a grand Victorian garden reworked by Russell Page in the 1930s. The new Lord Bath has conserved the best and is invigorating the rest of Longleat. Worth another visit.

Oare House
Oare, Marlborough SN8 4JQ
☎ 01672 62428

OWNER Henry Keswick
LOCATION In village, west side of A345
OPEN 2 pm – 6 pm; 27 April & 27 July
ADMISSION Adults £2; Children Free
FACILITIES Parking; dogs permitted; loos; light refreshments
FEATURES Good collection of trees; herbaceous borders; modern roses; tall hedges of field maple
ENGLISH HERITAGE GRADE II

Oare has an approach along lime avenues and tall hedges whose grandeur is echoed by the main garden behind: a huge apron of walled lawn, with majestic mixed borders at the sides, lead the eye over a half-hidden swimming pool to a grand ride beyond and on to the Marlborough Downs beyond. Intimacy exists only in some small enclosed gardens to the side and in the kitchen garden. Here are a magnificent herbaceous border in reds and yellows, a tunnel of fruit trees and vegetables in neat rows. A delight.

The Old Vicarage
Edington, Westbury BA13 4QF
☎ & ℻ 01380 830512

OWNER John d'Arcy
LOCATION On B3098 in Edington village
OPEN NGS open days or by appointment
ADMISSION £2.50
FACILITIES Plants for sale
FEATURES Alpines; herbaceous borders; gravel or scree garden; plantsman's garden; young garden; particularly good in July-August
NCCPG NATIONAL COLLECTIONS Oenothera

2 acres of intensively cultivated plantsmanship. The owner is a distinguished plant collector: his garden is immaculately maintained and bristles with new species (Salvia darcyi) and living holotypes.

Pound Hill House
West Kington, Chippenham SN14 7JG
☎ 01249 782822   ℻ 01249 782953

OWNER Mr & Mrs Philip Stockitt
LOCATION Signposted in village
OPEN 2 pm – 5 pm; Tuesday – Sunday & Bank Holidays; all year. 29 June for NGS
ADMISSION Adults £2; parties by appointment
FACILITIES Parking; loos; access for the disabled; adjacent to West Kington Nurseries Plant Centre; refreshments
FEATURES Alpines; fruit of special interest; modern roses; old roses; woodland garden; play area for children

The private garden of a discriminating nurseryman, Pound Hill has been developed as a year-round showplace. Stylish new plantings make it a garden to watch: Betula jacquemontii underplanted with pulmonarias and 'Queen of Night' tulips.

Roche Court
East Winterslow, Salisbury SP5 1BG
☎ 01980 862244   ℻ 01980 862447

OWNER The Earl & Countess of Bessborough
LOCATION Just south of A30 at Lopcombe Corner
OPEN 11 am – 4 pm; daily; all year
ADMISSION Free
FACILITIES Parking; dogs permitted; access for the disabled
FEATURES Herbaceous borders; garden sculpture; woodland garden

As a garden, nothing special, but a show place for Lady Bessborough's contemporary sculpture shop. Everything is for sale, so the garden is ever changing. The Sculpture Park runs to 20 acres, and many of the pieces are modern classics.

Sheldon Manor
Chippenham SN14 0RG
☎ 01249 653120   ℻ 01249 461097

OWNER Antony Gibbs
LOCATION Signposted from A420 west of Chippenham & A350 bypass
OPEN 12.30 pm – 6 pm; Thursdays, Sundays & Bank Holidays; Easter to the first Sunday in October
ADMISSION Adults £3.50
FACILITIES Parking; dogs permitted; loos; access for the disabled; plants for sale; shop in house; lunch & tea on open days; parties by arrangement
FEATURES Old roses; flowering cherries and ornamental apples
ENGLISH HERITAGE GRADE II

The best things about these romantic gardens and its Cotswold manor house are the informal roses (climbers and shrubs), the welcome from the owners and the delicious food in the old stables. Highly recommended.

Stourhead
Stourton BA12 6QD
☎ & ℻ 01747 841152

OWNER The National Trust
LOCATION 3 miles north of Mere, signposted off the A303/B3092

OPEN   9 am – 7 pm, or dusk if earlier (4 pm 24 to 26 July); daily; all year

ADMISSION   Adults £4.30; Children £2.30

FACILITIES   Parking; loos; facilities for the disabled; National Trust shop near entrance; new plant centre; famous hotel/pub opposite gate

FEATURES   Good collection of trees; bluebells; fine conifers; follies and garden buildings; lake; rhododendrons and azaleas; garden sculpture; snowdrops; interesting for children; good autumn colour; tallest tulip tree *Liriodendron tulipifera* (37m.) in the British Isles, and twelve other record tree species

ENGLISH HERITAGE GRADE   I

Whatever the weather or season, Stourhead conveys a sense of majesty and harmony. Try it early on a May morning, before it opens officially, when the air is sweet with azaleas. Or scuff the fallen leaves in late November. Think of it 200 years ago, without the rhododendrons, when all the beech trees were interplanted with spruces. Ponder the 18th century aesthetic, which esteemed tones and shades more highly than colours. Spot the change from classical to Gothic, from Pope to Walpole. And wonder at the National Trust's ability to maintain it so well with only 6 gardeners.

Stourton House
Stourton, Warminster BA12 6QF
☎ 01747 840417

OWNER   Mrs Anthony Bullivant

LOCATION   Next to Stourhead, 2 miles north of A303 at Mere

OPEN   11 am – 6 pm; Wednesdays, Thursdays, Sundays & Bank Holiday Mondays; 31 March to 30 November

ADMISSION   Adults £2; Children 50p; Groups (12+) £1.50

FACILITIES   Parking; loos; facilities for the disabled; plants & dried flowers for sale all year; teas; light lunches; sticky cakes

FEATURES   Herbaceous borders; particularly good in July–August; Victorian conservatory; elegantly curving hedges; 270 different hydrangeas; hosts of daffodils, in innumerable shapes, sizes and colours; new (1995) borders with Kiwi plants

This five acre Old Vicarage garden, next to Stourhead, is famous for its dried flowers, thanks to the energy and personality of Elizabeth Bullivant. Strongly recommended at any season: fascinating collection of split-corona daffodils in spring.

Thompson's Hill
Sherston, Malmesbury SN16 0PZ
☎ 01666 840766

OWNER   Mr & Mrs Sean Cooper

LOCATION   At Sherston village church turn left down hill, then right, up hill

OPEN   2 pm – 6.20 pm; 15 June, and by appointment

ADMISSION   £2

FACILITIES   Parking; plants for sale

FEATURES   Herbaceous borders; old roses; young garden

Half-acre modern garden, growing up quickly and changing all the time. Well planted and neatly maintained by owners' own efforts. Much featured in the glossies.

Wilton House
Wilton, Salisbury SP2 0BJ
☎ 01722 743115   📠 01722 744447

OWNER   Earl of Pembroke/Wilton House Trust

LOCATION   In village, 3 miles west of Salisbury on A30

OPEN   11 am – 6 pm; daily; 24 March to 2 November

ADMISSION   Adults £6.50; Senior Citizens £5.50; Children £4

FACILITIES   Parking; loos; access for the disabled; plants for sale in adjoining Wilton House garden centre; self-service restaurant

FEATURES   Old roses; interesting for children; handsome cedars; famous Palladian bridge; magnificent golden-leaved oak; new 'cloister garden' within the inner courtyard of the house (1996); adventure playground

ENGLISH HERITAGE GRADE   I

Sublime 18th-century park around classical Inigo Jones pile famous for its paintings. Recently courting popularity, Wilton has a pretty new rose garden and water garden, but an ugly new visitor centre.

NORTH YORKSHIRE

Beningbrough Hall
Shipton-by-Beningbrough, York YO6 1DD
☎ 01904 470666   📠 01904 470002

OWNER   The National Trust

LOCATION   8 miles north-west of York off the A19

OPEN   11 am – 5 pm; Saturday – Wednesday, plus Fridays in July & August; 29 March to 2 November. Plus Good Friday

ADMISSION   Adults £3; Children £1.50: Family £6

FACILITIES   Parking; loos; facilities for the disabled; National Trust gift shop; morning coffee; hot & cold lunches; afternoon teas

FEATURES   Herbaceous borders; fruit of special interest; plantings by Graham Thomas; American garden; good conservatory on house; traditional Victorian kitchen garden undergoing restoration (1997); 'Lady Downe's Seedling' grape, raised at Beningbrough in 1835; vast Portuguese laurel *Prunus lusitanica*

ENGLISH HERITAGE GRADE   II

Beningbrough is approached by an avenue of limes through stately parkland. Apart from a gloomy Victorian shrubbery, the gardens are modern – and pretty in a National Trust sort of way. Two small formal gardens, one with reds and oranges and the other with pastel shades, lie on either side of the early Georgian house. A sumptuous mixed border, graded from hot colours to cool, runs right to the gate of the walled kitchen garden. Here there are exciting plans for further developments.

Burnby Hall Gardens
Pocklington YO4 2QF
☎ 01759 302068

OWNER   Stewarts Trust

LOCATION   Off A1079 13 miles east of York

OPEN   10 am – 6 pm; daily; 5 April to 28 September

ADMISSION   Adults £2.20; Senior Citizens £1.70; Children 75p; Groups (20+) £1.40

FACILITIES Parking; loos; facilities for the disabled; plants for sale; snacks & salads, home-made cakes

FEATURES Herbaceous borders; fine conifers; lake; rock garden; museum; winner of *Age Concern* award; fortnightly band concerts

NCCPG NATIONAL COLLECTIONS *Nymphaea*

Famed for its water lilies, planted by Frances Perry in the 1930s, but there is much more to Burnby Hall. A rock garden, cheerful modern rose garden and good collection of conifers all contribute to its visitor-friendly style. Follow the tarmacadam path around the lake: Burnby is a grand place for a promenade.

Burton Agnes Hall Gardens

Burton Agnes, Driffield YO25 0ND
☎ 01262 490324   📠 01262 490513

OWNER Burton Agnes Hall Preservation Trust Ltd
LOCATION On A166 Driffield-Bridlington road
OPEN 11 am - 5 pm; daily; 1 April to 31 October
ADMISSION Adults £2; OAPs £1.75; Children £1
FACILITIES Parking; dogs permitted; loos; facilities for the disabled; plants for sale; café & ice-cream parlour
NCCPG NATIONAL COLLECTIONS *Campanula*

The old walled garden has been redesigned with such unconventional features as a life-size games board for snakes & ladders, and exuberantly planted with herbaceous plants.

Burton Constable Hall

Burton Constable Hall, Hull HU11 4LN
☎ 01964 562400   📠 01964 563229

OWNER Burton Constable Foundation
LOCATION Via Hull B1238 to Sproatley follow HH signs
OPEN 12 noon - 5 pm (last admission 4.15); Sunday - Thursday; Easter Sunday to 30 September. Plus Saturdays in July & August
ADMISSION Adults £4
FACILITIES Parking; dogs permitted; loos; facilities for the disabled; shop; light snacks
FEATURES Herbaceous borders; landscape designed by Capability Brown; lake; woodland garden; interesting for children; fine 18th-century orangery
ENGLISH HERITAGE GRADE II
FRIENDS Details from The Secretary, Friends of Burton Constable, Burton Constable, Hull HU11 4LN

Essentially a Capability Brown landscape (his original plans are still shown), but the 19th-century pleasure gardens are being restored and the whole estate will undoubtedly develop excitingly in future.

Castle Howard

York YO6 7DA
☎ 01653 648333   📠 01653 648462

OWNER Castle Howard Estates Ltd
LOCATION 15 miles north-east of York, off A64
OPEN 10 am - 4.30 pm (last entry); daily; 14 March to 2 November
ADMISSION House & grounds: Adults £7; Children £3.50; Senior Citizens £5.50. Grounds only: Adults £4.50; Children £2.50. (1996 prices)

FACILITIES Parking; dogs permitted; loos; access for the disabled; shop and plant centre; cafeteria
FEATURES Herbaceous borders; follies and garden buildings; modern roses; old roses; garden sculpture; woodland garden; tallest elm *Ulmus glabra* (37m.) in British Isles; major replanting of roses (1994-95)
ENGLISH HERITAGE GRADE I

Heroic megapark (1200 ha) laid out with five axes by the 3rd Earl of Carlisle, Vanburgh and Hawksmoor with important buildings (Temple of the Four Winds, Mausoleum). Grand 1980s rose gardens (slightly Surrey) designed by Jim Russell, with every type of rose from ancient to modern. Ray Wood is a fine and historic collection of rhododendrons and other ericaceous plants, meticulously labelled, and destined to develop as one of the greatest woodland gardens in Europe. A must for botanist and gardener alike - be prepared to spend all day here - and essential visiting for anyone with a sense of history.

Duncombe Park

Helmsley YO6 5EB
☎ 01439 770213   📠 01439 771114

OWNER Lord Feversham
LOCATION Off A170; signed from Helmsley
OPEN 11 am - 5.30 pm or dusk if earlier; Saturday - Wednesday; all year. But daily from May to September
ADMISSION Adults £2.95; Children £1.50
FACILITIES Parking; loos; access for the disabled; plants for sale; gift shop; restaurant
FEATURES Follies and garden buildings; garden sculpture; Rysbrack statue of Old Father Time
ENGLISH HERITAGE GRADE I

Major early 18th-century landscape, a grass terrace which sweeps between Vanburgh's Ionic rotunda and a Tuscan temple with views across the valley to Helmsley and the moors, matched only by views from its sister terrace at Rievaulx, in the care of the National Trust.

Harlow Carr Botanical Gardens

Beckwithshaw, Harrogate HG3 1QB
☎ 01423 565418   📠 01423 530663

OWNER Northern Horticultural Society
LOCATION Crag Lane off Otley Road (B6162), 1½ miles from Harrogate centre
OPEN 9.30 am - 6.00 pm, or dusk if earlier; daily; all year
ADMISSION Adults £3.40; Senior Citizens £2.60; Students £1.60; Children (under 16) free; Parties (20+) £2.60. Special winter rate (Nov - Feb). RHS members Free
FACILITIES Parking; loos; facilities for the disabled; plants for sale; gift shop; licensed restaurant
FEATURES Good collection of trees; bluebells; daffodils; fruit and vegetables of special interest; gravel or scree garden; herbs; rock garden; heathers and alpines; good autumn colour; tallest native rowan tree *Sorbus aucuparia* in the British Isles
NCCPG NATIONAL COLLECTIONS *Calluna*; *Dryopteris*; *Hypericum*; *Polypodium*; *Rheum*

Harlow Carr is quite the best place for northern gardeners to learn about gardening: the Wisley of the north.

Newby Hall

Ripon HG4 5AE
☎ 01423 322583　　📠 01423 324452

OWNER　Robin Compton DL, VMH
LOCATION　Off B6265, 2 miles from A1
OPEN　11 am – 5.30 pm; Tuesday – Sunday & Bank holiday
Mondays; April to September
ADMISSION　Adults £3.80; Senior Citizens £3.30; Children
& Disabled £2.50 (1996)
FACILITIES　Parking; loos; facilities for the disabled; shop and
plant stall; licensed restaurant
FEATURES　Herbaceous borders; daffodils; plantsman's gar-
den; rock garden; climbing roses; old roses; woodland garden;
HHA/Christie's Garden of the Year in 1986; tallest *Acer
griseum* (15m.) in UK; adventure playground
ENGLISH HERITAGE GRADE　II*
NCCPG NATIONAL COLLECTIONS Cornus

The garden with everything: firm design, an endless variety of
features, great plantsmanship, immaculate maintenance. Its axis
is a bold, wide, double border stretching endlessly down to the
River Ure. Second only to Hidcote as an example of 20th-cen-
tury gardening. Visit Newby at any season and expect to spend
all day there.

Parcevall Hall Gardens

Skyreholme, Skipton BD23 6DE
☎ 01756 720311

OWNER　Walsingham College (Yorkshire Properties) Ltd
LOCATION　Off B6160 from Burnsall
OPEN　10 am – 6 pm; daily; Good Friday to 31 October;
winter visits by appointment
ADMISSION　Adults £2; Children (5-12) 50p
FACILITIES　Parking; dogs permitted; loos; plants for sale
FEATURES　Fine conifers; lake; rhododendrons and azaleas;
rock garden; climbing roses; woodland garden; candelabra
primulas

Breathtaking architectural layout, and views. Planted by Sir
William Milner 70 years ago and best now for its wonderful
rhododendrons growing alongside limestone outcrops, daffodils (including 'W F Milner') and *Primula florindae* given by
Kingdon Ward now naturalised round the lily pond.

Ripley Castle

Ripley, Harrogate HG3 3AY
☎ 01423 770152　　📠 01423 771745

OWNER　Sir Thomas Ingilby Bt
LOCATION　3½ miles north of Harrogate, off A61
OPEN　11 am – 5 pm (4 pm in March, 3.30 pm November –
December); daily; 1 March to 23 December, but closed
Monday – Wednesday in March
ADMISSION　Adults £2.25; Senior Citizens £1.75; Children
£1
FACILITIES　Parking; loos; facilities for the disabled; gift shop
with plants, fruit and vegetables; castle tea-room
FEATURES　Herbaceous borders; landscape designed by Ca-
pability Brown; subtropical plants; interesting for children;
particularly interesting in winter; birds of prey sanctuary
ENGLISH HERITAGE GRADE　II

NCCPG NATIONAL COLLECTIONS Hyacinthus orientalis
14th-century castle (restored); temples; smashing Regency
conservatory; Victorian formal garden; evergreen shrubberies
(handsome yews); rare vegetables from HDRA; hundreds of
thousands of bulbs (daffodils in hosts). A garden with something for everyone.

Sledmere House

Sledmere, Driffield YO25 0XG
☎ 01377 236637　　📠 01377 236560

OWNER　Sir Tatton Sykes
LOCATION　Off A166 between York & Bridlington
OPEN　11.30 am – 5.30 pm; daily except Mondays & Satur-
days; 1 May to 30 September
ADMISSION　Adults £1.75; Senior Citizens & Children £1
FACILITIES　Parking; dogs permitted; loos; facilities for the
disabled; craft & gift shop; tea-terrace & cafeteria
FEATURES　Landscape designed by Capability Brown; fine
conifers; climbing roses; deer park
ENGLISH HERITAGE GRADE　I

Sledmere has a classical Capability Brown landscape: his
originals plans can be seen in the Library. An Italianate formal
garden was added in 1911, with Greek and Roman busts
swathed in climbing roses. A new knot garden is growing up
quickly. Definitely a garden on the up.

Sleightholmedale Lodge

Fadmoor, Kirkbymoorside YO6 6JG
☎ 01751 431942

OWNER　Mrs R James
LOCATION　Signed from Fadmoor
OPEN　For NGS: see Yellow Book. And by written appoint-
ment
ADMISSION　£1.50
FACILITIES　Parking; dogs permitted; loos
FEATURES　Herbaceous borders; herbs; plantsman's garden;
modern roses; old roses; woodland garden

This family garden – Mrs James is the third generation to
garden here – is a plantsman's paradise right on the edge of the
moors. As well as magnificent *Meconopsis* and hardy herbaceous plants it has Mexican and Mediterranean rarities (a
Cistus walk, for example) which are a triumph for good
cultivation and manipulation of the microclimate. And there
are roses of every sort – hundreds of them, perhaps thousands.

Studley Royal

Fountains, Ripon HG4 3DZ
☎ 01765 608888　　📠 01765 608889

OWNER　The National Trust
LOCATION　3 miles west of Ripon off B6265, via the Visitor
Centre
OPEN　10 am – 5 pm (7 pm in summer) or dusk if sooner;
daily; all year, except Fridays from November to January and
24 & 25 December
ADMISSION　Adults £4.20; Children £2; Family £10. Group
rates available
FACILITIES　Parking; dogs permitted; loos; facilities for the
disabled; National Trust visitor centre shop; tea-room

FEATURES Lake; snowdrops; good topiary; World Heritage site; 400-acre deer park; newly restored (1997) water garden; biggest *Prunus avium* (bird cherry) in British Isles
ENGLISH HERITAGE GRADE I

Inextricably linked to Fountains Abbey, which forms the focus of an unsurpassed surprise view from Anne Boleyn's Seat, Studley is a classical, geometrical landscape of major importance. Best seen high up from the banqueting house lawn and the Octagon tower — the formal canal, Moon pools, Grotto Springs, rustic bridge and Temple of Filial Piety.

Sutton Park
Sutton-in-the-Forest, York YO6 1DP
☎ 01347 810249   ☒ 01347 811251
OWNER Mrs N M D Sheffield
LOCATION 8 miles north of York on B1363
OPEN 11 am – 5 pm; daily; Easter to 1 October
ADMISSION Adults £2; Children 50p
FACILITIES Parking; loos; plants for sale occasionally; refreshments on Sundays in summer
FEATURES Herbaceous borders; landscape designed by Capability Brown; plantsman's garden; old roses; woodland garden; frequent Yorkshire & Humberside in Bloom winner; new pond garden in walled garden (1994)

Capability Brown was here 200 years ago, but the joy of Sutton is the formal garden laid out on terraces below the house by Percy Cane in the 1960s and planted by Mrs Sheffield with exquisite taste. Quite the prettiest garden in Yorkshire.

Thorp Perrow Arboretum
Bedale DL8 2PR
☎ & ☒ 01677 425323
OWNER Sir John Ropner Bt
LOCATION On the Bedale-Ripon road, 2 miles south of Bedale
OPEN Dawn to dusk; daily; all year
ADMISSION Adults £3; Children, Senior Citizens & Students £2
FACILITIES Parking; dogs permitted; loos; facilities for the disabled; plants for sale; tea-room
FEATURES Good collection of trees; bluebells; daffodils; eighteen different champion trees
ENGLISH HERITAGE GRADE II
NCCPG NATIONAL COLLECTIONS *Fraxinus*; *Juglans*; *Tilia*
FRIENDS Friends of Thorp Perrow (details from Curator)

Important modern arboretum undergoing restoration after some years of neglect. Wonderful avenues of laburnum, glades of cherries and coniferous groves.

The Valley Gardens, Harrogate
Harrogate Borough Council, Harrogate
☎ 01423 500600 x 3211 ☒ 01423 504426
OWNER Harrogate Borough Council
LOCATION Harrogate
OPEN Dawn – dusk; daily; all year
ADMISSION Free

FACILITIES Dogs permitted; loos; access for the disabled; small cafeteria
FEATURES Herbaceous borders; rock garden; interesting for children; wonderful *Meconopsis* & primulas alongside the stream; children's play area; band concerts every Sunday afternoon 25 May to 24 August
ENGLISH HERITAGE GRADE II

The best example of plantsmanship in a public garden in England, laid out 1880-1910: the Sun Colonnade, which incorporates an elegant pergola, has just been restored. Alpine rarities in spring, a romantic dell, magnificent dahlia display in late summer and the best colour bedding in Yorkshire.

SOUTH YORKSHIRE

Brodsworth Hall
English Heritage, Brodsworth, Doncaster
☎ 01302 722598   ☒ 01302 337165
OWNER English Heritage
LOCATION 6 miles north-west of Doncaster
OPEN 12 noon – 6 pm; daily except Mondays; 22 March to 26 October. Then 11 am – 4 pm; weekends only; until Christmas
ADMISSION House & garden: Adults £4.50; OAPs £3.40; Children £2.30. Garden only: Adults £2.50; OAPs £1.90; Children £1.30. RHS members free after 22 March
FACILITIES Parking; loos; facilities for the disabled; shop; licensed restaurant
FEATURES Fine conifers; Victorian bedding
ENGLISH HERITAGE GRADE II

English Heritage's latest acquisition, unkempt for 50 years and now restored as first laid out in 1860. Brodsworth offers Italianate terraces, statues and classical follies, a rose garden where ramblers are trained on ironwork arcades, magnificent trees, including monkey puzzles and 30 ft. *Arbutus* trees, and bright Victorian bedding. The fern dell, flower garden and target range will all be open for the first time this year.

Sheffield Botanical Gardens
Clarkehouse Road, Sheffield S10 2LN
☎ 0114 250 0500   ☒ 0114 255 2375
OWNER Sheffield Town Trust (administered by City Council)
LOCATION Jct 33 of M1, follow A57 signs to Glossop, left at Royal Hallamshire Hospital, 500m. on left
OPEN 8 am (10 am at weekends) – 8 pm (4 pm in winter); daily; all year
ADMISSION Free
FACILITIES Dogs permitted; loos; facilities for the disabled
FEATURES Herbaceous borders; fine conifers; rock garden; modern roses; particularly interesting in winter; conservatories by Paxton; peat garden; heath garden
NCCPG NATIONAL COLLECTIONS *Diervilla*; *Weigela*
FRIENDS Friends (Tel. 0114 2500500); good lecture programme

Founded in 1833 by public subscription and still burgeoning with civic pride. Good camellias and magnolias, ericas and *Sorbus*. Splendid summer bedding too, and lots of seats and waste bins: an exemplary combination of botany and amenity.

Wentworth Castle Gardens

Northern College, Wentworth Castle, Stainborough,
Barnsley S75 3ET

☎ 01226 285426   [FAX] 01226 284308

OWNER   Barnsley Metropolitan District Council
LOCATION   Signed 'Northern College'. 3 miles south of
Barnsley; 2 miles from M1
OPEN   10 am – 5 pm; Spring Bank Holiday (Sunday and
Monday). Parties by arrangement. Guided tours in May &
June on Tuesdays at 10 am and Thursdays at 2 pm (assemble
in car park)
ADMISSION   Adults £2; Unwaged, Students & Children £1
FACILITIES   Parking; dogs permitted; loos; access for the dis-
abled; refreshments and plants for sale at Spring Bank Holiday
FEATURES   Rhododendrons and azaleas; woodland garden;
interesting for children; newly excavated 19th-century rock
garden; educational collection of rhododendrons
ENGLISH HERITAGE GRADE   I
NCCPG NATIONAL COLLECTIONS   Rhododendron (Fal-
coneri series)
FRIENDS   Friends of the Gardens Society

Major landscape garden currently undergoing development as
an educational and cultural resource. Twinned with the Kun-
ming Academy of Sciences. A garden to watch.

WEST YORKSHIRE

Bramham Park

Wetherby LS23 6ND

☎ 01937 844265   [FAX] 01937 845923

OWNER   George Lane Fox
LOCATION   5 miles south of Wetherby on A1
OPEN   1.15 pm – 5.30 pm; Tuesday – Thursday & Sundays;
22 June to 7 September. Plus 29–31 March, 3–5 May & 24–26
May & 25 August
ADMISSION   Gardens only: Adults £2.50; Senior Citizens £2;
Children £1
FACILITIES   Parking; dogs permitted; loos; facilities for the
disabled
FEATURES   Herbaceous borders; daffodils; follies and garden
buildings; garden sculpture
ENGLISH HERITAGE GRADE   I

Very important pre-landscape formal gardens, laid out in the
grand manner by a pupil of Le Nôtre in the early 18th century.
Long straight rides cut through dense woodland, with ornamental ponds, cascades, loggias, temples and an obelisk.

Canal Gardens

Roundhay Park, Street Lane, Leeds LS8 2ER

☎ 0113 266 1850   [FAX] 0113 237 0077

OWNER   Leeds City Council
LOCATION   3 miles north-west of city centre, off A6120 ring
road
OPEN   All year, but Tropical World closes at dusk
ADMISSION   Free
FACILITIES   Parking; dogs permitted; loos; access for the dis-
abled; souvenirs; cafeteria by lakeside

FEATURES   Glasshouses and conservatories to visit; lake;
modern roses; subtropical plants; particularly interesting in
winter; good carpet bedding; orchids; new Desert & Nocturnal
houses
ENGLISH HERITAGE GRADE   II

Tropical World glasshouses containing South American rain
forest plants, bromeliads, hoyas, cacti and Butterfly House. A
wonderful retreat from a Yorkshire winter and a triumph of
municipal horticultural excellence.

Golden Acre Park

Otley Road, Bramhope, Leeds LS16 5NZ

☎ 0113 278 2030

OWNER   Leeds City Council
LOCATION   4 miles north on A660 Otley Road
OPEN   Dawn – dusk; daily; all year
ADMISSION   Free
FACILITIES   Parking; dogs permitted; loos; access for the dis-
abled; gifts/souvenirs; restaurant
FEATURES   Lake; rock garden; large heather garden
NCCPG NATIONAL COLLECTIONS   Primula auricula;
Syringa

Part park, part botanic collection, part demonstration garden,
part test ground for Fleuroselect and Gardening Which?;
perhaps the best of the five impressive public gardens in Leeds.

Harewood House

The Estate Office, Harewood, Leeds LS17 9LQ

☎ 0113 288 6331   [FAX] 0113 288 6467

OWNER   The Earl of Harewood
LOCATION   Between Leeds and Harrogate on A61
OPEN   10 am – 5 pm; daily; 15 March to 26 October
ADMISSION   Grounds: Adults £4; OAPs £3; Children £2
FACILITIES   Parking; dogs permitted; loos; access for the dis-
abled; plants for sale; refreshments
FEATURES   Landscape designed by Capability Brown; orien-
tal features; woodland garden; interesting for children; adven-
ture playground; Japanese garden; rhododendrons; current
holder of Sandford Award
ENGLISH HERITAGE GRADE   I
NCCPG NATIONAL COLLECTIONS   Hosta

Capability Brown landscaped Harewood, but Repton and
Loudon also had a hand in this grandest of Yorkshire gardens.
Charles Barry added the grand Italianate terrace, recently
restored with an EC grant. Best of all, Harewood is well
maintained and welcomingly run.

The Hollies Park

Weetwood Lane, Leeds LS16 5NZ

☎ 0113 278 2030   [FAX] 0113 247 8277

OWNER   Leeds City Council
LOCATION   3 miles north of city off A660
OPEN   Dawn – dusk; daily; all year
ADMISSION   Free
FACILITIES   Parking; dogs permitted; loos
FEATURES   Woodland garden; rhododendrons; eucryphias
NCCPG NATIONAL COLLECTIONS   Deutzia; Hemerocal-
lis (Coe hybrids); Hosta (large-leaved); Philadelphus;
Syringa

Slightly dilapidated plantsman's garden, under-resourced but well run by a hard-pressed and enthusiastic team.

Land Farm Gardens
Colden, Hebden Bridge, Halifax HX7 7PJ
☎ 01422 842260

OWNER John Williams
LOCATION On right, 2 miles from Hebdon Bridge on Colden road
OPEN 10 am – 5 pm; Saturdays, Sundays & Bank Holiday Mondays; 1 May to 31 August
ADMISSION Adults £2
FACILITIES Parking; loos; plants for sale; art gallery; refreshments pre-booked for parties
FEATURES Herbaceous borders; fine conifers; new woodland garden (2 acres), Meconopsis; Tropaeolum

A pioneering plantsman's garden, 1,000 ft up in the Pennines. Now 4 acres with a range of plants that is an eye-opener.

Lotherton Hall
Aberford, nr Leeds
☎ 0113 281 3259   FAX 0113 281 3068

OWNER Leeds City Council
LOCATION Off A1, ¾ mile east on B1217
OPEN 7.30 am – 8 pm or dusk, if earlier; daily; all year
ADMISSION Free
FACILITIES Parking; loos; facilities for the disabled; shop; cafeteria
FEATURES Oriental features; modern roses
ENGLISH HERITAGE GRADE II

Edwardian showpiece garden, given to the Council in 1968 and now recovering from neglect. It offers gazebos, formal walks, yew hedging, rose gardens, and a lily pond recently replanted with period varieties. A garden that is on the move again.

Temple Newsam Park
Manager's Office, Temple Newsam Park, Leeds 15
☎ 0113 264 5535

OWNER Leeds City Council
LOCATION 3 miles south-east of city, off A63 Selby Road
OPEN Dawn – dusk; daily; all year
ADMISSION Free. Admission charge to house
FACILITIES Parking; dogs permitted; loos; access for the disabled; plants for sale; souvenirs; restaurant
FEATURES Herbaceous borders; landscape designed by Capability Brown; glasshouses and conservatories to visit; modern roses; old roses; rhododendrons
ENGLISH HERITAGE GRADE II
NCCPG NATIONAL COLLECTIONS Aster; Delphinium; Phlox paniculata

A prodigious house on a windy bluff, surrounded by 1200 acres of parkland, now a 'green lung' for Leeds. Massive rhododendron rides in the woodland, and austere borders in the old walled garden. Somewhat dilapidated in the past, now improved by some recent softening plantings.

York Gate
Back Church Lane, Adel, Leeds LS16 8DW
☎ 0113 267 8240

OWNER The Gardeners' Royal Benevolent Society
LOCATION Behind Adel Church, off A660
OPEN 2 pm – 5 pm; 16 March. 2 pm – 6 pm; 7 & 8 June & 20 July. Parties by appointment. No coaches on Open Days
ADMISSION Adults £2.50; Children Free. Groups £3
FACILITIES Loos; tea & biscuits
FEATURES Plantsman's garden; good topiary; mini-pinetum; nut walk; an espaliered Cedrus atlantica 'Glauca'

Now safely in the care of the Gardeners' Royal Benevolent Fund, this is quite the busiest small garden in England. It is a masterpiece of tight design, invention, colour sense and sheer creative opportunism.

WALES

CLWYD

Bodnant Gardens
Tal-y-Cafn, Colwyn Bay LL28 5RE
☎ 01492 650460   FAX 01492 650448

OWNER The National Trust
LOCATION 8 miles south of Llandudno and Colwyn Bay on A470. Entrance ½ mile along Eglwysbach Road
OPEN 10 am – 5 pm; daily; 15 March to 31 October
ADMISSION Adults £4.20; Children £2.10. RHS members Free
FACILITIES Parking; loos; access for the disabled; plants for sale; light lunches, teas, refreshments
FEATURES Good collection of trees; herbaceous borders; camellias; follies and garden buildings; plantsman's garden; rhododendrons and azaleas; magnolias; good autumn colour; tallest Californian redwood Sequoia sempervirens (47m.) in the British Isles and 18 further record-breaking tree species – more than any other garden in Wales
NCCPG NATIONAL COLLECTIONS Embothrium; Eucryphia; Magnolia; Rhododendron forrestii

The greatest garden in Wales, some would say in all Britain. The grand Italianate terraces above a woodland 'dell' are only part of its renown: Bodnant is famous for its laburnum tunnel, white wisterias, vast Arbutus × andrachnoides, the 1730s gazebo called the Pin Mill, the green theatre, Viburnum × bodnantense, hybrid camellias, huge rhododendrons, flaming embothriums, the two Lords Aberconway, father and son, both past-Presidents of the Royal Horticultural Society, and the three generations of the Puddle family who have been Head Gardeners.

Chirk Castle
Chirk LL4 5AF
☎ 01691 777701   FAX 01691 774706

OWNER The National Trust
LOCATION 1½ miles west of Chirk off A5
OPEN 11.30 am – 6 pm (last admission 4.30); Wednesday – Sunday; 2 April to 29 September. Mondays in July & August. Saturdays, Sundays & Bank Holiday Mondays; 5 to 27 October

ADMISSION Adults £2.20; Children £1.10
FACILITIES Parking; loos; facilities for the disabled; shop; restaurant & tea-room
FEATURES Herbaceous borders; follies and garden buildings; rhododendrons and azaleas; rock garden; modern roses; old roses; garden sculpture; snowdrops; good topiary; woodland garden; eucryphias; hydrangeas; lime avenue; current holder of Sandford Award
ENGLISH HERITAGE GRADE I

Chirk has handsome 19th-century formal gardens, one planted with roses and another with billowing yew topiary. There is also a good 1930s collection of trees and shrubs, the relics of a garden by Norah Lindsay. But some say the whole garden is 'a little too National Trust' now.

Erddig
Wrexham LL13 0YT
☎ 01978 355314   [FAX] 01978 313333

OWNER The National Trust
LOCATION Signposted from A483 and A525
OPEN 11 am – 6 pm (5 pm after 30 September); Saturday – Wednesday; 22 March to 2 November
ADMISSION House & garden: Adults £5.40; Children £2.70; Groups pre-booked (15+) £4.40
FACILITIES Parking; loos; access for the disabled; plants for sale; restaurant, tea-room
FEATURES Fruit of special interest; lake; old roses; woodland garden; spring bulbs; current holder of Sandford Award
ENGLISH HERITAGE GRADE I
NCCPG NATIONAL COLLECTIONS Hedera

More of a re-creation than a restoration, Erddig today majors on domestic life in the early 18th century. There are old-fashioned fruit trees, an avenue of pleached limes, and a long canal to frame the house, but all are slightly awed by the Victorian overlay – avenues of monkey puzzles and wellingtonias.

DYFED

Cae Hir
Cribyn, Lampeter SA48 7NG
☎ 01570 470839

OWNER W Akkermans
LOCATION In village
OPEN 1 pm – 6 pm; daily except Mondays (but open on Bank Holiday Mondays)
ADMISSION Adults £2; Senior Citizens £1.50; Children 50p
FACILITIES Parking; dogs permitted; loos; plants for sale; light refreshments
FEATURES Bog garden; herbaceous borders; lake; colour gardens; bonsai; new water garden and new white garden (1995)

Young and expanding garden, begun in 1985 and already featured twice on Channel 4. Six acres have been taken from meadows and made into a series of beautiful colour-conscious gardens by the present owner. Trees, shrubs and herbaceous plants, often used in original ways. Immaculately tidy: Mr Akkermans' energy and achievement are an inspiration.

Colby Woodland Garden
Amroth, Narberth SA67 8PP
☎ 01834 811885

OWNER The National Trust
LOCATION Signposted from A477
OPEN 10 am – 5 pm; daily; 1 April to 1 November
ADMISSION Adults £2.60; Groups (15+) £2.10; Children £1.30. Guided walks by arrangement
FACILITIES Parking; dogs permitted; loos; access for the disabled; plants for sale; shop; light refreshments
FEATURES Fine conifers; rhododendrons and azaleas; woodland garden

A grand woodland garden, best in May when the rhododendrons are in full flower.

The Dingle (Crundale)
Crundale, Haverfordwest SA62 4DJ
☎ 01437 764370

OWNER Mrs A J Jones
LOCATION On the A40 to Haverfordwest turn right on first two roundabouts, fork right then 1st right
OPEN 10 am – 6 pm, Wednesday – Sunday; 12 March to 12 October
ADMISSION Adults £1; Children 50p
FACILITIES Parking; loos; access for the disabled; nursery; tea-room
FEATURES Herbaceous borders; gravel or scree garden; lake; rock garden; old roses; woodland garden; young garden; bluebells; primroses

This excellent young garden was started in 1982 to display the plants which Mrs Jones grows in the adjoining nursery – roses, clematis, herbaceous plants and alpines – but it has the feel of a private garden. Plants are arranged to show off their form as well as their flowers and leaf-colours. A good garden – it works well.

Picton Castle Trust
Picton Castle, Haverfordwest, Pembrokeshire SA62 4AS
☎ & [FAX] 01437 751326

OWNER Picton Castle Trust
LOCATION 4 miles east of Haverfordwest off A40
OPEN 10.30 am – 5 pm; Tuesday – Sunday & Bank Holidays; 1 April to 30 September
ADMISSION Adults £2.50; Children £1
FACILITIES Parking; dogs permitted; loos; facilities for the disabled; plants for sale; garden shop selling surplus garden produce; restaurant
FEATURES Camellias; rhododendrons and azaleas; woodland garden

Essentially a 50-acre woodland garden with rhododendrons and similar shrubs planted over the last fifty years, but the Trust is replanting the kitchen garden as a flower garden and visitors can expect further improvements.

Post House Gardens
Cwmbach, Whitland SA34 0DR
☎ 01994 484213

OWNER Mrs Jo Kenaghan

LOCATION 7 miles north of St Clears (A40)
OPEN 9 am – sunset; daily; 1 April to 30 June. And by appointment, 1 July to 31 October
ADMISSION Adults £1.50; Senior Citizens £1; Children 50p
FACILITIES Parking; loos; plants for sale; tea & coffee
FEATURES Herbaceous borders; plantsman's garden; rhododendrons and azaleas; rock garden; old roses; wood anemones; bluebells; lots of recent planting (1994/95), especially bog plants & shrubs

Four acres of plantsmanship on a long, narrow site above the River Sien, so steep that it appears much larger. Hardy trees and shrubs are the main feature, especially rhododendrons which are also available for purchase, but there are alpines, gunneras, *Meconopsis* and wonderful wild woodland flowers too.

GWENT

Lower House Farm
Nantyderry, Abergavenny NP7 9DP
☎ 01873 880257   FAX 01873 880108
OWNER Mr & Mrs Glynne Clay
LOCATION 500 yards from Chain Bridge
OPEN For NGS and by appointment
ADMISSION Adults £1.50; Children 50p
FACILITIES Parking; loos; access for the disabled; plants on NGS days; teas on NGS days
FEATURES Good collection of trees; herbaceous borders; fine conifers; herbs; plantsman's garden; old roses; *Lathraea clandestina*; good autumn colour

A modern garden, substantially made by the present owners. Many good features, notably the bog garden and fern island, and unusual young trees.

Penpergwm Lodge
Abergavenny NP7 9AS
☎ 01873 840208
OWNER Mrs C Boyle
LOCATION 3 miles from Abergavenny on B4598, opposite King of Prussia pub
OPEN 2 pm – 6 pm; Thursday – Saturday; 1 April to 31 October
ADMISSION Adults £1.50; Children Free
FACILITIES Parking; dogs permitted; loos; access for the disabled; Nursery for unusual plants; teas on Sundays
FEATURES New vine walk, planted for autumn colour; new avenue of *Malus transitoria* (1996)

The show garden attached to an established garden school. Clever design and satisfying planting. Recommended.

GWYNEDD

Bodysgallen Hall
Llandudno LL30 1RS
☎ 01492 584466   FAX 01492 582519
OWNER Historic House Hotels Ltd
LOCATION On right, off A470 to Llandudno
OPEN Daily; all year

ADMISSION Open only to Hotel Guests
FACILITIES Parking; loos; access for the disabled; refreshments at hotel
FEATURES Follies and garden buildings; fruit of special interest; herbs; lake; rock garden; old roses; woodland garden; knot garden; parterres; splendid new 64ft obelisk (1993) of local stone

Good gardens and good grounds for a good hotel. Partly 1920s and partly modern, the gardens include a knot garden divided into eight segments, an extremely busy kitchen garden, woodland walks, a little sunken garden with a lily pond and a modern parterre with white floribundas in the old walled garden. Handy for Bodnant.

Bryn Bras Castle
Llanrug, Caernarfon LL55 4RE
☎ 01286 870210   FAX 01286 870210
OWNER Mr & Mrs Nevile E Gray-Parry
LOCATION Signposted from A4086 at Llanrug (½ mile)
OPEN Groups by arrangement
ADMISSION Adults £3.50; Children £1.75
FACILITIES Parking; loos; tea-room & tea-garden for Welsh teas
FEATURES Rhododendrons and azaleas; woodland garden; stream with pools and waterfalls

There is much to commend the gardens at Bryn Bras: excellent herbaceous borders, an old/new knot garden and delicious walks through 30 acres of rhododendron woodland. If only more people knew of it.

Cefn Bere
Cae Deintur, Dolgellau LL40 2YS
☎ 01341 422768
OWNER G M Thomas
LOCATION At Cae Deintur, behind primary school, up short steep hill, left at top, 4th house
OPEN By appointment from early spring to late autumn
ADMISSION Contribution to NGS
FACILITIES Parking; cuttings & seeds available
FEATURES Glasshouses and conservatories to visit; plantsman's garden; old roses; troughs

A plantsman's garden within a disciplined design: the owners say that it encapsulates their own development as gardeners over the last forty years. A great variety of rare plants within a small compass, especially alpines, dwarf conifers, ferns and evergreens. Wonderful views.

Penrhyn Castle
Bangor LL57 4HN
☎ 01248 353084   FAX 01248 371281
OWNER The National Trust
LOCATION 3 miles east of Bangor on A5122, signposted from A55 – A5 junction
OPEN 11 am – 6 pm (10 am to 6 pm in July & August); daily except Tuesday; 26 March to 2 November
ADMISSION Adults £3; Children £1.50. Tours by arrangement
FACILITIES Parking; dogs permitted; loos; facilities for the disabled; plants for sale; light lunches in licensed tea-room

FEATURES   Fine conifers; subtropical plants; woodland garden; 1920s walled garden; rhododendrons; trees planted by royals; *Fuchsia* pergola walk; 'wet' garden

A Norman castle (actually a Victorian fake) with a distant walled garden of parterres and terraces merging into the slopes of rhododendrons and camellias. There is much of dendrological interest (ancient conifers, holm oaks and naturalised arbutus trees) and a 'dinosaur landscape' of tree ferns, gunneras and aralias.

Plas Brondanw Gardens
Llanfrothen, Panrhyndeudraeth LL48 6SW
☎ 01766 770484

OWNER   Trustees of the Second Portmeirion Foundation
LOCATION   On Croesor road off A4085
OPEN   9 am – 5 pm; daily; all year
ADMISSION   Adults £1.50; Children 25p
FEATURES   Good topiary; folly

Highly original and architectural Edwardian garden laid out by Clough Williams-Ellis seventeen years before he began Portmeirion, and now assiduously restored by his granddaughter Menna. One of the best-kept secrets in North Wales, full of slate stonework and such original design ideas as the arbour of four red-twigged limes. The garden rooms are inward looking and almost cottagey in their planting, but the mountain peaks are ever present.

Plas Newydd
Llanfairpwll, Anglesey LL61 6EQ
☎ 01248 714795   FAX 01248 713673

OWNER   The National Trust
LOCATION   2 miles south-west of Llanfairpwll on A4080
OPEN   11 am – 5 pm; Sunday – Friday; 27 March to 29 September. Fridays & Sundays; 1 to 27 October
ADMISSION   Adults £4.20; Children £2.10; Group £3.40; Family £10.50. Garden only: £2
FACILITIES   Parking; loos; access for the disabled; plants for sale; National Trust shop; tea-room
FEATURES   Fine conifers; follies and garden buildings; lake; landscape designed by Humphry Repton; azaleas; magnolias; rhododendrons; maples; spectacular agapanthus; new plantings in Italianate garden (1994)

A grand collection of rhododendrons (plus azaleas, magnolias and acers) within a Repton landscape on a spectacular site above the Menai Straits. The rhodos came as a wedding present to Lord & Lady Anglesey from Lord Aberconway at Bodnant. The fine Italianate garden below the house is 1930s, most surprising.

Plas-yn-Rhiw
Rhiw, Pwllheli LL53 8AB
☎ 01758 780219

OWNER   The National Trust
LOCATION   12 miles from Pwllheli on south coast road to Aberdarow
OPEN   12 noon – 5 pm; daily except Tuesday; 27 March to 30 September. Closed on Wednesdays between 27 March & 19 May
ADMISSION   Adults £2.60; Children £1.30; Family £6.50

FACILITIES   Parking; loos
FEATURES   Herbaceous borders; formal gardens

Pretty garden, small and formal, with box-edged parterres filled with rambling roses and billowing cottage garden flowers. Tender trees and shrubs flourish in the mild coastal climate.

Portmeirion
LL48 6ET
☎ 01766 770228   FAX 01766 771331

OWNER   Portmeirion Ltd
LOCATION   Between Penrhyndeudraeth and Porthmadog
OPEN   9.30 – 5.30; daily; all year
ADMISSION   Adults £3.50; Children £1.75
FACILITIES   Parking; loos; plants for sale; several shops; refreshments, and hotel
FEATURES   Follies and garden buildings; rhododendrons and azaleas; subtropical plants; woodland garden; giant yuccas; exuberant summer bedding; tallest *Maytenus boaria* (18m.) in the British Isles

Portmeirion is where the architect Clough Williams-Ellis worked out his Italianate fantasies. The gardens are carved out of a rhododendron woodland but formal, with a mixture of Mediterranean plants and exotic palms, and full of architectural bric-a-brac of every period. Fun.

POWYS

The Dingle (Welshpool)
Welshpool
☎ 01938 555145   FAX 01938 554734

OWNER   Mr & Mrs Roy Joseph
LOCATION   Left turn to Nurseries off A490 to Llanfyllin
OPEN   9 am – 5 pm; daily except Tuesdays; all year except Christmas week
ADMISSION   £1 (1995)
FACILITIES   Parking; dogs permitted; loos; access for the disabled; good nursery attached; cold drinks & ice-creams
FEATURES   Fine conifers; rhododendrons and azaleas; rock garden; woodland garden; colour borders; woodland garden expanded (1994-95)

Steep and stony garden attached to a successful wholesale nursery, but essentially a private garden still. Mainly trees and shrubs, mulched with bark, but some herbaceous plants too, and a stream with bridges leading to a pool.

Dolwen
Cefn Coch, Llanrhaedr-ym-Mochnant SY10 0BL
☎ 01691 780411

OWNER   Mrs Frances Denby
LOCATION   Right at Three Tuns Inn, 1 mile up lane
OPEN   2 pm – 4.30 pm; Fridays; 6 May to 13 September. Plus last Sunday in month from May to August
ADMISSION   £1
FACILITIES   Parking; loos; plants for sale; tea-room
FEATURES   Herbaceous borders; gravel or scree garden; lake; plantsman's garden; old roses; garden sculpture; woodland garden; garden school

A plantsman's garden on a steep 4-acre site, energetically made by Mrs Denby over the last 20 years. Beautiful plantings around three large ponds, fed by natural springs and connected by waterfalls. One of the best young gardens in Wales, of ever-growing interest.

Glansevern Gardens

Glansevern, Berriew, Welshpool SY21 8AH

☎ 01686 640200   ▣ 01686 640829

OWNER   Neville Thomas
LOCATION   On A483, 4 miles south-west of Welshpool
OPEN   2 pm – 6 pm; Fridays, Saturdays & Bank Holiday Mondays; 2 May to 27 September
ADMISSION   Adults £2; OAPs £1.50; Children Free
FACILITIES   Parking; dogs permitted; loos; access for the disabled; plants for sale; garden shop; galleried tea-room
FEATURES   Herbaceous borders; lake; rock garden; modern roses; good trees

The handsome Greek-revival house sits in a landscaped park, complete with its lake, rhododendrons and splendid Victorian specimen trees. The 1840s rock garden incorporates a spooky grotto. But it is the modern planting which distinguishes Glansevern: luxuriant primulas in the water-garden, island beds around the house and roses in the walled garden.

Powis Castle

Welshpool SY21 8RF

☎ & ▣ 01938 554336

OWNER   The National Trust
LOCATION   1 mile south of Welshpool off the A483
OPEN   11 am – 6 pm; Wednesday – Sunday plus Bank Holiday Mondays; 26 March to 31 May & 3 September to 2 November. Plus Tuesdays from June to August
ADMISSION   Adults £4; Children (under 17) £2; Family £10
FACILITIES   Parking; loos; facilities for the disabled; plant shop & gift shop; restaurant for light lunches & teas
FEATURES   Herbaceous borders; good topiary; woodland garden; plantings by Graham Thomas; particularly good in July-August; tender climbers; colour plantings; good autumn colour; largest (i.e. thickest trunk) sessile oak *Quercus petraea* in the British Isles, and four other record trees
NCCPG NATIONAL COLLECTIONS *Aralia; Laburnum*

Famous hanging terraces swamped by bulky overgrown yews and wonderfully rich with colour planting by Graham Thomas. Smashing in early autumn when maples colour the lower slopes and again in May when rhododendrons fill the surrounding woodland. Rare and tender plants on the walls include a hefty *Feijoa sellowiana*. The aspect is south-east, so Powis is best seen in the morning light: photographers please note.

SOUTH GLAMORGAN

Dyffryn Botanic Garden

St Nicholas, Cardiff CF5 6SU

☎ 01222 593328   ▣ 01222 591966

OWNER   Vale of Glamorgan Council
LOCATION   Jct 33 M4 on A48 then follow signs

OPEN   10 am – 5.30 pm; daily; 1 April to 30 September. 10.30 – dusk; Wednesday – Saturday; 1 October – 31 March
ADMISSION   Adults £2; Senior Citizens & Children £1.50; Groups (20+) £1.50
FACILITIES   Parking; dogs permitted; loos; access for the disabled; plants for sale; plants for sale on Bank Holidays; refreshments
FEATURES   Herbaceous borders; rhododendrons and azaleas; modern roses; woodland garden; spring bulbs; summer bedding; tallest purple birch *Betula pendula* 'Purpurea' in the British Isles (and ten other record trees)

55 acres of sumptuous gardens designed by Thomas Mawson around an Edwardian prodigy house. Intended partly for display – there is even a Roman garden with a temple and fountain – and partly for the owners' own pleasure, Dyffryn has a huge collection of good plants built up by Reginald Cory in the early years of this century. In the surrounding oakwoods, thousands of Japanese maples are used as underplanting. The garden as a status symbol.

WEST GLAMORGAN

Clyne Gardens

Mumbles Road, Black Pill, Swansea

☎ 01792 298637   ▣ 01792 635408

OWNER   Swansea City Council
LOCATION   3 miles west of Swansea on coast road
OPEN   Dawn to dusk; daily; all year
ADMISSION   Free
FACILITIES   Parking; dogs permitted; loos; facilities for the disabled; occasional light refreshments
FEATURES   Herbaceous borders; lake; oriental features; rhododendrons and azaleas; woodland garden; Clyne-in-Bloom Festival all May
NCCPG NATIONAL COLLECTIONS *Pieris; Enkianthus; Rhododendron* (Triflora & Falconera subsections)
FRIENDS   Details of Friends organisation from Ivor Stokes

Clyne is a stupendous woodland garden, the best in South Wales, well cared for by enthusiastic and knowledgeable staff. Best as a magic rhododendron valley in May, but the range of rare and tender plants provides interest all year. The car park is small, and tends to fill up early in the day.

Margam Park

Port Talbot SA13 2TJ

☎ 01639 881635   ▣ 01639 895897

OWNER   Neath Port Talbot County Borough Council
LOCATION   Follow directions from Jct 38 M4
OPEN   10 am – 7 pm (5 pm in winter); daily; all year
ADMISSION   Adults £3.50; OAPs & Children £2.50; Family £10 (1996)
FACILITIES   Parking; dogs permitted; loos; facilities for the disabled; gift shop; restaurant & light refreshments
FEATURES   Good collection of trees; follies and garden buildings; oriental features; modern roses; garden sculpture; interesting for children; bedding out; daffodils; rhododendrons; maze; orangery; tallest bay tree *Laurus nobilis* (21m.) in the British Isles

A popular country park with lots to interest the garden historian and plantsman. A wonderful range of conservatories and glasshouses, including the orangery for which Margam is famous, big trees and rhododendrons (some grown from Kingdon Ward's seed), and cheerful bedding out. Recent additions include a collection of dwarf conifers, a permanent exhibition of modern sculptures, a maze (one of the largest in Europe) and a new pergola 450 yards long: further work is promised.

Plantasia

Parc Tawe, Swansea SA1 2AL
☎ 01792 474555/298637 [FAX] 01792 652588

OWNER Swansea City Council
LOCATION Off main Eastern approach to Swansea
OPEN 10 am – 5 pm; Tuesdays – Sundays & Bank Holidays; all year. Closed 1 January, 25 & 26 December
ADMISSION Adults £1.50; Concessions 90p
FACILITIES Parking; loos; access for the disabled; plants for sale; souvenirs; soft drinks
FEATURES Glasshouses and conservatories to visit; interesting for children; particularly interesting in winter; new butterfly house (1995); aviary and tropical fish

A major modern amenity commitment by the go-ahead City Council. Plantasia is a large glasshouse (1600 sq m) with three climatic zones (arid, tropical, and rain forest) and each is stuffed with exotic plants – palms, strelitzias, tree ferns, nepenthes, cacti and such economic plants as coconuts and pineapple. The perfect goal for a winter expedition, and not expensive.

SCOTLAND

BORDERS

Abbotsford

Melrose TD6 9BQ
☎ 01896 752043 [FAX] 01896 752916

OWNER Mrs P Maxwell-Scott
LOCATION Off A7, two miles from Melrose
OPEN 10 am – 5 pm (but 2 pm – 5 pm on Sundays in April, May & October); daily; 17 March to 31 October
ADMISSION Adults £3.40; Children £1.70
FACILITIES Parking; loos; access for the disabled; gift shop; self-service tea-room
FEATURES Fine walled garden; orangery

Sir Walter Scott laid out the gardens at Abbotsford in the 1820s: he designed the formal Court garden by the house and planted the surrounding woodlands. The walled garden centres on a handsome orangery, with roses, fruit trees and herbaceous borders planted for late summer effect.

Dawyck Botanic Garden

Stobo EH45 9JV
☎ 01721 760254 [FAX] 01721 760214

OWNER Royal Botanic Garden, Edinburgh
LOCATION 8 miles south-west of Peebles on B712
OPEN 10 am – 6 pm; daily; 15 March to 22 October
ADMISSION Adults £2; Senior Citizens £1.50p; Children 50p; Family £4.50

FACILITIES Parking; loos; plants for sale; gift shop; light refreshments
FEATURES Herbaceous borders; lake; particularly interesting in winter; Meconopsis; Chinese conifers; Dawyck beech; Douglas fir from original seed; tallest Fagus crenata (21m.) in the British Isles, and eighteen further record trees

A woodland garden, run as an annexe of the Royal Botanic Garden in Edinburgh and long famous for its trees. The Dawyck beech is the upright, fastigiate form, first found in the policies in the mid 19th century. Edinburgh have underplanted with interesting shrubs, and some herbaceous plants. Dawyck is a getting-better garden. It can also boast the first Cryptogamic Sanctuary.

Floors Castle

Roxburghe Estates Office, Kelso TD5 7SF
☎ 01573 223333 [FAX] 01573 226056

OWNER The Duke of Roxburghe
LOCATION Signposted in Kelso
OPEN 10 am – 4.30 pm (4 pm in October); daily; Easter to October
ADMISSION Adults £3.80; OAPs £3
FACILITIES Parking; dogs permitted; loos; access for the disabled; garden centre in walled garden; licensed restaurant & shop
FEATURES Herbaceous borders

Not a great garden, but there are handsome traditional herbaceous borders in the walled garden and the siting of the castle in its parkland is very impressive.

Kailzie Gardens

Kailzie, Peebels EH45 9HT
☎ 01721 720007

OWNER Lady Angela Buchan-Hepburn
LOCATION On B7062 2 miles east of Peebles
OPEN 11 am – 5.30 pm; daily; 7 April until 31 October. Plus daylight hours in winter
ADMISSION Adults £2; Children 50p
FACILITIES Parking; dogs permitted; loos; access for the disabled; plants for sale; shop; restaurant & teas
FEATURES Daffodils; snowdrops; woodland garden

Kailzie has been revived over the last 20 years. The large walled garden has a mixture of flowers and produce: a laburnum alley, a rose garden and double herbaceous borders are some of the attractions. There are Meconopsis and primulas in the rhododendrons woodland walks outside.

Manderston

Duns TD11 3PP
☎ 01361 883450 [FAX] 01361 882010

OWNER Lord Palmer
LOCATION On A6105 2 miles east of Duns
OPEN 2 pm – 5.30 pm; Sundays & Thursdays; 18 May to 28 September, plus 26 May & 25 August. Parties at any time by appointment
ADMISSION Not available at time of going to press
FACILITIES Parking; dogs permitted; loos; cream teas & ice-cream

FEATURES Herbaceous borders; fine conifers; lake; rhododendrons and azaleas; good topiary; woodland garden; good bedding out

The house is sort-of-Georgian. Below it are four expansive terraces, with rich planting around clipped yews and hollies. Unfortunately it is possible to visit only a small part of this formal garden. Below are a small lake, a Chinese-style bridge (18th-century) and a woodland garden with modern rhododendrons and azaleas. All is planted and maintained in the grand manner.

Mellerstain
Gordon TD3 6LG
☎ 01573 410225   ☎ 01573 410388

OWNER Mellerstain Trust
LOCATION 1 mile west of A6089 Kelso – Edinburgh road
OPEN 12.30 pm – 5 pm. 28 – 31 March, then daily except Saturdays; 1 May to 30 September
ADMISSION £1.50
FACILITIES Parking; dogs permitted; loos; access for the disabled; tweed and gift shop; tea-room
FEATURES Lake; modern roses; good topiary; Italian terraced garden by Sir Reginald Blomfield (1909)

The house has extensive views south to the Cheviots. Below it lies Blomfield's formal garden planted with floribundas and lavender. Beneath it runs the landscape laid out by William and Robert Adam, sauntering down to a lake. Uncompromisingly grand.

Mertoun Gardens
St Boswells, Melrose TD6 0EA
☎ 01835 823236   ☎ 01835 822474

OWNER Mertoun Gardens Trust
LOCATION B6404, 2 miles north-east of St Boswells
OPEN 2 pm – 6 pm; Saturdays, Sundays & Public Holiday Mondays; 1 April to 1 October
ADMISSION Adults £1; Children 50p
FACILITIES Parking; loos; access for the disabled
FEATURES Herbaceous borders; daffodils; glasshouses and conservatories to visit; herbs; vegetables of interest

Originally part of the Duke of Sutherland's estates, Mertoun is best known for its traditional kitchen garden. A long herbaceous border within it has just been replanted.

Monteviot House Gardens
Jedburgh TD8 6UQ
☎ 01835 830380   ☎ 01835 830288

LOCATION Off A68 north of Jedburgh & B6400 to Nisbet
OPEN 2 pm – 5 pm; Monday – Thursday; April to August
ADMISSION Adults £2; OAPs £1; under-14s free
FACILITIES Parking; dogs permitted; loos; plants for sale; for pre-booked groups
FEATURES Good collection of trees; water garden; Victorian rose garden

A substantial garden, attached to a large estate. The rose garden, recently replanted, is Victorian in origin: much of the rest came from Percy Cane in the 1930s. The modern water garden is good. But the trees in the arboretum are exceptional

and recent clearing has displayed them in their glory. Guided tours are available by prior arrangement.

Priorwood Garden
Melrose TD6 9PX
☎ 01896 822493

OWNER The National Trust for Scotland
LOCATION Next to Melrose Abbey
OPEN 10 am (1.30 pm on Sundays) – 5.30 pm; daily; 1 April to 30 September. 10 am (1.30 pm on Sundays) – 4 pm; daily; 1 October to 24 December
ADMISSION Adults £1
FACILITIES Parking; dogs permitted; access for the disabled; plants for sale; dried flower shop and NTS gift shop
FEATURES Herbaceous borders; fruit of special interest; herbs

Best known for its shop, which was recently extended and improved. Everything at Priorwood is geared towards dried flowers. Inspirational.

Traquair House
Innerleithen EH44 6PW
☎ 01896 830323   ☎ 01896 830639

OWNER Mrs Maxwell Stuart
LOCATION Signposted from Innerleithen
OPEN 12.30 pm (10.30 in July & August) – 5.30 pm; daily; 29 March to 30 September. Plus Fridays, Saturdays & Sundays in October
ADMISSION House & grounds: Adults £4; Concessions £3.50; Children £2
FACILITIES Parking; dogs permitted; loos; access for the disabled; plants for sale; gift shop; restaurant serving lunch & tea
FEATURES Herbaceous borders; modern roses; woodland garden

The main attraction is a large maze, planted in 1980 of beech and Leyland cypress. The house is a Catholic time-warp: the Bear Gates in the park, once the main entrance to the estate, have been closed ever since Bonnie Prince Charlie passed through them for the last time in 1746.

DUMFRIES & GALLOWAY

Arbigland
Kirkbean DG2 8BQ
☎ 01387 880283

OWNER Arbigland Estate Trust
LOCATION South of Kirkbean on A710 Solway Coast Road
OPEN 2 pm – 6 pm; Tuesday – Sunday, and Bank Holiday Mondays; 1 May to 30 September
ADMISSION Adults £2; Senior Citizens £1.50; Children 50p
FACILITIES Parking; dogs permitted; loos; access for the disabled; plants for sale; home-made teas
FEATURES Lake; old roses; woodland garden; interesting for children; rhododendrons; maples

A woodland garden, with many different features. Best is the area called Japan, where ancient Japanese maples surround a water garden. But there are also a hidden rose garden, splendid large-leaved rhododendrons, and paths down to the sandy shore.

Broughton House & Gardens

National Trust for Scotland, 12 High Street, Kirkcudbright
DG6 4JX

☎ & FAX 01557 330437

OWNER Hornel Trust (managed by National Trust for Scotland)
LOCATION Signed in centre of Kirkcudbright
OPEN 1 pm – 5.30 pm; daily; 28 March to 31 October
ADMISSION Adults £2.30; Concessions £1.50. Party rates
available
FACILITIES Parking; loos
FEATURES Oriental features

E A Hornel the artist laid out the Japanese garden, which is
the best known part of the garden here and featured in many
of his portraits. Most of the rest is given to a nondescript
'Scottish' garden.

Castle Kennedy Garden

Stair Estates, Rephad, Stranraer DG9 8BX

☎ 01776 702024   FAX 01776 706248

OWNER Lochinch Heritage Estate
LOCATION 5 miles east of Stranraer on A75
OPEN 10 am – 5 pm; daily; Easter to 30 September
ADMISSION Adults £2; Senior Citizens £1.50; Children £1
FACILITIES Parking; dogs permitted; loos; access for the dis-
abled; plants for sale; plant centre; tea-rooms
FEATURES Herbaceous borders; woodland garden; rhodo-
dendrons; embothriums; eucryphias; monkey puzzle avenue;
tallest *Pittosporum tenuifolium* (17m.) in the British Isles,
and four other record-breaking trees

A huge garden, with early 18th-century rides, avenues and
allées, a complete 19th-century pinetum, rhododendrons from
Hooker's Himalayan expedition, a vast collection of trees and
shrubs, and handsome herbaceous plantings in the walled
garden. Important and impressive.

Galloway House Gardens

Garlieston, Newton Stewart DG8 8HF

☎ 01988 600680

OWNER Galloway House Gardens Trust
LOCATION Off B7004 at Garlieston
OPEN 9 am – 5 pm; daily; 1 March to 31 October
ADMISSION Adults £1.50; Senior Citizens £1; Children 50p
FACILITIES Parking; dogs permitted; access for the disabled
FEATURES Camellias; daffodils; rhododendrons and azaleas;
snowdrops

Galloway House is where Capt Neil McEacharn learnt to
garden, before moving to Lake Maggiore to create the great
gardens of Villa Taranto. A vast *Davidia involucrata* dates
from his ownership.

Glenwhan Garden

Dunragit, by Stranraer DG9 8PH

☎ 01581 400222

OWNER Mr & Mrs William Knott
LOCATION 1 mile off A75 at Dunragit Village
OPEN 10 am – 5 pm; daily; 1 April to 30 October
ADMISSION Adults £2; Senior Citizens £1.50; Children
(over 14) £1

FACILITIES Parking; loos; facilities for the disabled; shop;
nursery attached; garden restaurant
FEATURES Lake; plantsman's garden; old roses; woodland
garden; bluebells; trees and shrubs; many new *Rhododen-*
dron species planted (1997); new woodland walk and bog
garden (1994)

A new garden on a large scale (12 acres and still growing),
started by the owners in 1979 and worked by them and one
gardener. Very much a plantsman's garden, but it uses plants
to create effects, and capitalises upon the lie of the land to
produce different habitats. The achievement to date is commendable: definitely a garden to watch.

Logan Botanic Gardens

Port Logan, Stranraer DG9 9ND

☎ 01776 860231   FAX 01776 860333

OWNER Royal Botanic Garden, Edinburgh
LOCATION 14 miles south of Stranraer on B7065
OPEN 10 am – 6 pm; daily; 15 March to 31 October. 25 May
for SGS
ADMISSION Adults £2; Concessions £1.50; Children 50p
FACILITIES Parking; loos; facilities for the disabled; plants for
sale; shop selling books, gifts and local crafts; light meals &
refreshments
FEATURES Herbaceous borders; subtropical plants; particu-
larly good in July-August; tree ferns; cardiocrinums; gunnera;
cordylines; trachycarpus palms
FRIENDS Part of the Friends of the Royal Botanic Garden at
Edinburgh

The extraordinary effects of Logan are created by palms,
cordylines and tree ferns within the semi-formal setting of a
walled garden. Huge gunneras and cardiocrinums pile on the
message, but the richness extends also to diversity, for here is
one of the great botanic collections of tender exotica, worth a
long journey on a sunny day in summer.

Threave School of Horticulture

Castle Douglas DG7 1RX

☎ & FAX 01556 502575

OWNER The National Trust for Scotland
LOCATION 1 mile west of Castle Douglas
OPEN 9.30 am – sunset. Visitor Centre closes at 5.30 pm
ADMISSION Adults £3.70; Senior Citizens & Children
£2.50. Group rate £3
FACILITIES Parking; loos; facilities for the disabled; plants for
sale; shop; restaurant & snacks
FEATURES Good collection of trees; herbaceous borders;
fruit of special interest; glasshouses and conservatories to visit;
plantsman's garden; rock garden; modern roses; old roses;
woodland garden; peat garden; heath garden; tallest *Alnus*
rubra (23m.) in the British Isles, and two other record trees

A teaching garden with a very wide range of attractions –
something to interest every gardener, in fact. Developed over
the last 30 years with the needs of students at the School of
Horticulture, garden-owners and tourists all in mind, Threave
has quickly acquired the reputation of a Scottish Wisley. You
can spend all day here.

FIFE

Cambo Gardens

Kingsbarns, St Andrews KY16 8QD

☎ 01333 450054   [FAX] 01333 450987

OWNER   Mr & Mrs T P N Erskine

LOCATION   On A917 between Kingsbarns & Crail

OPEN   10 am – 6 pm (or disk, if sooner); daily; all year

ADMISSION   Adults £2; Children Free

FACILITIES   Parking; dogs permitted; loos; access for the disabled; plants for sale

FEATURES   Daffodils; old roses; snowdrops; snowflakes; colchicum meadows; autumn colour; new ornamental potager (1997)

Victorian walled garden built around the Cambo Burn with a waterfall and elegant oriental bridge. Spectacular when the snowdrops and snowflakes flower.

Falkland Palace

Falkland KY15 7BU

☎ 01337 857397

OWNER   The National Trust for Scotland

LOCATION   On A912, 11 miles north of Kirkcaldy. 10 miles from M90, Jct 8

OPEN   11 am – 4.30 pm, Monday – Saturday; 1.30 pm – 4.30 pm, Sundays; 1 April to 31 October

ADMISSION   Adults £2.10; Children £1.10 (1996 prices)

FACILITIES   Parking; loos; facilities for the disabled; gift shop

FEATURES   Herbaceous borders; fruit of special interest; autumn colour; spectacular delphinium border

Percy Cane's reconstruction of a Scottish renaissance garden, with a herb garden, an astrolabe walk and formal parterres prettily planted in pastel colours.

Hill of Tarvit

Cupar KY15 5PB

☎ 01334 653127

OWNER   The National Trust for Scotland

LOCATION   Off A916, 2½ miles south of Cupar

OPEN   9 am – sunset (or 9 pm if earlier); daily; all year round

ADMISSION   £1

FACILITIES   Parking; loos; facilities for the disabled; shop in house (open in summer)

FEATURES   Herbaceous borders; plantsman's garden; old roses; woodland garden; heathers

Essentially a plantsman's garden, opulently planted and maintained in keeping with the Lorimer house. The Edwardian plantings, now splendidly mature, have been complemented by modern additions. The Trust has begun to restore and replant the borders on the top terrace in the Edwardian style. Highly satisfying.

Kellie Castle

Pittenweem KY10 2RF

☎ 01333 720271

OWNER   The National Trust for Scotland

LOCATION   Signposted from main roads

OPEN   9.30 am – sunset; daily; all year

ADMISSION   Adults £1; Concessions 50p

FACILITIES   Parking; loos; access for the disabled; gift shop; tea-room

FEATURES   Herbaceous borders; fruit of special interest; old roses; particularly good in July-August; strong design; extended collection of historic vegetables

Robert Lorimer's family house: it was he who remade the garden in its present form, though much of the planting is modern. Only one acre, but strong lines and thick planting create a sense of both space and enclosure. Kellie has much to teach modern gardeners.

The Murrel Gardens

The Murrel, Aberdour KY3 0RN [FAX] 01383 860157

OWNER   Mrs M J Milne

LOCATION   On south side of B9157

OPEN   10 am – 5 pm; Monday – Friday; 1 April to 30 September, or by written appointment

ADMISSION   £1.50

FACILITIES   Parking; loos; plants for sale

FEATURES   Herbaceous borders; lake; plantsman's garden; old roses

The house is Arts & Crafts, and the garden was laid out in 1910, but thickly replanted by the present owner in 1980. Its protected position allows many tender plants to grow in this normally cool and difficult part of Scotland.

St Andrews Botanic Garden

The Canongate, St Andrews KY16 8RT

☎ 01334 477178/476452

OWNER   Fife Council

LOCATION   A915, Largo Road, then entrance in The Canongate

OPEN   10 am – 7 pm (4 pm October – April); daily; all year. Greenhouses closed at weekends October – April

ADMISSION   Adults £1.50; Senior Citizens & Children 50p; under-fives free

FACILITIES   Parking; loos; access for the disabled; plants for sale

FEATURES   Good collection of trees; glasshouses and conservatories to visit; gravel or scree garden; lake; rhododendrons and azaleas; rock garden; woodland garden; interesting for children; particularly interesting in winter; peat beds; ferns; heath garden; order beds; new landscaped orchid house (1996)

FRIENDS   Very active Friends organisation, with lectures, workshops, garden visits, a newsletter and seed scheme: details from Honorary Curator, St Andrews Botanic Garden, St Andrews KY16 8RT

The University botanic garden has taken a new lease of life since the Council took on its administration. The garden's main asset, the peat, rock and water complex (crag, scree, moraine, alpine meadow and bog) is being repaired and replanted. The cactus house has been completed, a new alpine house is now open, and the orchid house reopened last year too. The garden caters particularly well for children.

GRAMPIAN

Brodie Castle

Brodie, Forres, Moray IV36 0TE

☎ 01309 641371   [FAX] 01309 641600

OWNER   The National Trust for Scotland

LOCATION   Signposted from A96

OPEN   11 am – 5.30 pm (opens 1.30 pm on Sundays); daily, but Saturdays & Sundays only in October; 28 March to 26 October

ADMISSION   Adults £4; Concessions £2.70

FACILITIES   Parking; dogs permitted; loos; facilities for the disabled; NTS shop; small tea-room in castle

FEATURES   Daffodils; pond; rhododendrons and azaleas; woodland garden

NCCPG NATIONAL COLLECTIONS Narcissus

Famous for its daffodils, many bred here at the turn of the century: a glorious sight when they bloom in the lawns around the baronial castle.

Crathes Castle

Banchory AB31 5QJ

☎ 01330 844 525   [FAX] 01330 844 797

OWNER   The National Trust for Scotland

LOCATION   15 miles west of Aberdeen

OPEN   9.30 to sunset; daily; all year

ADMISSION   Adults £4.50; Senior Citizens & Children £3

FACILITIES   Parking; loos; facilities for the disabled; plants for sale; NTS shop; restaurant/café open April to October

FEATURES   Fine conifers; plantsman's garden; modern roses; old roses; woodland garden; two ice houses; specimen trees; colour borders; current holder of Sandford Award; tallest Zelkova × verschaffeltii in the British Isles, and four further tree records

NCCPG NATIONAL COLLECTIONS Viburnum; Dianthus (Malmaison carnations)

Famous for its walled garden, with eight distinct theme gardens: a white border, a yellow enclosure, a blue garden, and dreamy high summer borders with pastel shades for long Highland evenings. Only four acres but intensively planted.

Cruickshank Botanic Garden

University of Aberdeen, Dept of Plant and Soil Science, St Machar Drive, Aberdeen AB24 3UU

☎ 01224 272704   [FAX] 01224 272703

OWNER   Aberdeen University

LOCATION   Follow signs for Aberdeen University and/or Old Aberdeen

OPEN   9 am – 4.30 pm; Monday – Friday; all year. Plus 2 pm – 5 pm; Saturdays & Sundays; 1 May to 30 September

ADMISSION   Free

FACILITIES   Dogs permitted; loos; access for the disabled

FEATURES   Good collection of trees; herbaceous borders; lake; rock garden; old roses; stone troughs; peat beds

FRIENDS   Active and well established Friends group, with plant sales, lectures, excursions and a seed list. Contact 01224 272704

12 acres of classic botanic garden, with every educational element: rock gardens, an arboretum, collections of native plants, beds which illustrate the history of the rose, water plants and systematic beds. Well worth exploration.

Damside Garden Herbs

by Johnshaven, Montrose DD10 0HY

☎ 01561 361496

OWNER   Ian & Sheena Cruickshank

LOCATION   Signposted off A92 at Johnshaven

OPEN   10 am – 5 pm (4.30 pm in winter); daily; Good Friday to 24 December

ADMISSION   Adults £1; Senior Citizens & Children 80p

FACILITIES   Parking; loos; access for the disabled; plants for sale; excellent herb shop; non-smoking restaurant & light refreshments

FEATURES   Herbs; lake; promising young arboretum

A garden-cum-nursery which sets out to educate, interest and please its visitors. A series of gardens illustrates the history, variety and uses of herbs in such designs as the Celtic Knot garden, the Roman garden and the Monastic garden.

Drum Castle

Drumoak, Banchory AB31 3EY

☎ 01330 811406

OWNER   The National Trust for Scotland

LOCATION   Off A93, 10 miles west of Aberdeen

OPEN   Grounds: 9.30 – sunset; daily; all year. Garden: 10 am – 6 pm; daily; 1 May to 22 October

ADMISSION   Adults £1.50; Concessions 80p (1996 prices)

FACILITIES   Parking; dogs permitted; loos; plants for sale; small tea-room

FEATURES   Old roses

A historic garden of roses, with the best collection of Scottish roses (hybrids of Rosa pimpinellifolia) in Britain.

Kildrummy Castle Gardens

Kildrummy, Alford AB33 8RA

☎ 019755 71203/71277

OWNER   Kildrummy Castle Garden Trust

LOCATION   On A97, off A944

OPEN   10 am – 5 pm; daily; 1 April to 31 October

ADMISSION   Adults £1.70; Children (over 5) 50p

FACILITIES   Parking; dogs permitted; loos; access for the disabled; plants for sale; tea & coffee

FEATURES   Good collection of trees; lake; plantsman's garden; old roses; interesting for children; autumn colour; heathers; play area & nature trails

A romantic glen-garden, laid out nearly 100 years ago. Richly planted pools and ponds, a plantsman's collection on the hillside, and a large mature rock garden made from the natural sandstone. One of the most romantic gardens in Scotland.

Leith Hall

Kennethmont, Huntly AB54 4QQ

☎ 01464 831 269

OWNER   The National Trust for Scotland

LOCATION   On B9002 west of Kennethmont

OPEN   9.30 am – sunset; daily; all year

ADMISSION Adults £1.50; Children 80p (1996 prices)
FACILITIES Parking; loos; refreshments from May to September, 2 pm – 6 pm
FEATURES Herbaceous borders; rock garden; modern roses; particularly good in July-August; bluebells; ice house; recent restorations & improvements; garden walks throughout the season (phone for dates); new sculptures in woodland walk

Richly planted borders are the pride of Leith Hall: they are full of colour all through the summer. Also impressive is the rock garden, restored and replanted by that most successful of societies, the Scottish Rock Garden Club. Leith gets better and better.

Old Semeil Herb Garden
Strathdon AB36 8XJ
☎ 019756 51343

OWNER Mrs Gillian Cook
LOCATION At Strathdon
OPEN 10 am – 5 pm; daily (but not Thursdays in September, and weekends only in April); Easter to 30 September
ADMISSION Free
FACILITIES Parking; loos; access for the disabled; specialist herb nursery attached; light lunches & teas
FEATURES Herbs

A remarkable garden-cum-nursery 1,000ft up in the Highlands where over 200 varieties of herb are grown by organic methods.

Pitmedden
Ellon AB4 7PD
☎ 01651 842352

OWNER The National Trust for Scotland
LOCATION 1 mile west of Pitmedden on A920
OPEN 10 am – 5.30 pm (last admission 5 pm); daily; 1 May to 30 September
ADMISSION Adults £3.50; Concessions £2.30
FACILITIES Parking; loos; facilities for the disabled; plants for sale; tea-room
FEATURES Herbs; gazebos; parterres

A 17th-century formal garden meticulously created by the National Trust for Scotland 40 years ago. It has 3 miles of box hedging and uses 40,000 bedding plants every summer. The result is impressive, satisfying and peaceful, but lacks authenticity.

HIGHLAND

Allangrange
Munlochy, Black Isle IV8 8NZ
☎ 0146 3811249   [FAX] 0146 3811407

OWNER Major Allan Cameron
LOCATION Signposted off A9, 5 miles north of Inverness
OPEN 2 pm – 5.30 pm; 11 May, 8 June & 13 July; or by appointment
ADMISSION £1.50
FACILITIES Parking; dogs permitted; loos; facilities for the disabled; plants for sale; teas in house

FEATURES Lake; old roses; woodland garden; primulas; rhododendrons; colour borders
Colour gardening by Mrs Cameron, a botanical artist, has made this one of the loveliest summer gardens in the British Isles. Good spring flowers, too.

Cawdor Castle
Cawdor Castle, Nairn IV12 5RD
☎ 01667 404615   [FAX] 01667 404674
OWNER The Dowager Countess Cawdor
LOCATION Between Inverness and Nairn on B9090
OPEN 10 am – 5.30 pm; daily; 1 May to 1 October
ADMISSION Adults £2.70
FACILITIES Parking; loos; facilities for the disabled; gift shop; licensed restaurant in castle
FEATURES Herbaceous borders; fruit of special interest; old roses; woodland garden; new maze & paradise garden (1994); good late summer plantings, *trompe l'oeil*; newly restored 17th-century walled garden (1994)

A Victorian garden which has been replanted and, in part, redesigned in recent years by the addition of a holly maze, laburnum walk and colour schemes. Earth, Purgatory and Paradise are somehow represented in the new plantings, but they are best enjoyed as colours and shapes. The effect is neither cranky nor grand, just extremely charming, while the house is as Scottish a castle as ever was seen.

Dochfour Gardens
Inverness IV3 6JY
☎ 01463 861218   [FAX] 01463 861336
OWNER Lord & Lady Burton
LOCATION 5 miles south-west of Inverness on the A82
OPEN 10 am – 5 pm, Monday – Friday; 2 pm – 5 pm, Saturdays & Sundays; 1 April to 31 October
ADMISSION £1.50. Reductions for Senior Citizens & Children
FACILITIES Parking; access for the disabled; plants for sale; no shop, but pick-your-own fruit in season
FEATURES Rhododendrons and azaleas; good topiary; naturalised daffodils; parterres; water gardens; tallest *Thuja occidentalis* 'Lutea' in the British Isles, plus three further tree records

A substantial garden, landscaped and terraced down to the River Ness. Best when the daffodils and rhododendrons colour the hillside.

Dunrobin Castle Gardens
Golspie, Sutherland KW10 6RR
☎ 01408 633177   [FAX] 01408 634081
OWNER The Sutherland Trust
LOCATION 1 mile north of Golspie on A9
OPEN Dawn to dusk; daily; all year round. Castle: 10.30 am (1 pm on Sundays) – 5.30 pm (4.30 in April, May & October); Monday – Saturday; 28 March to 15 October
ADMISSION Castle & garden: Adults £4.80; OAPs £3.20. Reductions for groups. Gardens free when castle closed
FACILITIES Parking; loos; gift shop; tea-room in castle
FEATURES Herbaceous borders; modern roses; good topiary; woodland garden; formal gardens

Grand terrace gardens, designed by Nesfield, striding down to the Dornoch Forth. Recently replanted and partially restored. New features have been added, including rhododendrons: there will be further improvements.

Inverewe
Poolewe, Ross and Cromarty IV22 2LQ
☎ 01445 781200   ☒ 01445 781497

OWNER   The National Trust for Scotland
LOCATION   On A832, 6 miles north of Gairloch
OPEN   9.30 am – 9 pm (5 pm from 23 October to 31 March); daily; all year
ADMISSION   Adults £4.50; Senior Citizens & Children £3; Group £3.60
FACILITIES   Parking; loos; facilities for the disabled; plants for sale; large shop; excellent new restaurant
FEATURES   Good collection of trees; herbaceous borders; fine conifers; fruit of special interest; lake; plantsman's garden; rock garden; subtropical plants; woodland garden; particularly good in July-August; autumn colour; meconopsis; candelabra primulas; lilies; tallest *Eucalyptus cordata* (30m.) in the British Isles, and three further record trees
NCCPG NATIONAL COLLECTIONS *Olearia*; *Brachyglottis*; *Ourisia*; *Rhododendron* (Barbatum series)

One of the wonders of the horticultural world, a subtropical garden in the north west Highlands. Fabulous large-leaved Himalayan rhododendrons, magnolias, eucalyptus, tree ferns, palms and tender rarities underplanted with drifts of blue poppies and candelabra primulas. Best on a sunny dry day in May, before the midges breed.

Lochalsh Woodland Garden
Balmacara, By Kyle of Lochalsh, Ross IV40 8DN
☎ 01599 566231

OWNER   The National Trust for Scotland
LOCATION   On A87 near Kyle
OPEN   9 am – dusk; daily; all year
ADMISSION   Adults £1; Children 50p
FACILITIES   Parking; dogs permitted; loos
FEATURES   Fine conifers; plantsman's garden; subtropical plants; woodland garden

This woodland garden is becoming much better known, and deservedly. The structure is about 100 years old – tall pines, oaks and beeches with ornamental underplantings started about 30 years ago. Rhododendrons from Euan Cox at Glendoick came first: newer plantings include collections of hardy ferns, bamboos, fuchsias, hydrangeas and *maddeni* rhododendrons, as well as plants from Tasmania and New Zealand. The season of interest extends from early spring well into autumn.

LOTHIAN

Dalmeny House
Rosebery Estates, South Queensferry EH30 9TQ
☎ 0131 331 1888   ☒ 0131 331 1788

OWNER   The Earl of Rosebery
LOCATION   B924 off A90

OPEN   12 noon – 5.30 pm; Mondays & Tuesdays; 1 pm – 5.30 pm, Sundays; 1 July to 2 September. Also one Sunday in snowdrop time for SGS
ADMISSION   Grounds only: free
FACILITIES   Parking; loos; access for the disabled; refreshments
FEATURES   Fine conifers; lake; snowdrops; woodland garden; rhododendrons & azaleas; wellingtonias

The grounds at Dalmeny are extensive, and visitors are encouraged to see the valley walk with rhododendrons, wellingtonias and other conifers.

Inveresk Lodge Garden
24 Inveresk Village, Musselburgh EH21 7TE
☎ 0131 665 1855

OWNER   The National Trust for Scotland
LOCATION   A6124 south of Musselburgh, 6 miles east of Edinburgh
OPEN   10 am – 4.30 pm, Monday – Friday; 2 pm – 5 pm, Sundays; all year. Plus Saturdays from March to October
ADMISSION   Adults £1; Children & OAPs 50p. Honesty box
FACILITIES   Parking; loos
FEATURES   Herbaceous borders; old roses; plantings by Graham Thomas; raised beds; peat beds

A modern garden, tailor-made for a modest NTS estate and maintained to a high standard. Graham Thomas designed the rose borders. Good climbing plants.

Malleny House Garden
Balerno EH14 7AF
☎ 0131 449 2283

OWNER   The National Trust for Scotland
LOCATION   In Balerno, south-west of Edinburgh, off A71
OPEN   9.30 am – 7 pm (4 pm in winter); daily; all year. For SGS: 2 pm – 5 pm, 25 June
ADMISSION   Adults £1; Senior Citizens & Children 50p
FACILITIES   Parking; loos; access for the disabled
FEATURES   Herbaceous borders; glasshouses and conservatories to visit; climbing roses; old roses; good topiary; particularly good in July-August; Scottish National Bonsai Collection
NCCPG NATIONAL COLLECTIONS *Rosa* (19th-century shrubs)
FRIENDS   The Friends of Malleny enjoy garden visits, lectures and other benefits. The Secretary is Mrs Evlyne Danskin, 13 Marchbank Drive, Balerno EH14 7ER. Tel: 0131 449 2826

One of the NTS's best gardens, much praised for its 'personal' quality. The 19th-century shrub roses are underplanted with herbaceous plants which take the display into the autumn. The bonsai collection creates quite another dimension, as do the magnificent conservatory and the huge cones of yew topiary. Very peaceful.

Royal Botanic Garden, Edinburgh
Inverleith Row, Edinburgh EH3 5LR
☎ 0131 552 7171   ☒ 0131 552 0382

OWNER   Scottish Office Board of Trustees
LOCATION   1 mile north of Princes Street

OPEN 10 am – 6 pm, 1 March to 30 April; 10 am – 8 pm, 1 May to 31 August; 10 am – 6 pm, 1 September to 31 October; 10 am – 4 pm, 1 November to 28 February. Closed 25 December & 1 January

ADMISSION Free

FACILITIES Parking; loos; facilities for the disabled; shop; recently enlarged plant sales area; licensed terrace café

FEATURES Alpines; good collection of trees; herbaceous borders; fine conifers; ecological interest; glasshouses and conservatories to visit; gravel or scree garden; herbs; lake; oriental features; rhododendrons and azaleas; rock garden; modern roses; old roses; garden sculpture; subtropical plants; woodland garden; interesting for children; particularly interesting in winter; peat beds; 45 UK record-breaking trees, more than any other Scottish garden

FRIENDS Active Friends of the RBG. Lectures, newsletter, seeds: details from the Friends' Office at the garden

Edinburgh outclasses Kew in several ways – better rock gardens, peat beds, rhododendrons and woodland gardens. And entry is free. Wonderful cantilevered glasshouses and good facilities for people with special needs – children, disabled persons and the blind. Edinburgh also has the highest standards of maintenance. No visitor can fail to respond, above all, to the friendly welcome and helpfulness of all the staff.

Suntrap Garden

43 Gogarbank, Edinburgh EH12 9BY
☎ 0131 339 7283

OWNER Oatridge Agricultural College

LOCATION 1 mile west of Edinburgh bypass, between A8 & A71

OPEN 10 am – 4.30 pm; daily; all year, but weekdays only from October to March, and closed for Christmas fortnight

ADMISSION Adults £1; Children Free

FACILITIES Parking; dogs permitted; facilities for the disabled

FEATURES Alpines; herbaceous borders; daffodils; glasshouses and conservatories to visit; oriental features; pond; modern roses; vegetables of interest; woodland garden; 'Italian' garden; peat walls; new raised beds and colour borders (1996)

FRIENDS Friends of Suntrap. Annual subscription £3. Events & visits. Details from Edwin Arthur: 01875 815541

A three-acre demonstration garden attached to Oatridge Agricultural College, one of the best places in Lothian to learn how to be a better gardener.

STRATHCLYDE

Achamore Gardens

Isle of Gigha PA41 7AD
☎ 015835 267/254   📠 015835 244

OWNER Holt Leisure Parks Ltd (Mr D N Holt)

LOCATION Take Gigha ferry from Tainloan (20 mins) then easy walking for 1½ miles

OPEN Dawn – dusk; daily; all year

ADMISSION Adults £2; Children £1

FACILITIES Parking; dogs permitted; loos; lunches & teas at Gigha Hotel

FEATURES Subtropical plants; woodland garden; rhododendrons; azaleas; biggest *Larix gmelinii* in the British Isles

One of the best rhododendron gardens in the British Isles, and only 50 years old. Mainly planted by Sir James Horlick with advice from Jim Russell. The collection of large-leaved Himalayan rhododendrons is breathtaking.

Achnacloich

Connel, Oban PA37 1PR
☎ 01631 710221   📠 01631 710796

OWNER Mrs J Nelson

LOCATION On A85, 3 miles east of Connel

OPEN 10 am – 6 pm; daily; 24 March to 31 October

ADMISSION Adults £1.50; OAPs £1; Children Free

FACILITIES Parking; dogs permitted; loos; plants for sale

FEATURES Rhododendrons and azaleas; woodland garden

A substantial woodland garden made in three stages. First there were the Victorian conifers, which have grown to great heights. Then came the large-scale plantings of rhododendrons, particularly the Triflorum series which have begun to naturalise. The latest stage has been the creation of a plantsman's garden using the tender shrubs and trees which flourish on the west coast on Argyll. Some of the embothriums are taller than the native oaks.

An Cala

Isle of Seil PA34 4RF
☎ & 📠 01852 300237

OWNER Mr & Mrs T Downie

LOCATION In village of Easdale

OPEN 10 am – 6 pm; daily; April to October

ADMISSION £1

FACILITIES Parking; dogs permitted

FEATURES Bog garden; rock garden; new rockery planted entirely with alpine rhododendrons (1996)

Sheltered garden on the wild west coast, with a natural rock garden and several streams which have been dammed and planted with moisture-loving species. The result is a garden of great lushness.

Angus Garden

Barguillean, Taynuilt PA35 1HY
☎ 018662 333   📠 018662 652

OWNER Sam Macdonald

LOCATION Turn south off A85 at Taynuilt: 3 miles on right

OPEN 9 am – dusk; daily; 1 March to 31 October

ADMISSION Adults £1.50; Children Free

FACILITIES Parking; dogs permitted; Barguillean Nursery adjoins the garden

FEATURES Rhododendrons and azaleas; woodland garden

This young garden in a beautiful setting on the shores of Loch Angus has a particularly fine collection of modern rhododendrons in light oak woodland. It doubles up as a test ground for new hybrids introduced from USA by the adjacent Barguillean Nurseries. There are plans for a substantial expansion of the gardens to create more summer and autumn interest. Rather short on labels, but a garden to watch.

Ardanaiseig Hotel Garden
Ardanaiseig, Kilchrenan, by Taynuilt PA35 1HE
☎ 01866 833333   [FAX] 01866 833222

OWNER   Bennie Gray
LOCATION   On Loch Awe, 4 miles up from Kilchrenan
OPEN   9 am – 9 pm, or dusk if earlier; daily; all year
ADMISSION   Adults £2; Children Free
FACILITIES   Parking; dogs permitted; loos; hotel open to garden visitors
FEATURES   Bluebells; herbaceous borders; daffodils; rhododendrons and azaleas; woodland garden; maples; magnolias

A fine woodland garden with an important collection of rhododendrons and azaleas in a stunning position on a promontory. The hotel is famous for its Good Food.

Ardchattan Priory
Connel, Oban PA37 1RQ
☎ 01631 750274
LOCATION   5 miles east of Connel Bridge, on the north shore of Loch Etive
OPEN   9 am – 6 pm; daily; 1 April to 31 October
ADMISSION   Adults £1; Children Free
FACILITIES   Parking; dogs permitted; loos; access for the disabled; plants for sale; craft shop; light lunches & teas daily 11 am – 6 pm
FEATURES   Herbaceous borders; daffodils; rhododendrons and azaleas; good collection of Sorbus species; huge Hebe bushes

Best in spring, when daffodils flower in light ornamental woodland, but Ardchattan is also planted for high summer, with an emphasis on roses and herbaceous borders.

Ardkinglas Woodland Garden
Cairndow PA26 8BH
☎ & [FAX] 01499 600263
OWNER   S J Noble Esq
LOCATION   On A83 at Cairndow
OPEN   Daylight hours; daily; all year
ADMISSION   £1.50
FACILITIES   Parking; dogs permitted; loos
FEATURES   Fine conifers; rhododendrons and azaleas; woodland garden; tallest tree in all Europe Abies grandis (63m.), and 7 further UK record trees

Formerly known as Strone Gardens, Ardkinglas is famous for its magnificent conifers. Among the rhododendrons are many hybrids bred by Sir Michael Noble, the late Lord Ardkinglas, when he was Secretary of State for Scotland.

Ardtornish Garden
Lochaline, Morvern by Oban PA34 5XA
☎ 01967 421288   [FAX] 01967 421211
OWNER   Mrs John Raven
LOCATION   2 miles north of Lochaline
OPEN   10 am – 5 pm; daily; 1 April to 31 October (1994 times)
ADMISSION   £2
FACILITIES   Parking; dogs permitted; loos; plants for sale
FEATURES   Bluebells; fine conifers; plantsman's garden; kitchen garden; gunnera; rhododendrons

This is Faith Raven's other garden – see Docwra's Manor in Cambridgeshire – and a complete contrast: 28 acres of rocky hillside full of Edwardian hybrid rhododendrons like 'Pink Pearl' and 'Cynthia'. Mrs Raven has actively improved it with a great range of interesting plants. Remote, but worth every inch of the journey.

Arduaine Garden
Arduaine, by Oban, Argyll PA34 4XQ
☎ & [FAX] 01852 200366
OWNER   The National Trust for Scotland
LOCATION   On A816 between Oban & Lochgilphead
OPEN   9.30 am – sunset; daily; all year
ADMISSION   Adults £2.30; Senior Citizens £1.50; Family £6
FACILITIES   Parking; loos; access for the disabled; no refreshments in the garden, but Loch Melfort Hotel is next door
FEATURES   Subtropical plants; rhododendrons; tallest Nothofagus antarctica (26m.) in the British Isles and 6 further records
NCCPG NATIONAL COLLECTIONS Ampelopsis; Parthenocissus

A luxuriant woodland garden in a sheltered, south-facing valley at the edge of the sea. Stout conifers and 40ft thickets of Griselinia protect the rhodos which two nurserymen planted in the 1970s. Primula denticulata and Narcissus cyclamineus have naturalised in grassy glades. Arduaine is now in excellent condition and handsomely maintained: we can vouch for it.

Bargany Gardens
Bargany Estate Office, Girvan KA26 9QL
☎ 01465 871249   [FAX] 01465 714191
OWNER   John Dalrymple Hamilton
LOCATION   4 miles on left, B734 from Girvan to Dailly
OPEN   10 am – 7 pm; daily; 1 March to 31 October
ADMISSION   Donation
FACILITIES   Parking; dogs permitted; access for the disabled; plants for sale
FEATURES   Daffodils; rhododendrons and azaleas; snowdrops; woodland garden; lily pond

A charming woodland garden with banks of rhododendrons and azaleas around a lily pond. Little known, but undeservedly.

Biggar Park
Biggar ML12 6JS
☎ 01899 221085
OWNER   Captain & Mrs David Barnes
LOCATION   South end of Biggar on A702
OPEN   For SGS, and by appointment
ADMISSION   £2
FACILITIES   Parking; dogs permitted; loos; by arrangement
FEATURES   Herbaceous borders; lake; plantsman's garden; rock garden; old roses; woodland garden; daffodils; fritillaries; Meconopsis

Ten acres of plantsmanship, with drifts of naturalised fritillaries in spring, and deep traditional herbaceous borders in summer when the garden has its open day.

Brodick Castle

Isle of Arran KA27 8HY

☎ 01770 302202   [FAX] 01770 302312

OWNER   The National Trust for Scotland

LOCATION   Ferry from Ardrossan to Brodick, follows signs

OPEN   9.30 am – dusk; daily; all year

ADMISSION   Adults £2.30

FACILITIES   Parking; dogs permitted; loos; facilities for the disabled; plants for sale; NTS shop; tea-rooms open Easter to October

FEATURES   Good collection of trees; herbaceous borders; lake; subtropical plants; interesting for children; candelabra primulas; *Meconopsis*; lilies; four new garden trails; good bedding; tallest *Drimys winteri* (21m.) and *Embothrium coccineum* (20m.) in the British Isles (& 3 further records); several new trails (1995)

NCCPG NATIONAL COLLECTIONS *Rhododendron* (sub-sections Falconera, Grandia and Maddenia)

Ravishing 60-acre rhododendron garden on sloping woodland in a mild wet climate. Good magnolias, camellias, crinodendrons and olearias too, but they are never a match for the rhododendrons, many from collectors' seed (Forrest, Kingdon Ward etc.): a new Plant Hunters' Walk was opened last year.

Colzium Walled Garden

Colzium-Lennox Estate, Stirling Road, Kilsyth G65 0RZ

☎ & [FAX] 01236 823281

OWNER   Cumbernauld & Kilsyth District Council

LOCATION   Signposted from Kilsyth on B803

OPEN   Noon – 7 pm; daily; April to September. Noon – 4 pm; Saturdays & Sundays; October to March

ADMISSION   Free

FACILITIES   Parking; loos; access for the disabled

FEATURES   Trees & shrubs

An up-and-coming young garden, which the Council has developed on an ancient site since 1978. A wide range of plants is grown within the protection of high walls, particularly ornamental trees and shrubs, and the standards of maintenance and labelling are excellent.

Crarae Gardens

Crarae, by Inverary PA32 8YA

☎ 01546 886614

OWNER   The Crarae Garden Charitable Trust

LOCATION   South of Inveraray on A83

OPEN   9 am – 6 pm; daily; Easter to 31 October. Daylight hours; daily; 1 November to Easter

ADMISSION   Adults £2.50; Children £1.50

FACILITIES   Parking; dogs permitted; loos; plants for sale; small shop selling books, china & local crafts; light refreshments

FEATURES   Woodland garden; camellias; rhododendrons; autumn colour; tallest *Acer pensylvanicum* in the British Isles (and twelve further tree records)

NCCPG NATIONAL COLLECTIONS *Nothofagus*

FRIENDS   Major appeal ongoing

Fifty acres of romantic woodland, centred on a steep glen spanned by wooden bridges. The long narrow climb up the glen is a pilgrim's progress for plantsmen, past all manner of exotic plants displayed for effect, but especially large-leaved rhododendrons. At the top, you pass out of the enchanted garden into wild moorland: no other garden offers such catharsis. Best in the morning, and in late May.

Culzean Castle & Country Park

Maybole, Ayrshire KA19 8LE

☎ 01655 760269   [FAX] 01655 760615

OWNER   The National Trust for Scotland

LOCATION   Off A719, west of Maybole & South of Ayr

OPEN   9.30 am – dusk; daily; all year

ADMISSION   Park & Garden only: Adults, £3; Children & Concessions £2

FACILITIES   Parking; dogs permitted; loos; facilities for the disabled; plants for sale; good shop; self-service restaurant; light refreshments in car park

FEATURES   Herbaceous borders; follies and garden buildings; glasshouses and conservatories to visit; herbs; lake; woodland garden; interesting for children; deer park; formal garden; adventure playground; tallest Irish yew *Taxus baccata* 'Fastigiata' (19m.) in the British Isles (plus two further tree records); current holder of the Sandford Award

An important historic landscape, the flagship of the NTS, recently restored and seriously open to the public (400,000 visitors a year). Good trees as well as a Gothic camellia house, an ice house, gazebos and a pagoda.

Finlaystone

Langbank PA14 6TJ

☎ 01475 540 285

OWNER   George Macmillan

LOCATION   On A8, 10 mins west of Glasgow

OPEN   10.30 am – 5 pm; daily; all year

ADMISSION   Adults £2; OAPs & Children £1.20

FACILITIES   Parking; dogs permitted; loos; access for the disabled; gift shop; light meals, 11 am – 5 pm, March – September

FEATURES   Bluebells; daffodils; rhododendrons and azaleas

A traditional west coast garden of woodland walks and rhododendrons which has been transformed by the present owner's imaginative new designs and plantings, including a Celtic paving garden, a 'smelly garden' and a modern folly.

Glasgow Botanic Garden

730 Great Western Road, Glasgow G12 0UE

☎ 0141 334 2422   [FAX] 0141 339 6964

OWNER   Glasgow City Council

LOCATION   On A82 2 miles from city centre

OPEN   Grounds: 7 am – dusk; daily; all year. Glasshouses & Kibble Palace: 10 am – 4.45 pm (4.15 pm in winter); daily; all year. Main range open during afternoon only at weekends

ADMISSION   Free

FACILITIES   Dogs permitted; loos; facilities for the disabled

FEATURES   Good collection of trees; herbaceous borders; fine conifers; glasshouses and conservatories to visit; herbs; lake; rock garden; modern roses; old roses; good topiary; particularly interesting in winter; beautiful glasshouse (the 'Kibble Palace'); systematic beds

NCCPG NATIONAL COLLECTIONS *Begonia*; *Dendrobium*; Dicksoniaceae

FRIENDS Active Friends organisation with lectures, garden visits and a bi-monthly newsletter. Details from the Gardens' office

Most of the elements of the botanic garden are here, including systematic beds and chronological beds, but the glory of Glasgow is the two glasshouses – the Kibble Palace and the Main Range. From tree ferns to palms and from cacti to orchids, the Main Range is an essay in plant types. The Kibble Palace however is divided between geographical areas – South Africa, Australia, China, South America, the Canaries and so on. There is no better place to enjoy a winter's day in Glasgow.

Glenarn
Rhu, Helensburgh G84 8LL
☎ 01436 820493   FAX 0141 21 8450

OWNER Mr & Mrs Michael Thornley
LOCATION Turn up Pier Road at Rhu Marina, first right is Glenarn Road
OPEN Dawn to dusk; daily; 21 March to 21 July
ADMISSION Adults £1.50; Senior Citizens & Children 75p
FACILITIES Dogs permitted; access for the disabled; plants for sale; refreshments may be booked in advance
FEATURES Fine conifers; plantsman's garden; rock garden; rhododendrons; embothriums; new bog garden (1996)

Ten acres of woodland garden, with some rhododendrons dating from Sir Joseph Hooker's Himalayan expedition and others from the 1930s trips of Kingdon Ward and Ludlow and Sheriff. Good hybrids too – the original Gibson plants. But plenty of magnolias, camellias, *Pieris*, and other good plants.

Greenbank Garden
Flenders Road, Clarkston, Glasgow G76 8RB
☎ 0141 639 3281   FAX 0141 616 0550

OWNER The National Trust for Scotland
LOCATION One mile along Mearns Road from Clarkston Toll, take 1st left
OPEN Garden: 9.30 am – sunset; daily; all year
ADMISSION Adults £2.80; Concessions £1.90
FACILITIES Parking; dogs permitted; loos; facilities for the disabled; plants for sale; NTS gift shop; light refreshments & drinks (Easter – October)
FEATURES Herbaceous borders; fruit of special interest; rock garden; woodland garden; garden for the disabled; roses of every kind
FRIENDS Friends of Greenbank organise events throughout the year. The chairman is Mrs Kathy Rice, 23 Langtree Avenue, Glasgow G46 7LJ. Tel: 0141 638 7361

Greenbank is a demonstration garden: it was left to the Trust in 1976 on condition that it was developed as a teaching resource for people with small gardens. The walled garden has therefore been divided into a great number of sections which represent different interests and skills: a rock garden, fruit garden, dried flower plot, raised beds, winter garden, and so on. Does it *work*? Yes, definitely.

Mount Stuart
Isle of Bute PA20 9LR
☎ 01700 503877   FAX 01700 505313

OWNER The Mount Stuart Trust
LOCATION 5 miles south of Rothesay
OPEN 10 am – 5 pm; daily except Tuesdays & Thursdays; 2 May to 12 October. Plus 19, 20, 26 & 27 April
ADMISSION Adults £3; Children £2; Family £8. Group & concession rates available
FACILITIES Parking; loos; facilities for the disabled; plants for sale; tea-room
FEATURES Fine conifers; glasshouses and conservatories to visit; rhododendrons and azaleas; woodland garden

A vast and fascinating garden for a sumptuous house. Its 300 acres include: a Victorian pinetum, recently expanded by a further 100 acres dedicated to RBG Edinburgh's Conifer Conservation Programme; a two-acre rock garden designed by Thomas Mawson and stuffed with rare collected plants; a 'wee' garden of five acres, planted with tender exotics from Australia and New Zealand; and a kitchen garden recently redesigned by Rosemary Verey and planted with David Austin's roses. Add in the relics of an 18th-century landscape, a tropical greenhouse, acres of bluebells and established rhododendrons, and you have the measure of a long and fascinating visit.

Torosay Castle & Gardens
Craignure, Isle of Mull PA65 6AY
☎ 01680 812421   FAX 01680 812470

OWNER Mr C James
LOCATION 1 mile from Craignure on A849 to Iona
OPEN 9 am – 7 pm (dawn – dusk in winter); daily; all year
ADMISSION House (open 27 March to 11 October only) & gardens: Adults £4.50; Concessions £3.50; Children £1.50
FACILITIES Parking; dogs permitted; loos; facilities for the disabled; plants for sale; shop; tea-room (summer only) with light lunches
FEATURES Oriental features; rock garden; garden sculpture; water garden; *Eucalyptus* walk; new conservation plantings with conifers from RBG Edinburgh

The best feature of the gardens at Torosay is the Italian Statue Walk, lined with 19 figures by Antonio Bonazza. The Japanese garden and rock garden add to the sheer variety. The woodland garden is stuffed with interesting specimens: *Eucryphia*, *Embothrium* and *Crinodendron* among many.

The Younger Botanic Garden, Benmore
Dunoon PA23 8QU
☎ 01369 706261   FAX 01369 706369

OWNER Board of Trustees/Royal Botanic Garden, Edinburgh
LOCATION 7 miles north of Dunoon on A815
OPEN 10 am – 6 pm; daily; 15 March to 31 October
ADMISSION Adults £2; Senior Citizens £1.50; Children 50p; Family £4.50
FACILITIES Parking; dogs permitted; loos; facilities for the disabled; plants for sale; gift shop; tea-room
FEATURES Good collection of trees; fine conifers; woodland garden; interesting for children; giant redwood avenue planted

in 1863; rhododendrons; ferns; red squirrels; new Chilean plant collection

Benmore has been an annexe of the Royal Botanic Garden at Edinburgh since 1929. The mild, wet climate makes possible the cultivation of tender plants from lower altitudes of the Sino-Himalaya, Bhutan, Japan and the New World. Benmore is a living textbook of the genus *Rhododendron*. Their background is of conifers planted early in the 19th century, perhaps the best collection in Scotland. But the whole garden is spacious, educational and beautifully maintained.

TAYSIDE

Bell's Cherrybank Gardens
Cherrybank, Perth PH2 0NG
☎ 01738 627330/452317   FAX 01738 452415

OWNER   United Distillers plc
LOCATION   In Perth, on A9
OPEN   9 am – 5 pm; daily; 30 March to 5 October
ADMISSION   Adults £2; OAPs & Children £1
FACILITIES   Parking; loos; facilities for the disabled; heathers for sale; light refreshments & drinks
FEATURES   Heathers
NCCPG NATIONAL COLLECTIONS   *Erica*

18 acres of immaculately maintained show gardens which make good use of water and incorporate some striking modern sculptures. Best known for its collection of heaths and heathers, the most comprehensive in the British Isles (900 varieties).

Branklyn Garden
Dundee Road, Perth PH2 7BB
☎ 01738 633199

OWNER   The National Trust for Scotland
LOCATION   Off Dundee Road, on eastern edge of Perth, ½ mile from Queen's Bridge
OPEN   9.30 am – sunset; daily; 1 March to 31 October
ADMISSION   Adults £2.10; Senior Citizens £1.40
FACILITIES   Parking; loos; access for the disabled; plants for sale; small NTS gift shop
FEATURES   Gravel or scree garden; plantsman's garden; rock garden; rhododendrons; alpines; *Meconopsis grandis* 'Branklyn'
NCCPG NATIONAL COLLECTIONS   *Cassiope; Paeonia*

The apotheosis of Scottish rock gardening, a small suburban garden absolutely stuffed with rare plants in an ideal micro-climate.

Cluny House
by Aberfeldy, Perthshire PH15 2JT
☎ 01887 820795

OWNER   Mr J & Mrs W Mattingley
LOCATION   3½ miles from Aberfeldy, on the Weem to Strathtay Road
OPEN   10 am – 6 pm; daily; March to October
ADMISSION   Adults £2; Children under 16 Free
FACILITIES   Parking; plants for sale

FEATURES   Good collection of trees; plantsman's garden; *Meconopsis*; primulas; cardiocrinums; tallest *Prunus maackii* in the British Isles

A plantsman's garden, largely made in the 1950s by Mrs Mattingley's father, who subscribed to the Ludlow and Sherriff expeditions. Superb rhododendrons and, above all, candelabra primulas – sheets of them from April to July.

Drummond Castle Gardens
Muthill, Crieff PH7 4HZ
☎ 01764 681257   FAX 01764 681550

OWNER   Grimsthorpe & Drummond Castle Trust Ltd
LOCATION   South of Crieff on A822
OPEN   2 pm – 5 pm; daily; 1 May to 31 October (3 August for SGS)
ADMISSION   Adults £3; Senior Citizens £2; Children £1
FACILITIES   Parking; dogs permitted; loos; teas on SGS day
FEATURES   Fruit of special interest; important formal garden

Drummond has probably the most important formal garden in Scotland, laid out c.1830 as a St Andrew's cross, with complex parterres filled with roses, statues, clipped cones, herbaceous plants, gravel and lots more beside. The result is order, shape, structure, mass, profusion and colour.

Edzell Castle
Edzell, Angus DD9 7VE
☎ 01356 648631

OWNER   Historic Scotland
LOCATION   On B966 to Edzell Village, then signed for 1 mile
OPEN   9.30 am – 6 pm, Monday – Saturday; 2 pm – 6 pm, Sundays; 1 April to 30 September. 9.30 am – 4 pm, Monday – Wednesday & Saturdays; 2 pm – 4 pm, Sundays; 1 October to 31 March
ADMISSION   Adults £2; Senior Citizens £1.25; Children & Students 75p (1996 prices)
FACILITIES   Parking; dogs permitted; loos; access for the disabled; plants for sale; shop
FEATURES   Formal garden new herbaceous border (1995)
FRIENDS   Historic Scotland

A 1930s formal garden in the 17th-century style, designed to be seen from the ruined keep. A quincunx, of sorts, with yew bobbles, box edging and roses in the beds. The four main segments have the motto of the Lindsey family DUM SPIRO SPERO cut round their edges in box. Fun, though not a garden to linger in.

Glendoick Gardens
Glendoick, Perth PH2 7NS
☎ 01738 860205   FAX 01738 860630

OWNER   Mr & Mrs Peter A Cox
LOCATION   A90 between Perth & Dundee
OPEN   2 pm – 5 pm; 3, 10, 17, 24 May
ADMISSION   £2
FACILITIES   Parking; loos; famous garden centre attached
FEATURES   Plantsman's garden; woodland garden; rhododendrons; new arboretum in memory of Euan Cox (1995)
NCCPG NATIONAL COLLECTIONS   *Kalmia; Enkianthus*

Everyone knows of the Glendoick nursery, but the garden is even more important. Started by Farrer's friend Euan Cox in the 1920s, it has one of the best collections of plants, especially rhododendron species, forms and hybrids, in the British Isles. More's the pity that it is so seldom open.

Gowranes

Kinnaird, by Inchture PH14 9QY
☎ 01828 686752

OWNER   Professor & Mrs W W Park
LOCATION   Midway between Perth & Dundee, 1½ miles North of A90
OPEN   By appointment only
ADMISSION   £3
FACILITIES   Parking; loos; access for the disabled; refreshments by arrangement
FEATURES   Fine conifers; lake; plantsman's garden; rock garden; woodland garden

A newish plantsman's garden on a steeply sloping site above a burn which has been dammed to create pools and waterfalls. Rhododendrons, camellias, Pieris and similar shrubs in the woodland parts: gunneras and candelabra primulas down among the boggy bits.

House of Dun

Montrose, Angus DD10 9LQ
☎ 01674 810264

OWNER   The National Trust for Scotland
LOCATION   On A395, halfway between Montrose & Brechin
OPEN   10 am – dusk; daily; all year
ADMISSION   Adults £1 (honesty box)
FACILITIES   Parking; loos; facilities for the disabled; plants for sale; NTS shop; tea-room, open with house
FEATURES   Fine conifers; daffodils; fruit of special interest; old roses; woodland garden; ice house; new woodland garden (1997)

The first thing you notice at House of Dun, particularly in winter, is the magnificent line of mature wellingtonias, but there are sheets of spring bulbs, a Victorian rose garden for summer, a border of Nerine bowdenii over 100m. long, and a collection of old fruit trees of interest in autumn.

House of Pitmuies

House of Pitmies, by Forfar, Angus DD8 2SN
☎ 01241 828245

OWNER   Mrs Farquhar Ogilvie
LOCATION   Off A932 Forfar to Arbroath Road
OPEN   10 am – 5 pm; daily; 1 April to 31 October
ADMISSION   £2
FACILITIES   Parking; dogs permitted; loos; access for the disabled; plants for sale; home-raised plants & produce in season
FEATURES   Herbaceous borders; fruit of special interest; glasshouses and conservatories to visit; lake; modern roses; old roses; alpine meadow; ferns; colour schemes; new 'woodland garden' (1996); tallest Ilex aquifolium 'Argenteomarginata' in the British Isles

One of the most beautiful modern gardens in Scotland, and still expanding. Laid out and planted in the Hidcote style, Pitmuies has wonderful shrub roses in mixed plantings, clever colour schemes, and innumerable different gardens within the garden: a delphinium border, cherry walk, an alpine meadow for wild flowers, rhododendrons glades, vast hollies and splendid monkey puzzles inherited from Victorian times. Enchanted and enchanting.

Kinross House

Kinross KY13 7ET

OWNER   Sir David Montgomery Bt
LOCATION   In Kinross
OPEN   10 am – 7 pm; daily; May to September
ADMISSION   Adults £2; Children 50p
FACILITIES   Parking; access for the disabled
FEATURES   Walled garden; beautiful situation

Kinross is the most beautiful house in Scotland, with extensive views across Loch Leven. It is approached along a magnificent avenue of lime trees. The elegant walled garden has herbaceous borders and roses and, above all, a 17th-century sense of proportion.

Scone Palace

Perth PH12 6BD
☎ 01738 552300   📠 01738 552588

OWNER   The Earl of Mansfield
LOCATION   Signed from A93
OPEN   9.30 am – 5 pm; daily; 28 March to 13 October
ADMISSION   Adults £2.50; Children £1.40
FACILITIES   Parking; dogs permitted; loos; facilities for the disabled; gift shop; restaurant in old kitchens; self-service coffee-shop
FEATURES   Fine conifers; daffodils; rhododendrons and azaleas; tallest Tilia platyphyllos (37m.) in the British Isles, and 4 further record trees

Famous for its pinetum and for the Douglas firs (Pseudotsuga menziesii) grown from original seed sent back by their discoverer David Douglas, who was born on the estate here.

University of Dundee Botanic Garden

Riverside Drive, Dundee DD2 1QH
☎ 01382 566939   📠 01382 640574

OWNER   University of Dundee
LOCATION   Signposted from Riverside Drive (A85), near its junction with Perth Road
OPEN   10 am – 4.30 pm (3.30 pm from 1 November to 29 February); Monday – Saturday; all year. Plus 11 am – 4 pm (3 pm from 1 November to 29 February); Sundays; all year
ADMISSION   Adults £1; Senior Citizens & Children 50p
FACILITIES   Parking; loos; access for the disabled; plants for sale; some small souvenirs for sale; DIY soft drinks
FEATURES   Fine conifers; ecological interest; glasshouses and conservatories to visit; herbs; lake; subtropical plants; drought-resistant plants; carnivorous plants
FRIENDS   Friends: Individual £5, Family £8 per annum minimum. Newsletters, botanical excursions and illustrated lectures

A fine botanic garden which caters well for visitors. As well as historic plant collections, systematic and chronological borders, there are areas which illustrate native plant communities, including both montane and coastal habitats.

NORTHERN IRELAND

CO. DERRY

Guy Wilson Daffodil Garden

University of Ulster, Coleraine BT52 1SA

☎ 01265 44141   [FAX] 01265 40912

OWNER   University of Ulster at Coleraine

LOCATION   Signposted from sports centre, or entry via Portstewart Road

OPEN   Dawn – dusk; daily; all year

ADMISSION   Free

FACILITIES   Parking; loos; facilities for the disabled

FEATURES   Exceptional collection of daffodils; best in second half of April

NCCPG NATIONAL COLLECTIONS   *Narcissus*

The name says it all – this is both a celebration of Guy Wilson as a daffodil breeder and a museum of his hybrids. Drifts of his hybrids, and others of Irish raising, sweep through the university gardens.

CO. DOWN

Castlewellan National Arboretum

Castlewellan Forest Park, Castlewellan BT25 9KG

☎ 013967 78664   [FAX] 013967 71762

OWNER   Department of Agriculture, Forest Services

LOCATION   30 miles south of Belfast, 4 miles west of Newcastle

OPEN   10 am – sunset; daily; all year

ADMISSION   £3 per car

FACILITIES   Parking; dogs permitted; loos; access for the disabled; light refreshments at peak times

FEATURES   Good collection of trees; fine conifers; woodland garden; particularly interesting in winter; autumn colours; embothriums; eucryphias; tallest *Chamaecyparis nootkatensis* 'Lutea' (22m.) in the British Isles, plus 13 other tree records; new 'fragrant garden' around a Lutyensesque tea house

Castlewellan means trees: several record-breakers and many rarities. The heart of the collection is in a huge walled garden, interplanted with rhododendrons and other shrubs. The central path has mixed borders at the top: dwarf rhododendrons are prominent even here. Labelling is good, and the standard of maintenance high. There are plans to make the collections of *Taxus* and *Eucryphia* comprehensive.

Mount Stewart

The National Trust, Mount Stewart Estate, Grey Abbey, Newtownards BT22 2AD

☎ 012477 88636

OWNER   The National Trust

LOCATION   East of Belfast on A20

OPEN   10.30 am – 6 pm; daily; 1 April to 30 September; plus weekends only in October

ADMISSION   Adults £2.70; Children £1.35

FACILITIES   Parking; dogs permitted; loos; facilities for the disabled; souvenir shop; refreshments from 1.30 pm

FEATURES   Good collection of trees; herbaceous borders; follies and garden buildings; lake; old roses; snowdrops; good topiary; vegetables of interest; woodland garden; plantings by Graham Thomas; rare and tender shrubs galore; topiary in Shamrock Garden newly restored (1994)

NCCPG NATIONAL COLLECTIONS   *Phormium*

One of the best gardens in the British Isles and very little known outside Ireland. The formal gardens by the house are utterly original: a Spanish garden, statues of mythical beasts, and the red hand of Ulster set in a shamrock surround. Good plants too: *Rosa gigantea* grows on the house walls, and the herbaceous and woodland plantings are brilliant with colour and variety. Better still is the walk around the lake, where rhododendrons flood the woodlands. They are underplanted in places with *Meconopsis* and candelabra primulas and, at one point, you catch a glimpse of a white stag in a glade. For design, variety, plants and plantings, Mount Stewart is a place of miracles. Allow lots of time for your visit.

Rowallane Garden

Saintfield, Ballynahinch BT24 7LH

☎ 01238 510131   [FAX] 01238 511242

OWNER   The National Trust

LOCATION   One mile south of Saintfield on A7

OPEN   10.30 pm – 6 pm, Monday – Friday; 2 pm – 6 pm, Saturday & Sunday; 1 April to 31 October. 10.30 am – 5 pm; Monday – Friday; 1 November to 31 March

ADMISSION   Adults £2.50 (£1.40 from November to March); Children £1.25; Groups £1.75

FACILITIES   Parking; dogs permitted; loos; facilities for the disabled; National Trust shop; new Information Centre; light refreshments 2 pm – 6 pm May to August & weekends in April & September

FEATURES   Good collection of trees; plantsman's garden; rhododendrons and azaleas; rock garden; snowdrops; good autumn colour; tallest *Cupressus duclouxiana* (14m.) in the British Isles

NCCPG NATIONAL COLLECTIONS   *Penstemon*

52 acres of rhododendrons and azaleas, which started near the house and expanded into the fields beyond as the seedlings came and needed to be planted. No garden can match it on a sunny day in April or May, as you amble from a glade of R. *augustinii* forms to a line of R. *macabeanum* or back through R. *yakushimanum* hybrids.

CO. FERMANAGH

Florence Court

The National Trust, Florence Court, Enniskillen BT92 1DB

☎ 01365 348249   [FAX] 01365 348873

OWNER   The National Trust

LOCATION   8 miles south-west of Enniskillen

OPEN   House: 1 pm – 6 pm; daily except Tuesday; 1 May to 31 August; plus Saturday, Sunday & Bank Holidays in April & September. Grounds: 10 am – 7 pm (4 pm October to March); daily. Closed Christmas Day

ADMISSION Adults £2.80; Children £1.40; Family £7; Groups (12+) £2.50; Garden/Estate £2 per car

FACILITIES Parking; dogs permitted; loos; facilities for the disabled; National Trust shop; light lunches & teas, picnics welcome

FEATURES Good collection of trees; woodland garden; interesting for children; ice-house; water-powered sawmill; current holder of Sandford Award

Classic 18th-century parkland, with some fine trees, notably the original 'Irish Yew' *Taxus baccata* 'Fastigiata' and a beautiful form of weeping beech with a broad curving crown. The sawmill is fun for children.

CO. WICKLOW

Valclusa Gardens & Nursery

Waterfall Road, Enniskerry
☎ 00 353 1 286 9485   FAX 00 353 1 286 1877

OWNER Duncan & Susan Forsythe

LOCATION Signposted from Enniskerry to waterfall

OPEN 11 am – 8 pm; Saturdays, Sundays & Bank Holiday Mondays; April to October. Plus Wednesdays & Fridays in May & June. Groups at other times by appointment

ADMISSION Adults I£2.50; Children Free. Group rates available

FACILITIES Parking; loos; access for the disabled; plants for sale; cream teas

FEATURES Good collection of trees; plantsman's garden; new subtropical planthouse & wildflower meadow (1997)

The garden has a plum position by the famous waterfall. Among its established trees (huge specimens of redwood, embothriums, *Cornus capitata* and a weeping form of *Liriodendron tulipifera*) is a modern plantsman's garden of rhododendrons, grasses, hostas and over 100 geraniums.

EIRE

CO. CARLOW

Altamont Garden

Altamont Garden Trust, Altamont, Tullow
☎ 00 353 503 59128   FAX 00 353 503 59128

OWNER Mrs North

LOCATION Signed from N80 & N81

OPEN 2 pm – 6 pm; Sundays & Bank Holidays; 1 April to 31 October. And by appointment

ADMISSION Adults I£2; Children (under 10) free

FACILITIES Parking; loos; access for the disabled; large garden centre; craft shop; art gallery; home-made teas

FEATURES Lake; rhododendrons and azaleas; woodland garden; cyclamen; new arboretum

Charming and romantic woodland gardens, stretching to nearly 100 acres, and full of huge specimens of rare plants. A place of contemplation and wonder, and very old-world Irish.

CO. CORK

Annes Grove Gardens

Castletownroche, Mallow
☎ 00 353 22 26145

OWNER Patrick Annesley

LOCATION 1 mile north of Castletownroche on N72

OPEN 10 am – 5 pm, Monday – Saturday; 1 pm – 6 pm, Sundays; 17 March to 30 September

ADMISSION Adults I£2.80; Senior Citizens & Students I£1.50; Children I£1

FACILITIES Parking; dogs permitted; loos; plants for sale; lunches & teas by arrangement for groups

FEATURES Herbaceous borders; plantsman's garden; woodland garden; rhododendrons from wild seeds; rare trees; tallest *Azara microphylla* (11m) in the British Isles

Annes Grove has long been famous for its 30-acre garden, begun in 1907: 'Robinsonian' is the word most often used to describe it. The walled garden is a flower garden, with a 17th-century mount and a Victorian Gothic summer house on top. The river garden is lushly wild with lysichiton, gunnera and candelabra primulas around the pools. In the glen garden lies a wonderfully dense collection of rhododendrons and azaleas, many from Kingdon Ward's seed.

Ballymaloe Cookery School Garden

Ballymaloe, Shanagarry
☎ 00 353 21 646785   FAX 00 353 21 646909

OWNER Tim & Darina Allen

LOCATION Ballymaloe, signposted from Castlemartyr & Shanagarry

OPEN 9 am – 6 pm; daily; 1 April to 31 October

ADMISSION I£3

FACILITIES Parking; loos

FEATURES Herbaceous borders; fruit and vegetables of special interest; old roses; magnificent formal parterres for herbs

The garden attached to the famous Ballymaloe cookery school is full of unusual fruit, vegetables and herbs. Seldom is a functional garden so stylishly designed and planted, or so extensive.

Creagh Gardens

Skibbereen
☎ & FAX 00 353 28 22121

OWNER Gwendoline Harold-Barry Trust

LOCATION 4 miles from Skibbereen on the Baltimore road

OPEN 10 am – 6 pm; daily; all year

ADMISSION Adults I£3; Children I£1.50

FACILITIES Parking; loos; access for the disabled; refreshments for groups by arrangement

FEATURES Camellias; pond; rhododendrons and azaleas; subtropical plants; woodland garden; serpentine mill pond; traditional organic walled garden

Twenty acres of exotic woodland on the edge of a sea estuary and lushly planted by the late Peter & Gwendoline Harold-Barry in the style of a Douanier Rousseau painting. Wildly wonderful.

Fota
Fota Island, Carrigtwohill

☎ 00 353 21 812728   [FAX] 00 353 21 270244

OWNER   Fota Trust Company Ltd

LOCATION   9 miles from Cork city, off Cobh road

OPEN   10 am – 6 pm (11 am – 6 pm on Sundays); 2 April to 31 October

ADMISSION   Cars I£1; Pedestrians free of charge

FACILITIES   Parking; dogs permitted; loos; facilities for the disabled

FEATURES   Good collection of trees; fine conifers; ecological interest; lake; woodland garden; interesting for children; wildlife park; tallest Italian cypress *Cupressus sempervirens* (25m.) in the British Isles, plus 18 other record trees

Fota has a handsome formal garden and walled garden, now undergoing restoration, but is famous above all for its trees. As well as a fine collection of Victorian conifers (huge redwoods and wellingtonias), there are flowering mimosas, a wonderful *Cornus capitata* and such tender trees as the Canary Islands palm *Phoenix canariensis*.

Hillside
Annmount, Glounthane

☎ 00 353 21 353119

OWNER   Mrs Mary Byrne

LOCATION   From Cork, turn left at Glounthane Church, up hill, under bridge, 100 yards on right

OPEN   11 am – 5.30 pm; daily; 7 – 16 June. And by appointment throughout the summer

ADMISSION   I£3

FACILITIES   Plants for sale

FEATURES   Alpines; plantsman's garden; rhododendrons and azaleas

Intensely cultivated garden in a setting of mature trees and rhododendrons, but burgeoning with alpines in every part – stone troughs, a scree bed and gravel areas.

CO. DONEGAL

Ardnamona
Lough Eske

☎ 00 353 73 22650   [FAX] 00 353 73 22819

OWNER   Mr & Mrs Kieran Clarke

LOCATION   On Lough Eske, 5 miles north-east of Donegal

OPEN   Daily; all; by prior appointment

ADMISSION   I£2

FACILITIES   Parking; dogs permitted; bed & breakfast offered

FEATURES   Fine conifers; lake; woodland garden; ancient rhododendrons

A wilderness of huge rhododendrons, some as much as 60ft high, like a Himalayan forest, now taken in hand, cleared and revitalised with the aid of sixteen young people on a youth employment scheme. They have already made a big impact on the 40 acres of *Rhododendron ponticum*.

Glenveagh Castle
Churchill, Letterkenny

☎ 00 353 74 37040   [FAX] 00 353 74 37072

OWNER   Minister for Arts, Culture & the Gaeltacht

LOCATION   14 miles north-west of Letterkenny on R251

OPEN   10 am – 6 pm (7 pm on Sundays, June – August); 29 March to 2 November. Garden tours 2 pm (arrive 1.15 pm) on Tuesdays & Thursdays in July & August. Groups (20+) by appointment

ADMISSION   Adults I£2; Senior Citizens I£1.50; Students I£1

FACILITIES   Parking; loos; access for the disabled; restaurant at visitor centre; tea-room at castle

FEATURES   Good collection of trees; herbaceous borders; fruit of special interest; glasshouses and conservatories to visit; plantsman's garden; old roses; garden sculpture; subtropical plants

NCCPG NATIONAL COLLECTIONS *Pieris*

Glenveagh was built for its view down the rocky slopes of Lough Veagh, and part of the gardens is known as the View Garden. Lanning Roper laid out a formal Italianate courtyard garden. Jim Russell advised on planting. There are wonderful borders and conservatories as well as rhododendrons and camellias. The unusual shrubs are magnificent: tree-like griselinias and *Michelia doltsopa*, for instance.

CO. DUBLIN

Ardgillan Park
Balbriggan

☎ 00 353 1 849 1200

OWNER   Fingal County Council

LOCATION   Coast road between Skerries and Balbriggan

OPEN   10 am – 5 pm; daily; all year

ADMISSION   Free

FACILITIES   Parking; loos; facilities for the disabled; refreshments

FEATURES   Herbaceous borders; follies and garden buildings; fruit of special interest; herbs; rock garden; modern roses; old roses; ice house; 200-year-old yew walk; restored Victorian glasshouse in rose garden

Ardgillan was all but lost in the troubles, but restored ten years ago by the Council as a public amenity. A new rose garden and herbaceous borders have been added. The four-acre walled garden is being developed too – it has a herb garden now and fruit trees grown against the walls.

Dillon Garden
Ranelagh, Dublin 6

☎ 00 353 1 4971308   [FAX] 00 353 1 4971308

OWNER   Helen & Val Dillon

LOCATION   Jct of Sandford Road and Marlborough Road

OPEN   2 pm – 6 pm; daily; March, July & August. Plus Sundays, April to June, & September. Groups by appointment

ADMISSION   Adults I£3; Senior citizens I£2

FACILITIES   Loos; access for the disabled; plants for sale

FEATURES   Herbaceous borders; glasshouses and conservatories to visit; plantsman's garden; front garden replanted
(1996); raised beds

This much acclaimed plantsman's garden offers a fantastic
range of rarities, from snowdrops and hellebores in spring, to
tropaeolums in autumn. Unlike some collectors' gardens, this
is immaculately maintained and beautifully designed as a series
of garden rooms.

Fairfield Lodge
Monkstown Avenue, Monkstown
☎ & FAX 00 353 1 2803912

OWNER   John Bourke
LOCATION   In Monkstown village
OPEN   2 pm – 6 pm; Sundays, Wednesdays & Bank Holi-
days; 1 May to 30 September. And by appointment
ADMISSION   Adults: I£2.50
FACILITIES   Parking; loos; plants for sale; refreshment
FEATURES   Herbaceous borders; climbing roses; old roses;
colour combinations

A small town garden, made to appear much larger by division
into a series of outdoor rooms. Formal design, informal planting
and clever colour combinations: a modern classic.

Fernhill
Sandyford
☎ 00 353 1 295 6000

OWNER   Mrs Sally Walker
LOCATION   7 miles south of central Dublin on the Enniskerry
Road
OPEN   11 am – 5 pm (2 pm – 6 pm on Sundays); Tuesday –
Sunday (& Bank Holidays); 1 March to 30 November
ADMISSION   Adults I£2.50; Senior Citizens I£1.50; Children
I£1
FACILITIES   Parking; loos
FEATURES   Good collection of trees; herbaceous borders;
rock garden; woodland garden; sculpture exhibitions; rhodo-
dendrons

A popular garden on the outskirts of Dublin, with a good
collection of rhododendrons and other woodland plants and
some magnificent trees 150 years old. Steep woodland walks
and an excellent nursery thrown in.

National Botanic Gardens, Dublin
Glasnevin, Dublin 9
☎ 00 353 1 8374388   FAX 00 353 1 8360080

OWNER   Office of Public Works
LOCATION   1 mile north of Dublin near Glasnevin cemetery
OPEN   9 am – 6 pm (4.30 in winter); daily except 25 December. Open at 11 am on Sundays
ADMISSION   Free
FACILITIES   Loos; facilities for the disabled; refreshments by
arrangement
FEATURES   Good collection of trees; herbaceous borders; fine
conifers; ecological interest; fruit of special interest; glasshouses and conservatories to visit; lake; plantsman's garden;
rock garden; old roses; subtropical plants; particularly interesting in winter; carpet-bedding; fern house; tallest variegated

Plane tree *Platanus* × *hispanica* 'Suttneri' (21m.) in the
British Isles, plus 25 further tree records
NCCPG NATIONAL COLLECTIONS *Garrya*;   *Potentilla
fruticosa*

Glasnevin garden greets you with beautiful old-fashioned summer bedding and a bed of *Rosa chinensis* 'Parson's Pink',
known here as 'The Last Rose of Summer'. Very much a
botanic garden in the old tradition: public education and
amenity hand in hand. Richard Turner's elegant curvilinear
range of glasshouses, built in 1847, has just been restored
(1995). Interesting plant collections and some good trees, most
notably a weeping Atlantic cedar: allow a full day to do its 48
acres justice.

Primrose Hill
Primrose Lane, Lucan
☎ 00 353 6280373

OWNER   Robin & Cicely Hall
LOCATION   Lucan village, at top of Primrose Lane, through
black iron gates
OPEN   2 pm – 6 pm; daily; July & August. And by appointment
ADMISSION   I£3
FACILITIES   Parking; loos; plants for sale
FEATURES   Herbaceous borders; plantsman's garden; snow-
drops

Four acres of intensive plantsmanship, particularly interesting
for its rare forms of herbaceous plants and its snowdrops. The
planting continues, and includes a small arboretum.

Talbot Botanic Gardens
Malahide Castle, Malahide
☎ 00 353 1 8462456   FAX 00 353 1 8462456

OWNER   Fingal County Council
LOCATION   10 miles north of Dublin on Malahide Road
OPEN   2 pm – 5 pm (or by appointment); daily; 1 May to
30 September
ADMISSION   I£2 (1996)
FACILITIES   Parking; loos; facilities for the disabled; souvenir
shop and refreshments in castle
FEATURES   Good collection of trees; fine conifers; plantsman's
garden; woodland garden; Tasmanian plants; new scree bed
planted (1994); old Victorian glasshouse 'Messenger' in walled
garden (1994)
NCCPG NATIONAL COLLECTIONS *Olearia*

The garden at Malahide was the work of Milo Talbot, a
passionate amateur botanist with a particular interest in Tasmanian flowers. He built up a collection of 5,000 different taxa
and, since the soil is limey, all are calcicole. Best visited on
Wednesday afternoons when guided tours are offered of the
walled garden (not otherwise open).

Trinity College Botanic Garden
Palmerston Park, Dartry, Dublin 6
☎ 00 353 1 4972070   FAX 00 353 1 6081147

OWNER   Trinity College
LOCATION   3 miles south of city centre, near Ranelagh, opposite Municipal Park
OPEN   9 am – 5 pm; Monday – Friday; by prior arrangement
only

ADMISSION Free
FACILITIES Loos
FEATURES Good collection of trees; herbaceous borders; ecological interest; glasshouses and conservatories to visit; gravel or scree garden; rock garden; old roses; woodland garden

A charming old-fashioned botanic garden, full interesting plants, including a collection of Irish natives.

CO. KERRY

Derreen
Lauragh, Killarney
☎ 00 353 64 83103

OWNER The Hon David Bigham
LOCATION 15 miles from Kenmare on the Castletown Road
OPEN 11 am – 6 pm; daily; 1 April to 1 October
ADMISSION Adults I£2.50; Children I£1
FACILITIES Parking; dogs permitted; loos; facilities for the disabled; tea-room
FEATURES Rock garden; subtropical plants; woodland garden; tree ferns; rhododendrons; natural rock garden

Derreen is quite extraordinary. The rocky outcrops come right to the front door, but the fast lush growth of its trees and shrubs is boundless. Tree ferns *Dicksonia antarctica* and myrtles *Myrtus communis* have gone native, and seed themselves everywhere. Moss, lichen and ferns abound. Large-leaved rhododendrons grow to great heights. Wonderful on a sunny day in late April.

Muckross House & Gardens
Muckross, Killarney
☎ 00 353 64 31440   [FAX] 00 353 64 33926

OWNER Office of Public Works
LOCATION 4 miles south of Killarney on N71
OPEN Dawn – dusk; daily; all year except one week at Christmas
ADMISSION Free
FACILITIES Parking; dogs permitted; loos; facilities for the disabled; lunches, hot & cold snacks daily
FEATURES Good collection of trees; fine conifers; lake; rock garden; woodland garden; rhododendrons; azaleas; good new collection of *Daboecia* (1994); splendid new guide book (1995)

Killarney National Park provides a most beautiful setting for the gardens of Muckross House. There are a young arboretum (25 acres and now fully open to visitors) and some enormous old rhododendrons, but the native woodland is of Scots pines and arbutus trees and, even more exciting for a garden-visitor, the rock garden is a natural one, of carboniferous limestone. Well maintained.

CO. KILDARE

Coolcarrigan Gardens
Coolcarrigan, Naas
☎ 00 353 45 863512   [FAX] 00 353 45 8641400

OWNER John Wilson-Wright

LOCATION 12 miles north of Naas
OPEN By appointment only, from April to August
ADMISSION I£3
FACILITIES Parking; loos; access for the disabled; plants for sale; refreshments by arrangement
FEATURES Good collection of trees; bluebells; herbaceous borders; daffodils; lake; plantsman's garden; rhododendrons and azaleas; rock garden; snowdrops

This garden owes everything to a gale which knocked the heart out of the established plantings in 1974. Harold Hillier advised on the replanting and the result is one of the best modern collections of trees and shrubs in Ireland. The owners, keen plantsmen, have added late summer borders and a rock garden.

Japanese Gardens
Tully, Kildare Town
☎ 00 353 45 21617   [FAX] 00 353 45 22129

OWNER Irish National Stud
LOCATION Signposted in Kildare
OPEN 9.30 am – 6 pm; daily; 12 February to 12 November
ADMISSION I£5 Adults; I£3 Senior Citizens; I£2 Children; Family I£10
FACILITIES Parking; loos; plants for sale; souvenir shop; light refreshments
FEATURES Famous Japanese garden

The garden is a sequence which symbolises Man's journey through life. It was made for Lord Wavertree by Japanese gardeners in the early years of this century.

Lodge Park Walled Garden
Straffan
☎ 00 353 1 628 8412   [FAX] 00 353 1 627 3477

OWNER Mr & Mrs Robert Guinness
LOCATION Follow signpost to Steam Museum Straffan from Maynooth & Kill
OPEN 2 pm – 6 pm; Tuesday – Friday (plus Sunday in June/July); June to August
ADMISSION I£2
FACILITIES Parking; loos; access for the disabled; plants for sale; gift shop at Museum
FEATURES Herbaceous borders; modern roses

An 18th-century walled garden planted for the owners' use and pleasure, with everything from fruit and vegetables to sweet peas and roses. The Victorian greenhouse is being restored this year.

CO. KILKENNY

Kilfane Glen & Waterfall
Thomastown
☎ 00 353 56 24558   [FAX] 00 353 56 27491

OWNER Nicholas & Susan Mosse
LOCATION Off N9, 2 miles north of Thomastown
OPEN 2 pm – 6 pm; Tuesday – Sunday; 11 May to 15 September
ADMISSION Adults I£3; Children I£2; Family I£9
FACILITIES Parking; loos; plants for sale; teas on Sundays, and daily in August

FEATURES   Bluebells; follies and garden buildings; woodland garden

A romantic landscape garden laid out in the 1790s and vigorously restored by the present owners. Sit in the tiny *cottage ornée*, admire the exquisite form of the waterfall across the ravine, and dream of Rousseau.

CO. LAOIS

Gash Gardens
Gash, Castletown, Portlaoise
☎ 00 353 502 32247

OWNER   Noel Kennan
LOCATION   ½ mile from main Dublin-Limerick road
OPEN   10 am – 5 pm; daily; 1 May to 30 September
ADMISSION   I£2.50. Group rates by appointment. Small children discouraged
FACILITIES   Parking; loos; Nursery at entrance
FEATURES   Plantsman's garden; rhododendrons and azaleas; rock garden; old roses

Young award-winning plantsman's garden, full of unusual plants and maintained to very high standard. Four acres, on either side of the River Nore, with streams and other water features.

Heywood Gardens
Ballinakill
☎ 00 353 502 33563

OWNER   Office of Public Works
LOCATION   In grounds of Ballinakill College
OPEN   Dawn – dusk; daily; all year
ADMISSION   Free
FACILITIES   Parking
FEATURES   Planted by Gertrude Jekyll; lake; designed by Lutyens; woodland garden

A ravishing garden, originally designed by Lutyens and planted by Jekyll, which was taken into State care late in 1993 and is in the middle of careful restoration and replanting. Go now, to see what an Edwardian garden looked like when newly made.

CO. LIMERICK

Ballynacourty
Ballysteen
☎ 00 353 61 396409   FAX 00 353 61 396733

OWNER   George & Michelina Stacpoole
LOCATION   3 miles from Askeaton, on River Shannon
OPEN   By appointment
ADMISSION   I£3
FACILITIES   Parking; loos; access for the disabled; refreshments by arrangement
FEATURES   Herbaceous borders; old roses

A fine modern family garden: four densely planted acres won from open farmland. Interesting, too, for its selection of lime-tolerant trees and shrubs.

Glin Castle
Glin
☎ 00 353 68 34173   FAX 00 353 68 34364

OWNER   Desmond Fitzgerald, Knight of Glin
LOCATION   On N69, 32 miles west of Limerick
OPEN   10 am – noon & 2 pm – 4 pm; daily; 1 May to 30 June. Groups by appointment. Guided tours every half-hour
ADMISSION   Adults I£3; Groups I£2; Children I£1
FACILITIES   Parking; loos; facilities for the disabled; gate shop
FEATURES   Bluebells; camellias; daffodils; rhododendrons and azaleas; subtropical plants; vegetables of interest; new woodland walk (1996); new grotto & shell-house (1997)

Simple formal gardens run down towards the park and merge with the surrounding woodland. Not a great garden but, taken with the gothicised castle and magnificent position on the Shannon estuary, a place of rare enchantment.

CO. MEATH

Butterstream
Kildalkey Road, Trim
☎ 00 353 46 36017   FAX 00 353 46 31702

OWNER   Jim Reynolds
LOCATION   Outskirts of Trim on Kildalkey Road
OPEN   11 am – 6 pm; daily; 1 April to 30 September
ADMISSION   I£3
FACILITIES   Parking; loos; plants for sale
FEATURES   Herbaceous borders; fruit of special interest; lake; plantsman's garden; modern roses; old roses; colour borders

Ireland's Sissinghurst, only 20 years old, and still expanding. A series of garden rooms (13 at the last count) in the modern style around an old farmhouse. Each is different but connected to the next. They include a green garden, a white garden, a hot-coloured garden, a Roman garden, a pool garden (with Tuscan portico reflected in it), an obelisk garden, and many others. The plants are determined by the soil – heavy, cold, limey clay.

CO. OFFALY

Birr Castle Demesne
Birr
☎ 00 353 509 20336   FAX 00 353 509 21583

OWNER   Earl of Rosse
LOCATION   Rosse Row in Birr, Co. Offaly
OPEN   9 am – 6 pm or dusk; daily; all year
ADMISSION   Adults I£3.50; Children I£1.50
FACILITIES   Parking; dogs permitted; loos; access for the disabled; plants for sale; craft shop; good guide books; morning coffee, lunch & tea at gates
FEATURES   Good collection of trees; herbaceous borders; herbs; lake; plantsman's garden; old roses; good topiary; *Paeonia* 'Anne Rosse'; *Magnolia* 'Anne Rosse'; pretty Victorian conservatory restored in 1994; winner of all-Ireland Property of the Year Award in 1992; tallest *Acer monspessulanum* (15m.) and boxwood *Buxus sempervirens* (12m.) in the British Isles, plus 49 other record species

FRIENDS   Friends of the Birr Castle Demesne organisation: I£18 p.a. or I£33 p.a. for family

The best garden in the Irish Midlands. Birr has 50ha of grounds, a huge collection of trees and shrubs, and a wonderful walled garden with a tunnel down the middle. Many of the plants are grown from original collectors' material: some were collected in the wild by the owner's parents, Michael and Anne Rosse. Birr also has the tallest box hedges in the world. In the grounds is the famous telescope, once the largest in the world, now fully restored (1997) and witness to the polymath abilities of the owner's family over the generations.

CO. WATERFORD

Curraghmore

Portlaw

☎ 00 353 51 387102   FAX 00 353 51 387481

OWNER   The Marquess of Waterford
LOCATION   14 miles west of Waterford: enter by Portlaw gate
OPEN   2 pm – 5 pm; Thursdays & Bank Holidays; Easter to 31 October
ADMISSION   I£2
FACILITIES   Parking; loos; access for the disabled
FEATURES   Good collection of trees; landscaped park

A magnificent estate, with a classical landscape garden, a fine Victorian arboretum, and the pretty baroque shellhouse (1754). Curraghmore deserves to be better known.

Lismore Castle

Lismore

☎ 00 353 58 54424   FAX 00 353 58 54896

OWNER   Lismore Estates
LOCATION   Centre of Lismore
OPEN   1.45 pm – 4.45 pm; daily; 26 April to 14 September
ADMISSION   Adults I£2.50; Children I£1.50
FACILITIES   Parking; dogs permitted; loos
FEATURES   Old roses; woodland garden; magnolias; spring bulbs

Best for the castellated house: the gardens are interesting rather than exceptional, but there is a pretty grove of camellias and a double yew walk planted in 1707. The upper enclosure is even older, a Jacobean survivor. Visit the walled garden for some fine traditional kitchen gardening: the vinery was designed by Paxton.

CO. WESTMEATH

Tullynally Castle Gardens

Castlepollard

☎ 00 353 44 61159   FAX 00 353 44 61856

OWNER   The Hon. Mr & Mrs Thomas Pakenham
LOCATION   Signposted from Castlepollard
OPEN   2 pm – 6 pm; daily; 1 May to 30 September
ADMISSION   Adults I£2.50; Children I£1
FACILITIES   Parking; dogs permitted; loos; access for the disabled; tea-room open mid-June to mid-August

FEATURES   Bluebells; daffodils; lake; woodland garden; grotto; biggest beech tree *Fagus sylvatica* in the British Isles and tallest *Griselinia littoralis* (20m.)

A grand garden for a grandly turreted house. Formal terraces lead down to the park and into the woodland gardens. A fine avenue of centennial Irish yews is the centrepiece of the walled garden. Tom Pakenham wrote the acclaimed *Meetings with Remarkable Trees* (Weidenfeld, 1996. £25), some of whose photographs were taken at Tullynally.

CO. WEXFORD

The John F Kennedy Arboretum

New Ross

☎ 00 353 51 388171   FAX 00 353 51 388172

OWNER   The Office of Public Works
LOCATION   8 miles south of New Ross off R733
OPEN   10 am – 8 pm, 1 May to 31 August; 10 am – 6.30 pm, April and September; 10 am – 5 pm, 1 October to 31 March
ADMISSION   Adults I£2; Senior Citizens I£1.50; Children & Students I£1; Family I£5; Groups (20+) I£1.50
FACILITIES   Parking; dogs permitted; loos; facilities for the disabled; souvenirs; cafeteria for teas/refreshments in summer
FEATURES   Good collection of trees; fine conifers; interesting for children; eight different tree records for the British Isles

A memorial arboretum founded by Irish/American citizens on 623 acres adjoining the Kennedy home town. Thirty years on, the statistics are impressive: 4,500 types of trees and shrubs arranged on 200 plots both taxonomically and by geographical distribution, and planted with artistry. All meticulously labelled. There are picnic areas, viewpoints, signposted walks, a vigorous visitors' centre and plots of experimental forestry.

Johnstown Castle Gardens

Wexford

☎ 00 353 53 42888   FAX 00 353 53 42004

OWNER   TEAGASC (Food & Agriculture Development Authority)
LOCATION   4 miles south-west of Wexford
OPEN   9 am – 5.30 pm; daily; all year except Christmas day
ADMISSION   I£2.80 per car & passengers
FACILITIES   Parking; dogs permitted; loos; access for the disabled; plants for sale; coffee-shop with snacks, July and August only
FEATURES   Fine conifers; glasshouses and conservatories to visit; lake; woodland garden; walled gardens; tallest *Cupressus macrocarpa* (40m.) in the British Isles

50 acres of ornamental grounds with good trees, tall cordylines, three lakes and the Irish Agricultural Museum.

Ram House Garden

Coolgreany, Gorey

☎ 00 353 402 37238   FAX 00 353 402 31205

OWNER   Godfrey & Lolo Stevens
LOCATION   N11 to Inch and turn inland 1½ miles to Coolgreany
OPEN   2.30 pm – 6 pm; Saturdays & Sundays; Easter to 14 September. Plus 5 pm – 8 pm; Fridays; 1 June to 31 August

ADMISSION   I£2.50

FACILITIES   Parking; loos; paintings for sale; seeds for sale; tea-room

FEATURES   Herbaceous borders; pond; climbing roses; woodland garden; water garden; new gazebo (1995)

Two acres laid out in the modern style as a series of garden rooms, full of good plants and clever plantings. Utterly charming and forever expanding and improving.

Mount Usher Gardens
Ashford

☎ 00 353 404 40205   FAX 00 353 404 40116

OWNER   Mrs Madelaine Jay

LOCATION   Ashford, 30 miles south of Dublin on the N11

OPEN   10.30 am – 6 pm; daily; 14 March to 2 November

ADMISSION   Adults I£3; Senior Citizens & Children I£2.50; Groups (20+) I£2.50 & I£2 respectively. Guided tours for groups available

FACILITIES   Parking; loos; access for the disabled; courtyard shops with pottery, books, furniture, etc.; tea-room with home-baked food

FEATURES   Good collection of trees; fine conifers; plants-man's garden; subtropical plants; woodland garden; spring bulbs; pretty bridges across the river; tallest Cornus capitata (18m.) in the British Isles, plus 28 other record tree species

20 acres of garden with the River Vartry through the middle, crowded with unusual trees and shrubs – 5000 different species, some very rare. The self-sown Pinus montezumae are justly famous. Good herbaceous plants too, and lilies in July. A truly remarkable plantsman's garden made by four generations of Walpoles 1868–1980.

National Garden Exhibition Centre
Kilquade, Kilpedder

☎ 00 353 1 2819890   FAX 00 353 1 2810359

OWNER   Tim & Suzanne Wallis

LOCATION   7 miles from Bray

OPEN   10 am – 6 pm (1 pm – 6 pm on Sunday); daily; all year. Guided tours available in summer

ADMISSION   Adults I£2.50; Senior Citizens I£2; Groups (10+) I£2

FACILITIES   Parking; loos; garden centre; teas & drinks

Permanent exhibition of contemporary styles attached to a big nursery and garden centre. Seventeen linked but distinct gardens: the Herb Garden; the Geometric Garden; the Contemplative Garden; the Seaside Garden; the 'Pythagoras at Play' Garden; and so on. Each was made by a different designer and construction team. The best of modern Irish design for small gardens.

Powerscourt Gardens
Powerscourt Estate, Enniskerry

☎ 00 353 1 2867676   FAX 00 353 1 2863561

OWNER   Powerscourt Estate

LOCATION   12 miles south of Dublin off N11

OPEN   9.30 am – 5.30 pm (10.30 am – dusk in winter); daily; all year

ADMISSION   Adults I£3; Students & Senior Citizens I£2.50; Children I£2

FACILITIES   Parking; dogs permitted; loos; access for the disabled; plants for sale; garden centre; tea-rooms with light lunches

FEATURES   Good collection of trees; fine conifers; lake; oriental features; garden sculpture; woodland garden; interesting for children; 'pepper pot' folly re-opened (1996); tallest Abies spectabilis (32m.) in the British Isles, plus 10 other record tree specimens

Powerscourt is a wonderful mixture of awesome grandeur and sheer fun. It is also extremely well organised for visitors. The main Italianate garden, a stately 1860s staircase down to a lake, has Great Sugarloaf Mountain as an off-centre backdrop. It is lined with bedding plants, statues and urns (look out for the sulky cherubs). To one side is the Japanese garden – not strongly Japanese – but full of twists and hummocks and scarlet paintwork. In the arboretum, Alan Mitchell designed a tree trail. Powerscourt is busy in summer, but you can escape into solitude along the avenue of monkey puzzles. The house has been restored and will open for the first time this year.

29

Garden Features

Graham Thomas

Graham Stuart Thomas' contribution to English gardening is seen everywhere – above all, in his books and in his gardens. We have however never found a list of the gardens on which he worked when Gardens Adviser to the National Trust. This list is an attempt to put the record straight. They are gardens in which to study his work, whether as a restorer and maintainer of other men's plantings or as an original garden designer and plantsman himself.

Beningbrough Hall, North Yorkshire
Benthall Hall, Shropshire
Claremont Gardens, Surrey
Cliveden, Buckinghamshire
The Gardens of the Rose, Hertfordshire
Hidcote Manor Garden, Gloucestershire
Inveresk Lodge Garden, Lothian
Knightshayes Garden, Devon
Little Moreton Hall, Cheshire
Lytes Cary Manor, Somerset
Mottisfont Abbey, Hampshire
Mount Stewart, Co. Down, Northern Ireland
Polesden Lacey, Surrey
Powis Castle, Powys
Sezincote, Gloucestershire
Sheffield Park Garden, East Sussex
Shugborough Hall, Staffordshire
Wallington, Northumberland
Winkworth Arboretum, Surrey

Interesting for Children

Garden visiting is seldom such a pleasure to children as it is for adults: children are quickly bored if a garden has nothing to interest or occupy them. Finding gardens where children can be relied upon not to spoil the outing for older members of the party is difficult. All the gardens we list here pass the boredom test easily, but for widely differing reasons. Some such as Bowood and Wilton House have adventure playgrounds. Others have special facilities, often educational, which explain everything to children in such a way that their interest is aroused. Many of the gardens which have won Sandford awards fit in here, as do such brilliant examples of child-management as Trebah. Some have such exciting plants and design features that the gardens themselves can be made to interest the young.

Alton Towers, Staffordshire
Arbigland, Dumfries & Galloway
Bateman's, East Sussex
Bede's World Herb Garden, Tyne & Wear
Belton House, Lincolnshire
Bicton Park Gardens, Devon
Biddulph Grange Garden, Staffordshire
Birmingham Botanical Gardens & Glasshouses, West Midlands
Blenheim Palace, Oxfordshire
Borde Hill Garden, West Sussex
Boughton House, Northamptonshire
Bowood House, Wiltshire
Brodick Castle, Strathclyde
Brogdale, Kent
Burton Constable Hall, North Yorkshire
Capel Manor, London
Castle Bromwich Hall, West Midlands
Castle Drogo, Devon
Chatsworth, Derbyshire
Cragside, Northumberland
Croxteth Hall & Country Park, Merseyside
Culzean Castle & Country Park, Strathclyde
Dalemain, Cumbria

Dunham Massey, Greater Manchester
Florence Court, Co. Fermanagh, Northern Ireland
Fota, Co. Cork, Eire
Furzey Gardens, Hampshire
Goldney Hall, Gloucestershire
Hampton Court Palace, London
Harewood House, West Yorkshire
Holdenby House Gardens, Northamptonshire
The John F Kennedy Arboretum, Co. Wexford, Eire
Kildrummy Castle Gardens, Grampian
Lackham Country Attractions, Wiltshire
Leeds Castle, Kent
Levens Hall, Cumbria
Longleat House, Wiltshire
Longstock Water Gardens, Hampshire
Margam Park, West Glamorgan
Oxford Botanic Garden, Oxfordshire
Paignton Zoo & Botanical Gardens, Devon
Plantasia, West Glamorgan
Powerscourt Gardens, Co. Wicklow, Eire
Queen's Wood Arboretum & Country Park,
   Hereford & Worcester
RHS Garden, Rosemoor, Devon
Ripley Castle, North Yorkshire
Royal Botanic Garden, Edinburgh, Lothian
Royal Botanic Gardens, Kew, London
Ryton Organic Gardens, Warwickshire
Shugborough Hall, Staffordshire
Sir Harold Hillier Gardens & Arboretum, Hampshire
St Andrews Botanic Garden, Fife
Stapeley Water Gardens Ltd, Cheshire
Stourhead, Wiltshire
The Swiss Garden, Bedfordshire
Syon Park, London
Tapeley Park, Devon
Toddington Manor, Bedfordshire
Trebah Garden Trust, Cornwall
Tresco Abbey, Cornwall
Tudor House Garden, Hampshire
The Valley Gardens, Harrogate, North Yorkshire
Ventnor Botanic Garden, Isle of Wight
Wentworth Castle Gardens, South Yorkshire
Wilton House, Wiltshire
Wimpole Hall, Cambridgeshire
Woburn Abbey, Bedfordshire
Wyld Court Rainforest, Berkshire
The Younger Botanic Garden, Benmore, Strathclyde

Late Opening Hours

Many working people like to visit a garden on summer evenings after they have left their workplace. It is difficult to find good gardens, apart from the best of the public parks: Regent's Park in London is open from dawn to dusk, but is even better at 7 am than 7 pm. But few gardens are more magical than Winkworth Arboretum on a mid May evening, or the great rhododendron collections of Brodick Castle and the Valley Gardens in Windsor Great Park at the same time of the year. Some gardens open late for a few special days each year: it is worth finding out about the evening openings during peak rose time at Mottisfont Abbey, not least because you avoid the afternoon crowds. And if you visit Glenveagh Castle or Inverewe late in the day you may have the gardens entirely to yourself.

Achamore Gardens, Strathclyde
Alton Towers, Staffordshire
Angus Garden, Strathclyde
Ardanaiseig Hotel Garden, Strathclyde
Ardchattan Priory, Strathclyde
Arduaine Garden, Strathclyde
Brodick Castle, Strathclyde
Burrow Farm Gardens, Devon
Canal Gardens, West Yorkshire
Cannizaro Park, London
Castle Ashby Gardens, Northamptonshire
Castlewellan National Arboretum, Co. Down,
   Northern Ireland
Chiswick House, London
Clyne Gardens, West Glamorgan
Crossing House Garden, Cambridgeshire
Culzean Castle & Country Park, Strathclyde
Dartington Hall, Devon
Dawyck Botanic Garden, Borders
Dyffryn Botanic Garden, South Glamorgan
Elvaston Castle County Park, Derbyshire
The Ernest Wilson Memorial Garden,
   Gloucestershire
Glasgow Botanic Garden, Strathclyde
Hampton Court Palace, London
Harlow Carr Botanical Gardens, North Yorkshire
Heale House, Wiltshire
Highdown, West Sussex
The Hollies Park, West Yorkshire
Isabella Plantation, London
Killerton, Devon
Lochalsh Woodland Garden, Highland
Lotherton Hall, West Yorkshire
Malleny House Garden, Lothian

Marwood Hill Gardens, Devon
The Mill Garden, Warwick, Warwickshire
Muckross House & Gardens, Co. Kerry, Eire
Newstead Abbey, Nottinghamshire
Ram House Garden, Co. Wexford, Eire
RHS Garden, Rosemoor, Devon
Royal Botanic Garden, Edinburgh, Lothian
Royal Botanic Gardens, Kew, London
Sheffield Botanical Gardens, South Yorkshire
Somerleyton Hall & Gardens, Suffolk
Stourhead, Wiltshire
Syon Park, London
Temple Newsam Park, West Yorkshire
Torosay Castle & Gardens, Strathclyde
Valclusa Gardens & Nursery, Co. Wicklow
The Valley Gardens, Surrey
Ventnor Botanic Garden, Isle of Wight
Wakehurst Place, West Sussex
Westonbirt Arboretum, Gloucestershire
Winkworth Arboretum, Surrey

Young Gardens

Newly made gardens are a great inspiration to visitors who are starting to make gardens for themselves. The examples we list here are all comparatively young – a few are very new indeed. Some show what plants grow quickly: others reveal the latest ideas on design. The best will motivate you to get going in your own garden.

Bosvigo, Cornwall
Brandy Mount House, Hampshire
Brickwall House & Gardens, East Sussex
Bridgemere Garden World, Cheshire
Bryan's Ground, Hereford & Worcester
Cowley Manor, Gloucestershire
The Dingle (Crundale), Dyfed
East Ruston Old Vicarage, Norfolk
Holme Pierrepoint Hall, Nottinghamshire
Lakeside, Hereford & Worcester
Lamorran House, Cornwall
The Old Vicarage, Wiltshire
Pinewood House, Surrey
RHS Garden, Rosemoor, Devon
Sticky Wicket, Dorset
Stone House Cottage Garden, Hereford &
    Worcester
Thompson's Hill, Wiltshire
White Windows, Hampshire

Seldom Open to the Public

We often find that a garden that we wanted to visit has already had its annual visitors' day. This is a check list for some of the gardens which open seldom. If you have long nurtured the ambition to visit such gardens as Badminton, Shrubland Hall or Munstead Wood, you should look up its open days in the main chapter on gardens, and make a note of the dates when it receives visitors. Then plan your other garden visiting round it.

Abbotswood, Gloucestershire
Badminton, Gloucestershire
Bank House, Lancashire
Barningham Park, Co. Durham
The Beale Arboretum, Hertfordshire
Bolehyde Manor, Wiltshire
Brandy Mount House, Hampshire
Brook Lodge Farm Cottage, Surrey
Chyverton, Cornwall
Cowdray Park, West Sussex
Dam Farm House, Derbyshire
Darley House, Derbyshire
Elsing Hall, Norfolk
Fairfield House, Hampshire
Folly Farm, Berkshire
Glendoick Gardens, Tayside
Great Barfield, Buckinghamshire
Greenways, Oxfordshire
Hardwicke House, Cambridgeshire
The Harris Garden, Berkshire
Hillbarn House, Wiltshire
Lime Close, Oxfordshire
Long Barn, Kent
Longstock Water Gardens, Hampshire
The Manor House, Bledlow, Buckinghamshire
Mottistone Manor, Isle of Wight
Munstead Wood, Surrey
Old Rectory Cottage, Berkshire
The Old Vicarage, Wiltshire
Overbury Court, Hereford & Worcester
Riseholme Hall, Lincolnshire
Shrubland Hall, Suffolk
Stancombe Park, Gloucestershire
Stonehurst, West Sussex
Tirley Garth Trust, Cheshire
Westwell Manor, Oxfordshire
White Windows, Hampshire
Whitfield, Hereford & Worcester
Yew Tree Cottage, West Sussex

Good to Visit in the Summer Gap

It is easy for a garden to look good in May or June, but much more difficult for it to hold the visitor's interest in the dog days of August. Many people take their annual holidays then and are mildly disappointed to discover that there are no camellias, magnolias or rhododendrons in flower at Trengwainton or Caerhays. Some gardens, however, make a point of building up to a climax of colour in late summer.

> Alton Towers, Staffordshire
> Barrington Court, Somerset
> Blickling Hall & Garden, Norfolk
> Bressingham Gardens & Steam Museum, Norfolk
> Bridgemere Garden World, Cheshire
> Cambridge University Botanic Garden,
>   Cambridgeshire
> The Gardens of the Rose, Hertfordshire
> Great Dixter, East Sussex
> Greenways, Oxfordshire
> Hampton Court Palace, London
> Hever Castle, Kent
> Highclere Castle, Hampshire
> Inverewe, Highland
> Kellie Castle, Fife
> Lackham Country Attractions, Wiltshire
> Leith Hall, Grampian
> Logan Botanic Gardens, Dumfries & Galloway
> Longleat House, Wiltshire
> Malleny House Garden, Lothian
> The Manor House, Walton-in-Gordano, Somerset
> Marwood Hill Gardens, Devon
> Old Rectory Cottage, Berkshire
> The Old Vicarage, Wiltshire
> Powis Castle, Powys
> The Priory, Gloucestershire
> RHS Garden, Wisley, Surrey
> The Savill Garden, Surrey
> Sir Harold Hillier Gardens & Arboretum, Hampshire
> Spetchley Park, Hereford & Worcester
> Stone House Cottage Garden, Hereford &
>   Worcester
> Stourton House, Wiltshire
> Tintinhull House, Somerset
> Trelissick Garden, Cornwall
> Tresco Abbey, Cornwall

Underrated – A Personal Choice

We have all visited gardens which were a disappointment. Sometimes, however, we are lucky to tumble on a really smashing garden which no-one seems to know about. Here are some gardens we particularly want to visit again soon, and encourage our readers to do so too. Some are well known, but underrated, while others are little known but undeservedly.

> Athelhampton House & Gardens, Dorset
> The Beale Arboretum, Hertfordshire
> Chenies Manor, Buckinghamshire
> Cottesbrooke Hall, Northamptonshire
> Crowe Hall, Somerset
> East Ruston Old Vicarage, Norfolk
> Fairhaven Gardens Trust, Norfolk
> Galloway House Gardens, Dumfries & Galloway
> Hinton Ampner House, Hampshire
> How Caple Court Gardens, Hereford & Worcester
> Isabella Plantation, London
> Kingston Maurward Gardens, Dorset
> Lower Hall, Shropshire
> Mount Stewart, Co. Down, Northern Ireland
> Parcevall Hall Gardens, North Yorkshire
> Sleightholmedale Lodge, North Yorkshire
> Spetchley Park, Hereford & Worcester
> St Paul's Walden Bury, Hertfordshire
> Stancombe Park, Gloucestershire
> Thorp Perrow Arboretum, North Yorkshire
> Wrest Park, Bedfordshire

Winter Gardens

Sometimes the urge to go visiting gardens in winter is very strong, especially in late winter when the sun is higher in the sky and the first signs of new life appear. There are three types of garden worth visiting in winter. First are those with good glasshouse collections: most botanic gardens are therefore rewarding to explore whatever the season or weather. Second, there are those which have good collections of evergreen trees and shrubs, set off perhaps by the colour of bark and twigs: Bedgebury National Pinetum and Westonbirt Arboretum are both perfect for a brisk winter exploration. Third, there are gardens with a strong floral display in winter, particularly towards the end: such gardens as Great Barfield are thick with hellebores, crocus, *Leucojum* and many other genera, while those in milder regions have camellias, rhododendrons and the first primroses early in the year. Some gardens qualify on all three counts, though they are few.

The Royal Horticultural Society's garden at Wisley is perhaps the best example.

Abbotsbury Sub-Tropical Gardens, Dorset
Bedgebury National Pinetum, Kent
Belsay Hall, Northumberland
Cambridge University Botanic Garden, Cambridgeshire
Canal Gardens, West Yorkshire
Castle Ashby Gardens, Northamptonshire
Castlewellan National Arboretum, Co. Down, Northern Ireland
Cliveden, Buckinghamshire
Dawyck Botanic Garden, Borders
Dunster Castle, Somerset
Elvaston Castle County Park, Derbyshire
Glasgow Botanic Garden, Strathclyde
Great Barfield, Buckinghamshire
The Harris Garden, Berkshire
Hill House Garden, Devon
Killerton, Devon
Marwood Hill Gardens, Devon
Myddelton House Gardens, London
National Botanic Gardens, Dublin, Co. Dublin, Eire
Osterley Park, London
Plantasia, West Glamorgan
RHS Garden, Hyde Hall, Essex
RHS Garden, Rosemoor, Devon
RHS Garden, Wisley, Surrey
Ripley Castle, North Yorkshire
Royal Botanic Garden, Edinburgh, Lothian
Royal Botanic Gardens, Kew, London
The Savill Garden, Surrey
Sheffield Botanical Gardens, South Yorkshire
Sir Harold Hillier Gardens & Arboretum, Hampshire
St Andrews Botanic Garden, Fife
Stapeley Water Gardens Ltd, Cheshire
Stowe Landscape Gardens, Buckinghamshire
Trebah Garden Trust, Cornwall
Tresco Abbey, Cornwall
Ventnor Botanic Garden, Isle of Wight
Waddesdon Manor, Buckinghamshire
Wakehurst Place, West Sussex
Wallington, Northumberland

Gardens – Awards to Gardens

Two schemes for awarding recognition to gardens have started up in recent years. Both are private initiatives and, though quite different in their aims, Holker Hall in Cumbria has had the distinction of winning the Garden of the

Year Award in 1991 while also being a current holder of the Sandford Award.

The Garden of the Year Award was introduced jointly by the Historic Houses Association (HHA) and Christie's in 1984. It is designed to recognise the importance of gardens, either in their own right or as settings for historic houses. It reflects public enjoyment of those privately owned gardens which are open regularly to the public, rather than their horticultural excellence, although many winners can claim that too.

All HHA members and friends of the HHA may vote for any garden which is owned by a member of the HHA, and open regularly to the public. Voting takes place during the course of the year and is never completed until November. Marks are awarded for features of special interest, such as recent restoration work or unusual selections of plants, trees and shrubs. The award carries no cash prize but the resulting publicity is helpful in raising visitor numbers. The award winners since its institution have been:

1984 Heale House, Wiltshire
1985 Hodnet Hall, Shropshire
1986 Newby Hall, North Yorkshire
1987 Arley Hall, Cheshire
1988 Barnsley House, Gloucestershire
1989 Brympton d'Evercy, Somerset
1990 Parham Park, West Sussex
1991 Holker Hall, Cumbria
1992 Forde Abbey, Dorset
1993 Haddon Hall, Derbyshire
1994 Levens Hall, Cumbria
1995 Hever Place, Kent

Details of the 1996 winner will be revealed when the award is presented in spring 1997.

The **Sandford Awards** should be better known. They are given by the Heritage Education Trust to historic properties in recognition of the educational facilities they offer school parties. The Trust maintains that a welcome is not enough: the trip must present an educational opportunity. The awards are a measure of how well adapted a house or garden is to ensuring that visitors get maximum educational value. An award lasts for five years and is then reviewed. It is neither financial nor competitive but always based on properties meeting five educational criteria:

1. Good liaison between the owners and potential school visitors.

2. Imagination applied to developing the educational potential.

3. The design of educational materials and facilities.

4. Encouraging preparation for a visit, managing that visit effectively and offering good follow-up.

5. The use of interpretative facilities to relate the visit to a school curriculum, and to encourage exciting and imaginative work.

The Heritage Education Trust is principally concerned with historic buildings. It follows that a property can get an award even though it does not use its garden for educational purposes. In practice that happens rarely: educational facilities are usually offered both inside and outside the house.

Two or three properties with gardens receive a Sandford Award every year. Current holders include: Blenheim Palace, Oxfordshire; Boughton House, Northamptonshire; Chirk Castle, Clwyd; Crathes Castles, Grampian; Croxteth Hall & Country Park, Merseyside; Dunham Massey, Cheshire; Erdigg Hall, Clwyd; Florence Court, Co. Fermanagh; Harewood House, West Yorkshire; Holdenby House, Northamptonshire; Kingston Lacey, Dorset; Moseley Old Hall, Staffordshire; Norton Priory, Cheshire; Rockingham Castle, Northamptonshire; Shugborough Hall, Staffordshire; Sir Harold Hillier Gardens, Hampshire; Tatton Park, Cheshire; Wightwick Manor, Isle of Wight; Wimpole Hall, Cambridgeshire.

The places which have given thought to the educational needs of visiting children are just as interesting for grown-ups. It saves a great amount of disappointment if everyone can be sure that the place will be well equipped. The presence of a Sandford Award is a guarantee that all manner of educational aids will be available for you to learn more from your visit and thus to enjoy it more fully.

Further details are available from: The Heritage Education Trust, Pickwick, Vicarage Hill, Badby, Daventry, Northamptonshire NN11 3AP. Tel/Fax 01327 77943. Secretary: David Hill.

30

Historic Gardens

During the 1980s, the Historic Buildings and Monuments Commission for England compiled a register of gardens and parks of special historic interest. The aim was to draw attention to the nation's heritage, so that designed landscapes were not overlooked, for example in plans for new development. The register was largely the work of the distinguished garden historian Dr Christopher Thacker. There are three gradings:

Grade I – Parks and gardens which by reason of their historic layout, features and architectural ornaments considered together are of exceptional interest.

Grade II* – Parks and gardens which by reason of their historic layout, features and architectural ornaments considered together are, if not of exceptional interest, nevertheless of great quality.

Grade II – Parks and gardens which by reason of their historic layout, features and architectural ornaments considered together are of special interest.

These gradings reflect the importance of the garden or park concerned in comparison with other gardens or parks in England as a whole. They are not influenced by the presence of a listed building within the limits of a registered garden or park. If there is such a listed building, its grade may not necessarily be the same, since the building and the garden or park are seldom of equal importance. The register introduced no new regulations and had no effect upon existing planning or building controls.

Only gardens and parks with historic features dating from 1939 or earlier were included in the register. Additions since that date were of no account, because the register was only concerned with a garden's historic interest. In practice that rule was sometimes broken in the case of an influential modern garden: Great Dixter and East Lambrook Manor might not have merited Grade I status in 1939. Parks and gardens differ enormously: a public square

or a municipal cemetery may be more important than a good Victorian collection of trees. It has also been suggested that gradings were influenced by the park or garden's actual state and condition.

Much has been achieved by Dr Thacker's able successor Dr Harriet Jordan. New research and fresh evaluations, especially of such Edwardian designers as Thomas Mawson, have led to some upgrades: the Rothschild megagarden at Mentmore Towers in Buckinghamshire was moved from Grade II to Grade II* in October 1987. So was the park which Capability Brown laid out for the first Viscount Palmerston at Broadlands in Hampshire. Some of the new admissions to the register are a direct indication of how perceptions have changed: two designed landscapes which were recently added to the register are the Bestwood and Papplewick Pumping Stations in Nottinghamshire. These were part of the infrastructure of a 19th century water company and their ornamental landscaping was intended in part to encourage members of the public to buy water from them. One or two properties have been downgraded – notably Braxted Park in Essex from Grade I to Grade II* – but none has been dropped from the register even though English Heritage does now take into account the actual state and condition of a park or garden. Early this year, it was announced that English Heritage would carry out a comprehensive upgrade of the Register, with the aim of publishing a fully revised edition by the year 2000.

Many graded parks and gardens are open to the public and appear in the main Gardens section of this book, but many others are in private ownership. The Commission was at pains to emphasise that including a garden in the register did not mean that there was any public right of access, other than along public rights of way. That remains the position today. The register is in forty-six parts, one for each of the 1974 English counties. Copies are available from English Heritage, Fortress House, 23 Savile Row, London W1X 2HE at a price of £3.50 or £4 per county. The information they contain about the individual gardens is very comprehensive. It covers the site; area; dates and designers of key surviving elements; surviving features of the garden or park; and other interesting aspects such as historic associations. There is also a list of published references.

CADW, the Welsh Historic Monuments Commission, has begun a Register of Parks and Gardens of Special Historic Interest in Wales, with aid from ICOMOS. This has been the work of Elisabeth Whittle who wrote the standard modern work on the subject *The Historic Gardens of Wales* (HMSO, 1992). The Register is based on English Heritage's and the criteria for selection and grading are comparable. The Registers for Gwent and Clwyd have already been published and copies are available from CADW at a price of £15 and £20 respectively. We list the names and grades of the parks and gardens of those two counties below. It was intended that the Registers for Gwynedd and Dyfed should be published in 1996, but their issue has been delayed and CADW now hopes that they will be published during the course of this year, closely followed by Glamorgan and Powys.

The basis of protection for historic gardens in Scotland is the *Inventory of Gardens & Designed Landscapes*

in Scotland which was published in four volumes in 1987, although unfortunately not all are still in print. The Inventory lists 275 sites, which are graded in a more specific way than the gardens on the English register, for example according to the value of their horticultural content or historic importance on a scale of 1 to 6. Historic Scotland has begun to extend the Inventory and Caroline Kernan, the historian working on the Inventory, expects to be able to add some further 90 sites. The additions which she has already completed identify and describe the new gardens with exemplary thoroughness. It is regrettable, however, that the work of extension will only be done in central parts of Scotland: it will leave Highland, Borders and parts of Strathclyde and Grampian to be re-assessed at some future date.

There is as yet no Register of Parks and Gardens in Northern Ireland, but one is likely to be started during the course of this year, listing about 120 sites. By way of background, the Northern Ireland Gardens Committee commissioned Belinda Jupp to compile a survey of the province in association with the Institute of Irish Studies at Queen's University, Belfast and the result was published in 1992 as *The Heritage Gardens Survey*. It is an extremely comprehensive list of parks, gardens and demesnes, each with a location, a list of its principal features and a short description.

Avon
Grade I
  Badminton
  Prior Park
Grade II*
  Ashton Court
  Blaise Hamlet
  Clevedon Court
  Dodington House
  Dyrham Park
  Goldney House
  St Catherine's Court
  Tyntesfield
Grade II
  Abbey Cemetery
  Arno's Vale Cemetery
  Barrow Court
  Beckford's Ride
  Blaise Castle
  Brentry House
  Claverton Manor
  Crowe Hall
  Kelston Place
  King's Weston
  Leigh Court
  Newton Park

Oldbury Court
Rayne Thatch
Royal Victoria Park
Stoke Park
Sydney Gardens
Thornbury Castle
Tortworth Park
Warmley House
Widcombe Manor

Bedfordshire
Grade I
  Woburn Abbey
  Wrest Park
Grade II*
  Luton Hoo
  Old Warden House
  Swiss Garden
  Southill Park
Grade II
  Ampthill Park
  Battlesden Place
  Bedford Cemetery
  Bedford Park
  Bushmead Priory
  Chicksands

Flitwick Manor
The Hasells
Hinwick Hall
Hinwick House
Ickwell Bury
The Lodge, Sandy

Berkshire
Grade I
  Windsor Great Park
Grade II*
  Ascot Place
  Bearwood College
  The Deanery, Sonning
  Folly Farm
  Frogmore Gardens
  Inkpen House
  Park Place
  Purley Hall
Grade II
  Aldermaston Court
  Basildon Park
  Benham Park
  Caversham Court
  Caversham Park
  Ditton Park

Donnington Grove
Englefield House
Eton College
Farley Hall
Forbury Garden,
  Reading
Hamstead Marshall
Newbold College
Prospect Place, Reading
Sandleford Priory
South Hill Park
Swallowfield
Wasing Park

Buckinghamshire
Grade I
  Cliveden
  Stowe
  West Wycombe Park
Grade II*
  Ascott
  Bulstrode Park
  Chenies Place
  Chicheley Hall
  Fawley Court
  Hall Barn

Hartwell House
Mentmore Towers
Shardeloes
Tyringham
Waddesdon Manor
Wotton Underwood

Grade II
Berry Hill
Chequers
Claydon
Denhams Place
Dropmore
Gayhurst Court
Halton House
Harleyford
Hughenden Manor
Huntercombe Manor
Langley Park
Latimer Park
Milton's Cottage
Misserden Abbey
Nashdom Abbey
Stoke Poges, Garden of
   Remembrance
Stoke Park
Taplow Court
Wycombe Abbey

Cambridgeshire
Grade I
The Backs
Wimpole Hall
Grade II*
Anglesey Abbey
Botanic Gardens,
   Cambridge
Burghley House
Childerley Hall
Christ's College
Elton Hall
Emmanuel College
King's College
Longstowe Hall
Milton Hall
Pampisford Hall
St John's College
Thorpe Hall
Trinity College
Grade II
Abbots Ripton Hall
Bourn Hall
Chippenham
Croxton Park
Dullingham
Gamlingay
Hamerton
Hatley Park
Hilton Maze
Leighton Bromswold

Hadingley Hall
Pampisford Hall
Peckover House
Queen's College
Sawston Hall
Swaffham Hall
Trinity Hall
Wilbraham Temple

Cheshire
Grade II*
Adlington Hall
Arley Hall
Eaton Hall
Gawsworth Hall
Lyme Park
Tatton Park
Grade II
Cholmondeley Castle
Combermere Abbey
Crewe Hall
Doddington Park
Dorfold Hall
Mellor's Garden
Ness Botanic Gardens
Peover Hall
Rode Hall
Tabley House

Cleveland
Grade II*
Wynyard Park
Grade II
Albert Park
Ward Jackson Park

Cornwall
Grade I
Mount Edgcumbe
Port Eliot
Tresco
Grade II*
Boconnoc
Caerhays Castle
Lanhydrock
Tregothnan
Tregrehan
Trewithen
Grade II
Antony
Carclew
Catchfrench
Chyverton Park
Cotehele
Downes Enys
Glendurgan
Heligan
Lamellen
Lismore

Menabilly
Pencarrow
Penheale
Penjerrick
Prideaux Place
St Michael's Mount
Trebah
Trelissick
Trelowarren
Trengwainton
Trewarthenick
Werrington Park

Cumbria
Grade I
Levens Hall
Grade II*
Appleby Castle
Belle Isle
Dalemain
Holker Hall
Muncaster Castle
Sizergh Castle
Grade II
Askham Hall
Corby Castle
Dallam Tower
Hutton-in-the-Forest
Lowther Castle
The Image Garden,
   Reagill
Rydal Hall
Rydal Mount
Workington Hall

Derbyshire
Grade I
Chatsworth
Haddon Hall
Hardwick Hall
Kedleston Hall
Melbourne Hall
Grade II*
Bolsover Castle
Buxton Pavilion Gardens
Calke Abbey
Derby Arboretum
Elvaston Castle
Heights of Abraham
Renishaw Hall
Swarkstone Hall
Grade II
Ednaston Manor
Locko Park
Sudbury Hall
Sydnope Hall
Thornbridge Hall
Whitworth Institute

Devon
Grade I
Bicton
Endsleigh
Grade II*
Castle Drogo
Castle Hill
Dartington Hall
Killerton
Knighthayes Court
Lindridge
Luscombe Castle
Mamhead
Saltram House
Tapeley Park
Ugbrooke Park
Wood House
Grade II
A la Ronde
Arlington Court
Bridwell
Cadhay
Castle Tor
Coleton Fishacre
Combe House
Flete
Hayne Manor
Langdon Court Hotel
Lindridge
Lupton Park
Overbecks
Oxton House
Plympton House
Powderham Castle
Rockbeare House
Ranston
Saunton Court
Shobrooke Park
Stover Park
Sydenham House
Watcombe Park
Youlston Park

Dorset
Grade I
Abbotsbury Gardens
Athelhampton
Grade II*
Chantmarle
Charborough Park
Compton Acres
Cranborne Manor
Creech Grange
Eastbury
Encombe
Forde Abbey
Kingston Maurward
Mapperton House

Melbury Park
Milton Abbey
Parnham
St Giles' House
Sherborne Castle
Pleasure Gardens,
  Bournemouth
Grade II
Anderson Manor
Beaminster Manor
Boveridge House School
Bridehead
Crichell House
Downe Hall
Kingston Lacy
Lulworth Castle
Minterne
Ranston
Stepleton House
Waterston Manor
Wimborne Rd
  Cemetery,
  Bournemouth

Durham
Grade II*
Raby Castle
Rokeby Park
Grade II
Auckland Castle Park
Bowes Museum
Brancepeth Castle
Burn Hall
The Castle, Castle Eden
Croxdale Hall
Hardwick Park
Lartington Hall
South Park, Darlington

Essex
Grade I
Audley End
Grade II*
Braxted Park
Bridge End Gardens
Copped Hall
Hylands Park
Spains Hall
Thorndon Park
Grade II
Belchamp Hall
Belhus Park
Blake Hall
Boreham House
Colchester Castle Park
Danbury Park
Down Hall
Faulkbourne Hall

Glazenwood
Gosfield Hall
Hatfield Priory
Hill Hall
The House, Harlow
Langleys
Layer Marney Tower
Marsh Lane House
The Maze, Saffron
  Walden
New Hall, Boreham
Quendon Park
Riffhams
St Osyth Priory
Saling Grove
Saling Hall
Shortgrove Park
Terling Place
Thorpe Hall
Warley Place
Weald Park
Water Gardens, Harlow
Wivenhoe House

Gloucestershire
Grade I
Batsford Park
Cirencester Park
Frampton Court
Hidcote Manor
Sezincote
Stancombe Park
Stanway House
Westonbirt Arboretum
Westonbirt House
Grade II*
Abbotswood
Barnsley Park
Berkeley Castle
Cowley Manor
Daylesford House
Highnam Court
Kiftsgate Court
Lypiatt Park
Miserden Park
Painswick House
Rodmarton Manor
Sudeley Castle
Westbury Court
Grade II
Adlestrop Hall
Adlestrop Park
Alderley Grange
Alderley Mount
Barrington Park
Bourton House
Bradley Court
Chavenage House
Clearwell Castle

Dixton Manor
Eyford Park
Flaxley Abbey
Gatcombe Park
Great Rissington Manor
Hatherop Castle
Church House,
  Lechlade
Lodge Park
Nether Lypiatt Manor
Newark Park
Notgrove Manor
Owlpen Manor
St Mary's, Painswick
Pinbury Park
Pittville Park
Sherborne House
Snowshill Manor
Stowell Park
Toddington Manor
Woodchester Park

Greater London
Grade I
Bushy Park
Chelsea Physic Garden
Chiswick House
Greenwick Place
Hampton Court
Hyde Park
Kensington Gardens
Kew Gardens
Regent's Park
Richmond Park
St James' Park
Syon Park
Grade II*
Battersea Park
Bedford Square
Belair
Buckingham Palace
  Gardens
Cannizaro Park
City of London
  Cemetery
Crystal Palace Park
Dulwich Park
Fulham Palace
Gray's Inn
Grovelands
Hall Place
Ham House
Highgate Cemetery
The Hill
Kensal Green Cemetery
Kenwood
Lambeth Palace
Lincoln's Inn Fields
Marble Hill

Osterley Park
St George's Gardens
Victoria Embankment
  Gardens
Victoria Park
Waterlow Park
Wimbledon Park
Grade II
Abney Park Cemetery
Addington Palace
Alexandra Palace
Arnold Circus
Belgrave Square
Berkeley Square
Bloomsbury Square
The Boltons
Brockwell Park
Brompton Cemetery
Broomfield House
Cadogan Place
100 Cheyne Walk
Clissold Park
Coram's Fields
Danson Park
Down House
Eaton Square
Eccleston Square
Edwardes Square
Finsbury Circus
Finsbury Park
Foots Cray Place
Forty Hall
Garrick's Villa
Green Park
Grims Dyke
Grosvenor Square
Grove House
Gunnersbury Park
Hampton Court House
Hans Place
Hogarth's House
Holland Park
Holwood Park
Horniman Gardens
Island Gardens
Keats' House
Kennington Park
King George's Park
Ladbroke Square
Lamorbey Park
Manchester Square
Manor House Gardens
Morden Hall
Myatt's Fields
Myddelton House
Norwood Grove
Nunhead Cemetery
Parliament Square
Peckham Rye Park

Pope's Grotto
Portman Square
Putney Vale Cemetery
The Rookery, Streatham
Royal Hospital, Chelsea
Ruskin Park
Russell Square
St James' Square
St Luke's Gardens,
  Chelsea
St Marylebone Cemetery
St Michael's Convent
St Pancras Gardens
St Peter's Square
Southwark Park
Springfield Park
Strawberry Hill
Strawberry House
Sundridge Park
The Temple
Trent Park
Trafalgar Square
Valentine Park
Victoria Tower Gardens
Walpole House
Walpole Park
Wandsworth Park
Wanstead Park
Warwick Square
Well Hall
West Norwood
  Cemetery

Greater Manchester
Grade II*
  Dunham Massey
Grade II
  Alexandra Park,
    Manchester
  Alexandra Park, Oldham
  Cheadle Royal Hospital
  Haigh Hall
  Heaton Park
  Mesnes Park
  Philips Park
  Stamford Park
  Vernon Park
  Wythenshaw Park

Hampshire
Grade I
  Hackwood Park
  Highclere Park
Grade II*
  Avington Park
  Bramshill Park
  Broadlands
  Compton End
  Cranbury Park

Exbury House
Hale Park
Houghton Lodge
Lainston House
Leigh Park
March Court
Moundsmere Manor
Pylewell Park
Rotherfield Park
Tylney Hall
The Wakes
Warbrook House
Grade II
  Amport Park
  Awbridge Danes
  Basing House
  Bramdean House
  Breamore
  Brockenhurst Park
  Cadland House
  Central Parks
  Chawton House
  Dogmersfield Park
  Elvetham Hall
  Embley Park
  The Grange, Northington
  Hinton Ampner
  Hurstbourne Park
  Laverstock Park
  Little Boarhunt
  Manor House, Upton
    Grey
  Minley House
  Mottisfont Abbey
  Old Alresford House
  Rhinefield
  Southampton Central
    Parks
  Southampton Old
    Cemetery
  Stratfield Saye Park
  Stratton Park
  Townhill Park
  Victoria Park,
    Portsmouth
  The Vyne
  Warnford Park

**Hereford &
Worcester**
Grade I
  Croome Court
  Hagley Hall
Grade II*
  Berrington Hall
  Croft Castle
  Downton Castle
  Eastnor Castle
  Garnons

Hergest Croft
Hewell Grange
Holme Lacey
Kentchurch Court
Madresfield Court
Moccas Court
Overbury Court
Rous Lench Court
Spetchley Park
Sufton Court
Witley Court
Grade II
  Arley House
  Brampton Bryan
  Brockhampton Park
  Broxwood Court
  Eywood
  Foxley
  Gatley
  Hanbury Hall
  Hartlebury Castle
  Hill Court
  Homme House
  Hope End
  Kyre Park
  The Manor House,
    Cleeve Prior
  Shobdon
  Springhill House
  Stoke Edith
  Westwood Park
  Whitfield

Hertfordshire
Grade I
  Hatfield House
  St Paul's Walden Bury
Grade II*
  Ashridge
  Bayfordbury
  The Garden House,
    Cottered
  Knebworth
  Moor Park
  Panshanger
  Putteridge Bury
  Scott's Grotto
  Woodhall Park
  Youngsbury
Grade II
  Aldenham House
  Amwell Grange
  Ashwell Bury
  Ayot House
  Balls Park
  Benington Lordship
  Broadway, Letchworth
  Brocket Hall
  Cassiobury Park

Cokehatch
Fanhams Hall
Gobions
Gorhambury
Hexton Manor
Homewood, Knebworth
The Hoo, Kimpton
Howard Park,
  Letchworth
Julians
Markyatecell Park
Pishiobury
Poles Park
Stanstead Bury
Temple Dinsley
Tewin Water
Tring Park
Wormleybury
Wrotham Park

Humberside
Grade I
  Sledmere House
Grade II*
  Londesborough Park
Grade II
  Burton Constable
  Dalton Hall
  Houghton Hall
  Thwaite Hall

Isle of Wight
Grade II*
  Osborne
Grade II
  Appuldurcombe
  Norris Castle
  Nunwell House
  Swainston
  Westover

Kent
Grade I
  Godington Park
  Hever Castle
  Knole
  Penshurst Place
  Scotney Castle
  Sissinghurst Castle
Grade II*
  Chartwell
  Chevening
  Chilham Castle
  Cobham Hall
  Combe Bank
  Godmersham Park
  Goodnestone Park
  Groombridge Place

Hall Place
Japanese Garden,
  Bitchet Wood
Leeds Castle
Linton Park
Long Barn
Mereworth Castle
Northbourne Court
Oxen Hoath
Port Lympne
Grade II
  Bayham Abbey
  Belmont Park
  Benenden
  Boughton Place
  Calverley Park
  Chatham Dockyards
  Chiddingstone Castle
  Chilston Park
  Dane John Gardens
  Doddington Place
  Emmets Garden
  Franks Hall
  Great Maytham
  Hatch Park
  Hush Heath Manor
  Ightham Court
  Lees Court
  Mabledon Park
  Mount Ephraim
  Olantigh Towers
  Redleaf
  Riverhill House
  The Salutation
  Sandling Park
  Sissinghurst Court
  Sissinghurst Park
  Somerhill
  Squerryes Court
  Stonewall Park
  Swaylands
  Waldershare Park
  Walmer Castle

Lancashire
Grade II*
  Stanley Park
  Stonyhurst College
Grade II
  Ashton Memorial
    Gardens
  Astley Hall
  Avenham Park
  Bold Venture Park
  Capernwray Hall
  Clitheroe Castle
  Corporation Park
  Cuerden Hall
  Gawthorpe Hall

Haslam Park
Hoghton Tower
Lever Park
Lytham Hall
Moor Park
Rivington Gardens
Scarisbrick Hall
Sunnyhurst Woods
Whitehall Park
The Willows
Woodfold Park
Towneley Park
Worden Park

Leicestershire
Grade II*
  Coleorton Hall
  Staunton Harold Hall
Grade II
  Abbey Park, Leicester
  Baggrave Hall
  Belvoir Castle
  Bradgate Park
  Burley on the Hill
  Exton Park
  Garendon
  Langton Hall
  Lowesby Hall
  New Walk, Leicester
  Prestwold Hall
  Quenby Hall
  Stamford Hall
  Stapleford Hall
  Victoria Park, Leicester
  Whatton House

Lincolnshire
Grade I
  Belton House
  Brocklesby Park
  Grimsthorpe Castle
Grade II*
  Doddington Hall
  Harlaxton Manor
Grade II
  Aynscoughfee Hall
  Boultham Park
  Caythorpe Court
  Coleby Hall
  Culverthorpe Hall
  Easton Park
  Fillingham Castle
  Gunby Hall
  Hackthorn Hall
  Hainton Hall
  Harrington Hall
  Hartholme Park
  Lincoln Arboretum
  Marston Hall

Rauceby Hall
Revesby Abbey
Riseholme Hall
Scrivelsby Court
Stoke Rochford Hall
Well Hall

Merseyside
Grade I
  Birkenhead Park
Grade II*
  Ince Blundell Hall
  Sefton Park, Liverpool
Grade II
  Anfield Cemetery
  Botanic Gardens,
    Southport
  Croxteth Park
  Hesketh Park, Southport
  Knowsley Hall
  Prince's Park, Liverpool
  Speke Hall
  Stanley Park, Liverpool
  Thornton Manor
  Windle Hall

Norfolk
Grade I
  Holkham Hall
  Houghton Hall
Grade II*
  Blickling Hall
  Catton Hall
  Felbrigg Hall
  Gunton Park
  Heydon Hall
  Kimberley Hall
  Melton Constable Hall
  The Pleasaunce,
    Overstrand
  Sandringham House
  Sheringham Hall
Grade II
  Barningham Hall
  Beeston Hall
  Breccles Hall
  Eaton Park
  Elmham Hall
  Hanworth Hall
  Heigham Park
  Honing Hall
  Hunstanton Hall
  Intwood Hall
  Langley Park
  Lexham Hall
  Lynford Hall
  Mannington Hall
  Mile Cross Gardens

Narford Hall
The Old Rectory, Lyng
Oxburgh Hall
Pickenham Hall
Plantation Garden,
  Norwich
Rainthorpe Hall
Raveningham Hall
Raynham Park
Salle Park
Sennowe Hall
Shadwell Park
Stiffkey Old Hall
Stradsett Hall
Waterloo Park
Wensum Park
Wolterton Hall

Northamptonshire
Grade I
  Althorp
  Boughton House
  Castle Ashby
  Drayton House
Grade II*
  Canons Ashby
  Easton Neston
  Great Harrowden Hall
  Harrington
  Holdenby House
  Kirby Hall
  Lyveden New Bield
  Rockingham Castle
Grade II
  Ashby St Ledgers
  Aynhoe Park
  Barnwell Manor
  Boughton Park
  Cottesbrooke Hall
  Courteenhall
  Deene Park
  Fawsley
  Horton Park
  Lamport Hall
  Stoke Park
  Sulgrave Manor

Northumberland
Grade I
  Alnwick Castle
  Belsay Hall
Grade II*
  Cragside
  Seaton Delaval
  Wallington
Grade II
  Blagdon
  Chillingham Castle

Hesleyside
Howick Hall
Kirkharle Hall
Lindisfarne Castle
Nunwick
Tillmouth Park

Nottinghamshire
Grade I
   Clumber Park
   Newstead Abbey
   Thoresby Park
Grade II*
   Annesley Hall
   Flintham Hall
   Papplewick Hall
   Shireoaks Hall
Grade II
   Babworth Hall
   Bestwood Pumping
      Station
   Highfields Park
   Holme Pierrepont Hall
   Newark Castle Grounds
   Nottingham Arboretum
   Papplewick Pumping
      Station
   Rufford Abbey
   Welbeck Abbey

Oxfordshire
Grade I
   Blenheim Palace
   Christ Church
   Magdalen College
   New College
   Nuneham Courtney
   Oxford Botanic Garden
   Rousham
   Shotover
   Stonor
Grade II*
   Ashdown House
   Beckley Park
   Broughton Castle
   Buckland House
   Buscot
   Chastleton House
   Cornbury
   Corpus Christi
   Ditchley
   Garsington Manor
   Greys Court
   Heythrop College
   Merton College
   St Hugh's College
   St John's College
   Sarsden House

Tackley
Trinity College
Worcester College
Wroxton Abbey
Grade II
   Ascott
   Compton Beauchamp
   Cornwell Manor
   Eynsham Hall
   Friar Park
   Hinton Manor
   Kiddington Hall
   Kirtlington Hall
   Kirtlington Park
   Park Town, Oxford
   Pusey House
   Sandford House
   Shipton Court
   Shirburn Castle
   Sutton Courtenay Manor
   Swerford
   Wadham College
   Yarnton Manor

Shropshire
Grade I
   Hawkstone
Grade II*
   Attingham Park
   Davenport House
   Ludstone Hall
   Millicope Hall
Grade II
   Acton Burnell
   Albrighton Hall
   Aldenham Park
   Badger Dingle
   Boscobel House
   Brogyntyn
   Burwarton House
   Chetwynd Park
   Condover Hall
   Court of Hill
   Dudmaston
   Ferney Hall
   Hatton Grange
   Henley Hall
   Hodnet Hall
   Lilleshall Hall
   Linley Hall
   Longner Hall
   Oakly Park
   Orleton Hall
   Pitchford Hall
   Pradoe
   Quarry Park
   Stokesay Court
   Walcot Hall

Walcot Park
Wenlock Abbey

Somerset
Grade I
   Dunster Castle
   East Lambrook Manor
   Hestercombe
   Mells Manor
   Montacute House
Grade II*
   Ammerdown House
   Barrington Court
   Barwick Park
   Bishop's Palace, Wells
   Brympton d'Evercy
   The Chantry
   Cricket House
   Halswell Park
   Nynehead Court
   Orchardleigh
Grade II
   Babington House
   Burton Pynsent
   Cothelstone Manor
   Crowcombe Court
   The Deanery, Wells
   Fairfield
   Hatch Court
   Hazelgrove House
   Hinton House
   Lytes Cary Manor
   Marston House
   Mells Park
   Milton Lodge
   Nettlecombe Park
   Newton Surmaville
   Pundisford Park
   Redlynch Park
   St Audries
   Ston Easton Park
   Tintinhull House
   Ven House
   Wayford Manor

Staffordshire
Grade I
   Alton Towers
   Biddulph Grange
   Shugborough
Grade II*
   Chillington
   Enville
   Trentham Park
   Weston Park
Grade II
   Burslem Park
   Hanley Park

Himley Park
Keele Hall
Maer Hall
Sandon Park
Patshull Hall

Suffolk
Grade I
   Helmingham Hall
   Shrubland
Grade II*
   Campsey Ashe Park
   Euston Park
   Heveningham Park
   Ickworth Park
   Kentwell Hall
   Melford Hall
   Somerleyton Park
   Trinity Hospital
Grade II
   Chantry Park
   Chilton Hall
   Christchurch Mansion
   Culford Park
   Henham
   Tendring Hall Park

Surrey
Grade I
   Albury Park
   Claremont
   Munstead Wood
   Painshill
   Savill Garden
   Virginia Water
Grade II*
   Busbridge Lakes
   Great Fosters
   Orchards
   Polesden Lacey
   St Ann's Hill
   Wisley Gardens
   Wotton
Grade II
   Brookwood Cemetery
   Clandon
   The Deepdene
   Gatton Park
   Greathed Manor
   Hethersett
   Merrow Grange
   Moor Park
   Nonsuch Park
   Norbury Park
   Oatlands
   Pyrford Court
   Reigate Priory
   Titsey Place

Vann
Woodburn

East Sussex
Grade I
Great Dixter
Sheffield Park
Grade II*
Ashburnham Place
Brickwall
Buckhurst Park
Charleston Manor
Eridge Park
Glynde Place
Herstmonceux Castle
The Hoo
Penns in the Rocks
Rotherfield Hall
Grade II
Batemans
Battle Abbey
Bayham Abbey
Brightling Park
Buxted Park
Compton Place
Cotchford Farm
Firle Place
Hammerwood Park
Heathfield Park
Kemp Town, Brighton
Kidbrooke Park
Newick Park
Old Buckhurst
Plumpton Place
Preston Manor
Queen's Park, Brighton
Royal Pavilion, Brighton
Wadhurst Castle
Wych Cross Place

West Sussex
Grade I
Goodwood House
Leonardslee
Parham
Petworth House
Stansted Park
Grade II*
Arundel Castle
Borde Hill
Brockhurst
Cowdray House
Gravetye Manor
Heaselands
The High Beeches
Highdown
Hollycombe House
Little Thakeham
Nymans

Uppark
Wakehurst Place
West Dean
Grade II
Bignor Park
Blackdown House
Burton Park
Cooke's House
Knepp Castle
Lavington Park
Pitshill
Rymans
Sedgwick Park
Slaugham Place
Stonehurst

Tyne & Wear
Grade II
Gibside
Grade II
Axwell Park
Bradley Park
Jesmond Dene
Leazes Park
Mowbray Park,
  Sunderland
Newcastle General
  Cemetery
Saltwell Park
Woolsington Park

Warwickshire
Grade I
Compton Verney
Farnborough Hall
Packwood House
Warwick Castle
Grade II*
Arbury Hall
Baddesley Clinton Hall
Charlecote Park
Combe Abbey
Honington Hall
Radway Grange
Ragley Hall
Stoneleigh Abbey
Upton House
Grade II
Alscot Park
Anne Hathaway's
  Cottage
Clifford Manor
Dunchurch Lodge
Hill Close Gardens
Jephson Gardens
Kenilworth Castle
Merevale Hall
Newnham Paddox

Packington Hall
Ryton House
Shakespeare Gardens
Wooton Hall
Wroxhall Abbey

West Midlands
Grade I
The Leasowes
Grade II*
Birmingham Botanic
  Gardens
Castle Bromwich Hall
Grade II
Aston Hall
Brunswick Park
Edgbaston Hall
Great Barr House
Highbury Hall
Key Hill Cemetery
London Rd. Cemetery,
  Coventry
Sutton Park
Warley Park
West Park

Wiltshire
Grade I
Bowood House
Iford Manor
Longleat House
Stourhead
Wilton House
Grade II*
Amesbury Abbey
Belcombe Court
Corsham Court
Fonthill
Heale House
Larmer Tree Gardens
Longford Castle
The Moot, Downton
Tottenham Park
Wardour Castle
Grade II
Biddesden House
Conock Manor
The Courts, Holt
Dinton House
Great Chalfield Manor
The Hall,
  Bradford-on-Avon
Hatch House
Hazelbury Manor
Lacock Abbey
Lake House
Littlecote House
Lydiard Park

Marlborough College
North Canonry
Oare House
Ramsbury Manor
Rushmoor Park
Sheldon Manor
Trafalgar House
Wilbury House

North Yorkshire
Grade I
Castle Howard
Duncombe Park
Forcett Hall
Hackfall
Rievaulx Terrace
Studley Royal
Grade II*
Aldby Park
Aske Hall
Ebberston Hall
Mulgrave Castle
Newby Hall
Plumpton Rocks
St Nicholas, Richmond
Scampston Hall
Grade II
Allerton Park
Arncliffe Hall
Beningbrough Hall
Broughton Hall
Constable Burton Hall
Gilling Castle
Gledstone Hall
Long Walk,
  Knaresborough
Museum Gardens, York
Newburgh Priory
Norton Conyers
Nun Appleton Hall
Nunnington Hall
Ribston Hall
Ripley Castle
Rudding Park
Swinton Castle
Temple Grounds,
  Richmond
Thorpe Perrow
Valley Gardens,
  Harrogate
Weston Park

South Yorkshire
Grade I
Wentworth Castle
Grade II*
Sandbeck Park
Wentworth Woodhouse

Grade II
  Brodsworth Hall
  Cusworth Hall
. Hickleton Hall
  Norfolk Park, Sheffield
  Wortley Hall

West Yorkshire
Grade I
  Bramham Park
  Harewood House
Grade II*
  Nostell Priory
  Oulton Hall
  People's Park, Halifax
Grade II
  Bretton Hall
  Heathcote
  Ledston Hall & Park
  Lister Park
  Lotherton Hall
  Roundhay Park
  Saltaise Park
  Temple Newsam

WALES

Clwyd
Grade I
  Chirk Castle
  Hawarden Castle
  Leeswood Hall
  Wrexham: Erddig
  Wynnstay
Grade II*
  Bodrhyddan
  Garthgynan
  Gwrych Castle
  Gwysaney
  Kinmel Park
  Llangedwyn Hall
  Mostyn Hall
  Pedbedw
  Plas Newydd, Llangollen
  Rhual
  Soughton Hall

Talacre
Voelas
Whitehurst
Grade II
  Argoed Hall
  Bachymbyd
  Bettisfield Hall
  Bodelwyddan Castle
  Bryn Iorcyn
  Brynbella
  Bryngwyn Hall
  Brynkinalt
  Bryntisilio
  Coed Coch
  Colomendy
  Cotswold Ave., Colwyn
    Bay
  Pierce Memorial
    Garden, Denbigh
  Downing
  Erbistock Hall
  Eyarth Hall
  Eyarth House
  Fferm
  The Flagstaff, Colwyn
    Bay
  Foxhall Newydd
  Garthewin
  Golden Grove
  Gredington Park
  Gwaynynog
  Gyrn Castle
  Hafodunos
  Halkyn Castle
  Hartsheath
  Horsley Hall
  Iscoyd Park
  Llannerch Hall
  Llanrhaiadr Hall
  Llantysilio Hall
  Lower Soughton Hall
  Nantclwyd House,
    Ruthin
  Nerquis Hall
  Pantasaph
  Pen-y-lan
  Pentrehobyn

Perth-y-maen
Plas Heaton
Plas Newydd, Llanfair
Plas Teg
Plas Uchaf, Llannefydd
Rosehill
Ruthin Castle
St Beuno's College
St Mary's Churchyard,
  Overton
Tower
Trevalyn Hall
Trevalyn House
Trevor Hall
Valle Crucis Abbey
Vivod
Wrexham Cemetery

Gwent
Grade I
  Clytha Park
  Llanfihangel Court
  Piercefield Park
  Raglan Castle
Grade II*
  Dewstow House
  Dingestow Court
  The Hendre, Tredegar
    Park
  High Glanau
  Llanover Park
  Mathern Palace
  Mounton House
  Pontypool Park
  Shirenewton Hall
  Troy House
  Wyndcliffe Court
Grade II
  Abergavenny Castle
  Abergavenny New
    Cemetery
  Abergavenny Priory
    Deer Park
  Bedwellty Park, Tredegar
  Beechwood Park,
    Newport
  Bellevue Park, Newport

Bertholey House
Brynderwen, Bettwys
  Newydd
Bryn Glas, Newport
Cefn Tilla
Chapel House,
  Monmouth
Chippenham,
  Monmouth
Coldbrook House
Glen Usk
Hilston Park
Itton Court
Kemeys House
Llanarth Court
Llangybi House
Llantarnam Abbey
Llantilio Court
Llanwern Park
Lower Dyffryn
Machen House
Maes Manor Hotel
Moynes Court, Mathern
Pant y Goitre House
Pencoed Castle
Penhein
Plas Machen
St John's, Monmouth
St Pierre Park
St Woolos Cemetery,
  Newport
Talycoed Court
The Argoed
The Kymin
Treowen
Trewyn
Wyelands

31

Restoration Projects

The restoration of the Victorian garden at Biddulph Grange in Staffordshire is now complete. In April last year the wellingtonia avenue was formally re-opened. Despite its name, the original avenue was alternately planted with wellingtonias and deodars. The cedars were to act as nurses for the redwoods but, in the event, it was the wellingtonias which were cut down at the end of the 19th century, leaving the cedars to grow to a considerable height. Unfortunately, the cedars were too ragged and few to save and the National Trust rightly decided to fell them and replant the original avenue with both species. It is not yet known whether the deodars or the wellingtonias will be felled when the two get too crowded again: besides, the decision is unlikely to have to be made for at least 40 or 50 years. Other details which have been restored at Biddulph include the stumpery, and the upside-down tree.

The National Trust has been active in restoring and improving many of the historic parks and gardens attached to its properties. One such improvement last year involved further works of restoration at its classical Dutch garden at Westbury Court in Gloucestershire. Almost the first feature which visitors to Westbury encounter when they enter the garden is the elegant pavilion which looks down the length of a long, straight canal. It is clear from a Kip engraving that this axis was originally terminated by two further pavilions, whose reconstruction would be impracticable because they were sited in what is now part of the public road. However, they were fronted by a circular pool with a fountain in the middle, and it is these features, together with the associated paving, that the Trust has now restored. Instead of the two pavilions, the view is terminated by a newly planted yew arbour, with two seats set into it. There was, as often happens, some doubt as to the accuracy of the original Kip print which was the inspiration for this latest piece of restoration. Kip was known to anticipate works that the owner of a grand estate had in

mind to carry out, so that features appear in his drawings which were never put into effect. But excavations by garden archaeologists revealed the clay base of the circular pool surrounding the fountain, so this detail would appear to be a valid part of the original formal garden, which was built in 1699 or 1700.

The National Trust is willing to work closely with sponsors in order to raise funds for its mission. The New Covent Garden Soup Company launched a National Trust soup last year which was sold in selected supermarkets as well as at some Trust properties. In return for this concession the company gave £40,000 to the Trust's garden at Fenton House in north London. Meanwhile Hillier Nurseries has donated 50p from the sale of every plant of *Lonicera periclymenum* 'Graham Thomas' sold during the year towards the conservation of the garden at Mottisfont Abbey in Hampshire. Graham Thomas was the National Trust's Gardens Adviser from 1955 to 1974 and it was at Mottisfont that he created the best collection of old roses in Britain.

The National Gardens Scheme always contributes generously to garden conservation projects run by the National Trust. Last year, for example, they donated £250,000. The money will be used for projects that the Trust would otherwise not be able to fund, and spread between some twelve gardens. They include £100,000 to be spent at Tatton Park in Cheshire on the employment of a garden foreman for five years to oversee the recreation of the Victorian kitchen garden and to provide training for volunteer gardeners. Other projects to benefit include the restoration of the orangery at Dyrham Park in Gloucestershire, the creation of a perimeter walk at Anglesey Abbey in Cambridgeshire to provide winter interest, and the restoration of the steps in the yew tree walk at Cliveden in Buckinghamshire which run down from the great parterre to the banks of the river Thames.

Archaeologists working for the National Trust at Prior Park in Somerset have uncovered a mosaïc floor in the grotto. It lay under three inches of accumulated leaf-mould and revealed an elaborate pattern in the shape of sunrays, made from pebbles, inlaid with fossils and bones. The grotto was built by Ralph Allen in 1740 with advice from Alexander Pope. Pope also gave the Allens a puppy from his Great Dane, which they named 'Miss Bounce'. She is buried underneath the grotto by an epitaph which reads 'Weep not, Tread lightly my grave, Call me Pet'.

Concern still surrounds the long-term future of the great Welsh gardens of Dyffryn House near Cardiff. They were originally leased to Glamorgan County Council by Sir Cenydd Traherne, on condition that they remained open as a place for horticulture to be enjoyed by the public. When Mid and South Glamorgan county councils (successors to Glamorgan County Council) themselves ceased to exist at the end of last March, the new unitary authorities declined to accept responsibility for the maintenance costs of the house and gardens, and Dyffryn was therefore taken over by the Residuary Body for Wales for a period of twelve months. One of the new authorities, Vale of Glamorgan Borough Council, has since applied for lottery funding for the garden, but it is regrettable that the future of such an important landscape and garden should depend upon such support being forthcoming.

At the end of 1995 it was announced that several horticultural projects had won grants from the Heritage Lottery Fund. Chelsea Physic Garden was awarded £100,000 towards a £146,000 project to build a permanent education base for schools, a greenhouse area and research facilities. The Woodland Trust won £67,000 to preserve the wooded landscape of the Grade I historic park at Hackfell near Ripon in North Yorkshire as a nature conservation area. In fact, the Woodland Trust has been awarded a total of £6.5m towards a £19m project to create 200 community woodlands in England and Wales, much to the delight of tree nurserymen. And Scunthorpe Borough Council was allocated £210,000 towards the cost of renovating and re-creating the historic kitchen garden at Normanby Park, using traditional plant varieties and cultivation methods. The walled garden was closed to the public in 1987 because it was considered unsafe for members of the public to visit. One of the largest grants made towards managing parkland was of £825,000 for Osterley Park in West London announced at the beginning of February. But by far the largest was the grant of nearly £5m towards the purchase and restoration of Croome Court in Hereford & Worcester. This important 18th-century landscape was designed by Capability Brown. The park was about to be put on the market, in which case its 675 acres would have been broken up between several owners.

At the end of January, the Heritage Lottery Fund declared 1996 to be the year of the urban park. It announced that the revitalisation of our public parks and gardens was to be a priority area for grants, and issued guidelines to local authorities on what sort of work would be eligible for a grant. It included not just plans for restoration, but the cost of preparing feasibility studies themselves. Many observers have commented that the quality of maintenance in public parks has declined over the last 20 years. As they are highly valued by the many people who use them, and a source of much local pride, their restoration is an opportunity to create maximum benefit. 'Nothing is more important than the restoration of parks, public gardens and open spaces in towns and cities' declared the Heritage Lottery Fund. 'Contributing to the regeneration of public parks... uses lottery money to maximum public benefit and converts the legacy of the past into a vital asset for the future'.

In February the Millennium Commission announced funding of £21.7m for the creation of a national botanic garden for Wales. This amounts to some 50% of the expected cost of the funding to create a Welsh botanic garden at Middleton Hall in Dyfed. The focal point of the gardens will be a great glasshouse with five climatic zones to house plants from all over Africa, and an arboretum. At the beginning of April, three more public parks benefited from the Heritage Lottery Fund's stated aim to help with their resuscitation. Thamesdown Borough Council received £685,000 towards the total cost of £1,185,000 of acquiring and restoring the 72ha 19th-century Stanton Park near Swindon. The Fund also gave £144,000 towards the £474,000 cost of renovating Cadzow Linear Park in Hamilton, Strathclyde, and £137,750 towards the £197,750 needed for a project at Victoria Park in Cardiff. A MORI poll commissioned by the National Heritage Memorial Fund revealed that 74% of people thought that the improvement of public parks was an important and useful channel for Lottery profits.

Painshill Landscape Garden in Surrey was awarded £848,000 by the Heritage Lottery fund to ensure that the park can open fully to the public this year. The grant will pay 75% of the costs of a new access road, a landscaped car park, a foot bridge to connect the car park to the landscape park itself, a ticket office and other items of infrastructure which will make visiting this important historic garden easier. Other garden projects which received grants from the Heritage Lottery Fund included £45,300 towards the restoration of the garden at Leighton House in London, designed under the influence of Gertrude Jekyll; a grant of £19,000 to Southampton City Council towards the cost of a feasibility study on the redevelopment of its Victorian central parks; and £300,000 towards the acquisition of former parkland at Witley Court, in Surrey.

It must be said that most of these grants depend upon matching funding being found by the promoters of these schemes and, although both the National Heritage Memorial Fund and the Millennium Fund play down the likelihood, it is possible that some may never be completed.

32

Organisations

ADAS
ADAS Headquarters, Oxford Spires Business Park, The Boulevard, Kidlington, Oxfordshire OX5 1NZ
☎ 01865 842742

All Year Round Chrysanthemum Growers Association
30 Pern Drive, Botley, Hampshire SO30 2GW
☎ 01489 786638
CONTACT   The Secretary

Formed to represent the industry and distribute information to growers. Acts as a liaison between the growers, the government and other bodies. In the past their work has included pest control and the new plant passport scheme. They have recently become involved in publicity, and are promoting British chrysanthemums.

Ancient Monuments Society
St Ann's Vestry Hall, 2 Church Entry, London EC4V 5HB
☎ 0171 236 3934

Arboricultural Advisory & Information Service
Alice Holt Lodge, Wrecclesham, Farnham, Surrey GU10 4LH
☎ 01420 220022

This agency aims to develop the highest standards of arboricultural expertise and practice, and to advance professional development. It advises on everything to do with trees, from problems on legal matters to advice on diseases, pruning and planting grants.

Arboricultural Association
Ampfield House, Romsey, Hampshire SO51 9PA
☎ 01794 368717
CONTACT   The Secretariat

A registered charity and the professional body for arboriculturists. The AA publishes a useful directory of consultants and contractors who have met the organisation's stringent standards for training, work and insurance: contact the Secretariat for details. A range of other publications is also available. There is a local group structure, and keen amateurs can join as part of the Tree Club.

Architectural Association
34-36 Bedford Square, London WC1B 3ES
☎ 0171 636 0974

Excellent collection of prints, drawings and photographs: an essential resource for anyone concerned with historic gardens.

Association of Botanic Gardens
c/o Oxford Botanic Garden, High Street, Oxford OX1 4AX
☎ 01865 276920
CONTACT   Timothy Walker (Secretary)

A new organisation set up to represent and co-ordinate the interests of UK botanic gardens.

Association of Garden Trusts
8 Glasshouse Lane, Kenilworth, Warwickshire CV8 2AJ
☎ 01926 852976
CONTACT   Linda Cheeseman (Secretary)

The association provides a co-ordinating structure for the county gardens trusts and a focus for political lobbying. It supports the work of 24 local or regional trusts: 10 new ones are in the process of formation.

Association of National Park Officers
c/o The Old Vicarage, Bondgate, Helmsley, North Yorkshire YO6 3BP
☎ 01439 70657
CONTACT   S. Copeland

Association of Playing Field Officers & Landscape Managers
1 Cowley Road, Tuffley, Gloucester GL4 0HT
☎ 01452 417693
CONTACT   K. Hill

Bio-Dynamic Agriculture Association
Woodman Lane, Clent, Stourbridge, West Midlands DY9 9PX
☎ 01562 884933

Offers help to bio-dynamic growers: bio-dynamics are based on the anthroposophical theories of Rudolph Steiner and combine organic principles with celestial ones. The phase of the moon is believed to influence planting times.

Biotechnology & Biological Sciences Research Council
Polaris House, North Star Avenue, Swindon, Wiltshire SN2 1UH
☎ 01793 413200

BBSRC took over the work of the Agriculture & Food Research Council in 1994, along with parts of the programme of the former Science & Engineering Research Council. It supports and funds research into all biological fields. This includes work at HRI Wellesbourne and the John Innes Institute and by graduate students at universities.

Botanic Gardens Conservation International

Descanso House, 199 Kew Road, Richmond, Surrey TW9 3BW
☎ 0181 332 5953
CONTACT Dr P. Wyse-Jackson (Secretary General)

Britain in Bloom

Tidy Britain Group, The Pier, Wigan, Lancashire WN3 4EX
☎ 01942 824620
CONTACT Carolyne Lobban

Split into about 15 regions throughout the UK. Entry forms and advice are available from the regional organisers.

British Agricultural & Garden Machinery Association

14–16 Church Street, Rickmansworth, Hertfordshire WD3 1RQ
☎ 01923 720241

British Agrochemicals Association

4 Lincoln Court, Lincoln Road, Peterborough PE1 2RP
☎ 01733 349225

Trade association for manufacturers, distributors and retailers of pesticides. It publishes a useful Handbook and a list of its own many helpful publications – among them, a guide to the products available for amateur gardeners.

British Association of Landscape Industries (BALI)

Landscape House, Henry Street, Keighley, West Yorkshire BD21 3DR
☎ 01535 606139

The national body representing Landscape Contractors, founded in 1972. BALI promotes the interests of its members at national and regional level, and works to maintain high standards in the industry. Member firms cover the full spectrum of landscaping, both interior and exterior, design, construction and maintenance. They are required to carry adequate insurance, to abide by the code of conduct, and to maintain a certain standard in their work (which is subject to inspection). Probationary membership is available for companies which have been trading for less than two years.

British Association of Leisure Parks, Piers & Attractions

25 Kings Terrace, London NW1 0JP
☎ 0171 383 7942
CONTACT Joseph P. Grant (General Secretary)

Founded in 1936 as the trade association for most of the UK's private-sector leisure parks, piers and attractions, its 90 members now include managers of theme parks and wildlife attractions.

British Association of Seed Analysts

3 Whitehall Court, London SW1A 2EQ
☎ 0171 930 3611
CONTACT Paul Rooke (Secretary)

British Association Representing Breeders (BARB)

9 Portland Street, King's Lynn, Norfolk PE30 1PB

Formerly the British Association of Rose Breeders. Collects payments due under Plant Breeders' Rights, and promotes protected varieties.

British Bedding & Pot Plant Association

22 Long Acre, London WC2E 9LY
☎ 0171 235 5077
CONTACT The Secretary

Now funded in part by a Horticultural Development Council levy, the association is actively concerned with establishing standards and practice codes for the industry, as well as marketing and publicity.

British Bee-Keepers' Association

National Agricultural Association, Stoneleigh, Warwickshire CV8 2LZ
☎ 01203 696679

The BBA represents about 13,000 beekeepers, mainly in England. It produces leaflets, runs seminars and conventions, supports local groups of beekeepers and supervises examinations. It also represents the industry at UK and European government levels.

British Christmas Tree Growers Association

12 Lauriston Road, London SW19 4TQ
☎ 0181 946 2695
CONTACT Tony Richardson

Mainly to represent the growers and wholesalers but the association does publish a list of retailers selling Christmas trees.

British Commercial Glasshouse Manufacturers Association

c/o Cambridge Glasshouse Co Ltd, Barton Road, Comberton, Cambridge, Cambridgeshire CB3 7BY
☎ 01223 262395
CONTACT Mike Kendall (Chairman)

The association has about a dozen members and was set up to provide a common forum for commercial glasshouse manufacturers, research authorities, government controlling bodies and customers. Its members have a common purpose in maintaining high standards of manufacture, customer service, training and safety.

British Dragonfly Society

The Haywain, Hollywater Road, Bordon, Hampshire GU35 0AD
☎ 01420 472329
CONTACT Dr William Wain

The Society aims to promote and encourage the study and conservation of dragonflies and their natural habitats, especially in the UK. It has about 1,300 members and 30 local groups. Members may attend the Society's meetings and field days, and receive a Newsletter and Journal.

British Ecological Society
26 Blades Court, Deodar Road, Putney, London SW15 8HU
☎ 0181 871 9797
CONTACT   Dr Hazel Norman (Executive Secretary)

British Heather Growers Association
Cromwell House, 15 Andover Road, Winchester, Hampshire SO23 7EN
☎ 01962 63500

Marketing and promotions organisation for commercial heather growers. Its mascot 'Heather Hedgehog' (6ft tall & pink) is sometimes a little too conspicuous.

British Hedgehog Preservation Society
Knowbury House, Knowbury, Ludlow, Shropshire SY8 3LQ
Research into preservation and advice on the care of sick hedgehogs.

British Herb Trade Association
NFU, 22 Long Acre, London WC2E PLY
☎ 0171 331 7415
CONTACT   Rachel Moseley
The trade organisation for commercial herb growers.

British Herbal Medicine Association
Sun House, Church Street, Stroud, Gloucestershire GL5 1JL
☎ 01453 751389
CONTACT   R. A. Hill
BHMA was founded in 1964 to advance the science and practice of herbal medicine. It aims to defend the right to choose herbal remedies, to encourage wider knowledge and recognition of the value of herbal medicine, and to foster research into phytotherapy. BHMA is a member of the European Scientific Cooperative for Phytotherapy.

British Independent Fruit Growers' Association
'Aylsham', Broad Oak, Brenchley, Tonbridge, Kent TN12 7NN
☎ 01892 722080
CONTACT   Mrs J. Perry (Secretary)
A marketing and advisory organisation for some of the independent fruit growers in Great Britain. They have about 40 members.

The British Landscape Industry Training Organisation
11a North Queen Street, Keighley, West Yorkshire BD21 3DL
☎ 01535 691179
Established in 1993 to co-ordinate training for the landscape sector.

British Mycological Society
Department of Biology, University of Newcastle upon Tyne, Newcastle upon Tyne, Tyne & Wear NE1 7RU
☎ 0191 222 60001
CONTACT   Dr G. Beakes
The society promotes the study of all types of fungi, from mushrooms to moulds. It celebrated its centenary last year.

British Naturalists' Association
48 Russell Way, Higham Ferrers, Wellingborough, Northamptonshire NN10 8EJ
☎ & [FAX] 01933 314672
CONTACT   June F. Pearton (General Secretary)
The Association exists to encourage education, study and research in all branches of natural history and wildlife conservation. Lord Skelmersdale is the President and David Bellamy is President of the Youth Section.

British Orchid Growers Association
38 Florence Road, College Town, Camberley, Surrey GU15 4QD
☎ 01276 32947
CONTACT   Janet Plested
A trade association for orchid nurserymen and sundry traders to promote and maintain standards.

British Pest Control Association
3 St James' Court, Friar Gate, Derby, Derbyshire DE1 1ZU
☎ 01332 294288
CONTACT   Richard Strand (Executive Director)
Trade association for everyone concerned with pest control.

British Pharmacological Society
Royal Free Hospital, School of Medicine, Rowland Hill Street, London NW3 2PF
☎ 0171 794 0500
CONTACT   D. T. Maclagan

British Retail & Professional Florists Association
49 Meadway, Enfield, London EN3 6NX
☎ 01992 767645
CONTACT   W. Hart

British Rose Growers Association
4 Peewit Road, Hampton, Evesham, Hereford & Worcester WR11 6NH
☎ & [FAX] 01386 342307
CONTACT   Deidre Sutton (Secretary)
A vigorous trade association which works for the well-being of the rose-growing industry and for the promotion of the rose itself. Roses sold under the BRGA logo have a guarantee of quality.

British Seeds Council
Agriculture House, 25 Knightsbridge, London SW1X 7NJ
☎ 0171 235 5077

British Society of Plant Breeders

Woolpack Chambers, Market Street, Ely, Cambridgeshire
CB7 4ND
☎ 01353 664211

Represents the interests of commercial and state sector plant breeders covering farm crops, vegetables and ornamentals. The Society issues sub-licences and collects royalties from sub-licensees on behalf of plant breeders. It is an officially recognised body for conducting trials that are a legal requisite for National Listing of new varieties.

British Tourist Authority

Thames Tower, Black's Road, Hammersmith, London
W6 9EL

A list of British tourist information centres is available. Local centres can often provide information on gardens and events in their area.

British Trust for Conservation Volunteers (BTCV)

36 St Mary's Street, Wallingford, Oxfordshire OX10 0EU
☎ 01491 839766

Carries out practical conservation projects, including tree-planting. They run training courses and offer working conservation holidays, including some involving garden restoration.

Bulb Distributors Association

Springfield Gardens, Camelgate, Spalding, Lincolnshire
PE12 6ET
☎ 01775 724843
CONTACT   P. Atkinson

A trade organisation, founded in 1945, which now has 30 corporate members. It aims to organise and protect the interests of distributors of bulbs, and to co-operate in and deal collectively with all matters concerning the industry.

Butterfly Conservation

Box 222, Dedham, Colchester, Essex CO7 6EH
☎ & ⚏ 01206 322342

A thriving society with 7,000 members.

Cadw: Welsh Historic Monuments

Brunel House, 2 Fitzalan Road, Cardiff CF2 1UY
☎ 01222 867305

Centre for Alternative Technology

Machynlleth, Powys SY20 9AZ
☎ 01654 702400

The centre demonstrates a range of sustainable technologies, including organic food production. It also runs courses, sells books and publishes information leaflets on environmental approaches to gardening.

The Civic Trust

17 Carlton House Terrace, London SW1
☎ 0171 930 0914

Commercial Horticultural Association

Links View House, 8 Fulwith Avenue, Harrogate, North
Yorkshire HG2 8HR
☎ 01423 879208
CONTACT   Brian Dunsby

A trade organisation for manufacturers and suppliers of goods and services to the commercial horticultural industry. The CHA Suppliers Guide is available to professional horticulturists and the trade.

Common Ground

Seven Dials Warehouse, 44 Earlham Street, London
WC2H 9LA
☎ 0171 379 3109

Motivating force for projects which preserve and promote links between the environment and social culture. They publicise National Apple Day, and have worked on the *Flora Britannica* project. Pomologists should investigate their publications list.

The Conservation Foundation

1 Kensington Gore, London SW7 2AR
☎ 0171 823 8842

Manages, creates and funds environmental programmes with business sponsorship, and assists conservation groups with publicity and financing. Among its larger sponsors are Ford Motors, Wessex Water and Lloyds Bank.

Conservatory Association

2nd Floor, Goodwin House, George Street, Huntingdon,
Cambridgeshire PE18 6BU
☎ 01480 458271

A trade organisation for manufacturers and retailers of conservatories which seeks to protect the public by establishing and maintaining high standards of manufacture, sales and installation.

Council for Environmental Education

University of Reading, London Road, Reading, Berkshire
RG1 5AQ
☎ 01734 756061

The national body for the co-ordination and promotion of environmental education in England, Wales & Northern Ireland. Formed in 1968, it represents and works with the 80+ national organisations which are its members.

Council for National Parks

246 Lavender Hill, London SW11 1LJ
☎ 0171 924 4077

An independent charity which promotes the conservation, quiet enjoyment and understanding of the National Parks in England and Wales.

Council for the Protection of Rural England

Warwick House, 25 Buckingham Palace Road, London
SW1W 0PP
☎ 0171 976 6433

Country Houses Association
41 Kingsway, London WC2B 6UB
☎ 0171 836 1624
CONTACT R. D. Bratby

Founded in 1955 to save buildings (including their grounds and gardens) of historic and architectural merit for the public benefit, the association now has about 2,400 members. It owns some of the most beautiful historic houses in southern England, all of which offer residential accommodation for active retired people from all walks of life.

Country Landowners Association
16 Belgrave Square, London SW1X 8PQ
☎ 0171 235 0511

Countryside Commission
John Dower House, Crescent Place, Cheltenham, Gloucestershire GL50 3RA
☎ 01242 521381

Countryside Council for Wales
Plas Penrhos, Ffordd Penrhos, Bangor, Gwynedd LL57 2LQ
☎ 01248 370444

Cut Flower Growers' Group
Druimsallie, Peewit Road, Hampton, Evesham, Hereford & Worcester WR11 6NH
☎ & 🖷 01386 442307
CONTACT John Sutton

A new initiative to establish a trade organisation to represent the interests of members of the cut flower producers.

Department of Agriculture for Northern Ireland
Dundonald House, Upper Newtonards Road, Belfast, Co. Down BT4 3SG
☎ 01232 529100

Dry Stone Walling Association of Great Britain
YFC Centre, National Agricultural Centre, Kenilworth, Warwickshire CV8 2LG
☎ 0121 378 0493

English Heritage
Fortress House, 23 Savile Row, London W1X 1AB
☎ 0171 973 3000

English Nature
Northminster House, Peterborough, Cambridgeshire PE1 1UA
☎ 01733 340345

English Tourist Board
Thames Tower, Black's Road, London W6 9EL
☎ 0181 846 9000

Fauna & Flora International
Great Eastern House, Tenison Road, Cambridge CB1 2DT
☎ 01223 461471
CONTACT Mike Read

The society was founded in 1903, which makes it the world's oldest conservation society: it now has over 5,000 individual members. Much of its energy is currently directed at the trade in wild-collected bulbs and creating indigenous plant areas in such countries as Turkey.

Federation to Promote Horticulture for the Disabled
252 The Ridgeway, Enfield, London EN2 8AP

Fertiliser Manufacturers Association
Greenhill House, Thorpe Road, Peterborough PE3 6GF
☎ 01733 331303
CONTACT Mrs Jane Salter

Trade organisation for manufacturers: it advises on storage, handling, transport, health & safety, as well as producing market information and educational material and representing the industry to governments in the UK and Europe.

Flower Council of Holland
Catherine Chambers, 6-8 Catherine Street, Salisbury, Wiltshire SP1 2DA
☎ 01722 337505/6
CONTACT Jonathon Read

Established in 1980 to promote Dutch cut flowers and pot plants worldwide, the Council has offices in Paris, Milan and Düsseldorf, as well as its head office in Leiden. The UK is a prime market: we buy less *per capita* than most EU nations, and the Council is keen to encourage us to spend more.

Flowers & Plants Association
Covent House, New Covent Garden Market, London SW8 5NX
☎ 0171 738 8044

Formed in 1984 to promote the sale of flowers and plants, the Association now has 135 members in the cut flowers and indoor pot plants industry.

Forestry Commission
Forest Research Station, Alice Holt Lodge, Wrecclesham, Farnham, Surrey GU10 4LH
☎ 01420 23000

Research advisory service operates from the above address, and from: Northern Research Station, Roslin, Lothian EH25 9SY (Tel: 0131 445 2176; Fax: 0131 445 5124).

Forestry Commission
231 Corstorphine Road, Edinburgh, Lothian EH12 7AT
☎ 0131 334 0303

The Forestry Trust
The Old Estate Office, Englefield Road, Theale, Reading, Berkshire RG7 5DZ
☎ 01734 323523

Education and conservation trust dedicated to sustainable forestry. They have a network of 'Link Woods' and produce an annual guide, *Woodlands to Visit*.

The Garden Centre Association
38 Carey Street, Reading, Berkshire RG1 7JS
☎ 01734 393900

Industry body: 200 of the best garden centres belong. Members are independently inspected.

Garden Industry Manufacturers Association
225 Bristol Road, Birmingham, West Midlands B5 7VB
☎ 0121 446 6688
CONTACT   Mrs M. E. Slater

Garden Writers' Guild
14-15 Belgrave Square, London SW1X 8PS
☎ & FAX 0171 245 6943
CONTACT   Angela Clarke

Membership is open to anyone who earns a significant part of their income from writing, broadcasting or photographing related to horticultural matters. The Guild aims to improve the standing of its members and to raise the quality of their work. A significant number of the best gardening writers are not members.

Gardenex – Federation of Garden & Leisure Manufacturers
60 Claremont Road, Surbiton, Surrey KT6 4RH
☎ 0181 339 9259
CONTACT   Amanda Sizer

The Federation's function is to promote and expand exports of British garden and leisure products to the EC and overseas markets. It has about 120 corporate members.

Gardening for the Disabled Trust
c/o Hayes Farmhouse, Hayes Lane, Peasmarsh, East Sussex TN31 6XR
CONTACT   The Hon. Secretary

Advice, grants and information on every aspect of gardening for disabled people.

Geologists Association
Burlington House, Piccadilly, London W1V 9AG
☎ 0171 387 7050

The Georgian Group
6 Fitzroy Square, London W1P 6DX
☎ 0171 387 1720

Good Gardeners Association
Pinetum Lodge, Churcham, Gloucestershire GL2 8AD
☎ & FAX 01452 750402
CONTACT   J. D. Wilkin

This organic association believes that the earth does not belong to man, but man to the earth. It promotes the practice of companion planting: for example, beetroot likes to be with onions and kohlrabi, but not with beans.

Guernsey Growers Association
Grange House, The Grange, St Peter Port, Channel Islands
☎ 01481 724227

Health & Safety Executive (HSE)
Information Centre, Broad Lane, Sheffield S3 7HQ
☎ 0114 289 2345

The HSE should be the first point of reference on any matter relating to gardening health and safety, particularly as it affects the workplace.

Historic Houses Association (HHA)
2 Chester Street, London SW1X 7BB
☎ 0171 259 5688

A representative association of private owners which campaigns on their behalf. Of the 1,300 members nearly 300 houses are open to the public. Membership of the Friends of the HHA gives free admission to these properties. The association's brief includes gardens and designed landscapes.

Historic Scotland
Longmore House, Salisbury Place, Edinburgh, Lothian EH9 1SH
☎ 0131 668 8600

Responsible for the maintenance of historic houses and gardens in the care of the Secretary of State for Scotland.

Horticultural Association of Retail Traders (HART)
Hallams Court, Littleford Lane, Chilworth, Guildford, Surrey GU4 8QZ
☎ 01483 894808

The trade organisation for independent non-multiple garden centres. Aims to increase its members' market profitability and share by consolidated negotiations and marketing initiatives.

Horticultural Development Council
18 Lavant Street, Petersfield, Hampshire GU32 3EW
☎ 01730 263736

HDC is a statutory body whose function is to commission research on behalf of the horticultural industry. It is funded by an annual levy on growers. There are many projects currently under way relating to bulbs, field vegetables, hardy nursery stock, glasshouse crops and fruit.

Horticultural Research International
Wellesbourne, Warwickshire CV35 9EF
☎ 01789 470382

The main English organisation for scientific research into all aspects of horticulture, with further stations at East Malling and Wye in Kent, Efford in Hampshire, Kirton in Lincolnshire and Cawood in North Yorkshire.

Horticultural Therapy
Goulds Ground, Vallis Way, Frome, Somerset BA11 3DW
☎ 01373 464782

This charity is dedicated to helping people with special needs gain independence, new skills and quality of life through gardening. Its has set standards through its pioneering work in the community, helping projects and groups, and assisting individuals with information and educational opportunities.

Horticultural Trades Association (HTA)
Horticulture House, 19 High Street, Theale, Reading, Berkshire RG7 5AH
☎ 01734 303132

The trade association for amenity and leisure horticulture, with around 1,800 members. They publish a magazine, *Nurseryman and Garden Centre* and a useful reference *Yearbook*: both are also available to non-members. Business advice and negotiated discounts are provided to members. They promote horticulture generally, including the HTA National Garden Gift Tokens.

Institute of Grassland and Environmental Research (IGER)
Aberystwyth, Dyfed SY23 3EB
☎ 01970 828255

IGER incorporates the Welsh Plant Breeding Station, founded in 1919, and best known for breeding new grasses and disease-resistant cereals.

Institute of Groundsmanship
19–23 Church Street, The Agora, Wolverton, Milton Keynes MK12 5LG
☎ 01908 312511

Founded in 1934 to improve the status of groundsmen and the standards of groundsmanship, the Institute is a respected professional organisation which publishes its own journal *The Groundsman* and supervises the training and education of groundsmen.

The Institute of Horticulture (IoH)
14–15 Belgrave Square, London SW1X 8PS
☎ 0171 245 6943
CONTACT The Secretary

The professional body for horticulturists of all descriptions. The strict membership requirements demand a combination of education and experience. Membership confers recognised professional status. Student membership and career advice are available. The IoH acts as a forum for the collection and dissemination of horticultural information to its members and the public. It also promotes and represents the horticultural industry.

Institute of Leisure and Amenity Management (ILAM)
Lower Basildon, Reading, Berkshire RG8 9NE
☎ & 🖷 01491 874222

The professional body for leisure professionals. ILAM represents every aspect of leisure, cultural and recreational management and seeks to improve management standards throughout the industry.

International Association of Horticultural Producers
Postbus 93099, NL-2509 AB 's-Gravenhage, The Netherlands
☎ 00 31 70 381 4631

An international association for horticultural producers, including cut flowers, nursery stock and bulbs.

International Federation of Park & Recreation Administration
The Grotto, Lower Basildon, Reading, Berkshire RG8 9NE
☎ & 🖷 01491 874222

International Garden Centre Association
Pompmolenlaan 18, NL-3447 GK Woerden, The Netherlands
☎ 00 31 348 430676

The association has nearly 2,000 members in 27 countries.

International Institute of Biological Control
Silwood Park, Buckhurst Road, Ascot, Berkshire SL5 7TA
☎ 01344 872999

A research centre which publishes advice and information on biological control of insect pests and weeds.

International Institute of Entomology
56 Queen's Gate, London SW7 5JR
☎ 0171 584 0067

International Institute of Parasitology
395A Hatfield Road, St Albans, Hertfordshire AL4 0XU
☎ 01727 833151

International Mycological Institute
Bakeham Lane, Englefield Green, Egham, Surrey TW20 9TY
☎ 0181 940 4086

International Plant Propagators Society
Wegg's Farm, Common Road, Dickleburgh, Diss, Norfolk IP21 4PJ
☎ & 🖷 01379 741999
CONTACT D. J. Adlam (Secretary)

The Great Britain and Ireland region of an international society. The IPPS is aimed at practical and academic horticulturists. Its motto 'Seek and Share' reflects its aim of bringing together and distributing information about propagation and production techniques.

International Tree Foundation
Sandy Lane, Crawley Down, Crawley, West Sussex RH10 4HS
☎ 01342 712536

Formerly Men of the Trees. International tree planting and conservation organisation. Membership costs £12.50.

Irish Organic Farmers & Growers Association
Killegland Farm, Ashbourne, Co. Meath, Eire

John Innes Manufacturers Association
Links View House, 8 Fulwith Avenue, Harrogate, North Yorkshire HG2 8HR
☎ 01423 879208
CONTACT Brian Dunsby

The trade organisation for manufacturers of John Innes seed and potting composts. Members have to meet the quality standards: they can then display the seal of approval. JIMA actively promotes the use of loam-based composts by amateur gardeners.

The Landscape Foundation
14 Doughty Street, London WC1
☎ 0171 242 3301
CONTACT   Gillian Darley

Formed to encourage and promote sensitive design and best practice in relation to all matters affecting the landscape. 'Best practice' means combining the best of design with the best planning and business practices.

The Landscape Institute
6–7 Barnard Mews, London SW11 1QU
☎ 0171 738 9166

The professional body for the landscape profession: landscape architects, landscape managers and landscape scientists. The LI sets and maintains standards and accredits educational courses. It represents the profession's interests and disseminates information to its members. Members hold the qualification ALI: a directory of firms where at least one of the principals is a registered member is available from RIBA Publications (0171 251 0791). The Landscape Institute can advise potential clients free of charge about suitable firms for large or specialised projects.

Landscape Research Group
Leuric, North Road, South Kilworth, Lutterworth, Leicestershire LE17 6DU
☎ 01858 575530

A multi-disciplinary body to encourage education, interest and research in landscape.

Leisure and Outdoor Furniture Association Ltd (LOFA)
P O Box 233, Redhill, Surrey RH1 4YU
☎ 01737 644016

LOFA is a trade association to represent and promote some 56 companies in the garden furniture and barbecue market.

The Linnean Society of London
Burlington House, Piccadilly, London W1V 0LQ
☎ 0171 434 4479
CONTACT   Dr J. C. Marsden (Executive Secretary)

The Linnean Society was founded in 1788, which makes it the world's oldest active biological society. It is named after Carl Linnaeus (1707 – 1778), the founder of the modern system of binomial classification, and owns Linnaeus's collection of plants, animals, papers and books. The aim of the Society is 'the cultivation of the Science of Natural History in all its branches'.

Metropolitan Public Gardens Association
3 Mayfield Road, Croydon, Surrey CR4 6DN
☎ 0181 689 4197

Ministry of Agriculture, Fisheries and Food
3 Whitehall Place, London SW1A 2HH
☎ 0171 270 8080

General enquiries on the above number. See your local telephone directory (under 'Agriculture') for the addresses of MAFF's regional centres. There is an Information Division Helpline on 0645 335577.

Museum of Garden History
Lambeth Palace Road, London SE1 7LB
☎ 0171 401 8865
CONTACT   Mrs Rosemary Nicholson

The only museum of its kind, housed in the (now disused) church where the two John Tradescants, father and son, were buried.

National Association of Decorative & Fine Art Societies (NADFAS)
8 Guilford Street, London WC1N 1DT
☎ 0171 430 0730

National Farmers Union
22 Long Acre, London WC2E 9LY
☎ 0171 331 7200

The farmers' trade association has a horticulture section which represents growers. Associated organisations include BGLA Ltd (organisers of two trade exhibitions), British Bedding and Pot Plant Association, British Herb Trades Association, and Farm Shop and PYO Association. Specialist advisers can help members with law, taxation, employment and plant health.

National Gardens Scheme
Hatchlands Park, East Clandon, Guildford, Surrey GU4 7RT
☎ 01483 211535

The National Institute of Medical Herbalists
56 Longbrook Street, Exeter, Devon EX4 6AH
☎ 01392 426022

A professional group of practitioners of herbal medicine (phytotherapy). Entry is by examination following a four-year training course.

National Playing Fields Association
25 Ovington Square, London SW3 1LQ
☎ 0171 584 6445

National Small Woods Association
Red House, Hill Lane, Birmingham, West Midlands B43 6LZ
☎ 0121 358 0461

National Trust
36 Queen Anne's Gate, London SW1H 9AS
☎ 0171 222 9251

Conservation body with many outstanding gardens and landscapes under its care. Membership gives admission to all the Trust's properties, and numerous events are organised throughout the year.

National Trust for Scotland
5 Charlotte Square, Edinburgh EH2 4DU
☎ 0131 226 5922

This Scottish conservation body has a number of excellent gardens in its care; members also receive free entry to National Trust properties under a reciprocal arrangement. Self-catering and working holidays are available.

Natural History Museum
Cromwell Road, London SW7 5BD
☎ 0171 938 9123

Gardeners will be interested in the Insect Information & Advisory Service which is offered by the Entomological Department on 0171 938 9462.

NIAB
Huntingdon Road, Cambridge CB3 0LE
☎ 01223 276381

The National Institute of Agricultural Botany carries out testing of seeds and other laboratory and environmental research on behalf of the government and commercial customers. The Wisley Handbook, *Vegetable Varieties for the Gardener*, by J. Chowings and M. J. Day, passes on the results of NIAB tests.

Northern Ireland Horticulture and Plant Breeding Station
Department of Agriculture, Manor House, Loughgall, Co. Armagh BT61 8JB
☎ 01762 891206

Famous for the breeding of new amenity grasses with tolerance to herbicides, but most of the research work at Loughgall is directed at supporting local growers like top fruit nurserymen and hardy ornamental stock producers.

Northern Ireland Tourist Board
St Anne's Court, 59 North Street, Belfast BT1 1NB
☎ 01232 231221

The Organic Food & Farming Centre
86 Colston Street, Bristol BS1 5BB
☎ 0117 9290661

The Soil Association, British Organic Farmers and the Organic Growers Association are based here.

Permaculture Association
8 Hynter's Moon, Totnes, Devon TQ9 6TJ
☎ 01803 867546

Encourages the practice of permaculture, the conscious use of ecological principles for self-sustaining food production. Information on design, planting, and the different approaches – organic, ecological and bio-dynamic.

Pesticides Trust
Eurolink Business Centre, 49 Effra Road, London SW2 1BZ
☎ 0171 274 8895

Plant Breeding International
Maris Lane, Trumpington, Cambridge CB2 2LQ
☎ 01223 840411

Plant Publicity Holland
Goudse Rijweg 1, Postbus 81, NL-2770 AB Boskoop, The Netherlands
☎ 00 31 172 217550

Established in 1952 to promote Dutch nursery stock, mainly through marketing and public relations. It operates through a system of levies on growers in the Netherlands. The value of Dutch exports to UK in 1994/95 was over £40m.

Plant Variety Rights Office and Seeds Division
White House Lane, Huntingdon Road, Cambridge CB3 0LF
☎ 01223 277151

The main function of this division of the Ministry of Agriculture is to receive, consider and reach decisions on applications for the grant of rights in new varieties of plants – in short, to implement the *Plant Varieties and Seeds Act*, 1964. It also acts as a postbox for the European Union Community Plant Variety Office. The office issues a very useful *Guide to Plant Breeders' Rights*.

Plantlife
The Natural History Museum, Cromwell Road, London SW7 5BD
☎ 0171 938 9111

The only conservation charity in Britain solely devoted to saving wild plants. It has 6000 members and the individual subscription is £20. Projects include rescuing individual species, protecting peat bogs, and the Great Hedge Project.

The Professional Gardeners Guild
North Lodge, Upper Winchendon, Aylesbury, Buckinghamshire HP18 0ES
☎ 01296 651957
CONTACT Membership Secretary

Founded in 1977 as a professional organisation for head gardeners, garden managers and similar persons employed in private gardens. It has 400 members, including some overseas, and works to improve management, training and contacts between gardeners.

Ramblers Association
1–5 Wandsworth Road, London SW8 2XX
☎ 0171 582 6878

The Ramblers' Association was founded in 1935 and now has over 170,000 members and 370 local groups.

Royal Entomological Society
41 Queen's Gate, London SW7 5HU
☎ 0171 584 8361

A learned society, whose fellows are for the main part academics. They provide expert witnesses and publish scientific reports but are not the people to ask for advice on insects in your garden: members of the RHS should write to Wisley instead.

Royal Forestry Society of England, Wales & Northern Ireland
102 High Street, Tring, Hertfordshire HP23 4AF
☎ 01442 822028

An active society which seeks to encourage the conservation, improvement and expansion of Britain's woodlands by positive management. It has over 4,300 members in 21 divisions, each with its own programme of events. The *Quarterly Journal of Forestry* is the industry leader.

Royal Institute of British Architects (RIBA)
66 Portland Place, London W1N 4AD
☎ 0171 580 5533

Royal Scottish Forestry Society
62 Queen Street, Edinburgh, Lothian EH2 4NA
☎ & [FAX] 0131 225 8142
CONTACT   Michael Osborne

Royal Society for the Protection of Birds
The Lodge, Sandy, Bedfordshire SG19 2DL
☎ 01767 680551

This charity takes action for wild birds and the environment. It is the largest wildlife conservation charity in Europe, with nearly 900,000 members.

Rural Development Commission
141 Castle Street, Salisbury, Wiltshire SP1 3TP
☎ 01722 336255

A government agency concerned with the economic and social well-being of England's rural communities. It does *not* concern itself with agriculture or horticulture.

Scotland's Garden Scheme
3 Castle Terrace, Edinburgh EH1 2EL
☎ 0131 229 1870

Scottish Crop Research Institute
Invergowrie, Dundee, Tayside DD2 5DA
☎ 01382 562731

Employs about 370 staff and undertakes research on horticultural crops, their pests and diseases, and on processes common to all plants which improve the quality of life and the environment.

Scottish Natural Heritage
12 Hope Terrace, Edinburgh EH9 2AS
☎ 0131 447 4784

SNH's mission is 'to work with Scotland's people to care for our natural heritage'. This includes safeguarding Scotland's natural, genetic and scenic diversity, and encouraging environmental sustainability.

Scottish Seed & Nursery Trade Association
12 Bruntisfield Crescent, Edinburgh, Lothian EH10 4HA
☎ 0131 447 1035

Scottish Tourist Board
23 Ravelston Terrace, Edinburgh EH4 3EU
☎ 0131 332 2433

The source of all useful information about travel in Scotland.

Scottish Wildlife Trust
25 Johnston Terrace, Edinburgh, Lothian EH1 2NH
☎ 0131 226 4602

Society of Botanical Artists
1 Knapp Cottages, Wyke, Gillingham, Dorset SP8 4NQ
☎ 01747 825718
CONTACT   Pamela Henderson (Executive Secretary)

Founded in 1985 to 'honour and strive to continue in the great tradition of talent, beauty and infinite care apparent in the art of botanical painting through the ages'. The society has an expanding membership, holds regular open exhibitions and can act as a channel for commissions.

The Society of Floristry
70a Reigate Road, Epsom, Surrey
☎ 01372 463688
CONTACT   The Secretary

The society, which was started in 1951, works to maintain standards in professional floristry. Part of this work includes professional awards at intermediate level and above. Preliminary qualifications are handled by the City and Guilds of London. The National Diploma of the Society of Floristry is the highest floristry qualification. Members are drawn from all sectors of the industry. The society stages displays and demonstrations, including a stand at the Chelsea Flower Show.

Society of Garden Designers
6 Borough Road, Kingston upon Thames, Surrey KT2 6BD
☎ & [FAX] 0181 974 9483
CONTACT   The Secretary

The leading professional body for full-time garden designers. Only about 65 of its 600 members are recognised as Full Members or Fellows. Membership depends upon a combination of training and experience, and work is inspected. The society distributes information about its members to enquirers free of charge: contact The Secretary. Full members use the initials FSGD and MSGD.

Soil Association
86-88 Colston Street, Bristol, Gloucestershire BS1 5BB
☎ 0117 929 0661

Sports Turf Research Institute
Bingley, West Yorkshire BD16 1AU
☎ 01274 565131

Founded in 1929 to carry out research into grasses and turf management. The institute advises the National Trust and private owners, at home and overseas, as well as sports associations and golf course managers.

Swimming Pool & Allied Trades Association Ltd (SPATA)
Lorne Park House, 1 Lorne Park Road, Bournemouth, Dorset BH1 1JJ
☎ 01202 789224

The national organisation for trading and consumer standards in the swimming pool industry. Members must observe the Association's standards. Publications include *The Swimming Pool Guide*, *The Pool Owner's Handbook* and a list of members for owners and would-be owners to approach for advice.

The Tree Council
51 Catherine Place, London SW1E 6DY
☎ 0171 828 9928

Tree News is sent free to all Friends of the Tree Council.

Tree Register of the British Isles
77a Hall End, Wootton, Bedfordshire MK43 9HP
☎ 01234 768884
CONTACT   Mrs P. Stevenson (Secretary)

The Register aims to aims to identify and record full details of exceptional trees. Its Newsletter is a fascinating read for anyone who enjoys the sheer variety and size of old trees.

The Victorian Society
1 Priory Gardens, London W4 1TT
☎ 0181 994 1019

Wales Tourist Board
Brunel House, 2 Fitzalan Road, Cardiff CF2 1UY
☎ 01222 499909

Information on places to visit and holidays in Wales is available in the Welsh regional brochures and the *Wales* magazine – telephone 01222 457000. Ask the nearest main Tourist Information Centre for information on local events.

Wildfowl & Wetlands Trust
Slimbridge, Gloucester, Gloucestershire GL2 7BT
☎ 01453 890333

The Wildlife Trusts
The Green, Witham Park, Waterside South, Lincoln LN5 7JR
☎ 01522 544400

The Wildlife Trusts is the new name for the Royal Society for Nature Conservation – an ill-conceived name change if ever there was one – and the RSNC Wildlife Trusts Partnership is made up of the local wildlife trusts, many of whom are listed in our societies section, and some 50 urban groups. They manage nature reserves, campaign on conservation issues, and encourage people to become involved in conservation.

Women's Farm & Garden Association
175 Gloucester Street, Cirencester, Gloucestershire GL7 2DP
☎ 01285 658339

A useful voluntary organisation for women whose livelihood is connected with the land. Among its activities is the Women's Returners to Amenity Gardening Scheme which arranges placements in private gardens for women wishing to return to work.

Woodland Trust
Autumn Park, Dysart Road, Grantham, Lincolnshire NG31 6LL
☎ & [FAX] 01476 74297

This charity is concerned solely with the conservation of Britain's woodland heritage of broadleaved trees. It now owns and manages over 700 woods across Britain.

World Conifer Data Pool
Treetops, Buzzacott Lane, Combe Martin, Devon EX34 0NL
☎ 01271 883761
CONTACT   Humphrey Welch and Gordon Haddow

Acts as a collecting agency for data on new conifer introductions from around the world. They have recently published *The World Checklist of Conifers* through Landsman's Bookshop.

Worshipful Company of Gardeners
25 Luke Street, London EC2A 4AR
☎ 0171 739 8200
CONTACT   Col. N.G.S Gray (Clerk)

A City Guild, incorporated in 1605. It has always played an active part in horticultural affairs.

Index